PHOTOSYNTHESIS
AND RELATED PROCESSES

•

VOLUME II
Part 2

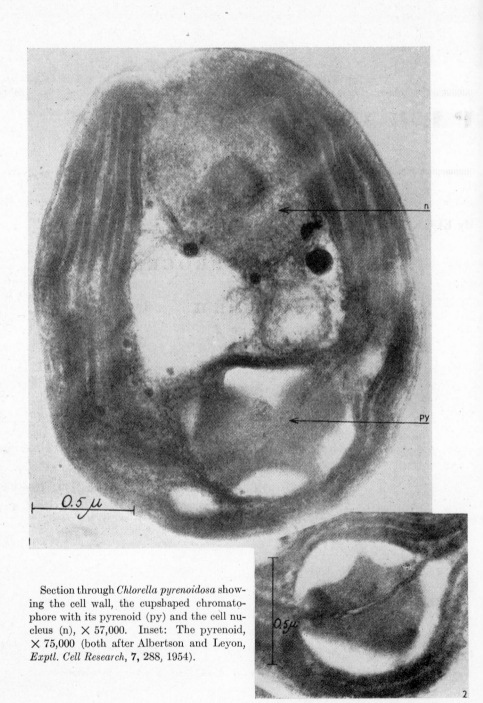

Section through *Chlorella pyrenoidosa* showing the cell wall, the cupshaped chromatophore with its pyrenoid (py) and the cell nucleus (n), × 57,000. Inset: The pyrenoid, × 75,000 (both after Albertson and Leyon, *Exptl. Cell Research*, **7**, 288, 1954).

PHOTOSYNTHESIS
and Related Processes

By EUGENE I. RABINOWITCH

*Research Professor, Photosynthesis Research Labora-
tory, Department of Botany, University of Illinois.
Formerly Research Associate, Solar Energy Research
Project, Massachusetts Institute of Technology.*

VOLUME II · *Part 2*
Kinetics of Photosynthesis (*continued*);
Addenda to Volume I and Volume II, Part 1

1956

INTERSCIENCE PUBLISHERS, INC., NEW YORK
Interscience Publishers Ltd., London

Library of Congress Catalog Card Number 45-7293

CHEMISTRY

Cat for Chemistry

INTERSCIENCE PUBLISHERS, Inc., 250 Fifth Avenue, New York 1, N. Y.

For Great Britain and Northern Ireland:
INTERSCIENCE PUBLISHERS Ltd., 88/90 Chancery Lane, London W. C. 2

PRINTED IN THE UNITED STATES OF AMERICA
BY MACK PRINTING COMPANY, EASTON, PA.

PREFACE

to Volume II, Part 2

This volume brings to completion the review of *Photosynthesis and Related Phenomena* which the author rashly undertook to prepare, for his own orientation, in the summer of 1938. Two months at Woods Hole, with its splendid library, seemed, at that time, an adequate period to complete the undertaking; and Interscience Publishers temptingly offered to publish the result in book form. Seventeen years and 2000 printed pages later, it is time to stop—even if this closure has to come in the midst of rapid and promising developments in several areas covered by the narrative.

A mistake, which proved almost fatal to the completion of the task, was to postpone the publication of the whole manuscript in 1943, when it was first finished in draft form, at a time when the war had imposed a hiatus upon the progress of non-applied research. Instead, only one half of the manuscript was prepared for publication at that time (and actually published, as Volume I, in 1945); while the second half was set aside for final revision until after the war. When, in 1946, the author returned from the Manhattan District to the Solar Energy Research Project at the Massachusetts Institute of Technology (to move on, soon afterward, to the Photosynthesis Laboratory at the University of Illinois), the rapidity with which new research data began to accumulate made it difficult to digest and fit them into the framework of the monograph. As a result, the "second volume" in turn burst its confines, and became divided in two. The first half (Volume II, Part 1) was published in 1951; completion of the second has taken five more years.

Chapters 31 to 34 of the present volume (II, Part 2) follow the original outline, bringing to a close the discussion of Kinetics of Photosynthesis begun in Chapter 25. Chapters 35 and 36 deal with two areas of knowledge that have been vastly enlarged since 1945—the Photochemistry of Chlorophyll (in solution and in chloroplast preparations), and Chemical Path of Carbon Dioxide Reduction. Chapter 37 was originally intended as a catch-all for new information in the various areas covered by Volumes I and II,1; but in the course of preparation, division into four parts became advisable: 37A (Structure and Composition of Chloroplasts), 37B (Chemistry of Pigments), 37C (Spectroscopy and Fluorescence of Pigments), and 37D (Kinetics of Photosynthesis), the latter bringing up-to-date,

v

but not to a close, among other things, the controversial subject of maximum efficiency.

This arrangement left out many not unimportant "miscellaneous" topics, such as the more recent work on photosynthesizing and chemo-synthesizing bacteria, photochemical nitrate metabolism, etc. The monograph as a whole therefore does not quite live up to the ambitious standard of coverage set in the first volume.

No attempt has been made to treat the problems of large-scale culturing of microscopic algae for food (and other practical purposes), to which so much public attention has been drawn lately. Reference must be made in this connection to the symposium "Algal Culture, from Laboratory to Pilot Plant," edited by J. S. Burlew, and published by the Carnegie Institution of Washington in 1953 (Publication No. 600), which contains contributions by leading investigators in this field.[1]

Each of the three volumes—I, II,1 and II,2—contains an Author Index of the Main Investigations. A Subject Index was provided in Volume I, but not in II,1; the present Volume II,2 contains a comprehensive Subject Index for all three volumes.

If the writing of this monograph were to be started now, a somewhat different plan would have been adopted, with a different distribution of emphasis. Some chapters now resemble a scaffolding, erected years ago, behind which no building has appeared, and which one would now be inclined—perhaps too hastily—to dismantle. There is, however, relatively little material, even in the earliest chapters, which does not contribute to the establishing of a proper perspective in the whole field. The policy—adopted at the beginning of the work—of discussing all alternatives and suggestions, has paid off in leaving the author free of commitment to any by now flagrantly obsolete theory. In fact, systematic reading—which is more than can be expected for a monograph of this bulk—would reveal that many of the current "new" ideas in photosynthesis have been proposed or discussed somewhere in it.

At the end of the book (p. 1994) the author expresses hope that it will not rapidly become obsolete, even if the rate at which new developments follow in the field makes it inevitable that it will be *incomplete* already at the date of its publication. Some of the developments of the years 1954–55 could at least be mentioned in the "Epilogue" (Chapter 38); others were published (or came to the author's attention) too late for this purpose.

The electron microscopic study of the chloroplast structure has entered a promising new stage with the improvement of techniques for the preserva-

---

[1] More recent summaries, presented at the Phoenix, Arizona, Conference on Applied Solar Energy (Oct. 30–Nov. 4, 1955) will be published in the proceedings of this conference.

tion of the intimate structure of the specimens (some striking pictures obtained with this technique are reproduced in Chapter 38).

Leyon,[2] and Vatter,[3] have reported interesting new data concerning the ontogenetic development of the chloroplast structure.

Important new observations were made concerning the *photochemical activity of chloroplast preparations.* Thomas and Haans[4] thought that the loss of much or all of the chloroplast stroma in the preparation of granular chloroplast fragments from leaves may be responsible for their incapacity to utilize carbon dioxide as photochemical oxidant. They accordingly prepared macerates from stroma-free, laminar chloroplasts of *Spirogyra,* and found that these preparations could take up manometrically measurable amounts of carbon dioxide and liberate roughly equivalent amounts of oxygen in light.

Arnon and co-workers[5] expanded, in a series of papers, the interesting findings to which brief reference only could be made on pp. 1537 and 1982. They found that whole chloroplasts, separated from protoplasmic particles (mitochondria), as well as fragments of such protoplasma-free chloroplasts, have very little aerobic metabolism—respiration and correlated ATP-formation from inorganic phosphate. On the other hand, they show evidence of two photosynthetic processes—the uptake of CO_2 (revealed by tracer measurements), with C(14) incorporation in sugar phosphates and carbohydrates (starch) and liberation of oxygen (measured manometrically, after qualitative gas identification by luminous bacteria); and of *anaerobic* formation of high-energy phosphate ("photosynthetic phosphorylation"). The photochemical processes can be directed preponderantly towards photosynthesis, or towards ATP accumulation, by varying external conditions or adding appropriate inhibitors.

In chloroplast *fragments* (as contrasted to whole chloroplasts) the "photosynthetic" CO_2 fixation could be observed only upon the addition of an aqueous extract from chloroplast maceration. The anaerobic formation of ATP in light could be stimulated, in such fragments, by "co-factors," which included Mg^{++}-ions, vitamin-K type compounds (*e.g.*, menandione), riboflavin, and ascorbic acid, until it was much stronger than in intact chloroplasts. The photochemical CO_2-incorporation was not stimulated (or even inhibited) by these additions, with the exception of ascorbic acid. The apparent necessity of the latter (in amounts much larger than that of

[2] Leyon, H., *Exptl. Cell Reserch,* **7**, 609 (1954).

[3] Vatter, A. E., *Thesis,* Univ. of Illinois, 1955.

[4] Thomas, J. B., and Haans, A. M. J., *Biochim. et Biophys. Acta,* **18**, 287 (1955).

[5] Arnon, D. I., Whatley, F. R., and Allen, M. B., *J. Am. Chem. Soc.,* **76**, 6324 (1954); Allen, M. B., Arnon, D. I., Capindale, F. R., Whatley, F. R., and Durham, L. J., *ibid.,* **77**, 4149 (1955); Arnon, D. I., *Science,* **122**, 3157 (1955); Arnon, D. I., *et al.,* Gatlinburg Conference on Photosynthesis of the NAS, Oct. 1955 (in press).

carbonate) appears as a complication in the interpretation of these observations, particularly if one recalls the complex action of ascorbic acid on the Hill reaction (*cf.*, p. 1568) and its role in the Krasnovsky reaction (*cf.*, pp. 1514–1522). The difference between the C(14)-tagged intermediates identified in Arnon's photosynthesizing chloroplast preparations and those found by Calvin and co-workers in intact photosynthesizing cells also needs clarification.

In any case, the observations of Arnon, and of Thomas, bring nearer to closure the gap between the photochemical activities of chloroplast preparations and whole cells, and between the Hill reaction and true photosynthesis (first narrowed by the coupling of Hill reaction to the malic enzyme system *via* pyridine nucleotides, described on pp. 1578–1585).

Vishniac[6] reported that the colorless "acetone powder," prepared from chloroplasts, can be restored to photochemical activity (reduction of TPN in light) by addition of chlorophyll solution. Similar activation of macerates from white leaves by added chlorophyll was described by Rodrigo[7]; the material obtained in this way was weakly fluorescent and had an absorption maximum at 678 mμ.

Kok[8] has made new flash light experiments, and suggested a simple two-step enzymatic mechanism, permitting the observations made with instantaneous flashes (Emerson and Arnold) to be reconciled with those obtained by means of flashes lasting several milliseconds (Tamiya). This mechanism, if correct, means that of the two constants previously derived from flash light experiments, one, $\mathbf{F}^{max}$ ($= 5 \times 10^{-4}$ Chl$_0$), retains its significance as titer (multiplied by a simple fraction, $1/n$) of a "stabilizing" enzyme; but that the other, designated in Chapter 34 as k_{EA} (50 sec.$^{-1}$) loses its significance as rate constant of the same enzyme, and becomes a function of the rate constants of the two enzymes, catalyzing the two reaction steps; under certain conditions, it may be practically equal to the rate constant of the second of them. The course of the reaction decay in the dark period is, in this case, more complex than that expected for a simple first order reaction—in agreement with the flash light findings of Gilmour, and Kok, and with the chemiluminescence data of Arnold and Strehler.

New contribution to the *minimum quantum requirement problem* were published by Yuan, Evans, and Daniels,[9] and by Bassham, Shibata, and Calvin[10]; the first-named study supported the view that this requirement

    [6] Vishniac, W., Gatlinburg Conference on Photosynthesis of the NAS, Oct. 1955 (in press).

    [7] Rodrigo, T. A., *Thesis*, Univ. of Utrecht, 1955.

    [8] Kok, B., Gatlinburg Conference on Photosynthesis of the NAS, Oct. 1955 (in press).

    [9] Yuan, E. L., Evans, R. W., and Daniels, F., *Biochim. et Biophys. Acta*, **17**, 185 (1955).

    [10] Bassham, J. A., Shibata, K., and Calvin, M., *ibid.*, **17**, 332 (1955).

is close to 8, the second one suggested that it may be 6.5 or 7.0 in strong light, and as low as about 4 in weak light (as suggested earlier by Kok).

Significant new observations of the *reversible changes in absorption spectrum and fluorescence of chlorophyll in vivo* have been described by Witt,[11] as well as by Chance and co-workers,[12] by Strehler and Lynch,[13] and by Coleman, Holt, and Rabinowitch.[14] The latter suggested that in *Chlorella*, chlorophyll undergoes, in light, a reversible change (probably reduction), leading to a bleaching in the red and the appearance of a band at 525 mμ. However, discrepancies between the observations of Coleman *et al.*, on the one hand, and of Duysens (and Strehler and Lynch), on the other, call for further study, especially in the red region of the spectrum.

The *chemical reduction path of carbon dioxide*, elaborated by Calvin, Benson, and co-workers on the basis of C(14) studies (*cf.*, Chapter 36) has received a suggestive confirmation in the demonstration by Racker[15] that reduced pyridine nucleotide, adenosine triphosphate, and bicarbonate will in fact produce sugar if provided with the eleven enzymes postulated in Calvin and Benson's cycle.

Franck[16] made the interesting suggestion that the transfer of hydrogen from hydrated chlorophyll to an acceptor, such as the carboxyl group in PGA, is achieved by the intervention of an *excited triplet state* of the pigment, formed by cooperation of two photons—one producing the metastable triplet state, and the other (supplied by resonance transfer from near-by chlorophyll molecules) transferring the metastable molecule into the excited state. Obviously, this mechanism requires a minimum of 8 photons per reduced CO_2 molecule. The existence of a *triplet metastable state* of chlorophyll *b* has been confirmed, and its energy found equal to about 33 Kcal./mole, by phosphorescence studies of Becker and Kasha.[17]

This is only a short (and arbitrary) selection of important new facts and speculations added to the field under review within a few months after this monograph was "completed!"

The author's thanks are due to Dr. Robert Emerson, the Photosynthesis

[11] Witt, M. T., *Naturwissenschaften*, **42**, 72 (1955); *Z. physik. Chem.*, **4**, 1920 (1955); *Z. Elektrochem.*, **59**, 981 (1955); Gatlinburg Conference on Photosynthesis of the NAS, Oct. 1955 (in press).

[12] Chance, B., Gatlinburg Conference on Photosynthesis of the NAS, Oct. 1955 (in press).

[13] Strehler, B. L., and Lynch, V. M., *Science*, **123**, 462 (1956).

[14] Coleman, J., Holt, A. S., and Rabinowitch, E., Second Gatlinburg Conference on Photosynthesis of the NRC, Oct. 1955 (to be published); *Science* (in press).

[15] Racker, E., *Nature*, **175**, 249 (1955).

[16] Franck, J., *Daedalus*, **86**, 17 (1955) (Rumford Medal Lecture, American Academy of Arts and Sciences in Boston).

[17] Becker, R. S., and Kasha, M., in *The Luminescence of Biological Systems*, Princeton Univ. Press, Washington, 1955, p. 25.

Laboratory, and the Botany Department of the University of Illinois for the patience with which they have allowed him to use their facilities for the completion of this work. The author owes much to discussion with his co-workers, Dr. A. Stanley Holt and Dr. E. E. Jacobs. Mr. Paul Latimer, Mr. John Coleman, and Dr. Sylvia Frank have helped in the preparation of the index. Miss Natalie Davis kindly supplied one of the drawings.

Miss Carolyn Prouty has helped to minimize, in this volume, the vexatious errors in bibliography, much too many of which have been permitted to go undiscovered in Volume I; she and Mrs. Ruth Adams have also helped with proofreading. Interscience Publishers have shown infinite patience and forbearance with the author's unreliability, procrastination, and tendency to enlarge and change the text up to the very last moment. The author's warm thanks are due Dr. Eric S. Proskauer and his staff.

The author early acquired a prejudice against dedicating scientific treatises to parents, teachers, or wives; it somehow seemed to him that such homage should be reserved to more personal works of art, and those who inspired them. This prejudice has prevented him from expressing his thanks to the one man to whom he owes both his interest in photochemistry and photobiology, and whatever special qualifications he may have to deal with these subjects, in the most natural and adequate way—by dedicating this monograph to him. The author has had the privilege of studying or working with several great scientists of our time; but Dr. James Franck is the one of whom he likes to consider himself a pupil—not only in the narrower field of common scientific specialization, but in the whole approach to the world of atoms and molecules. While the author has not been able to match the persistence, concentration, and clarity of thinking that have made James Franck one of the great pathfinders in this enchanted world (not to speak of acquiring his humility and deep understanding of the world of men), he can plead that these have been among the strongest influences he has experienced, and guiding lights he has tried to follow.

I hope Dr. Franck will accept these words of gratitude at the end of the long work, in lieu of a dedication which was due to him on its first page.

EUGENE I. RABINOWITCH

Urbana
April 1956

CONTENTS

PART FOUR

KINETICS OF PHOTOSYNTHESIS

(continued)

CHAPTER 31

THE TEMPERATURE FACTOR

Photosynthesis is a sequence of photic and catalytic chemical reactions, combined with physical processes of diffusion and convection. The primary photochemical reaction probably is independent of temperature; but all other partial processes of photosynthesis, physical as well as chemical, must be influenced by it. The adsorption and hydration equilibria, which affect the colloidal state of the protoplasm and of the chloroplasts and thus, indirectly, alter the efficiency of the photosynthetic apparatus, also are sensitive to heat or cold. Therefore, the influence of temperature on photosynthesis is a complex phenomenon. The rate of photosynthesis can be expected to be insensitive to temperature changes—at least within a certain range—only in the "light-limited" state, in which the velocity of the over-all process is equal to that of the primary photochemical reaction.

Under all other conditions, the rate of photosynthesis will change with temperature, and the character of this change will depend on what factor exercises the strongest influence on the rate under the specific conditions of the experiment.

It was mentioned on page 1137 that the maximum experimentally realizable quantum yield of photosynthesis may be smaller than the theoretical photochemical quantum yield because a certain fraction of the products may be lost by back reactions, independently of light intensity. This proportion, and thus the maximum quantum yield, could depend on temperature. In other words, photosynthesis could be somewhat dependent on temperature even in the light-limited state.

Before considering the "temperature curves" of photosynthesis (*i. e.*, curves in which rate is plotted against temperature, at constant light intensity and carbon dioxide concentration), we will first discuss the difference between the internal temperature of plants and the temperature of the surrounding medium. Obviously, this internal temperature, rather than the temperature of the medium, should be used as the independent variable in the analysis of the temperature curves.

A. INTERNAL TEMPERATURE OF PLANTS*

The internal temperature of plants can be higher or lower than that of the ambient medium. It may be different in different parts of the

* Bibliography, page 1254.

plant, *e. g.*, the chloroplasts, which absorb light, may be warmer than bidermis of the leaf, which is cooled by evaporation.

Fifty years ago, Timiriazev (1903) thought that local heating of chloroplasts by light absorption may be sufficient for thermodynamic reversal of combustion processes, and that this may explain photosynthesis. However, it has since become clear that the mechanism of activation of chemical reactions by light is different from that of activation by heat. The former is based on the formation of electronically excited molecules, or of free radicals, while the latter depends on the production of molecules with high kinetic energies.

Unlike warm-blooded animals, plants have no mechanism for automatic regulation of oxidation and transpiration processes, capable of maintaining the organism at a constant temperature. However, they, too, continuously produce heat by exothermal metabolic processes, and a plant enclosed in a dark vessel full of saturated water vapor (to prevent both transpiration and photosynthesis) warms itself up until the internal evolution of heat is compensated by increased conduction losses to the gas and by thermal radiation losses to the walls.

If plants are allowed to absorb light, and to transpire, the above three items of energy exchange are augmented by two additional terms: energy supply by light absorption and energy losses by transpiration. A certain fraction of the former is lost, from the point of view of heat balance, by conversion into chemical energy (photosynthesis).

Brown and Escombe (1905) and Brown and Wilson (1905) made the first attempt to calculate the stationary temperature of plants by estimating all these energy terms. They concluded that the stationary temperature of ordinary leaves, enclosed in a *dark* space *saturated* with water vapor, can rise only a few hundredths of a degree above the temperature of the medium. The difference may be somewhat larger in plant organs in which the volume/surface ratio is small, such as fruits, stalks and succulent leaves.

In *strongly illuminated leaves*, the conversion of light into heat is by far the largest item on the credit side of the heat balance, this physical process outweighing by far the chemical heat production by respiration and other exothermal metabolic processes. On the debit side, too, the two physical energy-consuming processes, *transpiration* and *heat transfer* (the latter we consider to include thermal conduction, convection and radiation losses), account for a much larger amount of energy than the chemical process of photosynthesis. Photosynthesis is most important in weak light (of the order of 1000 lux), where it may consume 30% or more of absorbed light energy; but in direct sunlight this proportion does not exceed 5% (*cf.* chapter 28). Consequently, the internal temperature of leaves exposed to the sun can be attributed (in the first approximation) to the balance of three physical processes: light absorption, transpiration and heat transfer.

A controversy has arisen as to the relative importance of the two last-named processes. Brown and Escombe (1905) considered transpiration by far the most important of the heat-dissipating processes; and this view was supported by the experiments of Shull(1919), Eaton and Belden (1929), Arthur and Stewart (1933) and Clements (1934). Eaton and Beldon (1929) pointed out that only transpiration can account for the fact that sun-exposed leaves often are *cooler* than the air.

Smith (1909) and Clum (1926), on the other hand, came to the conclusion that transpiration has a relatively small effect in preventing an excessive rise of temperature in strongly illuminated leaves. According to Clum, the leaves in which transpiration is prevented by a layer of vaseline are, in direct sunlight, only 2 or 3° C. warmer than similar, freely transpiring leaves. He therefore suggested that heat transfer is the main factor responsible for keeping the temperature of sun-exposed leaves within narrow, comfortable limits. Watson (1933, 1934) pointed out that even if it were true that heat transfer normally dissipates less energy than transpiration, its relative importance must increase with increasing difference in temperature between leaf and air. The low estimate of the energy loss by heat transfer made by Brown and Escombe might have been due, at least in part, to the neglect of *infrared reradiation*; an item, the importance of which was pointed out in particular by Curtis (1936[1,2]).

The concept of transpiration as the all-important heat-dissipating and temperature-regulating process in green leaves, which was for a time generally accepted in plant physiology, needs correction. The combined heat-dissipating effect of convection currents and thermal radiation may some time equal or even exceed that of transpiration. The relative importance of the several heat-dissipating processes depends on the structure of the leaf, and on atmospheric conditions, such as wind, exposure to cold surfaces and the humidity of the air. Because of these special conditions (and also because of the use of insufficiently reliable experimental methods), the data given in the literature for the temperature of illuminated leaves vary widely.

Table 31.I contains the most important results. A discussion of the experimental methods can be found, *e. g.*, in Miller's *Plant Physiology* (1931) and in an article by Seybold and Brambring (1933).

The earliest investigations were carried out by means of mercury thermometers with bulbs pressed against, or wrapped into, leaves. Later, small thermoelements were substituted for thermometers; some authors used them to measure the *surface temperature* of the leaves, whereas others attempted to introduce them into the leaves to determine the *internal temperature* of the latter.

Table 31.I shows that Shreve (1919), Miller and Saunders (1923), Eaton and Belden (1929), and Seybold and Brambring (1933) found only

TABLE 31.I

TEMPERATURE OF ILLUMINATED LEAVES

Author	Method	Plant	Illumination	Temp. diff. between plants and air, ° C.
Askenasy (1875)	Hg thermometer	Succulents (Sempervivum, Opuntia)	Sun	+15 to +20
Ursprung (1903)	Hg thermometer	Succulents (Opuntia Sempervivum, Mammilaria)	Sun	+16 to +22
		Nonsucculents	Sun	+7
		Ulmus betula	Sun	+8
		Saxifraga	Shade	Up to +3
Blackman, Matthaei (1905)	Thermocouple in midrib	Prunus laurocerasus	Sun	+7 to +16
			Shade	Up to +15
Smith (1909)	Thermocouple in leaf	Succulents and nonsucculents	Tropical sun	−1.5 to +4
			Shade	Up to +8
Ehlers (1915)	Thermocouple in leaf	Pinus laricio austriaca	Winter sun (shade temp. −12° C.)	Up to +9
			Winter sun (shade temp. +3°)	+1 to +2
			Cloudy winter day	−0.1 to +0.7
			Winter night	
Shreve (1919)	Thermocouple in contact with leaf surface	Eucelia farinosa	Open sun	+1.5
		Tradescantia	Greenhouse	+1.3
Miller, Saunders (1923)	Thermocouple in contact with leaf surface	Field Crops		
		Corn, sorghum, soybeans, pumpkin, watermelon	Average from morning to evening	±0.1
		Alfalfa	Average from morning to evening	−1
Clum (1926)	Thermocouple in leaf	Fuchsia speciosa, Phaseolus vulgaris	Sun on open field	Up to +13
		Brassica oleracea, Syringa vulgaris	Sun in greenhouse	Up to +16

	Thermocouple against		Sun; dry, hot air (up to 40° C.) 1 cal/cm.² min.[a]
Eaton, Belden (1929)	Thermocouple against leaf surface	Cotton leaves	
		Turgid	Up to −5.3
		Wilted	Up to ±2
Seybold, Brambring (1933)	Thermocouple against leaf surface	Xeromorphs	
		Ficus elastica	
		Upper side	" +4.1
		Lower side	" +3.7
		Hedera helix	
		Upper side	" +4.8
		Lower side	" +2.7
		Hygromorphs	
		Tropaeolum majus	
		Upper side	" +3.6
		Lower side	" +3.6
		Vicia faba	
		Upper side	" +2.8
		Lower side	" +1.9
		Succulents	
		Sedum spectabile	
		Upper side	" +3.4
		Lower side	" +2.5

[a] According to Seybold and Brambring, the temperature difference is proportional to incident light intensity (in the region between 0.1 and 1 cal/cm.² min.).

comparatively small temperature differences between leaf and air. According to Miller and Saunders, the *average* surface temperature of leaves in the field is practically equal to that of the air. (In direct sunlight, the surface temperature of the leaf often was, in their experiments, 1 or 2° *above* that of the air; but, when the sun was covered by a passing cloud, transpiration caused the leaf temperature to drop immediately to 1 or 2° *below* that of the surrounding atmosphere. Averaging over all atmospheric conditions gave a mean value of temperature difference close to zero.) Eaton and Belden (1929) found that turgid leaves of cotton plants had a temperature *lower* than that of the air during the greater part of the hot and dry summer day; only on mornings and evenings was this relation reversed. *Wilted* cotton leaves, on the other hand, showed positive temperature differences during the whole day. (The authors considered these results evidence of the strong influence of transpiration.)

In contrast to these examples of negligible or even negative temperature differences between illuminated leaves and air, others, from Askenasy (1875) to Clum (1926), have observed in direct sunlight, internal temperatures 10°, 15° or even 20° C. above the temperature of the ambient air. The fact that Miller and Saunders conducted their experiments with much thinner leaves than Blackman and Matthaei, and Clum may explain some of the discrepancies. Askenasy (1875) first suggested that thick succulent leaves are particularly liable to overheating in the sun. Table 31.I shows that this conclusion was confirmed by Ursprung (1903), but not by Smith (1909). The figures of Seybold and Brambring in this table (*cf.* also fig. 31.1) also show no significant differences among the temperatures of xeromorphic, hygromorphic and succulent leaves. This is not as strange as it may appear; because of the lower ratio of surface to volume, succulents undoubtedly are handicapped in the *dissipation* of heat; but, since light absorption is proportional to the area rather than to the volume (while heat capacity is proportional to the volume) of the leaf, the heating by light absorption also is much slower in the case of succulents than in that of thin leaves (*cf. Bryophyllum* curve in fig. 31.1). (Conditions are different in the dark, since heat production by respiration is approximately proportional to the *volume* of the tissue.)

The difference between leaf temperature and air temperature may be of paramount importance for the photosynthetic activity of evergreens in winter. According to Ehlers' data in Table 31.I, the needles of conifers may have, during a winter day, an internal temperature 7 or 8° C. above that of the air. The temperature of *alpine plants* may rise even higher, because of the intense radiation to which they are exposed, even while the temperature of the air may be quite low.

The danger of overheating is particularly great in experiments with leaves exposed to artificial light of high intensity, because this light may contain ten times more infrared rays than sunlight of equal visual brightness. Although leaves are comparatively transparent above 800 mμ (*cf.* chapter 22), they absorb enough in this region to affect their heat balance seriously. In the experiments of Seybold and Brambring, illuminated white leaves, which absorb only infrared light, acquired temperatures not much lower than those reached by green leaves (which absorbed both infrared and visible light). For example, the temperature difference was +2.7° C. for the upper surface of a white *Pelargonium* leaf, and +3.0° for the upper surface of a green leaf of the same species (*cf.* fig. 31.1); the corresponding figures for *Abutilon* were +2.3° and +3.7° C., respectively.

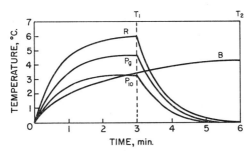

Fig. 31.1. Changes in leaf temperature upon illumination and darkening (after Seybold and Brambring 1933): *R, Rhododendron hybridum; P$_g$, Perlargonium zonale*, green leaf; *P$_{10}$*, same, white leaf; *B, Bryophyllum*, succulent leaf.

Karmanov (1951) found that leaves exposed to a flux of 1000 kerg/ (cm.^{2} sec.) from a 750 watt incandescent lamp, acquired a temperature up to 20° C. above that of the ambient air.

Franck and French (1941) found the temperature of *Hydrangea* leaves, illuminated by collimated light from a 1000 watt lamp (about 80,000 lux) to be 1.3° C. above that of the medium; these leaves were cooled by rapid circulation of gas in a thermostated vessel.

Because of the effective cooling of *aquatic plants* by the surrounding water, such plants have no opportunity to acquire internal temperatures markedly different from those of the medium, even if subjected to very intense illumination. They thus provide the most appropriate material for the quantitative study of the influence of temperature on the rate of photosynthesis.

B. Temperature Range of Photosynthesis*

All life processes are restricted to a certain "biokinetic" range of temperatures. Above and below this range, the organisms suffer a more or

* Bibliography, page 1254.

pid, and more or less irreversible "chill injury" or "heat injury." If
te of a specific biochemical process *in vivo* is measured as a function of
rature, one often finds a region of temperatures in which the effect of
heating is reversible, and similar to that observed in the study of simple
reactions *in vitro*. However, at the two ends of this range, the reversible
influence of temperature becomes obscured by irreversible, destructive
processes, such as changes in the colloidal structure of the protoplasm,
which affect indirectly all chemical reactions in the living organism.

In the case of photosynthesis, the region of reversible changes extends,
for plants adapted to moderate climates, only from about 0° to about 30° C.
Below $+5°$, and above $+25°$ C., a slow chill injury or a slow heat injury
may set in, so that the observed rate of photosynthesis depends not only
on the momentarily prevailing temperature, but also on how long the plant
has been exposed to it.

The exact limits of the biokinetic range of photosynthesis depend on
the individual (ontogenetic) adaptation of the plants, as well as on the
phylogenetic adaptation of the species. Analogous to the existence of
heliophilic and umbrophilic species and individuals (described in chapter
28), certain plants exhibit *thermophilic*, others *cryophilic* properties. This
"thermal adaptation" will be discussed in section 3.

1. Lower Temperature Limit and Chill Injury

Conifers, mosses and lichens retain their chlorophyll in winter,
even though the temperature of the air may drop to $-50°$ C. It has been
observed (*cf*. Ehlers 1915) that the starch deposits in conifers sometimes are
replenished in winter (while those of evergreen deciduous plants are used
up during the same period); this points to continued photosynthetic activity of conifers in cold weather. How low the temperature must be to
inhibit all photosynthesis has not yet been determined by reliable experiments under laboratory conditions; while observations made in the open
gave contradictory results. Boussaingault (1874) found no photosynthesis
below the freezing point, not even in conifers. Kreusler (1887, 1888), on
the other hand, noticed photosynthesis in *Rubus* at $-2.4°$ C., and Jumelle
(1891) claimed to have observed oxygen evolution by conifers (*Picea ex-
celsa, Juniper communis*), and lichens (*Evernia prunastri*) even at $-30°$
and $-40°$ C. These extreme results found little acceptance; Ewart (1896,
1897), among others, rejected them as erroneous, asserting that tropical
plants cease to reduce carbon dioxide at temperatures as high as $+4°$ or
$+8°$ C., that subtropical and aquatic plants stop reduction at 0° or $+2°$ C.,
and that land plants from temperate, arctic and alpine zones do so slightly
below the freezing point. Ewart noted that oxygen production ceases

upon cooling gradually rather than suddenly, e. g., in some tropical plants, after 1 hour exposure to 5°, and after 15 minutes exposure to 1° C. Matthaei (1904) found that the photosynthesis of cherry laurel leaves declines rapidly below 0° and ceases practically immediately at −6°. An extension of the temperature range of active photosynthesis, down to −16° for certain alpine phanerogams and to −20° for alpine lichens, was again claimed by Henrici (1921). In the interpretation of her results, the possibility of wide difference in temperature between the interior of the leaves and the surrounding air should be taken into account. In the mountains, where strong irradiation combines with low air temperature, the heating of leaves by light absorption may be particularly strong. Ivanov and Orlova (1931) found photosynthesis in pine trees down to −7° C., Printz (1933), only down to −2° or −3°. Freeland (1944) noted that apparent photosynthesis still was positive, in three *Pinus* species, at an external temperature of −6°.

It was mentioned above that the inhibition of photosynthesis by cold requires time. Conversely, once photosynthesis has been stopped by cold, plants may require a certain time for the recovery of their photosynthetic ability. Ewart (1896) found that, when *Elodea* was chilled to 0° for 6 hours and then transferred to warm water, photosynthesis did not reappear before 10 or 15 minutes; after chilling for 1 or 2 days, the recovery required 3 hours, and after 5 days, from 5 to 24 hours.

The suspension of photosynthesis in chilled leaves and its recovery upon thawing is one aspect of the broad problem of frost resistance of plants, which is of vital importance in agriculture. Largely because of this practical importance, extensive investigations have been carried out on the way in which plant cells are injured by cold. Ice formation—inside as well as outside the cell—certainly is a factor of importance, and frost resistance has often been associated with the capacity of the protoplasm for undercooling. Some plants can be cooled to −20° C. or lower without visible formation of ice. This capacity for undercooling has been associated with the living state of the protoplasm; thus, Lewis and Tuttle (1920) found that ice was first formed in living cells of *Pyrola rotundifolia* at −32° C., while in leaves of the same species, killed by immersion into solid carbon dioxide, water was observed to freeze at −3.5° C.

Ice formed on the outer walls drains water from inside the cells and thus causes injuries similar to those induced by drought. Ice formed inside the cell can cause injury by mechanical pressure.

Warburg (1919) found that *Chlorella* cells can resist immersion into liquid air for several hours without loss of their capacity for photosynthesis. He attributed this striking property to the fact that the single chloroplast contained in a *Chlorella* cell has the form of a bell, spread over the inside of the sturdy cell walls; this position may enable the chloroplast to sustain without injury a pressure that would destroy the chloroplasts freely suspended in the protoplasm.

Whatever the macroscopic and microscopic cause of frost injury to plant cells, the *submicroscopic* phenomenon is probably always a change in the colloidal structure of the cytoplasm or of the chloroplasts. It is a fundamental fact of life that the protoplasm colloids become granulated or coagulated under the influence of mechanical forces. Mechanical stresses, rather than direct temperature effects, probably explain the destruction of cells by freezing. This is why dried cells, in which no ice formation is possible, can sustain much lower temperatures than the same cells while they still contain water. (These questions are discussed in the book of Lepeschkin 1924.)

One immediate effect of cooling below about 10° C. is a rapid *increase in viscosity* and *decrease in permeability* of protoplasm. This change must impede the diffusion of carbon dioxide to the chloroplasts, as well as the translocation of the intermediates and products of photosynthesis. It can thus contribute to the rapid decline of the photosynthetic efficiency, which most plants experience in this temperature region.

2. Optimum and Upper Temperature Limits; Heat Injury

Above the lower temperature limit, the rate of photosynthesis increases with temperature, first rapidly, then more slowly, until an optimum is reached, followed by a rapid decrease to zero. For land plants in moderate climates, the optimum is situated at 30–35° C. However, it lies much lower for land plants and algae adapted to low temperatures, and much higher for "thermophilic" algae that live in hot springs, and for tropical desert plants. Some authors, *e. g.*, Henrici (1921), Lundegårdh (1924). Ehrke (1929, 1931) and Stocker (1927, 1935), have observed temperature curves with several (two or three) maxima. Even if these results (to be discussed in more detail in section C) are correct (which is doubtful), the occurrence of several temperature optima certainly is an exception and not the rule.

The decline of the net gas exchange $(P - R)$ at high temperatures (which eventually leads to a change in sign) is partly caused by a continued rapid rise in respiration. (The latter increases exponentially up to 45 to 50° C.) However, even if correction is made for enhanced respiration, the true photosynthesis (P) also is found to possess an optimum, even though it is less sharp, and is situated at a higher temperature, than the maximum of net oxygen liberation (*cf.* fig. 31.2).

Thomas (1950) found for the purple bacterium, *Rhodospirillum rubrum*, a peak of efficiency at 40° C., followed by a sharp drop.

As previously mentioned, P becomes time-dependent when the limit of the "biokinetic" range is approached, usually even before the optimum has been reached.   The position of the optimum thus becomes a function of the duration of the experiment.   Matthaei (1904) found slow heat injury to cherry laurel leaves at temperatures above 25° C.; figure 31.3 was

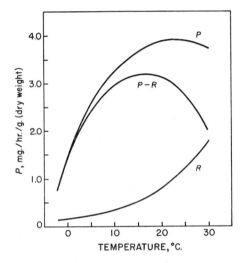

Fig. 31.2. Temperature curves of respiration (R) and photosynthesis (P) in the lichen *Ramalina farinacea* (after Stålfelt 1939).

constructed from her data by Jost (1906).   By extrapolating them to zero time, Blackman (1905) extended the exponentially ascending temperature curve of the photosynthesis of cherry laurel leaves up to 37.5° C. Decker (1944) observed a decline of 45% in the (apparent) photosynthesis of two species of pine between 30° and 40° C., in light of about 40,000 lux. Green algae behave similarly: Wurmser and Jacquot (1923) found complete stoppage of photosynthesis in *Ulva* after 2 minutes exposure to 45° C.

Stålfelt (1939) found in *Usnea dasypoga* (a lichen) time dependence above 21° C., independently of light intensity (2–32 klux), but subject to adaptation to the temperature of the ambient medium.

Noddack and Kopp (1940) found that the photosynthesis of *Chlorella* became time-dependent above 22° C.   By using experiments of not over 30 minutes duration, they could extend the exponentially ascending curve up to 30° C.; but a 150 minute exposure to the latter temperature gave an average rate 25% less than that found in 30 minute experiments (*cf.* fig. 31.4).   Craig and Trelease (1937) found no marked time effect in *Chlorella* up to 46° C., if the exposure was restricted to 20 minutes.

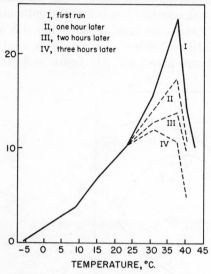

Fig. 31.3. Temperature curves of photosynthesis of cherry laurel (Jost 1906, after Blackman and Matthaei 1905).

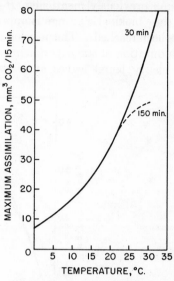

Fig. 31.4. Temperature curve of photosynthesis in *Chlorella* (after Noddack and Kopp 1940).

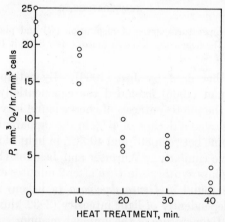

Fig. 31.5. Effect of heat treatment (at 45° C.) on photosynthesis of *Chlorella* (after Kennedy 1940).

The use of rapid recording devices (*cf.* chapter 25) may permit following the ascending temperature curve of photosynthesis beyond the range attained by Blackman and Noddack.

If a plant is subjected to superoptimal temperatures for more than a few minutes, reversible thermal *inhibition* may be replaced by an irreversible (or only slowly reversible) thermal *injury*. Van Amstel (1916) observed thermal injury to the photosynthetic apparatus of *Elodea* at 40° C. Wurmser and Jacquot (1923) observed that the inhibition of photosynthesis in

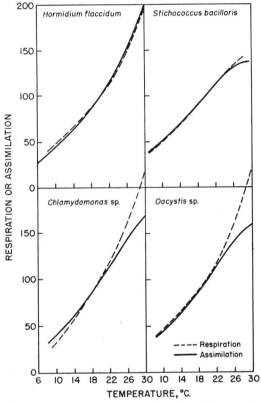

Fig. 31.6. Temperature curves of photosynthesis and respiration of four algae (after van der Paauw 1934).

green, red or brown algae, caused by a 2 minute exposure to temperatures of 36–45° C., was not entirely reversible, but left a permanent decrease in photosynthetic efficiency after return to 16°.

Kennedy (1940) studied quantitatively the effects of preheating to 40 and 45° C. on the photosynthesis of *Chlorella* at 25°. One hour exposure to 40° had no effect on chlorophyll concentration and respiration, but caused a decline in photosynthesis by about 30%. Exposure to 45° caused a very rapid decline in the capacity for photosynthesis at 25° (*cf.*

fig. 31.5).   Kennedy argued that if this heat injury were caused by the inactivation of an enzyme, as suggested by Blackman, its influence could be balanced, in flashing light experiments (*cf.* chapter 34) by longer dark intervals between flashes (as is actually possible in the case of cyanide poisoning; *cf.* chapter 12, page 307).   However, he found that the reduction in oxygen yield per flash, caused by 15 minutes preheating to 45°, was the same, whether the dark intervals lasted 0.0175 or 0.37 second.   (The cyanide effect would disappear in the latter case; *cf.* fig. 34.12.)

Progressive heat injury is not a specific property of the photosynthetic apparatus, but is common to all biochemical functions, as well as to many enzymatic reactions *in vitro*.   However, photosynthesis is more sensitive to heat than most other life processes.   Respiration of yeast, for example, shows the first signs of inhibition at 46° C. and is rapidly destroyed only by temperatures in excess of 50° (*cf.* van Amstel and van Iterson 1911).   A comparison between the temperature curves of photosynthesis and respiration of the lichen *Ramalina farinacea* was given in figure 31.2; figure 31.6 gives a similar comparison for four unicellular algae.

Sooner or later, all vital functions of the cell become totally inhibited by heat.   What ensues is known as "heat coma."   In its first stages, it is still reversible, but finally it leads to "thermal death."   With most leaves and algae, this happens at 55–60° C., although for organisms adapted to extreme cold (or heat) the lethal temperatures may be considerably lower (or higher).

The comparatively early onset of the thermal injury of photosynthesis seems to indicate that its origin lies in an impairment of the photosynthetic apparatus itself, rather than in the general decline in the "vitality" of the protoplasm.   The fact that, with short exposures, the ascending temperature curve can be followed for some distance above the optimum indicates that the thermal inhibition is caused by a destructive process (*e. g.*, slow deactivation of an enzyme), and is not associated with an intrinsic property of the kinetic mechanism of photosynthesis (such as thermal dissociation of the ACO_2 complex, as was suggested by Willstätter and Stoll).

Attempts have been made to calculate the activation energy E_a of the process responsible for heat injury, by measuring its rate at different temperatures (*cf.* Bělehrádek 1935, page 174).   Values between 51 and 95 kcal have been calculated for the heat inhibition of photosynthesis between 20 and 65° C., with the smaller values derived from measurements at the lower temperatures.   Several hypotheses have been suggested as to the nature of the process to which this remarkably high activation energy may correspond.   *Denaturation and coagulation of proteins* was the first explanation; and it finds much credence despite the fact that the "heat inhibition" of photosynthesis occurs at temperatures considerably below those usually associated with the denaturation of proteins. The *destruction of enzymes*, which also was suggested as a possible cause of the decline of photosynthesis at high temperatures (Blackman 1905) may be but a consequence of changes in structure of their proteinaceous components. *Lipides* (the role of which in the composition of the chloroplasts was discussed in chapter 14) also may be responsible for heat sensitivity. (It was mentioned in chapter 14, page 361, and in chapter 24, page 817, that the "melting" of grana in chloroplasts, observed under the fluorescence microscope, was attributed by Metzner to a liquefaction of lipides.)

It may be asked whether the rapidly reversible thermal *inhibition* (by comparatively low temperatures and short exposures) is fundamentally different from the irreversible, or only slowly reversible, *injury* caused by higher temperatures and longer exposures. In addition to reversible shifts of chemical equilibria, such as the one responsible for the formation of the ACO_2 complex, various other reversible changes could affect reversibly the rate of photosynthesis at high temperatures. One of them is the increased *viscosity* of the protoplasm. It wa smentioned on page 1220 that, at low temperatures, the viscosity of the protoplasm, like that of most other materials, decreases upon heating. Characteristically, however, it passes through a minimum, usually in the neighborhood of 15° C., and then increases again. This increase can slow down the diffusion of carbon dioxide and thus bring photosynthesis from the carbon dioxide-saturated into the carbon dioxide-limited state. Like the effect of the dissociation of the ACO_2 complex, this kind of thermal inhibition should disappear upon an increase in the concentration of carbon dioxide. Thus, in order to clarify the role of viscosity in the decline of photosynthesis at low and high temperatures, it would be useful to measure these effects at different concentrations of carbon dioxide, and to compare the results with the change in viscosity. Much quantitative work remains to be done in this field.

Thermal deactivation of enzymes by the denaturation of proteins also may be more or less rapidly reversible, depending on how far the denaturation has been allowed to proceed. Reversible denaturation as an explanation of the temperature effect on enzymatic processes has been discussed, *e. g.*, by Johnson, Brown and Marsland (1942) on the basis of experiments with luciferase.

3. Thermal Adaptation

Ewart's figures, given on page 1219, indicated already that the lower limit of photosynthesis differs in plants from different climatic zones, and thus reveals a considerable degree of "thermal adaptation." This adaptation also affects the positions of the *optimum* and of the *upper limit* of photosynthesis. While higher plants and algae adapted to moderate climates attain the maximum rate of photosynthesis at 30–35° C. and suffer rapid injury above 40°, *cold-adapted* (cryophilic) plants often show a maximum of true photosynthesis below 10°, and a maximum of net oxygen evolution near the freezing point. Some of them have been found to suffer thermal injury at temperatures as low as 12° (*Phaeocystes poucheti*).

Arctic land plants, polar sea algae and the flora of snow fields and glaciers ("red snow") are examples of such cold-adapted species. Plants

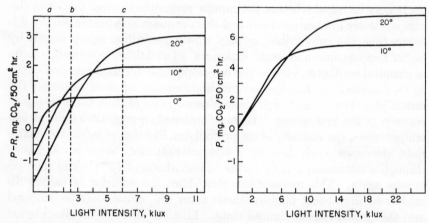

Fig. 31.7. Light curves of two arctic plants—*Salix glauca* (left) and *Chamaenerium latifolium* (right) at different temperatures (after Müller 1928).

adapted to high temperatures do not reach the maximum rate of net photosynthesis before 40° C.; they are capable of organic synthesis even at 50° and survive without permanent injury at 80° or even 90°. Algae that live in hot springs and tropical desert plants are extreme examples of such "thermophilic" plants.

Among studies of the temperature dependence of photosynthesis of cold-adapted species, we can mention that of Müller (1928) with *Salix glauca* and *Chamaenerium latifolium* at Disco, Greenland. Figure 31.7 shows the relative positions of light curves of *net* oxygen evolution by the two plants at 0°, 10° and 20°. In weak light (ordinate *a*) the largest oxygen production is obtained at 0°; at 2000 lux (ordinate *b*), the optimum of net synthesis is shifted to 10°, while in stronger light (ordinate *c*), it lies at (or above) 20° C. Similar behavior is shown by cryophilic marine *algae*. Thus, Harder (1915) found that *Fucus serratus* liberates, in weak light, twenty times as much oxygen at 0 as at 17° C. It must be pointed out, however, that within the linear range of the light curves, where *true* photosynthesis is independent of temperature, the *net* oxygen evolution of *all* plants—cryophilic as well as thermophilic—must decrease with temperature (because of accelerated respiration). In cryophilic plants, this behavior is accentuated by the early "thermal saturation" of true photosynthesis (which is not paralleled by an equally early saturation of respiration). Furthermore, these plants live in regions where the average intensity of sunlight is low, and this shifts their maximum efficiency under natural conditions toward lower temperatures. In July, the average illumination at Disco is only 450 lux, a light intensity at which the optimum of net oxygen production by *Salix* lies close to 0° C.

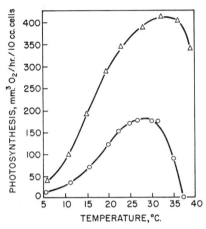

Fig. 31.8. Variation in rate of photosynthesis with temperature at high light intensities for *Nitzschia closterium* (○) and *N. palea* (△) (after Barker 1935).

The temperature optima of *true* photosynthesis probably never lie as low as one may think from the consideration of the net gas exchange of cryophilic plants. Barker (1935) (*cf.* fig. 31.8) found that the optimum of true photosynthesis of the marine diatom *Nitzschia closterium* lies at 27° C., although this organism usually lives at 8–12°. The fresh water diatom *Nitzschia palea* had an optimum at 33°. (This high optimum temperature probably enables the species to withstand the high temperatures that shallow waters may reach on warm summer days.)

At the opposite extreme from the arctic plants, adapted, as far as their net organic synthesis is concerned, to temperatures near the freezing point, we find some algae (*e. g., Phormidium*) as well as certain sulfur bacteria thriving in hot springs, with temperatures up to 80 or 90° C. (*cf.*, for example, Harvey 1924). Their cells must be capable of sustaining such high temperatures without injury. Furthermore, unless the water in which they live cools down perceptibly during certain periods of the day or season, these algae must be able to carry out photosynthesis at a temperature that would bring immediate and complete thermal inhibition—in fact, thermal death—to most other plants. Photosynthesis of these "thermophilic algae" certainly is worth closer investigation, under natural as well as under laboratory conditions. Inman (1940), who studied some algae from Yellowstone Park geysers, was concerned primarily with the proof of the spectroscopic identity of their chlorophyll with that of ordinary plants; the only observation he made concerning their photosynthesis was that they liberate oxygen when irradiated at room temperature.

Desert plants, exposed to direct sunlight, sometimes are heated to temperatures approaching those of hot springs. Their photosynthetic apparatus, too, must remain uninjured by heat. MacDougal and Working (1921) found that *Opuntia* actually continues to grow, and thus presumably to carry out photosynthesis, at 58° C.; growth is stopped, and shrinkage ensues, when the temperature reaches 62°. Wood (1932) found that the optimum of photosynthesis of some Australian desert plants lies between 40° and 50°, and that their net oxygen production does not become zero until 55°.

Extended heat resistance of thermophilic algae, bacteria and desert succulents must be due to a different structure of the protoplasmic constituents responsible for heat injury. Lipides might, perhaps, bear the main responsibility for this difference, because it is known that the thermal stability of fats and lipides depends on the temperature at which they have been formed in the organism.

One chemical peculiarity of thermophilic algae was noted by Harvey (1924): they contain no catalase, a unique occurrence in the whole plant world. Harvey suggested that thermal algae have no need for catalase because, at the high temperatures at which they live, the decomposition of hydrogen peroxide proceeds rapidly enough by itself. This caused him to speculate generally on the possibility of a primeval "life without enzymes" in a medium hot enough for the organisms to dispense with catalysts. However, thermophilic algae are more likely to represent adaptations of normal species to high temperatures, than remnants of such prehistoric, enzyme-free flora. (To prevent misunderstanding, it must be pointed out that thermophilic algae contain many enzymes—*e. g.*, oxidases—and are only deficient in catalase.)

A very interesting result was obtained by Sorokin and Myers (1953) in the course of experiments on mass cultivation of *Chlorella*. By starting with inocula from warm local surface water, and incubating the cultures at 32° C., several strains were isolated which showed decided "thermophilic" behavior. One of them grew fastest at 39° C.; fig. 31.8A shows its growth rate as a function of temperature, compared to that of an ordinary strain of *Chlorella pyrenoidosa*. The rate of growth of the two strains appears the same below 25° C., but the thermophilic strain grows much faster at the higher temperatures; a much higher light intensity is needed to reach growth "saturation" in this case. Preliminary manometric studies of the thermophilic strain at 39° C. indicated a rate of glucose respiration equivalent to 18 volumes of oxygen, and a rate of photosynthesis equivalent to 186 volumes of oxygen per volume of cells per hour (Sorokin 1954)—by far the highest rate ever observed with any organism!

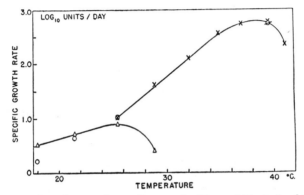

Fig. 31.8A. Growth rates of an ordinary and a thermophilic strain of *Chlorella* (Sorokin and Myers 1953): (Δ) *Chlorella pyrenoidosa* (Emerson's strain) at 1600 foot-candles; (×) Tx 71105 at 1600 foot-candles; (○) Tx 71105 at 500 foot-candles; (φ) Tx 71105 at 2800 foot-candles.

We have spoken so far of the adaptation of whole species (or strains) to heat or cold. As in the case of heliophilic and umbrophilic plants, this "phylogenetic" thermal adaptation is paralleled, although on a reduced scale, by the adaptation of individual organisms. Harder (1924) studied, as an example, the behavior of the aquatic plants *Elodea canadensis*, *Fontinalis antipyretica*, *Hypnum*, *Chara* and *Chladophora*, grown at 4.6° and

TABLE 31.II

PHOTOSYNTHESIS OF *Fontinalis* PLANTS GROWN AT 4.6° AND 20° C. (AFTER HARDER 1924)

I, lux	Temp., ° C.	P, relative units	
		Cold-adapted	Warm-adapted
1,017	8	224	162
	18	151	182
29,545	8	1564	944
	18	1894	2639

20° C. The specimens showed no difference in appearance, but their
responses to temperature were quite different. An example is given in
Table 31.II. In weak light, the photosynthesis of cold-adapted *Fontinalis*
plants *declined* between 8° and 18° C. while that of the warm-adapted
plants increased; in strong light, it increased in the same range, but proportionately much less than the photosynthesis of the warmth-adapted individuals.

Since the figures in Table 31.II appear to represent *true* photosynthesis, and not *net*
gas exchange, the negative sign of the temperature effect in the case of cold-adapted
plants in weak light is noteworthy.

The analogy between light and temperature adaptations caused
Harder to ask whether cold-adapted plants have an enhanced capacity
for photosynthesis at low temperatures (analogous to the higher efficiency
of shade-adapted plants in weak light). He carried out no experiments
with plants of equal dry weight (or equal leaf surface), but attempted instead to answer this question by analyzing the figures given in Table 31.II
for plants of unknown weight and leaf area. He concluded that at low
temperatures cold-adapted individuals actually are more efficient than
warmth-adapted ones. Theoretically, the situation in cryophilic plants is
somewhat different from that in the umbrophiles; in the latter case, an
improved efficiency (rate per unit area) in weak light could be easily explained by a higher chlorophyll content and consequent enhanced absorption of light (*cf.* page 422). For cryophilic plants to have an enhanced efficiency at low temperatures (in strong light), they should contain a higher
concentration of rate-limiting enzyme; and if this is the case, one can ask:
why have they not a superior efficiency at the higher temperatures as well?
One conceivable explanation is to assume that two different enzymatic
processes limit the rate at the two temperatures.

In contrast to the low respiration of umbrophilic plants, the respiration of cryophilic plants is, according to Harder, not weaker, but even
stronger than that of the thermophilic individuals; consequently, their
compensation points are higher.

Plants that do not interrupt photosynthesis in winter experience a reversible adaptation to cold during this season as shown, *e. g.*, by measurements of Stålfelt (1937, 1939) on lichens. The temperature curve of
respiration is practically unaffected by the season, while the optimum of
photosynthesis, and consequently also that of net organic synthesis, is
shifted in winter toward lower temperatures. For the eight species investigated by Stålfelt the average shift of the optimum of net photosynthesis
was from 18.5° in summer to 14.1° C. in winter. The fact, observed by
Beljakov (1930), that barley plants suddenly cooled to 3–10° interrupt

photosynthesis for a while, but resume it afterward, also can be interpreted as an example of individual thermal adaptation. (This phenomenon contrasts with the *gradual suspension* of photosynthesis in chilled plants, observed by Ewart, and mentioned on page 1219.)

Similar questions have been much discussed in connection with the increase in the abundance of algae observed as one proceeds northward in European waters. Kniep (1914) and Harder (1915) suggested that this is due to the greater excess of photosynthesis over respiration at the lower temperatures. This theory received support from experiments by Ehrke (1931); but Lampe (1935), who conducted experiments on numerous green, red and brown algae, under laboratory conditions and in natural habitats, concluded that the average light intensity under natural conditions often is not low enough to permit application of the Kniep-Harder theory. Furthermore, he observed that some algae can adjust themselves within a few days to higher or lower temperatures; the position of the optimum of net organic synthesis is shifted, by this adaptation, nearer to the temperature of the medium. These algae can act as cryophiles in winter and as thermophiles in summer. Only some deep water red algae, and the umbrophilic green algae, have rigid cryophilic characteristics, and actually increase in weight more rapidly in cold water (and dim light).

C. TEMPERATURE COEFFICIENT AND HEAT OF ACTIVATION OF PHOTOSYNTHESIS*

As stated before, if we leave aside the two extreme ends of the "biokinetic range" of photosynthesis, and restrict ourselves to its middle part, where no time-dependent inhibition effects occur, we can obtain a short segment of a temperature curve that apparently reflects the direct effect of temperature on the kinetic mechanism of photosynthesis. The shape of this temperature curve depends on several parameters, such as light intensity and carbon dioxide supply. This was not sufficiently realized by earlier plant physiologists, who gave figures for the "temperature coefficient" of photosynthesis without identifying the specific conditions under which this coefficient was determined. In weak light and in the presence of an adequate supply of carbon dioxide, the rate of the over-all process of photosynthesis is practically equal to that of the primary photochemical reaction, and the temperature curve reflects the influence (or, more likely, lack of influence) of temperature on this primary reaction. When the supply of carbon dioxide is low, the temperature coefficient may be essentially that of the supply process, *e. g.*, of the diffusion of carbon dioxide through an aqueous phase. In this case, Q_{10} (the proportional increase in rate caused by an increase in temperature by $10°$ C.) will be of

* Bibliography, page 1255.

the order of 1.2 or 1.3. If the supply of all reactants, as well as of light, is abundant, the over-all rate will be determined by the efficiency of a non-photochemical "bottleneck" reaction, and the temperature coefficient may reach or exceed 2 (which is the common value for enzyme reactions *in vitro* and *in vivo*). Obviously, by working in intermediary regions, one can obtain values of Q_{10} ranging all the way from 1 to 2 or more (as illustrated by figs. 28.6 and 28.7).

Most of the earlier investigators worked under "natural" conditions, which means partial or complete light saturation, but usually incomplete saturation with carbon dioxide. No wonder a controversy arose as to whether the temperature coefficient of photosynthesis is about 1.3 or about 2. Prjanishnikov (1876), Kreusler (1887, 1888, 1890) and Lubimenko (1906), among others, found Q_{10} values of less than 1.5, whereas Matthaei (1904), Blackman and Matthaei (1905) and Blackman and Smith (1911) obtained values close to 2. Blackman was the first to realize that high temperature coefficients were associated with high light intensities. He took this as an indication that photosynthesis involves, in addition to the photochemical reaction proper, also an enzymatic process, which becomes rate-determining when light and carbon dioxide are supplied in abundance.

This conclusion was criticized by Brown and Heise (1917), who referred to the above-mentioned papers of Prjanishnikov and others for proof that the temperature coefficient of photosynthesis is lower than that of typical enzymatic reactions; this criticism was rejected by Smith (1919) as showing a lack of understanding of the dependence of the temperature coefficient on external conditions.

The designation of the nonphotochemical stages of photosynthesis as the "Blackman reaction," first used by Willstätter and Stoll in 1918 and Warburg in 1919, was based on this argument of Blackman. We know now that photosynthesis involves not one, but many nonphotochemical catalytic reactions; therefore, references to *the* Blackman reaction should be avoided. Whenever possible, one should specify which of the several known or suspected catalytic reactions one has in mind.

1. Absence of Temperature Influence in Weak Light

Primary photochemical processes ordinarily are independent of temperature. This is so because light usually provides more than the required minimum activation energy, so that no additional thermal activation is needed. Exceptional situations occur, however, in which light energy alone is insufficient to accomplish a certain transformation that becomes possible if a certain amount of thermal energy is supplied during the excitation period.

When it was generally assumed that 4 quanta are sufficient to reduce one molecule of carbon dioxide, the scarcity of energy available in 4 quanta of red light caused Franck and Herzfeld (1937) to examine the possibility that light energy might be supplemented by thermal energy, available in the many degrees of freedom of the chlorophyll molecule. However, recourse to such hypotheses becomes unnecessary if the latitude of at least 6 quanta per molecule of carbon dioxide is allowed to the theorists. Another potential source of temperature effects in the light-limited state (*i. e.*, of a temperature dependence of the maximum quantum

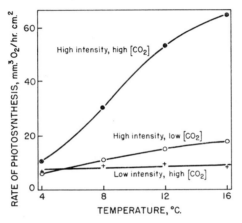

Fig. 31.9. Rate of *Gigartina* photosynthesis plotted against temperature (after Emerson and Green 1934). 60 w. incandescent lamps 8 cm. below vessel; 10% transmission filter used for low light curve. Artificial sea water; $35 \times 10^{-5} M$ CO_2/l. for "high CO_2," and $2.5 \times 10^{-5} M CO_2/l$. for "low CO_2."

yield of photosynthesis) also was discussed before (page 1138)—the possible influence of temperature on the relative probability of the forward and the back reaction of the primary photochemical products. This effect, if it exists, must be determined by the difference of two activation energies, and therefore could be comparatively small.

Experimental results speak against any theory requiring a *strong* temperature dependence of the rate in low light. Wherever the illumination was weak and the supply of carbon dioxide adequate, the rate of photosynthesis was found to be more or less exactly constant over a considerable range of temperatures. Thus, Matthaei (1904) found that the rate of production of oxygen by cherry laurel leaves in weak light is practically constant between 0° and 20° C. Warburg (1919) observed that the temperature coefficient of photosynthesis of *Chlorella*, $Q = P$ (20° C.)$/P$ (10° C.), roughly equal to 2 in strong light ($I = 16$–45 relative units), declined to unity at $I = 1$. Figure 31.9 shows similar results obtained more recently by Emerson and Green (1934) with the red alga *Gigartina*; here the rate obtained at the lower light intensities (and with an ample supply of carbon dioxide) is practically independent of temperature between 4° and 16° C. Emerson and Lewis (1940, 1941) in their work on the maximum quantum yield, γ_0, of photosynthesis in *Chlorella* (*cf.* chapter 29) found no significant differences between the γ_0 values at 0°, 10° and 20° C. Similar results were obtained by Wassink, Vermeulen, Reman and Katz (1938) and Noddack and Kopp (1940), (*cf.* figs. 28.6 and 28.7).

Figure 28.7A refers to experiments in white light, and figure 28.7B, to those in monochromatic (red) light. It will be remembered (*cf.* page 1160) that Noddack and Eichhoff found that the "light curves" bend early in white light, but remain linear until close to saturation in red light. The difference between figures 28.7A and B corresponds to these findings. In the first case, the rate is independent of temperature only in extremely weak light, whereas, in the second one, the light curves corresponding to 10° and 20° C. (corrected for respiration) coincide over a considerable range of light intensities. We said (pp. 1098 and 1162) that the origin of differences between the shapes of light curves in white and red light, claimed by Noddack and co-workers, is obscure; here we must be satisfied with the fact that, whether the light curves bend early or late, the rate is independent of temperature so long (and only so long) as they are linear. In other words, temperature dependence becomes evident as soon as some dark process interferes to reduce the over-all rate below the maximum value allowed by the primary photochemical process.

TABLE 31.III

COMPENSATION POINT AND TEMPERATURE

Observer	Organism	I_c (in lux)		
		0° C.	10° C.	16° C.
Ehrke (1931)	*Entheromorpha compressa*	—	299	457
	Fucus serratus	—	270	408
	Plocamium coccineum	—	247	299
Müller (1938)	*Salix glauca*	300	750	—
	Chamaenerium latifolium	175	500	—

Of course, the rate can be independent of temperature only within the "biokinetic" range. The drop in efficiency at the two ends of this range cannot be avoided, however weak the illumination. Blackman and Matthaei (1905) found that the rate of photosynthesis of cherry laurel leaves declines sharply below 0° C., in weak as well as in strong light. There appear to be no data available on the rate of photosynthesis in weak light at temperatures above 30°; but one can expect that, sooner or later, superoptimal temperatures will affect photosynthesis also in the light-limited state. However, if the exceptional sensitivity of photosynthesis to heat is due mainly, or partly, to the enzyme that limits the rate in strong light, the quantum yield in weak light may remain unimpaired, at least for some time, even at temperatures at which the saturation rate is strongly depressed.

Speaking of the temperature independence of photosynthesis in weak light, one thinks, of course, of *true* photosynthesis and not of *net* gas exchange. Since respiration is accelerated by heating, while true photosynthesis in weak light is independent of temperature, the net oxygen liberation in weak light must decline with increasing temperature; the compensation point is thus shifted toward the higher light intensities. This fact already was mentioned in chapter 28 (page 984); Table 31.III gives some additional examples.

2. Temperature Effect in Strong Light

We now consider another extreme case—that of strong illumination and ample supply of carbon dioxide. The transition from temperature-independent photosynthesis in weak light to temperature-dependent photosynthesis in strong light is best illustrated by light curve families with temperature as parameter (figs. 28.6 and 28.7), and temperature curve families with light intensity as parameter (fig. 31.9). In Table 31.IV are collected the results of a number of investigations dealing with the effect of temperature on photosynthesis in light- and carbon dioxide-saturated state. We have omitted measurements in which light and carbon dioxide saturation probably was incomplete, for example those of van Amstel (1916), carried out in light of only 2500 lux, and of Lundegårdh (1924), Yoshii (1928), Beljakov (1930) and Stålfelt (1939), in which ordinary air was used as the source of carbon dioxide. (We saw in chapter 27 that most plants require considerably more than the 0.03% CO_2 in the atmosphere for the saturation of their photosynthetic mechanism.)

Table 31.IV contains values of the temperature coefficient, Q_{10}, and of the heat of activation, E_a,* as characteristics of the temperature effect. The theoretical significance of these constants will be discussed in section 6. The constancy of E_a over a certain temperature range indicates that the rate in this range follows the Arrhenius function:

(31.7) $$\log P = A + (B/T)$$

where A and B are constants and T is the temperature on the absolute scale.

Figures 31.10 to 31.14 serve as illustrations to Table 31.IV. They clearly show the difference between the results of van der Paauw on *Chlamydomonas*, Craig and Trelease on *Chlorella* and Noddack and Kopp

---

* The similarity of this symbol and of the symbol E_A used throughout this book for the carbon dioxide-fixing catalyst should cause no confusion.

TABLE 31.IV

TEMPERATURE DEPENDENCE OF PHOTOSYNTHESIS IN THE LIGHT-SATURATED STATE

1. LAND PLANTS

Observer	Plant	Light source	CO_2 supply	Temp. range, °C	Q_{10}	E_a	Remarks
Matthaei (1904), calcd. by Willstätter, Stoll (1918)	Prunus laurocera-sus	Keith gas burner	CO_2-enriched air	15–24	1.52	7	
Blackman, Matthaei (1905), calc. by Kanitz (1915)	Prunus laurocera-sus	Sun	CO_2-enriched air	0–10	2.40	13	Time-dependent above 25°. Arrhenius law approximately valid
				10–20	2.12	12	
				20–30	1.76	10	
				30–37.5	1.81	11	
	Helianthus tubero-sus	Sun	CO_2-enriched air	20–30	2.6	17	
Willstätter, Stoll (1918)	Ulmus, green leaves	Incandescent lamp, 50,000 lux	5% CO_2 in air	15–25	1.53	7	
	Ulmus, aurea leaves		5% CO_2 in air	15–25	1.35	5	
Singh, Kumar (1935)	Raphanus sativus	28,650 lux	0.03 to 0.3%	16–46	—	—	Only at 0.03% enough points to determine Q_{10}
Shri Ranjan (1940)	Eugenia jambolana	1500 w. bulbs 1 ft. away	0.2% CO_2 in air	20–30	2–16	—	Corrected for assumed change of respiration in light
				25–35	1–53	—	

2. AQUATIC HIGHER PLANTS

Observer	Plant	Light source	CO_2 supply	Temp. range, °C	Q_{10}	E_a	Remarks
Blackman, Smith (1911)	Elodea canadensis		0.02% CO_2 in water	7–13	2.05	11.4	

3. GREEN ALGAE

Observer	Plant	Light source	CO_2 supply	Temp. range, °C	Q_{10}	E_a	Remarks
Osterhout, Haas (1919)	Ulva rigida	Sun	Sea water	17–27	1.81	10	
Warburg (1919)	Chlorella vulgaris	1500 w. lamp, 20 cm. distance	4% CO_2 over Knop's solution	5–10	4.3	23	P assumed to be a linear function of temperature.
				10–20	2.1	12	
				20–30	1.6	8	
Yabusoe (1924)	Chlorella vulgaris	"Saturating light"	5% CO_2 over Knop's solution	10–20	2.45	15	
				20–30	1.35	5	

Reference	Organism	Light	Medium	Temp. range (°C)	Q_{10}	μ	Remarks
Emerson (1929) (Fig. 31.13)	Chlorella pyrenoidosa	"Strong light"	Carbonate-bicarbonate buffer No. 9	4–8	7.6	33	No effect of varying chlorophyll concentration; Arrhenius law invalid.
				8–12	4.8	22	
				12–16	2.5	15	
				16–26	1.54	7	
Craig and Trelease (1937) (fig. 31.11)	Chlorella pyrenoidosa	22,000 lux	Buffer No. 9	15–25	3.2	20.0	No effect of heavy water. Arrhenius law valid.
Wassink, Vermeulen, Reman, Katz (1938)	Chlorella pyrenoidosa	1.75×10^4 erg/cm.^{2} sec.	Buffer No. 9	10–16.3	3.25	20.0	
				16.3–22.5	2.85	17.7	
Noddack, Kopp (1940) (fig. 31.12)	Chlorella pyrenoidosa	55,400 lux	Buffer No. 9	0–30	2.0	11.9	Time effect above 22° C.; Arrhenius law valid
van der Paauw (1932, 1934) (fig. 31.10)	Hormidium flaccidum	150 w. lamp, 14–16 cm. distance	Buffer (0.375 M NaHCO$_2$ +0.125 M Na$_2$CO$_3$)	5–15	2.8	17	
				10–20	2.2	12	
				15–25	2.0	11.6	
				20–30	1.9	11	
	Chlamidomonas	150 w. lamp 14–16 cm. distance		10–20	2.5	15	
				15–25	2.1	12.6	
				20–30	1.7	9	
	Stichococcus bacillaris	150 w. lamp 14–16 cm. distance		10–20	2.0	11.5	Arrhenius law approximately valid up to 25° C.
				15–25	1.7	9	
				20–30	1.4	5.5	
	Oocystis	150 w. lamp 14–16 cm. distance		10–20	2.2	13	
				15–25	1.9	10.9	
				20–30	1.6	8.5	
Tamiya et al. (1948)	Chlorella ellipsoidea	25 klux	CO$_2$-satd., pH 4.6	1–28	—	6; 27	2 consecutive reactions assumed
			CO$_2$-satd., pH 7.0	1–28	—	6; 27	
			CO$_2$-deficient (1 × 10^{-6} m./l.)	1–28	—	0; 6; 27	3 consecutive reactions assumed

4. RED AND BROWN ALGAE

Reference	Organism	Light	Medium	Temp. range (°C)	Q_{10}	μ	Remarks
Emerson, Green (1934) (fig. 31.14)	Gigartina harveyana (red alga)	4 × 60 w. lamps, 8 cm. distance	3.6 × 10^{-4} m./l. CO$_2$ in water	4–8	13.5	47	Arrhenius law invalid everywhere
				8–12	4.2	24	
				12–16	1.7	8.7	
Barker (1935)	Nitzschia closterium (diatoms)	"High"	"High"	5–15	—	30	
	N. palea (diatoms)	"High"	"High"	5–25	—	30	

also on *Chlorella*, on the one hand, and those of Emerson, and Emerson and Green on *Chlorella* and *Grigartina*, on the other. The first-named investigators (as well as Blackman and Matthaei) found the Arrhenius equation

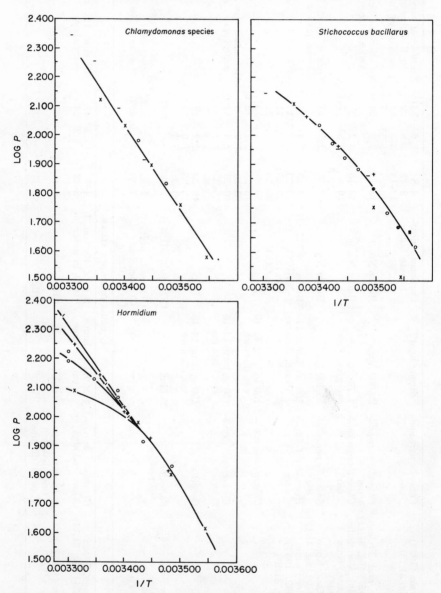

Fig. 31.10. Heat of activation of photosynthesis (after van der Paauw 1934): $\log P = f(1/T)$.

to be valid, at least approximately, over a considerable range of temperatures; whereas the log $P = f(1/T)$ curves of the second group of investigators (which also includes Warburg and Yabusoe) show practically no straight section at all. The observations of van der Paauw on *Hormidium* and *Stichococcus* also indicate continuous curvature of the logarithmic temperature curve, even if this curvature is less strong than in Emerson's curves.

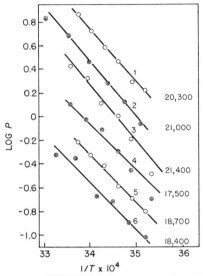

Fig. 31.11. Rate of photosynthesis as a function of temperature in the range 10–30° C. (after Craig and Trelease 1937). $\log P = f(1/T)$ for *Chlorella*. Figures on curves are E_a values; curves 1–3 for H_2O; curves 4–6 for D_2O. Ordinate scale given is for curve 3; curve 1 moved up 0.6; curve 2, up 0.2; curve 4, up 0.05; curve 5, down 0.1; curve 6, down 0.25.

In the region around 15° C., the activation energies found by most observers are in approximate agreement ($E_a = 10$–12 kcal), although Barker gave $E_a = 30$ kcal for diatoms, and Craig and Trelease, and Wassink and co-workers found for *Chlorella* $E_a = 20$ and 18 kcal, respectively. Larger discrepancies are encountered below 10° where the activation energies measured by some investigators were about the same as at higher temperatures, whereas those found by others were up to 30 or even 40 kcal/ mole. At 20–30° the E_a values sometimes were found to remain constant, and sometimes to decrease to as little as 5 or 8 kcal.

Tamiya, Huzisige and Mii (1948) found that the temperature curve of the photosynthesis of *Chlorella ellipsoidea* can be interpreted, between 1° and 28° C., in the carbon dioxide saturated state, by two consecutive reactions with activation energies of 6 and 27 kcal, respectively. This applied to measurements at pH 4.6 as well as at pH 7.0; however, the first reaction was slowed down by a decrease in pH, while the second one was unaffected by this change.

The decline in E_a above 20° undoubtedly is associated with an incipient heat inhibition. Since the temperature at which this inhibition first occurs, and its rapidity, are quite different for different species or strains, it may well explain the variability of the apparent E_a values in the upper temperature range. Some of these discrepancies could perhaps be removed if all investigators would take the precaution of reducing the time of exposure at the higher temperatures to a few minutes, or of extrapolating the results to zero time, as was done by Blackman and by Noddack and Kopp. More

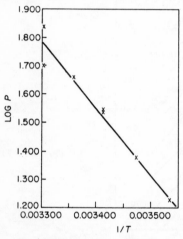

Fig. 31.12. log $P = f(1/T)$ for *Chlorella pyrenoidosa* (after Noddack and Kopp 1940).

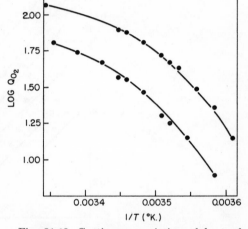

Fig. 31.13. Continuous variation of heat of activation for *Chlorella* at two different chlorophyll concentrations (after Emerson 1929): log $P = f(1/T)$.

difficult to interpret are the high E_a values observed by some authors (particularly by Emerson and Green 1934, and Emerson 1929) in the low temperature region ($<10°$ C.), a region in which Blackman, and Noddack and Kopp, for example, noticed no increase in temperature coefficient above the values observed at 10–20° C. (The theory of nonlinear "Arrhenius curves" will be discussed in section 5.)

The low temperature coefficients obtained by Willstätter and Stoll (*cf.* Table 31.IV) also are noteworthy. In their experiments the light was strong (over 50,000 lux) and the carbon dioxide supply ample (5% CO_2); nevertheless, the observed Q_{10} values, at 15–25° C., were as low as 1.5 for green leaves and 1.3 for yellow leaves. As mentioned before, Willstätter suggested that the increase in the velocity of the limiting enzymatic process with temperature is counteracted by the thermal dissociation of the ACO_2 complex, and that this reduces Q_{10} below the "normal" value of 2. However, if this were so, the situation could be amended by an increase in the concentration of carbon dioxide—which is not the case. Results obtained with *Chlorella* suspensions also make

Willstätter and Stoll's hypothesis improbable. It seems as if in their experiments the rate was not free of carbon dioxide supply limitations, despite the high external value of [CO₂].

The marked difference between the temperature coefficients of green and chlorophyll-deficient leaves, found by Willstätter and Stoll, also offers a problem for interpretation. Perhaps the yellow leaves were incompletely light-saturated under the conditions of the experiment. Emerson (1929), working with chlorotic *Chlorella* cells, found that the temperature curves in the region 4–6° C. had the same slope for chlorophyll concentrations

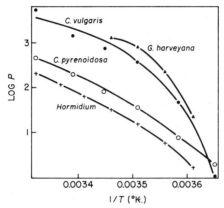

Fig. 31.14. Comparison of log $P = f(1/T)$ for *Gigartina harveyana*, *Chlorella vulgaris*, *Chlorella pyrenoidosa* and *Hormidium* (after Emerson and Green 1934).

varying in the ratio of 1 to 6 (*cf.* fig. 31.13); in the case, apparently, light intensity was sufficiently high to produce light saturation at all temperatures and chlorophyll concentrations. It should be recalled (*cf.* page 968) that Emerson found no dependence of the saturating light intensity on chlorophyll concentration in *Chlorella*, whereas such a difference was noted by Willstätter and Stoll in green and *aurea* leaves (*cf.* fig. 32.2).

Warburg (1919) and Yabusoe (1924) suggested that the rate of photosynthesis is a *linear*, rather than exponential, function of temperature, and considered this an essential characteristic of this process. (For the respiration of the same algae, they found the normal exponential curve.) As pointed out by Emerson (1929), the number of points determined (only three in Yabusoe's paper) was insufficient to warrant the unusual conclusion.

Emerson and Arnold (1932[2]) found that, in flashing light, intervals of about 0.02 second between flashes are necessary at room temperature (25° C.) to obtain the maximum oxygen yield per flash—*i. e.*, to let the rate-limiting dark reaction run to completion before the next flash. Similar experiments at 5° C. (*cf.* Emerson and Arnold 1932[1]) showed that at this temperature dark intervals required for "flash saturation" are longer—of the order of 0.08 second. This difference corresponds to a Q_{10} of about 2, or an activation energy of about 12 kcal, in agreement with the steady light results of Noddack and Kopp and many others, listed in Table 31.IV. This supports the view that in *Chlorella*, at least, the same "finishing" dark reaction that limits the maximum yield per flash also limits the rate in strong continuous light.

3. Temperature Curves in the Carbon Dioxide-Limited State

No systematic measurements of the temperature dependence of photosynthesis in the "carbon dioxide-limited" state (*i. e.*, in strong light and with a reduced concentration of carbon dioxide) are available in the literature. The case nearest to this limiting one, which was much studied, was that of free atmosphere (0.03% CO_2). In this case, the carbon dioxide concentration, although not strictly "limiting," exercises a strong influence on the rate, and the effect of heating may be largely due to the accelerated supply of carbon dioxide. It was mentioned on page 1232 that Prjanishnikov (1876), Kreusler (1887, 1888, 1890) and Lubimenko (1906) found, for photosynthesis in the open air, Q_{10} values between 1 and 1.5. Similar or smaller values were found by Stålfelt for mosses and lichens (Table 31.V).

TABLE 31.V

Q_{10} VALUES FOR THE PHOTOSYNTHESIS OF MOSSES AND LICHENS
(AFTER STÅLFELT 1937, 1939) (0.03% CO_2)

Species	0–10°	10–20°	20–30° C.
MOSSES			
Hylocomium proliferum............	1.56	1.13	0.74
Hylocomium triquetrum............	1.43	1.00	0.60
Hylocomium squarrosum...........	—	1.13	0.65
Hylocomium parietinum...........	1.52	1.13	0.60
Ptilium crista castrensis...........	1.43	1.15	0.69
Sphagnum Girgensohrii	2.67 (5–15°)	1.35	0.66
LICHENS			
Usnea dasypoga..................	2.65	0.97	0.43
Cladonia silvestris................	2.42	1.04	0.63
Ramalina fraxinea................	1.55	1.15	0.62
Ramalina farinacea...............	1.95	1.03	0.68
Umbilicaria pustulata.............	1.40	0.86	0.48
Evernia prunastri.................	2.07	1.14	0.75
Cetraria islandica................	1.08	0.81	0.46
Peltigera aphtosa.................	1.06	1.14	0.73
Cetraria glauca..................	1.0	0.84	0.62

In figure 31.9, the middle curve referred to the temperature dependence of photosynthesis in a red alga (*Gigartina*) in high light and comparatively low carbon dioxide concentration (initial concentration, $[CO_2]_0 = 2.5 \times 10^{-5}$ mole/l., about twice that in air). The rate is about doubled between 4 and 14° C., corresponding to $Q_{10} = 2$; but the influence of temperature still is very much weaker than in the presence of abundant carbon dioxide (upper curve), where the rate is increased, in the same temperature interval, by more than a factor of six.

Tamiya, Huzisige and Mii (1948) found that, at 1×10^{-6} mole/l. CO_2, the temperature curves of *Chlorella ellipsoidea* could be interpreted by a sequence of three reactions, with $E_a = 0$, 6, and 27 kcal, respectively (*cf.* above their results obtained at CO_2 saturation). Only the first reaction depends on CO_2 concentration.

The factor that may be important for the temperature dependence of photosynthesis at low temperatures, in the carbon dioxide-limited state, is the viscosity of the protoplasm (with the stomata fully open, the main diffusion resistance between air and chloroplasts may be in the aqueous phase within the cell; *cf.* chapter 27, page 916). According to Weber (1916) the temperature coefficient of the viscosity of the protoplasm is about 1.4 (between 10° and 20° C.).

Miller and Burr (1935) noted (in experiments described on page 898) that, at approximately 20,000 lux, potted plants of *Pelargonium, Tolmica, Coleus, Bryophyllum, Eichhornia, Primula, Saxifraga, Zebrina* and *Begonia*, as well as an unidentified *Crassulacea*, reached a balance between respiration and photosynthesis at approximately 0.01% CO_2 in the air, at all temperatures between 4° and 37° C. (This balanced state was maintained for many hours at temperatures <30°, but was soon disturbed, apparently by a progressive heat inhibition of photosynthesis, at 35–37° C.) Since, at 0.01% CO_2 and 20,000 lux, carbon dioxide supply probably is the main rate-limiting factor in photosynthesis, one could consider these results as proof of a practical equality of the temperature coefficients of respiration and carbon dioxide supply. This would be remarkable, since the temperature coefficient of respiration is high ($Q_{10} \simeq 2$). However, it must be taken into account that, in the state of compensation, a large part of the carbon dioxide used for photosynthesis is supplied internally, by respiration, and therefore has only a very short diffusion path (or is even used directly *in situ*). The temperature coefficient of photosynthesis may thus be that of the carbon dioxide production by respiration.

4. Temperature Curves with Several Optima

It was mentioned on page 1220 that temperature curves with two or more optima have been observed with some plants.

The first such observation was made by Henrici (1921) on alpine lichens. Lundegårdh (1924) found, in the study of tomato, potato and cucumber leaves, a main maximum at 30–35° C., which was most prominent in strong light and with an abundant supply of carbon dioxide, and two subsidiary maxima at 20° and 10°; in weak light (e. g., 1/25 of full sunlight) and relatively low carbon dioxide concentration (e. g., 0.03%), the 20° maximum became more prominent than the one at 30°.

Subsequent studies of bean leaves by Yoshii (1928) and of barley leaves by Beljakov (1930)—in Lundegårdh's laboratory—also gave temperature curves with several maxima. An example is shown in figure 31.15. Beljakov found that the relative prominence of the two main maxima—in the region of 20° and 30° C.—was different for two barley strains, and he considered this a sign of phylogenetic adaptation to different climatic conditions.

Stocker (1927) found two maxima in the temperature curves of northern lichens (thus confirming the observation of Henrici with alpine lichens) and later (1935) also

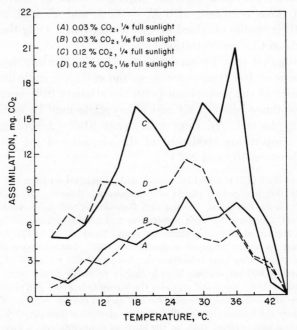

Fig. 31.15. Temperature curves of bean leaves showing
several maxima (after Yoshii 1925).

in the temperature curves of tropical trees. Stålfelt (1939), however, found only one optimum for northern lichens (cf. fig. 31.1). Ehrke (1929, 1931) found very irregular temperatures curves, with several "waves," for marine algae (e. g., the brown *Fucus* and the red *Plocamium*). Similar curves were obtained by him also for the respiration of these algae—a process for which a smooth ascent to an optimum is generally accepted.

We strongly doubt whether the multiple maxima of Henrici, Lundegårdh, Stocker and Ehrke are at all real, and not caused by experimental errors. Theoretically, no *sequence* of reactions with different temperature coefficients can give rise to curves of this type; it is, however, undoubtedly possible for systems of *competing* reactions to exhibit such complex relation to temperature.

Henrici (1921) associated the decline in the $P = f(T)$ curves between 20° and 30° C. with the formation of starch in the chloroplasts, and its inhibiting effect on photosynthesis (*cf.* Vol. I, page 331), and attributed the renewed rise of the rate between 25° and 30° to the disappearance of starch by accelerated conversion into sugars and dislocation of the latter from the chloroplasts.

5. Temperature Effect on Fluorescence

Knowledge of the influence of temperature on the yield of chlorophyll fluorescence in the living cell may contribute to the understanding of the nature of the temperature effect in photosynthesis. For a given fluorescent molecule and given composition of the complex in which this molecule is imbedded, the yield of fluorescence should be (at least, in the first approximation) independent of temperature, because the probabilities of absorption, of reradiation, of "quenching" by photochemical reaction within the complex and of energy dissipation by "internal conversion" can be expected not to be strongly affected by minor changes in temperature. Therefore, whenever a *strong* dependence of fluorescence intensity on temperature is observed, the most likely explanation is a change in the composition of the fluorescent complex. The effect of temperature changes on the light curves of fluorescence in living plants was described in chapter 28 (page 1055). These effects were observed by Kautsky and Spohr (1934) and Franck, French and Puck (1941) in leaves, by Wassink, Vermeulen, Reman and Katz (1938) in *Chlorella*, Wassink and Kersten (1945) in diatoms and by Katz, Wassink and Dorrestein (1941) and Wassink, Katz and Dorrestein (1942) in purple bacteria. The characteristic results are represented in figures 28.36–28.40.

In most cases, the yield of fluorescence was found to be higher at lower temperatures. Franck and co-workers found, more specifically, that lowering of temperature caused in *Hydrangea* leaves a downward shift of the light intensity, I_c, at which the quantum yield of fluorescence changed from the "low light value," φ_1, to the "high light value," φ_2 ($> \varphi_1$) (*cf.* page 1049 and fig. 28.26). The observations of Wassink and co-workers with purple bacteria (fig. 28.40) can be interpreted in the same way.

On the other hand, Wassink, Vermeulen, Reman and Katz (1938) found no effect of temperature on φ in *Chlorella* (fig. 28.36) and Wassink and Kersten (1945) observed, in *Nitzschia*, light curves of the shape shown in figure 28.39, in which the transition from φ_1 to φ_2 occurred at lower light intensity at 25° than at 5° C., and φ_2 was lower, instead of higher, than φ_1.

In interpreting the light curves of fluorescence in chapter 28, we suggested that a change in the yield of fluorescence is indicative of failure of a process that supplies reactants (oxidants or reductants) to the chlorophyll complex to keep pace with the consumption of these reductants by the photochemical process proper; this failure leads to "denudation" of chlorophyll, or its association with substances other than the normal reactants in photosynthesis. Franck suggested an additional cause of fluorescence changes: failure of the oxygen-liberating enzyme to keep pace with the production of "photoperoxides" by the primary photochemical process, resulting in the formation of a "narcotic" poison, that displaces the normal reactants from association with the chlorophyll complex.

Of the processes supplying the reactants, Franck considered, in particular, the formation of the oxidant ACO_2 from carbon dioxide and the acceptor A, catalyzed by the enzyme E_A. He saw in the transition from the low light yield, φ_1, to the (higher) high light yield, φ_2, evidence of exhaustion of the reactant ACO_2. The fact that this exhaustion occurred earlier at the lower temperatures can then be looked upon as evidence that the ACO_2-forming catalytic process has considerable activation energy. The observation that, at high temperatures, saturation of photosynthesis may occur at a lower light intensity than the transition $\varphi_1 \rightarrow \varphi_2$, while at lower temperatures the two phenomena occur simultaneously, then indicates that the activation energy of the carbon dioxide fixation process is *higher* than that of the enzymatic process (presumably, according to Franck, the stabilization of the primary photoproducts by the catalyst E_B), which is responsible for light saturation at high temperatures. Franck was thus led to the hypothesis that the (higher) temperature coefficient of photosynthesis observed in measurements in the lower temperature range (such as 5–15° C.) is characteristic of the carbon dioxide-fixation process, while the (lower) temperature coefficient observed around room temperature (15–25°) is determined by the "finishing" reaction, catalyzed by E_B.

In confirmation of this hypothesis, one may quote the observation (noted on page 1057) that the effect on fluorescence of lowering the temperature is quite similar to that of carbon dioxide deprivation.

The results of Wassink and Kersten with diatoms do not fit well into this picture, because, apart from the reversal of the relationship between φ_1 and φ_2, the effect of carbon dioxide deprivation on the light curve of fluorescence was found, in this case, to be similar to that of an increase, rather than of a decrease, in temperature. The effect of carbon dioxide deprivation on the light curves of fluorescence of *Chromatium* (fig. 28.30) also proved to be different and more complex than from the effect of low temperature (fig. 28.40). Altogether, it is not at all clear to what extent the transition from the "E_A-limited" state to the "E_B-limited" state, postulated by Franck, can be held responsible for the observed decrease of the temperature coefficient of photosynthesis with increasing temperature.

6. Theoretical Remarks

We have used above the values Q_{10} (temperature coefficient) and E_a (activation energy) to characterize the temperature dependence of photosynthesis. A few words are needed here on the theoretical meaning of these constants. The temperature coefficient, Q_{10}, is defined as the ratio of the reaction rates at two temperatures differing by $10°$ C.; the assumption that Q_{10} is a constant is equivalent to the postulate that the reaction rate, v, is an exponential function of temperature (van't Hoff's rule):

$$(31.2) \qquad v = \text{const.} \times e^T$$

Q_{10} is determined by the constant a in (31.2); it can be calculated from two rate measurements at temperatures differing by less (or more) than $10°$, by means of the equation:

$$(31.3) \qquad \ln Q_{10} = \frac{10 \ln (v_1/v_2)}{T_1 - T_2} = \frac{10 \, \Delta \ln v}{\Delta T}$$

Equation (31.2) is empirical. Arrhenius found that a better approximation to experimental results can be attained by representing $\ln v$ as a linear function of $1/T$ (rather than of T):

$$(31.4a) \qquad v = A \times e^{-E_a/RT}$$

$$(31.4b) \qquad \ln v = \log A - E_a/RT$$

Equations (31.4), originally also empirical formulae, later received theoretical justification, and it was shown that E_a is the "activation energy" required to bring the reaction about, whereas A is a frequency, or probability factor. From the point of view of theory, equations (31.4) are only approximate; the "constant" A must also be dependent on T. For example, in the simplest form of the collision theory of chemical reactions, in which activation is provided exclusively by the relative kinetic energy of the two colliding particles, the collision frequency (and consequently also the factor A) is proportional to $\sqrt{T}$, and the correct form of the rate equation must therefore be:

$$31.5) \qquad v = A' \sqrt{T} \, e^{-E_a/RT}$$

instead of (31.4a). If polyatomic molecules react by binary collisions, and the activation energy can be supplied not only by the translational degrees of freedom, but also by the degrees of freedom of rotation and vibration, the more complicated formula (31.6) must be substituted for (31.5):

$$(31.6) \qquad v = A' \sqrt{T} \, \frac{(E_a/RT)^{(n/2-1)}}{(n/2 - 1)!} \, e^{-E_a/RT}$$

Here, n is the number of degrees of freedom participating in the activation; for $n = 2$, expression (31.6) is reduced to (31.5). (Formula 31.6 is useful for even n values only; a generalization applicable to odd n values involves gamma functions instead of factorials.)

In the "activated complex" theory of absolute rates, the concentration of the activated complex is assumed to be proportional to $\sqrt{T}\ e^{-F_a/RT}$ (where F_a is the free energy of formation of the activated complex from the reaction partners), and the rate of its transformation into the final reaction product, proportional to $\sqrt{T}$, so that the rate equation has the form:

$$(31.7) \qquad v = cTe^{-F_a/RT} = ce^{S_a/R}\ Te^{-E_a/RT}$$

where S_a and E_a are the entropy and the heat of formation of the activated complex, respectively. The factor c in (31.7) contains—in addition to the usual concentration factors—almost exclusively universal constants, and therefore has approximately the same value for all reactants. Consequently, wide variations in the velocity constants of reactions having similar activation energies must be attributed, in this theory, to differences in the factor $e^{S_a/R}$—i. e., in the entropy (probability) of the activated complex. In the collision theory, on the other hand, variations of this kind are attributed to so-called "steric factors" (the fraction of collisions with the required energy that result in configurations making the reaction possible).

Whichever theory is used, the theoretical rate constant is always, to a first approximation, an exponential function of E_a/RT, since all other temperature-dependent factors in the above equations—except for the term in parentheses in equation (31.6) when n is large—change so slowly with temperature that they can be considered constant in the narrow range over which the velocity of a reaction is susceptible to experimental study. This is particularly true of reactions in living systems, which are restricted to the "biokinetic" range of approximately 0° to 40° C. (Between 270° and 300° K., T changes only by 10% and $\sqrt{T}$ only by 5%, whereas most reaction rates increase in this range by as much as a factor of eight or ten.)

According to all three formulae, the specific temperature dependence of a reaction is determined solely by its activation energy, E_a; *to a first approximation*, E_a can be calculated from the values of the rate constants at two temperatures, by means of the equation:

$$(31.8) \qquad E_a = -4.57\ \frac{\Delta \log v}{\Delta(1/T)}\ \text{(cal/mole)}$$

In equation (31.8), $\log v$ is a linear function of $1/T$; in (31.3), a linear function of T. However, in a narrow range of temperatures, the hyperbola $1/T = f(T)$ can be approximated by a straight line, and the two functions (31.4) and (31.8) are therefore not too different. For example, the values of $1/T$ for the temperatures 270°, 280°, 290°, 300° and 310° K. are 0.370, 0.357, 0.345, 0.333 and 0.322—i. e., they fall almost exactly on a straight line. Thus, if equation (31.8) applies, the values of Q_{10}, calculated from measurements at 0–10°, 10–20° and 20–30° C., although not exactly equal, will differ by not more than a few per cent, a variation insignificant in most kinetic measurements, particularly those in biochemistry. Thus, the Q_{10} formula (31.3) can be used as a practical substitute for the theoretically more significant Arrhenius equation (31.8). A simple relation exists between Q_{10} and E_a, namely:

(31.9) $$E_a = 0.457 T_1 T_2 \log Q_{10}$$

For $T_1 = 15°$ C. and $T_2 = 25°$ C., the relation becomes:

(31.10) $$E_a = 3.92 \times 10^4 \log Q_{10} \text{ (cal/mole)}$$

leading to the accompanying reduction table (Table 31.VI).

TABLE 31.VI

TEMPERATURE COEFFICIENT AND ACTIVATION ENERGY

Q_{10} (15–25° C.)	E_a (kcal/mole)	Q_{10} (15–25° C.)	E_a (kcal/mole)
1	0	3.5	21.3
1.5	6.9	4	23.6
2	11.8	4.5	25.6
2.5	15.6	5	27.4
3	18.7		

As discussed on page 1239, the temperature dependence of photosynthesis does not always follow equation (31.8) with a constant E_a; an apparent increase in activation energy usually is observed below 5° or 10° C., and a decrease above 20–25°; (formally, E_a becomes zero at the optimum temperature and *negative* above it). In some experiments (*cf.* figs. 31.13 and 31.14) the log $P = f (1/T)$ curve appeared to be nonlinear over its whole length.

Similar deviations from Arrhenius' law have been found in the study of most biological processes, and some authors, *e. g.*, Bělehrádek, in his monograph *Temperature and Living Matter* (1935), became altogether sceptical as to the usefulness of Arrhenius' formula in biochemistry. Bělehrádek found that the equation

(31.11) $$\log v = \text{const.} \times \log (T - \delta)$$

reproduces the rate of most biological processes more closely and over a wider range of temperatures than the formula (31.8). By an appropriate selection of the "minimum temperature," δ, the rate can be made to disappear at the lower limit of the "biokinetic" range.

Equation (31.11) is an empirical interpolation formula, and no theoretical interpretation has been suggested for it. Whether an empirical formula of an apparently wider, but still limited, range (it does not include, for example, the reversal of the trend above the optimum) is to be preferred to a theoretical equation, which is valid over a narrower range, depends on the use one wants to make of it—whether one is primarily interested in extrapolation, or in theoretical interpretation. Those who frown on the application of physicochemical theories to living systems will deprecate attempts to "impose" the Arrhenius law (or any other theoretical equation) on the complex processes in the living cell; others will see more significance in the existence of a temperature range, albeit a narrow one, in which a biochemical process follows the exponential formula, and will try to find a physicochemical explanation for deviations from it.

When the temperature course of a reaction is found to depart from the simple exponential law, it is often attempted to represent it by the combination of several temperature-dependent processes, each with its own activation energy. The reaction steps may be either competitive or consecutive. As an example of two parallel competing processes, we may consider a reaction that proceeds partly directly, and partly by means of a catalyst. The catalytic reaction normally has a smaller "temperature-independent" factor A in (31.4) (because of the low concentration of the catalyst, or a low affinity of the catalyst for the substrate) but a much lower activation energy. Consequently, at low temperatures, the catalytic reaction will predominate; while at higher temperatures, it may be replaced, more or less completely, by the direct uncatalyzed transformation. If we assume that the direct and catalyzed reactions are of the same order, e. g., of the first order (with respect to the substrate S) we obtain the scheme:

$$(31.12) \qquad S \left\{ \begin{array}{c} V = [S]\,A\,e^{-E_a/RT} \\ \xrightarrow{\quad\text{direct}\quad} \\ \xrightarrow{\text{with catalyst}} \\ v = [S]\,a\,e^{-e_a/RT} \end{array} \right\} \begin{array}{l} E_a > e_a \\ P \\ A \gg a \end{array}$$

where S stands for substrate, and P for product.

The two reactions velocities, V and v, are equal when:

$$(31.13) \qquad \ln (A/a) = (E_a - e_a)/RT_c$$

The transition temperature is thus:

$$(31.14) \qquad T_c = \frac{E_a - e_a}{4.57 \log (A/a)}$$

Above T_c, the temperature dependence of the over-all rate of conversion of S into P will approach that of the noncatalytic reaction; below T_c, it will approach that of the catalytic reaction. Thus, the absolute value of the slope of the log $v = f(1/T)$ plot will change, with increasing temperature, from a *smaller* to a *larger* absolute value. As shown by Burton (1936), among others, the transition will be *gradual*, rather than sudden, i. e., the log $\bar{v} = f(1/T)$ plot (where $\bar{v} = v + V$ means the total reaction velocity) will be curvilinear over a range of 20° or more, depending on the difference between the two activation energies.

Changes in the slope of the temperature curves also can be caused by a sequence of *consecutive* reaction steps—a so-called "catenary reaction series" (*cf.* chapter 26), which resembles a radioactive decay series (except that the velocity of each step depends on temperature). This concept has been much used in the explanation of the temperature dependence of biological and biochemical processes. It stems from Blackman's idea of "limiting factors," already discussed in chapter 26, and is thus historically connected with the theory of photosynthesis. As described in that chapter, Blackman first spoke vaguely of the "slowest factor" in a process determined by several external factors; this notion was later replaced (*cf.*, for example, Romell 1926, 1927) by the more precise concept of the slowest *step* in a sequence ("catenary series") of chemical reactions. This step was often called the "master process" or "master reaction," not because of its intrinsic importance for the chemical result of the transformation, but for its "limiting" effect on the rate. Pütter (1914) applied the master reaction concept to the interpretation of temperature coefficients. Crozier, in a series of papers (1924 and later), analyzed the temperature curves of numerous biological processes by dividing them into straight sections corresponding to different "master processes," connected by short curvilinear segments at the transition temperatures, T_c. This procedure was criticized, particularly by Burton (1936), who showed—for the case of a sequence of monomolecular reactions—that the transition regions can never be as narrow as suggested by Crozier.

In photosynthesis, the supply of carbon dioxide (by diffusion and carboxylation), and several enzymatic dark reactions of the primary photochemical products are steps in a "catenary series." It can thus happen that, starting with the state of "enzymatic limitation" (*i. e.*, saturation with respect to both light and carbon dioxide), we may pass, by a mere increase in temperature, into the state of "carbon dioxide limitation." In contrast to the first-considered case of two *competing* reactions (in which the reaction having the lower activation energy predominates at the lower temperatures) the case of two *consecutive* reactions is characterized by the fact that the one with the higher activation energy is rate-determining at lower temperatures.

In photosynthesis, the temperature coefficient declines with temperature, thus making an interpretation in terms of a series of consecutive reactions possible at least formally. An example of this kind of hypothesis is the above-mentioned suggestion of Franck, that the higher activation energy, E_a, which determines the temperature coefficient in the low temperature range, is characteristic of enzymatic carbon dioxide fixation (catalyst E_A), while the lower activation energy prevailing at room temperature is characteristic of a finishing enzymatic action.

The analysis of Burton (1937) indicates that the *gradual* change in E_a with temperature, as observed in photosynthesis, does not preclude such an explanation. However, it must be pointed out that in the kinetics of photosynthesis (as in the treatment of many biological processes) we usually deal with a *steady state*, rather than with the transformation of a limited quantity of a substrate. Burton (1937) thought that the concept of a master process cannot be applied to the steady state at all, since to reach this state, the rates of all processes in the catenary series must have adjusted themselves to that of the first irreversible step. This undoubtedly is true; but it is also true that, under different conditions, different steps in a catenary series can assume the role of the "first irreversible step." For example, if an enzymatic reaction consists of two stages:

(31.15)
$$S + E \underset{k_1'}{\overset{k_1}{\rightleftharpoons}} SE \overset{k_2}{\longrightarrow} P + S$$

(the first being the reversible formation of the substrate–enzyme complex SE, and the second its transformation into the reaction product P and the free enzyme S), the over-all rate equation (E_0 = total amount of enzyme) is:

(31.16)
$$v = d[P]/dt = k_1 k_2 [S] E_0 / (k_1' + k_2 + k_1 [S])$$

and this is reduced to:

(31.17)
$$v = d[P]/dt = k_2 E_0, \quad \text{if} \quad k_1[S] \gg k_1' + k_2$$

and to

(31.18)
$$v = k_1'[S] E_0, \quad \text{if} \quad k_2 \gg k_1' + k_1[S]$$

The transition from the case (31.17), in which the over-all rate is determined by the "first irreversible reaction," $SE \rightarrow P + E$, to the case (31.18), in which the reaction $S + E \rightarrow SE$ becomes "irreversible," can be brought about by a change in external conditions, e. g., an increase in temperature. Changes of this kind may well occur in photosynthesis.

Wohl (1937, 1940) thought that the high apparent activation energy of photosynthesis at low temperatures may be attributed to liberation of a complete glucose molecule from a "reduction center" to which it was attached by six links. This process obviously requires high energy, but can perhaps occur at comparatively low temperatures if it also has a high value of A in equation (31.4). According to the theory of the activated complex (*cf.* equation 31.7) a high value of A ($= ce^{(S_a/R)}$) means a large entropy, S_a of the activated state; and a reaction in which six bonds are disrupted simultaneously must increase the molecular disorder, *i.e.*, lead to an increase in entropy. (This hypothesis is similar to the theory of denaturation of proteins of Stearn and Eyring.)

Wohl analyzed the $P^{max.} = f(T)$ curves given by Warburg and by Emerson for *Chlorella*, and by Emerson and Green for *Gigartina*, by assuming two consecutive dark reactions, both occurring at the same "reduction site" (*i. e.*, at the same enzyme molecule), one requiring the time t_{d1} and the other the time t_{d2}. Under these conditions, the dark reaction time, t_d, derived from flashing light experiments (chapter 34) is simply the sum of the two consecutive reaction periods, $t_d = t_{d1} + t_{d2}$. Wohl found it possible to reproduce the experimental data closely by assuming that the first reaction has an A value in the Arrhenius formula characteristic of a bimolecular reaction (with the reaction partner present in a concentration of $10^{-1.3}$ to $10^{-5.2}$ mole/l.), and a low activation energy (0–9 kcal/mole), while the second one is a monomolecular reaction with a very high activation energy (23–58 kcal/mole), and a high activation entropy. This second reaction was the one he interpreted as the liberation of a complex (C_6) molecule, by simultaneous dissociation of several (six?) bonds attaching it to the enzyme. The bimolecular reaction accounts for 73–85% of the total dark reaction time at 15–25° C., and for only 12–24% at 5° C.

Wohl pointed out himself that with the four arbitrary constants available (two A values and two E_a values), the possibility of representing the experimental curves by the theoretical equation is not in itself significant; but he considered it significant that the two calculated reactions are so different in character, and, in particular, that the reaction that seems most important at low temperatures has the character of a monomolecular reaction with an extraordinarily high activation energy.

The attempt of Tamiya, Huzisige and Mii (1948) to analyze the temperature curves of photosynthesis, in terms of two or three consecutive dark reactions, each obeying the Arrhenius law, was mentioned in sections 2 and 3. The success of mathematical analyses such as those of Wohl and Tamiya does not prove that the assumption on which they are based is necessarily correct.

It may be doubted whether the rapid decrease in the rate of photosynthesis at low temperatures (as well as the similar phenomenon occurring above 30–35° C.) is at all due to a reaction that constitutes a step in the "catenary series" of photosynthesis. It seems more probable that these changes are due to alterations in the colloidal structure of the protoplasm, which affect, although to a different degree, all physiological processes taking place in the cell (as the freezing or evaporation of a solvent affects the kinetics of reactions between all the solutes which may be contained in it).

Bibliography to Chapter 31

The Temperature Factor

A. Internal Temperature of Plants

1875 Askenasy, E., *Botan. Z.*, **33**, 441.
1903 Ursprung, A., *Bibliotheca botanica*, **12**, 68.
      Timiriazev, C., *Proc. Roy. Soc. London*, **72**, 424.
1905 Blackman, F. F., and Matthaei, G. L. C., *ibid.*, **B76**, 402.
      Brown, H. T., and Escombe, F., *ibid.*, **B76**, 69.
      Brown, H. T., and Wilson, W. E., *ibid.*, **B76**, 122.
1909 Smith, A. M., *Ann. Roy. Botan. Gardens Peradnyia*, **4**, 229.
1915 Ehlers, J. H., *Am. J. Botany*, **2**, 32.
1919 Shreve, E. B., *Plant World*, **22**, 100, 172.
      Shull, C. A., *School Sci. and Math.*, **19**, 1.
1923 Miller, E. C., and Saunders, A. R., *J. Agr. Research*, **26**, 15.
1926 Clum, H. H., *Am. J. Botany*, **13**, 194, 217.
1929 Eaton, F. M., and Belden, G. O., *U. S. Dept. Agr. Tech. Bull.* No. 91.
1931 Miller, E. C., *Plant Physiology*. McGraw-Hill, New York, p. 362.
1933 Arthur, J. M., and Stewart, W. D., *Contrib. Boyce Thompson Inst.*, **5**, 483.
      Seybold, A., and Brambring, A., *Planta*, **20**, 201.
      Watson, A. N., *Ohio J. Sci.*, **33**, 435.
1934 Clements, H. I., *Plant Physiol.*, **9**, 165.
      Watson, A. N., *Am. J. Botany*, **21**, 605.
1936 Curtis, O. F., *ibid.*, **23**, 7.
      Curtis, O. F., *Plant Physiol.*, **11**, 343.
1941 Franck, J., and French, C. S., *J. Gen. Physiol.*, **25**, 309.
1951 Karmanov, V. G., *Compt. rend. (Doklady) acad. sci. USSR*, **77**, 913.

B. Temperature Range of Photosynthesis

1874 Boussaingault, J. B., *Agronomie, chimie agricole et physiologie*. Vol. V, Mallet-Bachelier, Paris.
1887 Kreusler, U., *Landw. Jahrb.*, **16**, 711.
1888 Kreusler, U., *ibid.*, **17**, 161.
1890 Kreusler, U., *ibid.*, **19**, 649.
1891 Jumelle, H., *Compt. rend.*, **112**, 1462.
1896 Ewart, A. J., *J. Linnean Soc. London, Botany*, **31**, 364.
1897 Ewart, A. J., *ibid.*, **31**, 554.
1904 Matthaei, G. L. C., *Trans. Roy. Soc. London*, **B197**, 47.
1905 Blackman, F. F., *Ann. Botany*, **19**, 281.
1906 Jost, L., *Biol. Zentr.*, **26**, 225.
1911 van Amstel, J. E., and van Iterson, G., *Proc. Acad. Sci. Amsterdam*, **19**, 106, 534.
1914 Kniep, H., *Intern. Rev. ges. Hydrobiol. Hydrog.*, **7**, 1.

1915   Harder, R., *Jahrb. wiss. Botan.*, **56**, 282.
1916   van Amstel, J. E., *Rec. trav. botan. néerland.*, **13**, 1.
1919   Warburg, O., *Biochem. Z.*, **1.**, **100**, 230.
1920   Lewis, F. J., and Tuttle, G. M., *Ann. Botany*, **34**, 405.
1921   Henrici, M., *Verhandl. Naturforsch. Ges. Basel*, **32**, 107.
      MacDougal, D. T., and Working, E. B., *Carnegie Inst. Yearbook*, **20**, 47.
1923   Wurmser, R., and Jacquot, R., *Bull. soc. chim. biol.*, **5**, 305.
1924   Harder, R., *Jahrb. wiss. Botan.*, **64**, 169.
      Harvey, R. B., *Science*, **60**, 481.
      Lepeschkin, W., *Kolloidchemie des Protoplasmas.* Springer, Berlin.
      Lundegårdh, H., *Biochem. Z.*, **154**, 195.
1927   Stocker, O., *Flora*, **121**, 334.
1928   Müller, D., *Planta*, **6**, 22.
      Yoshii, J., *ibid.*, **5**, 681.
1929   Ehrke, G., *ibid.*, **9**, 631.
1930   Beljakov, E., *ibid.*, **11**, 727.
1931   Ehrke, G., *ibid.*, **13**, 221.
      Ivanov, L. A., and Orlova, I. M., *Zhur. Russ. Botan. Obshchestva*, **16**, 139.
1932   Wood, J. G., *Australian J. Exptl. Biol. Med. Sci.*, **10**, 89.
1933   Printz, H., *Nytt Magazin Naturvidensk.*, **73**, 167.
1934   van der Paauw, F., *Planta*, **22**, 396.
1935   Bĕlehrádek, J., *Temperature and Living Matter.* Borntraeger, Berlin.
      Barker, H. A., *Arch. Mikrobiol.*, **6**, 141.
      Lampe, H., *Protoplasma*, **23**, 534.
      Stocker, O., *Planta*, **23**, 402.
1937   Craig, F. N., and Trelease, S. F., *Am. J. Botany*, **24**, 232.
1939   Stålfelt, M. G., *Planta*, **29**, 11.
      Stålfelt, M. G., *Svensk Botan. Tid.*, **33**, 383.
1940   Inman, O., *J. Gen. Physiol.*, **23**, 661.
      Kennedy, S. R., *Am. J. Botany*, **27**, 68.
      Noddack, W., and Kopp, C., *Z. physik. Chem.*, **A187**, 79.
1944   Freeland, R. O., *Plant Physiol.*, **19**, 179.
      Decker, J. P., *ibid.*, **19**, 679.
1950   Thomas, J. B., *Enzymologia*, **5**, 186.
1953   Sorokin, C., and Myers, J., *Science*, **117**, 330.
1954   Sorokin, C., Thesis, Univ. of Texas.

C. Temperature Coefficient and Heat of Activation of Photosynthesis

1876   Prjanishnikov, J., *V. Congress of Russian Naturalists*, Warsaw, 1876.
1887   Kreusler, U., *Landw. Jahrb.*, **16**, 711.
1888   Kreusler, U., *ibid.*, **17**, 161.
1890   Kreusler, U., *ibid.*, **19**, 649.
1904   Matthaei, G. L. C., *Trans. Roy. Soc. London*, **B197**, 47.
1905   Blackman, F. F., and Matthaei, G. L. C., *Proc. Roy. Soc. London*, **B76**, 402.
      Blackman, F. F., *Ann. Botany*, **19**, 281.
1906   Lubimenko, V. N., *Compt. rend.*, **143**, 609.
1911   Blackman, F. F., and Smith, A. M., *Proc. Roy. Soc. London*, **B83**, 389.

1914 Pütter, A., *Z. allgem. Physiol.*, **16**, 574.

1915 Kanitz, A., *Temperatur und Lebensvorgänge.* Borntraeger, Berlin.

1916 van Amstel, J. E., *Rec. trav. botan. néerland.*, **13**, 1.

1917 Brown, W. H., and Heise, G. W., *Philippine J. Sci.*, **C12**, 1.

1918 Willstätter, R., and Stoll, A., *Untersuchungen über die Assimilation der Kohlensäure.* Springer, Berlin.

1919 Osterhout, W. J. V., and Haas, A. R. C., *J. Gen. Physiol.*, **1**, 295.

      Smith, A. M., *Ann. Botany*, **33**, 517.

      Warburg, O., *Biochem. Z.*, **100**, 258.

1921 Henrici, M., *Verhandel. Naturforsch. Ges. Basel*, **32**, 107.

1924 Crozier, W. J., *J. Gen. Physiol*, **7**, 189.

      Lundegårdh, H., *Biochem. Z.*, **154**, 195.

      Yabusoe, M., *ibid.*, **152**, 498.

1926 Romell, L. G., *Jahrb. wiss. Botan.*, **65**, 739.

1927 Romell, L. G., *Flora*, **121**, 125.

      Stocker, O., *ibid.*, **121**, 334.

1928 Yoshii, Y., *Planta*, **5**, 681.

1929 Emerson, R., *J. Gen. Physiol.*, **12**, 623.

      Ehrke, G., *Planta*, **9**, 631.

1930 Beljakov, E., *ibid.*, **11**, 727.

1931 Ehrke, G., *ibid.*, **13**, 221.

1932 Emerson, R., and Arnold, W., *J. Gen. Physiol.* **15**, 391.

      Emerson, R., and Arnold, W., *ibid.*, **16**, 191.

      van der Paauw, F., *Rec. trav. botan. néerland.*, **29**, 497.

1934 Emerson, R., and Green, L., *J. Gen. Physiol.*, **17**, 817.

      van der Paauw, F., *Planta*, **22**, 396.

      Kautsky, H., and Spohn, H., *Biochem. Z.*, **274**, 435.

1935 Barker, H. A., *Arch. Mikrobiol.*, **6**, 141.

      Bělehrádek, J., *Temperature and Living Matter.* Borntraeger, Berlin.

      Miller, E. S., and Burr, G. O., *Plant Physiol.*, **10**, 93.

      Singh, B. N., and Kumar, K., *Proc. Indian Acad. Sci.*, **B1**, 736.

      Stocker, O., *Planta*, **24**, 402.

1937 Burton, A. C., *J. Cellular Comp. Physiol.*, **9**, 1.

      Craig, F. N., and Trelease, S. F., *Am. J. Botany*, **24**, 232.

      Franck, J., and Herzfeld, K. F., *J. Phys. Chem.*, **41**, 97.

      Wohl, K., *Z. physik. Chem.*, **B37**, 169.

      Stålfelt, M. G., *Planta*, **27**, 30.

1938 Müller, D., *Planta*, **29**, 215.

      Wassink, E. C., Vermeulen, D., Reman, G. H., and Katz, E., *Enzymologia*, **5**, 100.

1939 Stålfelt, M. G., *Planta*, **29**, 11.

1940 Emerson, R., and Lewis, C. M., *Carnegie Inst. Yearbook*, **39**, 154.

      Shri Ranjan, *J. Indian Botan. Soc.*, **19**, 91.

      Noddack, W., and Kopp, C., *Z. physik. Chem.*, **A187**, 79.

      Wohl, K., *New Phytologist*, **39**, 33.

1941 Franck, J., French, C. S., and Puck, T. T., *J. Phys. Chem.*, **45**, 1268.

Emerson, R., and Lewis, C. M., *Am. J. Botany*, **28,** 789.

Katz, E., Wassink, E. C., and Dorrestein, R., *Photosynthesis Symposium,* Chicago (unpublished).

1942 Johnson, F. H., Brown, D., and Marsland, D., *Science*, **95,** 200.

Wassink, E. C., Katz, E., and Dorrestein, R., *Enzymologia*, **10,** 285.

1945 Wassink, E. C., and Kersten, J. A. H., *ibid.*, **11,** 282.

1948 Tamiya, H., Huzisige, H., and Mii, S., *Bot. Mag. Tokyo*, **61,** 39.

Chapter 32

THE PIGMENT FACTOR*

1. Relation between Light Absorption and Pigment Content

The light energy used in photosynthesis is taken up by the pigments. In the reaction kinetics of photosynthesis, the "pigment factor" is therefore closely related to the "light intensity factor." The rate of absorption (number of quanta absorbed per unit time in unit volume) is affected by changes in the concentration of the absorbing pigments, c, as well as by alterations in the intensity of illumination, I. In a homogeneous system, the relation between these two factors is determined by Beer's law:

$$(32.1) \qquad A = I(1 - 10^{-\alpha cd})$$

where α is the absorption coefficient of the material and d the thickness of the absorbing layer. We note that, whereas I is a proportionality factor, c stands in the exponent. Therefore, the rate of absorption increases proportionately with light intensity, but slower than proportionately with the concentration of the absorbent. Only in the limiting case, when $\alpha cd \ll 1$, equation (32.1) can be replaced by the linear approximation:

$$(32.2) \qquad A = I\alpha cd \ln 10$$

in which both I and c are proportionality coefficients. In this case—realized when the absorbing layer is very thin, or the concentration of the absorbing material very low, or its absorption coefficient very small—the concentration factor and the intensity factor are interchangeable, $i.\ e.$, an increase in intensity by the factor χ and simultaneous reduction of the concentration by the factor $1/\chi$ leaves the absorption unchanged.

This situation practically never occurs in plants, since even a single cell, or isolated chloroplast, absorbs a considerable fraction of incident light. Therefore the use of the linear approximation (32.2) is out of question, except for extremely chlorotic cells, or etiolated plantules just beginning to form the green pigment. Furthermore, the influence of changes in the concentration of the pigment, [Chl],† on light absorption cannot be

---

* Bibliography, page 1310.

† For the sake of simplicity, we proceed here as if chlorophyll were the only pigment that matters. The role of other pigments will be discussed later in this chapter; it seems that their presence has an effect equivalent to that of an increase in the absorption coefficient of chlorophyll in certain spectral regions.

exactly calculated even by means of the exponential formula (32.1), because we are dealing, in plants, with non-homogeneous systems, in which the absorption depends not only on the total quantity of the coloring material in a given volume, but also on its distribution (*cf.* chapter 22). For example, doubling the chlorophyll content in a thin, faintly green tissue will have a different effect on light absorption, depending on whether this doubling is achieved by increasing the number of chloroplasts (in this case, light absorption will be nearly doubled, too), or by increasing the concentration of chlorophyll in each chloroplast (in this case, the effect on absorption will be much weaker). The same is true of cell suspensions which are thin enough for some light to be transmitted *between* the cells (*cf.* the discussion of the "sieve effect" in chapters 22 and 37C). Reliable estimation of the influence that a certain change in chlorophyll content will have on light absorption by a leaf, or a cell suspension, is particularly difficult when white (or, generally, nonmonochromatic) light is used, since in this case the average absorption coefficient, $\bar{\alpha}$, is itself a function of the pigment concentration.

Because of these complications, experiments on the relationship between chlorophyll concentration and the yield of photosynthesis should best be accompanied by direct determinations of light absorption; only then will it be possible to judge what part of the observed effect is "trivial" (*i. e.*, attributable to changes in light absorption), and what part, if any, requires a different explanation. This requirement was not satisfied by past investigations on this subject, and this makes it impossible to use them for any but preliminary, qualitative considerations.

If the effect of variations in chlorophyll concentration on the rate of photosynthesis were due *entirely* to changes in light absorption, the general shape of the "chlorophyll curves," $P = f[\text{Chl}]$, could easily be predicted. At first, these curves, drawn to appropriate scale, should coincide with the light curves, $P = f(I)$, which correspond to the same parameters (such as $[CO_2]$ or T); later, the chlorophyll curves should rise more slowly than the light curves (because absorption increases proportionately with I, and more slowly than proportionately with $[\text{Chl}]$). At the end, however, both should approach the same saturation level. These relations are shown schematically in figure 32.1A, while the solid curves in figure 32.1B show the position of two light curves corresponding to two concentrations of chlorophyll, one twice as high as the other. The ratio of the initial slopes of these two curves is between 1 and 2, because the more strongly pigmented system absorbs more light, but not quite twice as much as the less pigmented one. The curve that corresponds to $[\text{Chl}] = 1$ continues its linear rise longer than that corresponding to $[\text{Chl}] = 2$, and finally approaches the same saturation level. We expect to find this picture, *e. g.*, in the comparison of two *Chlorella* suspensions containing the same number of cells of identical volume, but with a different content of chlorophyll in each cell. The behavior will differ for two suspensions with identical chlorophyll content in their cells, but with a different number of cells per unit volume—a case illustrated by fig. 28.20(*1*), and, for a concentration ratio of 1:2, by fig. 32.1B. The broken curve in this figure begins with the same slope as the lower solid curve (presuming the absence of a "sieve effect"); but at higher intensities, the ratio [*P* (dense suspension)/*P* (dilute suspension)] *increases* to two, while the ratio [*P* (suspension of strongly pigmented cells)/ *P* (suspension of weakly pigmented cells)] *decreases* to unity. Whenever the

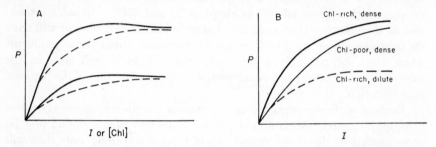

Fig. 32.1. (A) Light curves (—) and chlorophyll curves (--) of photosynthesis for two values of a parameter such as [CO_2] or temperature. (B) Light curves of photosynthesis; solid curves, two equally dense cell suspensions, one twice as rich in chlorophyll as the other; broken curve, chlorophyll-rich suspension, diluted to one half the original density.

observed effect of the [Chl] factor on photosynthesis agrees qualitatively with the picture presented by the solid curves in figure 32.1B, it can be attributed tentatively to change in light absorption. In this case, the effect should gradually disappear with increasing intensity of illumination. In some experiments, however, a strong dependence of the rate of photosynthesis on the concentration of chlorophyll was found also in intense light; in these cases, the chlorophyll concentration must have influenced photosynthesis not, or not only, by affecting the light absorption, but also in some other way.

In interpreting observations of this kind, one has to keep in mind that there is no simple way of varying the chlorophyll concentration in living cells. We are restricted in such studies to the use of natural specimens with different contents of the pigment, and of plants in which the pigment content has been affected by abnormal conditions of culture and growth, *e. g.*, deficiency of light, or lack of certain nutrient elements. All these treatments are apt to cause manifold changes in the composition and structure of the cells, and not merely variations in chlorophyll content.

From this point of view, and in consideration of the participation of the "accessory" pigments in the sensitization of photosynthesis, made probable by several studies described in chapter 30, it would be interesting to investigate the effect of changes in chlorophyll concentration on the rate of photosynthesis in the light absorbed by carotenoids or phycobilins (assuming their concentration could be kept constant while that of chlorophyll is changed). Experiments of this kind could perhaps be carried out with *aurea* leaves, in which practically all absorption in the blue-violet part of the spectrum must be due to the carotenoids.

2. Influence of Natural Variations of Chlorophyll Content on Photosynthesis

Lubimenko (1905, 1907, 1908, 1910) first pointed out that umbrophilic plants have a comparatively high chlorophyll content. Their high photosynthetic efficiency *in weak light* (*cf.* chapter 28, page 986) can be interpreted as a direct consequence of the fact that they absorb light more efficiently than the less strongly pigmented heliophilic plants.

Gabrielsen (1948) measured the photosynthesis of seventeen types of leaves, with chlorophyll contents between 0.2 and 8.7 mg. per 100 cm.², in weak incandescent light (up to 9000 lux); this series included *aurea, lutescens, chlorina* and normal varieties of twelve species. When the yield of photosynthesis at about 1500 lux was plotted as a function of chlorophyll concentration, a saturation type curve was obtained, showing saturation at about 6 mg. Chl ($a + b$) per 100 sq. cm. of leaf area. Comparison with the absorption data of Seybold and Weissweiler (pp. 678, 684) indicated general parallelism between absorption and rate of photosynthesis in such weak light. The chlorophyll-poor *aurea* varieties show, however, in Gabrielsen's table, a rate of photosynthesis even *lower* than could be anticipated from their chlorophyll content; Gabrielsen attributed this to the greater relative significance, in such pigment-poor leaves, of "inactive" light absorption by cell walls, nuclei and cell sap.

Whether this is true absorption by weakly colored components or by highly diluted pigments, or "false" absorption, simulated by scattering (not sufficiently taken into account in the evaluation of the measurements) cannot be said; plant physiologists often speak of "absorption of (visible) light by colorless cell components" as if this were not a contradiction in itself; *cf.* chapter 22, section A3.

Gabrielsen's observations on *aurea* leaves in weak light seem to contradict to some extent those of Willstätter and Stoll (*cf.* below).

In experiments to be described in detail in Chap. 37D (section 4), Brackett and co-workers (1953) noted a parallelism between the maximum quantum yield of photosynthesis in different *Chlorella* cultures, and their chlorophyll content; in other words, here, too, the effect of low chlorophyll content on the rate in weak light appeared stronger than could be explained by less effective absorption of light.

No "trivial" interpretation can be suggested for the behavior of shade-adapted plants in *strong light*. As stated on page 986, and illustrated by figures 28.16–28.18, these plants do not approach the same saturation values of photosynthesis as the heliophilic plants. (In other words, they do not conform to the behavior predicted in figure 32.1B for systems that differ *only* with respect to light absorption.) To the contrary, the photosynthesis of umbrophilic plants or leaves usually becomes light-saturated on a much *lower* level than the photosynthesis of plants or leaves adapted to strong light. Many umbrophiles suffer light inhibition (or permanent injury) whenever the light intensity is increased even a little beyond the saturating value.

If the light curves of all shade plants were of this "optimum type" (lowest curve, fig. 28.19), one could consider their low saturation as "apparent," by assuming that light *inhibition* occurs in these plants before true light *saturation* has been reached. However, the light curves of many shade plants, *e. g.*, those shown in figures 28.16 and 28.17, show an extended saturation plateau. We must assume that these umbrophiles, while containing *more* chlorophyll than the corresponding heliophiles, contain *less* of a catalyst that limits the rate in intense light (such as Franck and Herzfeld's "stabilizing catalyst," E_B).

This antiparallelism between [Chl] and $P^{max.}$, often found in the comparative study of sun plants and shade plants, is, however, by no means a general rule. Already in Table 28.V, we saw that, according to Willstätter and Stoll (1918), many plants with widely different chlorophyll contents have almost identical "assimilation numbers," ν_A; in other words, their rate of photosynthesis in intense light (about 45,000 lux) and in presence of abundant carbon dioxide (5%) is *directly proportional* to their content of chlorophyll. The ratio $\nu_A = P^{max.}/[Chl]$ (with $P^{max.}$ measured in grams carbon dioxide consumed per hour per gram chlorophyll present) is, for those plants, called "normal" by Willstätter and Stoll, of the order of 6 to 8. The ν_A values have been found to have this order of magnitude not only in many higher land plants, but also in a number of algae. For example, according to van den Honert (1930), the unicellular alga *Hormidium* has an assimilation number of 6.8; Emerson (1935) found values between 4 and 8 for *Chlorella*. The ν_A values given by Noddack and Kopp (1940) for the same species were somewhat but not much lower ($\nu_A = 4.5$ for a suspension grown in strong light and 2.6 for a shade-adapted suspension). Gessner (1943) studied the phytoplankton populations of fourteen Bavarian lakes, and found in twelve of these populations, consisting of varying proportions of *Chlorophyceae*, *Cyanophyceae* and diatoms, at different times of the year, ν_A values between 4.2 and 6.2. The plankton from one lake gave 2.6 and that from another, 9.0; but these were single determinations of doubtful precision.

From the kinetic point of view, a more relevant value than the assimilation *number* is the assimilation *time*, t_A. Willstätter and Stoll designated by this term the *minimum time required by a molecule of chlorophyll for the reduction of one molecule of carbon dioxide:*

(32.3) $\qquad t_A = (44 \times 3600)/(900 \times \nu_A) = 156/\nu_A$ (seconds)

(44 is the molecular weight of carbon dioxide, and 900 the approximate average molecular weight of chlorophyll).

For "normal" green leaves, the t_A values of Willstätter and Stoll were between 20 and 25 seconds. Values of this order of magnitude have been found for leaves the chlorophyll content of which differed by a factor of three or even more. The absorption of light by these leaves probably did not vary by more than 10 or 20% (even though some of them were "dark green" and others "light green"). In the saturation region, such a variation of absorption could not in itself cause a marked change in the rate of photosynthesis. Therefore, the fact that the saturation rate *did* change approximately proportionately with [Chl] is an indication that the velocity of the dark, rate-limiting process was in these plants *proportional to the content of chlorophyll.* Since the maximum rate of an enzymatic reaction usually is proportional to the available amount of the enzyme, we conclude that in this case the "limiting" catalyst was either chlorophyll itself, or a compound the quantity of which in "normal" plants is (approximately) *proportional* to that of chlorophyll. The possibility of identifying the rate-limiting catalyst with chlorophyll was discussed in chapter 28 (p. 1030). The alternatives, presented there, were either to attribute saturation (in continuous light) to a catalyst the concentration of which is roughly equivalent to that of chlorophyll (one such possibility being chlorophyll itself), and the working period of which is of the order of 10 seconds, or to attribute it to a catalyst whose concentration is a thousand times smaller and working time a thousand times shorter, *i. e.*, of the order of 0.01 sec. Flashing light experiments, to be described in chapter 34, were quoted there as demonstrating directly the existence of a catalyst of the second type, with respect to both concentration and working period. Chlorophyll could be a "competing" limiting factor, imposing a "ceiling" only slightly higher than that imposed by the catalyst revealed by flashing light experiments; but the deviations from constancy of ν_A, shown by the "abnormal" objects of Willstätter and Stoll (Table 28.V), do not support this hypothesis. These deviations can be as wide as 100% ($\nu_A = 15$) in green leaves and very much larger in *aurea* leaves. In Table 28.V we find, for three *aurea* varieties, the values $\nu_A = 78$, 82 and 117, respectively. If the photosynthesis of these plants were limited, in strong light, by the requirement that, after having participated in the primary photochemical act, each chlorophyll molecule has to spend 10 or 20 seconds in a photochemically inactive state, assimilation times of less than 10 seconds would be impossible; in fact, however, the above-quoted ν_A values of yellow leaves correspond to assimilation times of 1.5 to 2 seconds. Apparently, nature had deprived these leaves of nine tenths of the normal chlorophyll content, without a corresponding reduction in the concentration of the rate-limiting enzyme.

One can conclude, from the behavior of *aurea* leaves, that, intrinsically chlorophyll molecules do not require periods of the order of 10 sec. to complete the part of photosynthesis in which they are directly involved, but are available for a new photochemical act within a much shorter time.

Related to the same subject are the experimental results of Shcheglova (1940). She found that the light-green parts of leaves of *Polygonum sacchalinense* have a higher natural rate of photosynthesis in the first half of the summer than the dark-green ones, while in the second half of the summer (when the average light intensity is lower) the relation is reversed. In laboratory experiments with the same plant at different temperatures, she found that at 20–30° C., the light-green sections of the leaves (1.2–1.8 mg. chlorophyll per 100 sq. cm.) give a higher yield in strong light than the dark-green ones (2.2–3.1 mg. chlorophyll per 100 sq. cm.), and thus have a much higher assimilation number (6.6–5.5 *vs.* 3.7–2.5); while at 13–17° C., the relation is reversed, with the result that the assimilation numbers are about equal (2.2 and 2.4).

In interpreting differences in assimilation numbers as indicative of variations in the content of a rate-limiting enzyme, one has to keep in mind that the maximum rate of an enzymatic reaction may be affected, in addition to the concentration of the enzyme, also by the properties of the medium in which the enzyme has to act. Not only the reaction (the pH) of the medium, but also its colloidal properties may influence this rate. This is particularly true if the rate-limiting step is bimolecular (*e. g.*, if it involves the encounter of a substrate molecule with an enzyme molecule); but even if the rate-limiting step is monomolecular (transformation of the reaction complex {enzyme + substrate}), its rate nevertheless may be affected by association with colloidal particles.

Dastur (1924, 1925) and Dastur and Buhariwalla (1928) noted that in aging leaves the water content declined more rapidly than the chlorophyll content, and suggested that variations in water content could provide an explanation for the drop in the assimilation number, reported by Willstätter and Stoll for aging leaves. The state of hydration of the chloroplasts could perhaps affect the rate constant of the limiting enzyme, even if the concentration of the latter remains unchanged.

Conditions similar to those in *aurea* were found in some autumn leaves. According to Willstätter and Stoll, the autumnal decrease in photosynthesis usually parallels the disappearance of chlorophyll, so that the assimilation numbers remain approximately constant. Sometimes, however, the decrease of $P^{max.}$ lags behind that of [Chl], so that a transient increase in ν_A to 12–20 occurs in early autumn, before the final decline has set in.   On the other hand, leaves may remain green in the autumn and nevertheless show declining ν_A values; sometime these green but inactive leaves recover their efficiency after having been returned to higher temperature for several hours.   To sum up, Willstätter and Stoll's determinations of ν_A and t_A suggest that the concentration of the limiting catalyst has a tendency to change proportionately with [Chl], but that this rule admits of many, and sometimes of striking, exceptions.

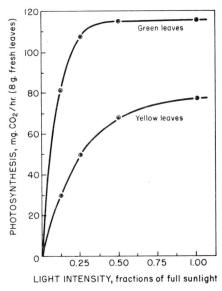

Fig. 32.2. Light curves of green and *aurea* leaves of *Sambucus* (after Willstätter and Stoll 1918).

In addition to numerous experiments on the assimilation numbers of various leaves in strong light, Willstätter and Stoll also determined the complete light curves of the green and *aurea* leaves of *Sambucus*. The results are represented in figure 32.2. The yellow leaves contained only 5–10% of the normal chlorophyll content, and probably absorbed not more than one third of the amount of white light absorbed by the green forms (*cf.* page 685). This difference may explain the slower rise in the rate of photosynthesis of yellow leaves in weak light, and their failure to reach complete saturation even in the strongest light used. The extrapolated saturation value of the yellow variety appears, however, to be equal to, or only slightly below, that of the green one. In other words, figure 32.2 agrees approximately with the prototype of the two solid curves in figure 32.1B (and differs from that of fig. 28.20(*1*)).

In some *aurea* leaves, characterized by *extreme* chlorophyll deficiency, the rate of photosynthesis in light of 45,000 lux was found to be much lower than in the moderately chlorophyll-deficient yellow leaves, to which figure 32.2 refers. For example, a leaf of *Sambucus* containing less than 0.1 mg. chlorophyll/10 g. fresh weight assimilated, in strong light, only 12 mg. CO_2/hr./10 g. (as against 90 mg. taken up by a leaf containing 0.75 mg. chlorophyll, and 150 mg. taken up by a fully green leaf with 23.5 mg. chlorophyll in 10 g.). These figures show that the assimilation number of the leaf with 0.5% of the normal quantity of chlorophyll was about the same ($\sim$120) as that of the leaf with 3% of the normal chlorophyll content, both being about eighteen times larger than the assimilation number of a normal leaf. However, by analogy with the curves in figure 32.2, it appears possible that the leaf with extreme chlorophyll deficiency was far from light-saturated at 45,000 lux. If the light curve of this leaf, followed to much higher intensities, would also approach the normal saturation value, this would mean an assimilation number of over 1000 (*i. e.*, an assimilation time of less than 0.15 second)! It would be interesting to find out whether such extremely high assimilation numbers actually occur.

It was mentioned above that Gabrielsen (1948) found the rate of photosynthesis of *aurea* leaves in weak light to be even lower than expected from their light absorption, and attributed this deficiency to "inactive" light absorption in cell walls, plasma and vacuoles. No such deficiency is apparent in Willstätter and Stoll's curves (fig. 32.2); these curves, however, cannot be evaluated quantitatively because of the absence of correlated absorption data. Gabrielsen's absorption estimates were based not on his own measurements, but on Seybold and Weissweiler's data (chapter 22); consequently, they, too, are not very reliable. Correct estimation of scattering losses is very important in the determination of true absorption by leaves, particularly when the latter are poor in pigments; and figures given in the literature for "inactive absorption" of visible light by "colorless" leaf constituents (p. 684) may be much too high because of unsatisfactory methods of integrating scattering losses.

Another experiment which also indicated the essential independence from chlorophyll of the catalyst that limits the rate of photosynthesis in strong light was described by Emerson (1935). He found that, when a suspension of *Chlorella* was illuminated by strong light for 16 hours, the volume of the cells was almost trebled, without appreciable change in the total quantity of chlorophyll. Thus, the *average* concentration of chlorophyll in the suspension was unchanged, but its concentration within the cells was smaller than before, by a factor of three. Photosynthesis was found to be about *twice* as large as before (ν_A about 4 before the treatment, and about 8 afterward). Only a small part of this improvement can be attributed to a more efficient absorption of light by the preilluminated suspension (caused by more uniform distribution of chlorophyll and consequent decline in the "sieve effect"); the result can therefore be taken as indication that, after multiplication, the cells contained about twice as much of the rate-limiting catalyst as was present in the original suspension, while their total content of chlorophyll was unchanged.

A striking demonstration of the existence of an enzymatic component that can limit the rate of photosynthesis, and is independent of chlorophyll (since it can be inactivated without noticeable damage to chlorophyll), is provided by the experiments of Davis (1948, 1952), who obtained *Chlorella* mutants containing normal chlorophyll, but incapable of photosynthesis.

3. Influence of Artificial Changes of Chlorophyll Content on Photosynthesis

The experiment of Emerson, described at the conclusion of the preceding section, forms a transition from the study of natural to that of artificial changes in chlorophyll content. Since we cannot extract or destroy a part of chlorophyll present in the cells without killing the cells, the desired artificial changes in chlorophyll content have to be obtained indirectly, by varying the conditions of culturing, so as to induce the plants to produce less (or more) than their normal complement of pigments.

As the first experiments of this kind, we may consider those in which Willstätter and Stoll (1918) found abnormally high v_A values in *etiolated* plants, *i. e.*, seedlings grown in the dark, just in process of becoming green. For example, the assimilation number of yellowish-green etiolated *Phaseolus vulgaris* plantules was as high as 133 (as compared with 9.4 in a green control plant).   The chlorophyll concentration was 0.7 mg. in 10 g. fresh leaves of the etiolated plant, and 18.6 mg. in the control specimen.

These results of Willstätter and Stoll disagreed with the earlier conclusions of Irving (1910) (who worked in Blackman's laboratory); the latter had found that etiolated seedlings do not photosynthesize at all until they have acquired a considerable amount of chlorophyll.   Inman (1935) found that the photosynthesis of etiolated plantules begins simultaneously with the appearance of green color.

Beber and Burr (1937) reported that, in etiolated oat seedlings, photosynthesis did not begin until some chlorophyll *b* was formed (not confirmed by Smith, *cf.* p. 1766).

Smith (1949) plotted the rate of photosynthesis (at 45 klux) of etiolated bean and corn seedlings in the process of greening, as observed by Willstätter and Stoll, as function of $(1 - e^{-\text{const. [Chl]}})$, and obtained a straight line. He interpreted this as an indication that the increase of P with [Chl] was a trivial consequence of increasing absorption. However, this kind of relationship is to be expected only in the light-limited state, and even if etiolated seedlings might not have been completely light-saturated at 45 klux, they are not likely to have been in the light-limited state in such intense illumination— particularly after the chlorophyll content had increased to 10–15 mg. in 10 g. (fresh weight).   Furthermore, Smith's interpretation disregards the high *absolute* assimilation numbers obtained by Willstätter and Stoll for etiolated leaves.

Smith (1949) also made observations of the rate of dyestuff reduction (Hill reaction) by chloroplasts extracted from etiolated barley seedlings at different stages of greening, and found a systematic increase in activity, similar to that observed for photosynthesis.

More recent studies of greening, indicating transient formation of a photosynthetically inactive chlorophyll form, will be described in chapter 37B (p. 1767).

Chlorotic plants, *i. e.*, plants in which the chlorophyll development has been arrested by nutritional deficiencies, also have been investigated by Willstätter and Stoll. The assimilation numbers of plants of *Helianthus annuus* and *Zea mais*, made chlorotic by iron deficiency, were found to be not very different from those of normal plants (sometimes smaller, sometimes larger). It thus seems that the development of the enzymatic apparatus has been held back together with that of chlorophyll.

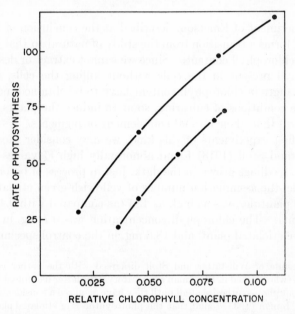

Fig. 32.3. Relation between chlorophyll concentration and photosynthesis of *Chlorella* in strong light (after Emerson 1929). Two series of experiments.

These results of Willstätter and Stoll were confirmed and amplified by Emerson (1929[1]), who investigated cultures of *Chlorella vulgaris* grown in nutrient solutions with a variable concentration of iron. Glucose was added to support growth in iron-deficient solutions. In this way, variations of [Chl] in the ratio 1:5 could be obtained. The maximum photosynthetic rate (in Warburg's buffer No. 9, and in light of about 10^5 lux) was found to increase regularly—but more slowly than proportionately—with the chlorophyll content (*cf.* fig. 32.3). The high light intensity used by Emerson made it improbable that the increase in P with [Chl] could be interpreted as a consequence of incomplete light saturation of the chlorophyll-deficient cells; this conclusion was confirmed by a second investigation (1929[2]), in which complete light curves were determined for two *Chlorella* cultures with chlorophyll contents differing in the ratio of 4:1. As shown by figure 32.4, the saturation yields of these two forms in fact differed widely (by a factor of 3.4, which is only 15% smaller than the ratio of the chlorophyll contents).

Emerson's light curves conform closely to the prototype of figure 28.20(1). In this case the reduction of the chlorophyll content by three quarters, brought about by iron deficiency, had the same effect on photosynthesis as would have been caused by removal of three fourths of all cells from a nonchlorotic suspension. In other words, chlorotic *Chlorella* suspensions, like Willstätter and Stoll's chlorotic leaves, behaved as "normal" leaves. However, since we have described above several cases in which the

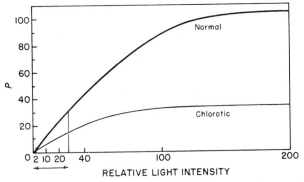

Fig. 32.4. Light curves of two *Chlorella* suspensions with different content of chlorophyll (after Emerson 1929). Double arrow indicates the "linear range."

relation was different (*aurea* leaves, autumn leaves, shade leaves and etiolated leaves), we are bound to conclude (as we did once before) that the two components of the photosynthetic apparatus—chlorophyll and the rate-limiting catalyst—are *not* identical; and that even if the ratio of their quantities often has a tendency to remain constant, this gives us no right to consider the two components as associated in a proportion that remains constant under all conditions.

The three different relationships between [Chl] and $P^{max.}$ are again compared in figure 32.5, where light curves A are those of Emerson's normal and chlorotic *Chlorella* cells ($P^{max.}$ *proportional* to [Chl]), while light curves B correspond to Willstätter and Stoll's green and yellow leaves ($P^{max.}$ roughly *independent* of [Chl]), and light curves C to the umbrophilic and heliophilic plants of Lubimenko ($P^{max.}$ *antiparallel* with [Chl]).

The dependence of $P^{max.}$ on *temperature* was found by Emerson to be unaffected by changes in the chlorophyll content of *Chlorella* cells. This result is different from Willstätter and Stoll's observations with *aurea* leaves, shown in Table 31.IV; but the reason for this difference may be simply that the *aurea* leaves were studied in a state of incomplete light saturation (*cf.* fig. 32.2), while Emerson used light intensity sufficient to saturate both the normal and the chlorophyll-deficient *Chlorella* cells (*cf.* fig. 32.4). Theoretically, there seems to be no reason why the temperature coefficient of $P^{max.}$ should change with [Chl], at least as long as the same dark reaction is rate-limiting in all the cell systems under comparison.

The photosynthesis of chlorotic *Chlorella* cells was found by Emerson to to be more strongly affected by *cyanide* than that of the normal ones. This may indicate that chlorotic cells contained less of the cyanide-sensitive carboxylating enzyme, E_A (*cf.* Volume I, page 306).

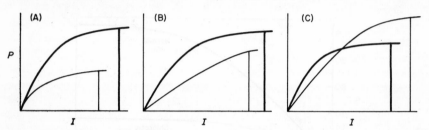

Fig. 32.5. Light curves of optically dense (—) and optically thin (—) systems: (A) normal and chlorotic *Chlorella* cells (*cf.* fig. 32.4); (B) normal and yellow *Sambucus* leaves (*cf.* fig. 32.2); and (C) shade and sun leaves (*cf.* fig. 28.16–18).

Fleischer (1935) repeated Emerson's experiments, varying the chlorophyll concentration of *Chlorella* by three types of changes in the nutrient medium: (*a*) changing the *iron* concentration, (*b*) changing the *nitrogen* concentration and (*c*) changing the concentrations of *magnesium* (*cf.* chapters 13 and 15). Results obtained by the methods *a* and *b*, (using Warburg's buffer No. 9, and light of 75,000 lux) were similar; like Emerson's observations, they showed an approximately linear increase in yield with the chlorophyll concentration. Method *c*, on the other hand, gave more complex results, indicating that magnesium deficiency had a specific effect on photosynthesis, beside the indirect influence caused by a lowering of chlorophyll concentration. Van Hille (1937), was unable to confirm Fleischer's results; he found a systematic decrease in both [Chl] and $P^{max.}$ in plants deprived of magnesium. However, the existence of a direct effect of magnesium concentration on the rate of photosynthesis was confirmed by Kennedy (1940) (*cf.* chapter 13, page 337).

In a second paper, van Hille (1938) reported that the photosynthetic capacity of *Chlorella pyrenoidosa* cultures decreased steadily with *age*, even if the chlorophyll content continued to increase. Experiments with varied nutrient solutions showed that this decline was connected with a developing deficiency of nitrogen; it could be remedied by repeated addition of nitrate to the suspension medium. (This influence of nitrogen concentration, too, was discussed in chapter 13; *cf*. page 339).

To sum up, experiments with nitrogen-deficient and magnesium-deficient cell cultures gave less consistent results as to the correlation between chlorophyll concentration and the capacity for photosynthesis than did experiments in iron-deficient media. However, in the latter case, too, we probably are dealing not with direct effects of changes in chlorophyll concentration, but with variations in the general development of the photocatalytic apparatus, which includes, in addition to chlorophyll, also the several catalysts participating in the "dark" stages of photosynthesis.

Myers (1946) noted that, when *Chlorella pyrenoidosa* was grown in a continuous growth apparatus, the chlorophyll content per unit cell volume increased by a factor of 5 when illumination was decreased from 360 to 6 foot-candles. At the same time, however, the number of cells in one cubic centimeter of packed cell material increased from 6×10^9 to 29×10^9 so that the average number of chlorophyll molecules in a single cell was almost unchanged, the small "shade cells" containing about as much chlorophyll as the large "light cells." Among these different cultures, the highest saturation rates of photosynthesis per *unit cell volume* were shown —in alkaline buffer as well as in acid Knop's medium—by those grown in light of 25–50 foot-candles; the saturation rate per unit cell volume declined sharply for cultures grown < 25 foot-candles and gradually for cultures grown >50 foot-candles. The saturation rate *per cell* (and thus, because of the above-mentioned constancy of the chlorophyll amount per cell, also the saturation rate *per chlorophyll molecule, i. e.,* the assimilation number), increased continuously with increasing intensity of the culture light. (It should be noted that the "saturation rate" was measured at 600 foot-candles—a light intensity that may be insufficient to completely saturate light-adapted *Chlorella* cells.)

Myers noted that the maximum rate of growth of *Chlorella* was reached at about 100 foot-candles, and suggested that in stronger light the cells are incapable of utilizing all the immediate products of photosynthesis, and develop a special mechanism of dissimilation ("light respiration," or photoxidation?) which disposes of surplus photosynthates. In other words, below 100 foot-candles growth is limited by the rate of photosynthesis, while above 100 foot-candles it is limited by a dark process (such as nitrogen assimilation), which the primary products of photosynthesis (carbohydrates?) must undergo to be converted into balanced cell material.

In Chapter 31, (p. 1228) we described Sorokin and Myers' discovery of a "thermophilic" *Chlorella pyrenoidosa* strain, with a peak capacity for growth at 39° C. (instead of the usual 26° C.). At its optimum temperature, this strain required a higher light intensity for saturation, and produced considerably more oxygen per unit cell volume per unit time than the ordinary strains of *Chlorella pyrenoidosa* do at their optimum temperature. The assimilation number of such thermophilic algae at 39° C. may be considerably higher, and their assimilation time correspondingly shorter, than those that other strains can reach under the most favorable conditions.

4. Chlorophyll Concentration and Yield of Photosynthesis in Flashing Light

In chapter 34, we will deal with experiments on photosynthesis in periodically interrupted light; we must here anticipate some of the results, which concern the relation between the chlorophyll content and the maximum amount of oxygen that can be liberated by a single short flash of light.

This quantity can be interpreted in different ways. The interpretation that seemed most natural and was therefore the first to be discussed was based on the identification of the maximum amount of substrate that can be reduced by a single flash, with the quantity of this substrate available in the cells, after a period of darkness, in a form suitable for immediate photochemical reduction (*e. g.*, as an acceptor–carbon dioxide compound or complex, $[CO_2]$ or ACO_2). In a dark-rested chloroplast, in presence of sufficient carbon dioxide, each acceptor molecule must be associated with a molecule of carbon dioxide. A sudden flash of light will send all these molecules through the photochemical reduction stage (or stages), and thus produce a quantity of primary photoproducts equivalent to the amount of the available acceptor. After this, a certain interval of time may be required for the "recharging" of the photosynthetic apparatus, *e. g.*, by the slow formation of a new quantity of the acceptor–carbon dioxide complex ("preparatory" dark reaction). The yield of oxygen, produced by a single strong flash, will then be equivalent to the quantity of the carbon dioxide acceptor present in the cells.

In discussing the nature of the carbon dioxide acceptor in chapter 8, we found that it is a compound the content of which in green cells is about equivalent to that of chlorophyll. In chapter 34, we will find evidence that this acceptor may itself be a transient product of photosynthesis, and therefore decrease in concentration in the dark and increase again as photosynthesis gets under way—perhaps approaching approximate equivalency with chlorophyll in the stationary state in strong light. If the maximum oxygen yield per flash were limited by the available quantity of this acceptor, we would expect this yield, too, to be approximately equivalent to the chlorophyll content of the cells; in other words, it should be of the order of 0.01 mole per liter of cells, or as much as 0.2 volume of oxygen per unit volume of cells per flash.

Emerson and Arnold (1932) found, however, in their first flashing light experiments with suspensions of *Chlorella pyrenoidosa*, that the maximum oxygen production per flash was less than 0.0001 cubic centimeter per flash per cubic centimeter of cells, corresponding to only one molecule of oxygen for each 2660 molecules of chlorophyll!   In a second paper (1932) the same observers investigated whether the maximum production per flash had any relation to the chlorophyll concentration at all.   For this purpose, they used *Chlorella* cells grown in light of different intensity or spectral

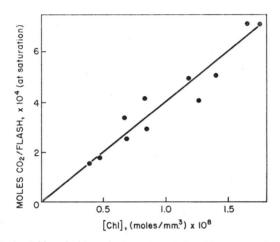

Fig. 32.6. Flash yield and chlorophyll content (after Emerson and Arnold 1932).

composition (neon tubes, mercury lamps and incandescent lamps).   The [Chl] values of these cultures ranged from 4×10^{-3} mole/l. to 16×10^{-3} mole/l. (referred to the volume occupied by the cells).   The oxygen yield per flash was found to be approximately *proportional to the chlorophyll content* (*cf.* fig. 32.6); but the proportionality factor (τ) was again found to be of the order of 5×10^{-4}, and not of the order of unity.   In Table 32.I we list the values of $1/\tau$ taken from the fundamental investigations of Emerson and Arnold (1931, 1932), as well as from the subsequent determinations of Arnold and Kohn (1934) and Emerson, Green and Webb (1940).

The last set of figures in Table 32.I shows that τ was found to decline steadily in aging cultures.   (The yield per flash diminished with age although the chlorophyll content remained constant or even increased.) This result reminds one of the observations of van Hille on the effect of age on rate of photosynthesis of *Chlorella* in continuous light (Vol. I, p. 239). Perhaps the striking decline of τ also could be checked, at least to a certain extent, by avoiding nutritional deficiencies.   With the exception of aged cultures, the τ values in Table 32.I obtained with plants belonging to five different phyla all lie in the range between 2000 and 5000.

The value of $1/\tau$ indicates the participation in the photosynthetic process of a catalytic component, x, the total available amount of which is from 2000 to 5000 times smaller than that of chlorophyll: $[x]_0 = 2$ to 5×10^{-4} $[Chl]_0$. We may consider $[x]_0 = 4 \times 10^{-4} [Chl]_0$ as the "normal" value.

This estimate may need a correction: If the catalytic component in question has to operate n times in order that one molecule carbon dioxide can be reduced to the carbohydrate level, the factor τ must be multiplied by n to obtain the number of catalyst molecules required. For example, if we assume $n = 8$ (a plausible assumption in an "eight-quanta theory"), the concentration of the yield-limiting catalyst required to explain the "normal" value of τ, will be $[x]_0 = 3.2 \times 10^{-3} [Chl]_0$. It is also possible that the limiting catalyst has to act only on one set of intermediates (e. g., on the reduction intermediates of carbon dioxide, and not on the oxidation intermediates of water, or, *vice versa*). In this case, τ will have to be multiplied by $n/2$ instead of by n and the "normal" value of $[x]_0$ will be $1.6 \times 10^{-3}[Chl]_0$. It is more difficult—although not impossible—to imagine

TABLE 32.I

MAXIMUM OXYGEN YIELD[a] IN FLASHING LIGHT

Observers	Species	$[Chl]$, (moles/mm.^{3}) $\times 10^8$	$1/\tau$
Emerson, Arnold (1932[1])	*Chlorella pyrenoidosa*	0.428	2,660
		0.606	1,980
		0.620	2,660
		0.766	2,380
Emerson, Arnold (1932[2])	*Chlorella pyrenoidosa* (25° C.) with variable chlorophyll content	0.756	2,010
		1.07	2,380; 2,780
		1.14	3,120
		1.49	2,310
		1.59	2,460
	Bryophyllum calycinum (31.5°)	—	2,500; 2,600
	Chlorella vulgaris (25°)	—	2,800
Arnold, Kohn (1934)	*Lemna* sp. (25, 26, 29°)	—	2,600; 3,200; 2,900
	Nicotiana longsdorffii (30, 29°)	—	2,800; 2,500
	Selaginella sp. (28°)	—	4,200
	Stichococcus bacillaris (25, 30°)	—	3,700; 5,000
Emerson, Green, Webb (1940)	*Chlorella pyrenoidosa*, different age		
	2 days[b]	—	3,750
	4 days[b]	—	6,180
	8 days[b]	—	11,120
	15 days[c]	—	6,650
	21 days[c]	—	11,000
	29 days[c]	—	14,500
Arnold (*cf.* van Niel 1941)	*Rhodospirillum rubrum*	—	400

[a] τ = oxygen yield, molecules per flash per molecule chlorophyll.
[b] Four 40 w. lamps 10 cm. from cultures during growth.
[c] One 40 w. lamp 15 cm. away.

mechanisms in which the limiting catalyst will have to act only once (or, more generally, less than four times) in the reduction of one molecule of carbon dioxide and the production of one molecule of oxygen.

Even with $[x]_0 = 8[Chl]_0\tau$, the concentration $[x]_0$ remains much too low for x to be identified with the carbon dioxide acceptor, A. It must thus be another component of the catalytic mechanism. According to the classification we have used often before, it may be either a *preparatory* or a *finishing* catalyst. The preparatory catalysts work on *stable* substrates; therefore nothing seems to prevent them from accumulating more and more products as the dark intervals between flashes increase in length; and this should permit the maximum yield per flash to increase indefinitely. The kind of preparatory catalysts to which this consideration does not apply are "acceptors" (similar to the repeatedly discussed carbon dioxide acceptor, A) that have a limited capacity and, once "filled," can be emptied only by, or in consequence of, the light reaction. We can postulate, *ad hoc*, such an acceptor, *e. g.*, on the "reduction side" as an additional intermediate between the first carbon dioxide compound, ACO_2, and the chlorophyll complex, or, on the "oxidation side," where a water acceptor compound, $A'H_2O$ (or, more generally, an intermediate hydrogen donor, RH_2), was postulated on previous occasions. Another, and more plausible possibility is, however, to relate the maximum yield per flash to the limited availability of a *finishing catalyst, i. e.*, a catalyst acting on the products of the primary photochemical process. Of course, if these intermediary photoproducts were stable (meaning by "stability" that their life-time is much longer than the working period, t_x, of the catalyst, x), then the catalyst could continue working, in the dark, until it has completely exhausted the products of the preceding flash; in this case, the yield per flash would again become capable of increasing indefinitely with the intensity of the flash, if the dark intervals between flashes are increased correspondingly. However, it is plausible to assume that the intermediary photoproducts are *unstable;* and, if their existence is so fleeting that a "second batch" cannot wait until the "first batch" had been processed and stabilized by the catalyst, the maximum yield per flash will be equal to the size of this first batch, and therefore equivalent to the available amount of the stabilizing catalyst (more exactly, it will be equal to this amount, [x], divided by the number of times the catalyst has to operate in the reduction of one molecule of carbon dioxide to carbohydrate). No useful purpose will be served, in this case, by further increasing the energy of the flash, or prolonging the dark intervals.

One could suggest that the figure obtained in this way ($3.2 \times 10^{-3}[Chl]_0$) is not necessarily equal to the concentration of the catalyst x, but may represent a multiple of it—the product of $[x]_0$ and the number of batches the catalyst is allowed to process after a flash. We have assumed that this number is 1, *i. e.*, that the life-time of the photoproduct is small compared with the working period of the catalyst. But what if this life-time is long enough to enable each molecule of the catalyst to work an average of two or three times before it has to stop because the substrate has disintegrated? If this were so, the necessary number of catalyst molecules would be only one half or one third of the above-calculated figures. However, the duration of the dark interval necessary to obtain the maximum yield per flash, would then change with increasing intensity of the flash. After a weak flash, a single working period would be sufficient to process all photoproducts; after a stronger flash, two such periods would be required, to permit a second "round" of catalytic activity, and so on, until the full life-time of the photoproducts is utilized. No such dependence of the length of dark intervals on flash intensity required to obtain the maximum yield per flash has been noted by Emerson and co-workers.

The attribution of the maximum flash yield to a back reaction destroying all photoproducts that cannot be immediately stabilized by a catalyst was suggested by Franck, and the concept was developed in detail by Franck and Herzfeld (1941) in conjunction with the reaction mechanism illustrated by scheme 7.VA, in which the "stabilizing" catalyst, E_B, is assumed to provide the limiting influence. However, the same hypothesis can be combined also with the other reaction schemes discussed in chapters 7, 9, 24 and 28, insofar as these schemes, too, contain "finishing" catalytic reactions that follow the primary photochemical process (or processes).

In chapter 28 we concluded, from an analysis of the phenomena of light saturation, and of changes in chlorophyll fluorescence in strong light, that the light saturation of photosynthesis is caused (usually, but probably not always) by the bottleneck of a finishing catalytic reaction. "Flash saturation" may thus be due to the same limiting agent as saturation in continuous light; and this hypothesis is strengthened by quantitative comparison of the two saturation yields.

In making this comparison, we assume that the maximum velocity of the rate-limiting catalytic reaction can be represented by a product of a concentration factor, such as $[E_B]$, and a velocity constant, k_B (i. e., that this reaction is a monomolecular transformation of a catalyst–substrate complex). If the maximum yield in continuous light is limited by the same "bottleneck" as the maximum yield per flash, the concentration of the catalyst limiting the rate in continuous light must have the value derived above from the ratio τ, namely (assuming $n = 4$), $[x] = 0.0016 \, [Chl]_0$. Since $P_{max.}^{max.}$ is of the order of 0.05 $[Chl]_0$ (t_A = about 20 seconds), we can write 0.0016 $[Chl]_0 \times k = P_{max.}^{max.} = 0.05 \, [Chl]_0$, and thus obtain $k = 30$ sec.$^{-1}$. When the yield per flash was measured as function of the length of the dark interval between flashes, a value of about 50 sec.$^{-1}$ was in fact found for the monomolecular rate constant of the reaction by which photosynthesis is completed after the flash. (For the description of these experiments, see chap. 34, section B2.) In other words, the product $k[E]$ derived from $P_{max.}^{max.}$, the saturation rate in continuous light, agrees with the product of the values $[E_B]$ and $[k_B]$ derived separately, from the saturation yield in flashing light and the flash yield dependence on the length of the dark intervals, respectively. The agreement supports strongly the assumption that saturation in continuous light and the maximum flash yield are determined by the same "bottleneck" reaction, brought about by a finishing catalyst present in a concentration of the order of 10^{-5} mole/l. ($\sim$0.1% of $[Chl]_0$) and having an "action period" of the order of 1/50 second (at room temperature).

No flashing light experiments have been carried out with objects for which abnormal assimilation numbers had been found in continuous light, such as *aurea* leaves, etiolated seedlings or autumn leaves. If the hypothesis that the rate-limiting reaction is the same in continuous and in flashing light applies to all of them (which is not necessarily true, because under abnormal conditions the limiting role may be taken over by a different reaction), then the plant objects showing exceptionally high assimilation numbers, ν_A, should exhibit also exceptionally high values of the ratio τ. In Myers' (1946) experiments with *Chlorella* cells grown in light of different intensity, the saturation rates per unit chlorophyll amount (and thus also the ratios ν_A) varied by a factor of 4 as the culture light increased from 6 to 360 foot-candles, and the chlorophyll concentration within the cells declined by a factor of 5. In table 32.I, Emerson and Arnold's figures show no significant change associated with chlorophyll concentration changes by a factor of 2, produced in a similar way (*i. e.*, by changes in illumination during the growth of the algae). However, only experiments performed on the same algae in both steady and flashing light could provide truly significant information as to the correlation between ν_A and τ.

In chapter 34 we will describe experiments by Tamiya and co-workers in which flash yields far exceeding the Emerson-Arnold limiting value of 5×10^{-6} $[Chl]$ have been obtained by further increasing the energy of the flashes and by prolonging the dark intervals beyond the Emerson-Arnold limiting duration of about 0.02 sec. For reasons to be presented there, we are reluctant to consider these experiments as sufficient to cast aside all the conclusions based on the observations of Emerson and Arnold; but a renewed experimental study of flashing light saturation seems necessary.

In identifying the limiting catalyst with the catalyst E_B in schemes 28.I and 28.II, we follow Franck and Herzfeld. In their scheme, (7.VA), E_B was supposed to act (with equal efficiency) on four (different) intermediate products "on the reduction side" and four (identical) intermediate products "on the oxidation side." The assumption of several processes on the reduction side, all catalyzed by E_B, can be avoided by postulating only one photochemical reduction process, followed by catalytic dismutations (in fact, E_B can be a "mutase" bringing about the first of these dismutations). The assumption of a stabilizing reaction on the oxidation side, also catalyzed by E_B, seems unnecessary, since the limitation of the yield of finished *reduction* products will automatically bring about also a limitation of the yield of finished *oxidation* products. (Whenever the production of $AHCO_2$ exceeds the capacity of E_B, the intermediates $AHCO_2$ will accumulate, until their back reaction with $A'HO$ will be able to compete with the oxygen-liberating reaction, catalyzed by E_C; the photosynthetic quotient will thus be rapidly reduced, after an initial, unbalanced "induction" period to the normal value of unity. Alternatively, if the stabilizing catalyst is assumed to operate on an instable *oxidation* product ($\{OH\}$ or $A'OH$), there would seem to be no need to assume also a stabilizing reaction on the reduction side.

The postulate of a single photochemical oxidation-reduction step, followed by dismutation, is found, in chemically more concrete form, in recent speculations on the mechanism of carbon dioxide reduction in photosynthesis, derived from $C(14)$ experiments (*cf.* chapter 36, section 12).

We will now consider, from the point of view of the theory of the "finishing bottleneck," the high quantum yield of photosynthesis and the absence of an extended induction period in weak light—these being the two kinetic observations that have played a decisive role in the development of the theory of the "photosynthetic unit" (to be described in section 5).

In the early discussions of this subject, Warburg's original value of the quantum yield ($\gamma = 0.25$) was used; but even if we substitute the smaller value ($\gamma = 0.12$–0.15), which now appears more plausible (*cf.* chapters 29 and 37D), it still remains true that probably all, or almost all, of the light quanta absorbed by chlorophyll in weak light actually can be utilized in the photosynthetic process.

The high quantum yield in weak light (the explanation of which offers some difficulty for a theory which would assume that only a small fraction of chlorophyll molecules are associated with appropriate reduction substrates) obviously does not embarrass a theory such as Franck's, which postulates that, except for cases of carbon dioxide deficiency or specific poisoning of the carboxylase, E_A, *all* chlorophyll molecules are associated with photosensitive complexes, even when light saturation sets in. The absence of an extended induction period in weak light (*cf.* chapter 33) requires, however, somewhat closer consideration.

This fact indicates that the collection of the 4 or 8 quanta required for the reduction of one molecule of carbon dioxide does not require that these quanta be absorbed by the same molecule of chlorophyll. In chapter 25 (page 838) we derived a relationship between light intensity and the frequency of absorption acts by a single molecule:

$$(32.4) \qquad n = 4 \times 10^{-21} \alpha N_{h\nu} \text{ sec.}^{-1}$$

where $N_{h\nu}$ is the rate of incidence of light quanta per second per square centimeter. The highest quantum yields of photosynthesis have been observed in light of the order of 100–1000 lux, corresponding to $N_{h\nu} = 10^{14}$–10^{15}; with $\alpha \simeq 10^4$, this means $n = 4 \times 10^{-3}$ to 4×10^{-2}, $i.\ e.$, each chlorophyll molecule absorbs a quantum every 25–250 seconds. If a carbon dioxide molecule were to remain anchored, during the whole reduction process, at one chlorophyll molecule, waiting for 4 (or 8) quanta to be absorbed by the latter, this should take, in the light of the above-mentioned intensity (100–1000 lux), from 100 to 1000 sec. for 4, and from 200 to 2000 sec. ($i.\ e.$, up to one half hour) for 8 quanta. In completely absorbing, dense cell suspensions, such as were used by Warburg and Negelein, Emerson and Lewis, and others, in quantum yield determinations, the $average$ light intensity was lower than 100 lux, and the frequency of absorption acts by a single chlorophyll molecule must have been only one every 10 or 20 minutes, corresponding to 1.5 to 3 hours for 8 quanta!

If one would start, after a dark period, with chlorophyll deprived of all intermediates, and all chlorophyll molecules associated with ACO_2 molecules, over 1 hr. of illumination would thus be required, under the assumed conditions, for the uptake of new carbon dioxide to reach the steady rate. The liberation of oxygen, on the other hand, could become steady after a quarter or an eighth of this period, because, in the most plausible reaction mechanisms, the final oxidized photoproduct (ROH in scheme 7.VA and A′OH in scheme 28.I, etc.) is obtained in consequence of a single photochemical step, and is converted to molecular oxygen entirely by dark reactions ($e.\ g.$, combination and dismutation of radicals, such as $2[OH] \rightarrow [H_2O_2] \rightarrow [H_2O] + O_2$).

Experiments have shown, however, that not only the liberation of oxygen, but also consumption of carbon dioxide begins very quickly upon illumination after a dark period, even in very concentrated suspensions. This fact can be explained, from the point of view adopted in this section ($i.\ e.$, without recourse to the hypothesis of a "photosynthetic unit") in two ways, depending on whether one adopts Franck and Herzfeld's scheme, (7.VA), in which the reduction of carbon dioxide is achieved by four consecutive photochemical steps, or chooses one of the reaction schemes ($e.\ g.$, scheme 28.IA) in which a single photochemical reduction step is combined with repeated catalytic dismutations.

In the first case, one has to assume either that the intermediate reduction products, $AHCO_2$, AH_2CO_2 ..., are so stable that they can survive a very prolonged period of darkness, or that the stock of these intermediates is continuously replenished in darkness in consequence of slow reversal of photosynthesis by an autoxidation process, different from normal respirations, occurring within the chloroplasts. In either of these two ways, the photosynthetic apparatus can be kept stocked, in darkness, with a full assortment of intermediates, so that, when illumination starts, carbon dioxide absorption can begin immediately, even in very weak light.

If we assume only one photochemical step, followed by catalytic dismutations, the co-operation of 4 or 8 light quanta in the reduction of one molecule of carbon dioxide can be explained, without the assumption of stable or continuously regenerated intermediates, by catalytic, nonphotochemical reactions among several identical, primary photochemical products. The velocity of these reactions is in no way limited by the rate of absorption of light quanta by a single chlorophyll molecule, since the intermediate photoproducts, formed by several chlorophyll molecules, can diffuse and react with each other. In this case, even if after a dark period the cells were entirely devoid of reduction intermediates, oxygen evolution and carbon dioxide consumption could begin immediately upon illumination.

5. Energy Migration and the Hypothesis of the Photosynthetic Unit

We consider the assumption of a "finishing" dark reaction of limited maximum rate as the cause of flash saturation (as well as of saturation in steady light) to be preferable to the assumption that this saturation is due to the limited quantity of the reduction (or oxidation) substrate. The arguments that influence our choice are (1) the observations of fluorescence, which make it probable that usually *all* chlorophyll molecules are associated with the photosensitive substrate, even after the light saturation has set in (*cf.* page 1075), and (2) the observations which indicate that the primary carbon dioxide absorber is present in the cells in a quantity roughly equivalent to that of chlorophyll. As described in chapter 28, this theory, proposed by Franck, can explain also the possibility of utilizing for photosynthesis all the light quanta absorbed by chlorophyll in weak light and the absence, under these conditions, of an extended induction period for the uptake of carbon dioxide.

Leaving aside for a while the arguments derived from fluorescence, and from the apparent abundance of the primary carbon dioxide absorber, we ask whether the alternative theory of "substrate limitation" could explain the two last-named phenomena: the high quantum yield and the absence of induction losses in weak light. Offhand this appears difficult. If, at best, only 0.1% of the chlorophyll molecules present in the cell can be associated with the reaction substrate (since this is the total amount of this substrate supposed to be available in the cells), how can the quanta absorbed by *all* chlorophyll molecules be made useful for photosynthesis? And if each chlorophyll molecule has to absorb 4, or, more likely, 8 quanta in order to complete the reduction of the carbon dioxide molecule associated with it, how can the uptake of carbon dioxide start immediately upon illumination, even in light which is so weak that individual chlorophyll molecules absorb quanta at an average rate of only one every 30 minutes?

The second difficulty could be eliminated by the assumption of a single photochemical reduction step, followed by nonphotochemical dismutations, while the first one could be resolved by the assumption that the reaction substrate (or an intermediate catalyst) moves freely through the photosynthetic apparatus, and can thus collect the required energy quanta from several excited pigment molecules. The quantity of the substrate, or catalyst, required for efficient energy collection may well be only 0.1 mole per cent of the amount of the pigment itself, particularly if the activation of chlorophyll is prolonged by transfer into a long-lived active state (*cf.* Vol. I, chapter 18).

An alternative, more exciting and more controversial interpretation has been suggested. It was submitted that the absence of an induction period in weak light, as well as the high quantum yield, can be explained by postulating the existence of a "photosynthetic unit" of 300–2400 chlorophyll molecules. This concept was developed by Gaffron and Wohl (1936) from initial suggestions by Emerson and Arnold (1932[1], 1932[2]).

In discussing, on the basis of substrate limitation, the figures in table 32.I, Emerson and Arnold (1932[1], 1932[2]) and Arnold and Kohn (1934) suggested that a "chlorophyll unit" of 2500 molecules may be associated with one "reduction center" (for example, a molecule of the carbon dioxide–acceptor complex, ACO_2) in such a way that all these pigment molecules can co-operate in bringing about the reduction of the molecule of carbon dioxide attached to the one "center."

In discussing the possible attribution of flash yield limitation to a finishing catalyst, we suggested that to calculate the available amount of this catalyst the factor τ should be multiplied by n (or $n/2$) (n being the number of quanta required for the reduction of one molecule of carbon dioxide), because the catalyst might have to operate n (or $n/2$) times in the reduction of one carbon dioxide molecule to the carbohydrate level and the liberation of one oxygen molecule. (For example, in the Franck-Herzfeld scheme, 7.VA, eight unstable intermediates must be stabilized by catalyst E_B.) In the hypothesis of flash yield limitation by the available substrate now under discussion, the necessity of dividing τ by n (or $n/2$) is less certain, because a reaction center can conceivably take up, during a single flash, all the n (or $n/2$) quanta that might be required to complete the reduction of the associated carbon dioxide molecule (and the oxidation of the associated water molecule).

It is, however, equally possible that each reaction center can utilize only 1 (or 2) quanta per flash, and that the intermediate photochemical products must complete their conversion into the final products, carbohydrate and oxygen, by nonphotochemical dismutations (or coupled reactions, discussed in chapter 9 under the name "energy dismutations"). If one of these mechanisms is used in photosynthesis, the number of needed reaction centers is n (or $n/2$) per oxygen molecule liberated in the flash. We therefore conclude that, in the "substrate limitation" theory of flash saturation, the required number of "reaction centers" can be $\tau[Chl]_0$, or $4\tau[Chl]_0$ or $8\tau[Chl]_0$ depending on whether the postulated reaction mechanism permits each center to utilize 1, 4 or 8 quanta in each flash.

Gaffron and Wohl (1936) sought an explanation of how the quanta absorbed anywhere in the "unit" can be utilized, without loss, for photochemical action in a single "center." They suggested that the "unit" may be a closely packed system in which the individual pigment molecules are so intimately associated that a light quantum absorbed by one of them can be exchanged, from neighbor to neighbor, until it reaches the reduction center. In other words, instead of the energy quanta being collected (as suggested above) by chemical agents diffusing through the system, the quanta themselves were supposed to move around until they find the substrate for photochemical action.

Weiss (1937) suggested that the "units" may be identical with the chloroplast grana (Vol. I, p. 357). Frey-Wyssling (1937) pointed out that each granum contains about 10^8 chlorophyll molecules, while "units" were supposed to consist of only about 10^3 molecules each. However, the unit may also be interpreted statistically as a structure containing about one molecule of an enzyme per about 10^3 molecules of chlorophyll. It could be suggested, for example, that each protein disc in the grana (cf. chapter 37A), carrying about 10^6–10^7 chlorophyll molecules, is provided with about 10^3–10^4 "reaction centers," e. g., molecules of an enzyme. Each of the latter can be conceived of as "servicing," preferentially an area, or being associated exclusively with an "island" of about a thousand chlorophyll molecules (cf. Rabinowitch 1951). The "servicing" may be accomplished either by the diffusion of material particles, or by energy migration between pigment molecules, or by a combination of both mechanisms.

Aside from any special assumption concerning the nature an ddistribution of the "reduction centers" in the cell, we may ask: Is the postulated efficient exchange of excitation energy between a large number of chlorophyll molecules physically possible? Can evidence be adduced for (or against) the occurrence of such an exchange in living chloroplasts?

The study of energy transfer in liquids or solids is a rather new development. It was known for a long time that in simple gases a transfer of excitation energy from molecule to molecule does occur in collisions, and that its efficiency is a function of the "resonance" between the collision partners. The closer the resonance, the stronger the interaction, the higher the probability of energy transfer, and the greater the distance over which it can occur. For example, when an excited helium atom approaches a normal atom of the same gas, the perfect resonance between the two states, (He* + He) and (He + He*), causes the energy early to begin fluctuating back and forth between the two atoms.   The frequency, ν, with which this fluctuation occurs, determines the interaction energy, E, according to the quantum-mechanical equation relating energy to frequency:

(32.4) $$E = h\nu$$

If $1/\nu$ is small compared with the duration of the collision (which, for average thermal velocities of the molecules, is of the order of 10^{-13} second) a large number of energy exchanges will occur during a single collision, and, when the atoms separate after the collision, the chance of finding the excitation energy associated with the formerly unexcited helium atom will be equal to that of finding it in the originally excited particle.

When identical molecules are present in close mutual proximity in a concentrated solution, a pure liquid or a crystal, the probability of excitation energy exchanges can be so high that the energy quantum will change its location several times before it is re-emitted as fluorescence, dissipated as heat or utilized for a photochemical transformation.   This phenomenon of energy migration includes two extreme cases (and all transitions between them).   In the one extreme, the frequency of intermolecular exchanges is much higher than that of intramolecular vibrations.   In this case, the excitation energy migrates from molecule to molecule without tarrying in any one of them long enough to warrant the application of the Franck-Condon principle; in other words, the electronic excitation energy is in and out of the molecule before the sluggish nuclei can adjust themselves to its presence.   The excited state then belongs to the system of many identical molecules as a whole, rather than to any individual molecule; the excitation energy "package" is in a condition reminiscent of that of an electron in the "conductivity band" of a metal (or a "pi electron" in the benzene ring).

In the other extreme case, the excitation energy stays with each molecule long enough for intramolecular vibrations to be acquired (or lost) in accordance with the Franck-Condon principle.   At each given moment, then, the excitation energy belongs to a definite molecule.   It moves from one molecule to another by a diffusion mechanism reminiscent of the Brownian movement of material particles.

There is some confusion in the terminology used to describe the different cases of resonance migration of energy.   The term "exciton" was first proposed by the Russian theoretical physicist Frenkel in a discussion of the "fast" propagation mechanism, and it has been suggested that this term should be reserved for this case (although Frenkel himself has used it later also in referring to "slow" migration).   The first phenomenon could also be described as "non-localized" or "communal" absorption of light quanta by a system of coupled resonators; while the second is reminiscent of repeated "collisions of the second kind," such as are responsible for sensitized fluorescence in gases; it has been therefore sometimes called, rather awkwardly, the "fluorescence mechanism." We will use the terms "fast" and "slow" migration, keeping in mind that the time yardstick by reference to which the two cases are distinguished is the period of intramolecular vibration, about 10^{-13} sec.

Theoretical estimates indicate, and experimental results confirm, that the exchange of excitation energy between resonating molecules can occur, in a condensed system, not only in actual collisions or (to use a term more appropriate for such systems) "encounters," but also while these molecules are separated by a solvent layer of several molecular diameters. The occurrence of such "remote" transfers was first derived from observations of the "concentration depolarization" of fluorescence in dyestuff solutions. When fluorescence of a dyestuff is excited by polarized light, the fluorescent light is found to be more or less strongly polarized. To explain this we have to assume that excitation by polarized light occurs preferentially in pigment molecules having a certain orientation, and that, in viscous media, this orientation is not, or not completely, lost by thermal agitation in the time between excitation and re-emission, thus resulting in an at least partly polarized fluorescence. The degree of polarization of the fluorescent light proves to be a function of concentration, being highest in very dilute solutions; this is the phenomenon of "concentration depolarization." This depolarization occurs without change in the absorption or fluorescence spectrum, the yield of fluorescence, or its life-time. It therefore cannot be attributed to dimerization (or generally, polymerization) of the dyestuff molecules or ions. The alternative is then between attributing depolarization to kinetic *encounters*, or to "remote" interactions between dyestuff molecules. Probably, both phenomena occur. Perrin (1932), Vavilov (1942–1950) and Förster (1946–1948, 1951) have been particularly concerned with the remote interaction. The following observation speaks in favor of this interaction as the main or only source of depolarization. The concentration at which depolarization reaches 50% is (in the case of fluorescein solution in glycerol) of the order of 10^{-3} mole/liter. Offhand, this seems sufficiently high for kinetic encounters to produce the observed effect; however, if encounters were actually responsible, the concentration of the dyestuff required for a certain degree of depolarization would increase with increasing viscosity of the medium. No observations of such a dependence have been made; furthermore, it was found that *concentration quenching* of the fluorescence of the same dye in sugar-glycerol solutions (which occurs in a much higher concentration range, 10^{-2} to 10^{-1} mole/l.) actually *is* independent of viscosity. The quenching thus appears to be a function of the average mutual distance of the pigment molecules (which is independent of viscosity) rather than of the frequency of their encounters (which decreases with increasing viscosity). *A fortiori*, this conclusion should also be applicable to depolarization, which occurs at concentrations ten or a hundred times lower than that required for quenching. (It seems unlikely that complete dissipation of excitation energy, implied in quenching, should occur by remote interaction while the much "gentler" depolarizing interaction required direct encounters.)

The concentration depolarization and concentration quenching of dyestuff solutions were again studied experimentally by Sevchenko (1944), and found to be in agreement with the predictions of the theory of "molecular induction" (which is another term for resonance exchange). Pekerman (1947) found that, when dyestuff solutions are taken up by sintered glass, whose pore diameters are such as to cause dye molecules to form one-dimensional trains, self-depolarization and self-quenching are decreased—probably because, under these conditions, resonance transfer is possible in one direction only, and is therefore less effective than in bulk solution.

According to this concept, concentration depolarization indicates (a) that a considerable proportion of the fluorescent light is emitted, not by the primary excited pigment molecules, but by molecules to which the excitation energy has been transferred between excitation and emission, and (b) that this transfer takes place without actual encounters of the emitting molecules with the primarily excited molecules.

(It may be useful to point out that the assumed mechanism of energy exchange is different from absorption and secondary re-emission of fluorescence, a phenomenon that also is possible in concentrated solutions. Estimates indicate that, because of the displacement of the fluorescence band toward the longer waves compared with the absorption band, the probability of "secondary fluorescence" of this type is much too small to account for the observed depolarization.)

If the energy transfer does not require (or prefer) parallel orientation of the molecules (an admittedly extreme assumption), the "self-sensitized" fluorescence will be completely unpolarized. In this case, the decrease of polarization with increased concentration will provide a direct measure of the average number of energy transfers during the excitation period. (Equal distribution of the probability of re-emission over the primarily excited and *one* secondarily excited molecule will produce 50% relative depolarization; distribution over three molecules, 67% depolarization, and so on.) In a 10^{-2} M solution of fluorescein in glycerol, the polarization is only 20% of that in dilute solution. If remote energy transfer is the *only* mechanism of depolarization, this figure indicates the distribution of the excitation probability over five pigment molecules.

At the same concentration, the fluorescence *yield* is reduced by about one half compared with dilute solutions. If this "self-quenching" effect also is ascribed to remote energy transfer, the two phenomena together indicate an energy exchange over an average of ten molecules. Perrin suggested that concentration quenching of fluorescence is generally due to remote energy transfer. This is certainly not true as a general rule, since in many dyestuffs (such as methylene blue) self-quenching is due predominantly to the formation of nonfluorescent dimers at the higher concentrations. Furthermore, at concentrations as high as 10^{-2} mole/liter, quenching (and depolarization) by actual kinetic encounters is unlikely to be entirely negligible even in a medium as viscous as glycerol.

In methylene blue and similar dyestuffs, the self-quenching occurs at concentrations at which dimer formation is revealed by changes in the absorption spectrum. In other dyestuffs, however, quenching occurs when the equilibrium concentration of dimeric molecules is too small to permit the assumption that only the light quanta directly absorbed by such molecules are lost for fluorescence. The concentration quenching can nevertheless be attributed to dimer formation, by means of either or both of the following two hypotheses: *first*, that short-lived, nonfluorescent dimers can be *formed* in encounters of excited and normal pigment molecules; and *second*, that the excitation can "seek out" the few dimeric molecules present in equilibrium, by making numerous jumps from molecule to molecule during the excitation period (Förster's hypothesis). According to Franck and Livingston (1949), migration of excitation energy could lead to quenching also by another mechanism, not requiring dimers: the perambulating quantum could be dissipated whenever in its travel it visits a molecule containing an abnormally high amount of vibrational energy, since, in such a molecule, electronic excitation may produce a configuration permitting conversion of the electronic energy into vibrations of the ground state (for an objection to this hypothesis, see Förster 1951, p. 252).

A mathematical theory of quenching by energy migration was developed also by Vavilov (1942, 1944, 1950), who postulated that each transfer of electronic energy from molecule to molecule involves a certain probability of its loss, without specifying the mechanism of this dissipation.

Perrin (1932) calculated, using a classical harmonic oscillator as a model of pigment molecules, that the probability of energy transfer from the originally excited to a second, resonating oscillator, becomes equal to the probability of re-emission of energy by the primary absorber, when the distance between the two oscillators is of the order of $\lambda/27$, corresponding to about 100 mμ for visible light. Neither the concentration quenching nor the depolarization occur at such extreme dilutions. Förster (1946) ascribed this to lack of *exact* resonance (assumed in Perrin's calculations). The resonance is not exact for two reasons: the displacement of the fluorescence band relative to the absorption band, and the finite width of both bands. Förster made a rough calculation, taking into account two requirements: (*a*) that the frequencies of the two interacting oscillators must be within the region where the fluorescence band and the absorption band overlap, and (*b*) that these frequencies must differ by not more than E/h (where E is the interaction energy). The result of this calculation is that the "critical distance" (*i. e.*, the intermolecular distance at which the probabilities of re-emission and transfer are equal) is reduced, compared with Perrin's estimate, by a factor of $[\Delta'\nu/\tau(\Delta\nu)^2]^{1/6}$:

$$(32.5) \qquad d_0 = (\lambda/27)[\Delta'\nu/t(\Delta\nu)^2]^{1/6}$$

Here, $\Delta'\nu$ is the range of overlapping fluorescence and absorption frequencies, $\Delta\nu$ the band width and t the average duration of excitation. With $\Delta'\nu/\Delta\nu = 0.1$, $t = 5 \times 10^{-9}$ second and $\Delta\nu \simeq 1.5 \times 10^{14}$, Förster calculated $d_0 \simeq 7.5$ mμ, corresponding to about 20 molecular diameters. An improved, quantum-mechanical calculation leads (Förster 1948, 1951) to the same order of magnitude for the distance over which excitation energy can be transmitted. The frequency of energy transfer is, according to this calculation, proportional to the *inverse sixth power* of the distance between molecules, and therefore directly proportional to the *square* of concentration. The following equation was obtained by Förster (1948) as a substitute for equation (32.5):

$$(32.6) \qquad d_0^6 = 3lcT'_\nu/8\pi^4 n^2 N'^2 \nu_0^2$$

where t = average life-time of excitation, c = velocity of light, n = index of refraction of the medium, N' = number of molecules in a millimole; ν_0, the frequency of the band (average of the frequencies of the absorption and fluorescence peaks); and T_ν the integral:

$$(32.4) \qquad T_\nu = 2.30^2 \int_0^\infty \alpha_\nu \alpha_{2\nu_0 - \nu} \alpha_\nu$$

which is a measure of the overlapping of the fluorescence and the absorption spectra (α_ν being the decimal molar extinction coefficient at frequency ν). Applying this equation to chlorophyll α in ether ($n = 1.35$) Förster obtained $d_0 = 8.0$ mμ as the distance at which energy transfer becomes equally probable with re-emission. This is the average intermolecular distance at 7.7×10^{-4} m./l. Treating chlorophyll grana as a homogeneous system 0.1 M in chlorophyll (*cf.* Vol. I, page 411), *i. e.*, neglecting the probable orderliness of the arrangement, Förster calculated that about 10^4 transfers can occur during the excitation period of 3×10^{-8} sec.

According to the equation $\Delta E = h\nu$ (where ν is the frequency of the energy exchange) this rate of exchange should cause a change, ΔE, in the energy of the excited state, equivalent to about 10 cm.$^{-1}$ $[10^4/(3 \times 10^{-8} \times 3 \times 10^{10}) = 10]$. This corresponds to a shift of the absorption band, leading to this state, by about 0.4 μ. It will be noted that, with 10^4 transfers per second, 30 to 300 molecular vibrations (with periods between 10^{-14} and 10^{-13} sec.) will be possible per visit; consequently, the band shape—determined by the coupling of electronic excitation and intermolecular vibrations (according to the Franck-Condon mechanism)—will be preserved more or less unchanged.

These estimates seemed to fulfill the requirements of the theory of the photosynthetic unit (300–2400 transfers during the excitation period) and to be at least not inconsistent with the spectroscopic facts (the red band shift *in vivo* is $\gg 0.4$ mμ, but it could be attributed largely to complexing with proteins; the shape of the red absorption band is approximately the same *in vivo* as *in vitro*).

However, the numerical values used in Förster's calculations require correction. He used $t = 3 \times 10^{-8}$ sec. as the average life-time of the excited state. A larger value, 8×10^{-8} sec., was derived on page 633 from the integral of the absorption curve, but much more recent calculations (*cf.* chapter 37C, section 1) gave only 1.3×10^{-8} sec. A much more radical correction is required by the fact—neglected by Förster—that the yield of fluorescence of chlorophyll in the living cell is low, perhaps only 0.1% (as against 10% in organic solvents). This indicates that the "natural" life-time of excitation (as derived from band intensity) is shortened—perhaps by a factor of 10^3—by energy dissipation. The effective t thus may be of the order of 10^{-11}, rather than 10^{-8} sec. Even a few hundred excitation jumps during this period will reduce the "visiting time" below 1×10^{-13} sec., and thus destroy the coupling with molecular vibrations. (Incidentally, a "visiting time" of such brevity should also affect unfavorably the probability that excitation will actually cause the photochemical change while "visiting" the chlorophyll molecule associated with the reaction center, since this energy transfer, too, depends on the conversion of electronic energy into the kinetic energy of atomic nuclei.)

From considerations of this type, Franck and Teller (1938) concluded that, in the living cell, energy propagation by the "slow" transfer mechanism cannot extend over the number of molecules required by the theory of the photosynthetic unit.

The concept was nevertheless revived by Duysens (1952). He derived from Förster's equations the conclusion that at a concentration $[k]_0 = 1000/N_A d_0^3$ (m./l.), where d_0 is the "critical distance" given in equation (32.6), and N_A, Avogadro's number (6×10^{23}), an average of about 15 energy transfers will occur during the lifetime of the excited molecule—assuming an at random distribution of the acceptor. With increasing concentration, $[k] > [k]_0$, the average number of transfers will increase proportionally. It was estimated above that with $t = 3 \times 10^{-8}$ sec., $[k]_0$ for chlorophyll a is 7.7×10^{-4} mole/l.; the pigment concentration in the grana is much higher, ~ 0.1 mole/l. True, the lower actual yield of fluorescence *in vivo* does not permit an estimation of the average extent of energy migration simply from this ratio of concentrations; nevertheless (using a natural life-time of 4×10^{-8} sec.) Duysens arrived at a relatively optimistic estimate by postulating an "intrinsic" fluorescence yield of 10% (the same *in vivo* as *in vitro*), and an actual yield of the order of 1%.

According to Duysens, at an average concentration of 0.1 mole/l. (which is a plausible value for the grana), the average number of energy transfers, during an excitation period of 4×10^{-9} sec., is about 750. If, before the end of the transfer chain, excitation hits a "reaction center" in which it is utilized for a photochemical reaction, fluorescence is quenched. Assuming that one such center exists per 200 chlorophyll molecules (in a random, three-dimensional array), the chance of hitting it before the transfer chain of 750 links is terminated can be estimated as 0.8; the fluorescence must then be reduced by 80%—from the "intrinsic" value of 10% to an "actual" value of about 2%. Duysens considered this figure as close to the actual true yield of fluorescence *in vivo* (about 1%, according to his estimates; *cf.* chap. 37C, section 7), and the whole calculation as proving that the concept of the photosynthetic unit, with energy exchange by the "slow" resonance transfer mechanism, *can* be reconciled with the spectroscopic evidence, if the unit is reduced to about 200 chlorophyll molecules (and the yield of fluorescence *in vivo* is assumed to be of the order of 1%).

About 750 transfers during 4×10^{-9} sec. means an exchange frequency of 2×10^{11} sec.$^{-1}$, corresponding to a band shift by only 7 cm.$^{-1}$ ($2 \times 10^{-11}/ 3 \times 10^{10}$), which is small compared to the actual red shift *in vivo* (about 200 cm.$^{-1}$). The vibrational structure of the absorption band will be unaffected by such slow transfer, and the band shift caused by it will be practically negligible.

A simplified procedure—similar to that repeatedly used above—would be to set 4×10^{-10} sec. as the available migration time (indicated by a 1% fluorescence yield), and to conclude that 200 transfers during this time mean an exchange frequency of 5×10^{11} sec.$^{-1}$, and a visiting time of 2×10^{-12} sec.—just enough to preserve the coupling with molecular vibrations with frequencies of the order of 10^{13} sec.$^{-1}$.

The theoretical migration range is cut to $1/3$ if t is only 1.3×10^{-8} sec.

The case of energy transfer to a minor constituent of the pigment system, mixed at random with the main pigment, and having an absorption band in resonance with the fluorescence band of the latter, is clearly analogous to the above-discussed case of energy transfer to a "reaction center" in a photosynthetic unit. Duysens (1952) considered from this point of view the—apparently highly effective—loss of excitation energy of chlorophyll *a* in red algae by transfer to an unidentified minor pigment (probably, chlorophyll *d*). To compete effectively with the "reduction centers" as ultimate energy acceptors, the "chlorophyll *d*" molecules must be present in a similar concentration (one for a few hundred chlorophyll molecules, which is compatible with experimental evidence). This assumes equal probability of transfer to both acceptors; the capacity of "chlorophyll d" to divert quanta from the "reduction centers" would be enhanced if the overlap integral for the transfer chlorophyll $a \rightarrow$ "chlorophyll d" were larger than for the transfer chlorophyll $a \rightarrow$ "reduction center"—as it may well be. (The "reduction centers" may be properly located or complexed molecules of chlorophyll a itself.)

One may ask whether all these estimates could be affected by the probable existence of a long-lived, metastable state of the chlorophyll molecule (or of the pigments-protein-lipide complex in the living cell). If the low yield of fluorescence of chlorophyll *in vivo* is the result of the transfer of most of the excited chlorophyll molecules (or complexes) into a metastable state containing considerable electronic energy, and *not* of total conversion of this energy into heat (or chemical energy), why should it not be possible for the electronic energy of the metastable state to be exchanged "at leisure," as it were, between adjacent molecules? (The time available for the exchange could be, in this case, a million—or more—times longer than the natural life time of the fluorescent state.) If the metastable state is a tautomeric form of the molecule, no resonance transfer of energy is possible, because it would require a displacement of the *nuclei;* but if the long-lived state is an electronic mesomer (*e. g.*, a triplet state, as envisaged by Terenin*) and by Lewis and Kasha, *cf.* pp. 486, 790), energy transfer is feasible. However, the rate of transfer by the "slow" mechanism is proportional to the *fourth* power of the transition probability between the ground state and the excited state; while the natural life-time of the excited state is inversely proportional to the *square* of the same probability. Therefore, if the natural life-time of the excited state is t_f, and that of the metastable state, t_m, the number of transfers during the full natural life-time of the latter will be smaller (by a factor of t_f/t_m)—and not larger than the number of transfers during the full life-time of the fluorescent state. If we assume that the low yield of chlorophyll fluorescence *in vivo* (0.1%, or 1%) is caused by the transfer of 99 (or 99.9%) of the excited chlorophyll molecules from the fluorescent into the metastable state (rather than by the dissipation of total energy of the fluorescent state by internal conversion), the number of energy transfers during the *actual* excitation period will be increased in consequence of this transfer, only if t_m is $<10^3$ (or 10^2) $\times t_f$. (We now compare the number of jumps during the full natural life-time of the metastable state with that during one-thousandth or one-hundredth of the natural life-time of the fluorescent state.) With $t_f = 4 \times 10^{-8}$ sec., this means that the existence of a metastable state could favor migration only if the natural life-time of this state were $<4 \times 10^{-5}$ (or 4×10^{-6}) sec. If the first figure is correct, a metastable state with a natural life-time of 4×10^{-6} sec. would increase the frequency—and thus also the range—of energy migration by a factor of 10, and a metastable state with a life-time of 4×10^{-7} sec., by a factor of 100—presuming this state actually survives for its full natural life-time. However, if this were the case, the metastable state would produce a marked phosphorescence. Since this state is situated considerably below the initial excitation state (as judged by the nonoccurrence of delayed red fluorescence, which could be caused by return from metastable to the fluorescent state by thermal energy fluctuations), an emission originating in this state should be located in the infrared. Until evidence is presented that chlorophyll *in vivo* does emit infrared phosphorescence, with a quantum yield higher than that of the known red fluorescence, we have to assume that the metastable triplet state, if it occurs *in vivo* at all, survives for only a small fraction of its "natural" life—and this should make it im-

* Terenin (1940, 1941) had suggested the interpretation of the metastable state of organic molecules as a triplet "biradical" state before this was proposed by Lewis and Kasha (1945), but his work did not become known abroad, because of wartime conditions, until considerably later. (For a review of the work by Terenin and co-workers, see Terenin's *Photochemistry of Dyes*, 1947.)

possible for this state to contribute significantly to resonance energy migration. In other words, the number of energy transfers that occur while the molecule is in the metastable state is smaller than those occurring in the brief period (4×10^{-10}, or 4×10^{-11} sec.) the molecule spends in the original excited state.

In chapter 23 (p. 795) we mentioned the—inconclusive—attempts by Calvin and Dorough to identify a long-lived, infrared fluorescence of chlorophyll *in vitro;* no similar experiments have been made with chlorophyll *in vivo.*

Terenin and Ermolaev (1952) saw evidence of energy exchange in the metastable state in benzaldehyde-sensitized phosphorescence of naphthalene in a frozen mixture of these two compounds. The energy content of the excited singlet state of benzaldehyde is too small to lift naphthalene into its excited singlet state. The authors suggested that excited benzaldehyde is first converted into the metastable triplet state, and that the energy of the latter is then transferred to naphthalene. The triplet state of naphthalene, resulting from this transfer, slowly decays by phosphorescence.

It was suggested long ago, from the study of sensitized fluorescence in gases, that, for the resonance transfer to be a "permitted" process, the *total* electronic spin of the system must remain constant—and that this condition can be fulfilled by the excitation of a "prohibited" singlet → triplet transition at the cost of another "prohibited" triplet → singlet transition, as well as by the more trivial replacement of one "permitted" transition by another. There is a certain contradiction between this statement and the argument used above in discussing the probability of energy migration in the metastable state, since in the latter the low oscillator strengths of the "prohibited" transitions were supposed to be unaffected by the mutual approach of the two partners in the exchange. Which of the two conclusions is correct must depend on the strength of the coupling between the electron spins of the two molecules at the distances over which the energy exchange occurs.

We will now consider whether the "fast" exchange mechanism ("communal absorption") could operate in the chloroplasts, and whether the spectroscopic properties of chlorophyll in the living cell are consistent with such an exchange. Since chlorophyll is not distributed uniformly in the granum (instead, it probably is arranged in monomolecular layers, *cf.* chapter 37A), resonance exchange may be considerably faster than was calculated by Förster from the *average* concentration of chlorophyll in the granum. If we attribute the total red shift of the absorption band *in vivo* (about 10 mμ from its position in ethereal solution, and about 25 mμ from its extrapolated position in vacuum), to such an exchange, we calculate for the exchange process a wave number of from 250 to 625 cm.$^{-1}$, and a frequency of from 7.5 to 20 $\times$ 10^{12} sec.$^{-1}$; this would permit 300–1200 exchanges, enough to satisfy the requirements of the "photosynthetic unit" during an excitation period as short as 4×10^{-11} sec. (not to speak of the 4×10^{-10} sec. available if Duysens' revised estimate of the fluorescence yield *in vivo* is correct).

A difficulty arises, however, when we consider the *shape* of the absorption band. As pointed out before, this shape is determined, in solution, by the coupling of electronic excitation with intramolecular vibrations; and one can expect this coupling to be destroyed if the excitation does not stay with each visited molecule $\gg 10^{-13}$ sec., to permit molecular vibrations to get excited according to the Franck-Condon mechanism. With a transfer occurring each 5–15 $\times$ 10^{-14} sec. this is impossible; excitation shoots through the molecules without setting them in vibration, like a bullet passes through a glass pane without shattering it. One therefore expects this type of energy exchange to strip the absorption band of its vibrational structure and, by preventing electronic energy dissipation into vibrations, to produce a high yield of fluorescence of the "resonance" type (*i. e.*, fluorescence with a wave length practically identical with that of the absorption band).

Absorption and fluorescence phenomena of this type have been observed by Scheibe *et al.* (1936–41; see also Katheder 1940; Jelley 1936) in concentrated solutions of certain dyestuffs. These investigators found that the absorption spectra of isocyanine, pinacyanol and certain other dyestuffs change radically when their concentration in aqueous solution is increased above a certain value. The original absorption band loses its intensity and a new sharp and narrow band appears on the long-wave side

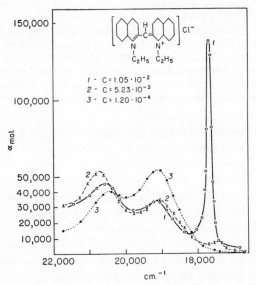

Fig. 32.7. Absorption spectrum of pseudo-isocyanine at three different concentrations, showing the formation of dimers at 5×10^{-3} mole/l. and of polymers with a sharp absorption band at 1×10^{-2} mole/l. (after Scheibe 1938).

of the original band. Figure 32.7 shows this phenomenon for pseudo-isocyanine. This change is due to linear *polymerization* of the dyestuff; it disappears sharply upon heating to a certain temperature. The extinction coefficient of the polymer *per single link* is of the same order of magnitude as that of the monomeric form, thus showing that the "super-molecule" acts as the sum of as many chromophores as it contains monometric molecules.

Figure 32.7 shows that, in a typical case, the polymer band is shifted about 1500 cm.$^{-1}$ from the position of the monomer band. This shift corresponds to a frequency of the order of 5×10^{13} sec.$^{-1}$, or to a sweep of the excitation over 10^5 pigment molecules during the life-time (if the latter remains of the order of 10^{-8} second).

The polymeric molecules of this type show strong *resonance fluorescence*, in agreement with the theoretical prediction; a striking result, because resonance fluorescence is usually associated with vapors of low pressure, consisting of free atoms or simple molecules, and not with complex molecules or condensed systems.

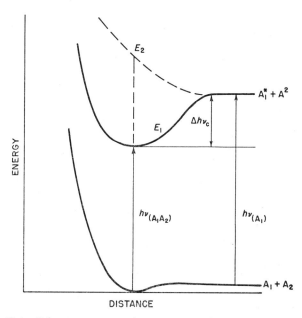

Fig. 32 8. Potential energy curves of two atoms with no bonding in the ground state and exchange bonding in the excited state (example: He_2).

Obviously, nothing similar to Scheibe's polymers exists in chloroplasts: the red absorption band of chlorophyll is about as broad, if not broader *in vivo* than *in vitro*, as if no uncoupling of intramolecular vibrations from electronic excitation has occurred. Furthermore, the fluorescence of green cells is weak and not of the resonance type.

These facts seem to preclude the interpretation of the red band shift *in vivo* as due to a "fast" resonance migration of excitation energy through a closely packed chlorophyll layer. They caused Franck and Teller (1938) to reject the "fast" energy migration mechanism as a possible basis of the "photosynthetic unit" concept; it was mentioned above that they have also rejected the "slow" mechanism because in their estimate it did not provide a sufficiently wide range of energy migration.

It is not quite certain, however, whether band sharpness and resonance fluorescence are *necessary* attributes of energy migration of the "fast" type. In the first place, the narrowness of the absorption band is predicated not only on the uncoupling of electronic excitation from intramolecular vibrations, but also on a strict selection of permitted transitions from a broad electronic excitation band.

The simplest case of energy resonance is that between two atoms, $A_1 + A_2$. Their mutual potential energy as a function of distance can be represented by the lower curve in figure 32.8. If one of the two atoms is excited, the resonance between the structures $A_1 + A_2$ leads either to attraction or to repulsion, giving rise to *two* excited electronic levels, E_1 and E_2. The first absorption line of the separated atoms, $h\nu_0$, is thus shifted to the red (*i. e.*, to the smaller energy quanta), the amount of the shift being determined by equation (32.4). The second absorption line, leading to the repulsion curve, is shifted to the short-wave side of the original band, and may be a "forbidden" line.

If this concept is extended from two atoms or molecules to three, four or more resonating systems, the addition of each new link will cause an increase in the number of levels, until a practically continuous band of energy levels will be formed. (This situation is similar to that in the series Na, Na_2 ... Na metal, with the difference that, in a metal, the multiplicity of levels is due to the exchange of *electrons*, and not excitons.) Under certain conditions, the probability of transition by light absorption will be high only to the *lowest* excited states, thus giving a sharp absorption and fluorescence band of the lowest possible frequency (*i. e.*, with the maximum possible shift toward the red from the position of the absorption band of a single molecule).

The sharp selection of the permitted electronic transitions appears to be valid for symmetry conditions prevailing in Scheibe's one-dimensional polymers; but under different symmetry conditions a broader electronic band could possibly arise, to replace, in the resonating system, the vibration-broadened but intrinsically sharp electronic transition in the monomeric molecule. A closer study is needed also to decide whether the transfer of energy from the electronic system to the vibrational degrees of freedom—including those of the system as a whole, rather than of individual molecules—can be effectively prevented, by rapid fluctuation of electronic excitation, in *all* two-dimensional or three-dimensional resonating systems, or whether this uncoupling, too, can be fully effective only under special spatial relationships, such as may exist between the electronic excitation and molecular vibrations (or, at least, a certain type of molecular vibrations) in one-dimensional polymers.

As to the lack of, or weakness of, fluorescence, this can be caused, in a large resonating system, not only by a residual coupling with inter- or intramolecular vibrations, but also by an efficient quenching of fluorescence by a relatively small number of molecules of an impurity—a "trapping" of electronic excitation in a "potential hole," in which it can then be dissipated in the usual way by conversion into vibrations.

Of some relevance here are the experiments on the absorption spectra and fluorescence of certain pigments (particularly chlorophyllides) in the crystalline state, described in chapter 37C, section 3.

These experiments showed that, in chlorophyllide crystals and monolayers, the red absorption band is shifted by as much as 80 mμ (up to 2000 cm.$^{-1}$; cf. table 37C.II) toward the longer waves. Theoretical calculations, using the actual density of the chromophores in the crystal, indicated that a shift of approximately this extent is to be expected in consequence of the interaction between closely packed chromophores (Kromhout 1952; Jacobs, Holt, Kromhout and Rabinowitch 1954; cf. also Heller and Marcus 1951).

In contrast to calculations of Förster et al., in which only the energy exchange between two molecules was considered, these estimates were based on simultaneous consideration of "virtual dipole" interactions between all pairs of molecules in a cubic lattice.

The calculations were carried out for an isotropic three-dimensional lattice. The chlorophyllide crystals have, however, a layered structure (illustrated by fig. 37B.9); and molecular interaction can be expected to be much stronger within each layer than between them. (A difference is likely also between two directions within each layer.) This expectation is confirmed by the observation that the spectra of monomolecular layers of chlorophyllide show almost as wide a red shift as those of crystals. The predominantly two-dimensional interaction must lead to a more rapid saturation of interaction energy with distance than in a three-dimensional system (since the integration of the resonance energies has to be carried out over circular belts, rdr, instead of spherical shells, r^2dr). Consequently, the relative contribution of the nearest neighbors to the total resonance energy of a molecule is greater in the layered structure than in an isotropic three-dimensional system. This has a bearing on the observations—described in chapter 37C—of the saturation of the band shift with increasing size of the microcrystals. Obviously, as a crystal begins to grow, the interaction effect must at first increase with the number of molecules in it; saturation will be reached when new molecules, added on the surface, are so far from an average molecule inside the crystal that they do not contribute significantly to its excitation energy. For an energy decreasing with inverse third power of distance (such as the mutual energy of two dipoles), the contribution of circular belts of increasing diameter to the energy of a molecule in the center declines with the *square* of the radius. If the ring of nearest neighbors contributes the interaction energy ΔE, the second ring will contribute (approximately) $\Delta E/4$, the third one, $\Delta E/9$, and so on, the total for an infinite number of rings being $(\pi^2/6)\Delta E$. The contribution of rings beyond the Nth one will be

$$\Delta E \left(\frac{1}{(N+1)^2} + \frac{1}{(N+2)^2} + \ldots \right) < \frac{\Delta E}{N}$$

or $<5\%$ for $N = 12$, and $<1\%$ for $N > 60$. The interaction energy of the layer should thus be $>99\%$ saturated—and the band shift should practically cease—when the radius of the layer has grown to sixty molecular diameters; the shift will reach the limit of reliability of our present measurements at 12–15 molecular diameters.

The crystals for which band shift saturation was observed, according to figure 37C.16, contained about 10^7 molecules; even if correction is made for scattering, and the true shift assumed to end at about 730 mμ, this limit still corresponds to crystals containing as many as 10^6 molecules each. Assuming equal development in three dimensions (which is admissible for the "small", as contrasted to the "large" microcrystals; *cf.* fig. 37B.8), such crystals consist, roughly, of 100 layers of 100 × 100 molecules each—somewhat in excess of the dimensions over which the interaction energy should be 99% saturated in a single two-dimensional layer. However, as the distance from the central molecule grows, the role of the crystal layer to which this molecule belongs becomes less dominant, and this should cause the energy saturation to be approached more slowly.

Spectral effects similar to those observed in chlorophyll derivatives must occur also in other molecular crystals, if the absorption bands of the molecules are intense enough to cause strong interaction. This subject was analyzed theoretically by Davydov (1948), specially in application to hydrocarbons (anthracene, naphthalene, etc.), whose absorption spectra have been described by Obreimov, Prikhodko and co-workers (*cf.* Prikhodko 1949). Similar to the chlorophyllide crystals, naphthalene crystals are thin, monoclinic sheets. Their absorption spectrum (for light falling normally to the sheets) depends on polarization, since electric oscillations can be excited parallel to one or the other of the two crystallographic axes located in the plane of the sheets. Some bands occur with only one (or predominantly one) polarization; others with both of them. Two of the latter can be correlated with known bands of naphthalene vapor, shifted toward the longer waves (by 500 and 2000 cm.$^{-1}$, respectively). Their vibrational structure is similar to that of the vapor bands. Bands leading to three other excited levels observed in crystals have no parallel in the vapor spectrum. One of them is about equally strong with both polarizations, the other two are strongly polarized. These three electronic levels, considered as "crystal levels," rather than "molecular levels," combine with a set of vibrational quanta not encountered in vapor, which must be attributed to the lattice as a whole.

One could suggest that bands leading to the "crystal levels" in naphthalene crystals are analogous to the sharp absorption bands of Scheibe's polymers, and that energy quanta absorbed in these bands are "communal property" of the lattice. In contrast to this, quanta taken up in bands leading to "molecular levels" can be considered as belonging to individual lattice points, and capable of migration only by the "slow" resonance mechanism.

From the point of view of the state of chlorophyll *in vivo*, the spectra of chlorophyll monolayers are of special interest. Of the two types of such layers (Jacobs *et al.* 1954), the "optically dense" (probably, bimolecular) layers show a band position entirely different from that of chlorophyll in the living cell; but the "optically thin" (undoubtedly, monomolecular) layers show the band in about the same position as the living cells (675 mμ; *cf.* table 37C.II). Two questions must be answered, however, before this coincidence is accepted as significant. Is the band position in the monolayer due to chromophore interaction, or to the binding of chlorophyll molecules to water? And, similarly, is the band position in the living cell due to chromophore interaction, or to the attachment of chlorophyll to other cell constituents (*e. g.*, water, or proteins)? If the red shift were as wide as in chlorophyllide monolayers (or in "dense" chlorophyll layers), its attribution to interaction between chlorophyll molecules would be much safer, since such shifts are unlikely to arise from solvation. Despite this uncertainty, it is at least a legitimate working hypothesis to assume that the band position *in vivo* is due mainly to the interaction between chlorophyll molecules within monolayers (which they probably form on protein discs).

The width of the absorption bands in chlorophyll crystals and monolayers make it likely (although, according to p. 1294, not quite certain) that no "fast" migration of excitation energy occurs in them; while the absence of fluorescence (or its shift into the infrared?) sets a rather low limit for the possible extent of "slow" resonance migration. It will be noted in this connection that the extensive band shift in crystals and monolayers, although it indicates a "stabilization" of the "red" excitation level by about 2000 cm.$^{-1}$ as compared to isolated chlorophyll molecules, can be adequately explained, in the first approximation, by virtual dipole interaction between the chromophores in the lattice, without recourse to quantum mechanical resonance phenomena, and therefore offers no evidence concerning possible excitation energy migration in the lattice.

In vivo, on the other hand, the small but measurable fluorescence yield leaves, as estimated on p. 1289, just enough leeway for resonance energy migration to satisfy the needs of a modest "photosynthetic unit." The red band shift *in vivo* may be the composite result of virtual dipole interaction between pigment molecules in a monolayer, the attachment of pigment molecules to proteins and other cellular constituents, and a small resonance stabilization, associated with a limited migration of excitation energy.

Returning now to the problems in connection with which the concept of the "photosynthetic unit" was first introduced on p. 1280—namely, the alternative between a "preparatory" or a "terminal" process limiting the maximum flash yield, we note that although the "unit" was first invented to be able to attribute the flash yield limitation to the number of available reduction sites (*i. e.*, of substrate molecules available for transformation in a flash), it can be equally well combined with the assumption of a "terminal" limitation—*e. g.*, by the amount of a "stabilizing" enzyme. In this form, the hypothesis does not contradict the observation that the "CO_2 acceptor" seems to be present, in photosynthesizing cells, in a concentration of the same order of magnitude as that of chlorophyll (and not $<1\%$ of it). As to the effect of carbon dioxide on chlorophyll fluorescence *in vivo*, this does not require, if energy migration occurs, the association of each chlorophyll molecule with a carbon dioxide molecule. (A case in point is presented by Scheibe's linear polymers, where, in a micelle containing up to 1000 dye molecules, the association of a single molecule with a quencher effectively quenches the fluorescence of the whole micelle.)

To sum up, the role of resonance energy migration between chlorophyll molecules in the photosynthetic process is still uncertain. Theoretical estimates show that excitation energy should have a chance to migrate, during an actual life-time of the order of 10^{-10} sec., over a small number (of the order of 10 or 100) of chlorophyll molecules, if the pigment is distributed at random in the grana, and over a larger number (of the order of 1000) of molecules, if these are arranged in densely packed monomolecular layers.

Whether this migration actually takes place, we do not know. To prove beyond doubt that energy migration *does* occur between chlorophyll molecules *in vivo*, and to determine its reach, would be of great importance for the understanding of the photochemical mechanism of photosynthesis; yet even after this proof one could not be certain that energy migration is the true cause of the kinetic phenomena (such as flash saturation) that had first led to the concept of a "photosynthetic unit." The now most plausible interpretation of these phenomena is in terms of an enzymatic component ordinarily present in a concentration of between 1/300 and 1/2400th of that of chlorophyll. Effective cooperation of this "limiting enzyme" with *all* chlorophyll molecules could be achieved in three ways—by migration of excitation energy from the chlorophyll molecules to the enzyme ("photosynthetic unit"), *or* by migration to the enzyme of photochemical products formed at the chlorophyll molecules, *or* by migration of the enzyme itself, collecting its substrate from hundreds or thousands of chlorophyll molecules, like a bee collects nectar from a plot of flowers.   Even if the phenomenon of energy migration were well established, this would not prove that the other two are nonexistent or irrelevant.

In the above discussion the analogy between "energy conduction" and electron conduction in crystals was mentioned.   The kind of resonance required for the diffusion of *energy* is, however, different from that underlying the diffusion of *electrons*.   The atoms of a metal are held together by *electron exchange forces* (the same effect that is responsible for the formation of hydrogen molecules, according to Heitler and London). In molecular lattices, the resonance effects are due to *excitation energy* resonances, as illustrated above by the example of a He_2 molecule.   In an H_2 molecule, the degeneracy, which leads to the bonding, is due to the fact that the two *electrons* can exchange their places without a change in energy; in He_2, formed from an *excited* He* and a normal helium atom, the degeneracy is due to the fact that the *excitation energy* may be exchanged between the two atoms in the molecule.   The first kind of resonance, extended to a system of many nuclei, leads to *electron conduction;* the second kind of resonance leads, in a similar case, to an *energy conduction.*

If the electron exchange in a crystal is strong in the ground state, the crystal shows *metallic* conduction.   If only excited atoms (or molecules) easily exchange their electrons, the crystal has insulating properties in the dark, and shows photoconductivity in light.   Chlorophyll in the chloroplasts is certainly not a metallic conductor; but can it be a *photoelectric* conductor?   This could lead to a variation of the theory of the photosynthetic unit in which an exchange of *electrons* between molecules would replace the exchange of *excitations*.   The primary effect of light on the "photosynthetic unit" would then be the same as that of ultraviolet light on an alkali halide crystal: to set an electron free.   This electron then could diffuse through the unit until it meets a "reduction center" that absorbs it, the whole process being equivalent to *oxidation* of a chlorophyll molecule and reduction of a substrate anchored somewhere else in a "reduction center."   However, the similarity between the absorption spectrum of molecularly dispersed chlorophyll and that of the chlorophyll in the cell seems to preclude the possibility that the excited state of chlorophyll *in vivo* is a "conductivity state" (which would be entirely different from the excited state *in vitro*).   Consequently this variation of the "photosynthetic unit" (proposed by Katz 1949) must be rejected.

6. Energy Transfer between Different Pigment Molecules

Related to the problem of energy transfer between *identical* molecules (e. g., between several chlorophyll *a* molecules in the hypothetical "photosynthetic unit") is that of energy transfer between *different* molecules, (*e. g.*, between chlorophyll *a* and chlorophyll *b*, or between carotenoids, phycobilins, and chlorophyll). It was repeatedly suggested in chapter 30 that the (by now well established) sensitizing action of so-called "accessory" pigments in photosynthesis may be based on the transfer of the energy quanta, absorbed by these pigments, to chlorophyll—perhaps, the only pigment that can (or, at least, the only one that does) act as the chemical "photocatalyst" in photosynthesis.

Theoretically, the probability of the resonance transfer of excitation energy between different molecules by the "slow" resonance mechanism is determined (similarly to that between identical molecules), by the overlapping of the fluorescence band of the primary light absorber (energy donor) and the absorption band of the energy acceptor. In a mixture of several chlorophylls this overlapping may be so wide that the probability of energy transfer between them can be of the same order of magnitude as for the energy transfer between two molecules of a single component. Förster (1947) estimated, for example, that the probability of energy migration from *b* to *a* is about one half that from one *a* to another *a*. The transfer in the opposite direction—from *a* to *b*—is, however, about 300 times less probable (Duysens 1952).

Band overlapping is considerable also between the phycobilins and the chlorophylls, since the fluorescence of the former pigments lies in the region where the latter ones absorb strongly. It is generally less extensive between the carotenoids and the phycobilins or chlorophylls.

Arnold and Oppenheimer (1950) first discussed the probability of resonance transfer of energy (a process they called "internal conversion") between two different photosynthetic pigments, using phycocyanin and chlorophyll in blue-green algae as an example. They estimated, from crude observations, that 1 or 2% of the quanta absorbed by phycocyanin in *Chroococcus* are re-emitted as phycocyanin fluorescence. Postulating that the relative probabilities of fluorescence and energy dissipation in the chromoproteid should be the same *in vivo* as *in vitro*, and noticing that in the pigment extract this ratio is about 1:4 (*i. e.*, about 80% of the absorbed quanta are dissipated, and 20% re-emitted), they concluded that dissipation can account, *in vivo*, for only 4–8% of the absorbed quanta. This leaves 90–95% unaccounted for by either fluorescence or dissipation—and thus, they postulated, transferred to chlorophyll. Arnold and Oppenheimer estimated that the transfer probability ("internal conversion coefficient") required for a transfer yield of 90–95%, lies within the theoretical limits one can calculate from the classical model of two coupled oscillators, by using the smallest and the largest plausible value, respectively, of the average distance between the molecules of the two pigments in the *Chroococcus* cell.

In chapter 24, we mentioned the fluorescence experiments of Van Norman, French and Macdowall (1948) which made it plausible (but did not prove definitely) that a transfer of excitation energy from phycocyanin to chlorophyll actually does occur in the red alga, *Gigartina harveyana*. Subsequently, French and Young (1952) developed a double-monochromator permitting the determination of the fluorescence spectra of algae with monochromatic excitation. These experiments will be described in Chapter 37C (section 7). They indicate that the energy absorbed by chlorophyll in the blue-violet band, is *not* transferred to the phycobilins (probably because the chlorophyll molecule in the upper state of the blue-violet band is changed practically instantaneously, by internal conversion, into the excited state reached directly by absorption in the red band, leaving the molecule with a quantum too small to be acceptable to phycoerythrin or phycocyanin). The quanta absorbed by phycoerythrin, on the other hand, *are* transferred to both phycocyanin and chlorophyll *a*, causing simultaneous cule with a quantum too small to be acceptable to phycoerylthrin or phyco- fluorescence of all three pigments (figs. 37C.41–47). The fluorescence spectrum excited by 453.5 mμ (a frequency absorbed mostly by phycoerythrin), undergoes a characteristic change upon heating: the phycoerythrin band increases in intensity relatively to the chlorophyll band indicating that the resonance coupling, responsible for the phycoerythrin-sensitized fluorescence of chlorophyll, has been destroyed or weakened by heating.

Systematic studies of sensitized fluorescence in algae and bacteria have been carried out by Duysens (1951, 1952); these, too, will be described in chapter 37C. They prove an effective transfer of excitation energy from all pigments present in photosynthesizing cells to the one pigment with the lowest excitation level (*i. e.*, one whose absorption band is located furthest towards the infrared). In purple bacteria, this ultimate energy acceptor is one of the several bacteriochlorophylls (BChl "890"); in green plants and algae, chlorophyll *a;* in red algae, it may be either chlorophyll *a* or a minor pigment with an absorption band located (*in vivo*) at about 700 mμ— perhaps chlorophyll *d*.

The efficiency of energy transfer from phycobilins or carotenoids to chlorophyll *a* (or to bacteriochlorophyll "890"), evidenced by sensitized fluorescence, parallels closely the contribution of these pigments to photosynthesis. This provides a strong support for the hypothesis that the quanta absorbed by the "accessory" pigments are utilized in photosynthesis by being first transferred to the main "photocatalytic" pigment—chlorophyll *a*. The observations of French and Young (chapter 37C, section 7) that in red algae only chlorophyll *a* fluorescence shows induction phenomena and a dependence of the yield on light-intensity (*i. e.*, indirectly, on the rate of photosynthesis) also support this hypothesis.

The following estimates of the efficiency of energy transfer *in vivo* were made by Duysens for purple bacteria:

Chromatium:

BChl "800" → BChl "850" → BChl "890":	100%
Carotenoids → BChl "850":	~40%

Rhodospirillum (molischianum or *rubrum):*

Carotenoids → BChl "890":	~40%

In the species *R. rubrum*—as contrasted to other purple bacteria—a striking difference between the absorption spectrum and the action spectrum of *phototaxis* was noted by Manten (1948), and interpreted as proof of phototactic inactivity of one of their most abundant carotenoids, spirilloxanthol. The action spectrum of *photosynthesis* of *Rhodospirillum rubrum* is in this respect similar to that of phototaxis (Thomas 1950); thus, spirilloxanthol seems to be inactive also in photosynthesis. The efficiency of energy transfer to BChl "890" (as determined from fluorescence measurements) is, however, according to Duysens, about the same for spirilloxanthol as for other carotenoids (namely, about 40%). Duysens suggested that two types of carotene-bacteriochlorophyll complexes occur in *Rhodospirillum rubrum*. The complexes containing spirilloxanthol (which predominate in older cultures) are inactive (both in photosynthesis and in phototaxis), while complexes containing other carotenoids (mainly, rhodopol), which predominate in younger cells, are photobiologically active; the fluorescence of BChl "890" is excited with the same efficiency by the carotenoids in both complexes. Later, Clayton found spirilloxanthol to be effective in phototaxis of another strain of *Rhodospirillum rubrum;* Duysens suggested that this may have been due to the use of much lower light intensities than those used by Manten.

Thomas and Goedheer (1953) again compared the action spectra of photosynthesis and phototaxis in *Rhodospirillum rubrum,* and confirmed the earlier observation (Thomas 1950) that, while the absence of the spirilloxanthol band is common to both of them, the two spectra differ in that the action spectrum of photosynthesis indicates a higher efficiency of the "active" carotenoids than the action spectrum of phototaxis. An explanation was suggested for this difference in terms of a two-fold photochemical function of carotenoids—first as energy suppliers to photosynthesis, and second as photocatalysts for the consumption of photosynthetic products (carotenoid-sensitized "photorespiration," *cf.* Emerson and Lewis, chap. 20, p. 568 and Warburg *et. al.,* chap. 37D, section 4). The second process reduces the accumulation of photosynthetic products in violet (compared to red) light, and this in turn reduces phototaxis (which, in purple bacteria—but not in algae or higher plants—seems to be stimulated by the products of photosynthesis).

In *green* algae (*Chlorella*), the following transfer efficiencies were calculated by Duysens:

Chlorophyll *b* → chlorophyll *a:*	100%
Carotenoids → chlorophyll *a:*	44%

The first figure was obtained by comparison of the yields of fluorescence excited by 670 and 650 mμ—i. e., by a frequency absorbed only by *a*, and one absorbed about equally by *b* and *a*. The second figure was derived from fluorescence yield at 480 mμ (using the assumption that the energy taken up by Chl b at this wave length is transferred to a with 100% efficiency).

The *spectrum* of fluorescence was found to be the same with excitation at 480 mμ (where b absorbs much light) and at 420 mμ (where a is the main absorber). No fluorescence band was noticeable around 650 mμ, where the peak of the fluorescence of chlorophyll b *in vivo* should be located. Both observations confirm the quantitative transfer of energy from b to a. (We note, however, that table 24.I lists several determinations of the chlorophyll b fluorescence peak in *Ulva* and *Elodea*, at 655–657 mμ; but perhaps these photographic data are unreliable.)

Energy transfer was also observed between the chlorophylls a and b in *solution* (about 1.2×10^{-3} M in each pigment), by comparison of the intensities of chlorophyll a fluorescence excited at 429 mμ (70% absorption by a, 30% by b) and 453 mμ (5% absorption by a, 95% by b). The ratio of the two intensities was only 1.7 (instead of 14, as expected in the absence of a transfer). This indicates a 40–50% efficiency of transfer from b to a. As shown in fig. 37C.23, a marked fluorescence of b itself is emitted in this case (because the transfer to a is not 100% effective). At 5×10^{-4} mole/l. the transfer efficiency was down to about 35%, and at 1.2×10^{-4} mole/l. to about 5%. According to Förster's calculations (equation 32.6), the probability of the transfer $a \rightarrow a$ is 50% at 7.7×10^{-4} mole/l., if a life-time of 3×10^{-8} sec. is assumed; with a life-time of 1×10^{-8} sec. (natural life-time 4×10^{-8} sec.; 25% fluorescence yield), this "critical" concentration, $[k]_0$, becomes $7.7 \times 10^{-4} \times \sqrt[3]{3} \simeq 1 \times 10^{-3}$ mole/l. As mentioned above (p. 1300), the efficiency of $b \rightarrow a$ transfer should be about one half of that between two molecules of chlorophyll a, or 0.25 at 1×10^{-3} mole/l. To bring it up to 50% the concentration should be increased by $\sqrt{2} = 1.4$, *i. e.* to about 1.5×10^{-3} mole/l., while Duysens' experimental value is about $1.2 \times 10^{-3} \times 11$ mole/l. (The probability of transfer increases, according to Förster, with the *square* of concentration; the above quoted estimates of Duysens—50% at 12×10^{-4} mole/l., 35% at 5×10^{-4} mole/l., and 5% at 1.2×10^{-4} mole/l.—do not agree well with this law, but claim no precision.)

In *brown* algae, the transfer of excitation energy from fucoxanthal to chlorophyll a, first demonstrated by Dutton, Manning and Duggar (1943) and confirmed by Wassink and Kersten (1946) (*cf.* chapter 24, p. 814), was again observed by Duysens (1952). According to the latter, the efficiency of energy transfer (as measured at 500 mμ) is:

Carotenoids (mainly fucoxanthol) $\rightarrow$ chlorophyll: $\simeq 70\%$

This value can be compared with the ratio of quantum yields of photosynthesis at 500 and 660 mμ, which, according to Tanada (*cf.* fig. 30.9A), is approximately 0.8.

Measurements of the action spectra of photosynthesis and of chlorophyll a fluorescence in the blue-green alga *Oscillatoria*, also made by Duysens (1952), showed (similarly to the experiments on red algae, see below) that quanta absorbed by phycocyanin are transferred with considerable (perhaps $> 90\%$) efficiency to fluorescent and photosynthetically active chlorophyll a; but that the greater part (55–60%) of chlorophyll a is present in a form which is nonfluorescent and photosynthetically inactive. With excitation at 528 mμ (absorbed mainly by phycocyanin), both phycocyanin and chlorophyll fluorescence are emitted and together account satisfactorily for the total fluorescence of the algae. With excitation at 420 mμ (absorbed mainly by chlorophyll a and the carotenoids, and slightly by phycocyanin), no chlorophyll a fluorescence band appears, but only a— relatively weak—fluorescence band of phycocyanin, and a broad fluorescence band of unknown origin (chlorophyll d?) at 720–750 mμ.

It may therefore by hypothesized that the "nonfluorescent" and photosynthetically inactive chlorophyll a is associated with a minor pigment (chlorophyll d?) which has an even lower excitation level and serves as a "sink" into which the energy of excited chlorophyll a disappears, producing fluorescence of the acceptor (chlorophyll d?), but no photosynthesis.

A possible reason for the loss of energy conveyed to "chlorophyll d" is that this pigment is present in a very small concentration. Because of this, energy trapped in its molecules has no chance of further migration, and may have little chance to reach a "reaction center" (assuming that resonance migration of energy to a reaction center is a necessary step in photosynthesis!). A small number of "traps" can be sufficient to catch most of the quanta on their way from chlorophyll a molecules to the reaction centers.

The spatial arrangement of the phycocyanin and the chlorophyll molecules in the cell may be such that the energy quanta absorbed by phycocyanin have a better chance to reach the reaction centers (even if they have to pass through some chlorophyll a molecules on the way), than the majority of quanta absorbed by chlorophyll a itself. The chemical properties of the phycobilins and of chlorophyll are so different that they cannot be uniformly mixed in the cell (or a cell organ, such as a chloroplast, or a granum). (This puts considerable theoretical strain on any hypothesis which would assume a 100% effective resonance transfer of quanta from the phycobilins to chlorophyll; and yet, such a hypothesis seems to be indicated by the fluorescence experiments.)

The contribution of carotenoids is small, both to the chlorophyll a fluorescence and to the photosynthesis of blue-green algae (*cf.* chapter 30, fig. 30.10A).

Similar results were obtained with the *red algae*, such as *Porphyridium cruentum*, by French and Young (*cf.* above p. 1301). In evaluating their (and his own) measurements, Duysens concluded that 80% or more of the quanta absorbed by phycoerythrin are transferred to phycocyanin (the fluorescence of the latter being proportional to the sum of absorption by both pigments). The transfer from chlorophyll to the phycobilins is negligible (<10%), even for excitation with λ 420 mμ.

Both 430 and 680 mμ quanta—absorbed mainly by chlorophyll a—are less effective in exciting chlorophyll a fluorescence in *Porphyridium* than 560 mμ quanta, absorbed mainly by phycoerythrin (or 630 mμ quanta, absorbed to a considerable extent by phycocyanin), the ratio being similar to that found in *Oscillatoria* (about 0.4). Experiments on another red alga, *Porphyra lacineata*, suggested that the energy absorbed by "non-fluorescent" and (according to Haxo and Blinks, *cf.* chapter 30, fig. 30.11, and to Duysens 1952) photosynthetically inactive fraction of chlorophyll a, are transferred to—and produce the fluorescence of—a minor pigment component, probably, chlorophyll d (identified in red algae by Manning and Strain, *cf.* p. 720). The fluorescence peak of this pigment lies at 725 mμ.

Duysens (1952) made an attempt to interpret all these experimental results quantitatively by applying Förster's theory of resonance transfer to mixed solutions of several pigments. He derived from Förster's equations the efficiency, E, of excitation energy transfer, E, from a molecule of type "j" to *any* of the molecules of type "k" in such a mixture, as function of concentration $[k]$, expressed in terms of a "critical" concentration, $[k]_0$. The latter is the concentration at which the theoretical transfer probability for a single pair (j, k) would be 0.5, if all molecules were arranged in a simple cubic lattice—in other words, the lattice constant were equal to the "critical distance," d_0, defined by Förster's equation (32.6). Following is Duysen's table:

$[k]/[k]_0$:	0.05	0.11	0.27	1.00	>1
E:	0.3	0.5	0.75	0.96*	$1 - 0.036 \dfrac{[k]_0^2}{[k]^2}$

To apply the above table to the calculation of energy transfer in plant cells, Duysens had to make rough estimates of the concentrations of the different pigments, their fluorescence yields (which determine the life-times available for transfer) and the "overlap integrals" between the absorption and fluorescence spectra of the several pigment pairs.

For example, to estimate the probability of energy transfer from *chlorophyll b* to *chlorophyll a in vivo*, Duysens assumed $\varphi = 0.01$ (*i. e.*, 1% yield of fluorescence for chlorophyll b *in vivo* in the absence of a, *cf.* chapter 37C, section 7), and calculated $[k]_0 = 0.046$ mole/l. Since the actual concentration of chlorophyll a in the grana is >0.046 mole/l., the transfer efficiency from b to a should be, according to the table, >96%; the reverse transfer, from a to b, calculated in the same way, turns out (as mentioned on p. 1300) to be 300 times less probable, and thus experimentally undetectable.

---

* If the transfer probability to a single neighbor is 0.5, that to *any* neighbor in a cubic lattice is 0.96.

For energy transfer from *phycocyanin* to *chlorophyll a* in blue-green algae, φ was assumed to be as high as 0.7 (*i. e.*, 70% yield of phycocyanin fluorescence *in vivo*, if no transfer were to occur). This gave for the "critical concentration" of chlorophyll a, $[k]_0 = 0.006$ mole/l. Actually, the concentration of chlorophyll in the cell is much higher; if one assumes $[k]_0 = 0.03$ mole/l. (concentration of chlorophyll a in *Chroococcus* cells according to Arnold and Oppenheimer 1950), the probability of transfer becomes >90%, and the yield of fluorescence of phycocyanin would thus be reduced from 70% to 0.1%. Observations of Arnold and Oppenheimer indicated, however, a yield of the order of 5%; Duysens saw in this an indication that in blue-green algae chlorophyll and phycocyanin are separated in different structural units. This view is supported by the fact that phycocyanin can be separated from chlorophyll by fractional precipitation or centrifugation. Chlorophyll seems to be contained in (grana-like) "chromophores" (*cf.* p. 1741), while phycocyanin seems to be located in the extragranular plasma. This separation would increase the average distance between a phycobilin and a chlorophyll molecule to something like 1000 Å.; offhand, this seems much too far to permit the observed, about 90% effective, energy transfer. Perhaps the difficulty can be overcome by assuming a migration of energy through numerous phycocyanin molecules in the cytoplasm, to the granum boundary, where it can be transferred to chlorophyll. Another possibility is that phycocyanin is located, in the main, not outside, but inside the grana in the protein layers, while chlorophyll occupies the interfaces between protein and the lipoidic layers. This assumption could bring the theoretical rate of energy transfer from phycocyanin to chlorophyll in line with the observed 5% residual fluorescence of phycocyanin; but it calls for the further hypothesis that in the smashing of the cells, phycocyanin is leached out of the grana, while chlorophyll remains bound to their "skeleton." More recently this hypothesis has found support in the observations of McClendon and Blinks (1952) that the loss of phycobilins can be prevented by the addition of high-molecular substances to the medium (*cf.* p. 1754).

Duysens estimated the probability of the transfer of energy from phycoerythrin to phycocyanin and chlorophyll in *Porphyridium cruentum*, assuming all three pigments to be present in a common phase, and concluded that because of the greater band overlap the transfer to phycocyanin should be about five times faster, and thus occur to a practical exclusion of that to chlorophyll. The transfer from phycocyanin to chlorophyll would than follow as a second step, with the efficiency estimated in the discussion of *Oscillatoria*. The overlap integral is negligible for the reverse transfers—from chlorophyll to any one of the phycobilins.

In *purple bacteria* the overlap between the fluorescence spectrum of bacteriochlorophyll "800" and the absorption spectrum of bacteriochlorophyll "850," as well as that between the fluorescence spectrum of bacteriochlorophyll "850" and the absorption spectrum of bacteriochlorophyll "890," is considerable, so that, with $\varphi = 0.01$, a $[k]_0$ value of about 0.025 mole/l. can be estimated for both transfers. This is presumably smaller than the actual concentration of the two bacteriochlorophylls serving as energy acceptors, and this makes a high efficiency of the transfers BChl "800" → BChl "850" → BChl "890" plausible; the direct transfer from BChl "800" to BChl "890" should play only a subordinate role.

To estimate theoretically the probability of resonance transfer from carotenoids to chlorophyll, Duysens assumed $\varphi = 10^{-4}$ (0.01% fluorescence yield of carotenoids in the absence of transfer). Assuming, for purple bacteria, a carotenoid fluorescence band at 590 mμ, a value of $[k]_0 = 0.13$ mole/l. can be calculated for the energy transfer to the three bacteriochlorophylls (which all have an absorption band near 590 mμ). This makes the observed high efficiency of this type of transfer in purple bacteria plausible. In *green algae*, on the other hand, the observed, relatively low efficiency of the carotenoids ($<50\%$) can be plausibly explained by a smaller band overlap. Whatever transfer does occur in this case, can be due largely to a primary energy transfer from the carotenoids to chlorophyll *b*, whose "blue" absorption band must be located, *in vivo* at about 465 mμ— close to the probable position of the fluorescence bands of the carotenoids. In red algae, a 50% efficiency of transfer from carotenoids to chlorophyll can be estimated theoretically to require 0.05 mole/l. phycoerythrin. The actual efficiency is lower (about 20% in *Porphyridium cruentum*), confirming, according to Duysens, the spatial separation of the chromoproteids from the lipochromes.

The exceptionally high efficiency of energy transfer from fucoxanthol to chlorophyll, indicated by Montfort's, Manning's and Tanada's experiments (chapter 30), cannot be explained entirely by a larger overlap integral; it may indicate either a relatively high intrinsic fluorescence yield of fucoxanthol or a close association of this pigment with chlorophyll.

The excitation quantum of chlorophyll, acquired in the blue-violet absorption band, is "acceptable" to carotenoids; but the high yield of red chlorophyll fluorescence *in vivo*, excited at 420 mμ, indicates that this transfer is improbable compared to internal conversion of the "blue" excited state into the "red" one, within the chlorophyll molecule.

Sensitized fluorescence of dyestuffs in solutions, indicating resonance transfer of energy from one dyestuff to another, was first observed by Perrin and Choucroun (1927, 1929), (phenosafranin → tetrabromoresorufin), then by Förster (1947, 1948) (fluorescein → erythrosin, in water) and (1949[1]) (trypaflavin → rhodamine B, in methanol). (The transfer chlorophyll $b \rightarrow$ chlorophyll a in solution was mentioned on p. 1303.) Förster proved, by quantitative measurements, that the observed effect could not be attributed to re-absorption of fluorescent light of the "donor" by the "acceptor" or to their association in a complex (the latter was shown by the demonstration of a competitive relation between the quenching of the trypoflavin fluorescence by rhodamine B and by iodide). The observed lack of an effect of glycerol addition indicated that the energy transfer occurred by long-range resonance, rather than by kinetic encounters. A theoretical analysis of the resonance energy transfer between two different molecules—similar to that given earlier for two identical molecules—was first undertaken by Förster (1949[2]). A value of $d_0 (= 5.8$ mμ) was calculated from experimental data for the "critical distance" (the distance where the probability of transfer becomes equal to that of emission), for a mixture of trypoflavin and riboflavin. An approximate theoretical calculation gave $d_0 = 6.3$ mμ. (This can be compared with $d_0 = 8.0$ mμ given on p. 1287 for the transfer between two chlorophyll a molecules.)

The resonance transfer of energy between different dyestuffs in solution has been investigated, theoretically and experimentally, also by Vavilov, Galanin and Pekerman (1949; *cf.* also Vavilov 1950), and later by Galanin and Franck (1951), and Galanin and Levshin (1951). They used mixtures containing a fluorescent and a nonfluorescent dye, and studied the quenching of fluorescence by increasing concentrations of the nonfluorescent component. The excitation energy, transferred by resonance from the fluorescent to the nonfluorescent molecule, is dissipated in the latter by internal conversion, so that no sensitized fluorescence of the acceptor occurs; the efficiency of the transfer is measured by the quenching of the fluorescence of the donor. The quenching effect proved to be dependent in the expected manner on the overlapping of the absorption band of the energy acceptor with the emission band of the donor. Furthermore, the half-life of the fluorescence decay was found to decrease proportionally with the yield of fluorescence, and the yield to be independent of viscosity. Both relationships are characteristic of resonance quenching; the second one because resonance quenching depends on the average distance between the fluorescer and the quencher, which is independent of viscosity. Quenching by collisions, on the other hand, is slowed down as viscosity increases.

Vavilov, Galanin and Pekerman (1949) and Vavilov and Galanin (1949) (*cf.* Vavilov 1950) described experiments in which dyestuff fluorescence was excited in a thin layer between a plane and a convex lens. The thickness of the layer could be determined by counting the Newton rings in reflected light. The fluorescent light was analyzed by a monochromator, and the ratio of intensities determined for two wave length bands—one subject to re-absorption in the layer (either by the fluorescent material itself or by another added dyestuff with an overlapping absorption band)

and another which was not re-absorbed.   By plotting these ratios as function of the thickness of the layer, curves were obtained which agreed with the theoretical equations (derived from Beer's law) as long as the layer was not thinner than the wave length of light.   In thinner layers, systematic deviations from the simple absorption theory were found which were interpreted as evidence that, in such thin layers, the loss of fluorescence quanta caused by resonance transfer became significant.

In following the picture of energy transfer still further into the field of nonresonating systems, one notes that, since the period of a single molecular vibration may be sufficient to achieve transfer of a quantum immediately after its absorption, the probability of transfer may be significant also if electronic resonance can be established for the duration of one (or a few) molecular vibrations during the process of internal energy dissipation in the primary absorber.   For example, a molecule that had absorbed an ultraviolet quantum, and is engaged in internal conversion of the latter into vibrational quanta, must, during this process, assume for a short time a configuration in which it is in electronic resonance with a molecule that absorbs only visible quanta.   It passes through this configuration so rapidly that no emission of visible fluorescence can be noticed (except perhaps by an ultrasensitive, photon counting method); and yet the time of passage may be long enough for the excitation energy to migrate by resonance.   In this way, one could perhaps explain (as first suggested by Franck and Livingston 1949) such phenomena as the dissociation of the myoglobin-carbon monoxide compound by ultraviolet light absorbed in the protein moiety of the porphyrin-protein complex (Bucher and Kaspers 1947). Two possible alternatives are, however: (1) resonance transfer of the ultraviolet quantum as such from the protein to the chromophore (which has absorption bands also in the ultraviolet!); and (2) conversion of electronic excitation into vibrational energy in the protein, followed by its spreading into the porphyrin ("intermolecular heat conduction").   The second alternative is not possible in the case of Bannister's (1953) study of the intensity of fluorescence of phycocyanin excited by various wave lengths between 230 and 360 mμ, in which he found the same quantum yield everywhere, including the absorption band at 277 mμ, where about 50% of the total absorption can be attributed to the protein moiety of the chromoproteid (characteristic band of the aromatic amino acids tyrosin and tryptophan!).   One of the two above-mentioned resonance transfer mechanisms must be operative in this case.

The energy transfer (sensitized fluorescence) between organic molecules in the vapor phase (aniline → indigo; benzene → aniline) was described by Prileshajeva and co-workers (1934, 1937) and Terenin (1943).   Energy transfer between molecules of this type in *crystals* was studied quite extensively, the best known case being that of naphthacene fluorescence sensitized by anthracene in mixed crystals. Considerable literature exists on this phenomenon; we can only refer here to its first description by Winterstein and Schön (1934) and Bowen (1938, 1944, 1947), and the more recent work by Moodie and Reid (1952).

Bibliography to Chapter 32

The Pigment Factor

1905   Lubimenko, V. N., *Rev. gén. botan.*, **17,** 381.

1907   Lubimenko, V. N., *Compt. rend.*, **145,** 1347.

1908   Lubimenko, V. N., *Rev. gén. botan.*, **20,** 162, 217, 253, 285.

1910   Irving, A. A., *Ann. Botany*, **24,** 805.

Lubimenko, V. N., *Trav. soc. naturalistes St. Pétersbourg*, **41,** 1.

1918   Willstätter, R., and Stoll, A., *Untersuchungen über die Assimilation der Kohlensäure.* Springer, Berlin.

1924   Dastur, R. H., *Ann. Botany*, **38,** 779.

1925   Dastur, R. H., *ibid.*, **39,** 769.

1927   Perrin, J. and Choucroun, *Compt. rend.*, **184,** 1097.

1928   Dastur, R. H., and Buhariwalla, N. A., *Ann. Botany*, **42,** 949.

1929   Emerson, R., *J. Gen. Physiol.*, **12,** 609.

Emerson, R., *ibid.*, **12,** 623.

Perrin, J., and Choucroun, *Compt. rend.*, **189,** 1213.

1930   van den Honert, T. H., *Rev. trav. botan. néerland*, **27,** 149.

1932   Emerson, R., and Arnold, W., *J. Gen. Physiol.*, **15,** 391.

Emerson, R., and Arnold, W., *ibid.*, **16,** 191.

Perrin, F., *Ann. phys.*, **17,** 283.

1934   Arnold W., and Kohn, H., *J. Gen. Physiol.*, **18,** 109.

Winterstein, A., and Schön, K., *Naturwissenschaften*, **22,** 237.

Prileshajeva, N., *Acta Physicochim. USSR*, **1,** 785.

1935   Emerson, R., *Cold Spring Harbor Symposia Quant. Biol.*, **3,** 1289.

Fleischer, W. E., *J. Gen. Physiol.*, **18,** 573.

Inman, O. L., *Plant Physiol.*, **10,** 401.

1936   Gaffron, H., and Wohl, K., *Naturwissenschaften*, **24,** 81, 103.

Kohn, H. I., *Nature*, **137,** 706.

Jelley, E. E., *ibid.*, **138,** 1009.

Scheibe, G., *Angew. Chem.*, **49,** 563.

1937   Beber, A. J., and Burr, G. O., *Abstr. Papers Amer. Soc. Plant Physiol.*, 214th Meeting.

Frey-Wyssling, A., *Protoplasma*, **29,** 279.

van Hille, J. C., *Proc. Acad. Sci. Amsterdam*, **40,** 792.

Jelley, E. E., *Nature*, **139,** 378, 631.

Prileshajeva, N., and Klimova, A., *Acta Physicochim. USSR*, **7,** 163.

Scheibe, G., *Naturwissenschaften*, **25,** 75, 474, 795; *Z. angew. Chem.*, **50,** 51, 218.

Weiss, J., *J. Gen. Physiol.*, **20,** 501.

1938   Bowen, E. J., *Nature*, **142,** 1081, **143,** 623.

Franck, J., and Teller, E., *J. Chem. Phys.*, **6**, 861.

van Hille, J. C., *Rec. trav. botan. néerland*, **35**, 680.

Scheibe, G., *Kolloid-Z.*, **82**, 1.

Scheibe, G., and Kandler, L., *Naturwissenschaften*, **26**, 412.

1939   Bowen, E. J., and Williams, A. H., *Trans. Faraday Soc.*, **35**, 765.

Scheibe, G., Schöntag, A., and Katheder, F., *Naturwissenschaften*, **27**, 499.

Scheibe, G., Schöntag, A., Kopske, J., and Henle, K., *Z. wiss. Phot.*, **38**, 1.

1940   Emerson, R., Green, L., and Webb, J. L., *Plant Physiol.*, **15**, 311.

Katheder, F., *Kolloid-Z.*, **92**, 299.

Katheder, F., *ibid.*, **93**, 28.

Kennedy, S. R., *Am. J. Botany*, **27**, 68.

Noddack, W., and Kopp, C., *Z. physik. Chem.*, **A187**, 79.

Shcheglova, O. A., *Eksperiment. Botanika*, **4**, 63.

Wohl, K., *New Phytologist*, **39**, 33.

Terenin, A. N., *Acta Physicochim. USSR*, **12**, 617.

Terenin, A. N., *ibid.*, **13**, 1.

1941   Terenin, A. N., *ibid.*, **14**, 566.

Franck, J., and Herzfeld, K. F., *J. Phys. Chem.*, **45**, 978.

Scheibe, G., *Z. Elektrochem.*, **47**, 73.

van Niel, C. B., in *Advances in Enzymology*. Vol. I. Interscience, New York, page 263.

1942   Vavilov, S. I., and Feofilov, P. P., *Compt. rend. (Doklady) acad. sci. USSR*, **34**, 220.

1943   Dutton, H. J., Manning, W. M., and Duggar, B. M., *J. Phys. Chem.*, **47**, 308.

Gessner, F., *Z. Botan.*, **38**, 414.

Vavilov, S. I., *J. Phys. USSR*, **7**, 141.

Terenin, A. N., *Acta physicochim. USSR*, **18**, 210.

1944   Bowen, E. J., *Nature*, **153**, 653.

Sevchenko, A. N., *Compt. rend. (Doklady) acad. sci. USSR*, **42**, 340.

Vavilov, S. I., *ibid.*, **42**, 331.

Vavilov, S. I., *ibid.*, **45**, 7.

1945   Lewis, G. N., and Kasha, M., *J. Am. Chem. Soc.*, **67**, 994.

1946   Förster, T., *Naturwissenschaften*, **33**, 166.

Myers, J., *J. Gen. Physiol.*, **29**, 419, 429.

Wassink, E. C., and Kersten, J. A. H., *Enzymologia*, **12**, 3.

1947   Bowen, E., and Mikiewicz, E., *Nature*, **159**, 706.

Bucher, Th., and Kaspers, J., *Biochim. et Biophys. Acta*, **1**, 21.

Förster, T., *Angew. Chem.*, **59**, 181.

Förster, T., *Z. Naturforsch.*, **2B**, 174.

Pekerman, F. M., *Compt. rend. (Doklady), acad. sci. USSR*, **57**, 559.

Terenin, A. N., *Photochemistry of Dyes* (in Russian). Acad. Sci. USSR, Moscow-Leningrad.

1948   Förster, T., *Ann. Physik*, **2**, 55.

Förster, T., *Angew. Chem.*, **60**, 163.

Davis, E. A., *Science*, **108**, 110.

Davydov, A. S., *Zhur. Eksptl. i Teort. Fiz.*, **18**, 210; *Izv. Akad. Nauk USSR.*, *Ser. Fiz.*, **12**, 608.

Gabrielsen, E. K., *Physiol. Plantarum*, **1**, 5.

Manten, *Thesis*, Univ. of Utrecht.

Van Norman, R. W., French, C. S., and Macdowall, F. D. H., *Plant Physiol.*, **23**, 455.

Wassink, E. C., *Enzymologia*, **12**, 362.

1949   Förster, T., *Z. Elektrochem.*, **53**, 93.

Förster, T., *Z. Naturforsch.*, **4a**, 321.

Franck, J., and Livingston, R., *Revs. Modern Phys.*, **21**, 505.

Prikhodko, A. F., *Zhur. Eksptl. i Teort. Fiz.*, **19**, 383.

Smith, J. H. C., *J. Chem. Education*, **26**, 631.

Vavilov, S. I., and Galanin, M. D., *Compt. rend. (Doklady) acad. sci. USSR*, **67**, 811.

Vavilov, S. I., Galanin, M. D., and Pekerman, F. M., *Izv. Akad. Nauk USSR, Ser. fiz.*, **13**, 18.

Katz, E., in *Photosynthesis in Plants*, Iowa State College Press, Ames, Iowa, p. 287.

1950   Arnold, W., and Oppenheimer, J. R., *J. Gen. Physiol.*, **33**, 425.

Thomas, J. B., *Biochim. et Biophys. Acta*, **5**, 186.

Vavilov, S. I., *Mikrostruktura Sveta* (Microstructure of Light), Acad. Sci. USSR, Moscow-Leningrad.

1951   Duysens, L. N. M., *Nature*, **168**, 548.

Förster, T., *Fluoreszenz organischer Verbindungen*, Vandenhoeck and Ruprecht, Göttingen.

Galanin, M. D., and Frank, I. M., *Zhur. Eksptl. i Teort. Fiz.*, **21**, 112.

Galanin, M. D., and Levshin, L. V., *ibid.*, **21**, 121.

Rabinowitch, E., *Ann. Rev. Phys. Chem.*, **2**, 361.

Heller, W. R., and Marcus, A., *Phys. Rev.*, **84**, 809.

1952   Duysens, L. N. M., *Thesis*, Univ. of Utrecht.

Davis, E. A., *Am. J. Botany*, **39**, 535.

French, C. S., and Young, V. K., *J. Gen. Physiol.*, **35**, 873.

Jacobs, E. E., *Thesis*, Univ. of Illinois.

Jacobs, E. E., and Holt, A. S., *J. Chem. Phys.*, **20**, 1326.

Kromhout, R., *Thesis*, Univ. of Illinois.

Moodie, M. M., and Reid, C., *J. Chem. Phys.*, **20**, 1510.

Terenin, A. N., and Ermolaev, V. L., *Compt. rend. (Doklady) acad. sci. USSR*, **85**, 547.

1953   Bannister, T., *Arch. Biochem. and Biophys.* **49**, 222.

Brackett, F. S., Olson, R. A., and Crickard, R. G., *J. Gen. Physiol.*, **36**, 563.

Thomas, J. B., and Goedheer, J. C., *Biochem. et Biophys. Acta*, **10**, 385.

Jacobs, E. E., Holt, A. S., and Rabinowitch, E., *J. Chem. Phys.*, **22**, 142.

1954   Jacobs, E. E., Holt, A. S., Kromhout, R., and Rabinowitch, E. (unpublished).

CHAPTER 33

TIME EFFECTS. I. INDUCTION PHENOMENA*

The preceding chapters dealt with kinetic relationships in the *stationary state*, even if we have not quite succeeded in eliminating all references to time, for example, when speaking of the effects of high temperature (chapter 31), or excessive light (chapter 28), or when discussing the influence of chlorophyll content on oxygen yield in flashing light (chapter 32). The following two chapters deal specifically with two types of "time effects": the phenomena occurring in the initial period of steady illumination (induction effects), and the consequences of regular alternation of darkness and light (photosynthesis in intermittent light).

When these chapters were first written a few years ago, one could be relatively optimistic about the possibility of organizing the various findings in the field of induction phenomena under a few simple headings. Induction appeared simply as *delayed start* of photosynthesis after a period of darkness, with the extent of the delay depending on the duration of the dark period and the conditions to which the cells had been exposed during this time.

Investigations of fluorescence changes at the beginning of illumination first revealed, and application of rapidly registering methods of oxygen and carbon dioxide determination subsequently confirmed, that induction is not, or not always, so simple. It may involve a brief initial burst of activity, followed by one or more waves of inhibition. Furthermore, the time courses of oxygen evolution and of carbon dioxide consumption during the induction period are not always parallel; instead, the photosynthetic quotient, $Q_P(=\Delta O_2/-\Delta CO_2)$ may vary during this period, deviating far from its normal value of $+1.0$, and occasionally even changing its sign (for example, carbon dioxide may be liberated simultaneously with oxygen).

The chapter was rewritten in the light of these new observations, and became, in this process, one of the longest in the whole monograph.

This, unfortunately, was not the end of the trouble. The controversy over the maximum quantum yield of photosynthesis (see chapters 29 and 37D) has caused several observers to study very closely the transient phenomena accompanying the transfer of cells from dark to light, or changes in the intensity of illumination, since the interpretation of these transient effects appeared highly important for many quantum yield cal-

* Bibliography, page 1429.

culations. In these studies, variations of gas exchange of unexpected extent, variety and duration have been uncovered. As the proofs of this chapter are being revised, it seems well nigh impossible to combine these new observations with the previously digested ones, in a single logical presentation. As an interim solution, the original organization of the chapter has been left unchanged, and the new results interpolated where this seemed most appropriate. The resulting picture is bewildering, although a few, repeatedly noted, regularities begin to emerge from the confusion.

A. Gas Exchange during the Induction Period*

1. "Long" and "Short" Induction

The changes that occur when a plant, after having been kept in darkness for a certain period of time, is brought into light are complex. In recent years, it has become increasingly clear that different investigators of this so-called "induction" have dealt with different phenomena. Even now, after the extensive studies of McAlister, Aufdemgarten, Blinks and Skow, Kautsky, Gaffron, Steemann-Nielsen, Emerson, Franck, van der Veen, Warburg, Österlind, Brackett, Hill, Whittingham and others, it is still difficult to correlate all observations, much less to explain them in terms of one simple mechanism. What is clear is that the induction phenomena are caused by several changes that the photosynthetic apparatus undergoes in the dark, and which are reversed by several reactions of different velocity after the plant had been returned into light. The relative prominence of the different induction phenomena depends on the nature and state of the plant, the duration of the dark period and the conditions that prevailed during this period.

In trying to bring some order into the multitude of observed phenomena, we will distinguish between "short" and "long" induction. The first usually consists of a sharp drop of the rate of photosynthesis in the first second or two of illumination, followed by a gradual rise to a steady level (often interrupted by a secondary depression), which comes to an end in from 2 to 5 minutes (at room temperature). These features may be fully developed after only a few minutes of "incubation" in the dark at room temperature.

"Long induction," on the other hand, is fully developed only after several hours of darkness, and is characterized by a slow change in rate, which may last for several hours. However, this simple relation between the lengths of incubation and induction is not always found. In the measurements of Steemann-Nielsen (1942) with *Fucus*, for example, no prolonged induction of oxygen liberation appeared even after dark periods of 15 to 16 hours. On the other hand, the graph showing the induction losses incurred

---

* Bibliography, page 1429.

in the first 10–20 minutes of illumination as a function of the duration of incubation (fig. 33.6) indicated that two different dark processes, one much slower than the other, were involved in bringing about the "short" induction. The same appeared to be the case in McAlister's observations of carbon dioxide uptake by wheat (fig. 33.9), and in Franck and Wood's measurement of fluorescence during the induction period.

Since it is generally difficult to maintain completely steady conditions of photosynthesis for extended periods, particularly in higher plants, it is uncertain whether "induction" phenomena lasting for as long as several hours can be treated as significant demonstrations of the working of the photosynthetic mechanism; many of them may be due to variations in the changes in colloidal properties of the protoplasm, and other transformations only indirectly related to the intrinsic mechanism of photosynthesis.

In the steady state, the photosynthetic quotient, $Q_P = -\Delta O_2/\Delta CO_2$, is unity. This makes it possible to speak of the "rate of photosynthesis" without specifying whether we have in mind absorption of carbon dioxide or liberation of oxygen. The observers who first studied induction took it for granted that the same must be true also during the induction period. This is not necessarily the case. Recent advances in the understanding of photosynthesis lead to the conclusion that the reduction of carbon dioxide and the oxidation of water are two more or less separable catalytic processes. In the steady state of photosynthesis, the two catalytic systems must work at the same rate. In the dark, however, these systems could be—and probably are—deactivated to different degrees. If the catalytic system engaged in the reduction of carbon dioxide has become oxidized in the dark, it may, upon illumination, utilize the hydrogen supplied by the photochemical process for its own reduction, before it starts transferring hydrogen to carbon dioxide; while the catalytic system that takes hydrogen from water and liberates oxygen will, from the beginning, work in the normal way. Inversely, reduction of the water-oxidizing catalytic system in the dark may delay oxygen liberation in the light, without affecting the reduction of carbon dioxide. The extent of such "asymmetric" induction losses is limited by the quantity of the catalysts available in the cells. It appears that the most abundant of them are present in concentrations similar to the concentration of chlorophyll. The "induction asymmetry" may therefore reach the order of magnitude of one carbon dioxide (or oxygen) molecule missing per chlorophyll molecule, which is equivalent to the maximum photosynthetic production in 20 or 30 seconds (cf. Table 28.V). This limitation imposed on induction losses affecting only oxygen liberation or carbon dioxide consumption does not apply to inhibition losses affecting photosynthesis as a *whole*.

It must be clear from the above remarks that no investigation of induction is complete without determination of both the carbon dioxide and the oxygen exchange—a requirement satisfied by very few of the available studies.

In addition to induction *losses*, induction *gains*, in the form of "bursts" or "gushes" of oxygen, or "gulps" of carbon dioxide, also have been observed, sometimes simultaneously, and sometimes independently of each other. We can speak in such cases of *inverse* or *positive* induction, in contrast to *normal* or *negative* ones. Here, again, the maximum volume of the bursts or gulps is restricted by the maximum amount of "carrier" or "acceptor" molecules that can accumulate in the cell in darkness.

The determination of the induction losses or gains is dependent, as are all measurements of photosynthesis, on the assumptions made concerning the course of respiration during the light period. Here, too, the picture is becoming more, rather than less, confused as a result of recent studies. The exchange of both oxygen and carbon dioxide, which has become constant (or only slowly changing) after a long dark period, undergoes considerable fluctuations after an illumination period, reminiscent of the induction phenomena in light, but in general more prolonged; in fact, it may take the respiration a half hour, or even longer, to settle again to a steady rate after a light period of the order of ten minutes.

Altogether, it seems that the chemical systems of respiration and photosynthesis are connected by channels, perhaps on several different levels of reduction, and that several chemical reservoirs in both systems are open to the atmosphere, *i. e.*, capable of exchanging oxygen or carbon dioxide with the medium (through the mediation of appropriate enzymes). While photosynthesis is suspended, all connecting reservoirs are filled to certain levels, depending on the intensity of the oxidative metabolism in the cell. When photosynthesis begins (or its rate changes suddenly), many reservoirs are forced to change their levels, by taking up or absorbing oxygen or carbon dioxide from the medium, until a new stationary state is reached. In addition to this readjustment of the stores of various respiratory and photosynthetic *intermediates*, induction effects may be further complicated by the deactivation, in the dark, of some *enzymes* needed for photosynthesis, and their gradual reactivation in light; this may cause some reservoirs to be filled, at the beginning of illumination, above their final steady level; delayed inhibition waves can be caused by such temporary roadblocks.

If, during the dark period, the plants are deprived of oxygen, they ferment (plants left in enclosed spaces can create anaerobic conditions by their own respiration). After a period of such fermentation the induction phenomena are changed. As shown by Gaffron (1935, 1937, 1939, 1940) they can involve, in certain algae, the absorption or liberation of *hydrogen* (*cf.* chapter 6, and section A7 of this chapter). In other organisms, where no such qualitative changes of metabolism occur, the recovery of full photosynthetic efficiency may require much longer than the usual 1 to 3 minutes (*cf.* ch. 13, and sect. 6 below). Both types of abnormal induction must be due to the influence of the products of dark anaerobic metabolism on the catalytic mechanism of photosynthesis. This influence may be nonspecific, due to reducing properties, or the acidity of the fermentation products; but it may also involve specific inhibition effects.

2. Oxygen Exchange during the Short Induction Period

The short induction was discovered by Warburg in 1920, in the first precise manometric study of photosynthesis in *Chlorella*. (Osterhout and Haas, 1918, in their earlier description of induction phenomena, probably dealt with a combination of "short" and "long" induction; *cf.* section 5.) Working in a buffer solution ($[CO_2] = 9.1 \times 10^{-5}$ mole/l.) Warburg found that, in strong light (10–20 klux), the integrated oxygen production in 10 minutes decreased when the illumination was subdivided into ten periods of 1 minute each: by 10% when the dark intervals lasted 1 minute, and by 75 or 85% when they lasted 5 minutes. Further extension of the intervals had no effect.

This was *indirect* evidence of the existence of an induction period, fully developed after 5 minutes of darkness. Warburg could not observe the induction directly, because of the inertia of the manometric system (*cf.* fig. 29.1); but, from experiments in which light periods of varying length followed dark periods of 5 minutes each, he estimated that the induction lasted for about 2 minutes in strong light; no signs of induction were found in *weak* light (400–800 lux).

The observation that induction disappears in weak light justified the use of short illumination periods in Warburg and Negelein's experiment's on the quantum yield of photosynthesis (page 1086). However, the absence of induction was derived from experiments in alkaline buffers, in which oxygen evolution alone was measured; whereas the quantum yields were measured in nonbuffered solutions, in which carbon dioxide contributed markedly to pressure changes. McAlister (1937) found that carbon dioxide consumption also shows no induction in weak light (*cf.* fig. 33.8); but his results were obtained with comparatively low concentrations of carbon dioxide (0.03 to 0.3%), whereas Warburg and Negelein used 4 or 5%. Emerson and Lewis (1941) found that in the one case not covered by either Warburg or McAlister—that of carbon dioxide exchange in an atmosphere of high carbon dioxide content—significant induction effects may occur even in weak light. More recently, measurements by Emerson and co-workers (1954) have confirmed this observation and revealed that transient phenomena of great complexity can occur in an atmosphere of high carbon dioxide content.

Van der Paauw (1932) studied the induction in another unicellular green alga, *Hormidium flaccidum*, and found that it lasted 1.5 minutes at 26° C.,

2 minutes at 20° and 3 minutes at 14°. A somewhat longer induction period was found by Emerson and Green (1934) in the red alga *Gigartina harveyana,* approximately 15 minutes at low carbon dioxide concentrations, and 20 minutes at higher ones.

The length of the induction period may be different for different species; but observations of McAlister (section 3) make it more likely that induction periods in excess of 5 minutes occur (in higher plants as well as in algae) only after extended periods of

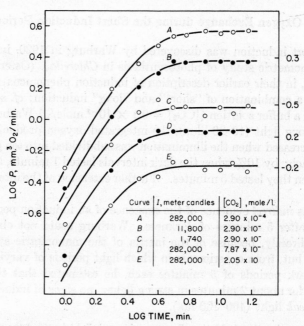

Curve	I, meter candles	[CO₂] ,mole/l.
A	282,000	2.90 x 10⁻⁴
B	11,800	2.90 x 10⁻
C	1,740	2.90 x 10⁻
D	282,000	7.87 x 10⁻
E	282,000	2.05 x 10

Fig. 33.1. Rate of photosynthesis as a function of time for different light intensities and. [CO₂] for *Cabomba* (after Smith 1937). Scale is correct only for curve *A;* the others are displaced as indicated at right of figure.

darkness, under conditions that favor the development of "long induction." The experiments of Osterhout and Haas with *Ulva* (1918), of Li Tsi Tung (1929) with higher aquatic plants and of Briggs (1933) with *Mnium* probably belong to this group. They were carried out after dark periods of one or several hours, and the observed induction periods were of the same order of magnitude. These experiments will be discussed in section 4.

The first investigation in which the induction phenomena in a higher plant were studied under conditions similar to those used by Warburg and van der Paauw with unicellular algae (*i. e.,* after dark periods of a few minutes) was that of Smith (1937). He used the aquatic plant *Cabomba caroliniana.* The procedure was indirect, similar to that followed by Warburg with *Chlorella*.   Figure 33.1 shows the oxygen evolution as a function of time.   The induction lasts approximately the same time (5 minutes) between 1740 and 282,000 lux; it is unaffected (at the higher light intensity) by changes in CO_2 concentration (from 2 to 29 $\times$ 10^{-5} mole/l.).

The curves in figure 33.1 were calculated by means of an interpolation formula:

(33.1) $$\log [(P_{max.} + P)/(P_{max.} - P)] = Kt$$

where t = time.   This equation, according to Smith, also fits the experimental results of Warburg, van der Paauw and Briggs.

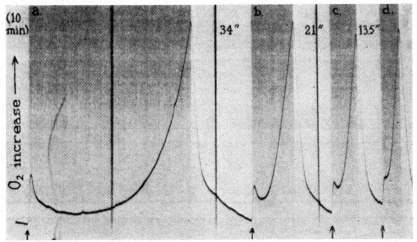

Fig. 33.2. O_2 liberation during induction period in *Ricinus* leaf (after Blinks and Skow 1938).

The first investigation in which the oxygen liberation during the induction period was followed by a direct "differential" method was that of Blinks and Skow (1938[2]).   They used the polarographic method described in chapter 25 (page 850).   To avoid time lags, a small-surface platinum or mercury electrode was pressed against a thallus or a submerged leaf.   With a polarization potential of 0.5 volt, the current was proportional to the oxygen concentration in the thin layer between plant and electrode.   The capacity of this layer was so small that fluctuations lasting for less than 0.02 second could be recorded.   The "time resolution" in Blinks and Skow's experiments was thus a thousand times higher than in the manometric experiments of Warburg, van der Paauw and Smith.   Where the latter noted only a smooth increase in oxygen liberation in the first 2 to 5 *minutes* of illumination, the polarographic curves now revealed an initial "gush" of oxygen, which was over in a few *seconds* (fig. 33.2).

In the experiment recorded in the figure the lower surface of a castor bean leaf (*Ricinus*) was pressed tightly against a stationary mercury electrode. The oxygen was down to nearly anaerobic levels due to respiration and reduction by the electrode. The leaf was then illuminated (through the agar) with light of about 7500 meter candles during the shaded parts of the record: in *a* after a 10 minute dark period, in *b* after 34 seconds, etc., as shown in the figure. We note the immediate, brief gush of oxygen. Vertical lines are time marks, 1 minute apart; arrows indicate beginning of

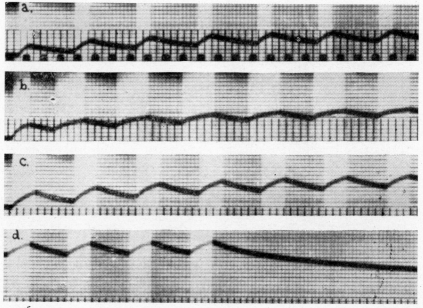

Fig. 33.3. O_2 liberation in light after dark intervals of the order of 1 sec. (after Blinks and Skow 1938). (a) 0.45 sec. light, 1.35 sec. dark; (b) 0.9 sec. light, 0.9 sec. dark; (c) 0.7 sec. light, 1.1 sec. dark; (d) later portion of c, with long dark period in last half of record. O_2 production begins within the period of the galvanometer, and is nearly constant during the flash, or slightly higher at the beginning. Time marks are 0.2 sec. apart. Full height in d represents O_2 content of water in equilibrium with air.

illumination. (Similar records were obtained with a platinum electrode and with marine algae (*e. g., Ulva*) without stomata or gas spaces.)

In accordance with Warburg's and van der Paauw's data the inhibition begins to disappear after about 1 minute of illumination, and oxygen liberation is well under way toward the end of the second minute.

Figure 33.3 shows that, even after dark intervals of only 1 second, the oxygen evolution during the first half second of illumination is slightly faster than in the second half second; this may or may not be the first sign of the "gush" and subsequent inhibition

In figure 33.3 the duration of flashes is indicated by the paler parts of the record, flashes were produced by a revolving disc in front of an incandescent source (6000 meter-candles).

Blinks and Skow associated the oxygen gush with the "inverse induction," observed by Gaffron in the investigation of the influence of anaerobiosis on green algae (*cf.* chapter 6); and therefore emphasized that in their experiments, in consequence of respiration and cathodic reduction, an anaerobic state was reached at the end of the dark period in the layer between electrode and plant. However, the effects of anaerobic incubation usually appear only after one or several hours in an oxygen-free medium (*cf.* section 6 below, and chapter 6).

Blinks and Skow observed the oxygen gush not only with the leaves of a higher land plant (*Ricinus*), but also with an aquatic plant (*Potomageton*) and an alga (*Ulva*).   They concluded that the gush is a general feature of

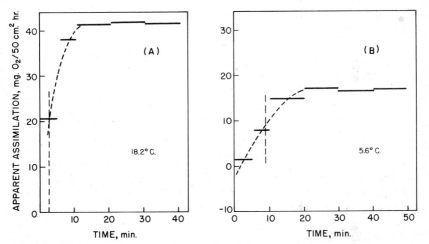

Fig. 33.4. Induction in *Fucus* after 16 hrs. in dark at 5.6° and 18.2° C. (after Steemann-Nielsen 1942):   (A) $R = 0.45$ mg. O_2/cm.^{2} hr.; (B) $R = 0.25$ mg. O_2/cm.^{2} hr.

the kinetics of photosynthesis.   We will see below that Warburg and co-workers reached a similar conclusion, and ascribed to it far-reaching theoretical implications, but that other experiments indicate extreme variability of the gush in duration and volume, and thus argue against its interpretation as an essential feature of photosynthesis.

A more extensive, if less precise, study of induction in the evolution of oxygen was carried out by Steemann-Nielsen (1942) with the multicellular brown alga, *Fucus serratus*.   He used Winkler's method of oxygen determination in water.   Steemann-Nielsen incubated the thalli for as long as 16–17 hours before exposure to light, in streaming sea water.   Nevertheless, the induction phenomena lasted for only about 10 minutes at 18° C.

and 20 minutes at 4°, and thus appeared to fall into the category of "short induction."

The method used by Steemann-Nielsen (involving measuring periods of 2.5 to 5 minutes) was much too slow to reveal the oxygen gush; but it showed clearly the gradual increase in the rate of oxygen production, which lasted for 20–30 minutes at 4–6° C., and for about 10 minutes at 18° (in light of 23,000 or 2300 lux, in 2.5×10^{-3} mole/l. bicarbonate solution). The same temperature was maintained during the incubation and the exposure.   Figure 33.4 illustrates the results.

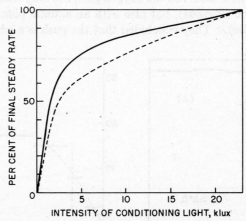

Fig. 33.5. Initial rate of photosynthesis in *Fucus* in 23 klux as function of previous illumination (after Steemann-Nielsen 1942).   Average for first 5 min. (solid curve); initial rate extrapolated to zero time (broken curve).

Steemann-Nielsen made observations on the repetition of induction upon stepwise transition from weaker to stronger light, a phenomenon previously noted by McAlister in experiments on CO_2 consumption (section 3 below).   After *Fucus* had reached the steady rate of photosynthesis in 2300 lux, an increase to 23,000 lux produced, in the first 5 minutes, only 65% of full rate; the latter was reached after 15 minutes additional induction (at 5° C.).   Similar results were obtained with other transitions (7000 → 23,000 lux, 6°, 82% of maximum rate in the first 5 minutes; 1200 → 23,000 lux, 5.5°, 45% of maximum rate in the first 5 minutes). Fig. 33.5 shows the first measured rate in strong light as a function of intensity of the "conditioning" illumination.   Steemann-Nielsen noted that the dotted curve (which represents the rate in strong light, extrapolated to the moment of light increase, as a function of conditioning intensity) is identical with the light curve of photosynthesis, $P = f(I)$, of the same plant.   He concluded that the "activation" of the dark-inhibited factors of the photosynthetic apparatus in light proceeds only to the level sufficient for the maintenance of the maximum steady rate possible at the prevailing light intensity (this maximum being determined by factors not involved in induction).   A similar conclusion was reached earlier by Gaffron and Franck (*cf.* part C).

Steemann-Nielsen's observations of the time required for the preparation of induction in the dark are illustrated by figure 33.6.   The curve showing the initial rate in light as a function of the length of the preceding

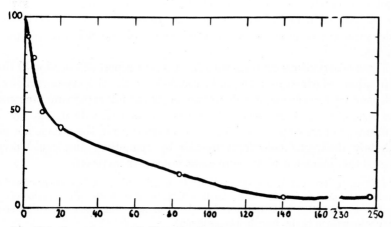

Fig. 33.6.   Average rate of O_2 liberation by *Fucus serratus* in first 5 min. of light of 23 klux at 4.8° C., as function of preceding dark incubation (after Steemann-Nielsen 1942).   Abscissa, minutes dark after activation to P_{max}. at 23 klux.   Ordinate, per cent of P_{max}. (net).

dark interval appears to consist of two parts: About one half of the total induction loss is developed after 10 minutes in darkness;   50 minutes of additional incubation are required to reduce the rate by another factor of 1/2.   A similar relation was found for the carbon dioxide exchange (McAlister, fig. 33.9).   This indicates the superposition of two different induction-producing dark reactions: one being completed in about 10 minutes (at 18° C.), the other requiring several hours.   Fluorescence measurements (part B) also revealed two dark deactivation processes—one appeared to reach saturation in about 1 minute;   the second one was much slower.

The duration of the dark period required to bring about a certain percentage inhibition was found by Steemann-Nielsen to be independent of temperature, if incubation and illumination were carried out at the same temperature.   Experiments in which only the incubation temperature was varied (while illumination temperature was kept constant) showed, on the other hand, that the *absolute* rate of the deactivation process was—as expected—strongly dependent on temperature; its temperature coefficient appeared to be about 2.

Steemann-Nielsen found, with *Fucus vesiculosus*, at 2.9° C., that the duration of the recovery period (~30 minutes) was not affected by absence of carbon dioxide during the first 10 minutes of illumination. If, however, the plants were deprived of carbon dioxide for as long as 40 minutes in light, the rate of oxygen production immediately after the readmission of carbon dioxide corresponded only to the level usually reached in 10 minutes after the beginning of illumination. Steemann-Nielsen saw in this an indication that *Fucus* contains an internal reserve of carbon dioxide, sufficient to maintain the normal course of activation for about 10 minutes.

These observations contrast with McAlister's report (*cf.* section 3) that "activation" of wheat in light can be *completed* in the absence of carbon dioxide, so that the carbon dioxide uptake begins at full rate instantaneously after readmission of this gas. (Of course, carbon dioxide uptake by replenishment of an empty "reservoir" of bicarbonate in the cells is not immediately distinguishable from uptake by reduction, and could occur without the liberation of an equivalent volume of oxygen.)

It is known (*cf.* Vol. I, chapter 19) that illumination of plants in absence of carbon dioxide causes photoxidation. The induction phenomena observed after a period of carbon dioxide starvation must therefore be related to induction phenomena that occur after photoxidation (to be described in section 6).

It will be noted that none of the experiments discussed so far has indicated the occurrence of a "second depression" of oxygen liberation, matching a depression often found in carbon dioxide uptake curves (*cf.* sect. 3), and the "second wave" of fluorescence (*cf.* part B). Franck, French and Puck (1941) therefore proposed an explanation of the second depression not requiring a parallelism between oxygen liberation and carbon dioxide absorption. Later, however, Franck, Pringsheim and Lad (1945) noted that a second depression actually did occur in the oxygen induction curves of *Chlorella*, as determined by the trypoflavine phosphorescence-quenching method (*cf.* chapter 25, p. 851). This method can be used only under anaerobic conditions; but Franck and co-workers considered these conditions irrelevant in this case and concluded that the experiments indicate a second depression of oxygen liberation occurring under the same conditions as the depression of carbon dioxide uptake.

Warburg and co-workers used the two-vessel manometric technique to calculate oxygen and carbon dioxide exchange, in light and darkness, in minute-to-minute intervals (for a description of the method, *cf.* chapter 25, p. 848; *cf.* also discussions in chapter 29, pp. 1109–1112, and chapter 37D, section 4).

Warburg, Geleick and Briese (1951) studied dilute *Chlorella* suspensions, illuminated with a red light beam, superimposed on white "background" illumination just sufficiently to compensate steady respiration. These "bright periods" of a few minutes duration alternated with similar periods of illumination with the white "background" light alone ("dim periods"). A very strong positive induction was noted at the beginning of both the bright and the dim periods. A gradually subsiding "burst" of oxygen was found in the first 1–2 minutes of "bright" illumination, and a gradually

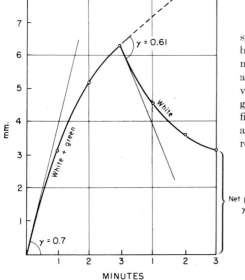

Fig. 33.6A. Splitting of photosynthesis into light reaction and dark back-reaction at 20 °C. (two-vessel measurements by Warburg, Geleick and Briese 1951). 100 μl. cells per vessel, compensating white background light; 546 mμ light added for first 3 minutes. 10.9% CO_2. Points: average of measurements at corresponding times in 16 cycles.

subsiding "gulp" of oxygen in the first 1–2 minutes of "dim" illumination. Fig. 33.6A shows this for a 3 minute light–3 minute dark cycle at 20° C. With the type of manometers used in this work, the precision of single minute-by-minute pressure change determinations was low; the points in the figure were therefore obtained by averaging the changes in the corresponding minutes of ten cycles.

Warburg *et al.* interpreted the results of the type of those in figure 33.6A (more specifically, the steep initial slopes of the "bright light" segments) as evidence that oxygen liberation begins, after a few minutes of darkness, with a quantum requirement as low as unity. The average ratio Q_P ($= \Delta O_2 / - \Delta CO_2$) calculated from the total gas exchange during ten three-minute periods of bright light, was about 0.85; this was considered as evidence that the burst was one of complete photosynthesis (for which the theoretical ratio is $Q_P = 1.0$).

The average ratio $Q_P (= \Delta O_2 / \Delta CO_2)$, calculated from the total gas exchange in ten three-minute "dim" periods, also was about 0.85; this was considered evidence that the "gulp" was due to a complete reversal of photosynthesis—*i. e.*, oxidation of a substrate of the approximate reduction level of a carbohydrate by molecular oxygen. From the initial slope of the "dim light" curve segments, it was calculated that immediately after the cessation of "bright light," the rate of this back reaction (which we may call "antiphotosynthesis," to distinguish it from ordinary respiration), can be ten or more times that of steady respiration of the same cells (measured over extended periods of darkness).

As reported in more detail in chapter 37D (section 4a), Warburg *et al.* interpreted the observed "bursts" and "gulps" of O_2 and CO_2 not as induction phenomena, but as revelations of the hidden mechanism of photosynthesis, showing it to consist of a forward, photochemical reaction with a quantum requirement of 1 (one quantum per O_2 produced and CO_2 consumed), and a thermal back-reaction that consumes a large proportion of the products of the forward reaction. This proportion must be large enough for the liberated chemical energy (added, *via* some "chemosynthetic" mechanism, to the one quantum of light energy used in the forward process) to reduce the net yield of the cycle to a value compatible with the law of conservation of energy ($\simeq 2.8$ quanta per O_2 molecule).

The postulated partial separation in manometric experiments of the forward photochemical, from the reverse thermal reaction implies that the back reaction has a rate constant as low as a reciprocal minute, so that the light-enhanced consumption of molecular oxygen needs a minute or two to get under way at the beginning of a light period, and is carried over for a minute or two into the following dim period, thus permitting tell-tale "bursts" and "gulps" to be caught by minute-to-minute manometric readings.

Warburg and co-workers (1951) noted that activity bursts of the above-described type are not observed in carbonate buffers, and suggested that the back reaction is much faster in these media; later (1953, 1954) they found that *Chlorella* cultures grown in a different way showed no activity bursts of similar duration also in carbon dioxide solutions.

Wide variations in the duration of the oxygen bursts and gulps was observed also by Damaschke, Tödt, Burk and Warburg (1953) with a rapid electrochemical method of oxygen determination. The method was similar to that used by Blinks and Skow, and the results were qualitatively similar to those described above on p. 1319. These measurements, too, showed a rapid oxygen burst at the beginning of illumination, and an oxygen gulp after its termination. (Fig. 33.6B shows the recordings of gulps after bright periods of 3, 8 and 28 seconds.)

In contrast to the qualitative observations of Blinks and Skow, the recordings of Damaschke *et al.* were used to evaluate the absolute yield of oxygen production during the burst, and its net yield in a complete light-dark cycle; these calculations will be dealt with in more detail in chapter 37D.   Depending on (unspecified) conditions, the duration of the "gulp" was found in these experiments to vary from a few seconds (as in fig. 33.6B), to one, or even ten minutes.   (Among widely varied conditions, one notes

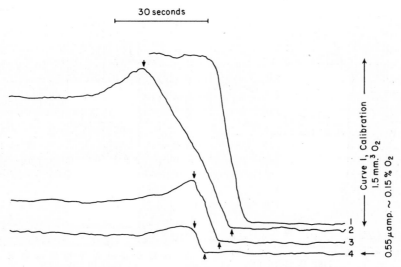

Fig. 33.6B. Polarographic recordings of O_2 liberation by *Chlorella* (160 mm.[3] cells per 80 cc.) exposed for 3, 8 and 28 sec. of additional illumination, on top of continuous light sufficient to compensate respiration (after Damaschke, Tödt, Burk and Warburg 1953).   Time scale from right to left; gulps of O_2 are seen to follow the exposures.   20% CO_2, 20° C., $\lambda = 644$ mμ.

the carbon dioxide concentration, which was 5%, 20% and even 54% in the several experiments illustrated in the paper.)

The wide variation in duration (and volume) of the oxygen bursts and gulps observed by Warburg and co-workers in manometric, as well as electrochemical measurements in differently pretreated *Chlorella* cultures, makes their interpretation as revelations of an intrinsic thermal component of the reaction sequence of photosynthesis rather implausible.   This view is supported by evidence from other investigations described in this chapter, such as the polarographic studies of Brackett, in which no oxygen burst was noted at all (while the gulp was clearly noticeable, but much less prominent than in Warburg's curves); and Brown's mass-spectrographic data (in which the respiratory oxygen consumption of *Chlorella* was found to be, as a rule, unchanged by illumination, while sudden, but relatively small, increases in respiration were occasionally noted *after the end* of an illumination period).

A similarly bewildering variety of carbon dioxide induction phenomena will be described in the next section—ranging from a photochemical carbon dioxide *gulp* (van der Veen, Warburg) to a photochemical carbon dioxide *burst* (Blinks, Emerson, van der Veen).

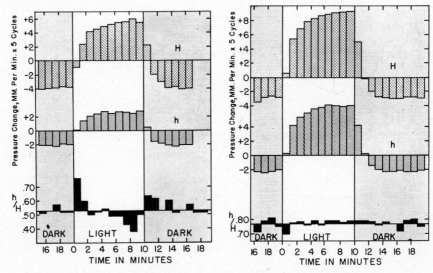

Fig. 33.6C. Two-vessel manometric measurements (after Emerson and Chalmers 1954). O_2 liberation by *Chlorella* in carbonate buffer, in vessel pairs of type H, h_1 (left) and H, h_2 (right) (*cf.* fig. 29.4A). Minute-by-minute pressure changes measured by twin differential manometers. The ratio of measured pressure changes varies in the two vessels on left, remains nearly constant on right, indicating synchronous reaction.

All these results leave one with the impression that rapid fluctuations of gas exchange after the transfer of cells from darkness to light (or light to darkness) are "transients," caused by readjustments of the catalytic systems (and intermediate products) to new steady states (in other words, typical induction effects), rather than "tail ends" of steady activities in the preceding periods.

This impression is further strengthened by new observations of Emerson and Chalmers (1954), who were able to improve considerably the precision of the two-vessel manometric method by using a double differential manometer, making simultaneous readings with two cathetometers. Two matched light beams from the same source were thrown onto two vessels, whose shape was carefully chosen to achieve the best possible synchronization of the gas exchange processes.

The importance of the shape of the manometric vessels for the reliability of two-vessel determination was mentioned before on p. 1111. Slight differences in the effectiveness of stirring in the two vessels can become crucial in the analysis of transient phenomena. Emerson and Chalmers (1954) showed this by comparing the manometric data obtained in vessel pairs of different shape with *Chlorella* cells suspended in carbonate buffers (where only one gas is exchanged). With a vessel pair of the type used by Warburg and co-workers (H and h_1 in fig. 29.4A), the course of pressure equilibration was markedly different in the two vessels, as illustrated by the left side of figure 33.6C; the synchronization was much better with vessels of the "Emerson type" (H and h_2 in fig. 29.4A), as shown by the steadiness of the ratio of the pressure changes during the transition from dark to light and back, on the right-hand side of the diagram. The reason for this difference must be that shaking at a certain rate has a different effect for different distances between liquid and ceiling.

Furthermore, vessels "matched" for one gas, are not *eo ipso* matched for others.

Emerson believes that, because of these experimental uncertainties, Warburg's quantitative analysis of manometric readings in the transient periods (and of the quantum yields derived from this analysis) are open to grave doubts; particularly uncertain is the determination of the carbon dioxide-oxygen ratio (which is the basis for the conclusion that the observed bursts involved photosynthesis and respiration as a whole).

Emerson and Chalmers' measurements (1954) with vessels of better synchronous behavior confirmed that an "oxygen burst" does occur sometimes in the first minute of illumination (as first noted by Blinks and Skow, and also indicated by the manometric measurements of Burk, Warburg *et al.*, and by the electrochemical measurements of Damaschke *et al.*). However, this burst is not a regular feature of photosynthesis in *Chlorella*; nor does it usually have the volume required by Burk and Warburg's theory. Quantum requirements of 3 (quanta per oxygen molecule), or even less, sometimes can be calculated by comparing oxygen production at the height of the burst (*i. e.*, in the first minute of illumination) with the peak oxygen consumption subsequent to the light period; however, the latter peak is reached, according to Emerson and co-workers, not immediately after the cessation of illumination, but several minutes later (fig. 33.6D).

The manometric method is too slow to catch gas bursts or gulps if they are not big enough to affect significantly the gas exchange in a whole minute. Therefore, Emerson's measurements can be used only as a check of Warburg, Geleick and Briese's conclusions concerning the volume and general significance of the bursts. They cannot be compared with the polarographic data of Blinks and Skow, and of Damaschke, Tödt, Burk and Warburg, whose instruments were able to record bursts and gulps lasting only a few seconds, irrespective of their volume.

The transient gas bursts in light (and the equivalent gulps at the beginning of darkness) increase, according to Emerson's observations, with the number of cells in the vessel, and the carbon dioxide concentration, while the steady rate of oxygen liberation or consumption (reached after 5 or 10

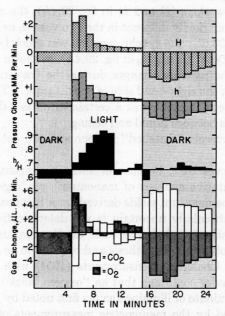

Fig. 33.6D. Example of transient gas exchange phenomena measured with "synchronized" manometric vessels (after Emerson and Chalmers 1954). Shows O_2 burst and CO_2 gulp in first minute, CO_2 burst in second to fourth minutes, steady photosynthesis, with $Q_P \simeq 1$ after the sixth minute.

minutes in light, and only after a considerably longer time in darkness), is much less affected by these factors (more about this in the next section, since these transients have been studied more extensively in carbon dioxide than in oxygen exchange).

Van der Veen (1949[1,2]) applied another rapidly registering method—the measurement of heat conductivity—to the study of induction. In air, or nitrogen, this method is used to determine the exchange of carbon dioxide independently from that of oxygen (cf. below, section 3); but if a hydrogen atmosphere is used, changes in both oxygen and carbon dioxide content affect the heat conductivity.   By absorbing carbon dioxide chemically before the gas enters the "diaferometer," it becomes possible to measure the oxygen exchange alone.   Van der Veen (1949[2]) demonstrated in this way that in heat-pretreated algae the surviving carbon dioxide gulp and gush (after exposure to light and darkness, respectively, *cf.* next section) are unaccompanied by any oxygen exchange (*cf.* fig. 33.6E)—a suggestive example of the independence of the exchange of carbon dioxide from that of oxygen during the transient periods.

The electrochemical data of Blinks and Skow, and of Damaschke *et al.*, can be compared with the results obtained by a similar method by Brackett and co-workers.

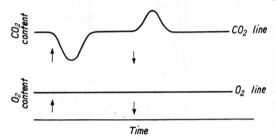

Fig. 33.6E. CO_2 gulp upon illumination (upward arrow) and burst upon darkening (downward arrow), of heat-treated leaves of *Holcus lanatus* (after van der Veen 1949[2]).   No uptake or release of O_2.   Measured with a diaferometer.

Olson and Brackett (1952) and Brackett, Olson and Crickard (1953[1,2]) studied the induction phenomena in *Chlorella* with a polarographic oxygen meter that permitted readings every 10 seconds.   They used dilute cell suspensions, illuminated simultaneously from two sides; the uniformity of illumination, achieved in this way, removed, according to their findings, some adventitious features of the induction picture.

Brackett, Olson and Crickard (1953[1]) found that the respiration of *Chlorella* underwent considerable changes in the first few minutes of darkness after exposure to light.   The typical picture of this respiration induction included a gulp of oxygen taking place in the first 10–20 seconds of darkness (probably related to the burst observed by Damaschke *et al.*, but apparently smaller in volume), a minimum, a second, flatter maximum reached in 1–4 minutes (probably related to the respiration peak noted manometrically by Emerson *et al.*), and a gradual decay to a steady level. (These observations are to be discussed again under "Photosynthesis and Respiration," section 3, Chapter 37, *cf.* figs. 37D.31 and 32.)   During the illumination period, Brackett *et al.* assumed respiration to change smoothly (and approximately logarithmically) from its level at the end of the pre-

ceding dark period to its level 0.5–1 minute after the beginning of the subsequent dark period, when the initial respiration burst has subsided. (This
meant assuming, in contrast to Warburg, that the burst was something
that happened entirely *after* the end of illumination, and not the "tail end"
of enhanced respiration during the light period.)   Brackett *et al.* used the

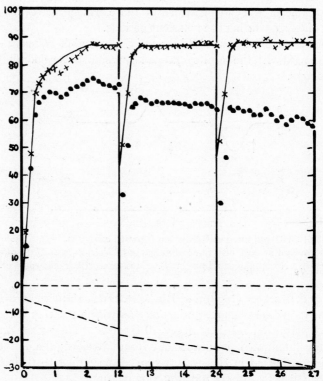

Fig. 33.6F. Aerobic O_2 induction in *Chlorella* measured potentiometrically in three
successive 3 minute light periods with 9 minute dark intervals: dashed line, interpolated
respiration;   circles, measured points;   crosses, points corrected for respiration (after
Brackett, Olson and Crickard 1953[2]).   Abscissa, time (min.).   Ordinate, rate of oxygen
evolution.

so interpolated time curve of respiration to correct the measurements of
oxygen production during the light period (*cf.* figs. 33.6F and 37D.32), and
obtained in this way curves showing only the normal negative induction in
light.   The latter lasted between 10 seconds and 2 minutes, and was followed by a very steady photosynthesis for the rest of the light period.   No
evidence of an oxygen burst in the first seconds of illumination is visible on
these curves.

Figure 33.6F, taken from the second paper (1953[2]) of the same authors, shows typical oxygen induction curves in three successive three minute light periods, interrupted by nine minute dark periods. The circles represent uncorrected rates, the crosses, rates corrected for interpolated respiration (dotted lines below). After thorough dark adaptation, the initial rate of oxygen liberation in light may be zero (or almost zero, *cf.* the conclusions of Franck *et al.* in section 6), and induction may cover up to 3 minutes, as in the first segment of figure 33.6F. The initial rate becomes higher, and the induction loss declines, in repeated cycles. The induction loss of oxygen production appears complementary to Emerson and Lewis's carbon dioxide burst (*cf.* below section 3); in fact, it can be accounted for approximately by assuming that, for each quantum of light diverted from the production of oxygen, one molecule of carbon dioxide is liberated.

In these experiments, too, there is no sign of an initial burst of oxygen in light ("positive" induction, interpreted by Warburg and co-workers as evidence of a "one-quantum process of photosynthesis"). It seems certain from Blinks' and Damaschke's polarographic measurements, however, as well as from Emerson's more recent manometric results, that such a burst *does* occur in some cases; however, its occurrence does not seem to have the generality (and therefore probably, also, the significance) attributed to it by Warburg, Burk and co-workers.

Brackett, Olson and Crickard (1953[2]) observed a second, shallow minimum of oxygen liberation on some of their induction curves (about 1 minute after the beginning of illumination). This, too, reminds one of the shape of Emerson and Lewis's carbon dioxide burst (as well as of that of Aufdemgarten's and van der Veen's carbon dioxide gulp, both of which show two or more successive waves, *cf.* section 3).

Brackett *et al.* plotted the oxygen liberation rate during the induction period (after complete dark adaptation) on a $\log (P_0/P) = f(t)$ scale, and found that different runs showed different deviations from the logarithmic approach to the steady rate—curvatures, breaks in slope, etc., seemingly indicating complexity and variability even of the "normal" negative oxygen induction.

The most significant evidence concerning Warburg's hypothesis of oxygen burst as evidence of strongly enhanced respiration in light was provided by isotopic tracer studies of Brown and co-workers.

Brown (1953) measured respiration during illumination, independently from photosynthesis, by using O(18)-enriched oxygen (*cf.* chapter 37D, section 3). He found, with *Chlorella*, either no change in respiration rate at all, or a sudden increase in respiration *at the end* of the illumination period. If this result were generally valid, it would make Brackett's method of interpolation of respiration in light (figs. 33.6F and 37D.32) inexact, affecting slightly the shape of the induction curves calculated by the latter (fig. 33.6F). Much more important is, however, the failure of Brown's measurements to support in any way Warburg and Burk's hypothesis of a strongly enhanced oxygen consumption in light, at least as far as *Chlorella* is concerned.

Much stronger changes of respiration in light were observed by Brown and Webster (1953) in the blue-green alga *Anabaena* (*cf.* chapter 37D, section 3); they ranged (in dependence on light intensity and partial pressure of oxygen) from complete *inhibition* of respiration within a minute or two after the beginning of illumination (in 0.2–0.4% O_2, and $P \simeq 3.5R$), to *stimulation* of respiration by a factor of two or more (in more intense light and higher oxygen concentration). Measurements of transient phenomena in cells of this type obviously could be entirely misleading if a constant (or continuously interpolated) respiration correction were applied to the pressure readings. It may be, however, that such extreme respiration changes in light can occur only in blue-green algae, in which the site of photosynthesis is not separated morphologically from the main site of cell respiration.

Hill and Whittingham (1953) used the hemoglobin conversion to oxyhemoglobin for rapid spectroscopic oxygen determination in the induction phase of *Chlorella:* the delay of response was thus reduced to <10 seconds, from about 1 minute in parallel manometric measurements. The course of induction was the same, corresponding to half-reactivation in 0.5 minute at 15° C. for dark incubation times of 13, 30 or 45 minutes; even 22 hours spent in darkness did not appreciably slow down the induction. Experiments in alternating light at different temperatures showed that at 7° C. induction losses were negligible after dark periods of 1 minute or 3 minutes, but noticeable after 10 minutes darkness; at 16° and 25° C. they became significant after 3 minutes in the dark. The half-time of reactivation after a given short dark period was shorter at the lower temperatures. No positive induction (oxygen burst) could be noted in any of the runs.

3. Carbon Dioxide Exchange during the Short Induction Period

Observations of short induction by carbon dioxide determination were first made by McAlister (1937, 1939, 1940) with wheat plants. He used the infrared spectrophotometric technique described on page 852. At first, the rate was calculated from carbon dioxide concentration measurements made at 0.5 minute intervals; later, it was recorded directly by a differential recorder.

Figure 33.7 gives an example of curves obtained by the earlier, point-to-point method. The downward trend of the curves corresponds to liberation of carbon dioxide, the upward trend to its consumption.   The induction periods last for about 2 minutes (four points) at 31° C., and 3.5 minutes (seven points) at 12°.   Figure 33.8 shows that, at a given temperature, the duration of the induction period is practically independent of light intensity between 214 and 1030 foot-candles (*i. e.*, between 2000 and 10,000 lux), but that induction is absent at 44 foot-candles (about 450 lux).   McAlister designated as "induction loss" (ΔP_i) the amount of carbon dioxide that would have been taken up but for induction.   It is determined, in figures 33.7 and 33.8, by the intercept of the solid straight lines (which

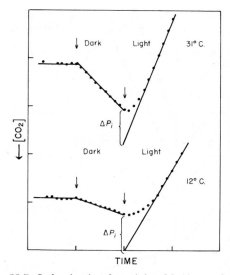

Fig. 33.7. Induction in wheat (after McAlister 1937).

correspond to steady assimilation) with the ordinates corresponding to the beginning of illumination.   The inset in figure 33.8 shows the induction loss as a function of light intensity.   Comparison of this curve with the light curve of photosynthesis, $P = f(I)$, for wheat (fig. 28.1) shows that ΔP_i is approximately proportional to P, except for the lowest light intensities (where ΔP_i disappears more rapidly than P).   At the higher light intensities, the induction loss at room temperature is equal to the photosynthetic production in approximately one minute of steady illumination.

In a second investigation (1939), McAlister compared the induction losses with the amount of chlorophyll in the plant, and also investigated the relation between this loss and the length of the preparatory dark period. Figure 33.9 shows the induction loss in multiples of the chlorophyll content (both in moles), plotted against length of the dark period.   The induction develops rapidly as the dark time increases to little more than a minute; when fully developed, it accounts—at room temperature—for the loss of about one molecule of carbon dioxide for two molecules of chlorophyll. (McAlister estimated that the induction losses of oxygen in the ex-

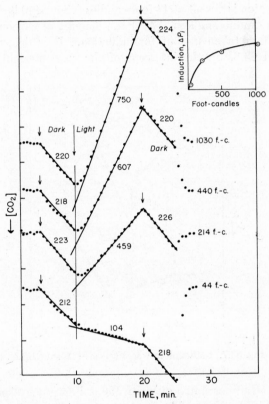

Fig. 33.8. Effect of intensity of illumination on the induction period in wheat (after McAlister 1937). Numbers are rates of CO_2 exchange by respiration or assimilation (true) in mm.[3] per 10 min. First arrow, beginning of experiment; second, switch from dark to light; third, return to darkness. Dotted line shows return to initial position at end of experiment.

periments of van der Paauw and Smith were of the same order of magnitude.) At low temperatures, the induction loss may be three to five times larger (cf. fig. 33.7).. A second induction-enhancing dark process becomes apparent when the dark period is extended to several hours; this process leads to a stationary state after about 7 hours in darkness, and then accounts for an induction loss of about five molecules of carbon dioxide per molecule of chlorophyll.   The duration of the induction period remains, however, of the order of magnitude of a few minutes, even after several hours of incubation.   The analogy between these observations and the findings of Steemann-Nielsen on oxygen liberation (fig. 33.6), was pointed out before.

The induction loss is, according to McAlister, larger in the carbon dioxide-limited state than in the light-limited state, even when the final rate is the same in both cases.   For example, the same steady rate of photosynthesis prevails at 0.03% CO_2 and 3000 foot-candles, and at 0.3% CO_2

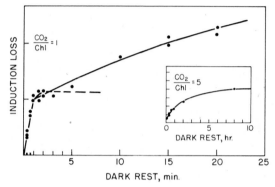

Fig. 33.9. Induction loss in wheat *vs.* dark rest (after McAlister 1937).   Broken line indicates "saturation" of the (short-) induction-preparing process.   Inset shows continued growth and final saturation of a second, slow induction-enhancing reaction.

and 1000 foot-candles; but the induction loss is much smaller in the second case.   If the plant is preilluminated in a carbon dioxide-free atmosphere, and carbon dioxide is admitted afterward, its uptake begins without delay.   (Related observations of Steemann-Nielsen on oxygen liberation were mentioned in section 2.)

Another interesting observation of McAlister—also confirmed by Steemann-Nielsen's observations on oxygen liberation—is that, if the light intensity is raised in steps, each increase is followed by a new induction period.   The sum of all carbon dioxide induction losses is approximately equal to the loss that would be incurred in a direct passage from darkness to full light.

McAlister and Myers (1940) recorded changes in the intensity of chlorophyll *fluorescence* simultaneously with the changes in the rate of carbon dioxide consumption.   The results will be discussed in detail in section B; some typical induction curves are shown in figures 33.21, 33.22 and 33.26. The upper curve in each of these figures refers to fluorescence, the lower to absorption of carbon dioxide. As far as the latter is concerned, two or three distinct types can be noted. One (type I) is obtained with wheat plants in an atmosphere of low carbon dioxide content (*e. g.*, normal air; *cf.* fig. 33.21A), and with *Chlorella* cells grown in an atmosphere rich in carbon dioxide (*cf.* fig. 33.22A). It is characterized by a smooth increase in

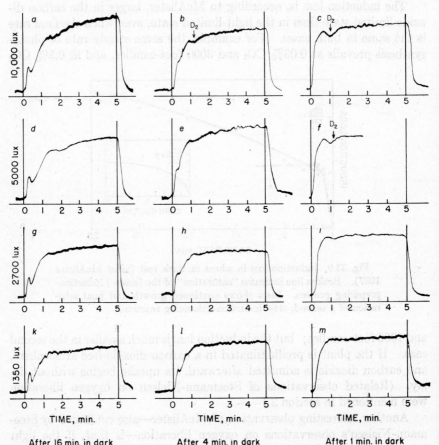

Fig. 33.10a. CO_2 absorption by *Stichococcus bacillaris* at 19° C., as a function of time (after Aufdemgarten 1939). 0.32% CO_2, varying light intensity.

carbon dioxide consumption during the whole induction period (3–4 minutes). On closer examination, one notices a slight inflection near the origin of the curves (at about 20–30 seconds). Because of the delayed response of the carbon dioxide-recording device, this position of the inflection probably means that the CO_2 consumption begins with a "gulp" immediately upon illumination (as indicated by the dotted curves in fig. 33.21).

Curves of a somewhat different type were obtained with wheat plants at higher concentrations of carbon dioxide (0.07 to 0.24%; no higher concentrations were used).   In these curves (*cf.* fig. 33.21B), the induction loss is considerably smaller than in the curves of the first type (as well as in the experiments used for the construction of the inset in figure 33.8).   The full rate is reached in less than 1 minute;   and a secondary depression occurs between 1.5 and 2 minutes simultaneously with a second "burst" of fluorescence.   An extreme form of this type of induction curves (type II) is illustrated by figure 33.22C, obtained with *Chlorella* grown and studied in

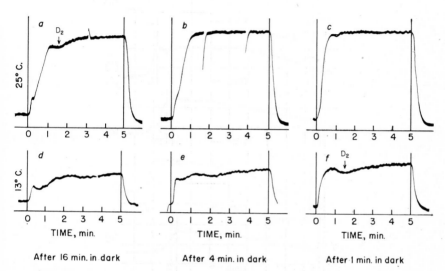

Fig. 33.10b. CO_2 absorption by *Stichococcus bacillaris* at varying temperatures (after Aufdemgarten 1939).   5000 lux, 0.32% CO_2.

normal air.   Here, the total induction loss is normal; but the initial carbon dioxide "gulp" is much more pronounced than in figures 33.21A and 33.22A, and the inflection is consequently replaced by a distinct peak 20–30 seconds after the beginning of illumination.   Characteristic in these curves is the *parallel* (rather than antiparallel) development of carbon dioxide consumption and fluorescence.   (The registration of fluorescence occurs without a time lag;   therefore the peak of fluorescence in figure 33.22C coincides approximately in time with the peak of carbon dioxide consumption, although the latter is registered 15 seconds later.)

The induction curves of McAlister are closely paralleled by the curves obtained by Aufdemgarten (1939).   As described in chapter 25 (page 853), Harder and Aufdemgarten (1938) developed a method of rapid carbon dioxide assay, based on measurement of thermal conductivity of the gas before and after passage through the plant chamber. Aufdemgarten studied by this method the induction in *Stichococcus bacillaris*. His results are shown in figures 33.10 and 33.11. We find in them the same three features noted above in the curves of McAlister and Myers: an initial *gulp* of carbon dioxide (registered, because of the time lag of the apparatus, about 15 seconds after the beginning of illumination), a *gradual increase*

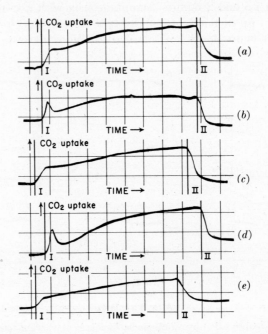

Fig. 33.11a. Time course of CO_2 uptake by *Stichococcus bacillaris* (after Aufdemgarten 1939). (*a* to *d*), *inorganic nutrition:* (*a*) 4 weeks light, 30 min. dark, Kolkwitz solution, pH 7.6; (*b*) 4 weeks light, 30 min. dark, Eiler solution, pH 5.8, 19° C.; (*c*) 10 days dark, Kolkwitz solution, 18.1° C.; (*d*) 10 days dark, Eiler solution, 18.9° C.; (*e*) *organic nutrition* in daylight; 15 min. dark, 4 min. 6 sec. light.

lasting for several minutes, and (in some curves) a *secondary depression*, D_2, which is registered between 1 and 1.5 minutes after the beginning of illumination. As in McAlister's curves, this depression can be most clearly seen on curves in which the main induction effect is weak, such as *c* and *f* in figure 33.10a, and *f* in figure 33.10b.

The analogy between the carbon dioxide exchange curves of the type *a* in figure 33.10a (or type *b* in figure 33.11a) and the oxygen exchange curves of the type of figure 33.2 is obvious. Quantitative comparison is impossible, because the oxygen curve is an integral curve, while the carbon dioxide curves are differential rate curves.   Furthermore, in figure 33.2, the oxygen liberation is partly compensated by rapid oxygen consumption by cathodic reduction.   If these factors are kept in mind, and the carbon dioxide curves are corrected for sluggishness, the similarity between the course of the oxygen liberation and that of carbon dioxide consumption becomes striking.   It would be interesting to compare quantitatively not only the timing of changes, but also the volumes of oxygen and carbon dioxide involved in them.   In a rough measurement, Aufdemgarten (1939) found no marked deviation of Q_P from unity during the first 10 minutes of illumination (19.5° C., 5000 lux, 0.6% CO_2).

Later, similar conclusions were reached and generalized by Warburg and co-workers, as described above in section 2; but measurements by

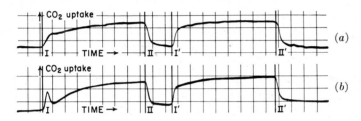

Fig. 33.11b. Time course of CO_2 uptake in *Stichococcus bacillaris* after varying periods of darkness (after Aufdemgarten 1939).   5000 lux, 1.0% CO_2, 15 min. dark, 4 min. light, 1 min. dark, 4 min. light.   (*a*) Kolkwitz solution, 18.4° C.; (*b*) Eiler solution, 18.7° C.

Emerson and co-workers, also reported there, revealed considerable minute-to-minute variations in Q_P, even in cases in which the time course of the exchange of the two gases is qualitatively the same; extreme deviations of Q_P from unity occur when the oxygen burst is combined with a carbon dioxide burst (see below).

The consumption of carbon dioxide during the gulp is independent of the dark period (between 1 and 16 minutes; *cf.* fig. 33.10a) as well as of temperature (between 13 and 25° C., *cf.* fig. 33.10b).   This behavior is typical also of the fluorescence burst (*cf.* part B).   The oxygen gush has not been studied at different temperatures, but we may presume that it, too, is unaffected by temperature.   If this is true, these three phenomena must be due to a straight photochemical reaction.   On the other hand, the subsequent inhibition, which dominates the short induction period, depends on the length of the dark interval as well as on temperature, and must therefore be associated with thermal reactions, both in its preparation (deactivation) and in its liquidation (reactivation of the photosynthetic mechanism).

In contradiction to other observers, Aufdemgarten found that the duration of the induction period was *not* independent of light intensity; it increased from 1.5 minutes at 1350 lux to 5 minutes at 10,000 lux (at 19° C.).

Aufdemgarten observed that the CO_2 gulp disappeared in the presence of 0.001 mole/l. *cyanide;* we will discuss this observation in part B (Sect. 2e), together with the effect of cyanide on fluorescence (which has been studied much more thoroughly). The same observer found the gulp to be absent from induction curves obtained with *higher plants;* but this cannot be a general rule, since the gulp was observed by McAlister in experiments with both *Chlorella* and wheat. Perhaps the leaves used by Aufdemgarten had a high diffusion resistance, which prevented rapid fluctuations of the carbon dioxide exchange in the leaf from affecting markedly the concentration of this gas in the atmosphere.

The gulp was also found by van der Veen (1949,[1,2] 1950) in experiments with grass blades, conifer needles and some algae; but in *Chlorella* (and certain other algae, or at least in certain cultures of these algae) it is replaced (or submerged) by a carbon dioxide *burst*, first discovered by Emerson and Lewis (*cf.* below).

In a second investigation (1939[2]), Aufdemgarten succeeded largely in eliminating the rapid oscillations (caused by unsteadiness of the apparatus) which marred the registration curves in figure 33.10. Using the same organism (*Stichococcus bacillaris*) he now studied the effect on induction of *pretreatment* of the algae. He used: (*a*) organic nutrition in daylight, which produced cells full of assimilates, in the form of oil droplets; (*b*) and (*c*) inorganic nutrition in acid and alkaline medium, respectively; and (*d*) starvation (inorganic medium in darkness). The (rather unexpected) result (fig. 33.11a) was that the composition of the inorganic medium proved to be of more decisive importance for the carbon dioxide gulp than the alternative of nutrition or starvation. Ten days spent in darkness in an organic medium had almost no influence on the shape of the induction curve (compare *a* and *c*, *b* and *d*). On the other hand, the gulp was much more pronounced in cells incubated in the acid Eiler medium (*p*H 5.8) than in cells incubated in the alkaline Kolkwitz medium (*p*H 7.6) (compare *a* and *b*, *c* and *d*).

It remains to be proved that acidity, and not other differences in the composition (such as the presence or absence of ammonia), was the decisive factor. This assumption is, however, favored by observations on the importance of acidity for anaerobic induction (*cf.* section 6).

Figure 33.11a shows that, when the dark period was reduced to one minute, the difference between the induction curves in the two inorganic media disappeared, not, as one would be inclined to say at first sight, because of disappearance of the carbon dioxide gulp, but rather because the strong decline of the inhibition effect as a whole makes the gulp unobservable.

The experiments described so far in this section indicated, in general, a parallelism between the course of induction as measured by carbon dioxide uptake, and the time course of oxygen liberation, as described in the first part of section 2, although, with the oxygen and carbon dioxide experiments performed by different observers and on different objects, only qualitative analogy can be asserted.   Later in section 2 we reported more recent investigations, indicating the occurrence of "positive induction" (oxygen gush) in the first minute of illumination; we recall that Warburg and co-workers assumed that the same applies also to carbon dioxide consumption ("CO_2 gulp"), but that Emerson and co-workers found this to be only occasionally correct (*e. g.*, in the first minute of illumination in fig. 33.6D); in other cases the oxygen gush was not accompanied by an equivalent carbon dioxide gulp.   We will now discuss experiments on the course of carbon dioxide uptake, which revealed strong "unilateral" carbon dioxide induction effects, not paralleled by similar changes in oxygen evolution.

(The discussion of some two-vessel manometric induction measurements in section 2, and of others in the present section is arbitrary, since all such measurements give both ΔO_2 and ΔCO_2; it is justified by the greater emphasis laid in Emerson and Lewis's work on the "carbon dioxide burst," and in Warburg's work on the "oxygen burst.")

Strong deviations of the photosynthetic quotient from unity during the induction period were first noted by Kostychev (1921).   He found that, in the initial 5 or 10 minutes of illumination of leaves or algae in an atmosphere containing 6% carbon dioxide, $-\Delta CO_2$ strongly *exceeded* ΔO_2 ($Q_P = 0.21 - 0.79$).   According to Kostychev, the excess carbon dioxide absorbed in the first minutes of illumination is compensated by a reduced uptake later, so that the average value of Q_P becomes unity after 15 or 20 minutes illumination.

Blinks and Skow (1938) and Emerson and Lewis (1941) observed, in contrast to Kostychev, an initial *deficiency of consumption* (or even a *liberation*) of carbon dioxide, not compensated by a slower evolution (or outright consumption) of oxygen;   this means Q_P values either > 1 or negative.

Blinks and Skow (1938[1]) used a rapid potentiometric method for the determination of the carbon dioxide exchange.   They measured ΔCO_2 by means of a glass electrode immersed in the algal suspension, or pressed against the surface of a leaf (*cf.* chapter 25, page 853).   The evolution of carbon dioxide revealed itself by a decrease, and its consumption by an increase in pH.   (Of course, similar effects could also be caused by formation or consumption of other acids.)   The response was so rapid that light flashes lasting only 0.04 second were recorded as distinct peaks on the pH curves.

The unexpected result of Blinks and Skow's measurements was the observation of a *gush of acidity* in the first moment of illumination. This gush was particularly strong after a prolonged dark rest, and could then be observed several times in succession—although with a declining strength—even after dark intervals of only a few seconds duration. Figure 33.12 shows three repetitions of the gush in a pond lily leaf (in this case, the dark intervals were of the order of 1 minute).

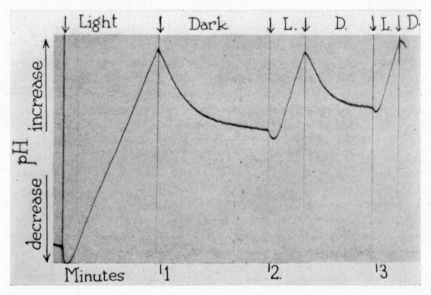

Fig. 33.12. Acidity change on illumination of pond lily (*Castalia*) (after Blinks and Skow 1938). Glass electrode pressed against upper surface of leaf (side that has stomata).

A temporary decrease of pH occurs immediately on illumination, preceding the regular rise of pH (alkalinity increase) due to assimilation of carbon dioxide. The anomalous pH decrease is most marked on the first illumination (after a long dark period) and becomes progressively less on successive exposures after shorter dark intervals.

Upon darkening, after a period of illumination, an *alkaline gush* was found to precede the regular increase in acidity due to respiration. The "acid gush" was observed by Blinks and Skow with marine algae (*e. g.*, *Stephanoptera*), fresh water plants (*e. g.*, *Potomageton* and *Castilia*) and land plants, and thus seems to be of fairly general occurrence.

The observations of Emerson and Lewis (1941) already were discussed in chapter 29.   In these experiments, the rates of exchange of both carbon dioxide and oxygen were measured manometrically, by means of two reaction vessels of different volume, containing the same amount of liquid. The experiments were carried out at low light intensities (near the compensation point), and high carbon dioxide concentration (5%), thus repeating the experimental conditions of Warburg and Negelein.   The results were shown in figure 29.3B.   If the ratio $\Delta O_2 / - \Delta CO_2$ were unity (for both respiration and photosynthesis), the two curves in the figure would be mirror images.   This relation is not reached until 20 or 40 minutes after the beginning of illumination.   At first, the picture is dominated by a

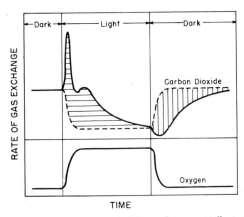

Fig. 33.13. Diagram showing the part of CO_2 exchange attributed to some process other than respiration and photosynthesis (after Emerson and Lewis 1941).

"carbon dioxide gush," which reaches its peak in the first minute of illumination (when the value of $\Delta O_2 / \Delta CO_2$ drops to -0.15).   It subsides slowly, perhaps with a secondary wave of carbon dioxide liberation, 5 or 10 minutes later.   The oxygen curve is much more regular (the slight maximum of oxygen consumption, coinciding with the carbon dioxide gush, may or may not be real).   Assuming—in contrast to Kostychev's suppositions—that the oxygen curve gives the true measure of photosynthesis during the induction period, and postulating that respiration is constant, Emerson and Lewis constructed from figure 29.3B the curve reproduced in figure 33.13, where the shaded areas represent extra liberation of carbon dioxide in light attributable to the gush (and its reversal in the dark).

The volume of the gush (shaded area, showing the difference between the assumed carbon dioxide exchange and the observed exchange) increases at first with increasing light intensity, but "light saturation" is reached in light of comparatively low intensity—above the compensation point, but well below the intensity required for the light saturation of photosynthesis. Horizontal shading is used in the diagram for areas above the dotted curve, indicating carbon dioxide production in excess of that due to respiration and photosynthesis. Vertical shading is used for areas below the dotted curve, indicating a deficit in the expected carbon dioxide production by respiration. It is not clear to what extent the *duration* of the gush depends on light intensity. (A part of what has been described by Emerson and Lewis as increase in *volume* may have been decrease in duration, and consequent greater prominence of the gush in the first few minutes of illumination.)

Successive gushes can be produced by increasing the light intensity in steps.

Emerson and Lewis estimated that the initial quantum yield of carbon dioxide liberation during the gush reaches (or even exceeds) unity; a total of about 20 mm.^{3} CO_2 can be liberated, in 3 minutes, from 100 mm.^{3} of *Chlorella* cells, containing about 20 mg. dry matter and about 1 mg. chlorophyll. This corresponds to approximately one carbon dioxide molecule per chlorophyll molecule, and shows that the size of the "reservoir" from which the carbon dioxide is taken is approximately equivalent to the amount of chlorophyll present.

Figure 33.13 indicates that the resorption of carbon dioxide in the dark occurs much more slowly than its release in light; but, since the two shaded areas are approximately equal, Emerson and Lewis concluded that, after a sufficiently long dark interval, the carbon dioxide loss suffered during the gush is completely recovered.

The extent of the uptake of carbon dioxide in the dark, and thus also the volume of the gush that occurs upon subsequent illumination, strongly depends on the concentration of carbon dioxide. Up to 0.5% CO_2, the uptake is small; this may explain why McAlister found no carbon dioxide gush in his induction experiments—he used only concentrations up to 0.24%. At 5%, the gush is very prominent (fig. 29.3A); it continues to increase with [CO_2] up to concentrations as high as 12%.

Phenylurethan, in a concentration of 0.005% (which causes a 50% inhibition of photosynthesis), leaves the carbon dioxide gush unaffected, at least in its initial stage. Higher urethan quantities, which completely inhibit photosynthesis, prevent also the carbon dioxide gush. Addition of malic, maleic, citric and other plant acids had no effect on the gush. (This experiment was conducted because Emerson and Lewis thought that the gush might be due to the photodecarboxylation of an acid of this type.) *Low temperatures* slowed down the gush, and reduced its total volume; below 10°, the gush required more than 10 minutes for completion, and the gulp in the dark was extended to an even much longer period.

Culture conditions and *micronutrients* were found to have an important effect on the size of the gush (as mentioned in chapter 29 in the discussion of the influence of these factors on the apparent quantum yield of photosynthesis). Anaerobic incubation prevented the gush (*cf.* section 6).

The formal analogy between the observations of Emerson and Lewis and of Blinks and Skow is unmistakable. Both observed an initial liberation of carbon dioxide in light, compensated by absorption in a subsequent dark period. However, the gushes of Blinks and Skow lasted for only a few seconds, as against several minutes in the experiments of Emerson and Lewis. Perhaps, the "cusps" visible on Blinks and Skow's curves were all that remained of the "Emerson-Lewis effect" at the (undefined, but probably low) carbon dioxide concentration used by these investigators. Blinks and Skow gave no hints as to the volume of the alkaline "gush"; but a glance at their figures makes this appear to be equivalent to the photosynthetic production in a few seconds of strong illumination, thus five or ten times smaller than the carbon dioxide gushes of Emerson and Lewis (stated above to be roughly equivalent to the amount of chlorophyll, and thus equal to the photosynthetic production in 20 or 30 seconds of strong illumination).

Warburg and co-workers (1948, 1950, 1951) did not usually observe a significant carbon dioxide gush ("Emerson effect") in *Chlorella* even while they worked with carbon dioxide concentrations of 10% or more. Nishimura, Whittingham, and Emerson (1951) suggested that physical lag in the equilibration of the manometer may have approximately compensated for the burst, and created the impression that both were absent. (Concerning claims of elimination of the lag by rapid shaking, *cf.* p. 1111.)

A clear and unambiguous confirmation of the occurrence of the CO_2 burst was provided more recently by Brown and Whittingham (1955) using the mass spectrographic method.

Warburg and co-workers (1951, 1953) concluded, from two-vessel manometric measurements, that a carbon dioxide *gulp*, rather than burst, took place in the first minute of illumination in *Chlorella*, parallel with the oxygen burst; since the Q_P ratio they calculated was about 0.85, the CO_2 gulp must have been even larger than the O_2 gush. (However, this ratio was an average for the total gas exchange in 6 minutes of illumination, leaving the distribution of carbon dioxide exchange over this period open; furthermore, the determination of Q_P was the least reliable part of these measurements.)

The induction curves of Emerson and Chalmers (1954), obtained with two-vessel technique of much improved precision, almost invariably showed a carbon dioxide burst, but its volume varied strongly in dependence on temperature, carbon dioxide concentration and cell density. A more rapid, transient gulp is sometimes superimposed upon the slower burst. Figure 33.6D (*cf.* also fig. 33.13), for example, shows a distinct carbon dioxide gulp in the first minute of illumination, paralleling a simultaneous oxygen burst (reminiscent of Blinks and Skow's, and Warburg's, findings); but a carbon dioxide burst supersedes the gulp in the second minute and lasts through the third and fourth minutes; only after that does the ratio Q_P become close to 1. In many other runs, the "positive" induction effects were much less prominent than in fig. 33.6D, or totally submerged under a much bigger carbon dioxide burst (*cf.* fig. 29.3B).

The dependence of the burst on cell concentration, even in the region of nearly complete light absorption (in which the rate of photosynthesis is almost independent of cell density), indicates, according to Emerson, that it is due to the emptying of a "reservoir" filled up during the dark period, and is not directly related to the kinetics of photosynthesis. It seems that most if not all the transient gas exchange phenomena are highly sensitive to conditions such as temperature, cell density and carbon dioxide concentration, while the steady rate of photosynthesis (in the light-limited state), is, in good approximation, independent of all of these factors.

Emerson and Lewis suggested that the "induction loss" of carbon dioxide consumption in strong light (as observed, *e. g.*, by McAlister and Aufdemgarten) may be merely another aspect of the carbon dioxide gush. The maximum volume of the gush is in fact about equal to the induction loss as measured by McAlister (page 1335). However, McAlister's induction losses were measured in 0.3 or 0.03% CO_2, a concentration region where the carbon dioxide gush should be negligible.

Pending further clarification of the relation between the two effects, it seems advisable to consider the carbon dioxide *gush* and the carbon dioxide *induction loss* as two independent effects.

Van der Veen (1949[1]), too, studied the carbon dioxide uptake during the induction period, using a "diaferometer"—a heat conduction meter similar to that of Aufdemgarten. With an entirely different plant material—leaves of tobacco and needles of *Sciadopitys*—he obtained results very similar to those found by Aufdemgarten with unicellular algae. He, too, observed curves that began with a brief carbon dioxide "gulp"; a wave of inhibition followed, decaying within 3–5 minutes to a steady rate. Sometimes the approach to the steady level was interrupted by another, or several, waves of inhibition.

The initial carbon dioxide gulp was small in normal air, and increased with carbon dioxide enrichment of the atmosphere; its time course was not much affected by the length of the dark period, or temperature variations. The highest rate of carbon dioxide uptake was reached in 1/2 to 3/4 minute under all the conditions used. (This might have been the measure of the sluggishness of the apparatus, the true uptake perhaps being highest at the very beginning of illumination.)   The inhibition that follows the gulp increased in duration, and the separation of the successive inhibition waves became wider, as the dark period was extended (fig. 33.13A). In tobacco leaves, for example, with $t_d = 2$ minutes, the existence of the two waves was revealed only by an inflection on the induction curve, while,

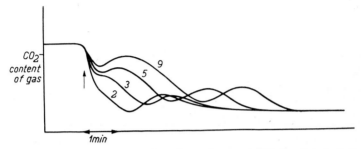

Fig. 33.13A. CO_2 induction in tobacco leaves at 20° C. after 9, 5, 3 and 2 min. darkness;   diaferometer record (after van der Veen 1949[1]).

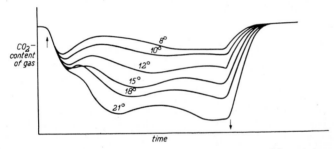

Fig. 33.13B. CO_2 induction curves of tobacco leaves at different temperatures; diaferometer record (after van der Veen 1949[1]): (↑) light on; (↓) light off.

at $t_d = 5$ minutes, the first inhibition peak was reached in about 1.5 minutes, and a well-separated second peak, 4.5 minutes later.   Judging from the shape of the induction curves after repeated short dark periods, the factor causing the inhibition requires several minutes of darkness to be built up (or else the factor responsible for activation in light survives in the dark for several minutes).

The inhibition waves can be slowed down (fig. 33.13B) also by lowering the temperature.   The duration of the dark period needed to produce a certain wave of inhibition decreases with increasing temperature.   At 40° C., inhibition becomes more or less permanent.

Figure 33.13C shows that the initial carbon dioxide gulp was unaffected

by heat pretreatment.   It persisted even after the cells had been heated to
47–53° C., reducing steady photosynthesis to zero.   In this way, the gulp
can be completely separated from normal photosynthesis.   It then proves
to be independent of the dark period (between 1 minute and 1 hour) and
temperature (between 6 and 30° C.).   The gulp depends on light intensity;

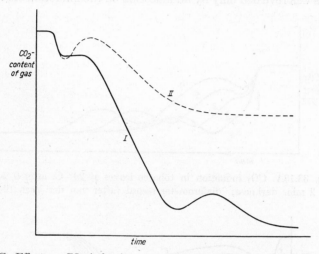

Fig. 33.13C. Effect on CO_2 induction curve of 3 min. preheating of leaves to 43° C.
(after van der Veen 1949[1]): (I) normal; (II) preheated.   Diaferometric record.

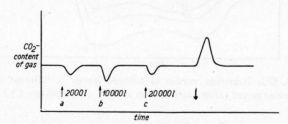

Fig. 33.13D. CO_2 uptake by heat pretreated *Sciadopitys* needles after
successive exposures to different illumination (2, 10, 20 klux), and its release
in dark (after van der Veen 1949[1]).   Diaferometer record.

stepwise increase in illumination produces a sequence of gulps, with saturation at about 20 klux.   The gulp can be produced in filtered red light, showing it to be chlorophyll-sensitized.   After switching the light off, the carbon
dioxide taken up in the gulp (or gulps) is released in a gush in the dark (fig.
33.13D).   In many of these details (but not, for example, in its independence from the length of the dark period), the phenomenon reminds one of the
"Emerson-Lewis effect"—with a reverse sign.

In these experiments, the CO_2 gush at the beginning of the dark period could be observed only with heat-inhibited plant material; later (*cf.* van der Veen, 1949) it was found that, in a hydrogen atmosphere ($+3\%$ CO_2), the gush becomes clearly observable also in non-preheated leaves.

The separation of the gulp from steady photosynthesis can be achieved also by cooling to $0°$ C.   At this temperature photosynthesis is suppressed, but the gulp is practically unchanged (fig. 33.13E).   It is not reversed by a gulp in the dark (or rather, the gulp is smeared out over 10–15 minutes). In experiments with preheating, the gush appeared to be independent of temperature (6–22° C.); since it must be due to a dark reaction, this result

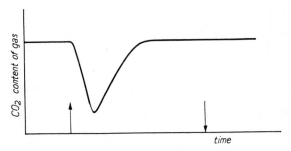

Fig. 33.13E. CO_2 uptake by *Sciadopitys* needles at $0°$ C. (photosynthesis suspended) (after van der Veen 1949[1]).   Uptake normal, release in dark absent (or delayed).   Diaferometer record.

is puzzling.   The slowing-down of the gulp at $0°$ C., on the other hand, seems natural.

The gulp observed at $0°$ C. is strongly dependent on the length of the preceding dark period, reaching "saturation" after about 15 minutes. (With preheated leaves, even the shortest dark period used—1 minute—was sufficient to prepare the gulp, *i. e.*, to release the carbon dioxide taken up in the preceding light period.)

Exposing *Sciadopitys* needles at $0°$ C., after dark periods of up to 15 minutes, to light flashes of varying duration, indicated that 20–30 seconds are needed to produce a gulp of maximum volume.   This is the order of magnitude of the "assimilation time" (chapter 32)—the shortest time in which a chlorophyll molecule can reduce a molecule of carbon dioxide in saturating light.

In a second paper (1949[2]) van der Veen observed more closely the secondary inhibition waves, using the grass *Holcus lanatus* as object.   He found that they occur only in saturating (or almost saturating) light.   For example (fig. 33.13F), only a faint indication of the second wave appeared at 10 klux (in 3% CO_2), while a strong second, and a clear third, wave were visible at 30 klux (3.7 and 6.0 minutes after the beginning of illumination, respectively; the first inhibition wave had its peak at 1.8 minutes). The

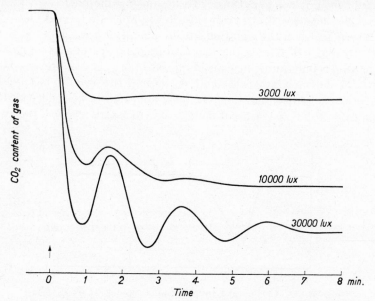

Fig. 33.13F. CO_2 induction curves of *Holcus lanatus* in light of different intensity; diaferometer record (after van der Veen 1949[2]).

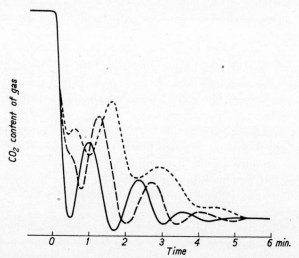

Fig. 33.13G. CO_2 induction curves of *Holcus lanatus* after different dark periods (20° C., 3% CO_2 in air): (—) 1 min. dark; (– –) 3 min. dark; (- -) 6 min. dark (after van der Veen 1949[2]). Diaferometer record.

longer the dark period (it varied between 5 seconds and 6 minutes), the slower were the inhibition waves.   After 3 or 6 minutes of darkness, a "preliminary" wave appeared at about 1/2 minutes (fig. 33.13G).   After a very

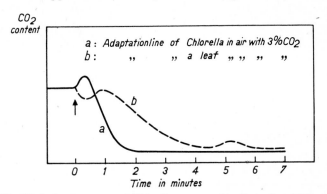

Fig. 33.13H. CO_2 induction curve of *Chlorella* compared to that of a dahlia leaf; both in air $+ 3\%$ CO_2; diaferometer record (after van der Veen 1950).

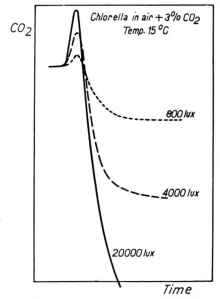

Fig. 33.13I. CO_2 burst in *Chlorella* at different light intensities; diaferometer record (after van der Veen 1950).

short dark period (5 or 15 seconds), photosynthesis was found to begin at a higher than the stationary rate; lowering the temperature had an effect similar to that of prolonging the dark interval.

After the observations of van der Veen (1949[1,2]) with needles and grass blades have demonstrated a "carbon dioxide gulp" at the beginning of illumination and a "carbon dioxide burst" after its end, in exact opposition to the findings of Emerson and Lewis with *Chlorella* (and of Aufdemgarten, 1939[1,2], with *Stichococcus* and *Hormidium*), van der Veen (1950) next used his apparatus on *Chlorella*. For this purpose, a suspension of *Chlorella* cells was spread over a piece of filter paper, and the gas stream passed over

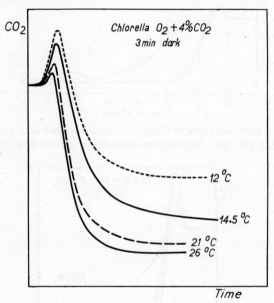

Fig. 33.13K. CO_2 burst in *Chlorella* at different temperatures; diaferometer record (after van der Veen 1950).

it into the diaferometer. Contrary to his expectations, van der Veen found a confirmation of Emerson and Lewis' results. Figure 33.13H shows the difference between the induction phenomena in *Chlorella* and in a higher plant (a leaf of dahlia). The same response as *Chlorella* was shown by another species of Chlorococcales, *Protococcus olivaceus*.

Figure 33.13I illustrates the effect of light intensity on the carbon dioxide burst, as observed by van der Veen in *Chlorella*. Figure 33.13K indicates that the burst increases in prominence as the temperature declines from 26 to 12° C. (in apparent contradiction to the manometric data of Emerson). It reaches its maximum volume after several hours of darkness. It is the same in air (+3% CO_2) and in O_2 (+3% CO_2); in hydrogen (also with 3% CO_2) it is less prominent; a second, smaller gush was noted in this gas a few minutes later.

The "light adaptation" stage of the induction process (which follows the initial gushes or gulps), has in *Chlorella*, according to van der Veen, a relatively short duration, and is largely independent from the length of the preceding dark period; (3, 24 or 60 minutes darkness gave similar adaptation curves; even after 16 hours in the dark, the light adaptation was about as fast as after 3 minutes darkness). This behavior differs from that observed by other observers with many other species (*cf.* figs. 33.6, 9, 11b).

On the whole, the results of van der Veen indicate that transient carbon dioxide exchange at the beginning of light periods may have either a positive or a negative sign, depending on species and treatment of the algae. Combining his results with those of Aufdemgarten, Emerson and co-workers, and Blinks and Skow, one gets the impression that the gulp may be a more general feature than the burst, but that its volume is small and it is usually over in much less than a minute; the burst, on the other hand, may be much more prominent, but slower, reaching a peak only in the second or third minute of illumination, and taking several more minutes to subside. It thus blankets the whole period of normal (negative) long induction. Carbon dioxide induction curves of *Chlorella*, obtained by Gaffron (1954) and Rosenberg (1954) by pH measurements, were published too late for detailed discussion here (*cf.* chapter 37D, section 1). They showed many complex and interesting features—in particular, 1–3 minute long "stops" (periods of zero gas exchange), interrupting the transition from CO_2 liberation in darkness to CO_2 consumption in light, and *vice versa*.

4. Induction after Change to Lower Light Intensity

Offhand, one would not expect new induction losses to occur after the cells have been working for a while at full rate at high light intensity, and the illumination then is reduced to a lower level (assuming the illumination was not so strong as to cause damage by photoxidation; induction effects caused by photoxidation will be described in section 7. Gessner (1938) noted that, in the first 15 minutes after an exposure to 80,000 lux, the (uncorrected) rate of photosynthesis of *Elodea* at 4600 lux was about 30% lower than before; but, in this case, both photoxidation and enhanced respiration might have contributed to the change. More significant are the results of Steemann-Nielsen (1942), obtained with *Fucus serratus* at low temperature. When the light intensity was reduced from 23,000 to 2300 lux at 19.8° C., no marked induction appeared; but, when the same experiment was carried out at 4.9°, the rate of oxygen liberation (corrected for respiration) was, in the first 5 minutes after the change, only 34% of the steady rate; the latter was reached after about 25 minutes. A rough check of the carbon dioxide liberation showed a similar induction loss. Experiments also were conducted with transitions from 4000 to 2300, from

23,000 to 7000, from 7000 to 2300, and from 2300 to 1200 lux, always at about 5° C. Induction losses occurred in all but the last-named case. After the transition from 54 to 2.3 klux, the first 5 minutes in weaker light gave a net consumption instead of liberation of oxygen. Figure 33.13L

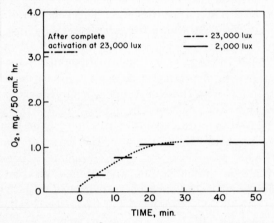

Fig. 33.13L. Induction in *Fucus serratus* after passage from 23,000 to 2000 lux (after Steemann-Nielsen 1942). 4.9° C.; $R = 0.18$ mg. O_2 per 50 cm.^{2} hr.

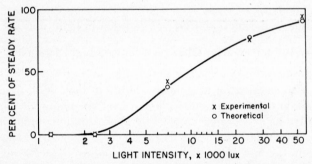

Fig. 33.13M. Relative induction loss as a function of light intensity (after Steemann-Nielsen 1942).

shows a typical set of results. Steemann-Nielsen suggested that, at the higher temperatures, induction may be too brief to be discovered by measurements of 5 min. duration. (Li, 1929, noted that, at room temperature the steady rate of bubble evolution from a submerged plant was reached about 1 minute after transition from stronger to weaker light; but results obtained by this method are too rough for exact interpretation.)

Steemann-Nielsen hypothesized that the relative inhibition observed in the first moment after the light intensity had been reduced from a "saturating" to a "limiting" value may be independent of the specific value of the final light intensity, and equal to the "rate deficiency" in conditioning light (meaning by this the ratio of the actual rate to the rate

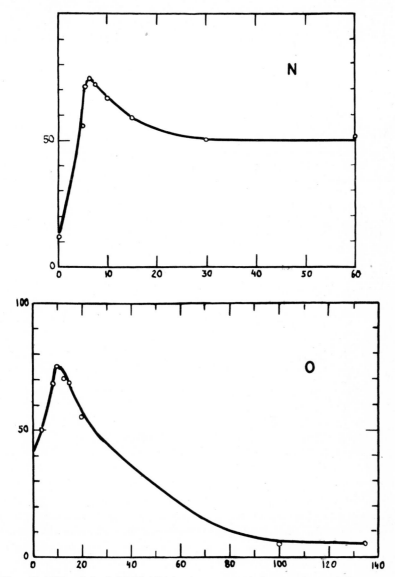

Figs. 33.13N and O. Initial inhibition in percent of photosynthesis of *Fucus serratus* at 2.3 klux, as function of the duration of "conditioning" to 23 klux (curve N), and of "deconditioning" in darkness after completed conditioning to 23 klux (curve O), 5° C. (after Steemann-Nielsen 1942).

that would prevail at the same light intensity if light saturation did *not* occur). To put it more simply, Steemann-Nielsen postulated that, upon a sudden decrease of light intensity, the quantum yield at first remains unchanged, and only gradually rises to the higher value characteristic of the weaker light. If generally valid, this would be a significant relation; however, it was derived from only seven not very precise, measurements (five at

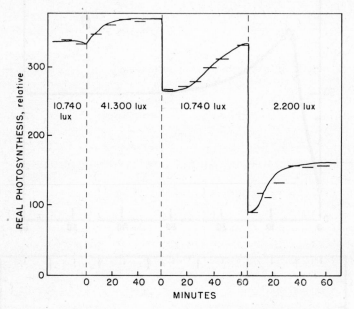

Fig. 33.13P. O_2 induction losses of *Cladophora insignis* after upward and downward changes in light intensity (after Steemann-Nielsen 1949). Winkler method.   18° C, 5×10^{-3} mole/l. HCO_3, pH 8.1.

variable conditioning light, I', and constant illuminating light, I'', and two at constant I' and variable I''). In figure 33.13M, the curve represents the initial inhibition as *calculated*, on the basis of this theory, from the light curve of photosynthesis of *Fucus;* the crosses represent the actually *observed* inhibitions.

Steemann–Nielsen also carried out experiments in which conditioning to the higher light intensity was incomplete. The results are shown in figure 33.13N, in which the ordinates represent the yields in the first 10 minutes of weaker illumination as a function of the duration of preillumination with stronger light. The curve shows a maximum after about 6 minutes conditioning. Figure 33.13O shows that a similar maximum corresponds to a certain degree of "deconditioning" in the dark; it is reached about 12 minutes after the cessation of strong illumination. In other words, it appears that at some time in the course of conditioning to strong light, and again at some time during "deconditioning" in the dark, the photosynthetic apparatus passes through a state capable of giving the highest initial rate in weaker light.   It is noteworthy that, even in the maximum of both curves, the initial rate is about 25% below the steady rate at 2300 lux. Steemann-Nielsen saw in this an indication that these inhibition effects are due to the competing action of *two* independent factors, one activating and the other inhibiting the photosynthetic apparatus, rather than to variation in the intensity of a single activating factor, the optimum value of which increases with light intensity.   (In the latter case, the maxima of the curves in figures 33.13N and O should be 100%.)   By further analysis of the curves on the basis of these concepts, Steemann-Nielsen constructed a curve showing the time development of the inhibiting factor at 23,000 lux;   the curve was sigmoid and showed a saturation after about 20 minutes (at $5.6°$ C.).

In section 7, we will describe observations of induction losses after a period of photoxidation, caused by various factors. One of them is excessive light.   It may be asked whether a relation exists between these experiments and the observations of Steemann-Nielsen. Offhand, it seems unlikely that significant photoxidation could occur at intensities as low as 7000 lux, even at temperatures close to $0°$ C.   (In the experiments described in section 7, light intensities of the order of 100,000 lux were used.) We will see below, however, that Steemann-Nielsen tends to consider the analogy as significant.

Steemann-Nielsen (1949) resumed the investigation of induction after reduction of light intensity, using this time *Cladophora insignis*.   In this fresh-water green alga, induction losses of this kind could be observed only on rare occasions, despite an improvement in the technique of the Winkler method which permitted one-minute oxygen determinations.   A number of curves were secured, however, which showed the effect.   In one experiment, a change from 31 to 2.6 klux was followed by 14 minutes induction (at $10°$ C.), and in another, a change from 10.7 to 2.2 klux, by 15 minutes induction (at $18°$ C.).   The effect was more pronounced after a change from 41 to 2.2 klux than after a change from 10.7 to 2.2 klux—although photosynthesis was saturated at both initial intensities; in agreement with this result, an induction loss was noted also upon transition from a higher to a lower intensity in the saturating range.   Figure 33.13P shows a set of measurements illustrating these findings.

In new experiments with two species of *Fucus*, the induction after light reduction could not be found (in contrast to earlier results with *Fucus serratus*).

Steemann-Nielsen concluded that photosynthesis includes one dark reaction, which *can* produce light saturation, but is not *usually* limiting and which involves reactivation of chlorophyll (somehow changed in the primary photochemical process).   Whenever this reaction becomes limiting in the light-saturated state (because of some special metabolic conditions), a sudden reduction of light intensity finds a part of chlorophyll in the inactive state incapable of contributing to oxygen production.   The initial quantum yield of oxygen liberation in weaker light could then be the same as it had been in the conditioning stronger light (as suggested in fig. 33.13M). Often, however, the initial rate deficiency is smaller; Steemann-Nielsen suggested that, in this case, light saturation was only partially determined by the rate of chlorophyll reactivation, and partially by another, chlorophyll-independent enzymatic factor, such as "catalyst B" of Franck and Herzfeld. In chapters 26 and 27, pp. 871 and 923, it was shown that cooperation of several reactions in the determination of the saturation level is to be expected theoretically if the "ceilings" imposed by them separately are not too different; on p. 1030, we discussed the possibility that a dark reaction involving chlorophyll and requiring about 20 seconds may impose a "ceiling" on the rate of photosynthesis that is not too different from the ceiling imposed by a reaction of "catalyst B," which requires about 0.01 second. Steemann-Nielsen's explanation is in principle the same, but the postulated chlorophyll recovery is much slower—requiring up to 30 *minutes* for completion. This means that the chlorophyll "deactivation," postulated by Steemann-Nielsen, can be permitted to occur only once in a large number of primary photochemical reactions—perhaps one in about two hundred. (Steemann-Nielsen estimated 1 deactivation per 40 reduced CO_2 molecules.)

Steemann-Nielsen (1949) discussed the above-mentioned possibility that the same inactivation of chlorophyll may account also for the decline of photosynthesis in excessively strong light. His first experiments with *Cladophora insignis* spoke against such a hypothesis. He observed that, when the algae were exposed to a very strong light (160 klux) until the rate had declined by about 30%, a sudden drop in intensity to 21 klux did not reduce the rate to the very low value which was to be expected if the cause of inhibition at 160 klux were the same chlorophyll inactivation to which induction losses after exposures to 20–40 klux have been attributed.

Later, however, Steemann-Nielsen (1952) found that, after one hour exposure of *Cladophora* to 100 klux (at 18° C.), during which the rate had declined by about 50%, a sudden drop of light intensity to 3 klux (implying transition to the light-limited state) did reveal a strong inhibition, the recovery from which required several hours. He concluded from this that exposure to excessive light affects not only a rate-limiting enzyme, which is not part of the photochemical apparatus proper (as suggested by Franck and French, *cf.* section 7 below), but inhibits the latter apparatus as well. The effect of a ten minute exposure to 100 klux proved to be the same as that of one hour exposure to 17 klux; it could be therefore suggested that inhibitions caused by exposure to excessive light are due, at least in part (and if the exposure is not too long, perhaps predominantly), to the same kind of inhibition (photoxidation?) of the photochemical mechanism proposed above as explanation of induction losses following transition from saturating (but not excessive) to limiting light.

The time required for reactivation is about the same, whether a certain degree of deactivation had been reached by brief exposure to excessively bright light, or moderate exposure to moderately strong light; it becomes, however, much longer if deactivation by bright light had been pushed so far as to produce almost complete suppression of photosynthesis.

5. Gas Exchange during the Long Induction Period

When Osterhout and Haas (1918) first described the induction of photosynthesis, they left the plant (*Ulva lactuca*) in the dark overnight and observed, in the morning, a gradual increase in the rate of carbon dioxide consumption, which lasted for about 1.5 hours.

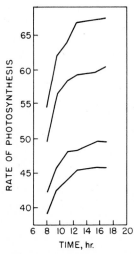 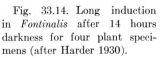 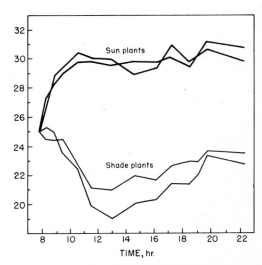

Fig. 33.14. Long induction in *Fontinalis* after 14 hours darkness for four plant specimens (after Harder 1930).

Fig. 33.15. Induction curves of sun-adapted and shade-adapted *Fontinalis* plants (18° C.) (after Harder 1933). Adaptation to sun: several months in an aquarium with southern exposure. Adaptation to shade: 6 days in shaded aquarium.

Comparison with the results of Warburg, van der Paauw, McAlister and Aufdemgarten shows that what Osterhout and Haas observed must have been the long, rather than the short, induction; more precisely, it was a superposition of the two phenomena. Many of the subsequent induction studies also were made under conditions that must have led to the superposition of the two induction effects, often with the long induction

predominating.   Because of the uncertainty of interpretation of this kind
of measurements, we will describe them only briefly.

Briggs (1933) kept the moss *Mnium undulatum* in the dark for 2 hours.   After this,
on the average, the induction periods in light lasted for about 30 or 50 minutes, but the
values scattered widely, and showed only a vague tendency to increase with increasing
ight intensity, decreasing temperature and extended dark incubation.

The experiments of Harder (1930) have been quoted once before in chapter 26.
Here, we are interested only in the part of Harder's complex time curves that can be attributed to the long induction.   Figure 33.14 shows, as an example, the gradual rise of

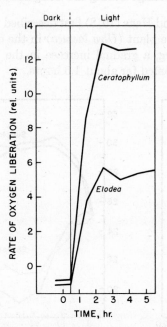

Fig. 33.16. Induction after 40 days dark rest (after Gessner 1937).

the rate of oxygen evolution by four *Fontinalis* plants after a dark rest of 14 hours.
The induction periods in this case lasted from 4 to 6 hours.   Later (1933) Harder found
that, if plants adapted to weak light ("shade plants") were brought into stronger light,
their photosynthetic efficiency *declined* at first, until they began to "readapt" themselves
to strong light (*cf.* lower curves in fig. 33.15).   We can look upon this decline as an expression of "light injury" (to which shade-adapted plants are easily susceptible; *cf.*
chapter 19, pp. 529, 532 and chapter 28, p. 995), and dismiss them as having no direct
relation to induction, unless it is suggested that a complete theory of the changes that
the photosynthetic apparatus undergoes in light and darkness should include "light
injury" and "light adaptation," too (*cf.* section 4 above).   In figure 26.8, we reproduced Harder's scheme of the time course of photosynthesis corresponding to different
ratios of conditioning and illuminating light.   The uppermost curve in this figure was a
pure induction curve, the lowest one a pure light injury curve, while the intermediate

curves were interpreted by Harder as the result of superposition of four processes: activation (= induction), deactivation (= light injury), re-adaptation to strong light (renewed rise) and "fatigue" (expressed in the final decline of the rate).

Other authors who have studied the course of photosynthesis over long periods obtained less complex curves. Bukatsch (1935), for example, noted with green algae (*Spirogyra*, *Zygnema*, *Mougeotia* and *Cladophora*), after an extended dark rest, only a smooth increase in rate that lasted for about 1 hour, and was followed by constant oxygen production. Gessner (1937) often found, in experiments with higher aquatic plants (*Elodea*, *Potomageton* and *Ceratophyllum*), no long induction periods at all; the rate was constant from the first hour of illumination. (Two such curves were reproduced in figure 26.9.) Other curves of the same observer showed, however, an increase in rate during the first 1 or 2 hours of illumination, especially after a prolonged period of darkness. However, the induction never exceeded 2.5 hours, even after dark periods of 40 days (*cf.* fig. 33.16). Finally, it was mentioned in section 2 that Steemann-Nielsen (1942) observed, in *Fucus*, only induction phenomena of 10–30 minutes duration, even after incubation periods of 16 hours.

Apparently, a long induction period after prolonged dark incubation is a fairly common, but not general, phenomenon; whether its occurrence is closely related to the kinetic mechanism of photosynthesis, or is more or less incidental, is as yet uncertain. Perhaps, vigorous circulation of the medium in the experiments of Gessner and Steemann-Nielsen had something to do with the absence of a prolonged induction period in their experiments.

It was mentioned in section 1 that, even if no prolonged induction occurs after a dark incubation of several hours, the extent of the "short" induction is affected in a manner showing the superposition of a slow deactivating process upon the fast deactivating reaction responsible for induction after a few minutes of dark rest. This twofold origin of short induction losses is clearly shown both by Steemann-Nielsen's (1942) curve of losses of oxygen liberation by *Fucus* (fig. 33.6), and by McAlister's (1939) curve of losses of carbon dioxide uptake by *Triticum* (fig. 33.9).

A special kind of induction phenomena has been recently described as following the transfer of certain algae from acid into alkaline media.

In chapter 37D, we will describe the experiments of Österlind (1951, 1952) on the photosynthesis of *Scenedesmus quadricauda* in carbon dioxide and in bicarbonate solutions. He noted the occurrence of a long induction period (order: 30–50 minutes) in algae grown in acid, carbon dioxide-rich solutions, and transferred into carbon dioxide-poor bicarbonate solution before exposure to light; the same algae showed none, or only the usual short, induction if exposed to light in the original carbon dioxide solution. Österlind suggested as explanation a slow photoactivation of a factor involved in the utilization of bicarbonate in photosynthesis—either in the transport of bicarbonate through the cell wall, or in its chemical transformation (in the latter case, this factor may be the enzyme, carbonic anhydrate). Similar observations were made by Briggs and Whittingham (1952) with *Chlorella*. They found, however, that induction continued if the illuminated algae were transferred from bicarbonate back into carbon dioxide solution, and therefore suggested a different explanation: that cells grown in a carbon dioxide-rich medium and therefore full of metabolites, suffer, when exposed to light in a solution that is low in carbon dioxide, "self-poisoning" by the formation of "narcotics" which cover the surface of chlorophyll, and that this causes a prolonged induction. This would place the observed phenomenon alongside certain other forms of "long" inductions, such as that after anaerobic incubation (*cf.* next section). Österlind (1952) could not confirm with his plant material the above-mentioned findings of Whittingham and Briggs with *Chlorella*. The long induction *Scenedesmus quadricauda* shows after transfer into bicarbonate solution may therefore have a different origin from that observed under the same conditions in *Chlorella*. This is not implausible, because (as we will see in chapter 37D), *Scenedesmus quadricauda* appears to be much better adapted to utilize bicarbonate for photosynthesis than *Chlorella pyrenoidosa*.

6. Influence of Anaerobiosis on Induction

In chapter 13, we discussed the question whether small quantities of oxygen are necessary for photosynthesis, and answered it in the negative. (The question has been revived more recently by Warburg; but new experiments seem to confirm the above conclusion, *cf.* chapter 37D, section 2b). Nevertheless, there is no doubt that green plants deprived of oxygen during a prolonged period of darkness, and then exposed to light, often show considerable initial inhibition. Boussingault (1865), Pringsheim (1887) and Willstätter and Stoll (1918) found that, after several hours of anaerobic incubation in the dark, the photosynthesis of higher land plants was practically completely inhibited, and required a considerable time for recovery. Green algae were found to suffer, too, but usually to a lesser degree.

From experiments of Franck, Pringsheim and Lad (1945) it appears that the maximum capacity of algae for photosynthesis is reduced by anaerobic incubation, not to zero, but to a low, finite level, which may be two. ten or several hundred times lower than the saturation rate in the aerobic state. The level of inhibition depends on the nature of the plant and the duration and specific conditions of the anaerobic treatment. The speed of recovery in light depends—in continued absence of external oxygen supply

—on how long it takes for the oxygen produced by residual photosynthesis to "burn up" the accumulated (and continuously produced) inhibitors arising from the anaerobic metabolism. Whether this is at all possible is determined by the extent of competition of other oxygen-consuming side reactions, as well as by the exact rate of the residual oxygen production. In hydrogen-adapted *Scenedesmus*, competition comes, for example, from the "oxyhydrogen" reaction $(2 H_2 + O_2 \rightarrow 2 H_2O)$. If all the oxygen liberated by photosynthesis is swept away by a stream of oxygen-free gas (as was done in the experiments of Franck, Pringsheim and Lad), "anaerobic inhibition" can be prolonged practically indefinitely, even in strong light, and reversible light curves of residual, anaerobic photosynthesis can be obtained.

Some algae (*e. g.*, *Scenedesmus*) acquire, simultaneously with anaerobic inhibition of oxygen production, the capacity for photochemical reactions that involve absorption or liberation of hydrogen (*cf.* chapter 6). It was the study of these phenomena that led Gaffron (1935, 1937[1,2], 1939[1,2], 1940) to the conclusion that the cause of induction generally lies in the deactivation of a catalyst or catalysts concerned primarily with the liberation of molecular oxygen (Franck's "catalyst C"). In *Scenedesmus*, this deactivation is coupled with the activation (probably, by reduction) of a "hydrogenase," capable of transferring molecular hydrogen; in most other green plants, no hydrogenase is produced, and the only effect of anaerobic incubation is therefore an enhanced initial inhibition of ordinary photosynthesis. In purple bacteria, which have no oxygen-liberating enzymatic system to begin with, but which do contain an active hydrogenase, anaerobiosis does not affect the capacity for photochemical metabolism at all; often it even represents the only condition under which this metabolism is possible (*cf.* chapter 5).

The question arises as to whether the persistent inhibition of photosynthesis observed under strictly anaerobic conditions is caused simply by a more complete deactivation (or even destruction) of the oxygen-liberating enzyme (the autocatalytic regeneration of which by photosynthesis is thus delayed), or by another, independent phenomenon. It seems that both factors play a role, so that "anaerobic inhibition" is the result of two processes —one affecting the activity of the oxygen-liberating enzymatic system, and the other, obstructing in a less specific way all catalytic agents, including chlorophyll and the "finishing catalyst" E_B (Franck's "catalyst B"). Perhaps the two inhibiting agents are identical, but widely different amounts are needed for the specific and the nonspecific "narcotic" action. (Perhaps the same hypothesis can be applied to "short" and "long" induction under aerobic conditions.)

Among experiments that demonstrate the production by anaerobic metabolism of a general diffusible, acidic and reducing inhibitor, are those of Noack, Pirson and Michels (1939) and Michels (1940). They observed that *neutralization* of the medium as well as aeration can remove the anaerobic inhibition, sometimes almost instantaneously. This is illustrated by

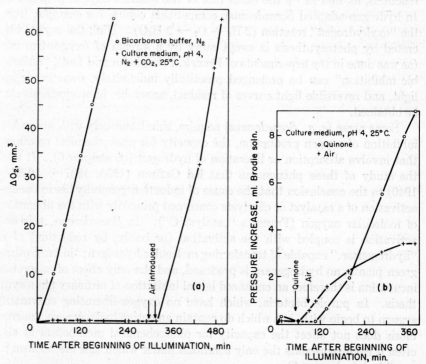

Fig. 33.17. (a) Induction in *Chlorella* after 13.5 hours of anaerobiosis in acid or alkaline medium. (b) Quinone added after 60 minutes light, or air bubbled through solution 60–105 minutes after beginning of illumination (after Noack, Pirson and Michels 1939).

figure 33.17, which shows the practically complete inhibition of photosynthesis of *Chlorella* by 13.5 hours of anaerobiosis in an acid nutrient solution, and the absence of a similar effect in an alkaline buffer. Figure 33.17b shows that the inhibition can be removed by aeration in the dark (in the course of which a considerable quantity of oxygen is taken up by the cells), and, even more rapidly, by the addition of quinone. The chemical nature of the easily oxidizable, acid fermentation products indicated by Noack's experiments is as yet unknown. Assays were made for lactic acid but it was found in only relatively small quantity (in agreement with Gaffron's observations on *Scenedesmus; cf.* chapter 6, page 138).

Franck, Pringsheim and Lad (1945) found much less pronounced effects of alkali and quinone on anaerobic inhibition than Noack, Pirson and Michels. Franck attributed this difference to the use of streaming gas which kept the local oxygen concentration safely below the "reactivation" level even in alkaline medium. Noack's experiments, on the other hand, were made in a closed system, where even partial removal or neutralization of the inhibiting material may have been decisive in determining the balance between oxygen accumulation by residual photosynthesis and oxygen consumption by side reactions not contributing to the reactivation of photosynthesis.

According to Franck and co-workers, an important factor determining the extent of inhibition of a cell culture by anaerobic incubation is, beside duration of the incubation period (the difference between the results of Franck and of Noack may have been due, in part, to the latter's using a thirteen hour incubation period and the former, a three to five hour incubation period), the concentration of the algae in the suspension. This indicates that inhibition is caused by a product capable of diffusing into and out of the cells. Since young cultures, placed in suspension media that previously contained old, anaerobically incubated algae, often show only little deterioration, one of the effects of anaerobic incubation (to which old cultures appear to be more sensitive) may be a change in the permeability of the cells for general, "narcotic" poisons.

It is obvious from the above that the induction curves observed after anaerobic incubation must depend on the balance of residual photosynthesis and various competing, oxygen-consuming processes and may therefore display a great variety of shapes. This applies to the course of photosynthesis in the first *minutes* (or *hours*) after the beginning of illumination; the phenomena in the first few *seconds* of exposure, on the other hand (best revealed by the observations of fluorescence), are simpler under anaerobic than under aerobic conditions. In general, anaerobic pretreatment makes the fluorescence start at a high level immediately upon illumination, thus eliminating all or most of the usual "fluorescence burst" (*cf.* fig. 33.47). Photosynthesis, on the other hand, begins under anaerobic conditions, at a low level (*i. e.*, the initial oxygen burst and carbon dioxide gulp probably are absent). It looks as if, in this case, the inhibiting action is fully developed in the dark, and requires no initiating photochemical reaction. Emerson and Lewis (1941) found that the photochemical carbon dioxide gush, too, is absent in *Chlorella* after anaerobic incubation.

As mentioned in sect. 2, the polarographic oxygen liberation curves of Blinks and Skow (fig. 33.2), even if they were obtained after exhaustion of oxygen in the layer between leaf and electrode, cannot be considered characteristic of anaerobic conditions. McAlister and Myers (1940) obtained a number of carbon dioxide consumption curves in pure commercial nitrogen (0.5% oxygen), but here, too, no attempt was made to realize truly anaerobic conditions (which have to be maintained for some time prior to the beginning of illumination in order to obtain the typical anaerobiotic inhibition effects). Consequently, McAlister and Myers' "low oxygen" curves reflected merely the known favorable effect on photosynthesis of a reduction in the partial pressure of oxygen (attributed in chapters 13 and 19 to the avoidance of photoxidation). The only effect of low oxygen concentration noticeable in these curves was a slight increase in rate, spread over most of the induction period. An investigation of the initial

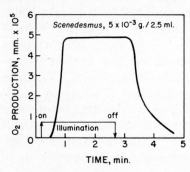 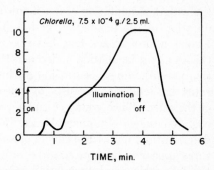

Fig. 33.18. Absence of induction in *Scenedesmus* after 3 hours anaerobiosis in N₂ (after Shiau and Franck 1947). $p(CO_2) = 20$ mm.

Fig. 33.18A. Induction in *Chlorella* after 3 hours anaerobiosis in N₂ (after Shiau and Franck 1947).

course of photosynthesis under strictly anaerobic conditions, in a stream of oxygen-free nitrogen or hydrogen, was made by Franck, Pringsheim and Lad (1945), using the phosphorescence-quenching method. It was mentioned before that reversible light saturation curves can be obtained under these conditions, the saturation level being from 50 to 0.1% of that under aerobic conditions, depending on the completeness of the incubation treatment.

In some experiments, no induction at all was observed under anaerobic conditions, as far as the inertia of the apparatus permitted one to judge. This inertia was of the order of 20 seconds. Figure 33.18 gives an example of this behavior in *Scenedesmus* after 3 hours anaerobiosis. Fluorescence experiments (part B, section 2f) make it likely that *brief* induction changes actually occur in the first few seconds.

After longer anaerobic pretreatment, curves with a clearly delayed ascent were obtained; their shape indicated a "second wave" of inhibition about 1 minute after the beginning of illumination. Oxygen liberation reached a constant level in about 2 minutes.   This type of induction curve is correlated with the occurrence of sigmoid light curves of steady photosynthesis; they occur more often in hydrogen than in nitrogen, and are favored by carbon dioxide deficiency.

With *Chlorella*, an even more pronounced second inhibition wave was observed (fig. 33.18A); it led to a *minimum* of oxygen production between 0.5 and 1 minute after the beginning of illumination. The "secondary induction loss" increases with the length of the dark period, although it was noticeable after only 1 minute in darkness (subsequent to a previous 3 hour incubation).   It is enhanced by low temperature—at 0° C. a deep depression at 0.5 minute extended over as much as 4 minutes before the

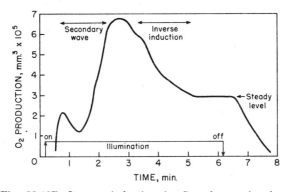

Fig. 33.18B. Inverse induction in *Scenedesmus* in absence of added CO_2 after 3 hours in pure streaming N_2 (after Shiau and Franck 1947).   0° C., 12.5×10^{-3} g. algae in 2.5 cc.

oxygen production finally picked up.   Poisoning by cyanide or extreme carbon dioxide deficiency acts in a similar way.

These experiments first showed that the "second wave" of induction can affect also oxygen liberation.   (It was previously observed only in carbon dioxide consumption, and in fluorescence.)   Franck, French and Puck (1941) previously had suggested that the second wave may be caused by a "blockade" of the chlorophyll surface by accumulated intermediate oxidation products ("photoperoxides") not removed rapidly enough by the inhibited "deoxygenase."   Such a blockade could increase fluorescence and prevent the uptake of carbon dioxide, but could not be expected to cause a decline in the rate of oxygen production.   An alternative explanation of the second depression was therefore suggested by Shiau and Franck (1947) (part B, section 2).

When carbon dioxide was absent or, more exactly, when only the small amount of carbon dioxide produced by fermentation was present, "inverse induction" was observed by Shiau and Franck, following the secondary induction wave (fig. 33.18B). A similar and sometimes even stronger permanent decline of oxygen production was produced by adding cyanide (10^{-3} M HCN, in the presence of 20 mm. CO_2). The decline from the peak of oxygen production to the final steady level was more pronounced the longer the preceding dark period; after several hours in the dark, the rate in the first minutes of illumination was three to eight times higher than in the subsequent steady state.

There is a parallelism between these results and the fluorescence induction curves obtained in the presence of cyanide (fig. 33.39). In both cases, the initial part of the induction curves is unaffected; a depression of photosynthesis and enhancement of fluorescence appear only after the "second wave."

In interpreting the phenomenon of "inverse induction" Franck and co-workers noted that it occurs under conditions of inhibited carbon dioxide supply (low carbon dioxide, presence of cyanide). The carbon dioxide supply deficiency is not so important at the beginning of illumination, after the carboxylation of the acceptor has had time to be completed in the dark. The insufficient rate of replacement of the carbon dioxide used up by photosynthesis begins, however, to be felt after one or several minutes of illumination.

Some more recent observations of the effect of oxygen deficiency on induction can be mentioned here.

Van der Veen (1949[2]) found that the induction curves of *Holcus lanatus* did not change substantially by substituting (instead of air) nitrogen containing only 0.3% oxygen (with unchanged content of carbon dioxide), except that the preparatory dark period was lengthened. (The induction curve was, for example, the same after 30 minutes dark incubation in 0.3% O_2 as after 2 minutes incubation in air.) This seems to indicate that the "de-adaptation" in the dark (which causes induction) is an autoxidation. When oxygen was removed altogether from the nitrogen atmosphere during the incubation period, the rate of steady photosynthesis of *Holcus* leaves remained low for hours afterwards. The effect was noticeable even after 1 minute anaerobiosis in darkness; after 30 minutes the steady rate was only a few per cent of normal. It could be completely restored by aerobic incubation in darkness.

The capacity for carbon dioxide uptake and release by heat-inactivated *Holcus* leaves was also destroyed by anaerobic incubation. In *Chlorella*, no gas gulps or bursts of any kind appeared in an atmosphere of pure oxygen or hydrogen without carbon dioxide. A small amount of oxygen was produced in light in the hydrogen atmosphere.

Higher plants, placed in pure hydrogen, produced an *oxygen* gush, followed by a steady, slow oxygen production. Van der Veen suggested that this gush originated from the reduction of carbon dioxide, accumulated in the plant (by some fermentation reaction) during the dark period; the subsequent steady liberation of oxygen could be based on continued slow carbon dioxide production by the same fermentation process.

Hill and Whittingham (1953) studied the induction phase in *Chlorella* and *Scenedesmus* by their spectroscopic method (*cf.* section 2) also under anaerobic conditions. They noted (in agreement with the earlier observations by Franck and co-workers) that the induction period was more strongly affected by dark anaerobiosis in *Chlorella* than in *Scenedesmus*. After anaerobic dark periods up to 80 minutes (at 15° C.) the half-time of reactivation was increased from 0.5 to 2–3 minutes, and after 17 hours, to about 7 minutes. In this case, as contrasted to that of aerobic incubation, the induction period is longer the lower the temperature; also, the reactivation is faster the stronger the illumination (while the duration of aerobic induction is independent of light intensity over a wide range, and even decreases in weak light). The anaerobic inhibition could be completely removed by addition of a small amount of oxygen in the dark, provided the anaerobic incubation had not lasted too long.

Because they noted an effect on induction even after an anaerobic incubation of only a few minutes, Hill and Whittingham suggested a return to the Willstätter-Kautsky-Warburg hypothesis of direct oxygen participation in photosynthesis, in preference to the concept of Gaffron, Franck and others, according to which anaerobic inhibition is due to the accumulation of fermentation products and inactivation of enzymes (see in this connection, chapter 13, p. 327, this chapter, p. 1365, and chapter 37D, section 3).

Olson and Brackett (1952) noted that anaerobic dark incubation of *Chlorella* leads to an initial total inhibition of oxygen evolution, which may last up to 2 minutes (after an incubation of 1–3 hours); after a shorter, or much longer, incubation period ($\ll 1$ hour or 18–24 hours), inhibition does not occur. Once the period of total inhibition is over, the "light adaptation" curve follows the same time course as after aerobic incubation.

Franck, Pringsheim and Lad made use of the high sensitivity of the phosphorescence method to study oxygen liberation by single light flashes, and found evidence of both primary and secondary induction losses in the flash yield as well. The first flash produced less oxygen than the second one, and so forth. In *Scenedesmus*, the yield per flash soon became steady, while in *Chlorella*, a second depression was noticeable.

7. Induction after Photoxidation

Since induction probably is a consequence of oxidation-reductions and autoxidations in the dark, we can expect characteristic induction effects to occur also after a period of photoxidation in light (brought about in one of the several ways discussed in chapter 19).

Observations on these aftereffects of photoxidation were made by

Franck and French (1941). They found that, if a carbon dioxide-starved leaf, after a period of photoxidation, was exposed to light in the presence of

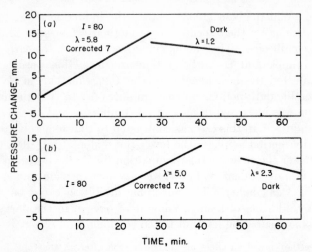

Fig. 33.18C. Photosynthesis in the presence of sufficient CO_2, (*a*) before and (*b*) after photoxidation (after Franck and French 1941). Straight lines on right show increase in respiration after photoxidation. Corrected for this increased respiration, the final rate of photosynthesis, 7.3, is about equal to that before photoxidation, but is reached only 20 minutes after admission of CO_2 in light.

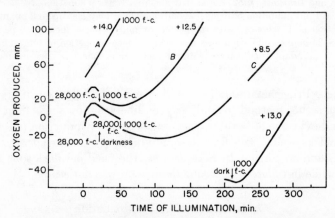

Fig. 33.18D. Progressive injury of cells by 28,000 foot-candles of light, and recovery in darkness (*D*) and in 1000 foot-candles (*B* and *C*) (after Myers and Burr 1940).

carbon dioxide, 10 or 20 minutes were needed to recover its full photosynthetic efficiency (fig. 33.18C). The exact length of the recovery period

depended on the duration and intensity of photoxidation.   If the latter
had gone too far, no complete recovery was possible.   The photosynthetic
capacity could be restored more or less completely also by a dark rest.

In chapter 19, we described a second method for replacing photosynthesis by photoxidation: very intense illumination.   A period of photoxidation induced in this way also is followed by an induction period upon return
to photosynthesis in more moderate light.   Figure 33.18D, taken from the
work by Myers and Burr (1940), shows that the longer the cell suspension
has been exposed to extremely strong light (28,000 foot-candles, or 300
klux), the slower and less complete is its recovery in moderate light (1000

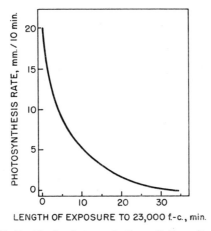

LENGTH OF EXPOSURE TO 23,000 f.-c., min.

Fig. 33.18E. Residual photosynthetic activity after varying exposures to 23,000 foot-candles (after Myers and Burr 1940).   Rate 20
equals 100% for this batch of cells under 7500 foot-candles.

foot-candles).   Curve D shows that in this case, too, recovery occurs in
darkness as well as in light.   After a long exposure (3–5 hours) to intense
light ($>$ 10,000 foot-candles) no recovery is possible at all.   Figure 33.18E
shows the residual photosynthetic efficiency (at 7500 foot-candles) as a
function of the duration of exposure to 23,000 foot-candles.

Franck and French suggested that the aftereffects of a period of photoxidation have
a double origin—the oxidation of some constituents of the enzymatic apparatus of
photosynthesis, and the burning up of the reserves of intermediate products.   The occurrence of the first effect is clearly demonstrated by the fact—mentioned in chapter 19
—that photoxidation *inhibits* photosynthesis and not merely counterbalances it.   The
natural explanation of such a "catalytic" effect is the destruction (oxidation) of one or
several members of the enzymatic system involved in photosynthesis.   (Franck and
French believe that the most probable substrate of oxidation is E_A, the catalyst responsible for the formation of the carbon dioxide–acceptor complex.)

However, Franck and French pointed out that the inactivation of "catalyst A" does not offer sufficient explanation for aftereffects lasting for 20 minutes and more, because from fluorescence experiments of Franck, French and Puck (1941) they concluded that E_A can be regenerated in less than 1 second. They therefore suggested that, in addition to the injury to E_A, photoxidation affects the capacity for photosynthesis also by burning the stocks of intermediate products of photosynthesis and respiration.

In section 4 above, we described the experiments of Steemann-Nielsen which made him believe that the induction which follows transition from saturating to limiting light intensity is caused by partial inactivation (perhaps photoxidation) of a part of the photochemical apparatus—either of chlorophyll itself, or of an enzymatic factor associated with chlorophyll so closely that its inhibition makes the corresponding part of chlorophyll in the cell incapable of contributing to photosynthesis. Steemann-Nielsen also concluded that inhibition by excessively strong light (≥ 100 klux) may have, at least partially, the same origin. Longer exposures to excessive light may cause both deactivation of the photochemical apparatus (as suggested by Steemann-Nielsen), and the photoxidation of an enzyme (or enzymes) kinetically independent of chlorophyll, as suggested by Franck and French (as well as photochemical burning-up of intermediates of photosynthesis and respiration).

8. Induction in the Photoreduction by Algae

The algae (*Scenedesmus, Raphidium*) that will *liberate hydrogen* after anaerobic incubation, if illuminated in an atmosphere of nitrogen, will *absorb hydrogen* if illuminated in an atmosphere of hydrogen (slowly in pure hydrogen, and much more rapidly in a mixture of hydrogen and carbon dioxide, in which the absorbed hydrogen can be utilized for the reduction of carbon dioxide). In chapter 6, this "photoreduction" of carbon dioxide was discussed as a significant variation of normal photosynthesis. In strong light, hydrogen liberation or photoreduction rapidly gives place to normal photosynthesis. If only the net pressure change is measured, very complex "induction curves" can be obtained (*cf.* Vol. I, fig. 14); the "positive induction" that characterizes many of these curves is caused by an initial liberation of *hydrogen*.

Hydrogen absorption by anaerobically adapted algae also has an induction period. But, contrary to ordinary photosynthesis, this induction period's duration *increases* with decreasing light intensity (*cf.* Vol. I, fig. 14). Franck and Gaffron (1941) suggested that "hydrogen induction" is due to the fact that carbon dioxide is first reduced at the cost of accumulated organic hydrogen donors (fermentation products), before the reduction at the cost of molecular hydrogen can get under way. If the disposal of accumulated reducing intermediates is achieved by a simple photochemical reaction, it should require less time in strong than in weak light. This hypothesis links the induction period of hydrogen assimilation with the "hydrogen burst" produced by the same algae in carbon dioxide-free nitrogen atmosphere. In both cases, the first effect of light is oxidation (dehydrogenation) of the accumulated fermentation products, the hydrogen being either utilized for the reduction of carbon dioxide, or released into the atmosphere.

The assumption of "photosynthesis at the cost of fermentation products" was also used by Franck, Pringsheim and Lad (1945) in the explanation of the cyanide-insensitive burst of oxygen production in the first minutes of illumination of anaerobically incubated algae. These authors have also contributed essentially to the understanding of the time curves of gas exchange in Gaffron's hydrogen-adapted algae, by showing that the return to normal photosynthesis can be postponed indefinitely by preventing the oxygen evolved by residual photosynthesis from accumulating in the closed system.

9. Induction in Hill Reaction

Clendenning and Ehrmantraut (1950) noted that no induction occurs in the liberation of oxygen by *Chlorella* cells with quinone as oxidant; the same cells showed the usual induction period of about 5 minutes in bicarbonate solution. No induction losses were found in the oxygen liberation by isolated chloroplasts with quinone or ferrocyanide as oxidants. The theoretical significance of these results will be discussed later.

No induction was observed in the Hill reaction of chloroplasts by Hill and Whittingham (1953) with the hemoglobin method of spectroscopic oxygen determination.

B. FLUORESCENCE AND ABSORPTION CHANGES DURING THE INDUCTION PERIOD*

1. Fluorescence Induction Phenomena in Leaves, Algae, Chloroplasts and Chlorophyll Solutions

It was said before that fluorescence is one of the few if not the only property of chlorophyll that can easily be measured simultaneously with photosynthesis. All determinations of gas exchange, even by electrical or optical methods, are sluggish, since the gas has to be moved from the interior of the plant cell to the locus of measurement (or *vice versa*). Fluorescence, on the other hand, is measured practically instantaneously; this

* Bibliography, page 1431.

permits one to follow the very rapid changes in the photosynthetic apparatus, such as must occur during the induction period. The recording of fluorescence has first led to the realization of the great complexity of the induction phenomena, particularly to the discovery of the developments that take place in the first one or two seconds of illumination.

That the fluorescence of chlorophyll changes in a characteristic way during the induction period of photosynthesis was first noted by Kautsky and Hirsch (1931).* Kautsky has since devoted a series of investigations to this subject (1931–1943). The reliability of his earlier observations (1931–1937) was limited by inadequate technique (which involved excitation by ultraviolet light, and visual estimation of fluorescence intensity). More recently, he has gone over to excitation by visible light and automatic registration of fluorescence, and more reliable data have been collected in this way, particularly by Kautsky and U. Franck (1943). Systematic determinations of the intensity of the chlorophyll fluorescence during the induction period have also been made by Wassink and co-workers (1939, 1942, 1944), McAlister and Myers (1940), Franck, French and Puck (1941) and Shiau and Franck (1947). Reviews of the subject have been written by Kautsky and U. Franck (1948), J. Franck (1949) and Wassink (1951).

Nothing is known so far of changes in the fluorescence *spectrum* of chlorophyll, which are not impossible, if the chemical structure of chlorophyll itself, or of its associates in the "photosensitive complex," undergoes changes in the transition from darkness to light and back.

Correlation of measurements of fluorescence intensity with gas exchange measurements would be much safer if experiments of both kinds were carried out with the same plant objects. Otherwise, there is a danger that, in attempting to present a comprehensive picture of induction phenomena, one may try to fit together pieces from several different jigsaw puzzles. A step in the right direction was taken by McAlister and Myers, who measured simultaneously the carbon dioxide absorption and the fluorescence intensity of wheat plants and *Chlorella* suspensions.

The analysis of the gas exchange leads to the conclusion that the most conspicuous induction phenomena observed under aerobic conditions can be formally explained by three processes: a *preparatory dark reaction*, which produces a "precursor," or "potential inhibitor" (or removes or inactivates a catalyst that, when active, prevents the accumulation of an inhibitor); a *photochemical reaction*, which "activates" the inhibitor; and a *second, nonphotochemical process* by which the inhibitor is removed. Special explanations are required for the occurrence of a second inhibition period, and for the carbon dioxide "burst" observed by Blinks and Skow

---

* It is worth recalling here that French and Young found no induction of the fluorescence of phycoerythrin *in vivo*, indicating that the composition and environment of its molecules remain unchanged by illumination.

and Emerson and Lewis. *Anaerobic* incubation accentuates the ordinary inhibition and, in addition, produces a second inhibiting factor that requires no photochemical activation.

(The above summary was based on the assumption that the normal course of induction consists of a brief burst of uninhibited—but not enhanced—gas exchange, followed by one main wave, and sometimes one or more secondary, waves, of inhibition; and that the only additional, unilateral effect superimposed on this standard sequence is the Emerson-Lewis carbon dioxide burst. More recent studies have shown that the true picture is more complex. In particular, the burst of oxygen liberation and

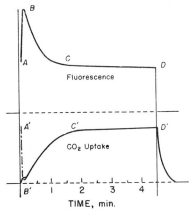

Fig. 33.19a. Course of fluorescence and photosynthesis in wheat during induction period (after McAlister and Myers 1940). Broken lines show CO_2 absorption curve corrected for slow response of the apparatus.

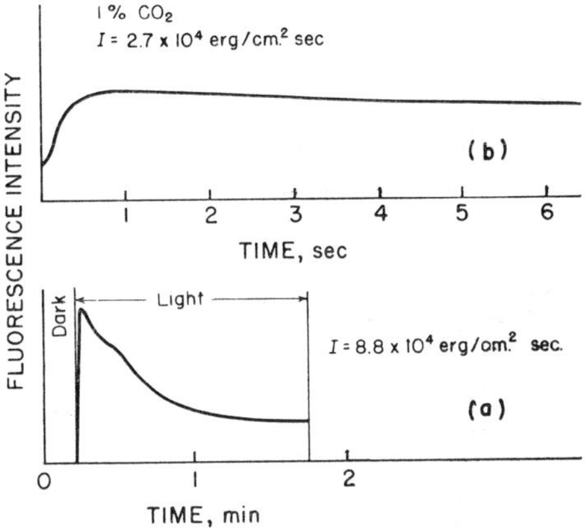

Fig. 33.19b. Fluorescence *vs.* time curves at 23° C. of *Hydrangea;* excitation by 400–600 mμ (after Franck, French and Puck 1941): (a) first half minute; (b) first 6 sec.

carbon dioxide consumption in the first few seconds (or first minute) of illumination may appear larger than could be produced by uninhibited, steady photosynthesis during this brief period, and therefore seems to involve (similarly to the carbon dioxide burst) a sudden photochemical transformation (deoxygenation, carboxylation, decarboxylation) of some material or materials accumulated in the cell during the dark period. The following discussion of the induction effects in fluorescence was written with the simpler picture of a few years ago in mind. In particular, it contains many references to "inhibition of photosynthesis" during certain induction phases, while we would now prefer to speak more specifically of inhibition of oxygen liberation, or inhibition of carbon dioxide uptake, or of both together, if this be the case, rather than of inhibition of photosynthesis as a whole.)

A sequence of three above-suggested processes is suggested also by the common shape of the fluorescence *versus* time curves found under aerobic conditions, which is shown in figures 33.19a and b. The fluorescence starts at the normal level, A, rises rapidly to a maximum, B (reached about 1 sec. after the beginning of illumination), and declines again to the initial level, CD, in about 1 min. These fluorescence curves are mirror images of the typical gas exchange induction curves (fig. 33.19a). Often, however, fluorescence measurements have led to induction curves of a somewhat different type, shown in figure 33.20. Here, the "first wave" of fluorescence, B, is low and decays very rapidly, and the induction picture is dominated by a *second wave*, D, the maximum of which occurs from $\frac{1}{2}$ to several *minutes*

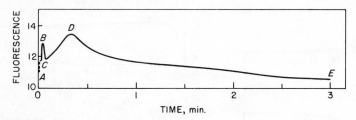

Fig. 33.20. Fluorescence curves of *Chlorella* with dominant second wave (after Wassink and Katz 1939). Buffer No. 9, 29° C., $I = 1 \times 10^4$ erg/cm.² sec.

after the beginning of the light period. This wave appears to be related to the second depression of the gas exchange, although the latter has been usually encountered above only as a relatively minor disturbance, and not a dominant feature of induction curves (*cf.* figs. 33.10, 11, 13A,B,F,G). Apparently, the transformation of the photosynthetic mechanism that gives rise to the second wave of fluorescence does not always affect the gas exchange equally strongly, and may sometimes have no influence on this exchange at all. Thus, while in fig. 33.21(B) the second wave of fluorescence coincides with a distinct depression in the curve of carbon dioxide absorption, no such correlation is apparent in figure 33.22(C): the second wave of fluorescence (which appears here about 0.5 minute after the beginning of illumination, and does not decay until sometime beyond 4 minutes), does not interrupt the steady increase of carbon dioxide consumption. As a result, the fluorescence curve and the carbon dioxide absorption curve assume a *parallel*, instead of the usual antiparallel, course.

Fluorescence measurements have shown that each of the two waves of fluorescence may possess a "fine structure," with features that reappear with remarkable persistence in curves obtained by different observers with different species. One such feature is a depression on the ascending part of the first wave, noticeable in figure 33.19b, and seen in more detail in figure 33.23 (where it is marked D_1). Kautsky suggested that this depression becomes the main feature of the induction curves under *anaerobic* conditions, or in the presence of certain poisons (*cf.* figs. 33.33A and 33.39).

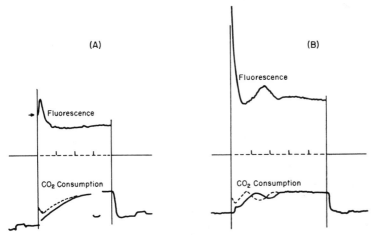

Fig. 33.21. Induction phenomena in wheat (after McAlister and Myers 1940). (A) Normal air (0.03% CO_2), strong light (5 $\times$ 10[5] erg/cm.[2] sec.) after 40 min. light and 12 min. dark, 24° C. (B) High CO_2 (0.36%) in air, strong light after 10 min. light and 10 min. dark, 24° C. Broken lines indicate approximate correction for time lag of gas exchange curve; time marks 1 min. apart.

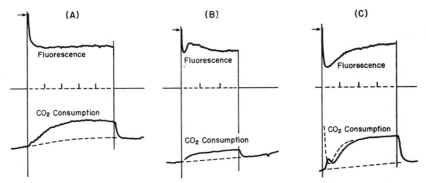

Fig. 33.22. Induction phenoma in *Chlorella* (after McAlister and Myers 1940). (A) Grown in 4% CO_2, studied in 0.24% CO_2; 6 min. light, 10 min. dark. (B) Grown in air, studied in 0.33% CO_2; 2 min. dark. (C) Grown and studied in normal air (0.03% CO_2); 3 min. light, 40 min. dark. Broken curve indicates approximate correction for time lag of gas exchange curve; time marks 1 min. apart.

A second, equally persistent feature is a "bulge" on the declining slope of the first peak (*cf.* lower fig. 33.19b). (Kautsky assumed the existence of two depressions, the first of them marked D_2 in figures 33.27 and 33.33B.) Sometimes this bulge develops into a maximum and can then be confused with the second main wave of fluorescence.

Even while we do not believe, with Kautsky (1943), that each ripple on the induction curve indicates a new photochemical reaction in the main sequence of photosynthesis, the persistent occurrence of these details shows that they are not accidental, but indicative of a complex interplay of activation and deactivation processes.

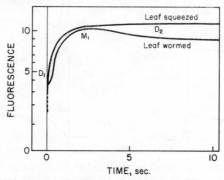

Fig. 33.23. Effect of mechanical injury on fluorescence curve of a leaf (*Saponaria officinalis*) (after Kautsky and Franck 1943): air, 20° C., 40 meter candles (about 4×10^4 erg/cm.² sec.).

Certain conditions appear to favor the occurrence of induction curves of "type I" (fig. 33.19) or "type II" (fig. 33.20). Curves of type I, with a peak value, φ_m, twice or three times as high as the steady yield, $\bar{\varphi}$, appear to be more common with higher land plants, while induction curves of type II are more often encountered with algae. Thus, figure 33.19a was obtained with wheat, and figure 33.19b with *Hydrangea*, while figure 33.20 was given by Wassink and Katz (1939) for *Chlorella*. Kautsky and U. Franck (1943) observed, in the green alga *Ulva lactuca*, curves with a comparatively weak first fluorescence wave (even in very strong light, the ratio $\varphi_m/\bar{\varphi}$ was not higher than 1.6), and a second wave more or less comparable in height with the first one (fig. 33.27).

Kautsky and Hirsch (1934), who studied 22 species, concluded that ferns and higher aquatic plants, as well as algae, show a more rapid decay of the first wave of fluorescence than is commonly observed with land plants.

The experiments of Franck, Pringsheim and Lad (1947) make it likely that the difference between unicellular algae and leaves is based, at least in part, on the different density of packing of the cells. The induction phenomena in algal suspensions may, for the same reason, depend on the density of the suspension.

In section A2, we stated that short induction lasts for approximately the same time in algae, higher aquatic plants and land plants. Some of the parallel curves of carbon dioxide absorption and fluorescence in wheat (McAlister and Myers) indicate that the induction period of fluorescence may be subject to stronger variation in length than that of the carbon dioxide uptake. For example, in figure 33.22A, fluorescence drops to a steady level after less than 1 minute, while carbon dioxide consumption continues to increase for about 3 minutes. It is, however, difficult to say how much of this discrepancy is caused by the sluggishness of gas measurements, and how much represents a genuine time lag between the transformation of the photosensitive complex (instantly reflected by changes in fluorescence) and the change in the uptake of carbon dioxide (which, after all, is only a more or less remote consequence of this transformation).

The shape of the fluorescence–time curves is further influenced by the *age* of the plants, or cell cultures. In the investigation of Franck, French and Puck (1941), young cultures of *Chlorella* and *Scenedesmus* gave "one-wave" curves of type I, whereas old cultures gave curves dominated by the second wave. According to Shiau and Franck (1947), young and very vigorous cultures of *Chlorella* and *Scenedesmus* sometimes show no induction phenomena at all, except after long anaerobic incubation; while old cultures may show abnormally long induction periods (up to 5 minutes in air, instead of the usual 1 minute). Young cultures, transferred into a medium that previously contained an old culture, sometimes show, after 24 hours, a marked increase in the duration and extent of induction.

In plants of a given species and age, the induction curve may depend greatly on the conditions to which the cells were exposed before and during the illumination. Carbon dioxide supply is one of them. McAlister and Myers (1940) obtained curves of type I with wheat in ordinary air (*cf.* fig. 33.21A); but, in air enriched with carbon dioxide (0.3 to 0.4% CO_2; no higher concentrations were used), the first fluorescence peak decayed very rapidly, and the second wave was strongly developed (*cf.* 33.21B). Its crest was reached 1.5 minutes after the beginning of illumination, compared with only 20 seconds in *Chlorella*, in figure 33.20. This may be due to stronger light and lower temperature (since figs. 33.27 and 33.33 show that both these factors delay the second wave).

With *Chlorella*, too, McAlister and Myers found that the type of the fluorescence curve depends on carbon dioxide concentration. Induction curves of type I (although with a faster fluorescence decay than in wheat) were obtained with cells grown in 4% CO_2, and studied in 0.24% CO_2 (fig. 33.22A). A second wave appeared in cells grown in ordinary air and studied in carbon dioxide-enriched air (fig. 33.22B), while, in cultures grown and studied in normal air, this wave was so extensive that, after the first few seconds of illumination, the development of fluorescence became parallel, instead of antiparallel, to that of carbon dioxide consumption (fig. 33.22C).

Shiau and Franck (1947) noted that the second wave is much more pro-nounced, and its crest occurs later, in nitrogen than in air (*cf.* fig. 33.47).

Fluorescence–time curves of the general type of figure 33.19 were obtained by Franck and Levi (1934) also with leaf extracts in acetone or alcohol; but all changes were much slower than *in vivo*. The activation took about 1 minute and the decay more than 10 minutes. It would be interesting to find out whether these changes bear more than accidental similarity to the fluorescence effects in living cells. Franck and Levi (1934) and Franck and Wood (1936) suggested that such a relation may be brought about by the presence, in leaf extracts, of lipophilic plant constituents with which chlorophyll can form photosensitive complexes, analogous to those postulated in living cells. How-ever, the fluorescence–time curves obtained by Knorr and Albers (1935) with solutions of pure chlorophylls *a* and *b* also showed a succession of maxima and minima (accom-panied by changes in the position of the fluorescence bands); these fluctuations con-tinued for several hours and ended with the bleaching of the solution.

Kautsky, Hirsch and Davidshöfer (1932) and Kautsky and Zedlitz (1941) reported that *grana precipitates*, obtained from mashed *Saponaria* leaves by the method of Noack (*cf.* chapt. 14, part B), also showed an initial increase of fluorescence, but only a very slow, if any, subsequent decay, (a feature that they associated with the incapacity of the grana for photo-synthesis). Under nitrogen, or in the presence of urethan, even the initial increase was absent, and the fluorescence–time curves of the grana were perfectly horizontal.

Shiau and Franck (1947) made analogous observations with *whole chloroplasts* isolated from spinach or tobacco. The initial rise was present both in air and in nitrogen, but was completely suppressed by urethan. However, this rise was comparatively slow: At 3.0×10^4 erg/cm.^{2} sec., and 4° C., the growth of φ continued for about 30 seconds, after which the curve became horizontal. Dark periods of as much as 5 minutes in air, or 15 minutes in nitrogen were required to repeat the curve (*cf.* the much lower figures for living cells on page 1383).

The rise of φ was "light-saturated" considerably earlier in isolated chloro-plasts than in whole cells; as in the latter, it was insensitive to cyanide, and to carbon dioxide starvation. *Ruptured* chloroplasts "aged" faster than whole chloroplasts (the symptom of aging being a decrease in the initial slope of the fluorescence–time curve).

Fluorescence–time curves, similar to those of free chloroplasts or grana, were obtained by Kautsky and U. Franck (1943) and Shiau and Franck (1947) also with *mechanically injured leaves* (fig. 33.23).

2. Influence of Different Factors on Fluorescence–Time Curves

(a) *Duration of Incubation*

The rise of the first fluorescence wave can be explained, as suggested above, by the combination of a thermal and a photochemical process, preparing the way for inhibition and activating the inhibitor, respectively. A second nonphotochemical process removes the inhibition and thus terminates the wave. According to this concept, the dark pause has a twofold effect; it completes the removal of the active inhibitor (if this was not completed in light), and replenishes the amount of the "precursor," if the latter has been exhausted in light. (We recall that the "precursor" may be a negative quantity—the absence of a catalytic component needed to *prevent* the formation of an inhibitor in light.) The first effect will be most conspicuous if illumination has been interrupted during the initial fluorescence burst, *i. e.*, after an illumination time of the order of a second,

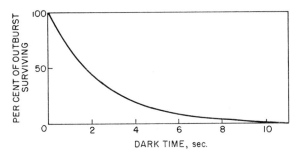

Fig. 33.24. Survival of fluorescence-promoting substances in the dark measured by the starting height of curves (after Franck, French and Puck 1941): 3 sec. illumination, followed by dark periods of various durations. Curve corresponds to equation $y = e^{-0.406t}$. Half-life = 1.7 sec.

while the second effect will be more important if the illumination had lasted long enough to approach the steady state (*i. e.*, for at least several minutes).

Kautsky, Hirsch and Davidshöfer (1932) noticed that, if light is turned off when fluorescence has just reached its peak (point B in figure 33.19a), the curve AB can be repeated after a few seconds, but that, if point C has been reached, several minutes of dark rest are necessary for the repetition of the whole curve ABC. In the first case, the rate of disappearance of the light-produced inhibitor is measured; in the second case, the rate of regeneration of the precursor (or the rate of deactivation of the protective catalyst).

The removal of the inhibitor in the dark can be studied quantitatively, by determining the initial intensity of fluorescence (height of point A in fig. 33.19a), after dark intervals of different duration. The results of such a study are shown in figure 33.24. It indicates that, in *Hydrangea*, the active inhibitor survives for about 10 seconds at room temperature; its disappearance is a first-order process, with a half-time of 1.7 seconds. The survival of this fluorescence-promoting and photosynthesis-inhibiting material can also be followed by illuminating the leaf with a flash of strong light and observing the fluorescence in light that is too weak to affect the induction phenomena. In this way, the mean life-time of the inhibitor was found to be 2 seconds at room temperature, and 5 seconds at 0° C. Systematic polarographic experiments, of the type described in section A2, could perhaps show whether the increase in the photosynthetic gas exchange, after its inhibition by 1 or 2 seconds of illumination, occurs exactly parallel with the decline of fluorescence.

It may be asked why *in light* the removal of the inhibition requires at least 1, and often 2 or 3, *minutes*, while the "survival" experiments in the dark indicate that the inhibitor has a life-time of only a few *seconds*. Partly, the prolongation of the induction period in light may be caused by the superposition of the "second wave"; but this cannot be the chief cause, especially in curves of the type in figures 33.19. Probably, the quantity of the "precursor" produced during the dark incubation is larger than needed to bring about the first fluorescence wave; consequently, the photochemical activation of the inhibitor continues, at a decreasing rate, even after the peak of fluorescence has been passed, thus slowing down the decay. In the dark, where no activation occurs, the photosynthetic apparatus can be freed from active inhibitor in a few seconds.

If the formation of the "precursor" means the depletion of a catalyst that, when active, prevents "self-inhibition" of photosynthesis by removing the photochemical products, a similar explanation applies. In the first moment of illumination, because of the absence of the protective catalyst, the rate of photochemical production of the inhibitor is much higher than the rate of its metabolic destruction; therefore the rate of photosynthesis declines, and the yield of fluorescence grows. Within a second, however, the reactivation of the catalyst has reduced the rate of formation of the inhibitor, while the rate of removal of the latter has grown proportionately to concentration, causing a reversal of the trend. The rate at which the fluorescence declines is determined by the superposition of the decay of the inhibitor, and its continuous photochemical formation. The steady state therefore is approached much more slowly than if the decay were the only relevant process.

The ascending slope of the first wave AB must depend on the initial amount of the "precursor" (or the initial deficiency of the protective catalyst) and on the intensity of illumination. The removal of the inhibitor, on the other hand, is a thermal process (probably related to the intensity of the autoxidative metabolism of the cells), and as such is strongly enhanced by a rise in temperature. Consequently, for given internal conditions, the height of peak B must increase with light intensity, and decline with increasing temperature; while its timing must be delayed by intense light, and accelerated by higher temperature. (For confirmations, see sections *b* and *c*.) At constant light intensity and temperature, height *B* must increase with the duration of incubation, until the accumulated amount of "precursor" will be so high that the rate of its photochemical activation ceases to depend on this amount (*i. e.*, probably, until it occurs with a quantum yield of unity).

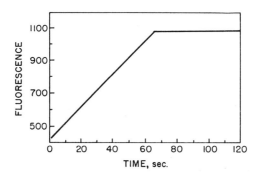

Fig. 33.25. Height of fluorescence peak (*B* in fig. 33.19) in relation to dark rest (after Franck and Wood 1936).

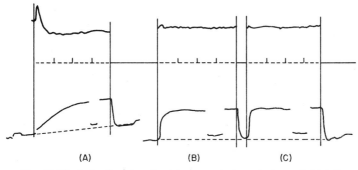

Fig. 33.26. Induction in wheat in normal air and strong light (after McAlister and Myers 1940): (A) 40 min. light, 12 min. dark; (B) 2 min. dark; (C) 1–2 min. dark. Upper curves, fluorescence; lower curves, CO_2 uptake.

These predictions can be compared with the experimental results of Franck and Wood (1936), who found the height of *B* to rise linearly with duration of the dark rest, until the latter reached about 60 seconds (*cf.* fig. 33.25). After this, the height of *B* continued to increase for a long time (as shown by experiments with plants that have rested overnight), but so much more slowly as to suggest an entirely different fluorescence-promoting reaction. This result bears obvious similarity to the effects of the duration of incubation upon the induction losses of oxygen and carbon dioxide, illustrated by figures 33.6 and 33.9.

Wassink and Katz (1939) found, similarly, with *Chlorella*, that the height of B can be maintained, in successive light flashes of 10 seconds duration, if these flashes are separated by dark intervals of at least 2 minutes. The required intervals were much shorter in cells grown in glucose solution and having strong respiration than in cells grown in an organic medium and having weak respiration, thus confirming the surmise that the inhibitor is removed by an oxidation process.

These results of Franck and Wood, and of Wassink and Katz, are in satisfactory agreement with determinations of Warburg, McAlister and others, which gave a value of about 1 minute for the dark interval required to repeat the induction curves of oxygen liberation and carbon dioxide absorption (*cf.*, *e. g.*, fig. 33.9). The observations of Aufdemgarten (figs. 33.10b and 33.11b) indicated a somewhat longer regeneration period of the "precursor" (>4 minutes), while McAlister and Myers noted (*cf.* fig. 33.26) that, in wheat in normal air, no burst of fluorescence at all occurred after 1 minute darkness, and only a faint burst was noticeable after 2 minutes.

(b) *Light Intensity*

Like induction losses of O_2 and CO_2, induction of fluorescence is not observed in *weak light* (fig. 33.27). (There are as yet no observations on

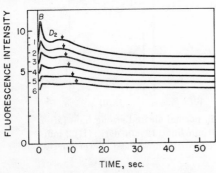

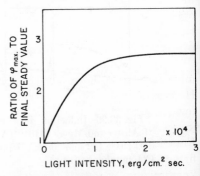

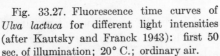

Fig. 33.27. Fluorescence time curves of *Ulva lactuca* for different light intensities (after Kautsky and Franck 1943): first 50 sec. of illumination; 20° C.; ordinary air.

Fig. 33.28. Fluorescence outburst in relation to light intensity in *Hydrangea* (after Franck, French and Puck 1941).

whether the CO_2 gush, which occurs even in weak light, is accompanied by variations of fluorescence.) With increasing light intensity, ascending slope of fluorescence wave AB becomes steeper, as anticipated. In *Hydrangea* leaves, according to Franck, French and Puck (1941), this increase continued until the light intensity has reached 20×10^4 erg/cm.^{2} sec., or approximately 40 klux. The height of point B, on the other hand, ceases growing much earlier, *e. g.*, in *Hydrangea* at about 1.5×10^4 erg/cm.^{2} sec. (see fig. 33.28; *cf.* the "light saturation" of the carbon dioxide induction loss, illustrated by fig. 33.8).

The maximum fluorescence yield, $\varphi_{max.}$, reached in point B, often is almost three times the steady yield $\bar{\varphi}$. Thus, the ratio $\varphi_{max.}/\bar{\varphi}$ can be considerably higher than the ratio φ_2/φ_1 ($\simeq 1.7$), of the yield of fluorescence in strong and weak light (*cf.* p. 1049). The fluorescence peak during the induction period therefore must be due to a change in the chlorophyll complex that enhances fluorescence more strongly than the transformation that occurs in strong, steady light. The maximum is reached so soon (in about 1 second) after the beginning of illumination that, at light intensities of the order of 2×10^4 erg/cm.^{2} sec. (*cf.* figs. 33.19a and 33.28), only a small fraction of the chlorophyll molecules (probably, less than one tenth) could have absorbed a quantum during this period, and thus passed into a chemically different form. To explain this result, we have the alternatives: either to assume that the form of the photosensitive complex produced during the burst fluoresces so strongly that even the conversion of only 10% of total chlorophyll into this form increases the average yield of fluorescence by a factor of three or four; or to postulate that the burst is caused by the formation of a fluorescence "protector," which prevents both chemical quenching and physical dissipation of energy (*i. e.*, acts like a narcotic), and that the amount of the protector activated by one quantum is sufficient to protect the fluorescence of ten chlorophyll molecules.

The first fluorescence wave may be accompanied by an almost complete inhibition of both oxygen liberation and carbon dioxide consumption. Here again, the question arises: How can a transformation in which only a few per cent of the total number of chlorophyll molecules can be actively involved, cause complete inhibition of the photosynthetic apparatus? Franck, French and Puck suggested that the inhibitor, activated in the first moment of illumination, acts in two ways: by settling down and "narcotizing" a part or all of the chlorophyll molecules (and thus promoting their fluorescence), and by associating with certain catalyst molecules, and thus inhibiting photosynthesis. Since, according to the above estimate, the concentration of this catalyst must be at least one order of magnitude lower than that of chlorophyll, they suggested the "stabilizing" catalyst, E_B (for which a concentration of only 0.1% of that of chlorophyll was deduced from flashing light experiments; *cf.* chapter 34).

Fluorescence bursts occur not only upon transition from darkness to light, but also upon sudden increase in light intensity, unless the weaker light was sufficient to saturate photosynthesis. For example, according to Franck, French and Puck, a burst occurs, in *Hydrangea*, upon an increase in light intensity from 0.5 to 5 $\times$ 10^4 erg/cm.^{2} sec., but not upon an increase from 7.4 $\times$ 10^4 to 12.2 $\times$ 10^4 erg/cm.^{2} sec. In wheat, on the other hand, a burst was observed (*cf.* fig. 33.29) even after an increase from 25 to 50 $\times$ 10^4 erg/cm.^{2} sec.—probably because the photosynthesis of young wheat plants is light-saturated only in very intense light (*cf.* Table 28.1).

The successive bursts of fluorescence parallel the successive induction losses of carbon dioxide (observed by McAlister; *cf.* Section A3) and of

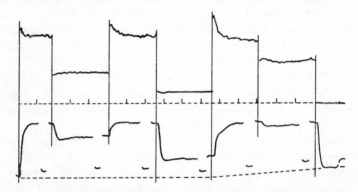

Fig. 33.29. Induction in wheat (after McAlister and Myers 1940). Light intensities 100, 49, 100, 21, 100, 74, 0 (100 $\cong$ 50 $\times$ 10^4 erg/cm.^{2} sec.). Ordinary air. Upper curves, fluorescence; lower curves, CO_2 uptake.

oxygen (described by Steemann-Nielsen, Sect. A2). This points to *catalyst deficiency* as a source of induction, and to an *autocatalytic activation* as the mechanism of its termination. Apparently, photosynthesis produces (or activates) at least one of its own catalysts (which is continuously deactivated by a dark reaction), so that the photostationary quantity of this catalyst is determined by the prevailing light intensity. When the latter is increased, more catalyst must be activated to take care of the increased supply of primary photochemical products. During this activation, the fluorescent capacity of the photosensitive complex increases temporarily (according to Gaffron and Franck, because the catalyst deficiency causes the accumulation of oxidation intermediates that act as direct or indirect inhibitors of photosynthesis, and promotors of fluorescence). Thus, the same condition that occurs in the transition from darkness to light is repeated each time an increase in light intensity leads to an increase in the steady rate of photosynthesis.

When the light intensity is suddenly *decreased, e. g.*, from 16×10^4 to 0.8×10^4 erg/cm.^{2} sec., the yield of fluorescence drops first to a level even lower than φ_1 (the value that ordinarily corresponds to weak illumination); and several minutes are required for the return to the steady value (*cf.* fig. 33.30). At low temperatures, this "undershooting" of the steady fluorescence intensity may be replaced by a "hysteresis," or slow adjustment of φ to its final value (*cf.* fig. 33.31), indicating that the conditions conducive to strong fluorescence—and thus presumably to low yield of photosynthesis —survive, at 0° C., for about a second after the transition from strong to weak light. This reminds us of the observations of Steemann-Nielsen, in

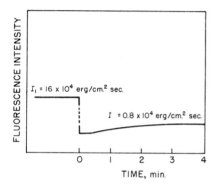
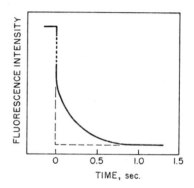

Fig. 33.30. Fluorescence changes in *Hydrangea* leaves after a sudden decrease of light intensity (after Franck, French and Puck 1941). At normal temperature, fluorescence first drops below the steady level, then recovers slowly.

Fig. 33.31. Fluorescence changes in *Hydrangea* leaves after sudden decrease of light intensity (after Franck, French and Puck 1941). At 0°, fluorescence requires about 1 sec. to decline to its steady level, showing the survival of the highly fluorescent material present in intense light.

which a qualitatively similar picture was found for oxygen liberation; however, the "induction after transition to weaker light" lasted in Steemann-Nielsen's experiments for several minutes (at 4° C.), as against only a second in figure 33.31.

We have dealt so far only with the effect of light intensity on the *first wave* of fluorescence. Figure 33.27 shows that the *second maximum* also is shifted with increasing intensity, in a way which indicates that it, too, is due to a photochemical reaction that promotes fluorescence, and to a counteracting thermal reaction. However, the relations seem to be more complex than in the first maximum. For example, Wassink and Katz (1939) noted that, in the presence of cyanide (which prevents the final decay, *DE* in fig. 33.19), the ascending slope, *CD*, is affected not only by light intensity, but also by temperature (*cf.* figs. 33.39 and 33.40). Figure 33.41 indicates that an "optimum" light intensity exists for the enhancement of the second maximum, D.

(c) Temperature

As mentioned before, Kautsky and Hirsch (1931) noticed that the "upward slope," AB, is independent of temperature, whereas the "downward slope," BC, is steeper the higher the temperature. Kautsky and Spohn (1934) measured this effect visually and found the period AB to be constant between 0 and 40° C., and the period BC to decrease from 800 seconds at 5° to 20 seconds at 35° (in *Pelargonium zonale*).

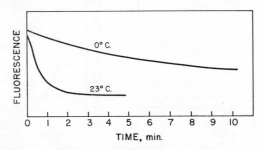

Fig. 33.32. Effect of temperature on rate of decay of fluorescence outburst in *Hydrangea* (after Franck, French and Puck 1941). $I = 44 \times 10^4$ erg/cm.² sec.

According to Franck and Wood (1936), the fluorescence decay, BC, is exponential at 25, 20 and 12° C., and can be attributed to a monomolecular reaction with a temperature coefficient of approximately 2. The curves obtained at low temperatures (*e. g.*, 3°) show an accentuation of the second wave. According to Franck, French and Puck (1941), the decay in *Hydrangea* lasts for 3 minutes at 23°, and for more than 10 minutes at 0° (fig. 33.32).

The curves obtained by Kautsky and Marx (1937) with different leaves confirmed the enhancement of the secondary wave by decreasing temperature. Leaves of different species showed analogous shapes at different temperatures, *e. g.*, the curve of *Piper amplum* at 25° was similar to that of *Ageratum mexicanum* at 35°.

Figure 33.33 shows the influence of temperature on fluorescence curves of *Ulva lactuca*. They confirm that decrease in temperature increases the heights of both the first and the second fluorescence peaks, and shifts them further from the beginning of illumination. At 0°, the second peak is shifted beyond the 3 minute registration limit.

The effect of temperature on the declining slope of D was studied also by Wassink and Katz (1939) with HCN-poisoned *Chlorella*. In this case, in contrast to fig. 33.33, maximum height of peak D was reached at the *highest* temperature (35°; *cf*. fig. 33.41). This can be explained by the fact that not only the decay, DE, but also the rise, CD, is accelerated by an increase in temperature. In nonpoisoned cells the influence of temperature on the purely thermal decay process is more important than its influence on the combined (photochemical *and* thermal) activation process; maximum D therefore *de-*

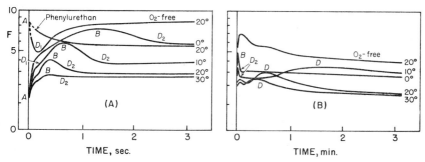

Fig. 33.33. Fluorescence time curves of *Ulva lactuca* at different temperatures, in presence of urethan, and in absence of oxygen (after Kautsky and Franck 1943): (A) first 3 sec., 10 lux; (B) first 3 min., 2.5 lux.

clines with increasing temperature. In cyanide-poisoned cells, on the other hand, the decay, DE, is inhibited, and the enhancing effect of temperature on the rise, CD, is the only remaining effect.

(d) Carbon Dioxide Concentration

We have to distinguish between two phenomena: the effect of *excess* carbon dioxide (in concentrations which cause a "narcotic" poisoning of photosynthesis; *cf*. chapter 13, page 330), and the effect of *low* carbon dioxide concentration, in the range where this concentration limits the efficiency of the photosynthetic apparatus.

The influence of *excess* carbon dioxide was first noticed by Kautsky and Hirsch (1935). The activation curve, AB, was unaffected, but the decay BC, lasted for 2 minutes at 4% CO_2, and 3 minutes at 10% CO_2, instead of 1 minute at <1% CO_2. The inhibiting effect of carbon dioxide concentrations >10% is confirmed by figure 33.34 of Franck, French and Puck. A sudden increase in carbon dioxide concentration, *e. g.*, from 1 to 20%, during the decay (or after its termination) caused an immediate burst, followed by a renewed slow decay, of fluorescence.

Figure 33.35 shows an almost complete disappearance of the first fluorescence wave of *Ulva* in concentrated carbon dioxide. The difference from the results of Franck, French and Puck (who found the height of peak B to be almost unaffected, even by 80% CO_2) may be due to the use of a different species, or of shorter dark intervals. (All curves in figure 33.34 were obtained after 1 hour dark rest, the decay of fluorescence in 80% CO_2 being very slow. Earlier repetition might have given a result much more like that shown in figure 33.35.)

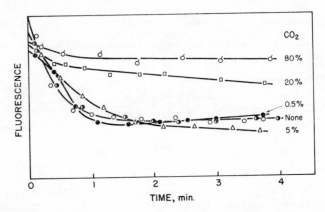

Fig. 33.34. Effect of excess carbon dioxide on decay of fluorescence outburst in *Hydrangea* (after Franck, French and Puck 1941). 4 min. exposure after 1 hour dark. $I = 1.7 \times 10^4$ erg/cm.^{2} sec.; Hg lines 436, 492, 546 mμ. (O) Control after the series, with no CO_2.

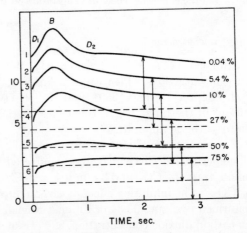

Fig. 33.35. Effect of excess carbon dioxide on fluorescence time curve of *Ulva lactuca* at 20° C. (after Kautsky and Franck 1943). $I = 40$ m. c. (equivalent).

The influence of carbon dioxide concentration in the range where it represents a strong "limiting factor" in photosynthesis (*i. e.*, below approximately 0.1%) is not shown clearly by figures 33.34 and 33.35. According to chapter 28 (page 1051), carbon dioxide limitation causes a shift toward lower light intensities of the transition from the "low" to the "high" steady fluorescence yield ($\varphi_1 \rightarrow \varphi_2$). In complete absence of carbon dioxide, one would expect the fluorescence yield to be equal to $\varphi_2 \simeq 1.7 \varphi_1$ even at the lowest light intensities. However, no difference between the steady yields at 0 and 0.5% CO_2 appears in figure 33.34. Figure 33.35 also shows no difference in shape between the curves corresponding to 0.04 and 5.4% CO_2; but, here, the absolute fluorescence values cannot be compared, because of the arbitrary adjustment of the scale.

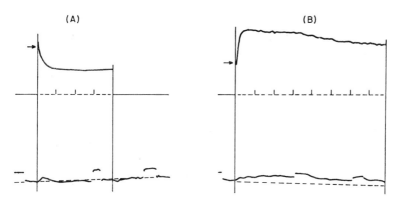

(A)   (B)

Fig. 33.36. Induction phenomena in wheat in the absence of CO_2 (after McAlister and Myers 1940). (A) O_2, 15 min. light, 10 min. dark. (B) N_2.

Figure 33.36A (McAlister and Myers 1940) agrees with figure 33.34 (Franck and co-workers) in that it, too, shows the first fluorescence burst to grow and decay normally even in the absence of carbon dioxide. In a *nitrogen* atmosphere, on the other hand, the decay of fluorescence after the burst is much slower in the absence than in the presence of carbon dioxide (*cf.* fig. 33.36B). This agrees with the hypothesis that removal of the inhibitor formed (or activated) in the first few seconds of illumination occurs by a reaction with oxygen (which, in nitrogen, must first be produced by photosynthesis).

The occurrence of the complete first fluorescence wave in the absence of carbon dioxide, demonstrated by figures 33.34 and 33.36A, recalls the observation of McAlister that preliminary illumination in carbon dioxide-free atmosphere can eliminate the induction loss of carbon dioxide upon subsequent admission of this gas. Despite the "autocatalytic" character of the process by which the induction is liquidated, no *complete* photosynthesis appears to be required for this purpose.

The absence of induction losses upon transition from a carbon dioxide-free atmosphere to an atmosphere containing carbon dioxide may be, however, not a general rule. At least, fluorescence has been observed to undergo a very characteristic change following an alteration of this concentration, by McAlister and Myers in wheat, and by Franck, French, and Puck in *Hydrangea*. As shown by figure 33.37A, the change consists of a dip of fluorescence, followed by a burst, a second dip and finally an approach to a new steady value (which may be lower than the value at the original, low concentration of carbon dioxide, if the latter was rate-limiting).

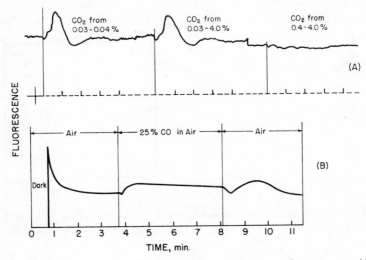

Fig. 33.37. Effect of changes of CO_2 concentration on fluorescence. (A) Wheat; high light intensity (after McAlister and Myers 1940). (B) *Hydrangea* (after Franck, French and Puck 1941).

According to figure 33.37A the effect disappears when the initial carbon dioxide concentration itself is saturating (*e. g.*, 0.4%; *cf.* third curve). Franck and co-workers observed, however, a wave of fluorescence upon a transition from 1 to 20% CO_2, and found that only the dip was absent if the initial concentration was saturating. A sudden *decrease* of carbon dioxide concentration (*e. g.*, from 25 to 0.03%) also caused a dip, followed by a wave of fluorescence (*cf.* fig. 33.37B).

Changes of carbon dioxide concentration often have a very pronounced effect on the *second* fluorescence wave. As mentioned in section A3, McAlister and Myers (1940) found in wheat one-wave curves in ordinary air, and two-wave curves, with a second maximum around 1.5 minutes in 0.1 to 0.3% CO_2 (*cf.* fig. 33.21B).

The association of two-maximum curves with increased carbon dioxide concentration was confirmed by Franck, French and Puck (1941), as shown by figure 33.38, obtained with *Hydrangea* leaves in 1% CO_2. In this case, the minimum occurs 1.5 minutes, and the secondary maximum 3 minutes after the beginning of illumination. It seems that different species require different carbon dioxide concentrations to develop the second fluorescence wave—some show it at 0.1% CO_2, others only at 1% or more. It has been mentioned above that, in *Chlorella*, a very pronounced second maximum was observed by McAlister and Myers even in ordinary air (*cf.* fig. 33.22B and C). Kautsky and Franck (1943) found that *Ulva lactuca* shows no second maximum in carbon dioxide-free medium, and a pronounced second maximum in 0.1% CO_2.

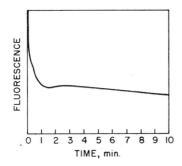

Fig. 33.38. Fluorescence curve of *Hydrangea* in 1% CO_2 (after Franck, French and Puck 1941). A second maximum occurs at about 3 min. $I = 0.82 \times 10^4$ erg/cm.^{2} sec.

The occurrence of the second fluorescence wave at the higher carbon dioxide concentrations, and the fact that it is often associated with a minimum of carbon dioxide absorption, suggests association with the carbon dioxide gush. However, as mentioned before, there is no direct evidence that the gush is accompanied by changes in fluorescence.

(e) Poisons

Kautsky and Hirsch (1935) noticed that the decay of fluorescence is retarded by the presence of *cyanide*. Franck and Wood (1936) confirmed this and found that the decay period, BC, is lengthened despite a decrease in the height of peak B. According to Franck, French and Puck (1941), this effect becomes apparent only at very high concentrations of the poison (*e. g.*, 2% HCN in air).

A detailed study of the cyanide effect on two-maximum curves of *Chlorella* was made by Wassink and Katz (1939). Figure 33.39 shows the influence of variations of cyanide concentration. With sufficient cyanide present, the decay disappears entirely and the fluorescence becomes stabilized at the level it had reached in the second maximum. (The influence on the *first* fluorescence wave is scarcely noticeable in this figure.)

Wassink and Katz used the cyanide-poisoned cells for the study of the effect of temperature, oxygen and other factors on the initial part of the fluorescence curve, assuming that elimination of the final decay must make the analysis easier. Insofar as these measurements concerned the first wave of fluorescence, ABC, they are discussed in sections (c) and (f), because in this part of the induction curve the effects of cyanide are minor. Here, we will discuss some results concerning the "second wave."

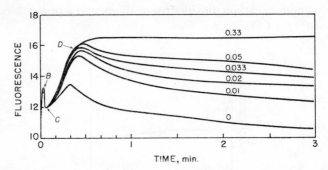

Fig. 33.39. Fluorescence–time relation in air at 29° C. as a function of inhibition of photosynthesis by cyanide (after Wassink and Katz 1939). Per cent KCN shown on curves; 0.1 ml. added to 2 ml. cell suspension.

Figure 33.39 shows that the decline of photosynthesis after the second maximum is much more sensitive to cyanide than the decline after the first peak. Even 5×10^{-4} per cent cyanide in solution (corresponding to 7.7×10^{-5} mole/l.) had a strong effect, while 1.65×10^{-2} per cent (2.6×10^{-3} mole/l.) eliminated the decay altogether. This compares with 2% HCN in air, or about 0.15 mole/l. in the equilibrated aqueous phase, which Franck and co-workers found to be the smallest quantity affecting the first wave of fluorescence. The two observations refer to different species, and it was shown in chapter 12 (*cf.* Table 12.V) that the sensitivity of plants to cyanide varies widely; however, in this case, the variation is so extreme that it can be taken as indicative of differences between the reactions that bring about the fluorescence decay after the first and the second maxima.

Figure 33.40 and 33.41 show the influence of light intensity and temperature on the ascending slope of the second wave, CD, in cyanide-inhibited *Chlorella* cells. The second wave behaves as if it were caused by a combination of a photochemical reaction with at least two thermal reactions. At low intensities, the slope CD is proportional to I and independent of T; at higher intensities, a "saturation" is reached—the lower T, the earlier. At still higher intensities, the rate decreases again (apparently due to the development of a second minimum, near 1 minute).

The retarding influence of phenylurethan on fluorescence decay was first observed by Kautsky and Hirsch (1935). Figure 33.42 shows this effect in *Ulva lactuca*, according to Kautsky and U. Franck (1943). At concentrations of the order of 10^{-3} mole/l., the first fluorescence wave is entirely eliminated, the fluorescence starts high, and a slight decline at the

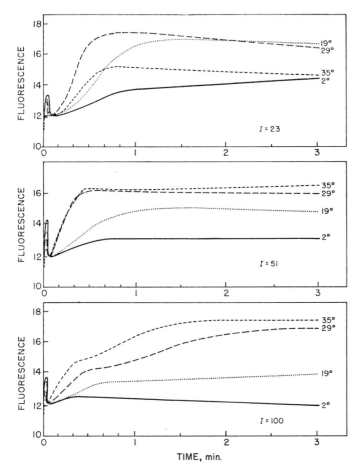

Fig. 33.40. Fluorescence–time relations as a function of temperature at three different light intensities (after Wassink and Katz 1939). Gas phase, air; total inhibition of photosynthesis by cyanide. Order of curves in first peak, from top down: 2°, 19°, 29°, and 35° C.

beginning of illumination replaces the normal increase. This decline lasts longer at lower light intensities (fig. 33.42B). The drop in φ from the initial level to the steady level is greatest at the lowest light intensity and highest temperature.

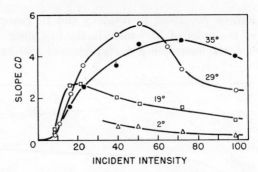

Fig. 33.41. Slope of second fluorescence wave as function of light intensity at various temperatures (after Wassink and Katz 1939). Gas phase, air; total inhibition of photosynthesis by cyanide.

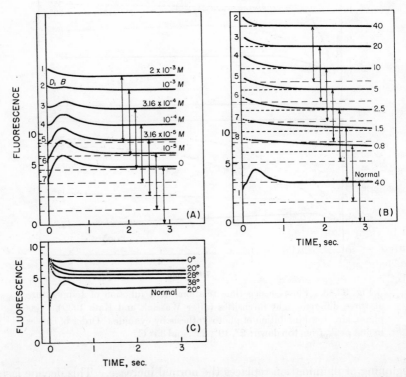

Fig. 33.42. Phenylurethan effect on fluorescence of *Ulva lactuca* (after Kautsky and Franck 1943). (A) Different phenylurethan concentrations; $I = 40$ m. c. (equiv.); 20° C. (B) Different light intensities (in equivalent meter candles); air; first 3 secs. (C) Different temperatures.

(f) Oxygen; Effects of Anaerobiosis

Since Kautsky believed, at first, that fluorescence quenching by oxygen, converting the latter to a metastable form, is the first step in photosynthesis, several of his papers were devoted to the study of the influence of oxygen on fluorescence during the induction period. However, the only definite result, obtained in the very first investigation (Kautsky, Hirsch and Davidshöfer 1932), was that changes in the concentration of oxygen between 0.5 and 100% have no marked effect on the fluorescence–time curves.

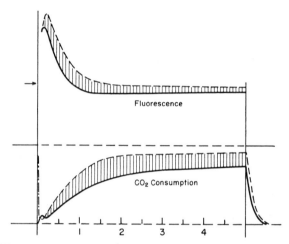

Fig. 33.43. Induction behavior of wheat under low (broken line) and under normal O_2 pressure (after McAlister and Myers 1940): 0.03% CO_2, high light, after 30 min. dark rest.

In chapter 24, we noted that an increase of oxygen concentration from 0.5 to 20% resulted in a certain *decrease* of steady fluorescence, probably related to the inhibiting effect of oxygen on photosynthesis. However, McAlister and Myers (1940) found that, during the induction period, not only fluorescence, but photosynthesis as well, were somewhat *higher* in nitrogen than in air (fig. 33.43). The explanation is uncertain, but we may recall that inhibition of photosynthesis by excess oxygen requires time (*cf.* chapter 19, fig. 60), and therefore may be absent in the first minutes of illumination. In other words, during the induction period, the quenching of chlorophyll fluorescence by oxygen (*cf.* chapt. 23, section A6) may be the main influence, while in the steady state the predominant effect is that due to the photoxidative inhibition of photosynthesis. In any case, the effect is small.

This result destroyed the original theory of Kautsky, and caused the latter to shift the search for the effect of oxygen on fluorescence to very low concentrations (in a hope of substituting a weakly dissociable complex, XO_2, for free oxygen as energy carrier). Marked changes in the fluorescence curves were, in fact, found in leaves almost completely deprived of oxygen; but whether these curves were caused, as alleged, by the absence of oxygen during the induction period (and not by *anaerobic incubation*) can be argued, since there is no way of depriving the cells of oxygen except by sweeping them with an oxygen-free gas for some length of time.

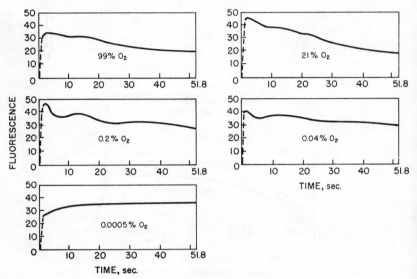

Fig. 33.44. Effect of O_2 on fluorescence in *Ageratum mexicana* leaves (after Kautsky and Hormuth 1937).

Kautsky (1939) said the "low O_2-curves" (fig. 33.44) cannot be attributed to anaerobic incubation for three reasons: *first*, because the sweeping out with nitrogen lasted only 60–90 minutes; *second*, because certain types of fluorescence curves were obtained at definite oxygen concentrations independently of the length of the incubation period; and *third*, because the normal shape of the induction curves was restored within 1 minute upon the admission of oxygen. None of these arguments is convincing: The duration of anaerobic incubation needed to produce "after effects" varies widely from species to species (as mentioned in section A6) the degree—perhaps even the character—of the anaerobic metabolism may depend on oxygen concentration; and 1 minute may be sufficient time to burn up the fermentation products obstructing chlorophyll.

Because of these considerations, the significance of the extensive collection of induction curves at different low oxygen concentrations, contained in the papers of Kautsky and co-workers, is uncertain. We will nevertheless give a short summary of their results.

Kautsky, Hirsch and Davidshöfer (1932) and Kautsky and Hirsch (1935) first found that, in complete absence of oxygen, the fluorescence wave, ABC (fig. 33.19), disappears, and the fluorescence–time curve becomes horizontal. Kautsky and Flesch (1936) observed that the slope AB first begins to flatten out in nitrogen containing less than 0.5% O_2. To achieve *complete* suppression of the "first wave" the system had to be swept by pure nitrogen for much more than 1 or 2 hours.

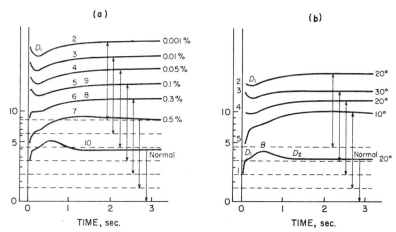

Fig. 33.45. Fluorescence curves of *Ulva lactuca* at low O_2 pressure (after Kautsky and Franck 1943): (a) variation of O_2 at 20° C.; (b) variations of temperature at 0.3% O_2. $I = 10$ m. c. (equiv.).

Later Kautsky and co-workers (1936, 1937) found no substantial variations in the fluorescence curves of *Ageratum* above 0.2% O_2, but noted a slight change in 0.04% O_2 and a strong change in pure nitrogen (estimated oxygen content, 0.0005%). After 2 hours of sweeping out with this gas, the fluorescence curve acquired the shape shown in figure 33.44.

The parallelism between these results and the observations on the effects of anaerobic incubation on gas production (chapter 13, part A) is obvious; it seems natural to correlate horizontal fluorescence–time curves with anaerobic inhibition of photosynthesis.

In transition from "aerobic" to the "anaerobic" fluorescence curves, the second fluorescence wave became prominent at a certain intermediary stage (0.2% O_2, in fig. 33.44). An enhanced second wave was found also on certain intermediate temperature curves obtained at a constant, low value of oxygen.

"Anaerobic" fluorescence curves of a more complex shape were obtained by Kautsky and Eberlein (1939) and Kautsky and U. Franck (1943) with the green alga *Ulva lactuca* (*cf.* fig. 33.45). The incubation time was 100 minutes. A new feature, recognizable in the detailed figure 33.45a, is an inflection on the ascending branch, *AB*, which may be the first indication of transformation into the "anaerobic" fluorescence curve. (The latter has a maximum at zero time.)

No effect of oxygen was observed in *Ulva lactuca* between 10 and 80% O_2; but, already at 1% (at 20° C.), the fluorescence wave was noticeably enhanced because of the delay in decay *BC*, and the initial fluorescence level was much higher than in air.

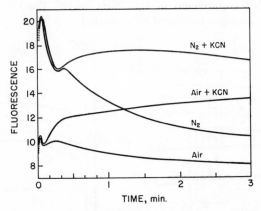

Fig. 33.46. Fluorescence–time relations in air and N_2 at 29° C., with and without cyanide (after Wassink and Katz 1939).

Experiments on the effect of oxygen on the fluorescence curves of *Chlorella* were carried out by Wassink and Katz (1939); their results (fig. 33.46) were quite different from those of Kautsky. In oxygen-free nitrogen, they found the fluorescence wave to be higher than in air, with decay *BC* taking more time, but decay *DE* accelerated. After 1 hour, the difference between the two curves disappeared (probably in consequence of the oxygen production by photosynthesis). A similar family of four curves (air with and without cyanide, and nitrogen with and without cyanide) was given by Shiau and Franck, except that, basically, their curves were of type I, while Wassink's curves in figure 33.46 are closer to type II. (For example, in fig. 33.46 the second wave was marked even in the absence of cyanide, while in the curves of Shiau and Franck this wave only appeared when cyanide was present.)

Most of the experiments of Wassink and Katz were carried out under complete inhibition of photosynthesis by cyanide, and consequent absence of the final fluorescence decay; the general shape of the curve was as shown in figure 33.39, and the authors studied the effect of oxygen concentration on maximum *B* and the second ascent, *CD*. Both were found to decline sharply with increase in $[O_2]$ up to about 2%, and become constant afterward. These results, even more than those of Kautsky and Eberlein, indicate a real effect of the *momentary* oxygen concentration on the fluorescence curves of *Chlorella* (whereas such effect seems to be almost nonexistent in the leaves of the higher plants studied by Kautsky, McAlister and Myers).

The observations of McAlister and Myers (1940) on the more pronounced effect of carbon dioxide deficiency in nitrogen (compared with air) were mentioned, and their explanation was given, on page 1393.

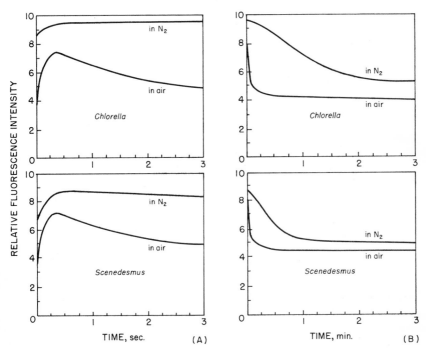

Fig. 33.47. Anaerobic fluorescence induction curves of *Chlorella* and *Scenedesmus* at 25° C. (after Shiau and Franck 1947): 3.0×10^4 erg/cm.^{2} sec. (A) First 3 sec.; (B) first 3 mins. Intensity units differ for the two algae.

Shiau and Franck (1947) made extensive comparisons of fluorescence–time curves of *Scenedesmus* and *Chlorella* in air and in very pure nitrogen. The results obtained with the two species were similar. Figure 33.47 shows the development of fluorescence during the first 3 minutes. In general, the picture is similar to that in Wassink and Katz's figure (Fig. 33.46, curves for nitrogen and air). About 15 minutes of darkness were needed to repeat the anaerobic induction curve starting at the same high value. These observers, too, found that, if oxygen from photosynthesis is permitted to accumulate, the difference between the two curves vanishes in about 1 hour. The enhancing effect of anaerobiosis on the "second wave" is shown by figure 33.48.

The curves obtained by Shiau and Franck in nitrogen and in air, in the presence of *cyanide*, also were mentioned on page 1402. Effects similar to those of cyanide could be brought about, as usual, by low temperature or by carbon dioxide deprivation.

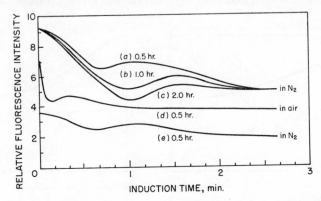

Fig. 33.48. Anaerobic fluorescence induction curves of *Chlorella* at 24° C., showing the second wave (after Shiau and Franck 1947). Time in darkness shown on curves. Light intensities are: (a) to (d), 3.0×10^4 erg/cm.^{2} sec.; (e) 2.2×10^4 erg/cm.^{2} sec.

Cells affected by long anaerobic incubation (as well as cells from old cultures) were found to be permeable to methylene blue, while young healthy cells were not stained by this dye. This points to cell permeability as one variable possibly responsible for variations in the shape of the induction curves.

The initial intensity of fluorescence of *isolated chloroplasts* was the same in nitrogen or air; there appears to be no inhibition of their photochemical activity by aerobic or anaerobic dark metabolism. The mechanism of the *photochemical* inhibition (revealed by the rise of φ at the beginning of illumination) may be the same as in whole cells, but the practical absence of the subsequent decay in light, and its extreme slowness in the dark, indicate the inefficiency of the respiratory mechanism removing the inhibitor (which in this case apparently cannot overcome the continued production of the inhibitor in light).

(g) Oxidants and Neutralizers

Related to the effect of oxygen is that of "substitute oxidants," such as quinone or ferric iron compounds. If anaerobic inhibition is due, to a large extent, to the accumulation of an acidic, reducing, fermentation product, this inhibitor could be removed by oxidation with oxygen or other oxidants, or by neutralization.

Kautsky and Zedlitz (1941) noted that the fluorescence–time curves of grana precipitates could be changed from the anaerobic type to the aerobic type either by aeration or by the addition of ferric oxalate or quinone. (Whether these two oxidants are especially useful, because of their capacity to serve as oxidants in the "Hill reaction" of isolated or broken chloroplasts, remains to be seen.)

Shiau and Franck (1947) investigated the effect of quinone or alkali on the fluorescence–time curves of *Chlorella* and *Scenedesmus*. In young healthy cultures they found no effect, in either air or nitrogen, except after 12 hours of anaeroboisis. After such long anaerobic incubation, the addition of 10^{-3} M quinone caused the induction to disappear and the steady state value of φ to drop considerably. Quinone still had an effect on φ even 15 minutes after the cells were exposed to air, showing the slowness of recovery after extensive anaerobic pretreatment. *Alkali* caused, after the same anaerobic pretreatment, first a transient increase and then a drop in fluorescence. *o-Phenanthroline* (10^{-4} to 10^{-5} M) was found to counteract the effect of quinone addition.

The same investigators also observed the effect of quinone and of alkalies on the fluorescence of isolated chloroplasts. The final fluorescence intensity was reduced, by 10^{-3} M *quinone*, about 10% below the initial value, and the "wave" of φ in the first second disappeared completely. Addition of 0.1 M *potassium phosphate* to a 12% sucrose solution (which changed the pH from 6 to about 7.5) produced a similar effect. The effect of alkalies on chloroplasts was slower than that of quinone, and had a high temperature coefficient (*e. g.*, no effect was observed in 2 hours at 0°); it was more rapid with ions of smaller radius (Na). The neutralization effect was very fast and independent of temperature in *disrupted* chloroplasts. With chloroplasts, *o*-phenanthroline had an effect similar to that of the alkalies, rather than an antagonistic effect, as in live algae.

The figures given in this chapter are but a small selection of the bewildering multitude of induction curves of gas exchange and fluorescence available in the literature. They are probably enough to create the impression of a field full of confusion and contradictions. However, we will see below that, in the main, the results are capable of a not-too-complex interpretation, based on the assumption of a twofold inhibiting effect: a fast deactivation of the oxygen-liberating enzyme system in the dark, and a relatively slow accumulation of surface-active inhibitors ("narcotics") as a result of dark, particularly anaerobic, metabolism.

3. Changes in Absorption Spectrum during Induction

It was mentioned on p. 1376 that all measurements of fluorescence-time curves are predicated on the assumption that the fluorescence *spectrum* remains the same, and only the yield of fluorescence changes. This is not certain; but the low intensity of fluorescence makes an experimental check difficult. Somewhat easier is the measurement of the absorption spectrum as a function of time; this could be achieved either (if the changes in the extinction coefficient are greater than about 10%) by means of one of the now available rapid spectrometers, which registers a complete spectrum in fractions of a second, or, in a more cumbersome way, by determining the extinction as a function of time for each wave length in a separate run. Experiments of the second type have been carried out by Duysens (1952, 1954[1-3]). The measuring time of his apparatus was of the order of magnitude of one second; the changes in extinction coefficient recorded were of the order of 0.1%. In as far as his experiments deal with the absorption spectra in the stationary state in light, they will be discussed in chapter 37C. Here, we will merely mention some preliminary results concerning the transition from darkness to light.

In *Rhodospirillum rubrum* (in peptone, under anaerobic conditions), conspicuous changes have been noted by Duysens both in the infrared, where they indicate some kind of chemical change in the bacteriochlorophyll (or molecules complexed with it), and in the violet, where the changes in weak light (10^4 erg/cm.^{2} sec.) seem to indicate the transformation of a compound of the type of cytochrome c from reduced into the oxidized state in the first 10 seconds of illumination. In very strong light (10^6 erg/cm.^{2} sec.), there is a second spectroscopic change, opposite in direction, following closely upon the cytochrome change; superimposed upon these fast changes there is a much slower one, taking a minute or more. All three changes are reversed in the dark.

Duysens (1954[3]) observed similar changes in *Chlorella* and *Porphyridium*, between 330 and 530 mμ. Some of them could be attributed to the oxidation of a cytochrome or reduction of a pyridine nucleotide in light; one new band in the green remained unexplained (*cf.* chapter 37C, section 6f). No kinetic measurements have been as yet made on these transformations.

This may be the place to mention the observations of Kandler (1950) and Strehler (1953) on the changes of ATP concentration in *Chlorella*. The ATP level established in the dark under anaerobic conditions, rises (and that established under aerobic conditions, falls) upon exposure to light. The rate of rise is proportional to light intensity, I, but the stationary level, reached after about 1 minute in light, has a maximum at a certain intensity. The change is independent of the presence of carbon dioxide.

C. Interpretation of Induction Phenomena*

1. Diffusion and Buffer Effects

In higher land plants, the gas exchange usually has to take the path through stomata and air channels, the diffusion resistance of which may become the main rate-limiting factor in photosynthesis, particularly when the slits are only partially open (*cf.* chapter 27, page 910). The stomata close regularly during the night, but may do so also during the day, particularly if the plants are temporarily darkened. Sluggish reopening could make photosynthesis in the first moments of illumination "carbon dioxide-limited," even when the outside concentration of carbon dioxide is high. Fortunately, most of the data used in this chapter were obtained either with stomata-free aquatic plants, or with higher plants under conditions minimizing the stomatal effects.

Lubimenko and Shcheglova (1932) suggested that the low initial value of the photosynthetic quotient found by Kostychev (*cf.* sect. A3) may be due to a delay in the outward diffusion of oxygen, caused by the necessity to build up its pressure in the leaf until it equals that in the air. However, the building up of a diffusion gradient should delay the movement of carbon dioxide *more*—and not less—than that of oxygen. In the first place, the diffusion coefficient of carbon dioxide is smaller than that of oxygen; consequently, the concentration gradient, required to maintain the same rate of flow, is larger for carbon dioxide than for oxygen. In the second place, the building up of the carbon dioxide pressure can be delayed by the presence of buffers; consequently, the exchange of a certain quantity of carbon dioxide for an equivalent quantity of oxygen, may create a smaller diffusion gradient for carbon dioxide than for oxygen. Lastly, prior to the beginning of illumination, the concentration gradient must have been higher for carbon dioxide than for oxygen (since in the dark, too, the flows of the two gases had to be equal). Thus, in the building up of the carbon dioxide gradient required for steady photosynthesis, the cells start further back, progress more slowly and have to go further than in the creation of the oxygen gradient. Consequently, the transition from carbon dioxide liberation into the atmosphere to carbon dioxide absorption from it (or *vice versa*), must take more time than the change in the direction of the oxygen flow.

Although diffusion effects should not be overlooked in the quantitative analysis of induction phenomena in higher plants, it will be noted that they can account only for a gradual approach to the steady rate of gas liberation (or consumption), and not for such phenomena as the oxygen "gush," or the carbon dioxide "gulp." Furthermore, all induction losses caused by buffer action or slow diffusion, must be reversible, *i. e.*, at the end of the illumination period, they must be compensated by a continued absorption of carbon dioxide (and evolution of oxygen) in the dark. This is not normally the case in photosynthesis, where the induction losses are nonrecoverable.

* Bibliography, page 1432

2. Building Up of Intermediates

Osterhout and Haas (1918), in the very first discussion of induction in photosynthesis, pointed out two possible mechanisms: the building up of intermediates, and the activation of catalysts. All subsequent explanations of the induction losses belong to one of these two general types. For positive induction, one can postulate utilization of intermediates accumulated in the preceding period (preceding dark period for positive induction in light, preceding light period for positive induction in dark). Transient *inactivation* of catalysts by light can also produce a kind of positive induction in the form of a temporary decline of gas exchange below the initial, normal level (*i. e.*, *not* in the form of a burst of gas exchange in excess of the steady level, which can be due only to the utilization of accumulated intermediates).

Closer analysis shows that the distinction between the two mechanisms is not as sharp as one may think. The kinetic role of catalysts that are reversibly changed during a chemical reaction (*e. g.*, by alternating oxidation and reduction, or carboxylation and decarboxylation) is in many respects similar to that of intermediates. For example, if carbon dioxide in the complex $A \cdot CO_2$ is hydrogenated, in the course of photosynthesis, in several steps, the compounds $A \cdot HCO_2$, $A \cdot H_2CO_2$, ... are reduction intermediates, while the free acceptor A is a catalyst; nevertheless, at the beginning of illumination, the concentration [A] may have to be built up in exactly the same way as the concentrations $[A \cdot HCO_2]$, etc., since at the end of a dark period all acceptor molecules may be in the form of the complex $A \cdot CO_2$, while a certain quantity of free A is required for the carboxylation reaction, $CO_2 + A \rightarrow A \cdot CO_2$, to keep pace with the photosynthetic process as a whole.

Similarly, if the hydrogen atoms move, during photosynthesis, from the reductant, $A' \cdot H_2O$, to the oxidant, $A \cdot CO_2$, through the intermediary of an oxidation-reduction catalyst, X/HX (*cf.* chapter 7), and if, after a dark period, all molecules of this catalyst are present in the same form (*e. g.*, the oxidized form, X) the concentration of the other form has to be built up, in light, like that of an intermediate, until the reaction in which this form takes part (*e. g.*, $HX + A \cdot CO_2 \rightarrow X + A \cdot HCO_2$) can keep pace with the over-all progress of photosynthesis.

The specific character of induction effects due to catalysts appears when their inactivation is brought about by *inhibition* (and not by accumulation in one form) and this inhibition is removed "autocatalytically" by the products of photosynthesis. In this case, induction may assume the form of "waves," so characteristic of many experimental induction curves of photosynthesis. The building up of intermediates, on the other hand, can in itself cause (similarly to diffusion) only a gradual approach of the gas exchange to the steady state. (Shiau and Franck, 1947, suggested that a *combination* of catalyst inactivation with a shift in the distribution of intermediates is a possible cause of the "second wave" of induction; *cf.* sections 2(a) and 4 below.)

The simplest example of induction based on the building up of intermediates is found in radioactive decay. For example, if uranium is freed of all its daughter elements, the production of emanation will at first be zero; it will increase with time, and reach a steady rate after an "induction period" of several thousand years (this being the time required to build up to a stationary level the intermediate elements between uranium and emanation, notably radium). Similarly, if the dark metabolism of plants eliminates all intermediates of photosynthesis left over from a preceding illumination period, the concentration of these intermediates must be built up to a stationary level before the formation of the final products will attain its full speed.

Two types of intermediates have to be considered—those that require light for further transformation and those that can complete their transformations in the dark ("photochemical" and "thermal" intermediates). Reaction schemes that assume only *one* primary photochemical process (*e. g.*, scheme 7.VI, 9.III or 24.I) contain thermal intermediates only. In reaction schemes based on two or several consecutive photochemical steps (*e. g.*, 7.V or 7.VA), the photochemical intermediates evoke the greatest interest; but these schemes usually also contain thermal intermediates (*e. g.*, the intermediary reductant, ROH, and the peroxide, ROOH, in scheme 7.VA).

(a) Photochemical Intermediates

The role of "photochemical" intermediates in induction has been discussed by Franck and co-workers (1941, 1945), whose scheme of photosynthesis (7.VA) contains five of them. Since these intermediates are incapable of completing their transformation without the aid of light, they must, at the end of illumination, either persist in the dark or disappear by back or side reactions, without contributing to the yield of photosynthesis.

Franck favored the first alternative. He argued that if photochemical intermediates were to be built up anew, at the beginning of each illumination period, the duration of the resulting induction period should increase with decreasing light intensity (which is not observed in nature); in moderate light, the induction should last much longer than is actually observed.

This relation between the light intensity and the length of the induction period follows from the consideration that in the linear part of the light curve the steady state of photosynthesis requires all photochemical reactions to run at the same rate, and that to achieve this "equipartition of light energy" an excited chlorophyll molecule must have the same chance of reacting with each of the several reduction substrates. For example, in scheme 7.VA, the reduction rate must be the same for $A \cdot CO_2$, $A \cdot HCO_2$, $A \cdot H_2CO_2$ and $A \cdot H_3CO_2$. Furthermore, in this and other schemes (such as 7.V) which postulate photochemical oxidation of water by oxidized chlorophyll in addition to photochemical reduction of carbon dioxide by reduced chlorophyll, the *photoxidation* must run at the same rate as the *photoreduction* (*i. e.*, chlorophyll must be distributed about evenly between the oxidized and the reduced forms).

If, at the end of the dark period, all acceptor molecules are in the state $A \cdot CO_2$, or all chlorophyll molecules are in the oxidized (or the reduced) state, the induction period required to redistribute the acceptor and the chlorophyll molecules so as to permit equipartition of quanta obviously must be inversely proportional to the intensity of illumination.

As a strict requirement, the equipartition of energy between the complexes $A \cdot CO_2$, $A \cdot HCO_2$, ... and between the oxidized and reduced forms of the sensitizer is mandatory only in the linear part of the light curves, where practically all the absorbed quanta have to be utilized for photosynthesis; this condition gradually loses its validity with approach to light saturation, where more and more light quanta are allowed to be wasted.

It will also be noted that, if, in the dark, all chlorophyll were to accumulate in the oxidized form, the evolution of oxygen should start at twice its steady rate, and then decrease gradually, while the consumption of carbon dioxide should start at zero, and gradually increase to the steady level. According to scheme 7.VA, the achievement of equipartition with respect to the reduction intermediates $A \cdot CO_2$, $A \cdot HCO_2$, $A \cdot H_2CO_2$ and $A \cdot H_3CO_2$ should require four times as many quanta as the achievement of equipartition with respect to oxidation and reduction (X and HX). If at the beginning of illumination, all acceptor is in the form $A \cdot CO_2$, and all chlorophyll in the oxidized form, X, the carbon dioxide consumption should require four times longer to *rise* to its steady rate, than the oxygen production to *decline* to a steady level.

Experimentally, the duration of the induction period is either independent of light intensity, or *increases* slowly with it; and as a general rule, no differences in sign or duration have been noticed between the carbon dioxide and the oxygen induction curves. This indicates that the building up of photochemical intermediates is *not* the essential cause of induction.

It was mentioned once before that Shiau and Franck (1947) have suggested an interpretation of the "second wave" of induction by the interplay of catalytic inhibition and redistribution of intermediates. This hypothesis assumes that the plant starts, after a period of darkness, with an equipartition of A among the intermediates, $A \cdot CO_2$, $A \cdot HCO_2$, $\cdots$ In strong light, however, this equipartition will be disturbed, if the photochemical reduction is not instantaneously compensated by carbon dioxide uptake by liberated acceptor molecules. If this uptake is not instantaneous, a stationary concentration of A is established. This is particularly likely if the carboxylation is delayed by a limiting amount of the carboxylase, E_A, or by a low concentration of carbon dioxide (*i. e.*, if saturation ceases to be determined exclusively or mainly by the finishing catalyst, E_B, and becomes a function of $[E_A]$ or $[CO_2]$).

This kind of redistribution of intermediates obviously should produce an *inverse induction;* at least, the rate of *oxygen production* should start high and gradually decline to a steady level. How, according to Shiau and Franck, the superposition of this depletion of the reduction substrates upon "ordinary" induction (due to photochemical activation of an inhibitor and its subsequent oxidative removal) can explain the occurrence of a "wave" of inhibition and enhanced fluorescence will be discussed in section 4 below.

The *absolute duration* of the induction period was mentioned above as a second argument against the attribution of induction to the replenishment of the stock of photochemical intermediates. Since the concentration of the carbon dioxide acceptor appears to be approximately equal to that of chlorophyll, and the acceptor has to receive an average of considerably more than 4 quanta per molecule to ensure close approach to equipartition, an induction period of this origin should last long enough for each chlorophyll molecule to absorb, say, 10 or 12 quanta. Franck and Gaffron (1941) pointed out that, in light just sufficient to bring about net liberation of oxygen, this may require as long as 2 hours (whereas no induction was observed at all in such weak light); in ten times stronger light, induction should take 12 minutes—about ten times the actual induction period in moderate light.

This estimate was based on the conditions prevailing in the quantum yield experiments of Warburg and Negelein. They used such dense *Chlorella* suspensions that, in weak light, the average frequency of absorptions by each individual chlorophyll molecule was only once every 12 *minutes*. In less concentrated suspension, used in induction work, this frequency is, of course, much higher, approaching, according to page 838, a limiting value of $1 \times 10^{-4} \times I$ (in lux), corresponding to once every 25 seconds at 400 lux or once every 2.5 seconds at 4000 lux. In an average leaf, the mean frequency of absorptions probably is not much less than once every 2 minutes at 400 lux and once every 12 seconds at 4000 lux. An induction period in a leaf, caused by replenishment of photochemical intermediates, should therefore last about 20 minutes at 400 lux, and 2 minutes at 4000 lux. These figures show that the argument based on the *absolute duration* of the induction period is less conclusive than the objections derived from the *direction* in which this duration changes with light intensity. (Shiau and

Franck's interpretation of the "second induction wave" is only possible because 1 or 2 minutes is all the time required for the whole chlorophyll complex to undergo photochemical transformation in moderate light, if the quantum yield is of the order of 1.)

The apparent absence of an induction period attributable to the replenishment of photochemical intermediates permits two interpretations: either such intermediates do not exist, or they are stable. The first alternative leads to reaction schemes with a single photochemical primary process. As stated before, Franck and co-workers (who based their considerations on scheme 7.VA) chose the second alternative, and postulated that the photochemical intermediates survive, without decomposition, dark periods of the order of several minutes. Furthermore, they suggested that, even if the dark periods last for several hours or days, the intermediates do not disappear completely—perhaps because they are regenerated by oxidation processes. More recent concepts of the chemical mechanism of photosynthesis (chapter 36) favor the alternative of a single photochemical reaction.

(b) *Thermal Intermediates*

The building up of "thermal" intermediates, *i. e.*, of photochemical products that can be converted in the dark to the final products of photosynthesis, could give rise to an induction period of any duration—depending on the quantity of these products required for the maintenance of a stationary state. This quantity is likely to increase in proportion with the rate of photosynthesis; therefore, the duration of the induction period of this origin could be more or less independent of light intensity (at least, in the region where the rate is approximately proportional to light intensity). In other words, the assumption of thermal intermediates as source of induction is not open to the two objections raised above against the attribution of this phenomenon to photochemical intermediates.

However, other arguments can be adduced against this hypothesis as well. In discussing slow diffusion as a possible source of induction, we noted that irreversibility of induction losses makes it impossible to accept diffusion as an adequate explanation. The same can be said about the attribution of induction to thermochemical intermediates. If an initial delay of the gas exchange is caused by the accumulation of an intermediate from which oxygen can be evolved (or which can absorb carbon dioxide) by a dark reaction, the accumulated intermediates should continue to evolve oxygen (or absorb carbon dioxide), after the cessation of illumination, for a period equal to the induction period.

As illustrated by figure 33.2, no such recovery of induction losses of photosynthesis in the dark has been observed in the study of oxygen liberation. In measurements of carbon dioxide consumption, a "dark uptake" of carbon dioxide after the cessation of illumination was noted by McAlister, Blinks and Skow and Emerson and Lewis (cf. next section), but only under very special conditions; usually induction losses of carbon dioxide are as irreparable as those of oxygen (cf. fig. 33.8).

To sum up: Two views are possible of the role of intermediates in induction. The first one—which fits best into the picture of photosynthesis as a single photochemical oxidation-reduction followed by dark, catalytic reactions—assumes that the only intermediates in photosynthesis are "thermal," and that these do not occur, in the steady state, in concentrations approaching that of chlorophyll. The second hypothesis, which follows if one postulates two or more successive light reactions, and thus admits the existence of one or several photochemical intermediates (with stationary concentrations of the same order of magnitude as that of chlorophyll), postulates that these intermediates are still present in the cells even after prolonged dark intervals. The two concepts are not mutually exclusive, since photosynthesis may involve both thermal *and* photochemical intermediates. In this case, we can assert that the first ones do not occur in quantities commensurate with those of chlorophyll, while the second ones do not disappear from the cells in the dark.

The possible function of *respiration intermediates* in the induction (particularly "positive" induction) will be discussed in section 5.

3. Role of the Carbon Dioxide Acceptor in Induction

It was stated before that, formally, the carbon dioxide acceptor, A, may play the role of an intermediate. After a dark rest, this acceptor is in thermodynamic equilibrium with external carbon dioxide; depending on the concentration of the latter and the dissociation constant, it may be either completely or partially carboxylated. As discussed in chapter 27, the carboxylation equilibrium may be disturbed in light, in consequence of rapid consumption of carbon dioxide by the photochemical system, and insufficient replacement (because of slow diffusion or slow carboxylation). In any case, the disturbed carboxylation equilibrium should be restored by a "pick-up" of carbon dioxide after the cessation of illumination, and this phenomenon has actually been observed under conditions favoring the denudation of the acceptor, such as strong light, low carbon dioxide supply, or cyanide poisoning of the carboxylase, E_A (cf. chapter 8, page 200, and figs. 21, 22 and 33.11).

Whenever a "pick-up" occurs at the end of illumination, this can be taken as indication that the concentration of the free acceptor, [A], has undergone an increase at the beginning of the light period.   The influence of this change on induction depends on whether the rate of carboxylation was determined by the concentrations [CO_2] and [A], or by the available quantity of the carboxylating catalyst, E_A.   It further makes a difference if the steady rate of photosynthesis depends on the quantity of $A \cdot CO_2$

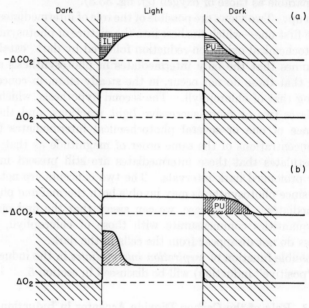

Fig. 33.49.   Induction effects that may be caused by CO_2 acceptor, A;   IL = induction loss;   PU = pick-up.   (a) Saturation light (saturation imposed by factors independent of CO_2 availability, *e. g.*, by E_B limitation).   (b) Transitional part of light curve, [CO_2] has effect on rate (E_A deficiency, *e. g.*, in consequence of cyanide poisoning).

complexes available for reduction, or is so limited by other catalytic factors (such as the availability of the finishing catalyst, E_B), to be practically insensitive to a depletion of the reduction substrate.

Let us assume, as an example, that the latter is the case;   furthermore, that the concentration of carbon dioxide is high enough to saturate the acceptor in the dark and that the rate of carboxylation is proportional to the momentary concentration of the free acceptor, [A].   In this case, the rate of *oxygen liberation* will be constant throughout the induction period (since according to our assumption a decrease in $A \cdot CO_2$ cannot affect this rate).   The initial rate of the *carbon dioxide* absorption, on the other hand, will be low;   it will gradually increase and the steady rate reached when [A] becomes high enough for carboxylation to keep pace with the photochemical utilization of $A \cdot CO_2$. The resulting carbon dioxide induction loss will be balanced by the "pick-up" (cf. fig. 33.49a).

As a second example, we can assume that the steady rate of photosynthesis is dependent on $[A \cdot CO_2]$, and that the rate of formation of $A \cdot CO_2$ is determined entirely by the available quantity of the catalyst E_A. In this case, oxygen liberation will show an "inverse induction"; it will begin at a higher rate and decline to a steady level. The carbon dioxide absorption, on the other hand, may be practically constant, or show a slight increase to a steady level. A pick-up will nevertheless occur, at the end of the light period, to compensate for the excess oxygen liberated during the "inverse induction" (cf. fig. 33.49b). A somewhat similar situation is postulated in Shiau and Franck's interpretation of the second induction wave (section 4).

These are only two examples of induction effects that may arise if the illumination causes a marked disturbance of the carboxylation equilibrium. The shape of the pick-up curves should show whether, under the conditions of the experiment, the carboxylation is of first order with respect to [A] (as in fig. 33.49a), or of zero order (as in fig. 33.49b). The latter relation can be expected, e. g., in cyanide-poisoned cells, where catalyst E_A is almost completely inactivated. (The extended duration of the pick-up in the presence of cyanide was noted by Aufdemgarten; cf. chapter 8, page 207.)

Since the total quantity of the carbon dioxide acceptor appears to be of the same order of magnitude as that of chlorophyll, a practically *complete* decarboxylation of this acceptor should lead to the pick-up of about one molecule of carbon dioxide per mole of chlorophyll (and to a corresponding induction loss of carbon dioxide, or induction gain of oxygen). The duration of the pick-up should be, in the nonpoisoned state, of the order of 10 or 100 seconds. The frequency with which a chlorophyll molecule absorbs quanta at the light intensity at which the pick-up becomes noticeable, $\sim$10,000 lux, is between 0.1 and 1 absorption per second; if 10 quanta are needed to make an "occupied" molecule A available for a new carbon dioxide molecule, the mean life-time of the acceptor in the occupied state will be between 10 and 100 seconds. In order that 50% of the complexes can be dissociated in the steady state, the average time required for recarboxylation also must be between 10 and 100 seconds.

In the E_A-deficient (e. g., cyanide-poisoned) state, the pick-up can be expected to last much longer; in this case, the depletion of $A \cdot CO_2$ (and the corresponding increase of fluorescence, cf. chapter 28, page 1051) should occur in light much weaker than 10,000 lux.

Another reversible induction effect, which may or may not be associated with the disturbance of the carboxylation equilibrium, is the *liberation* of carbon dioxide in light, described by Emerson and Lewis and illustrated by figures 29.5 and 33.13. Emerson and Lewis suggested that this gush (and the compensating slow uptake of carbon dioxide in the dark) is due to the presence of a photolabile compound not directly related to photosynthesis, the photochemical decomposition of which is superimposed upon the latter. Blinks and Skow, in discussing the "acidity gush" in light (and "alkalinity gush" in the dark), which they had observed in measurements with the glass electrode (cf. fig. 33.12), listed several possible interpretations: (1) release of carbon dioxide by a photolabile compound; (2) light-stimulated respiration; (3) production of an acid stronger than carbonic acid, as a first product of photosynthesis; (4) photodecomposition of plant acids (e. g., malic acid), with the liberation of carbon dioxide; and (5) photochemical consumption of a base (e. g., ammonia). Hypothesis 2 is improbable for reasons discussed in chapter 20; furthermore, it does not explain the reversibility of the gush. The latter also rules out hypothesis 4. Hypothesis 5 discounts the probable identity of the acid gush with the carbon dioxide gush of Emerson and Lewis. We are thus left with hypotheses 1 and 3 (the latter can explain a gush of gaseous carbon dioxide, if it is assumed that the synthesized acid reacts with a bicarbonate reserve in the cell).

In chapter 8, we described two reversible carbon dioxide uptake mechanisms operating in green plant cells. One is due to carboxylation and probably leads, among other products, to the immediate reduction substrate of photosynthesis. (We say "among other products" because it has recently become clear that reversible carboxylations also occur, in plant tissues as well as in animal tissues, without direct relation to photosynthesis, as a part of respiratory and fermentative reactions.) The second carbon dioxide uptake mechanism is based on buffer equilibria (involving alkaline earth carbonates and alkali phosphates), and is either unrelated, or only indirectly related to photosynthesis. Before postulating a new reversible carbon dioxide-absorbing mechanism to account for the results of Emerson and Lewis, and Blinks and Skow, one must consider the possibility that the gush is due either to the photochemical decomposition of the complex $A \cdot CO_2$, or to the decomposition of bicarbonate reserves, in consequence of the photochemical formation of a comparatively strong acid.

The first hypothesis was suggested by Franck (1942), and appears the more plausible, since we have no other indications that photosynthesis leads to acidification of the cell contents. Furthermore, the maximum volume of the carbon-dioxide gush, as measured by Emerson and Lewis, appears to correspond to the amount of the carbon dioxide acceptor complex, $A \cdot CO_2$, in the cells (i. e., it is about equivalent to the content of chlorophyll).

The strong dependence of the gush on carbon dioxide pressure is an argument against attributing it to a decomposition of the $A \cdot CO_2$ complex. According to Emerson and Lewis (*cf.* sect. A3), a gush becomes noticeable only when the cells have been exposed, in the dark period, to a carbon dioxide concentration of several per cent; it still increases between 5 and 10% CO_2—a behavior more similar to that of buffers (*cf.* fig. 19) than to that of the $A \cdot CO_2$ complex (which appears to be saturated with carbon dioxide below 0.1% CO_2).

If, despite this apparent difficulty, we follow Franck in attributing the carbon dioxide gush to a decomposition of the complex $A \cdot CO_2$, we have to answer two further questions: Why should this complex decompose in light at all, and why does this decomposition occur even in very weak light? To answer these questions, we would have to assume, *first*, that the normal photochemical reaction (*i. e.*, the reduction of $A \cdot CO_2$ to carbohydrate) is *blocked* during the gush, for example, by inactivation of the stabilizing catalyst, E_B, and, *second*, that the $A \cdot CO_2$ molecules which have undergone the first reduction step (to $A \cdot HCO_2$) and fail to be "stabilized," react back with the first oxidation product, $A' \cdot OH$ (or with oxidized chlorophyll, X), liberating carbon dioxide, *e. g.*:

(33.2) $$A \cdot HCO_2 + A'OH \longrightarrow A + A' + CO_2 + H_2O$$

or:

(32.3) $$A \cdot HCO_2 + X \longrightarrow HX + A + CO_2$$

The assumption that the primary products, not stabilized by catalyst E_B, react back was made before in chapter 28 (sect. B7) in the interpretation of light saturation, and of the relation (or rather lack of systematic relation) between the saturation of photosynthesis and the yield of fluorescence. The additional assumption made here is that the energy released in the back reaction splits $A \cdot CO_2$ into A and CO_2.

Complete inhibition of the catalytic mechanism somewhere beyond the carboxylation stage can thus explain why light causes the decomposition of the complex $A \cdot CO_2$; but it is more difficult to see why the recarboxylation is so slow that the gush begins with a net quantum yield of almost unity, the photostationary state appears to be entirely on the side of decarboxylation, even in very weak light, and the carbon dioxide uptake after cessation of illumination continues for as long as an hour. We recall that, according to the concept of saturation as a consequence of back reactions, which we considered most plausible in chapter 28, a large proportion (of the order of 1/8) of the light quanta not utilized for photosynthesis because of limitation by a finishing catalyst (in saturating light, this may mean >50% of all absorbed quanta) should bring about decarboxylation of $A \cdot CO_2$. The latter should therefore proceed, in strong steady light, 10 or 100 times more rapidly than in the weak light used by Emerson and Lewis. Nevertheless, we do not observe a decarboxylation of the acceptor (unless the light is *excessively* strong and pick-up begins to become noticeable). This indicates that the recarboxylation is rapid enough to replace all the $A \cdot CO_2$ complexes destroyed—both those utilized for photosynthesis, and those merely decomposed into A and CO_2. The pick-up experiments in fact show the recarboxylation time of the acceptor to be of the order of 10–20 seconds. In the case of the gush, the recarboxylation seems to be at least 100 times slower.

One may recall in this connection that, according to figure 8.21, the rate of carboxylation in the dark was found to be unexpectedly slow also in experiments with radioactive carbon dioxide. In this case, however, explanations could be sought in the occurrence of carboxylations not related to photosynthesis; furthermore, the observed rates may be at least in part those of the *replacement* of carbon dioxide in a carboxyl group by C^*O_2, rather than of the *uptake* of C^*O_2 by a free acceptor. Similar explanations are not possible in the case of the gush. Its occurrence in light indicates close connection to the photosynthetic apparatus; since the gush is revealed by manometric measurements, it is not an exchange phenomenon.

To sum up: The mechanism of the reversible carbon dioxide gush described by Emerson and Lewis is not clear, and its attribution to a shift of the carboxylation equilibrium of acceptor A, although plausible, remains uncertain.

Since this section was first written, the question of the hypothetical carbon dioxide acceptor in photosynthesis, A, has been brought closer to direct experimental elucidation by continued studies of the uptake and distribution of radiocarbon in photosynthesis (to be described in chapter 36). These studies indicate that one—and perhaps even the only—carboxylation which is directly related to photosynthesis leads to phosphoglyceric acid (PGA). The carboxylation substrate is, however, not yet identified; it seems likely that it is not a C_2 compound (which could give a C_3 acid by simple addition), but a longer-chain compound (a pentose) that breaks into two parts (e. g., C_3 and C_3) upon taking up a CO_2 molecule. The reaction that leads to PGA appears to be a carboxylation coupled with a TPN-specific oxidation-reduction. Finally, the compound A, which gives PGA by coupled carboxylation and chain fission, is itself an intermediate product of photosynthesis (since it rapidly incorporates radiocarbon). If this conclusion—which we have tentatively mentioned before—proves to be correct for all (or a large part) of the CO_2 acceptor in the cell, this would mean the likelihood of a deficiency of this acceptor at the beginning of a light period, and of an autocatalytic adjustment of its concentration in light to the level needed to maintain photosynthesis at the rate corresponding to the prevailing light intensity. The role of the carbon dioxide acceptor in the induction phenomena thus appears in a new light, in particular in the interpretation of those features of induction (such as the approximate independence of its duration of light intensity) that point to a factor activated in light only to the level sufficient to maintain the rate of the over-all reaction sequence at the level permitted by other limiting reactions.

4. Inactivation of the Catalytic System as the Primary Cause of Induction. Gaffron-Franck Theory of Induction

The assumption that the inactivation of one definite catalytic agent in the dark is the prime cause of the short induction period of photosynthesis was first made by Gaffron (1937, 1939, 1940), and later developed into a detailed theory by Franck and co-workers (1941, 1945, 1947, 1949). This theory represents the most comprehensive attempt to date to explain the induction phenomena, and we will give an account of it here, although in many details it is speculative, and new observations—particularly that of the autocatalytic formation of the carbon dioxide acceptor, and the consequences this may have for induction—may call for its re-examination. It must be kept in mind that the theory attempts to explain only the two waves of inhibition which characterize the short induction period and not the "bursts" and "gulps" of oxygen and carbon dioxide. (Franck has endeavored to interpret the latter in terms of invasion of the photosynthetic mechanism by respiration intermediates, as described in section 5 below.)

Gaffron suggested that the cause of irreversible induction losses is the inactivation of the oxygen-liberating catalyst (or catalysts). We recall that kinetic researches, beginning with those of Blackman, Warburg, and Willstätter and Stoll, led Franck and Herzfeld to contemplate three major catalytic factors in photosynthesis—a carboxylating catalyst (E_A), a "finishing" (or "stabilizing") catalyst (E_B) and one (or more likely, two; *cf.* chapter 6, page 133) oxygen liberating catalyst (E_C, and E_O in schemes 9.III, etc.

That the carboxylase, E_A, is not rate-limiting during the initial period of induction is shown, for example, by the insensitivity of the gas exchange and fluorescence during this period to cyanide (cyanide is a specific inhibitor for E_A).

Catalyst E_B, too, is not limiting at the beginning of induction. This has been demonstrated particularly clearly in anaerobic incubation experiments, where the yield per flash (determined by the available amount of

E_B, according to chapter 34) was found by Franck, Pringsheim and Lad to be unaffected by inhibition. Inactivation of E_B should affect immediately both carbon dioxide uptake and oxygen liberation, but according to chapter 28 *not* the yield of fluorescence.

The attribution of induction to the oxygen-liberating catalyst, the "de-oxygenase" (catalyst C in Franck's terminology; E_O rather than E_C in chapter 6 and chapter 9), is the remaining alternative; and it is sup-ported by several pieces of evidence. In the first place, anaerobic incuba-tion experiments with algae of the type of *Scenedesmus* have demonstrated directly that, after a dark anaerobic period (and, *a posteriori*, probably also after a dark period in air), the photochemical and catalytic mecha-nisms of photosynthesis are still intact, with the exception of the oxygen-liberating catalyst (since these algae are able to reduce carbon dioxide in light if hydrogen is supplied as substitute reductant).

Further arguments for the oxygen-liberating catalyst as the primary cause of induction can be derived from experiments with hydroxylamine (Vol. I, page 311). The latter appears to be a specific poison for the oxygen-liberating enzyme system; its uniform effect on the rate in weak and strong light leads to the surmise that this system is formed (or acti-vated) by photosynthesis itself, and *continuously deactivated* by a dark reac-tion, so that its stationary concentration adjusts itself to the prevailing rate of photosynthesis. A catalyst of this kind obviously must be com-pletely deactivated in the dark, and is thus likely to cause induction effects. The "autocatalytic" formation of the "deoxygenase" explains the repeti-tion of induction losses upon each successive increase of the steady rate of photosynthesis (whether it is brought about by a change of light intensity, temperature or carbon dioxide supply).

Since we have assumed that the inhibition of catalyst E_B does not affect fluorescence, one may ask why the same should not hold also for the inhibi-tion of the oxygen-liberating catalyst, since the latter, after all, occupies a similar "finishing" position in the scheme of photosynthesis.

If we assume the validity of a scheme such as 7.IV, E_B and E_C assume exactly symmetric positions, and inhibition of either of them should lead to disappearance of the primary photochemical product (such as $A \cdot HCO_2$ or HX and $A' \cdot OH$ or Z) by back reaction. Inhibition of the second catalyst on the oxidation side, E_O, could, on the other hand, lead to the accumula-tion of somewhat more stable intermediates (designated by $\{OH\}_2$ or $\{O_2\}$ in Vol. I). Franck suggested that these "photoperoxides," if not removed by E_O (or by the hydrogenase in hydrogen-adapted algae), tend to react with metabolic products (sugars?), converting the latter to substances capable of "narcotizing" chlorophyll (as well as E_B). In this way, the "finishing" catalyst, E_C, acquires the capacity of affecting indirectly the fluorescence of chlorophyll—a change that can be caused *directly* only by preparatory catalyst. (This hypothesis already was used in chapter 24.)

The totality of the events in the "first wave" of induction is attributed by Franck and co-workers (1941, 1945, 1947) to the photochemical production of an "internal narcotic." One may ask: Why introduce an unknown metabolite as an intermediate, and not assume direct action of the "photo-peroxides" on chlorophyll? The answer is: *first*, that a "blockade" of chlorophyll by oxygen-precursors would be unlikely to lead to a reduction in the rate of *oxygen liberation* (although it may produce a delay in carbon dioxide uptake, and an upsurge of fluorescence); *second*, the strong dependence of the first wave on species, age, culturing and conditions that prevailed during the dark period points to the intervention of metabolic products.

One puzzling question in connection with the "first wave" of induction is: How can a photochemical reaction lasting only 0.5 to 1 second, and thus permitting, at best, only one chlorophyll molecule in ten or fifty to absorb a quantum, bring about complete cessation of gas exchange, and an increase in fluorescence yield by as much as a factor of three?

As far as the chemical inhibition is concerned, a plausible answer can be provided by reference to a catalyst the concentration of which is much lower than that of chlorophyll. Flashing light experiments led to the conclusion (*cf.* chapters 32 and 34) that this is true of the finishing catalyst, E_B. This catalyst appears to be present normally to the extent of about one molecule per 400–2500 molecules of chlorophyll. Franck and coworkers pointed out that the amount of the internal narcotic produced within a half second of moderate illumination is likely to be sufficient to inhibit *all* of catalyst E_B, and thus to cause practical cessation of photosynthesis.

If this picture is correct, then, in the first moment of illumination, carbon dioxide consumption should begin at a comparatively high level, corresponding to the full rate of the primary photochemical process, while the liberation of oxygen should begin at a rate determined by the amount of the active deoxygenase. Unless illumination is very weak (in which case the residual amount of the oxygenase suffices to maintain the initial rate, and no induction wave occurs), the initial rate of oxygen liberation is much lower than that of the primary photochemical process. As a result, intermediate oxidants accumulate, and within a second inhibit practically all E_B (through the intermediary of the oxidizable metabolite), and thus stop more or less completely both the formation of oxygen and the consumption of carbon dioxide. According to the hypothesis used before, respiration removes the "narcotic" poison—into which the metabolite produced in the dark is converted in light—and thus causes the inhibition wave to subside rapidly in air, it extends over a much longer period under anaerobic conditions, where the only oxygen available is that produced by residual photosynthesis (*cf.* section 6).

How can one, however, explain the strong effect of the first induction wave on the yield of chlorophyll fluorescence? How can such an effect be caused by a "narcotic" available (assuming it is produced with a quantum yield of 1) only to the extent of 1 molecule to 10 or 100 molecules of chlorophyll? One is forced to assume either that 1 molecule of the narcotic can protect the fluorescence of 100 chlorophyll molecules, or else that the fluorescence of the protected molecules is so much more intense than that of the unprotected ones as to raise the *average* yield of fluorescence by a factor of two or three. Both assumptions seem artificial.

An explanation of the "second wave" of induction was first suggested in a paper by Franck, French and Puck (1941). They thought that, if the first wave is an *indirect* effect of accumulated photoperoxides (via an oxidizable metabolite), the second wave may be due to a direct effect of the same intermediates, which has to wait until their quantity had become sufficient to "block" all chlorophyll. (Assuming a quantum yield of ~ 1 for the production of the photoperoxides, this should require from one half to several minutes, depending on the intensity of illumination.)

This hypothesis could explain a "second depression" in the carbon dioxide uptake curves, and also the "second wave" of fluorescence—but not interruption of the steady increase in oxygen production (since the oxygen "precursors" remain present in excess). Therefore, when Franck, Pringsheim and Lad (1945) found a second wave also in oxygen liberation curves, a reinterpretation became necessary. This was provided by Shiau and Franck (1947); as mentioned before, their hypothesis was based on combination of normal induction with the depletion, in light, of the initially full reservoir of the reduction substrate, $A \cdot CO_2$. The suggested interplay is illustrated by fig. 33.50. In A, curve *a* represents induction (more specifically of fluorescence intensity) as it would be if the reactivation of the deoxygenase were the only determining factor, and if the reservoir of reduction substrates remained full. This curve shows the, at first slow, and then accelerated, decline of the "narcotization" of chlorophyll by the metabolic poison (the concentration of which follows that of the "photoperoxides," and thus, indirectly, the inactivation of the deoxygenase). If one assumes —which is the salient point of the hypothesis—that the reduction substrates compete with the "narcotic" for adsorption on chlorophyll (as two adsorbable gases would for the surface of charcoal), then, with a lower concentration of the reduction substrates, the "narcotic" would have a chance to occupy more chlorophyll, and a fluorescence–time curve of type *b* would result. If, at the beginning of illumination, the concentration of the reduction substrate is high, and, after a few minutes of illumination, drops to a steady value (curve a in fig. 33.50A), the fluorescence (which depends on the ratio [narcotic]/[reducible substance]), represented by curve c, will first follow curve a and then go over to curve b (fig. 33.50B), the transition being as indicated by the dotted curve.

Whether this "second wave" of narcotization of chlorophyll will cause, in addition to a fluorescence wave, simultaneous inhibition waves in the uptake of carbon dioxide and the liberation of oxygen, may depend on

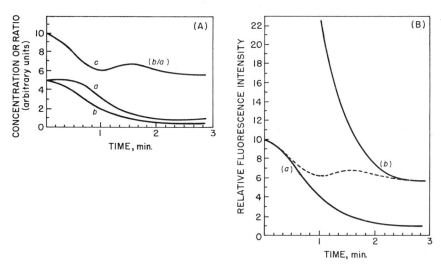

Fig. 33.50. Explanation of the second wave by competition of reducible substances and inhibitor for chlorophyll (after Shiau and Franck 1947): (A) concentration variation of narcotics (b), of photosynthetically reducible substances (a) and of their ratio; (B) theoretical fluorescence–time curves at two concentrations of photosensitive reducible substance, with transition curve shown as broken line.

whether these rates, at the moment when the narcotization wave appears, are limited by the amount of photochemically active chlorophyll, or the amount of active catalyst E_B. This may explain why during the second wave the usual antiparallelism between gas exchange and fluorescence is found often, but not always.

According to this interpretation of the second wave, it should be enhanced by all the factors that tend to depress the concentration of the reduction substrate, $[A \cdot CO_2]$, such as low carbon dioxide concentration, low temperature and cyanide poisoning. This is confirmed by many experimental curves, although the results obtained with variable $[CO_2]$ seem to be ambiguous (*cf.* p. 1339, 1381, 1391). Cyanide, in particular, clearly enhances the second wave and delays its decay practically indefinitely (*cf.* fig. 33.39).

We cannot recount here all the details of Franck's interpretation, by means of this induction theory, of all the variations in the shape of gas exchange and fluorescence–time curves uncovered in the experimental studies reported in parts A and B of this chapter. One general surmise of Franck should, however, be emphasized. He believes that the production of a "blanket" of a narcotizing metabolite on the surface of chlorophyll (and perhaps also on the surface of some catalysts) must be an important

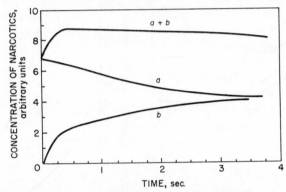

Fig. 33.51. Time course of concentration variation of two narcotics and their total concentration, which influences fluorescence intensity of chlorophyll (after Shiau and Franck 1947): (*a*) external inhibition; (*b*) internal inhibition.

protective device developed by the plants to prevent destructive photochemical reactions (such as photoxidations) from being sensitized by chlorophyll when photosynthesis is inhibited (for any possible reason).

The peculiarities of the induction phenomena after *anaerobic* conditions were explained by Franck, Pringsheim and Lad by the assumption of the combined action of an "external" and the above introduced "internal" inhibitor. The "external" inhibitor is the repeatedly mentioned diffusible acid and reducing material produced by fermentative metabolism and excreted into the medium. This material accounts for the effect of alkalies on anaerobic inhibition (Noack *et al.*), the importance of algal concentration (Franck, Pringsheim and Lad), the immediate high fluorescence yield at the beginning of illumination after prolonged anaerobic incubation, and many other characteristics of anaerobic induction. Variations in the premeability of cell membranes may play an important role in the inhibition phenomena caused by this factor, particularly in the different sensitivity of young and aged cells.

Figure 33.51 shows the hypothetical changes in the amounts of the two inhibitors at the beginning of illumination, and the resulting time course of fluorescence (the latter in agreement with the experiments).

5. Role of Respiration in Induction Phenomena

The above analysis of the possible mechanisms of induction was based on the concept of photosynthesis as a separate system of chemical and photochemical reactions, fundamentally independent of other metabolic mechanisms in the cell. This has been a legitimate and useful concept, since it permitted attention to be concentrated on a minimum number of factors, and to ask questions conducive to meaningful experimentation. It is likely that, in the main, the chemical schemes and kinetic relationships based on this approach will prove valid in the end. However, complete isolation of photosynthesis from other cellular processes undoubtedly was an oversimplification. More recently, evidence has begun to pile up concerning the mutual interplay of photosynthesis and other biochemical processes, above all, respiration. Instead of a separate, chemical structure with one inlet through which carbon dioxide and water molecules enter, and one outlet through which sugar and oxygen escape—we now look on photosynthesis as a more open structure, with several connections to the ambient medium and to the other metabolic reaction systems, on different reduction levels. Of course, even in the explanation of induction phenomena suggested in the preceding sections, Franck has assumed an interference of metabolites with the smooth working of the photosynthetic apparatus, most prominently in his concept of "internal narcotics" (produced, e. g., by fermentation, or by the action of excess photoperoxides on sugars), which were credited with inactivating the photochemical apparatus by settling on chlorophyll, or on catalysts in permanent association with this pigment.

The influence of such "internal poisons" appeared, however, as an incidental interference, which could only slow down or temporarily stop altogether the wheels of photosynthesis (although Franck also suggested that this interference may be providential when the danger exists that the photochemical apparatus, for lack of proper substrate, may begin to chew up itself).

The evidence for placing greater emphasis on the intrinsic character of cross-connections between photosynthesis and other metabolic processes came from two areas. Biochemical studies with isotopic carbon tracers have indicated that photosynthesis may have several intermediates which also occur in catabolic oxidative processes. It was found that several intermediates of respiration can participate reversibly in the carbon dioxide exchange with the medium (and not merely release carbon dioxide as inert final product of oxidation); and signs have been found that setting into motion or stopping the anabolic photochemical mechanism of photosynthesis affects the course and rate of the catabolic thermal processes more immediately than one could expect if their relation were due merely to the one process supplying substrates (sugars and carbon dioxide, respectively) for the other. These relationships will be discussed in chapter 36.

The other reason for considering the interlocking of photosynthesis with other metabolic processes lies in kinetic findings, in particular the occurrence of inverse induction, in which bursts of photochemical activity, considerably in excess of the steady rate, have been observed at the beginning of the illumination period (while bursts of nonphotochemical gas exchange have been observed in the initial periods of darkness, or reduced illumination). As mentioned before, the concept of photosynthesis as a closed reaction sequence could account for inverse induction if it meant starting photosynthesis at full normal rate and then going into a temporary slump, or if it meant starting at a higher-than-normal rate of exchange of one gas (O_2 or CO_2) but lower-than-normal rate of exchange of the other one (to readjust the proper balance of the oxidized and the reduced forms of the photosynthetic catalysts and intermediates). It seems, however, that the various observed bursts and gulps of oxygen and carbon dioxide cannot all be explained in this way, and require the assumption that the pools of photosynthetic intermediates communicate with other metabolic pools and reservoirs, and that the levels to which these pools are filled depend on the rates of both the photochemical and the nonphotochemical metabolic processes. Every time one of these rates is suddenly changed, through an increase or decrease of illumination, all the pools and reservoirs are partly drained, or filled up, to a new stationary level, and this readjustment can be accompanied by evolution or absorption of either oxygen, or carbon dioxide, or both gases. This is obviously a generalization of the picture in which the filling of the pools of intermediates was considered as a matter of photosynthesis alone. Superimposed on these changes in the amounts of intermediates—such as various organic acids, perhaps also peroxides (or other intermediates in the exchange with molecular oxygen)—is the readjustment of catalysts, which may involve the oxidation or reduction of intermediate redox systems (such as the cytochromes, *cf.* above section B7).

The attribution of gas "bursts" and "gulps" in the first minute of illumination to the filling up of the photosynthetic pools by respiration intermediates was first suggested by Franck (1949) as interpretation for the rate measurements by Warburg and co-workers in intermittent light. As stated before in this chapter, Burk and Warburg (1951) suggested that the bursts of activity they noted in the first minute of both light and darkness (or "bright" and "dim" light) were revelations of steady high rate of gas exchange in light—the high rate of anabolic photoprocess being revealed at the beginning of illumination, and the high rate of catabolic "anti-photosynthesis" at the beginning of darkness (where it takes seconds or minutes to be completed).   We have concluded before that this interpreta-tion is not in agreement with the totality of experiments, and that the ob-served bursts and gulps must be considered as transients rather than as "tail ends" of steady metabolisms before the change in illumination. Franck (1953) has attempted a quantitative analysis of the experiments described in Warburg's papers to show that these transients can be explained by assuming that respiration intermediates (of the reduction level of glyc-eric acid), accumulated during the dark period, become available for photo-chemical reduction in the first minute of illumination, and that this photo-chemical half-way reversal of respiration requires only two quanta (per one nonliberated molecule of CO_2 and one nonconsumed molecule of oxy-gen).   Because of the importance of this question for the controversy about the true minimum quantum requirement of photosynthesis, Franck's calculations will be given in more detail in chapter 37D (section 4d).

The absence of induction losses in the Hill reaction of *Chlorella* cells and isolated chloroplasts poses a question for the Franck-Gaffron theory of induction.   It appears offhand that the simplest explanation of this fact would be to renounce the concept that the origin of the induction loss lies on the "oxidation side" of the photochemical process proper (*e. g.*, in the inactivation of the oxygen-liberating enzyme), since processes there must be the same in photosynthesis and in the Hill reaction, and to seek this ori-gin on the "reduction side" of the primary photochemical process, where the Hill reaction differs from photosynthesis.   Franck suggested, however, that this argument is not necessarily convincing, provided one attributes the bulk of the induction loss to a "narcotization" of photochemical ap-paratus by oxidation products formed in consequence of the accumulation of photoperoxides when the oxygen-liberating enzyme is inhibited.   These "narcotics," he argued, may be unable to displace "substitute oxidants," such as quinone, from their position as hydrogen acceptors in contact with chlorophyll (and thus to inhibit temporarily the Hill reaction), while they are able to prevent the access to chlorophyll of hydrogen acceptors (such as phosphoglycerate) which must be reduced in photosynthesis.   Although this explanation is not implausible, it must be acknowledged that the at-tribution of induction to the inhibition of the oxygen-liberating enzyme as the primary cause rests on circumstantial evidence.   It could perhaps be revised without destroying the main ideas of Franck's induction theory, which include the inactivation, in the first moment of illumination, of some essential photosynthetic enzyme, the consequent blanketing of chlorophyll by a "narcotic," and the removal of this narcotic by respiration.

6. Other Theories of Induction

It is impossible to discuss here in detail the theories of induction suggested by other authors, particularly since they were mostly invented *ad hoc*, without relation to the totality of our knowledge of the kinetics of photosynthesis. The most elaborate speculations concerning the origins of the induction curves have been presented by Kautsky. They were based exclusively on the observation of fluorescence, in disregard of other aspects of the induction phenomena, not to speak of general kinetics of photosynthesis in constant or intermittent light.

In his first papers, Kautsky attributed induction to the interaction of excited chlorophyll with molecular oxygen (which he considered—*cf.* chapter 18, page 514—as the universal energy acceptor in dyestuff-sensitized reactions). After he himself had found that the fluorescence of living plants is insensitive to changes in oxygen concentration between 0.5 and 100%, Kautsky substituted, in the role of energy acceptor, an oxygen-acceptor compound, supposed to dissociate only below 1% O_2 in the atmosphere. He attributed the first rise of fluorescence to the transfer of excitation energy from chlorophyll to this compound (ΩO_2), which was assumed to be converted into an activated form, ΩO_2^* (perhaps a peroxide). While this form accumulates, the fluorescence rises to a peak (because only ΩO_2, and not ΩO_2^*, can act as a chemical quencher). In the second stage, ΩO_2^* reacts (thermally) with the substrates of photosynthesis, and is converted back into ΩO_2; this leads to the renewed decline of fluorescence. In absence of oxygen, ΩO_2 is dissociated and the fluorescence wave disappears.

Kautsky later added various additional assumptions intended to explain the details of the fluorescence curves. An elaborate development of the theory was given by Kautsky and U. Franck (1943), who postulated, in addition to the photochemical activation and thermal deactivation of the first energy acceptor, ΩO_2, a sequence of three photochemical activations and thermal deactivations of another energy acceptor, which they made responsible for those features of the fluorescence curves that do not disappear, but, to the contrary, are accentuated in the absence of oxygen. They thought that the four successive photochemical reactions between excited chlorophyll and the two energy acceptors, which they believed detectable in the ups and downs of the fluorescence curves, must correspond to as many primary photochemical processes of photosynthesis, and thus explain why the latter may require 4 quanta.

This explanation fails to deal with the basic problems. While attributing the variations of fluorescence to accumulation and disappearance of various intermediates of photosynthesis, Kautsky does not even ask why these intermediates accumulate to a maximum and then disappear again (instead of assuming a constant level), or why the first peak is reached after an illumination period so short that only a few per cent of chlorophyll molecules can be excited.

Later, Kautsky (1951) tried to bring his theory of induction in relation to Warburg and Burk's "new theory" of photosynthesis, which also ascribes to molecular oxygen an active role in the photosynthesis cycle.

Smith (1937) suggested that the induction curves he obtained with *Cabomba*, as well as those found by Briggs for *Mnium* and by van der Paauw for *Hormidium*, can be explained quantitatively by the assumption that chlorophyll has to be activated photochemically, to Chl*, by a reaction the yield of which is proportional to (const. $-$ [Chl*]^2), and is deactivated thermally by a reaction (with the substrate of photosynthesis) the yield of which is proportional to [Chl*]² (this reaction leading to the final product of photosynthesis: Chl + $h\nu \rightarrow$ Chl*, Chl* + substrate $\rightarrow$ Chl + product). No explanation was given for the occurrence of a square of concentration in both equations. In addition Smith's theory disregards the main objections against all induction theories based on the accumulation of thermal intermediates—the irreversible character of the induction losses.

Briggs (1933) discussed two forms of an "inhibitor theory" of induction. In the first one, the inhibitor was assumed to be of the "narcotic" type, *i. e.*, one which makes the sensitizer unavailable for photosynthesis by settling down on it. In the second theory, the inhibitor was assumed to be of the cyanide type, and to prevent the primary photoproducts from stabilization by the poisoning of an enzyme. Briggs derived, for these cases, equations representing the approach of photosynthesis to its final steady rate; but our present knowledge of the complexity of the induction curves makes us sceptical with regard to the value of all such theoretical functions, even if they were found to fit several experimental curves.

Some more recent experimental studies (Mehler, p. 1568; Gerretsen, p. 1588; Arnon *et al.*, p. 1537) drew attention to one additional possible source of "asymmetric" induction-photoxidation of ascorbic acid reserves. This may precede the utilization of water as reductant and delay the liberation of oxygen, while permitting carbon dioxide reduction to start immediately. (Initial reduction of "substitute reductants," instead of carbon dioxide, obviously must have the opposite effect, as repeatedly suggested above.)

Speaking in general, with the gradual clarification of the biochemistry of photosynthesis a tendency arises to inquire into the qualitative chemical sources of induction phenomena instead of analyzing the induction curves in terms of a minimum number of kinetic factors. This is inevitable and natural; but the considerable experimental work and ingenuity of interpretation invested in the study of induction kinetics (and of the kinetics of photosynthesis in general) should not be considered as wasted (as some biochemists may be inclined to believe). They are fundamental contributions toward the general edifice of photosynthesis—and biochemistry in general—as an exact science.

Bibliography to Chapter 33

Induction Phenomena

A. Gas Exchange during the Induction Period

1865   Boussaingault, J. B., *Compt. rend.*, **61**, 493, 605, 657.
1887   Pringsheim, N., *Sitzber. Akad. Wiss. Berlin*, **1887**, 763.
1918   Osterhout, W. J. V., and Haas, A. R. C., *J. Gen. Physiol.*, **1**, 1.
        Willstätter, R., and Stoll, A., *Untersuchungen über die Assimilation der Kohlensäure.* Springer, Berlin.
1920   Warburg, O., *Biochem. Z.*, **103**, 188.
1922   Kostychev, S. P., *Ber. deut. botan. Ges.*, **39**, 319.
1929   Li, Tsi Tung, *Ann. Botany*, **43**, 787.
1930   Harder, R., *Planta*, **11**, 263.
1932   van der Paauw, F., *Rec. trav. botan. néerland.*, **29**, 497.
1933   Briggs, G. E., *Proc. Roy. Soc. London*, **B113**, 1.
        Harder, R., *Planta*, **20**, 699.

1934 Emerson, R., and Green, L., *J. Gen. Physiol.*, **17**, 817.
1935 Bukatsch, F., *Jahrb. wiss. Botan.*, **81**, 419.
Gaffron, H., *Biochem. Z.*, **280**, 337.
1937 Gaffron, H., *Naturwissenschaften*, **25**, 460.
Gaffron, H., *ibid.*, **25**, 715.
Gessner, F., *Jahrb. wiss. Botan.*, **85**, 267.
McAlister, E. D., *Smithsonian Inst. Pubs. Misc. Collections*, **95**, No. 24.
Smith, E. L., *J. Gen. Physiol.*, **21**, 151.
1938 Blinks, L. R., and Skow, R. K., *Proc. Natl. Acad. Sci. Washington*, **24**, 413.
Blinks, L. R., and Skow, R. K., *ibid.*, **24**, 420.
Gessner, F., *Jahrb. wiss. Botan.*, **86**, 491.
Harder, R., and Aufdemgarten, H., *Nachr. Ges. Wiss. Göttingen*, **3**, 191.
1939 Aufdemgarten, H., *Planta*, **29**, 643.
Aufdemgarten, H., *ibid.*, **30**, 342.
Gaffron, H., *Biol. Zentr.*, **59**, 288.
Gaffron, H., *Cold Spring Harbor Symposia Quant. Biol.*, **7**, 377.
McAlister, E. D., *J. Gen. Physiol.*, **22**, 613.
Noack, K., Pirson, A., and Michels, H., *Naturwissenschaften*, **27**, 645.
1940 Gaffron, H., *Am. J. Botany*, **27**, 204.
McAlister, E. D., and Myers, J., *Smithsonian Inst. Pubs. Misc. Collections*, **99**, No. 6.
Michels, H., *Z. Botan.*, **35**, 241.
Myers, J., and Burr, G. O., *J. Gen. Physiol.*, **24**, 45.
1941 Emerson, R., and Lewis, C. M., *Am. J. Botany*, **28**, 789.
Franck, J., and French C. S. *J. Gen. Physiol.*, **25**, 309.
Franck, J., French, C. S., and Puck, T. T., *J. Phys. Chem.*, **45**, 1268.
Franck, J., and Gaffron, H., *Advances in Enzymology*, Vol. I, Interscience, New York-London, p. 199.
1942 Steemann-Nielsen, E., *Dansk Botanisk. Arkiv*, **11**, No. 2.
1945 Franck, J., Pringsheim, P., and Lad, D. T., *Arch. Biochem.*, **7**, 103.
1947 Shiau, Y. G., and Franck, J., *Arch. Biochem.*, **14**, 253.
1948 Warburg, O., *Am. of Botany*, **35**, 194.
1949 van der Veen, R., *Physiol. Plantarum*, **2**, 217.
van der Veen, R., *ibid.*, **2**, 287.
Steemann-Nielsen, E., *ibid.*, **2**, 247.
1950 Clendenning, K., A. and Ehrmantraut, H., *Arch. Biochem.*, **29**, 387.
van der Veen, R., *Physiol. Plantarum*, **3**, 247.
Kandler, O., *Z. Naturforsch.*, **5b**, 423.
Warburg, O., and Burk, D., *Arch. Biochem.*, **25**, 410.
1951 Österlind, S., *Physiol. Plantarum*, **4**, 514.
Warburg, O., Geleick, H., and Briese, K., *Z. Naturforsch.*, **6b**, 417.
Nishimura, M. S., Whittingham, C. P., and Emerson, R., *Symposia Soc. Exptl. Biol.*, **5**, 176.
1952 Steemann-Nielsen, E., *Physiol. Plantarum*, **5**, 334.
Österlind, S., *ibid.*, **5**, 403.
Olson, R. A., and Brackett, F. S., *Federation Proc.*, **11**, 115.

Briggs, G. E., and Whittingham, C. P., *New Phytologist*, **51**, 236.
1953   Brown, A. H., *Am. J. Botany*, **40**, 719.
Brown, A. H., and Webster, G. C., *ibid.*, **40**, 753.
Brackett, F. S., Olson, R. A., and Crickard, R. G., *J. Gen. Physiol.*, **36**, 529.
Brackett, F. S., Olson, R. A., and Crickard, R. G., *ibid.*, **36**, 563.
Franck, J., *Arch. Biochem. and Biophys.*, **45**, 190.
Hill, R., and Whittingham, C. P., *New Phytologist*, **52**, 133.
Damaschke, K., Tödt, F., Burk, D., and Warburg, O., *Biochim. et Biophys. Acta*, **12**, 347.
Strehler, B. L., *Arch. Biochem. and Biophys.*, **43**, 67.
Warburg, O., Krippahl, G., Buchholz, W., and Schröder, W., *Z. Naturforsch.*, **8b**, 675.
1954   Emerson, R. and Chalmers, R. V., Paper presented to *Nat. Acad. Sci.*, April 1954.
Emerson, R., and Chalmers, R. V., Paper presented at *Intern. Botany Congress*, Paris, July 1954.
Rosenberg, J. L., *J. Gen. Physiol.*, **37**, 754.
Gaffron, H., *IVth Symposium of the Society of General Microbiology*, Cambridge Univ. Press, pp. 152–185.
1955   Brown, A. H., and Whittingham. C. P., *Plant Physiol.*, **30**, 231.

B. Fluorescence and Absorption during the Induction Period

1931   Kautsky, H., and Hirsch, A., *Naturwissenschaften*, **19**, 694.
1932   Kautsky, H., Hirsch, A., and Davidshöfer, F., *Ber. deut. chem. Ges.*, **65**, 1762.
1934   Franck, J., and Levi, H., *Z. physik. Chem.*, **B27**, 409.
Kautsky, H., and Hirsch, A., *Biochem. Z.*, **274**, 423.
Kautsky, H., and Spohn, H., *ibid.*, **274**, 435.
1935   Kautsky, H., and Hirsch, A., *ibid.*, **277**, 250.
Kautsky, H., and Hirsch, A., *ibid.*, **278**, 373.
Knorr, H. V., and Albers, V. M., *Cold Spring Harbor Symposia Quant. Biol.*, **3**, 87.
1936   Franck, J., and Wood, R. W., *J. Chem. Phys.*, **4**, 551.
Kautsky, H., and Flesch, W., *Biochem. Z.*, **284**, 412.
Kautsky, H., and Marx, A., *Naturwissenschaften*, **24**, 317.
1937   Kautsky, H., and Marx, A., *Biochem. Z.*, **290**, 248.
Kautsky, H., and Hormuth, R., *ibid.*, **291**, 285.
1938   Kautsky, H., and Eberlein, R., *Naturwissenschaften*, **26**, 576.
1939   Kautsky, H., and Eberlein, R., *Biochem. Z.*, **302**, 137.
Wassink, E. C., and Katz, E., *Enzymologia*, **6**, 145.
1940   McAlister, E. D., and Myers, J., *Smithsonian Inst. Pubs. Misc. Collections*, **99**, No. 6.
1941   Franck, J., French, C. S., and Puck, T. T., *J. Phys. Chem.*, **45**, 1268.
Franck, J., and Gaffron, H., *Advances in Enzymology*, Vol. I, Interscience, New York-London, p. 199.
Kautsky, H., and Zedlitz, W., *Naturwissenschaften*, **29**, 101.

1942   Wassink, E. C., Katz, E., and Dorrestein, R., *Enzymologia*, **10**, 285.
1943   Kautsky, H., and Franck, U., *Biochem. Z.*, **315**, 139, 156, 176, 207.
1944   Wassink, E. C., and Kersten, J. A. H., *Enzymologia*, **11**, 282.
1945   Franck, J., Pringsheim, P., and Lad, D. T., *Arch. Biochem.*, **7**, 103.
1947   Shiau, Y. G., and Franck, J., *Arch. Biochem.*, **14**, 253.
1948   Kautsky, H., and Franck, U., *Naturwissenschaften*, **35**, 43, 74.
1949   Franck, J., "The Relation of Chlorophyll Fluorescence to Photosynthesis" in *Photosynthesis in Plants*. Iowa State College Press, Ames, 1949, pp. 293–348.
1951   Wassink, E. C., *Advances in Enzymology*, Vol. XI, Interscience, New York-London, p. 91.
1952   Duysens, L. N. M., *Thesis*, Univ. Utrecht.
1954   Duysens, L. N. M., *Nature*, **173**, 692.
      Duysens, L. N. M., *Science*, **120**, 353.
      Duysens, L. N. M., *ibid.*, **121**, 210.

C. Interpretation of Induction Phenomena

1918   Osterhout, W. J. V., and Haas, A. R. C., *J. Gen. Physiol.*, **1**, 1.
1932   Lubimenko, V. N., and Shcheglova, O. A., *Planta*, **18**, 383.
1933   Briggs, G. E., *Proc. Roy. Soc. London*, **B113**, 1.
1937   Gaffron, H., *Naturwissenschaften*, **25**, 460.
      Gaffron, H., *ibid.*, **25**, 715.
      Smith, E. L., *J. Gen. Physiol.*, **21**, 151.
1939   Gaffron, H., *Biol. Zentr.*, **59**, 288.
      Gaffron, H., *Cold Spring Harbor Symposia Quant. Biol.*, **7**, 377.
1940   Gaffron, H., *Am. J. Botany*, **27**, 204.
1941   Franck, J., French, C. S., and Puck, T. T., *J. Phys. Chem.*, **45**, 1268.
1942   Franck, J., *Am. J. Botany*, **29**, 314.
1943   Kautsky, H., and Franck, U., *Biochem. Z.*, **315**, 139, 156, 176, 207.
1945   Franck, J., Pringsheim, P., and Lad, D. T., *Archiv. Biochem.*, **7**, 103.
1947   Shiau, Y. G., and Franck, J., *ibid.*, **14**, 253.
1949   Franck, J., *Arch. Biochem.*, **23**, 297.
1951   Burk, D., and Warburg, O., *Z. Naturforsch.*, **6b**, 12.
      Kautsky, H. *ibid.*, **6b**, 292.
1953   Franck, J., *Arch. Biochem. and Biophys.*, **45**, 190.

CHAPTER 34

TIME EFFECTS. II. PHOTOSYNTHESIS IN INTERMITTENT LIGHT*

This chapter calls for the same preliminary remark made in chapter 33. When it was first written, "induction" appeared to be merely a gradual rise of photosynthesis, after a dark period, from a low initial rate to a steady final level; and the effects of light intermittency appeared fully explicable by the combined influence of induction losses (negative intermittency effect), and a continuation in the dark, for a time of the order of 0.03 second, of the limiting thermal reaction of photosynthesis (positive intermittency effect). This picture appears oversimplified now, after transient bursts and slumps of gas exchange have been shown to follow changes in the intensity of illumination. Combined with induction losses, these transients can make the time course of the exchange of carbon dioxide, or oxygen, or both, quite complicated.

Furthermore, it now seems likely that photosynthesis in intermittent light may be affected by interaction with respiration and other catabolic processes (which may be one of the causes of the above-mentioned "transients"). Intermediates of the catabolic metabolism can be drawn into the photosynthetic process in a subsequent light period; in other words, in intermittent light, illumination may reverse part-way some of the respiration begun, but not completed, during the dark periods (cf. chapter 37D, section 3).

Still another general remark is appropriate here: In cell suspensions, "intermittency effects" are also inevitable in "steady" light because of stirring, particularly in the case of dense suspensions illuminated by a narrow beam of light. Diluting the suspension and spreading the illumination uniformly over the whole surface of the vessel minimizes the intermittency of the light to which each single cell is exposed. However, even in the extreme case when practically no mutual shading of the cells occurs, individual chlorophyll molecules still receive variable amounts of light depending on the momentary orientation of the cell (since a single chloroplast absorbs up to 50% of incident light in the absorption peaks of chlorophyll). The closest approximation to uniform illumination can be obtained by using weakly absorbed (e. g., green) light, and a suspension layer containing, on the average, less than one cell in the path of each light beam.

*Bibliography, page 1483.

After these preliminary remarks, we now proceed with the discussion of intermittent light experiments.

In a quantitative discussion of the intermittency effect, a basis must first be established for the comparison of yields in intermittent and constant light. Three methods of comparison have been used (*cf.* fig. 34.5):

(*a*) The yield obtained during a certain total period of intermittent illumination (N light periods of t^* seconds each, and N dark periods of t_d seconds each) has been compared with the yield produced in the same total time, $t = N(t_d + t^*)$, by uninterrupted light of equal intensity. We may call the ratio of these two yields the *intermittency factor for equal intensity, and equal total time, i_{It}.* This method of comparison has to be used, *e. g.*, to answer the question: How will periodic interruptions of illumination by a rotating disc affect the yield of photosynthesis of a plant under a light source of constant intensity?

(*b*) The yield produced during N light periods of t^* seconds each can be compared with that of uninterrupted illumination of equal *actual duration*, Nt^* seconds (and equal intensity). This comparison answers the question: Given a certain total amount of light energy of definite intensity, will it be better utilized for photosynthesis by dividing it into several exposures separated by dark intervals, or will it be used best in one continuous stretch? The ratio of the yields obtained in these two ways—the *intermittency factor for equal intensity and equal total energy*—will be designated by i_{IE}. A simple relation exists between i_{It} and i_{IE}, namely:

$$(34.1) \qquad i_{It} = i_{IE} \frac{t^*}{t_d + t^*}$$

The quantity that Briggs (1941) called the "yield" of intermittency was: $i_{IE} - 1$.

(*c*) The yield obtained in intermittent light can further be compared with the yield produced by the same total amount of light energy distributed uniformly over the same total time; the *intensity* of the uninterrupted light is in this case smaller than that of intermittent light, in the ratio $t^*/(t_d + t^*)$. This method of comparison answers the question: Given a certain amount of light energy to be used within a certain period of time, will it be more advantageous to distribute this energy evenly over the whole available time, or to concentrate it in separate exposures with dark intervals between them? The ratio of the yields obtained in this way can be called the intermittency factor for equal energy and equal time; it will be designated by i_{Et}.

The relation between i_{Et} and the other two intermittency factors is as follows:

(34.2)
$$i_{Et} = \beta i_{It} = \beta i_{IE} \frac{t^*}{t_d + t^*}$$

Here, β designates the increase in rate of photosynthesis brought about by an increase in the intensity of continuous light by a factor of $(t_d + t^*)/t$. Equation (34.2) follows from the consideration that, if we first raise the intensity of continuous illumination by this factor, and then use a rotating sector to produce intermittent illumination with light periods of t^* seconds duration, the result must be the same as that obtained by concentrating the whole energy of the original illumination in exposures of t^* seconds each.

Equation (34.2) shows that the factor i_{Et} depends on the shape of the light curve, $P = f(I)$, in continuous light.

Section A of this chapter will deal with phenomena observed in intermittent light with equal light and dark periods, $t_d = t^*$, which we will designate as *alternating light*. In this case, $i_{tE} = 2\,i_{It}$ (*cf.* equation 34.1), and one of these two factors (rather than the factor i_{Et}) is commonly used for the characterization of the intermittency effect.

Section B will deal with *flashing light* $(t^* \ll t_d)$. For very short flashes $(t^* < 0.001$ second), the true momentary light intensity during the flashes seems to become unimportant. (About Burk's disagreement with this view, see p. 1475.) Plants react to such short flashes as if they were instantaneous, *i. e.*, the yield per flash depends only on the *total energy* of the flash (time integral of its intensity).

In photography—and in photochemistry in general—one is accustomed to consider the reduction of *average* light intensity by *rotating sectors* equivalent to the reduction cf *true* light intensity by *filters* (reciprocity law). This, however, does not apply to reactions which are subject to light saturation—*i. e.*, reactions that contain, in addition to a photochemical stage, a "dark" process of limited efficiency. In the saturation region, the two ways of reducing light intensity can have the same effect only if the duration of the dark periods is much shorter than the time required for the completion of all dark reactions.

A. Alternating Light*

1. Yield of Photosynthesis in Relation to Frequency of Alternations

In alternating light, the factor i_{IE} can be expected to be larger than unity $(i_{It} > 0.5)$ if the periods t_d and t^* are very long or very short, and less than unity in the intermediate region. Long intervals (of the order of several hours) can improve the utilization of light energy because during the dark "rest periods" the plant can recuperate from the injury or exhaustion that often follows a period of intense photosynthesis. Some phenomena involved in the natural adaptation of plants to the alternation

*Bibliography, page 1483.

of day and night probably belong to this class. Very short intervals (of the order of 1 second or less) also may cause an improvement of the energy conversion yield, because they allow the dark catalytic reactions of photosynthesis to run to completion, restoring the photosynthetic apparatus to its full efficiency at the beginning of each new light period.

In the intermediate range of frequencies—of the order of 1/min. or 1/hr.—alternating illumination can be expected to cause a depression of the yield ($i_{IE} < 1$, $i_{It} < 0.5$), because dark intervals of this length permit the development of induction phenomena, which occupy most of the subsequent light periods. Thus, plotting i_{IE} and i_{It} against log t, we can expect to obtain a curve of the shape shown in figure 34.1.

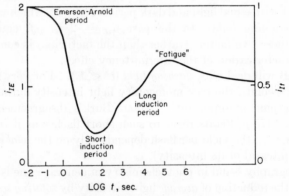

Fig. 34.1. Expected trend of intermittency factors for
equal dark and light periods.

(In this curve, the "bursts" and "gulps" which complicate induction phenomena have not been taken into consideration. This is legitimate when the volume of these extra components of the gas exchange is considerably smaller than that of the induction losses.)

The first observations of the actual effect of intermittent light on photosynthesis were made by Brown and Escombe (1905). They reported that, under certain conditions, as much as one half, or even three quarters, of the total incident light could be taken away by a rotating sector without significantly decreasing the yield of photosynthesis (this means $i_{It} \simeq 1$ and $i_{IE} \simeq 2$–4).

Willstätter and Stoll (1918) suggested that, since Brown and Escombe worked with strong light and a limited supply of carbon dioxide, their results could have been due to the exhaustion of carbon dioxide in the immediate neighborhood of the chloroplasts during each flash and thus bear no relation to the intrinsic kinetic mechanism of photosynthesis. This inter-

TABLE 34.I

INTERMITTENCY FACTORS FOR *Chlorella* IN ALTERNATING LIGHT[a] (AFTER WARBURG 1919)

t, sec.	15	1.5	0.38	0.15	0.038	0.015	0.0038	0.0038[b]	0.0038[c]
i_{IE}		1.14	1.36	1.46	1.56	1.77	1.72	1.96	1.88	1.0

[a] High light intensity, 25° C., $[CO_2] = 9.1 \times 10^{-5}$ mole/l.
[b] $[CO_2] = 136 \times 10^{-5}$.
[c] Low I.

pretation caused Warburg (1919) to undertake new experiments on the effect of alternating light, in which care was taken to provide an abundant supply of carbon dioxide. He found that the intermittency effect occurs also under these conditions, where the explanation of Willstätter and Stoll cannot apply. Table 34.I shows that the intermittency factor, i_{IE}, is considerably larger than unity at $[CO_2] = 9.1 \times 10^{-5}$ mole/l. (a concentration high enough to make carbon dioxide limitation implausible), and even

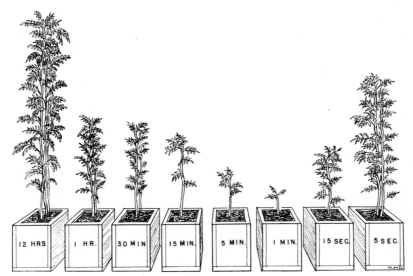

Fig. 34.2. Yellow cosmos (*Cosmos sulphureus*) grown with equal periods of light and darkness (after Garner and Allard 1931). Compare with fig. 34.1.

at $[CO_2] = 136 \times 10^{-5}$ mole/l. The last figure in the table shows that intermittency has no influence on the rate in *weak* light ($i_{IE} = 1.0$; $i_{II} = 0.5$). This is understandable; in weak light (more precisely, within the linear range of the light curves), the rate of photosynthesis is limited only by the frequency of the absorption acts; the catalysts can cope with all the intermediates produced by light without the formation of a backlog that could be utilized in the dark. In strong light, on the other hand, the photosynthetic apparatus could produce more if it were not for the slowness of certain enzymatic reactions—and these can be completed during the dark intervals. (Here, again, we neglect the fact that under certain conditions "bursts" of gas exchange have also been observed in weak light, where induction losses are negligible.)

Padoa and Vita (1928) repeated Warburg's experiments with the water plant *Elodea canadensis*. They found i_{IE} factors up to 2.71, with not less than five maxima (at 16, 80, 406, 650 and 887 alternations per second). Between these peaks, i_{IE} values declined to 1. The reality of these several maxima and minima, not noted by other investigators, is very doubtful.

The next step in the elucidation of the shape of $i_{IE} = f(t)$ curve was made in the well-known studies of Garner and Allard (1931) on the effect of intermittent light on the *growth* of plants. Figure 34.2, taken from their work, shows a striking minimum of the growth of potted plants of yellow cosmos when the alternations occur about once a minute. The growth curve rises steeply on both sides of the minimum; 5 second intervals are almost as favorable as the "natural" intervals of 12 hours.

It was often suggested that the basis of some intermittency effects in plant physiology may lie in the influence of intermittent light on photosynthesis. In confirmation of this, Portsmouth (1937) found that the growth curve of Garner and Allard runs closely parallel to the curve representing the yield of photosynthesis in relation to the frequency of light alternations. We recall that Willstätter and Stoll tried to attribute the intermittency effects, described by Brown and Escombe, to an inadequate supply of carbon dioxide. Gregory and Pearse (1937) suggested a similar explanation for the growth curve of Garner and Allard. They thought that it may be caused by incomplete opening of stomata in intermittent light, leading to carbon dioxide starvation. (Both the opening of stomata in light and their closure in the dark are not instantaneous; the ratio of their velocities determines the average aperture of the stomata in intermittent light.) Portsmouth thought that the sluggishness of the stomata may provide a clue also to the decline of photosynthesis in alternating light.

Gregory and Pearse measured the apertures of the stomata of *Pelargonium zonale* in alternating light, and found the slits to be particularly narrow when the periods of light and darkness were 5 seconds each. They thought this period to be sufficiently close to the minimum of the Garner-Allard growth curve to warrant the attribution of the latter to stomatal influences. However, figure 34.2 shows that, at $t = 5$ seconds, the plant development proceeded quite satisfactorily. Furthermore, we mentioned above that Warburg had observed intermittency effects in *Chlorella* cells, where no stomatal effects are possible. More recently, Iggena (1938) found that a growth curve similar to that observed by Garner and Allard with the higher land plants can be obtained also with stomata-free lower plants (green or blue algae). These plants, too, grew particularly slowly in light with an alternation frequency of 1/min., and much better at $t =$ 0.25 or 0.08 second, or $t > 1$ minute. More recent experiments on the growth of unicellular algae (*Chlorella*) in intermittent light gave a similar result (*cf.* part B, pp. 1476–1477).

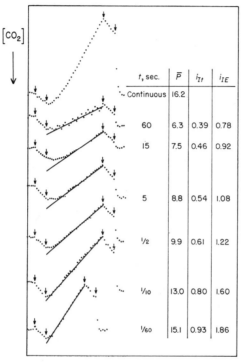

t, sec.	$\bar{P}$	i_{Tt}	i_{TE}
Continuous	16.2		
60	6.3	0.39	0.78
15	7.5	0.46	0.92
5	8.8	0.54	1.08
1/2	9.9	0.61	1.22
1/10	13.0	0.80	1.60
1/60	15.1	0.93	1.86

Fig. 34.3. Effect of intermittent illumination, with equal light and dark periods, on photosynthesis in wheat plants (after McAlister 1937). Arrows indicate beginning and end of illumination. Points represent spectroscopic CO_2 determinations in half minute intervals.

We conclude from these experiments that the inertia of the stomata can be, at best, only a contributing cause of the inhibition of plant growth by alternating light with a frequency of the order of 1/min. Comparison of figure 34.1 with the figures in chap. 33 makes it likely that the main cause of this behavior is induction, which is almost fully developed after 1 minute of darkness, and permits only little photosynthesis in the first minute of subsequent illumination.

Figure 34.3 shows that according to McAlister (1937) the average rate of consumption of carbon dioxide by wheat plants also is slowest at

$t = 60$ seconds; it increases gradually when t declines to $\frac{1}{60}$ second, or increases from 60 seconds to infinity. (The yields obtained at $t = 120$ and 300 seconds, not shown in figure 34.3, were intermediate between those obtained at 60 seconds and in continuous light.)

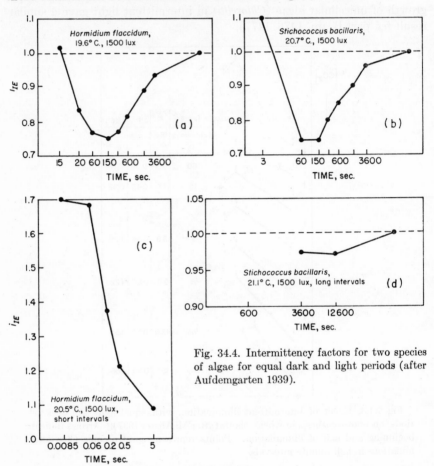

Fig. 34.4. Intermittency factors for two species of algae for equal dark and light periods (after Aufdemgarten 1939).

Factor i_{It} is determined in figure 34.3 by the ratio of the slope of the line representing the average consumption of carbon dioxide in intermittent light, and the slope of the corresponding line for continuous light. i_{It} is < 0.5 ($i_{IE} < 1$) for $t = 60$ and 15 seconds, and > 0.5 ($i_{IE} > 1$) for the smaller values of t. At $t = \frac{1}{60}$ second, i_{It} almost reaches unity ($i_{It} = 0.93$, $i_{IE} = 1.86$).

The findings of Warburg et al. (1951) that the gas exchange in alternating light, $t =$ 1–3 min., results from a photosynthesis enhanced up to 3 times and respiration enhanced up to 10 times (compared to steady conditions), and the failure of Brown (1953) and of Whittingham (1954) to confirm them will be discussed in chapter 37D.

Aufdemgarten (1939) measured the photosynthesis of *Hormidium flaccidum* in intermittent light, using van der Paauw's gas flow method. His results are shown in figure 34.4a, the shape of which resembles closely that anticipated in figure 34.1   The minimum lies somewhat above 1 minute (at t = 2.5 minutes); in some experiments, a second minimum was found at t = 10 minutes.

In a *Stichococcus bacillaris* suspension, a flat minimum stretched from 1 to 2.5 minutes (fig. 34.4b).   The factor i_{IE} rises sharply on the side of the short intervals as t declines to 0.06 second, then more slowly; at t = 0.0085 second, i_{IE} reaches 1.7 (*cf*. fig. 34.4c).   On the side of long intervals, i_{IE} remains below unity up to t = 1.5 hour (*cf*. fig. 34.4d).

Experiments with excised leaves (*Impatiens parviflora, Vitis vinifera,* etc.) gave less regular curves, but they, too, showed a distinct minimum in the region of t = 5 minutes.

2. Theoretical Discussion of the Effect of Alternating Light

There seems to be little doubt that the general shape of the $i_{IE} = f(t)$ curves in the region between 0.01 and 1000 seconds is strongly influenced by the interplay of two factors: the "Emerson-Arnold period," which causes the intermittency factor to be highest at alternations of the order of 100/sec.; and the induction period, which produces a minimum in the region between t = 1 and 5 minutes.   The course of the curve above 5 minutes seems to reveal the influence of the "long" induction period (*cf*. fig. 34.4c).   Whether "exhaustion" or "fatigue" effects produce a second hump, somewhere between t = 1 hour and ∞ (tentatively indicated in fig. 34.1), is not certain, and probably depends on special circumstances.

A *quantitative* interpretation of the intermittency factors in the region where the induction period is the decisive factor is complicated by the fact that, in alternating light, a change of frequency affects both the light and the dark periods, and thus produces two antagonistic effects.   A longer dark interval means a more complete preparation of the induction phenomena, while a longer light interval means more time for overcoming the initial inhibition.   The first effect can be expected to prevail at alternation frequencies of more than 1/min. (where induction phenomena blanket practically the whole illumination period), the second at alternation frequencies of less than 1/5 min. (where a further lengthening of the dark period can add only little to the induction losses; *cf*. fig. 33.6).   The exact position of the minimum must depend on kinetic equations that govern deactivation of the photosynthetic apparatus in the dark and reactivation in light (for a discussion of the kinetics of these reactions, see chapter 33, part C).

The disappearance of photosynthetic production losses due to induction at t-values below 1 minute should bring the factor i_{IE} back to unity, but could not make it *higher* than 1. The experimental intermittency factor increases, however, far above this value, and approaches 2 at alternation frequencies of the order of 100/sec. (*cf.* Table 34.I, and figs. 34.3 and 34.4c). This behavior becomes understandable if one assumes that short dark intervals can be efficiently utilized for the completion of the dark reaction that limits the rate of photosynthesis in strong continuous light. In the limiting case of very short intervals, the rate-determining catalyst will be as fully occupied during the dark interval as it is in light, leading to an intermittency factor of $i_{IE} \simeq 2$ ($i_{It} \simeq 1$). We may thus conclude, from the alternating light experiments, that the catalytic reaction that limits the rate of photosynthesis in strong light can continue for about 0.01 second after the cessation of illumination.

According to the theory of Franck and Herzfeld, this reaction is the transformation of the intermediates produced by the photochemical process proper, which prevents them from reacting back. The catalyst that brings about this "stabilization" was designated by E_B in several reaction schemes presented in chapters 7, 9 (Vol. I), 24 and 28 (Vol. II, 1). As stated before, this hypothesis of Franck and Herzfeld is not bound to the specific reaction mechanism suggested by these authors (scheme 7VA), but can be used also in conjunction with other reaction schemes.

The fact that the catalyst E_B can work in the dark only for a limited length of time (about 0.01 second at room temperature), irrespective of the intensity of the preceding flash, can be understood if it is assumed that this catalyst acts on an *unstable* substrate. If the flash had produced more light products than the catalyst can handle at one time, only the batch that has become associated with the catalyst immediately after the light reaction is saved from back reactions and contributes to the final yield. We have already used this picture in chapter 32 (sect. 4) in explaining the maximum number of oxygen molecules that can be produced by a flash. (We have postulated that this number is determined by the number of available molecules of E_B; it may be either equal to E_B^0, or smaller by a factor of n, depending on whether E_B has to operate once, or n times—perhaps, four or eight times—to bring about the liberation of one molecule of oxygen.)

Experiments in flashing light (to be discussed in section B) have permitted a more precise determination of the "working period" of E_B— about 0.02 second at 20° C. (*cf.* Table 34.II). If the intermittency effect in alternating light were determined, in the region $t < 1$ minute, *only* by this catalytic action period (which we will call the Emerson-Arnold period) the factor i_{IE} could exceed unity only for dark intervals of this order of magnitude. Instead, we find in Table 34.I that i_{IE} is higher than unity even for intervals as long as 15 seconds.

The results of McAlister (fig. 34.3) are somewhat less extreme: the i_{IE} values found by him are < 1 at 15 seconds, and practically equal to 1 at 5 seconds; but they reach 1.2 at 0.5 second and 1.6 at 0.1 second—periods which are still too long to be effectively occupied by the Emerson-Arnold reaction. Briggs (1941), too, found $i_{IE} = 1.6$ for $t = 0.6$ second, a value even somewhat higher than Warburg's values in Table 34.I.

Weller and Franck (1941) noted the need to explain the favorable effect of dark periods of the order of 1–10 seconds, and proceeded to repeat Warburg's experiments under a variety of conditions. In some cases, the i_{IE} values remained below unity until t reached the order of magnitude of the Emerson-Arnold period; but in others, they exceeded 1 even at much longer intervals. Weller and Franck suggested that this "premature" rise of i_{IE} occurs when a second catalytic reaction of photosynthesis becomes rate-limiting, and thus influences the phenomena of intermittency. According to Franck and Herzfeld, the stabilizing catalyst, E_B, is usually limiting in strong continuous light, and in the presence of abundant carbon dioxide. However, under certain conditions, the limiting influence may pass partially or completely to other factors, particularly those associated with the carbon dioxide supply.

When the carbon dioxide concentration is low, or the diffusion path offers high resistance (as in the case of closed stomata), the limiting process may be the *diffusion of carbon dioxide to the chloroplasts;* in this case, dark intervals can be utilized for the re-establishment of the carboxylation equilibrium by diffusion (as this was first suggested by Willstätter and Stoll in the discussion of the results of Brown and Escombe). The length of the dark period required for this purpose must depend on specific conditions.

Intermittency effects caused by slow diffusion are, however, unlikely to occur in unicellular algae suspended in buffer solutions (which were used in the Warburg experiments) and should be absent in the carbon dioxide-saturated state (since the diffusion supply can always be improved by an increase in the external concentration of carbon dioxide). However, a carbon dioxide supply limitation of a different nature may occur even under these conditions if the quantity of the available carboxylating enzyme, E_A, is insufficient. In this case, the maximum rate of supply of carbon dioxide to the acceptor—and thus also the maximum over-all rate of photosynthesis—cannot be improved by an increase in the external carbon dioxide concentration (as discussed in chapter 27, page 917). If, because of E_A deficiency, carboxylation becomes rate-limiting in strong continuous light, dark intervals can be utilized for recarboxylation of the "denuded" acceptor. The time required depends not merely on the *action period* of E_A, but also on its *concentration*. This difference from the case of limitation by a deficiency of E_B is caused by the fact that E_A acts on a *stable* substrate (carbon dioxide), and therefore can be used repeatedly during a single dark period (while E_B is supposed to act on unstable intermediates and is therefore available only once in each dark interval). Because of this difference, the frequency of alternations that gives the most favorable intermittency factor under the conditions of E_A limitation is not equal to one "action period" of this catalyst, but is determined in a more complex way by the time that the available quantity of E_A requires to saturate the acceptor with carbon dioxide to such an extent as to give the maximum possible yield of photosynthesis during the subsequent light period.

Franck has concluded, from the "pick-up" experiments described in chapter 8 (page 206, *cf.* also figs. 10 and 11 in chap. 33), that the time required to carboxylate *all* acceptor (once it has been totally decarboxylated) is about 20 seconds. This then must be the *upper limit* for the optimum frequency of alternations. (There certainly can be no advantage in extending the dark periods beyond the time required for *complete* recarboxylation; while the simultaneous extension of light periods is disadvantageous since in longer flashes the $A \cdot CO_2$ complex is more completely decarboxylated, thus causing an approach to the conditions of steady illumination and decreasing the favorable intermittency effect.) To obtain a *lower limit* of the most favorable frequency of alternations, one has to know the rate of processes by which the complex $A \cdot CO_2$ is decarboxylated in light. We presented in chapter 8 (page 167) and chapter 29 (p. 1086) evidence that led Franck to assume that *each* absorption act, whether it contributes to photosynthesis or not, may cause the decarboxylation of an acceptor molecule (because back reactions can result in a decomposition of $A \cdot CO_2$ into free acceptor and carbon dioxide). If this is so (some difficulties of this hypothesis were mentioned in chap. 33), the rate of decarboxylation in light is proportional to light intensity, even in the saturation range (at least, until we come into the intensity region where the yield of fluorescence increases, as described in chap. 28B, thus revealing a decrease in the rate of the primary photochemical process). From the frequency of absorption acts (estimated on page 838) and the concentration of the acceptor molecules (estimated on page 204), we can deduce that, in light of approximately 10,000 lux, the velocity constant of the photochemical decarboxylation of $A \cdot CO_2$ complexes (partly by reduction and partly by dissociation caused by back reactions) is of the order of 1/sec., and in light of 100,000 lux, of the order of 10/sec. 0.1 to 1 second must then represent the lower limit for favorable intermittency effects ($i_{IE} > 1$) in the case of E_A limitation. Combined with the above-mentioned upper limit (20 seconds), these estimates define a region that in fact roughly corresponds to the range in which intermittency factors larger than 1 have been found by Warburg, McAlister, Briggs and Weller and Franck. This lends support to Franck's attribution of this anomaly to an inadequate quantity of the carboxylating catalyst, E_A. This interpretation implies that, in plants that show the anomaly, the rate-limiting process in strong continuous light also is the "preliminary" carboxylation reaction, rather than the "stabilizing" reaction catalyzed by E_B. This should be recognizable, *e. g.*, by a greater sensitivity of the maximum rate to cyanide (*cf.* chapter 12, sect. A1). According to Weller and Franck, *Hydrangea* leaves generally behave as if they were deficient in enzyme E_A.

It may be useful to point out that in the case of E_A limitation, the maximum obtainable value of i_{IE} still is 2 ($i_{It} \leq 1$). Under no conditions can the average yield of photosynthesis in alternating light be higher than the rate of carboxylation; and the average rate of carboxylation in intermittent light can at best approach (but never exceed) the rate of carboxylation in continuous light. (E_A cannot work more efficiently in the dark than it does in light, when practically all acceptor is maintained in the decarboxylated state by intense photosynthesis.)

Briggs (1941) also has discussed the efficient utilization for photosynthesis of dark intervals of the order of several seconds (in addition to those of the order of 10^{-2} second), and suggested two catalytical components: one with a concentration approximately equal to that of chlorophyll, and a relatively long working period (of the order of several seconds) corresponding to the concentration of the carbon dioxide acceptor, A, and the working time of the carboxylating catalyst, E_A, in our hypothesis; and one with a concentration about 500 times smaller and a working period of the order of 0.01 second (corresponding to concentration and working time of catalyst E_B in Franck's picture). Briggs suggested that the second catalyst is an intermediate between chlorophyll and the carbon dioxide acceptor complex (cf. the position of the system HX/X in some of our schemes, e. g., scheme 7.I in Vol. I). However, the identification of the limiting catalyst, E_B, with an intermediate oxidation-reduction system in this position is improbable, because of fluorescence phenomena (cf. chapter 28, part B).

In part B of this chapter, when discussing more recent experiments with flashing light, we will again find evidence of the favorable effect of dark intervals of the order of 0.1–1 second on light energy utilization, and discuss several new attempts to interpret these results. It is particularly notable that Gilmour et al. (cf. section B7) found these effects also in the Hill reaction of chloroplast fragments, in which carbon dioxide takes no part at all; this seems to indicate that if two (or more) enzymatic reactions (of the type discussed by Franck and Weller, and by Briggs) are responsible for these complexities of induction and intermittency effects, both of them belong (or can belong, if more than two reactions are involved) to the part of the photosynthetic reaction sequence concerned with the photochemical oxidation of water and liberation of oxygen. Tamiya has attempted to show that all intermittent light results can be explained by a single enzymatic reaction with kinetic characteristics different from those postulated by Franck and Herzfeld (on the basis of the data of Emerson and Arnold); for a discussion of his suggestion, see section B6 below.

We see that, in all cases of catalytic yield limitation, the question asked at the beginning of this chapter: whether an *increase* in photosynthesis can be achieved by regular interruption of illumination, e. g., by means of a rotating sector, must be answered in the negative. The factor i_{It} never exceeds unity, and the factor i_{IE} never exceeds 2. (We have shown this for *alternating light;* we will see in part B that the same is true for the factor i_{It} in *flashing* light, but that the factor i_{IE} may acquire, in such light, values much higher than 2.) Whether the same is true when the poorly understood phenomena of "injury" and "fatigue" come into play, is uncertain. It is conceivable, for example, that plants may produce more organic matter in 12 hours of illumination followed by 12 hours of dark rest than they would in a uniform 24 hour illumination of the same intensity. The same may happen when photoxidation phenomena lead to a gradual inactivation of the photosynthetic apparatus (as may occur in an atmosphere poor in carbon dioxide, or in light of excessive intensity, or in the

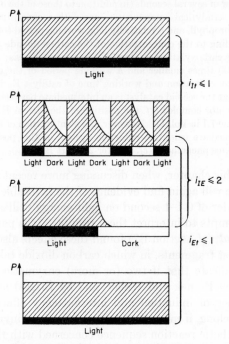

Fig. 34.5. The three intermittency factors (for equal light and dark periods). Intensity and duration of illumination is shown by black areas; photosynthesis by shaded area.

presence of excess oxygen; *cf.* chapter 19). In this case, the inhibition of photosynthesis has been found to grow autocatalytically, and it may be possible to prevent it by inserting dark recovery periods at appropriate intervals.

Early in this chapter we also asked another question—whether the *energy conversion yield* can be improved by intermittency (*i. e.*, whether the factor i_{Et} can become larger than unity). As far as enzymatic limitation in alternating light is concerned, this question, too, must be answered with a denial. To prove this we refer to equation (34.2). In weak light (when the light curve is linear), $\beta = 2$ and $i_{It} = 0.5$; thus $i_{Et} = 1$.

In saturating light, $\beta = 1$, while $i_{It} < 1$, so that i_{Et} is < 1. Thus, i_{Et} can only vary between 0.5 and 1.

We thus conclude that, if a certain amount of light energy is available to be spent within a certain interval of time, the best utilization of this energy for photosynthesis can be achieved by spreading it uniformly over the whole available period, rather than by using it in flashes. At least, this must be the case with *rapid* alternations of darkness and light. In the *medium* range of alternations (one every minute) the same is obviously true (because induction losses are the main intermittency effect in this range). Only with *slow* alternations (*e. g.*, one in several hours, or days) may there be a chance of obtaining i_{Et} factors higher than unity.

These conclusions apply to the continuous or intermittent illumination of the same plant, or the same cell in a suspension. Alternation can, however, improve the utilization of a continuous, uniform light flux (such as that from the sun) if the intervals in which one batch of cells completes its dark reactions are used to expose to the same flux another batch, *e. g.*, by replacing the cells in the upper layer of an algal suspension with new ones at a suitable rate. As part of the plans for large-scale growing of unicellular algae (for food, fodder or fuel), studies have been made of the possibility of using a turbulent flow of algal suspensions to create such favorable intermittencies of exposure; we will return to this topic on p. 1477.

The relationships between the three above-used intermittency factors are represented graphically in figure 34.5, which needs no further explanation.

B. Flashing Light*

1. Intermittency Factor in Flashing Light

Separate variation of dark and light periods enables one to find out more about the mechanism of the induction period and of the reactions going on during the dark intervals than can be derived from experiments in alternating light with equal periods of darkness and light. We have encountered the first example of their usefulness in describing how Warburg first determined the duration of the induction period and of the dark reaction that prepares it. Emerson and Arnold (1932) made an important contribution to the study of photosynthesis by introducing *flashing light*, meaning by this light with very short illumination periods, separated by longer dark intervals. This method permits separation of the primary photochemical process (together with such rapid nonphotochemical transformations as are practically instantaneous, *i. e.*, are completed within $<10^{-3}$ second) from all those chemical or physical components of photosynthesis that require measurable time for completion. Two experimental methods have been used to obtain the required intense light flashes:

* Bibliography, page 1483.

condensor discharges through gas-filled tubes (Emerson and Arnold 1932), and appropriately shaped rotating sectors (in combination with a constant light source of high intensity, *e. g.*, high-pressure mercury arcs) (Pratt and Trelease 1938, Weller and Franck 1941, Tamiya and Chiba 1949). In the discharge tube technique, the flashes are shorter (of the order of 10^{-5} second) and more intense, but the rotating disc technique offers easier access to a wide range of integrated flash energies.

In both types of experiments, the yield—determined by the usual technique, such as manometric measurement—is the *average* yield for a large number of identical flashes. Franck, Pringsheim and Lad (1945) were able to determine, by means of the phosphorescence-quenching technique, the oxygen production of a single flash. They used for this purpose photoflash bulbs, which produce much stronger flashes than are obtainable by the other methods. The flashes last for about 0.04 second, and reach a peak intensity of 1.4 million lumen.

It is easy to show that in flashing light (as in alternating light) the factor i_{It} must always be < 1 if the rate limitation is caused by catalyst deficiency. (The maximum yield in flashing light is reached when the rate-limiting catalyst is practically fully occupied for the whole duration of the dark intervals; it is then equal to the maximum yield in continuous light.) The factor i_{IE} (which, in alternating light, had a limiting value of 2) can reach much higher values in flashing light (*cf.* equation 34.1). For example, if $i_{It} \simeq 1$, and $t^*/t_d = 10^{-3}$ (*e. g.*, $t^* = 10^{-5}$ second and $t_d = 10^{-2}$ second), i_{IE} is approximately 1000.

However, these high values of i_{IE} are without real significance, for when the light periods are shorter than the "Emerson-Arnold period" the yield per flash depends only on the *total energy* of the flash (the time integral of its intensity) and not on these two factors separately. In other words, plants do not distinguish between a flash of a certain intensity that lasts for 10^{-4} second, and a flash of tenfold intensity that lasts for only 10^{-5} second. Under these conditions, the two intermittency factors for equal intensity, i_{It} and i_{IE}, lose their importance, and the only factor with which we need to be concerned is i_{Et}.

These considerations appear not to apply to intense flashes lasting for several milliseconds or longer; in this case, the yield becomes a function of the duration of the flash, and is affected by dark periods of the order of 0.1 or 1 second. We mentioned this complicating effect in discussing the "alternating light" phenomena in part A, and will return to it below in discussing the experiments and theoretical considerations of Weller and Franck, Tamiya, and Gilmour *et al.* We will also see that Burk and coworkers denied the validity of the photochemical "reciprocity law" in photosynthesis even for the very brief condensor discharge flashes.

For low integrated light intensities, $i.\ e.$, low values of the product (energy of a single flash $\times$ number of flashes per unit time), the factor i_{Et} must be unity (since in this case, all the absorbed light quanta can be utilized for photosynthesis, with the highest possible quantum yield, whether they are supplied continuously or in flashes). The factor i_{Et} will decline below unity when the flash energy becomes so high that more intermediates are produced in a single flash than the available catalyst E_B^0 can handle in one batch (since, according to our assumptions, the fraction of the intermediates that finds no free catalyst is lost by back reactions). Thus, if one plots the rate of photosynthesis in flashing light with

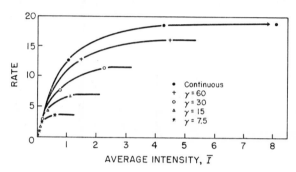

Fig. 34.6. Light curves for flashing light (after Weller and Franck 1941). The number of light flashes per second, γ, is the parameter in this set of curves.

different frequencies of flashes against the integrated intensity (or, what is essentially the same, the $average$ incident energy per unit time), one expects to obtain a picture of the type of figure 34.6, based on actual experimental results of Weller and Franck (1941). In this figure, the ratio of yields in flashing light and in continuous light with the same value of $\bar{I}$, is the factor i_{Et}. The figure confirms that this factor is unity for low values of $\bar{I}$. It declines below unity, first for widely spaced flashes (where, in order to achieve the same average intensity of illumination, one has to use stronger flashes), and later for flashes that are more closely spaced. When the dark intervals, t_d, approach zero, $i.\ e.$, when the flash frequency becomes very high, the light curve for flashing light must become identical with that for continuous light.

Figure 34.6 confirms that the yield in flashing light never $exceeds$ that in continuous light of the same integrated intensity; $i.\ e.$, that the factor i_{Et} never is larger than unity. A theoretical proof of this rule was given in part A for alternating light; the same proof can easily be generalized to include intermittent light with any ratio of t^* and t_d.

This proof is illustrated by figure 34.7. The shaded areas represent amounts of limiting catalyst actively engaged in photosynthesis (A) in saturating continuous light, and (B) in flashing light of the same integrated intensity, for two different flash frequencies (B_1, B_2). The average yield of photosynthesis, which is proportional to the sum of the shaded areas, is highest in A and lowest in B_2.

Instead of plotting the average yield of photosynthesis in flashing light against the *average* light intensity (as in fig. 34.6), one can plot the yield *per flash*, **P** against the *energy of a single flash*, **I**. Such "flash saturation curves" (fig. 34.8) can be constructed from the same data used in figure

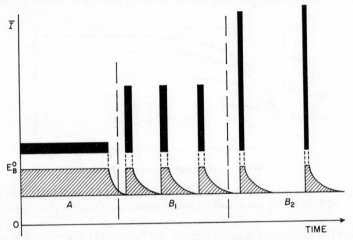

Fig. 34.7. Photosynthesis in continuous light and flashing light of the same integrated intensity, $\bar{I}$, for two different frequencies. Flashes are "saturating," *i. e.*, each produces enough intermediates to occupy all molecules of E_B. Photosynthesis begins at the saturation level (which is proportional to E_B^0), and declines exponentially during each dark interval. Black rectangles, light. Shaded areas, photosynthesis (*i. e.*, progress of the limiting dark reaction).

34.6.   At first, **P** is proportional to **I** and independent of τ ($= t^* + t_d$); this increase continues as long as practically all intermediates, formed during the flash, can be utilized by catalyst E_B during the subsequent dark period. With increasing flash energy, however, E_B, even if it is fully occupied during the entire dark interval, ceases to be able to transform all intermediates formed in the flash; therefore the flash saturation curves bend, one after another, and approach the horizontal. The saturation yield is proportional to the length of the dark intervals as long as the latter are very short compared with the working period, t_B, of E_B, and thus can be fully utilized for the dark reaction catalyzed by this agent. When t_d becomes commensurate with t_B, full utilization of the dark intervals becomes impossible (because of the exponential decline of the yield; *cf.* fig. 34.7). Finally, after the intervals had become so long that practically all intermediates associated with E_B after the flash are stabilized before the next flash ($t_d \ll$

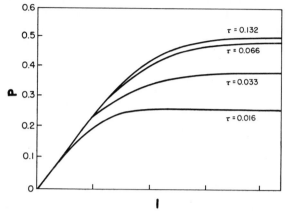

Fig. 34.8. Flash saturation curves calculated from fig. 34.6 (after Weller and Franck 1941); τ is the time between successive flashes ($\tau = t^* + t_d$).

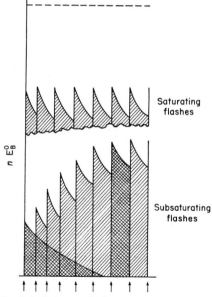

Fig. 34.9. Length of dark intervals has no effect on yield of nonsaturating flashes. E_B^0 is the total available amount of E_B. The two dark-shaded areas represent the yield of a single (subsaturating) flash with a long dark interval, and the yield per flash of same intensity in the "stationary" state with short dark intervals. They are equal.

t_B), further extension become useless, and the rate per flash reaches a maximum value independent of both I and t_d.

It may seem at first as if dark intervals of insufficient length ($t_d < t_B$) should reduce the yield of weak flashes in the same proportion as that of strong ones, since in both cases the same fraction of the E_B molecules, supplied with intermediates during the flash, will fail to complete their transformation during the subsequent dark interval. However, this is only true of the yield of the *first* (or the first few) flashes. As shown in figure 34.9, the proportion of working E_B molecules will be built up, by a series of subsaturating flashes, until it is high enough to transform the intermediates at the same average rate at which they are supplied by the flashes; only then will a "stationary state" be reached (assuming one may speak of a stationary state in intermittent light).

Clendenning and Ehrmantraut (1950) found that *Chlorella* suffers similar induction losses of oxygen (after a dark interval ≥ 2 minutes), whether it is exposed to continuous light, or to 40 neon discharge flashes per second; in both cases the steady state was reached only after about 10 minutes of exposure.

2. Maximum Flash Yield

Figure 34.10 shows the yield per flash as a function of the length of the dark intervals, according to the measurements of Emerson and Arnold

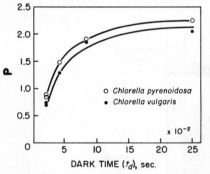
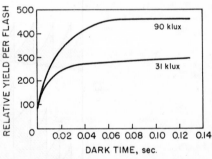

Fig. 34.10. Flash yield as function of dark time for *Chlorella* (after Emerson and Arnold 1932).

Fig. 34.11. Yield per flash for two different light intensities given for 4.5 msec. (after Weller and Franck 1941).

(1932). The shape of these curves is exponential, and they can be interpreted as revealing a reaction of the first order (*e. g.*, the monomolecular transformation of the complex I·E_B, where I stands for intermediate such as $\{HCO_2\}$ in chapter 7, or $E_B HCO_2$ in scheme 28.II). If, at the beginning of the dark interval, the quantity of this complex is [I·E_B]$_0$, the kinetic law of monomolecular decomposition (identical with the law of radioactive disintegration) determines that, after time t, the residue of unchanged $I \cdot E_B$ complexes will be:

(34.3)
$$[I \cdot E_B] = [I \cdot E_B]_0 \, e^{-k_{EA}t}$$

where k_{EA} is the monomolecular velocity constant of the Emerson-Arnold reaction. The yield per flash, which we assume to be equal to the amount of $I \cdot E_B$ transformed during the dark interval, is:

(34.4)
$$P = [I \cdot E_B]_0 - [I \cdot E_B] = [I \cdot E_B]_0 \, (1 - e^{-k_{EA}t_d})$$

One half the maximum yield is obtained when $e^{-k_{EA}} = \frac{1}{2}$, or:

(34.5)
$$t_{1/2} = \ln 2 / k_{EA}$$

(this being the well-known relation between "half-time" and velocity constant of a monomolecular process).

From what was said before about the influence of dark intervals on the yield of *nonsaturating* flashes, it is obvious that the above equations can be applied to saturating flashes only. Figure 34.11 is an illustration of this fact. The plot of P against t_d gives an exponential curve for saturating flashes (90 klux for 0.0045 second); but the lower curve, which corresponds to nonsaturating flashes, has no such simple shape.

Table 34.II contains the values of $t_{1/2}$ and k_{EA} calculated from the measurements of different authors. The column headed t_B shows the intervals required for the *completion* of the Emerson-Arnold reaction; since the law of decay is exponential, the figures in this column can be only approximate.

TABLE 34.II

RATE OF THE EMERSON-ARNOLD REACTION IN *Chlorella*
(Values in Parentheses are Rough Estimates)

Author[a]	Temp. ° C.	$t_{1/2}$, sec.	t_B, sec.	k_{EA}, sec.$^{-1}$
EA	1.1	0.04	0.4	20
WF	4.7	0.038	—	22
EA	5.9	—	(0.12)	—
EA	6.9	—	(0.08)	—
EA	13	0.02	0.2	40
WF	19.6	0.013	0.06	63
PT	23.9	(0.005)	0.029	(165)
PT	23.9	0.025[b]	0.062[b]	33

[a] EA = Emerson and Arnold (1932). WF = Weller and Frank (1941). PT = Pratt and Trelease (1938). See also Gilmour *et al.* (1953).
[b] In heavy water.

Since the Emerson-Arnold reaction is a dark catalytic process, it can be expected to possess a high temperature coefficient. The values of k_{EA} in

Table 34.II scatter rather badly, but show an unmistakable downward trend with increasing temperature, and indicate a temperature coefficient of approximately 2. Comparison of the figures in the last two rows shows that the Emerson-Arnold reaction is about five times slower in heavy than in ordinary water, a fact that can be explained by the assumption that the "stabilizing" reaction (which may be a dismutation) involves the transfer of a hydrogen atom.

The exponential curves in figures 34.10 and 34.11 can be defined by two parameters, e. g., the half-time, $t_{1/2}$, and the maximum yield per flash, $\mathbf{P}^{\max.}$. The latter constant was discussed in chapter 32; its values, determined by Emerson and Arnold (1932[1,2]), Arnold and Kohn (1934) and Emerson, Green and Webb (1940), were listed in Table 32.I (expressed in the form of a factor τ, the ratio flash yield/chlorophyll content). In healthy specimens of plants from various phyla, $\mathbf{P}^{\max.}$ was found to vary between 5×10^{-4} [Chl]$_0$ and 2×10^{-4} [Chl]$_0$; it declined below 1×10^{-4} [Chl]$_0$ in aged cultures of *Chlorella*. (Similar decline can be caused, according to section 4, by narcotization and by ultraviolet illumination.)

The yield $\mathbf{P}^{\max.}$ was identified, in equation (34.3), with [I·E$_B$]$_0$. Since we now apply this equation to saturating flashes, in which *all* molecules of the catalyst E$_B$ are occupied at the beginning of the dark period, we can write:

$$(34.6) \qquad \mathbf{P}^{\max.} = E_B^0/n$$

where E_B^0 is the total available amount of E$_B$, and $1/n$ the number of oxygen molecules produced by a single reaction of a molecule of $1/E_B$; $1/n$ may be 1, but is more likely to be $\frac{1}{4}$, or even $\frac{1}{8}$.

Franck and Herzfeld's (1941) interpretation of the maximum yield per flash as a measure of the available quantity of the limiting catalyst, E_B^0, implied in (34.6) was considered the most plausible interpretation of this constant in chapter 32. As an alternative, one could consider the hypothesis that the maximum yield per flash is equal to the amount of the *reaction substrate* present in the cells at the beginning of the flash, in a form suitable for immediate transformation (*cf.* Arnold, 1935). Because of the order of magnitude of $\mathbf{P}^{\max.}$, it is impossible to identify this substrate with the A.CO$_2$ complex. (It was estimated in chap. 8 that the concentration of the acceptor A is of the same order of magnitude as that of chlorophyll, while $\mathbf{P}^{\max.}$ is about a thousand times smaller.) An attempt can be made (as in the hypothesis of Briggs 1941; *cf.* sect. A2) to identify the "limiting" substrate with the intermediate oxidant, X (intervening between chlorophyll and A·CO$_2$), but this assumption does not explain the results of fluorescence experiments, (the latter indicating that *all* chlorophyll molecules—and not only one in several thousands—are parts of the photosensitive complex, such as {X·Chl·HZ}). In chapter 32, we also discussed the hypothesis of the *photosynthetic unit*, which attempted to avoid these contradictions by assuming that several thousand chlorophyll molecules are connected with *one* "photosensitive center" (*e. g.*, one molecule of the intermediate oxidant, X) by an efficient mechanism of energy conduction.

3. Effect of Cyanide on Photosynthesis in Flashing Light

Further support for the Franck-Herzfeld explanation of the flash yield was derived by Weller and Franck (1941) from experiments on cyanide inhibition in flashing light, which we mentioned before in chapter 12 (page 307), but must consider in more detail here. Emerson and Arnold (1932) noticed that the presence of cyanide (1.14 × 10⁻⁵ *M* HCN) decreased $P^{max.}$ in light with short dark intervals (*e. g.*, t_d = 0.035 seconds, at 13° C.) in the same proportion as the rate in continuous light (namely, by 50%), but that the influence of the inhibitor became weaker when the dark intervals were lengthened (only 12% inhibition was found at t_d = 0.106 second), and disappeared entirely at t_d = 0.212 second.

Brilliant and Krupnikova (1952[1]) measured the effect of cyanide on the oxygen production by filamentous algae in continuous and flashing light. With flashes of 5.9 msec., and dark intervals of 11 msec., 5 × 10⁻⁵ mole/1. KCN caused an inhibition by 31–76% (in different species); 5 × 10⁻⁸ mole/1. KCN had no effect. The results in continuous light were similar. With dark periods of 85 msec., oxygen liberation not only was not inhibited, but even increased (by 2 to 90% in 5 × 10⁻⁸ mole/1. KCN, and by up to 61% in 5 × 10⁻⁵ mole/1. KCN).

Emerson and Arnold first explained this result by "substrate limitation." They assumed that the rate-limiting reaction, which supplies new reduction substrate, A·CO₂, for the photochemical reaction (or frees the acceptor from the intermediate photoproducts and thus makes it available for "recharging"), is slowed down by cyanide, but, if given more time, still can provide the required amount of the complexes A·CO₂. This implies that the material on which the cyanide-poisoned catalyst is working is *stable*, and therefore can wait until the small residual amount of the catalyst left over in the presence of the inhibitor takes care of it.

In the Franck-Herzfeld theory, this explanation has to be modified, since the reaction that limits the flash yield is, in this theory, the transformation of unstable intermediates. This material cannot wait for the second or third "round" of catalyst action (which would enable a small residue of active catalyst to complete the task that usually requires a much larger amount). The alternative to the Emerson-Arnold explanation, suggested by Weller and Franck (1941), is that the reaction catalyzed by E_B and usually responsible for the rate limitation in strong continuous light, as well as for the maximum yield per flash, is practically insensitive to cyanide. The effect of cyanide on the flash yield is attributed, in this theory, to a second reaction, *not* rate-determining in the absence of cyanide, but assuming this role when a large fraction of its catalyst is inhibited by cyanide. In chapter 12, evidence was presented that the main source of cyanide sensitivity of photosynthesis is the carboxylation of the acceptor, A, catalyzed by the carboxylase, E_A; and we also concluded that this reaction is not usually rate-determining, but can become limiting in the presence of an inhibitor. (In this and subsequent discussions, we will use the concept of "rate-limiting" reactions in the crudest qualitative form. In any quantitative analysis of the data, the relationships derived in chapter 26, and used in analytical derivations in chapters 27 and 28, will have to be taken into account. It was shown there that the rate never actually "hits the ceiling," and that if several "rate ceilings" are provided by several physical or chemical reactions, of not too different maximum capacities, the rate is affected by *all* of them, and not only by the lowest one.)

According to Franck's theory, the maximum flash yield in the nonpoisoned state is essentially determined by the deficiency of the *finishing* catalyst, E_B, while the maximum flash yield in the cyanide-poisoned state is effectively limited by the deficiency of the reduction substrate, caused by inhibition of a *preparatory* catalyst, E_A.

Weller and Franck obtained confirmation of this hypothesis in the shape of the curves showing flash yield *vs.* dark time. Figure 34.12 presents two pairs of such curves—one determined with nonpoisoned cells and the other, with cells inhibited by 3×10^{-4} M cyanide. The first curve is exponential; the second begins as a straight line (as can best be seen in curves (A)), but later bends and approaches the same limit, $P^{max.}$, as the first curve (best seen in curves (B)). This difference in shape is precisely what one would expect if the flash yield in the noninhibited state were determined by the rate of a first-order transformation of a limited quantity of an intermediate, while the yield in the inhibited state were dependent on the rate of a zero-order transformation of a practically unlimited quantity of a material. In the first case, the number of working molecules of the limiting catalyst declines *exponentially* during the dark interval (as shown by the peaks in figs. 34.7 and 34.9); in the second case, *all* the available catalyst molecules can work uniformly throughout the dark periods, so that their production increases *linearly* with the duration of these periods. (The linear increase in $P^{max.}$ with t_d in poisoned cells obviously must cease with the approach to the limit imposed on the flash yield by the deficiency of the finishing catalyst, E_B, since obviously the yield in the presence of poisons, cannot be *higher* than in the noninhibited state.)

Since the maximum yield per flash corresponds to the liberation of about one molecule of oxygen per several thousand molecules of chlorophyll, and since about 8 quanta are probably required for the production of one molecule of oxygen, only one chlorophyll molecule in several hundred needs to adsorb a quantum during the flash for flash saturation to be reached. (Kohn, 1936, estimated that 99% flash saturation is reached when 1 quantum is absorbed during each flash by one out of a hundred chlorophyll molecules.) Since the concentration of the acceptor molecules, A, appears to be roughly equivalent to that of chlorophyll, it further

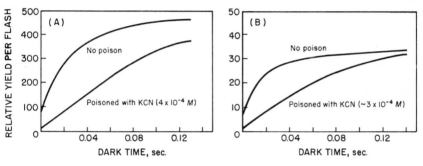

Fig. 34.12. Yield per flash with and without cyanide (after Weller and Franck 1941).

follows that to compensate for the consumption of $A \cdot CO_2$ complexes by photosynthesis in a saturating flash, about one acceptor molecule in a hundred has to be recarboxylated during each dark interval. This is the reason it was legitimate to consider recarboxylation a zero-order reaction. If the intervals were to become sufficiently long to allow a large part of the acceptor to be recarboxylated, the rate of carboxylation would finally slow down. However, complete recarboxylation requires as much as 20 seconds in the nonpoisoned state, and considerably more time in the presence of cyanide (as witnessed by the duration of the carbon dioxide "pick-up," described in chapters 8 and 33). Therefore, in experiments with dark intervals of less than 1 second, we always deal only with the initial, linear part of the carboxylation curve. If we accept Franck's suggestion that, in the case of E_B limitation, the light quanta *not* used for photosynthesis nevertheless cause decomposition of the complex $A \cdot CO_2$ (by back reactions; *cf.* page 167), we have to conclude that the number of acceptor molecules that need recarboxylation after each flash increases with the flash energy not merely up to flash saturation, but beyond it. Let us imagine that flashing illumination of a cyanide-poisoned cell begins after a dark rest long enough for the carboxylation equilibrium to be established (despite the inactivation of a large part of the carboxylating enzyme by cyanide). The first flashes should then give the usual maximum flash yield; only when the initial reserve of the $A \cdot CO_2$ complexes, formed in the long dark period, is exhausted, will the yield be limited to the number of $A \cdot CO_2$ complexes restored during the short dark interval immediately preceding the flash. By inserting after several flashes, a dark interval of sufficient length, it should be possible to produce enough reduction substrate, $A \cdot CO_2$, to assure the maximum yield in a new series of flashes, and so on. In other words, if the decrease in flash yield caused by cyanide is due to the retardation of a supply reaction that can effectively utilize dark intervals much longer than 0.01 second, such extended intervals need to be inserted only once after a series of flashes to remove completely the cyanide inhibition. This consideration led Rieke and Gaffron (1943) to carry out experiments in flashing light in which a rapid series of flashes was followed by a single long dark interval. (This was achieved by an appropriate arrangement of sectors in a rotating disc.) Table 34.III shows a typical result. When the 16 flashes/sec. were evenly spaced, the intervals (0.06 second) were insufficient for the cyanide-poisoned reaction to renew all the substrate used up during the flash, thus explaining the observed considerable inhibition (by 22%). It will be noted that the residual rate in flashing light (0.43 mm.^{3}/min.) was practically the same as in continuous

TABLE 34.III

INFLUENCE OF CYANIDE ON FLASH YIELD IN *Chlorella pyrenoidosa*
(AFTER RIEKE AND GAFFRON 1943)[a]

	Rate of O_2 production (corr. for respiration), in mm.^{3}/min.		
	Continuous light	16 flashes/sec., evenly spaced	16 flashes/sec., in groups of 4
No poison	2.08	0.55	0.34
3×10^{-4} M KCN	0.42	0.43	0.33
Inhibition (%)	80	22	<3

[a] Comparison of the rates in continuous and flashing illumination; thin suspension of algae in carbonate buffer (85 parts $M/10$ NaHCO$_3$ + 15 parts $M/10$ K$_2$CO$_3$); gas phase, air; 20% absorption of light of 0.578 mμ; intensity about twice that needed for saturation; temperature, 20° C.

light, being determined in both cases by the rate of formation of $A \cdot CO_2$ by the nonpoisoned fraction $[E_A]_r$ of the catalyst E_A. When, however, the 16 flashes were gathered in 4 groups of 4 flashes each, the cyanide had no effect on the rate—since, now, the long intervals between the groups were sufficient to supply all the required substrate even in the poisoned state. (The required quantity of $A \cdot CO_2$ was smaller than with regularly spaced flashes, because the dark intervals *within each* group were now shorter than $t_{EA} = 1/k_{EA}.)$

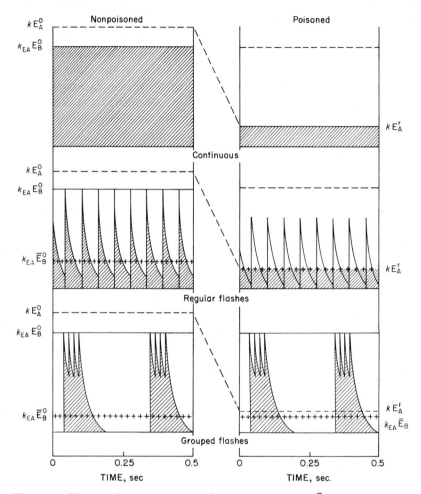

Fig. 34.13. Photosynthesis in nonpoisoned state determined by $\bar{E}_B$, the average working amount of E_B. Photosynthesis in poisoned state determined by formation rate of $A \cdot CO_2$ by E_A (except with grouped flashes, where it remains limited by E_B). Level $k[E_A^0]$ is arbitrary; other levels taken from Table 34.III. (—) effective ceiling on maximum momentary yield; (++) average yield in flashing light resulting from this limitation; (---) "potential ceilings" too high to affect the average yield decisively.

These results and their interpretation are illustrated by figure 34.13. In the nonpoisoned state, the rate is supposed to be determined by the catalyst E_B. In other words, the "ceiling" imposed on the rate by this catalyst, $P^{\text{max.}} = (k_{EA}/n)E_B^0$, is assumed to be considerably lower than the "ceiling" imposed by the $A \cdot CO_2$-supplying capacity of the carboxylase, kE_A^0. In flashing light, the average yield, under the conditions of E_B limitation, is (k_{EA}/n) $[\overline{E_B}]$, where $[\overline{E_B}]$ designates the average amount of actively engaged catalyst E_B. If the flash intervals are $> t_{EA}$, this rate can also be expressed as NE_B^0, where N is the number of flashes per second (sixteen in our example). In the poisoned state, on the other hand, the rate limitation is given by the rate of supply of the substrate by the residual carboxylase, kE_A^r. This applies to continuous light as well as to regular flashes. (Of course, the final products are liberated in the second case in bursts following each flash, as indicated by the peaked curves; but the total volume of these bursts is limited by the intake of carbon dioxide, which goes on uniformly.) With grouped flashes, however, the E_A-limitation remains practically ineffective even in the inhibited state (since, in this case, the "ceiling" $kE_A^r = 0.43$ mm.³/min. is considerably higher than the $[E_B]$-determined rate, 0.33 mm.³/min.). The experiments with flash groups provide the most convincing argument against the hypothesis of "substrate limitation" as an alternative to "limitation by a finishing catalyst."

4. Influence of Temperature, Carbon Dioxide Concentration, Narcotics and Ultraviolet Light on Flash Yield

Emerson and Arnold (1932[1]) found that decrease in temperature, though increasing required dark time, leaves $P^{\text{max.}}$ unaffected; fig. 34.14 shows

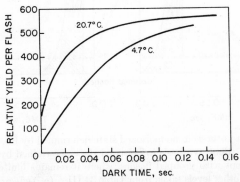

Fig. 34.14. Yield per flash curves for low and high temperature (after Weller and Franck 1941).

confirmation of this conclusion by Weller and Franck (1941). This result appears natural, since lower temperature leaves unaffected both the quantity of the intermediates available after a flash, and the quantity of the catalyst available for their transformation; it only slows down the rate of this transformation.

The maximum flash yield becomes dependent on temperature when, at the higher temperature, the duration of the flash ceases to be short compared with the working period of E_B (Franck, Pringsheim and Lad 1945).

At 4.7° C., the shape of the curve is not as close to exponential as at 20.7°, but indicates a linear beginning. This change is similar to that caused

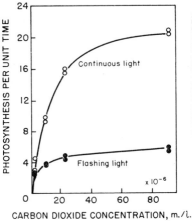

Fig. 34.15. Effect of [CO₂] on photosynthesis in continuous and flashing light (24 flashes/sec.) (after Emerson and Arnold 1932).

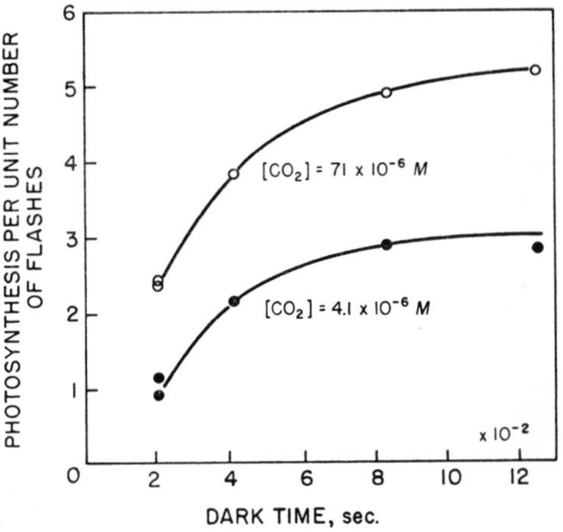

Fig. 34.16. Course of dark reaction at two different concentrations of CO_2 (after Emerson and Arnold 1932).

by cyanide poisoning (fig. 34.12), and could therefore be quoted in support of Franck's hypothesis that, at low temperature, the cyanide sensitive carboxylation reaction (catalyzed by E_A) replaces the cyanide-resistant finishing reaction (catalyzed by E_B) as the main yield-limiting factor (*cf.* chapter 31).

The effect of changes in the concentration of *carbon dioxide* on photosynthesis in flashing light offers an interesting problem. As shown by figure 34.15, Emerson and Arnold (1932) found the "carbon dioxide curves" in flashing light to be similar to those in continuous light. However, half saturation occurred in flashing light ($t_d = 0.04$ second) considerably earlier than in continuous light. This is natural, since carbon dioxide saturation must ensue as soon as the carbon dioxide supply reaction—which proceeds at a uniform rate throughout the dark periods—supplies enough material to cover the $A \cdot CO_2$ consumption of saturating *flashes*, which is considerably lower than that of saturating *continuous light*. Less easy to explain is figure 34.16, which shows the flash yield in relation to the length of dark periods, for two different concentrations of carbon dioxide. The two curves appear to retain an approximately constant ratio at all t_d values and not to approach a common limit—as we would expect if the maximum yield per flash were equal (or equivalent) to the available amount of the finishing catalyst, E_B. By using sufficiently intense flashes, it should be possible to produce enough intermediates to put *all* molecules of E_B to work, even if many of the absorbed quanta were lost because of the scarcity of carbon dioxide–acceptor complexes. The flashes used in the experiments of Emerson and Arnold were just strong enough to achieve flash saturation in the presence of abundant carbon dioxide; perhaps, no true saturation was obtained in the carbon dioxide-deficient medium (despite the evidence of the last two points on the curve). With the usual flashing-light technique (involving a long sequence of flashes) it is difficult to obtain flashes much more intense than those used by Emerson and Arnold, to see whether the two curves in figure 34.16 would converge at the higher intensities.

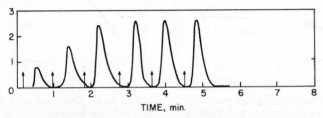

Fig. 34.17. Induction in oxygen liberation by flashes after anaerobic incubation (after Franck, Pringsheim, and Lad 1945).

We mentioned, however, that much higher intensities of *single* flashes can be produced by exploding flash bulbs, as was done in the phosphorescence measurements of Franck, Pringsheim and Lad (1945). Two points, however, have to be cleared before this method can be applied to the solution of our problem. In the first place, the phosphorescence technique requires absence of oxygen; under these conditions, the saturation yield in steady light may be only 1% of the normal, aerobic value. Is then the flash yield in the absence of air at all comparable with that obtained aerobically? The answer is that it is of the same order of magnitude, but may be smaller by a factor of five or even ten (corresponding to $Chl_0/P = 10,000–20,000$, instead of the usual 2000). This shows that the poison that accumulates during anaerobic incubation has much less effect on maximum yield per flash than on maximum yield in continuous light. This is confirmed by the observation that the maximum flash yield is independent of the density of the algal suspension (which is decisive for the extent of inhibition in continuous light, *cf.* chap. 33, sect. A6).   In describing anaerobic induction we noted its twofold character: an extremely strong effect, attributable to the production of an acid, diffusible, metabolic poison, and a weaker effect, apparently due to enhanced production of the (nondiffusible, nonneutralizable) "internal narcotic"—perhaps the same that is also responsible for the induction losses in the aerobic state.   Of

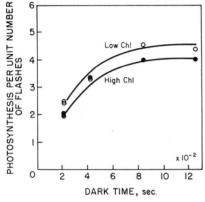

Fig. 34.18. Flash yield as function of dark time for cells with low chlorophyll concentrations (circles) and high chlorophyll concentration (dots). The ratio of the two concentrations is about 4:1; the saturation levels correspond to about 4 mm.^{3} O$_2$ and 1 mm.^{3} O$_2$ per mm.^{3} cells, respectively (after Emerson and Arnold 1932).

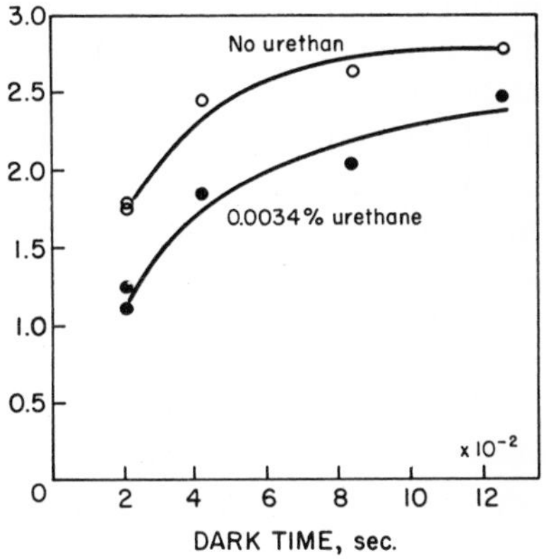

Fig. 34.19. Effect of phenylurethan on course of dark reaction (after Emerson and Arnold 1932).

these two aspects of anaerobic inhibition, only the second one appears to affect the oxygen production by single flashes. When several such flashes are produced in succession, the flash yield shows the typical short induction phenomenon, with or without a second minimum (fig. 34.17).

The absolute value of the maximum flash yield under anaerobic conditions, although smaller than in air, is not *so* much smaller as to make the application of the anaerobic method to the problem of [CO$_2$] influence on flash yield entirely unreasonable.

The second point to be considered is the duration of the flash bulb explosions. As mentioned before, it is 0.04 second longer than the Emerson-Arnold period at 20° C. Therefore, the maximum yield obtainable per flash could be somewhat higher than the amount produced by a single action of the available E$_B$ (since the catalyst can act more than once in each flash). The relation is reversed at 0° where the Emerson-Arnold period is considerably *longer* than the duration of the flash. The experiments in which E_B^0 is to be measured by the maximum flash yield with the help of flash bulbs must therefore be performed at low temperature.

At 0° C., the maximum anaerobic flash yield of a suspension of *Scenedesmus* was found to be 2.3×10^{-8} ml. in a carrier gas (nitrogen) without extra carbon dioxide (beyond that produced by respiration and fermentation of the algae), and 3×10^{-8} ml. in the presence of added carbon dioxide. The difference is so small as to suggest that (as expected in Franck's theory) the concentration of carbon dioxide has no effect on the maximum flash yield. (More precise confirmation obviously remains desirable.)

At room temperature, the flash yield as determined by this method was not only somewhat higher than at 0° C. (this was mentioned before), but also was much more dependent on the carbon dioxide supply. Both observations are explicable by reference to the fact that the duration of the flash at 20° is longer than the working period of the yield-limiting catalyst.

Emerson and Arnold (1932) found that the maximum flash yield is affected by *chlorophyll* deficiency (fig. 34.18). This dependence is another aspect of the problem discussed in chapter 32, section 2, in connection with the similar effect of [Chl] on $P^{\text{max.}}$ in continuous light. We concluded there—from the fact that the parallelism of [Chl] and $P^{\text{max.}}$ was absent in many plants, and not always present even in *Chlorella*—that no direct relation exists between these two magnitudes, but that a depression of $P^{\text{max.}}$ occurs when the decrease of [Chl] is brought about by treatment (such as iron starvation) that also reduces the concentration of other catalytic components of the photosynthetic apparatus, such as the usually rate-limiting catalyst, E_B. The same hypothesis could explain the parallelism between [Chl] and the maximum flash yield, $\mathbf{P}^{\text{max.}}$.

The effect of *narcotics* on $\mathbf{P}^{\text{max.}}$, also noted by Emerson and Arnold (1932), and illustrated by figure 34.19, could be similar to that of carbon dioxide deficiency. By enveloping the sensitizer molecules, narcotics could cause a dissipation of the energy of a considerable proportion of the absorbed light quanta. In this case, a higher flash energy would be required to produce flash saturation in the presence of narcotics, but the saturation level would be the same as in the nonpoisoned state. This is not clearly confirmed by figure 34.19. Explanation could be the same as suggested in the case of [CO_2]—failure to reach true saturation in the inhibited state; but it is also possible that narcotics inhibit not only the sensitizer, but also the limiting catalyst, E_B (since their influence is not as specific as that of the "catalyst poisons"). In this case, the flash saturation yield will be affected qualitatively in the same way as the yield of nonsaturating flashes. We recall that in chapter 12, part B, we made the same suggestion to account for the effect of narcotics on the rate of photosynthesis in strong continuous light.

Brilliant and Krupinikova (1952[2]) studied the effects of *dehydration* on the yield of photosynthesis in constant and intermittent light.

The observations of Arnold (1933) on the effect of *ultraviolet light* on photosynthesis in flashing light offer a similar problem. As described in chapter 13 (page 345), each quantum cf ultraviolet light (253.6 mμ) appears to "knock out" one catalytic "center" (these centers are not chlorophyll molecules, since chlorophyll remains intact, but their concentration is approximately equivalent to that of the green pigment). Arnold found that inhibition is proportionately the same in flashing and in continuous light, and that the full yield per flash cannot be restored by extending the dark intervals. The observation that the concentration of the sensitive catalytic centers is about equal to that of chlorophyll makes one think of the carbon dioxide acceptor, A, as the ultraviolet-sensitive target. If this is so, the inhibiting effect of ultraviolet light on the flash yield must be analogous to the effect of low carbon dioxide concentration.

The effect on the flash yield of variations in [CO_2], as well as that of the narcotics, could be explained without much difficulty on the basis of the theory of "substrate limitation" (*cf.* Arnold 1935) by assuming that at low [CO_2], or in the presence of narcotics, only a fraction of the normal number of substrate molecules are available for immediate reduction.

Another possibility for solving this type of kinetic difficulty is by assuming a morphological or kinetic "photosynthetic unit" (Gaffron and Wohl⁻ or "chlorophyll ensemble" (Tamiya) in which a number (say, 400–2000⁾ of chlorophyll molecules are associated with a single "reduction center" or a single molecule of an enzyme, in such a way that the intermediate photoproducts formed at these chlorophyll molecules can be further transformed only in this one reduction center or by this one enzyme molecule, and react back if they find this center or enzyme molecule occupied. (For a discussion of such kinetic mechanisms, see, *e. g.*, Rabinowitch 1951, and Gilmour *et al.* 1953.)

5. Flash Yield in Heavy Water

Pratt and Trelease (1938) found that substitution of *deuterium oxide* for ordinary water causes an extension of the Emerson-Arnold period to more than twice the original value, without affecting the maximum yield per flash (figure 34.20). The $\mathbf{P} = f(t_d)$ curve is changed in a way reminiscent of the effect cf cyanide—it is linear almost to the point of saturation. However, since the number of experimental points is small, this conclusion is not quite certain.

This result can be interpreted in several ways. Pratt and Trelease, considered two possibilities: deuterium oxide acting as a *poison*, and deuterium oxide acting as a *partner* in the Emerson-Arnold reaction (with a velocity smaller than that of ordinary water). They considered the second alternative the more probable. Weller and Franck agreed, and said that the retarding influence of deuterium oxide may indicate that the reaction catalyzed by E_B involves the transfer of hydrogen atoms. (We have repeatedly suggested that it may be a *dismutation*.) If it should be confirmed that the shape of the $\mathbf{P} = f(t_d)$ curve in heavy water is similar to that observed in the presence of cyanide, this explanation will have to be

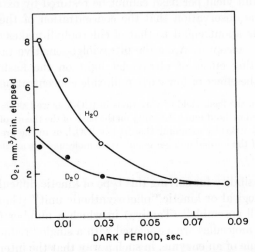

Fig. 34.20. Yield in flashing light as function of dark period in H$_2$O and D$_2$O (after Pratt and Trelease 1938).

changed. It is not necessary to revert to the other alternative of Pratt and Trelease and to assume that heavy water acts as a *poison*; the more plausible explanation is that the participation of deuterium oxide retards another dark reaction—*not* the usually limiting Emerson-Arnold reaction—to such an extent that it becomes rate-limiting. This reaction cannot be the carboxylation (as in the case of cyanide poisoning) since the latter involves no hydrogen, but it may be, *e. g.*, a preparatory reaction on the "oxidation side" of the primary photochemical process. We will see (section 8) that a reaction of the latter kind actually is rate-limiting in so-called "adapted algae," where hydrogen is supplied by a substitute donor, instead of by water.

6. Flashing Light Experiments Calling for Revision or Supplementation of the Emerson-Arnold-Franck Mechanism

The above-described results of the flashing light experiments of Warburg, Emerson and Arnold, Kohn, Franck and Weller, Rieke and Gaffron,
Clendenning and Ehrmantraut, and Ehrmantraut and Rabinowitch seemed
to add up to a consistent picture, and to provide one of the few firm factual
bases for the kinetic analysis of photosynthesis. It seemed to be well established that the normal maximum rate of photosynthesis in strong steady

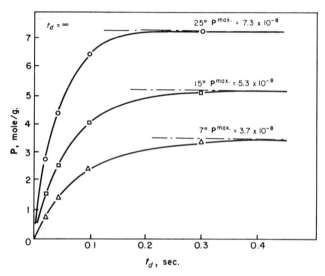

Fig. 34.21. Yield of flashes of saturating energy in *Chlorella ellipsoidea* as function of
dark interval (after Tamiya and Chiba 1949). The yields are expressed in moles O_2
per gram dry weight per flash; to express them in moles O_2 per mole chlorophyll, multiply the ordinates by about 2×10^4.

light ($P_{max.}^{max.}$ equal to about one molecule oxygen per molecule of chlorophyll
every 20–30 seconds), can be factorized into a concentration factor of the
order of $Chl_0/2000$ (or $Chl_0 n/2000$, with n a small number, perhaps 4 or 8)
and a monomolecular rate constant of the order of 100 sec.$^{-1}$ at 20° C.
These two separate constants accounted for flash saturation as function of
flash energy, and for flash saturation as function of the duration of dark
intervals, respectively. A remaining difficulty was the enhancing effect
on the (apparent, or true) light energy utilization ($i_{Et} > 1$) of dark intervals of the order of 1 second, or longer. Tentatively, this favorable effect
of relatively low frequencies of alternation could be related to CO_2 supply
limitations, or to the "bursts" and "gulps" described in chapter 33 (which
affect most strongly the gas exchange in the first seconds of exposure).

It could be hoped that a satisfactory explanation of these additional features of induction will also provide an interpretation of the additional intermittency effects, supplementing rather than replacing the original one. One could also hope that cell cultures showing no CO_2 supply limitations, and little or no "transients" would also show little or no complication of the Emerson-Arnold-Frank mechanism of flash saturation.

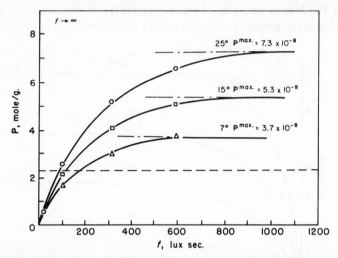

Fig. 34.22. Yield of flashes (with saturating dark intervals) in *Chlorella ellipsoidea* as function of flash energy (after Tamiya and Chiba 1949); for units, see preceding figure. (Closer approach to the extrapolated saturation level than shown in this figure is indicated by data in text of paper.)

We now have to discuss several flashing light studies which seem to call for a more thorough revision of the concepts derived from the above-enumerated earlier observations. The most important of them is an investigation by Tamiya and Chiba (1949). They used *Chlorella ellipsoidea*, a species similar to *Chlorella pyrenoidosa* of Warburg and Emerson. The cells were grown for 10 days in Knop's solution at 2–3 klux, and then incubated in the dark for 3 days. Its maximum steady photosynthesis at 25° C. in carbonate buffers was about 1.5 μmole/sec. per gram dry weight (0.77 μmole at 15° and 0.38 μmole at 7° C.). If one assumes a chlorophyll content of 5% (*cf.* table 25.I), this corresponds to an assimilation time of 33 sec. (at 25° C.) typical of normal shade cells (*cf.* table 28.V).

Tamiya and Chiba exposed these cells, in buffer No. 9, to flashes of 0.6 to 8 msec. duration, obtained by means of rotating discs, on which the image of a 750 watt incandescent lamp was focussed. The maximum illumination at the bottom of the suspension vessel was 120 klux. By varying flash duration and lamp voltage, flash energies from 10 to 1000 lux sec. could be obtained. (According to p. 838, this should mean from 1.4×10^{12} to 1.4×10^{15} incident quanta per cm.^{2} per flash, or from one absorption act per about 500, to one absorption act per about 5, chlorophyll molecules; these estimates could be too high because the copper sulfate filter must have affected the spectral composition and thus also the average absorption of the light reaching the suspension.)

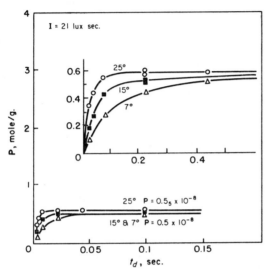

Fig. 34.23. Oxygen yield per flash as function of dark intervals in *Chlorella ellipsoidea* for subsaturating flash energy (after Tamiya and Chiba 1949).

The yield was measured manometrically in carbonate buffer No. 9, in 10 minute runs, with dark intervals from 0.015 to 0.60 sec., at 7°, 15° and 25° C. A suspension of 4 mg. algae covered an area of about 20 cm.^{2} (about 10^{-8} mole chlorophyll per cm.^{2}, indicating a probable absorption of <50% of incident light).

The results differed from earlier data in three significant ways.

(*1*) As shown in figure 34.21, the yield per flash increased with the duration of dark intervals up to 0.2 sec. at 25° C., 0.3 sec. at 15° C. and about 0.5 sec. at 7° C. (for saturating flashes)—ten times longer than in table 39.II.

(*2*) The absolute maximum flash yield at 25° C. was 7.3×10^{-8} mole oxygen per gram dry weight; with a chlorophyll concentration of about 5% this is equivalent to one molecule oxygen per 700 molecules chlorophyll— about three times the maximum flash yield observed in the earlier experiments. Fig. 34.22 shows the dependence of the yield on flash energy at saturating dark intervals; the "limiting yield" of Emerson and Arnold is indicated by a horizontal dashed line.

(*3*) The maximum yield per saturating flash depended on *temperature* (compare fig. 34.22 with fig. 34.14).

Tamiya and Chiba attributed the difference between their results and those of Emerson and Arnold to the use of higher flash energies, and submitted that the light emission of condensor discharges, lasting only 10^{-5} second, was insufficient for saturation. They pointed out that their own results at low flash energies gave a picture similar to that of the earlier observers (fig. 34.23), with a saturation level independent of temperature and reached after dark intervals of < 0.02 sec. at 25° C. and < 0.06 sec. at 7° C. However, the maximum yield in fig. 34.23 is only about one quarter that of Emerson and Arnold; with flash energies sufficient to equal the latter (about 100 lux sec.), Tamiya's curves show a strong dependence of saturation on temperature. Furthermore, their explanation does not apply to the observations of Weller and Franck, who used flashes, produced by a 1000 watt Hg lamp and rotating sector, with energies up to 450 lux sec., and nevertheless found (in agreement with Emerson and Arnold) no dependence of the maximum flash yield on temperature (fig. 34.14).

Tamiya (1949) suggested an interpretation of his experiments by a kinetic scheme in which the effect on the flash yield of back reactions in the primary photochemical apparatus was a function of temperature. This required no change in the mechanism of light saturation postulated by Franck, but merely a change in the relative values of the several rate constants. Both Franck's and Tamiya's picture can be illustrated by scheme 28.II (p. 1037) and the reaction sequence (28.41, a–e). (It is irrelevant for the kinetics whether the stabilizing reaction operates on the first reduction product of carbon dioxide, $AHCO_2$ in scheme 28.II, or the first oxidation product of water, AHO in the same scheme, or on some intermediate oxidation-reduction system.) Franck, in order to account for the independence of the maximum flash yield of temperature (observed by Emerson and Arnold, and confirmed by Weller and Franck), suggested (in essence) that the relative values of k' (the rate constant of the back reaction in scheme 28.II), k_e (rate constant of the photoproduct-enzyme complex formation), and k'_e (the rate constant of the transformation of this complex and reactivation of the enzyme E_B) are such that *all* products of the flash for which molecules of the enzyme E_B are available, are combined with this enzyme before they are lost by back reactions ($k' \ll k_e E_B^0$); but that by the time this first "batch" of photoproducts had been transformed, back reactions have taken care of all the remaining flash products, and no "second round" of the stabilizing reaction is possible ($k' \ll k'_e$). With this assumption, measurements of the maximum flash yield become titrations of E_B^0, and permit a separation of the factors k_e' and E_B^0 (whose product can only be derived from the maximum rate in constant light, *cf.* equation 28.47, or Tamiya's equation IV-3). Conversely, to explain the dependence of the maximum flash yield on temperature (which he has observed) Tamiya assumed (in essence) that the back reaction is *not* fast enough to prevent some enzyme molecules from operating twice (or more) in the wake of a single flash. (He retained Franck's first assumption, $k' \ll k_e E_B^0$, as needed to explain effective utilization of all absorbed quanta in weak light.) With the stabilization reaction now effectively competing with the back reaction, the flash yield becomes a function of their relative rate constants,

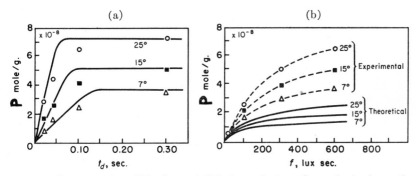

Fig. 34.24. Interpretation of Tamiya and Chiba's results by a first-order back reaction (after Tamiya 1949): (a) $\mathbf{P} = f(t_d)$ curves; (b) $\mathbf{P} = f(\mathbf{I})$ curves.

and, since the two reactions are likely to have a different dependence on temperature, also a function of the latter. The possibility of determining the total amount of the limiting enzyme, E_B^0, is lost in this scheme, since only the products $k_e E_B^0$ and $k_e' E_B^0$ occur in the kinetic equations.

By using the measured yields in constant and flashing light as parameters, Tamiya calculated the rate constants k', $k_e E_B^0$ and $k_e' E_B^0$ (designated by him as k_s, k_1 and k_2, respectively) at the three temperatures used ($k_e' E_B^0$ had to drop faster with decreasing temperature than $k_e E_B^0$ to account for the decrease in the flash yield). The rate constant, k', of the back reaction was estimated as about 200 sec.$^{-1}$ at 25° C., and 100 sec.$^{-1}$ at 7° C.— *i. e.*, *not* higher than Emerson and Arnold's values for the rate constant of the stabilizing reaction, k_e' (in contradiction to Franck's assumption).

Inserting the calculated values of the rate constants into the kinetic expressions derived for the flash yield as function of dark time, and for the flash yield as function of flash energy, Tamiya was able to reproduce with fair approximation the experimental course of the first-named function (fig. 34.24a), but not that of the second one (fig. 34.24b). The theoretical curves predicted flash saturation only at flash energies of the order of 10^5 lux sec., instead of $< 10^3$ lux sec. as observed by Tamiya.

A different kinetic postulate was therefore tried by Tamiya—that the back reaction is of the second order. In scheme 28.II, this would be the case if the two photoproducts, $AHCO_2$ and $A'HO$, were to become kinetically independent before reacting back; bimolecular secondary back reactions were provided (in addition to monomolecular primary back reactions) also in schemes 28.IA and 28.IB (pp. 1025–1026; reactions 28.20d and 28.21d).

The postulate of a bimolecular back reaction naturally leads to a more sudden approach to flash saturation (since the rate of the back reaction now

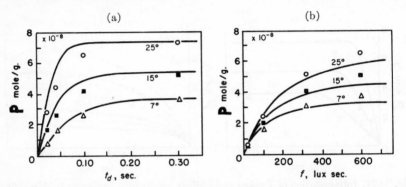

Fig. 34.25. Interpretation of Tamiya and Chiba's results by a second-order back reaction (after Tamiya 1949): (a) $P = f(t_d)$ curves; (b) $P = f(I)$ curves.

increases with the *square* of the concentration of the photoproducts). Kinetic equations of somewhat forbidding complexity were derived by Tamiya for this mechanism. The rate constants ($k_1\epsilon$, $k_2\epsilon$, and the bimolecular back reaction constant, k_s'') were calculated, by means of these equations, from the same experimental parameters as was done before for a first-order mechanism; a fairly good representation could be obtained this time not only for the flash yield *vs.* dark time experiments, but also for the flash yield *vs.* flash energy curves (fig. 34.25).

Tamiya suggested that the results of Emerson and Arnold could be accounted for quantitatively by the same equations, if one assumed that the flashes used by them had an integrated energy of about 100 lux sec. (*cf.* fig. 34.22). However, Tamiya's explanation requires the assumption that the flash yield of Emerson and Arnold was measured in the linear range of the yield *vs.* energy curve—which is incompatible with the experimental data, clearly showing an approach to (if not attainment of) saturation. Fig. 34.27 (p. 1479) of Ehrmantraut and Rabinowitch (1952), obtained with a higher discharge energy, shows even more clearly than the data of Emerson and Arnold, a levelling-off of the yield *vs.* energy curve at a height corresponding to $P = Chl_0/2000$, in disagreement with Tamiya's suggestion.

Assuming that both the measurements of Emerson and Arnold (and others) with *Chlorella pyrenoidosa*, and those of Tamiya with *Chlorella ellipsoidea*, are experimentally reliable, it appears that the flash yield is limited, in the first case, by a monomolecular back reaction with a rate constant $\simeq 100$ sec.$^{-1}$, permitting only a single "round" of the stabilizing reaction; and, in the second case, by a bimolecular back reaction allowing time for several such rounds. This is not impossible; but it seems a remarkable coincidence that the elimination (or slowing down) of the first-order back reaction should be coupled with the emergence of a second-order back reaction imposing almost the same ceiling on the maximum rate in continuous light. (It will be recalled, however, that in chapter 28 we did discuss the possibility that photosynthesis may contain several "bottleneck reactions" adjusted to about the same maximum capacity.)

In principle, the conclusion that both first-order back reactions (detautomerizations) and second-order back reactions (recombinations) can occur in photosynthesis is plausible. The same is generally true of reactions in which unstable intermediates are formed in the condensed state, *e. g.*, the decomposition of water by high-energy radiations.

The observations of Strehler and Arnold (1951), to be described in Chapter 37C, section 5, may be worth mentioning in this connection. They found a delayed re-emission of light quanta by chlorophyll *in vivo*, probably associated, as chemiluminescence, with a back reaction in photosynthesis. The decay of this emission was a second-order process at 6.5° C., and had an order of between one and two at 28° C. The absolute rate of the luminescence decay was considerably slower than the decay of the dark reaction derived from flashing light experiments: the period of half-decay was as long as 1.5 seconds at 28° C. (but only 0.5 second at 6.5°). It is, therefore, an open question whether this chemiluminescence is associated with the same two (or, at least, one of the two) back reactions revealed by the experiments of Emerson and Arnold, and of Tamiya and Chiba.

More extended measurements of the flash yield *vs.* flash energy curve, employing a variety of organisms undoubtedly are in order; the first need is for a device permitting high intensity instantaneous flashes (such as can be obtained from xenon discharge tubes) to be repeated at close intervals (0.01 second or less).

One fundamental question to be settled is whether it is true—as postulated at the beginning of this chapter—that for sufficiently brief flashes the integrated intensity (*i. e.*, the energy, E) of the flash is all that matters, while the true momentary intensity of illumination is irrelevant. Tamiya and Chiba reported having confirmed this assumption; but the figures they give show this confirmation to extend only up to 109 lux sec., while the measurements at which the Emerson-Arnold maximum flash yield was exceeded required flash energies of 200–1000 lux sec. It is therefore conceivable that the main reason for the difference between the results of Tamiya and Chiba, and of Emerson and Arnold, is to be sought in the use of flashes of very different duration—microseconds in one case and milliseconds in the other. Qualitatively, such a difference is to be expected, according to Franck's "single batch" theory, when the duration of the flash ceases to be negligible compared to the postulated working time of the limiting enzyme (about 3×10^{-2} sec. at 20° C.). In this case, some molecules of the stabilizing enzyme operate once *during* and once again after the flash. (In Tamiya's picture, an enzyme molecule could operate more than once *after* the flash!) As in Tamiya's theory, this repeated operation of the enzyme E_B must make the yield a function of temperature. However, it does not seem that the results of Tamiya and Chiba can be explained quantitatively in this way. In order that the yield *during* a saturating flash may become equal to the yield *after* the flash, its duration must equal the reciprocal (monomolecular) rate constant of the transformation process (for kt_f to equal $\int_0^\infty ke^{-kt}\,dt$, t_f must be equal to $1/k$). In Tamiya and Chiba's experiments, flash yields twice the Emerson-Arnold "maximum yield" were obtained at 15° C., with flashes lasting as little as 3 msec., while the reciprocal rate constant of the Emerson-Arnold reaction is about 40 msec. at 13°C. (*cf.* table 34.II).

It is obvious from this example that the correction for the finite duration of the flash is *not* negligible in experiments with rotating discs, and that an exact determination of flash duration is therefore important. (It can be argued that Tamiya's measurement of the "half-width" of the oscillograph record of the flash led to an underestimation of its effective length.)

That flash duration is not a sufficient reason for the difference between the results of Tamiya and of Emerson is further indicated by Weller and Franck's results, which, despite the use of "long" flashes, agreed with those of Emerson *et al.*

It seems that the assumption of (at least) two different reactions affecting the flash yield cannot be avoided. The first possibility—indicated above—is that *two back reactions* in the photosensitive complex may compete with a single rate-limiting reaction (such as the regeneration of the "finishing" catalyst, E_B). Weller and Franck (1941) suggested a different postulate—that of a second limiting reaction of the *preparatory* type (specifically, a stage in the carbon dioxide fixation). They used this hypothesis to explain the behavior of certain plants in flashing light, and, in particular, to interpret the effect of cyanide on the flash yield (*cf.* section B3 above). This postulate could provide a qualitative interpretation also of Tamiya's results (including the temperature dependence of the flash yield); but, quantitatively, this interpretation encounters the same difficulty as was mentioned above in discussing Tamiya's own theory: as a general rule, one would expect an alternative "ceiling" on the maximum rate to become effective only if it is *lower* than the usual one (*cf.* fig. 34.13); while the Weller-Franck theory can account for Tamiya's findings only if one credits Tamiya's cells with a much higher than usual content of the (normally limiting) "finishing" enzyme (E_B), and a content of active "preparatory" enzyme (E_A?) just sufficient to give the same maximum rate in constant light as is usually permitted by E_B (since Tamiya's algae showed, as mentioned above, a normal rate of photosynthesis in saturating steady light).

Another, as yet vague, explanation of Tamiya's results would be to relate them to the "oxygen bursts" described in Chapter 33, and suggest that perhaps with dark intervals of ≥ 0.1 sec. (needed to exceed the Emerson-Arnold maximum flash yield) a large part of the respiration intermediates, accumulated during the dark periods, is reduced in light, producing an oxygen burst and increasing the apparent yield of photosynthesis. In other words, one could suggest that light flashes effectively inhibit respiration during the whole period of exposure to flashing illumination. However, no such effect was noticed by Brown (1953) in mass spectrographic study of respiration in light (*cf.* chapter 37D). Also, one does not see offhand why the same effect should not have been produced also by instantaneous discharge flashes (after dark intervals of the same length). Refuge could be taken to the great variability which "transients" show in dependence on the metabolic history and nature of the cells; but the effects of dark intervals of the order of one second on flash yield crop up somewhat too regularly for such an explanation.

We can refer in this connection also to the findings of Gilmour *et al.* on chloroplast suspensions, and their kinetic interpretation in terms of a "reservoir" in which energy-rich photoproducts can be stored, to be released for "finishing" after the flash. These authors suggested a mechanism of the filling of the reservoir which makes it ineffective in instantaneous flashes, but operative in flashes of the same integral energy but longer duration (*cf.* section 7 below).

An even more radical departure from the conclusions reached in the earlier flashing light experiments was suggested by Burk and coworkers (1951, 1952, 1953). They asserted that not only Emerson and Arnold, but Tamiya and Chiba as well, have never even remotely approached flash saturation. The reaction mechanism postulated by Burk, Cornfield and Schwartz (1951, 1952) was in principle similar to that of Franck (or Tamiya): competition between a back reaction and a forward reaction for the primary photoproducts. Burk associated the competing back reaction with the "energy dismutation" mechanism. (This concept was first described in chapters 7 and 9, pp. 164 and 233, and later used by van der Veen, and by Burk and Warburg; the latter called it the "cyclic reaction," or the "one-quantum mechanism" of photosynthesis.) According to this concept, exothermal back reactions (such as reaction 28.41e on p. 1036, *cf.* scheme 28.II) are used in nature to store chemical energy for subsequent use as supplement to a quantum of light in the reduction of carbon dioxide. This special purpose of the back reaction does not affect the form of the kinetic equations, but only the assumptions concerning the *relative values* of the rate constants. Franck (and Tamiya) have assumed that the first forward reaction of the photoproduct (its association with the enzyme E_B) must be very fast compared to the back reaction (except when much of the enzyme E_B is occupied by the slow transformation of its complex with the photoproduct, with ensuing light saturation); this assumption was needed to permit effective utilization of quanta in weak light. Burk and Warburg, in their variant of the energy dismutation mechanism, postulated, to the contrary, that the back reaction must be at least twice as fast as the forward reaction (as needed to reduce the net quantum yield from 1 to the highest energetically possible value of about $1/3$).

Burk denied the existence of a "bottleneck enzyme" other than chlorophyll (for a discussion of this possibility, see p. 1030); the maximum expected flash yield thus became Chl_0/n, where n (≥ 3) is the "energy dismutation factor", *i. e.*, the number of quanta used for the net production of one molecule of oxygen. Burk thus reverted, in essence, to the early concept that in flash saturation each chlorophyll molecule must produce one molecule of oxygen. With $n \backsimeq 3$, this means a seven hundred times higher flash yield than obtained by Emerson and Arnold, or two hundred times greater than obtained by Tamiya and Chiba. At first, Burk *et al.* (1951, 1952) implied that such high flash yields actually are observable; a subsequent note (1953) indicated, however, that this was not the case. It was suggested that the failure to obtain the "theoretical" flash yields, $P = Chl_0/n$, is caused by a "solarization"—the same phenomenon that reduces the rate of photosynthesis in excessively strong, steady light (*cf.* chapter 19, section A3). As mentioned before, Burk *et al.* thus rejected the concept that, with very brief flashes, the momentary intensity of illumination is irrelevant, and all that matters is the total energy of the flash. Instead, they postulated that, if the momentary intensity of illumination exceeds—even for a few microseconds—the intensity which produces solarization in steady light, the yield of photosynthesis declines in the same proportion as if this intensity were applied for an extended period of time. According to Burk *et al.* (1953), the threshold of solarization for *Chlorella* lies at about 50 klux; this means that the maximum flash yield obtainable with flashes of 10 μsec. duration should be not much in excess of that corresponding to a flash energy of 0.5 lux sec. (which seems to be quite incompatible with observations), and flashes of 10 μsec. should yield, at best, not much more than the amount of oxygen corresponding to a flash energy of 500 lux sec. (close to where Tamiya found flash saturation).

This theory appears implausible (because "solarization," as described in chapter 19, is a cumulative rather than instantaneous response). It seems incapable of accounting quantitatively for the observations of Emerson and Arnold *et al.*; and if it were the correct explanation of Tamiya's observations, the latter should have noticed an "optimum" of flash energy. The theory appears as a reversion from Blackman's recognition of "limiting reactions" to the older concept of "cardinal points" (*cf.* chapter 26). A description of the actual experiments of Burk and coworkers must be awaited before judging whether they call for such drastic revision of our kinetic concepts.

Intermittency factors $E_{It} > 1$ offer obvious inducements to use intermittent light in experiments on mass culturing of algae. Of course, with a light source of a given intensity—*e. g.*, the sun—no advantage could be expected (on the basis of present kinetic knowledge) from the relation $E_{It} > 1$ if intermittency were achieved simply by blacking out the illumination for certain intervals (*e. g.*, by means of rotating sectors); but if the same interruption of illumination could be achieved by placing another batch of algae in the path of the light while the first one is "digesting" the flash products in darkness, $E_{It} > 1$ would mean also $E_{IE} > 1$, i. e., an increase in the utilization of solar energy (since, now, no light energy will be wastefully absorbed by black screens).

If the Emerson-Arnold reaction were the only one determining the intermittency effect, the maximum improvement in the efficiency of light utilization could be expected with light periods lasting just long enough to excite—with the available light intensity—one chlorophyll molecule out of between 250 and 2000 (to put all the enzyme E_B to work at the end of the flash), and dark periods lasting long enough to permit the Emerson-Arnold reaction to run to practical completion at the prevailing temperature, but short enough to avoid induction losses afterwards. According to p. 838, in direct sunlight at noon (~85 klux), a directly exposed chlorophyll molecule absorbs a photosynthetically effective quantum about once every 0.08 second. Therefore, one molecule in 2000 will absorb a quantum in a flash of direct sunlight 40 μsec. long, and one molecule in 250, in a flash of 300 μsec. duration. The dark period will have to last $\geq$ 30 μsec. (at 15–20° C.) to complete the Emerson-Arnold reaction. Finite optical density of a cell suspension will make the required length of the flash longer than 40–300 μsec.; while the above-discussed (but not definitely understood) capacity of dark intervals $\gg$ 0.03 sec. to enhance the yield of such "millisecond flashes," may shift the optimum towards dark intervals much longer than 3000 μsec.

Empirical studies of energy conversion yield as function of the "intermittency pattern" have been carried out on optically thin layers of *Chlorella* suspensions in connection with mass culturing of these algae, by Kok (1953) and Myers and coworkers (1953, 1954). Kok used rotating sectors which could be adjusted in width (varying t_f/t_d) and in speed of rotation (varying both t_f and t_d in the same proportion). The curves given in his paper show that with a ratio $t_d/t_f = 4.5$, a yield practically equal to that in constant light of the same intensity could be achieved in artificial light of about 70 klux at 1500 r.p.m., (i. e., $t_f = 3$ msec., $t_d = 13.5$ msec.). If this intermittency regime could be achieved by turbulent flow in a *Chlorella* suspension (instead of by wasteful black sectors), the gain in energy conversion (compared to nonstirred suspensions) would be by a factor of about 5. Since these cells were grown indoors and showed saturation in constant light at about 7 klux, still higher intermittency enhancement factors could be expected to result from an increase in the ratio t_d/t_f above 10 (so as to reduce the *average* intensity of flashing illumination below the steady saturating intensity). In fact, yields not significantly different from those in continuous light could be obtained, with such "indoor" cells, at $t_d \simeq 100$ msec., and $t_f = 4$ msec. These results confirm that dark intervals an order of magnitude longer than the Emerson-Arnold period of 10^{-2} sec. *can* be effectively utilized for photosynthesis after flashes lasting a few milliseconds (and having, in the above example, an integrated energy of the order of 70 $\times$ 4 = 280 lux sec.).

7. Hill Reaction in Flashing Light

Clendenning and Ehrmantraut (1950) studied the Hill reaction in flashing light, with quinone as oxidant, in whole *Chlorella* cells (*cf.* chapter 35, part C). A neon discharge tube (flash duration about 10 μsec.) was used. The flash yields as function of the duration of the dark period are shown in

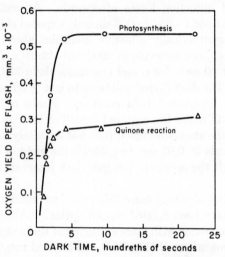

Fig. 34.26. Effect of dark intervals on flash yield of photosynthesis and quinone reduction by *Chlorella* (after Clendenning and Ehrmantraut 1941).

fig. 34.26; the curves follow a similar course for the quinone reaction and for photosynthesis (measured in the same *Chlorella* culture, but in bicarbonate solution instead of quinone-containing phosphate buffer). Saturation of both reactions requires dark intervals of 0.03–0.04 sec. at 10° C. The absolute flash yields in fig. 34.26 are 40–50% smaller in quinone than in bicarbonate at the same flash energy. However, subsequent experiments by Ehrmantraut and Rabinowitch (1952) led to the conclusion that this difference was caused by the higher energy needed (in flashing as well as in steady light) to saturate the Hill reaction. Fig. 34.27 indicates that the saturation level probably is the same for both reactions—namely, about 12 mm.³ oxygen per gram chlorophyll (*i. e.*, one molecule oxygen per 2000 molecules chlorophyll) per flash.   In these experiments, the energy of the flashes was increased by raising the discharge voltage to 5.8 kvolt; in the higher range of energies the flash yield of photosynthesis appeared quite constant between 30 and 80 (rel. units), indicating true saturation (*cf.* above, section B2); no equally convincing proof of complete flash saturation of the Hill reaction was possible in the accessible energy range.

In contrast to photosynthesis the Hill reaction in *Chlorella* showed no induction loss in flashing light.

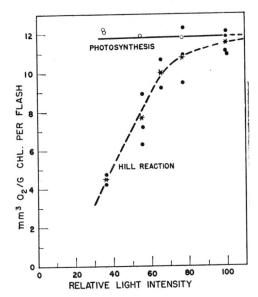

Fig. 34.27. Flash saturation of photosynthesis and quinone reduction
by *Chlorella* (Ehrmantraut and Rabinowitch 1952).

Gilmour, Lumry and Spikes (1953, 1954) made flashing light experiments with chloroplast preparations from *Beta vulgaris*, using ferricyanide as oxidant, and an oxidation-reduction electrode as measuring device. The chloroplast suspension was stirred during the measurement. Flash illumination was provided by a 1000 watt incandescent lamp, and chopped by rotating sectors.   The brightness at the vessel was up to 250 klux; with flashes lasting usually 2.8 msec. and in some experiments up to 16 msec., the flash energy was as high as 700, and sometimes even 4000 lux sec.

The largest flash yields observed were of the order of four Fe(III) atoms reduced (corresponding to one O_2 produced) per 3000 chlorophyll molecules—a yield considerably below the Emerson-Arnold maximum.   However, the maximum rate of Hill reaction in steady light was, in Gilmour's preparations, only about 10% of the normal saturation rate of photosynthesis (for equal amount of chlorophyll). In this sense, the observed yields in very strong flashes were, similarly to those of Tamiya, much higher than expected from the Franck-Emerson-Arnold relation between the yields in constant and flashing light. Reminiscent of Tamiya's observations was also the fact that in (relatively) weak flashes (about 100 klux) the flash yield was in the "proper" relation to the rate in constant light (one O_2 per 20,000 chlorophyll molecules per flash, or 10% of the Emerson-Arnold flash yield); complete saturation in respect to dark time was reached, in this case, after 0.04 sec. at 15.6° C., also in good agreement with the Emerson-Arnold observations on photosynthesis. With flash energies $\gg$ 100 lux sec., on the other hand, the flash yields kept growing with flash duration far past the Emerson-Arnold limiting period (again in agreement with Tamiya's results). The main content of the work of Gilmour et al. was the analysis of the flash yield, P, vs. dark time, t_d, curves under different conditions. In contrast to Tamiya, their interpretation was based on the assumption that the flash saturation curves of the Emerson-Arnold type are real, and that a kinetic theory must account for them, as well as for the "Tamiya type" curves (and, more generally, for the effect of dark periods $\gg$ 0.01 sec. on the energy utilization).

At "low" flash energies (50–100 lux sec.), the plots of $\Delta \log P$ vs. Δt_d (increment in flash yield vs. increment of dark period) were simple straight lines, indicating, as mentioned above, a single rate-limiting first-order dark reaction, with a half-time of about 0.016 sec. at 6.9° C., and 0.0113 sec. at 15.6° C.—in good agreement with the constants of the Emerson-Arnold reaction in photosynthesis as reported by various observers (cf. Table 34.II).

In some runs, a zero-order reaction was noticeable at the very beginning of the dark period. It was followed by an approximately temperature independent first-order reaction with a half-time of about 0.02 sec. (6.9–33.3° C.), and another zero-order reaction, with a rate constant of 4.3 $\times$ 10^{-3} at 6.9°, 4.7 $\times$ 10^{-3} at 15.6°, 2.5 $\times$ 10^{-3} at 23.6° and 0.83 $\times$ 10^{-3} at 33.3° C. (mole Fe^{3+}/mole chlorophyll/sec.). At the highest temperature used, 33.3° C., the plot showed two sharply separated linear segments, the above-mentioned, almost temperature independent first-order reaction being preceded by a faster one with a half-time of 0.007 sec. The latter may be identical with the temperature dependent first-order reaction (Emerson-Arnold reaction) which dominates the picture at the lower flash energies.

The superposition of a zero-order limiting reaction upon a second-order one recalls Weller and Franck's suggestion that a zero-order process, by which the reductant is supplied to the photosynthetic system, may be the reason for the effect of long dark intervals on the flash yield in some organisms (or under certain conditions, such as cyanide poisoning). One could extend the Weller-Franck hypothesis to the Hill reaction by assuming that the supply of the oxidant (ferricyanide, or an intermediate in its reduction) can become rate-limiting under certain conditions. Gilmour *et al.* offered a different concept. They suggested that the occurrence, after long and intense flashes of one (or two) zero-order limiting reactions, together with a (temperature independent) first-order reaction different from that which determines the yield of short flashes, can be interpreted by assuming a "reservoir" in which a part of the energy-rich products, formed in the flash, can be reversibly stored, escaping the back reaction and permitting the "Emerson-Arnold enzyme" to operate more than once in the wake of a single flash. Gilmour *et al.* elaborated a chemical mechanism for the filling and emptying of the "reservoir" which could justify the postulate that the reservoir has no effect on the yield of brief flashes (or on the rate in continuous light) but increases the yield of "long" flashes of the same total energy. In essence, this mechanism amounts to a combination of the Franck-Emerson-Arnold reaction system with a side reaction feeding into a reservoir, from which the Emerson-Arnold system can draw after a flash. If the reaction feeding into the reservoir is enzymatic, the amount of photoproducts drained into the reservoir during the flash will depend not only on the integrated intensity of the flash, but also on its duration (as in Tamiya's model). The addition to the flash yield, provided by the stored photoproducts, will then increase with the duration of the flash, and can be expected to depend also on temperature. The Emerson-Arnold reaction will nevertheless remain the bottleneck through which all photoproducts must pass, and which determines both the yield in steady light and the maximum yield of instantaneous flashes.

Further details of the reservoir filling and emptying mechanism (including two catalysts, one of which is photochemically activated) were suggested by Gilmour *et al.* to account for the above-mentioned complex features of the flash yield–dark time curves; experiments were also made (and interpreted by the same model) on the flash yield in chloroplast preparations partially inactivated by heat, cold, or ultraviolet light.

8. Flashing-Light Experiments with Bacteria and Hydrogen-Adapted Algae

The only result available on the photosynthesis of *purple bacteria* in flashing light is the observation of Arnold, quoted by van Niel (1941) and recorded in Table 32.I, that the ratio $P^{max.}/BChl_0$ is of the order of 1/400. This result can be interpreted as evidence that the limiting catalyst, E_B, is present in these bacteria in the ratio of one molecule for 400 BChl molecules—or 400n, where n may be $1/4$ or $1/8$. The duration of dark intervals required to achieve the full flash yield in bacteria—$i.$ $e.$, the constant k_{EA}^{B} is as yet unknown. However, it is likely that the rate-limiting reaction is the same in bacterial as in ordinary photosynthesis; and, if this is so, one sees no reason why the required dark intervals should be different. Confirmation would be of some interest.

Rieke and Gaffron (1943) conducted some experiments on the photoreduction of hydrogen-adapted *Scenedesmus* in flashing light. As discussed before, in chapter 6, the rate-limiting reaction is in this case the supply of hydrogen by the hydrogenase system. Whenever the rate of the

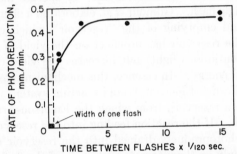

Fig. 34.28. Length of "stabilizing period" in photoreduction (after Rieke and Gaffron 1943). Rate of photoreduction as a function of time interval between flashes in a group of two.

primary photochemical process exceeds the maximum rate of the hydrogen supply, an accumulation of the intermediate oxidation products takes place, and causes a rapid "de-adaptation," $i.$ $e.$, return to normal photosynthesis. Limited hydrogen supply should have the same influence on flash yield as the limited carbon dioxide supply had in E_A-deficient ($e.$ $g.$, cyanide-poisoned) algae. This prediction was verified by Rieke and Gaffron by means of experiments with flashes grouped in pairs. When uniformly spaced flashes were used, the maximum yield of carbon dioxide reduction per flash was found to be approximately equal to that in non-adapted cells of the same species; but the dark intervals required for the full flash yield were much longer, since the supply of hydrogen during the intervals had to suffice for the reduction of all intermediates produced by a flash. Otherwise, not only would the yield per flash be smaller (as in the case of cyanide-poisoned plants), but the accumulation of oxidation intermediates would have brought about immediate "deadaptation."

When flashes were grouped in pairs—with the total number of flashes per minute unchanged—it was found that the interval between two flashes in a pair had to be >0.025 second in order to obtain a full yield from both of them (*cf.* fig. 34.28). As described in the analysis of the cyanide experiments, this is an indication that the reaction which limits the yield of the first few flashes in a series, after a sufficiently long "interserial" interval, requires not more than about 0.02 second for its completion. This is the same order of magnitude as in ordinary photosynthesis. Thus, both the maximum flash yield and the rate of the reaction that determines the duration of the dark intervals within a series of flashes required for maximum yield per flash, are not affected by adaptation. The slowness of the hydrogen supply in the adapted state merely leads to the necessity for inserting longer intervals between the flash series, in order to prevent deterioration of the flash yield after a small number of flashes. (The *average* rate of the primary photochemical process has to be kept at such a level that the slow but steady hydrogen supply can keep pace with it.)

Bibliography to Chapter 34

Time Effects. II. Photosynthesis in Intermittent Light

A. *Alternating Light*

1905 Brown, H. T., and Escombe, F., *Proc. Roy. Soc. London,* **B76,** 29.
1918 Willstätter, R., and Stoll, A., *Untersuchungen über die Assimilation der Kohlensäure.* Springer, Berlin.
1919 Warburg, O., *Biochem. Z.,* **100,** 230.
1928 Padoa, M., and Vita, N., *Gazz. chim. ital.,* **58,** 647.
1931 Garner, W. W., and Allard, H. A., *J. Agr. Research,* **42,** 629.
1937 Gregory, F. G., and Pearse, H. L., *Ann. Botany,* **1,** 3.
       McAlister, E. D., *Smithsonian Inst. Pubs. Misc. Collections,* **95,** No. 24.
       Portsmouth, G. B., *Ann. Botany,* **1,** 175.
1938 Iggena, M. L., *Arch. Mikrobiol.,* **9,** 129.
1939 Aufdemgarten, H., *Planta,* **29,** 643.
1941 Weller, S., and Franck, J., *J. Phys. Chem.,* **45,** 1360.
       Briggs, G. E., *Proc. Roy. Soc. London,* **B130,** 24.
1951 Warburg, O., Geleck, H., and Briese, K., *Z. Naturforsch.,* **6b,** 417.
1953 Brown, A. H., *Am. J. Botany,* **40,** 719.
1954 Whittingham, C. P., *Plant Physiol.,* **29,** 473.

B. *Flashing Light*

1932 Emerson, R., and Arnold, W., *J. Gen. Physiol.,* **15,** 391.
       Emerson, R., and Arnold, W., *ibid.,* **16,** 191.
1933 Arnold, W., *ibid.,* **17,** 135, 145.
1934 Arnold, W., and Kohn, H. I., *ibid.,* **18,** 109.
1935 Arnold, W., *Cold Spring Harbor Symposia Quant. Biol.,* **3,** 124.
1936 Kohn, H. I., *Nature,* **137,** 706.
1938 Pratt, R., and Trelease, S. F., *Am. J. Botany,* **25,** 133.

1940 Emerson, R., Green, L., and Webb, J. L., *Plant Physiol.*, **15**, 311.

1941 Briggs, G. E., *Proc. Roy. Soc. London*, **B130**, 24.

Franck, J., and Herzfeld, K. F., *J. Phys. Chem.*, **45**, 978.

van Niel, C. B., in *Advances in Enzymology*. Vol. I. Interscience, New York, pages 263, 320.

Weller, S., and Franck, J., *J. Phys. Chem.*, **45**, 1360.

1943 Rieke, F. F., and Gaffron, H., *J. Phys. Chem.*, **47**, 299.

1945 Franck, J., Pringsheim, P., and Lad, D. T., *Arch. Biochem.*, **7**, 103.

1949 Tamiya, H., and Chiba, Y., *Studies from Tokugawa Institute*, **6**, No. 2, 1.

Tamiya, H., *ibid.*, **6**, No. 2, 43.

1950 Clendenning, K. A., and Ehrmantraut, H. C., *Arch. Biochem.*, **29**, 387.

1951 Burk, D., Cornfield, J., and Schwartz, M., *Sci. Monthly*, **73**, 213.

Rabinowitch, E., *Ann. Rev. Phys. Chem.*, **2**, 361.

Strehler, B. L., and Arnold, W., *J. Gen. Physiol.*, **34**, 809.

1952 Burk, D., Cornfield, J., and Riley, V., *Federation Proc.*, **11**, No. 796.

Brilliant, V. A., and Krupnikova, T. A., *Compt. rend. (Doklady) Acad. Sci. USSR*, **85**, 1383.

Brilliant, V. A., and Krupnikova, T. A., *ibid.*, **86**, 1233.

Ehrmantraut, H. C., and Rabinowitch, E., *Arch. Biochem. and Biophys.*, **38**, 67.

1953 Burk, D., Hobby, G., Langhead, T., and Riley, V., *Federation Proc.*, **12**, No. 1, Abstract No. 601.

Gilmour, H. S. A., Lumry, R., Spikes, J. D., and Eyring, H., Report 11 (July 1, 1953) to the Atomic Energy Commission. [Contract No. AI (11-1)-82, Project No. 4].

Kok, B., in *Algal Culture*, by J. S. Burlew, ed., Carnegie Corp. Publ. No. 600, Chapter II.6, p. 63–75.

Myers, J., *ibid.*, p. 37–54.

Brown, A. H., *Am. J. Botany*, **40**, 719.

1954 Gilmour, H. S. A., Lumry, R., and Spikes, J. D., *Nature*, **173**, 31.

Phillips, J. N., and Myers, J., *Plant Physiol.*, **29**, 152.

PART FIVE

ADDENDA TO VOLUME I AND VOLUME II, PART 1

CHAPTER 35

PHOTOCHEMISTRY OF CHLOROPHYLL *IN VITRO* AND *IN VIVO**

(ADDENDA TO CHAPTERS 4, 18 AND 19)

Experiments with chloroplast suspensions and products obtained by their dispersion and fractionation have narrowed (but not quite bridged) the gap that had separated the photochemistry of chlorophyll in the living cell from the photochemistry of chlorophyll in solution. If this monograph were planned now, the part of it dealing with chloroplast-sensitized reactions would not have been tucked away among the unrelated and mostly wasted efforts described in chapter 4 ("Photosynthesis and Related Processes Outside the Living Cell"), but would have found its logical place at the end of chapter 18 ("Photochemistry of Pigments *in Vitro*"), forming a transition to chapter 19 ("Photochemistry of Pigments *in Vivo*"). Belatedly, we have adopted this plan in the present chapter, which thus constitutes an addendum to chapters 4, 18 and 19 of Volume I.

A. Photochemistry of Chlorophyll† in Solution*

1. Bleaching of Chlorophyll in Methanol

(First Addendum to Chapter 18, Section A2)

The reversible bleaching caused by illumination of oxygen-free chlorophyll solutions in methanol, first observed by Porret and Rabinowitch, was described in Vol. I, p. 486. McBrady and Livingston (1948) have continued the investigation of this phenomenon, which may provide clues to the function of chlorophyll in photosynthesis. Figure 35.1 gives a good illustration of the phenomenon. (The open circles represent the transmission of the solution in light, the black dots its transmission in the dark.) McBrady and Livingston (1948) confirmed Livingston's earlier suspicion that the rate of the back reaction, and with it also the extent of bleaching in the photostationary state, can vary considerably from case to case—

---

* Bibliography, page 1625.

† Very little is known about the photochemistry of other photosynthetic pigments. According to Krasnovsky, Evstigneev *et al.* (1952²), phycoerythrin solutions are much more stable in light than chlorophyll solutions; no reversible photochemical changes could be observed in them.

apparently under the influence of minor impurities. For example, the life-time of the bleached state in methanol solution was found by McBrady and Livingston to be of the order of 1 sec., in approximate agreement with the observations of Porret and Rabinowitch (1937), but about 100 times shorter than had been found in the earlier measurements of Livingston (1941). The life-time of the bleached state could be extended considerably by adding to methanol a small amount of carbon tetrachloride. Contrary to expectation, the rate of the dark back reaction (as well as the position of the photostationary state) was found to be insensitive to temperature changes, between 7.5° C. and 25° C.

Chlorophyll b showed a slightly stronger reversible bleaching (and a somewhat slower irreversible bleaching) than chlorophyll a.

Addition of 0.5 mole/liter allylthiourea, or 50% isoamylamine—substances whose autoxidation is sensitized by chlorophyll—as well as the presence of other *reductants*, such as phenylhydrazine or hydroquinone, had no

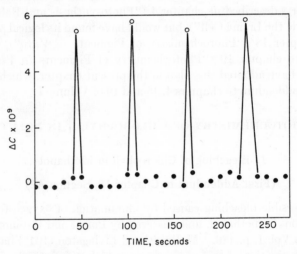

Fig. 35.1. Reversible photobleaching of chlorophyll in oxygen-free solutions (after Livingston 1949): (●) dark; (○) illuminated. Δc = decrease in concentrations (mole/liter) of the red-absorbing component (assuming the reaction product does not absorb red light at all).

depressing effect on reversible bleaching (*cf.* p. 437). However, allylthiourea counteracted the enhancing effect the presence of carbon tetrachloride had on bleaching, thus indicating that this enhancement must have been due to the presence of a reducible impurity in the ("reagent grade") carbon tetrachloride used. In contrast to earlier experiments, no enhancement of bleaching was found by McBrady and Livingston in the presence of 10^{-9} mole/liter *formic acid*; on the other hand, bleaching was enhanced by the addition of 10^{-4} mole/liter *oxalic acid* (threefold increase of steady-state bleaching, tenfold extension of the half-life of the bleached material). The back reaction was changed, by the addition of oxalic acid, from second to first order (in respect to the concentration of bleached material). An enhancement was produced also by the addition of *methyl red* (an azo dye whose reduction by phenylhydrazine is sensitized by chlorophyll); 10^{-5} mole/liter methyl red increased the stationary bleaching by a factor of four. A particularly strong enhancing effect was caused by *iodine* (10^{-5} mole/liter); for example, in one experiment the steady-state bleaching increased from 0.2 to 26%, and the half-life of the bleached state from 0.5 to 20 sec. In this case, too, the back reaction became a first-order reaction. Irreversible bleaching was completely suppressed by iodine. In pure carbon tetrachloride, reversible bleaching was noticeable, but it was largely obscured by irreversible bleaching, which was much faster than in methanol, and continued for some time in the dark. (Such an after-effect was not observed in methanol, or in methanol-carbon tetrachloride mixtures.)

The quantum yield of *irreversible* bleaching of air-saturated methanolic solution of chlorophyll a was estimated by McBrady and Livingston as $\gamma_{irr.} = 4 \times 10^{-5}$ (*cf.* similar earlier estimates on page 497, Vol. I). They also estimated the quantum yield of *reversible* bleaching (from the photostationary state and the rate of back reaction, or from the initial rate of bleaching), with the results shown in Table 35.I. The rate of the reverse process may change from case to case, by a factor of 200 or more, but the rate (quantum yield) of the forward reaction was found to change much less —only from 1.3×10^{-4} to 10×10^{-4} in the examples given in Table 35.I.

TABLE 35.I

KINETICS OF REVERSIBLE BLEACHING OF CHLOROPHYLL (AFTER McBRADY AND LIVINGSTON)*

| Solvent | Back reaction | | Forward reaction quantum yield, $\gamma \times 10^4$ |
	Order	Rate constant	
Methanol + oxalic acid..........1		0.28 sec. $^{-1}$	7
Methanol + CCl$_4$...............2		2.8×10^7 mole liter $^{-1}$ sec. $^{-1}$	1.3
Methanol (pure)................2		"At least 20 times higher"	~ 4
Methanol + I$_2$.................1		?	~ 10

* *Cf.* below for data of Livingston and Knight.

The values, $\gamma_{rev.} = 10 \times 10^{-4}$ and $\gamma_{rev.} = 3 \times 10^{-4}$, given earlier by Porret and Rabinowitch, and by Livingston, respectively, fall into the same range. (It is worth remembering that all these γ's are *minimum* values, since their calculation is based on the assumption that the reversibly bleached chlorophyll absorbs no red light at all.)

In dealing with the mechanism of reversible bleaching, McBrady and Livingston did not go beyond discussion of the several possibilities enumerated in Volume 1 (pages 489 and 514). One interesting new suggestion was that the inhibiting effect of oxygen may be due to the catalytic acceleration by oxygen of the "de-tautomerization" (or deactivation of a metastable triplet state) of chlorophyll:

$$(35.1) \qquad\qquad tChl \xrightarrow{\ O_2\rightarrow\ } Chl$$

a reversal of reaction (18.11a)—rather than to acceleration of an oxidation-reduction reaction which follows tautomerization, as was assumed, *e. g.*, in equations (18.12). The capacity of oxygen molecules to catalyze the destruction of tChl can be made plausible, according to McBrady and Livingston, by reference to the paramagnetism of the oxygen molecule, and to the probability that the long-lived state of chlorophyll, tChl, is a— mesomeric or tautomeric—triplet state and, as such, paramagnetic.

McBrady and Livingston mentioned an alternative explanation of the oxygen effect (suggested by Franck) involving the formation of a "mol-oxide" of tautomeric chlorophyll:

$$(35.2) \qquad\qquad tChl + O_2 \longrightarrow tChl\cdot O_2$$

capable of either reacting with hydrogen donors (such as an amine, AH_2):

$$(35.3) \qquad\qquad tChl\cdot O_2 + 2AH_2 \longrightarrow H_2O + 2\,A + Chl$$

or decomposing into ordinary chlorophyll and oxygen:

$$(35.4) \qquad\qquad tChl\cdot O_2 \longrightarrow Chl + O_2$$

Reaction (35.4) must be quite fast to be able to cause practically complete suppression of reversible bleaching; but reaction (35.3) must be even faster to account for the good quantum yield of sensitized photoxidation of amines. These two requirements seem difficult to reconcile.

Livingston and Ryan (1953) later adopted this scheme in the interpretation of flashing light experiments, *cf.* reactions (g) to (i) in sequence (35.12A), and calculated rate constants for reactions (35.2) and (35.4); they did not discuss the rate constant of (35.3).

McBrady and Livingston concluded that the earlier suggested mechanism of oxygen inhibition [reaction (18.12)] combined with a reaction of the tautomer with impurities or with the solvent (as discussed on page 491, Vol. 1) still affords the most plausible scheme of the oxygen effect:

$$(35.5a) \qquad\qquad Chl^* \longrightarrow tChl \qquad (\text{equation } 18.11a)$$

$$(35.5b) \qquad\qquad tChl + S \longrightarrow rChl + oS\ (\text{equation } 18.14)$$

$$(35.5c) \quad rChl + O_2 \longrightarrow Chl + HO_2\Big\}$$
$$(35.5d) \quad HO_2 + oS \longrightarrow S + O_2 \quad\Big\}\text{compare back reaction in equation (18.14)}$$

(here, S can stand for impurity, or solvent).

The following mechanism was suggested for the effect of iodine on reversible bleaching:

(35.6) $tChl + I_2 \longrightarrow tChl \cdot I_2$ (analogous to moloxide formation)

(35.7) $tChl \cdot I_2 \longrightarrow Chl + I_2$

These two reactions lead to enhanced stationary bleaching (extended life-time of the complex $tChl \cdot I_2$) and make the back reaction a first-order reaction.

Similar explanations could be suggested for the effects of oxalic acid on reversible bleaching.

Further experiments on the reversible bleaching of chlorophyll were made by Knight in Livingston's laboratory (*cf.* Livingston 1947, 1948, Knight and Livingston 1950). The effects of solvent, temperature, oxygen concentration, chlorophyll concentration and of certain additions were examined.

The extent of steady-state reversible bleaching of chlorophyll *a* in oxygen-free methanol was found to be 1.10 rel. units at 13.3° C., 1.00 at 27.3° C. and 0.98 at 39.5° C. This small but probably real *temperature coefficient* indicates a very small activation energy of the back reaction.

Experiments at three chlorophyll concentrations ($1 \times 10^{-6}, 2 \times 10^{-6}$ and 5×10^{-6} mole/liter) at 31° C., showed, quite unexpectedly, a slightly decreasing *absolute* bleaching: $\Delta[Chl] = 1.3, 1.0,$ and 1.0×10^{-8} mole/liter, respectively. Taking into account the increase in absorption, Livingston (1949) estimated that the extent of reversible bleaching at constant light absorption is inversely proportional to the *square root* of chlorophyll concentration. This implies that the rate of the back reactions is accelerated by an increase in chlorophyll concentration.

It was mentioned before that in pure methanol the back reaction is of second order with respect to $\Delta[Chl]$, indicating that it is brought about by the encounter of *two* tChl-molecules:

(35.8) $tChl + tChl \longrightarrow 2 Chl$

or more generally, of two molecules produced by bleaching, *e. g.*:

(35.9a) $rChl + oChl \longrightarrow 2 Chl,$ or

(35.9b) $rChl + oS \longrightarrow Chl + S,$ or

(35.9c) $oChl + rS \longrightarrow Chl + S$

(where S can stand, as before, for a molecule of the solvent, or an impurity). None of these schemes involves the participation of normal chlorophyll molecules in the back reaction. An apparent acceleration of the back reaction by nonexcited chlorophyll molecules thus remains to be made plausible. In Vol. 1 (p. 515), a similar effect of increased pigment concentration —the decrease in quantum yield of chlorophyll-sensitized reactions—was explained by the competition:

(35.10) $tChl \begin{cases} +A \longrightarrow oA + rChl \\ +Chl \longrightarrow oChl + rChl \end{cases}$

with the second reaction leading to recombination:

(35.11)   oChl + rChl ———→ 2 Chl

Livingston (1949) gave a somewhat different interpretation of the inhibiting effect of high pigment concentration on reversible bleaching:

(35.12)   tChl + Chl ———→ 2 Chl

However, this means that the back reaction ceases to be second order in respect to bleached chlorophyll—an implication not yet confirmed by experiment. It should also be taken into consideration that at higher chlorophyll concentration, absorption becomes less uniform and is concentrated in a thinner layer of solution; this favors second-order back reactions, such as tChl + tChl → Chl_2 (in the same way as would an increase in light intensity).

The observations (and speculations) concerning energy transfer between pigment molecules (chapter 32) and its role in the self-quenching of fluorescence (chapter 23, section A5, and chapter 37C, section 4b) suggest another possibility—that increased chlorophyll concentration could diminish reversible bleaching by dissipation of excitation energy in the course of its migration, as suggested in explanation of self-quenching. However, concentration effects were observed by Knight and Livingston in a range (10^{-6} M) which is far below that where concentration quenching becomes noticeable (10^{-3} M); they must be therefore attributed to the deactivation of metastable (and not of fluorescent) chlorophyll molecules. The only additional possibility derived from the energy migration concept is, then, that the deactivation reaction (35.12) may be caused by resonance rather than by actual kinetic encounters. (The probability of resonance exchange in the metastable state was mentioned in chapter 23, p. 785, and in chapter 32, p. 1290–1291.)

That the back reaction is not simple was indicated by the previously noted effect of *impurities*. In a renewed study, the influence of *traces of water* was investigated. It was found that the presence of 2% water in a 2×10^{-6} mole/liter solution of chlorophyll a in methanol increases the steady-state bleaching by as much as a factor of three. It also accelerates considerably the rate of irreversible bleaching. In *benzene* as solvent, no reversible bleaching could be observed at all, and only a very slow irreversible bleaching took place in the absence of oxygen. The presence of 1% methanol in benzene was sufficient, however, to produce as strong a reversible bleaching as that which occurs in pure methanol. In *carbon tetrachloride* (specially purified to remove the reductible impurity mentioned above) the irreversible bleaching is very strong. (Complete bleaching to a straw-yellow solution can occur within 3 min.; the product has an exceedingly high absorption peak at 400 mμ, and only a weak band in the red.)

Figure 35.2 shows the rate of irreversible bleaching and the extent of reversible bleaching as functions of *oxygen pressure*, $[O_2]$. The antiparallelism of the two developments—decrease in reversible bleaching and increase in irreversible bleaching—is easily apparent. In the neighborhood of 0.1 mm. O_2, the irreversible reaction is comparatively slow and the reversible reaction not yet completely inhibited. At 0.5 mm. O_2, irreversible bleaching has reached its maximum rate, and reversible bleaching has been

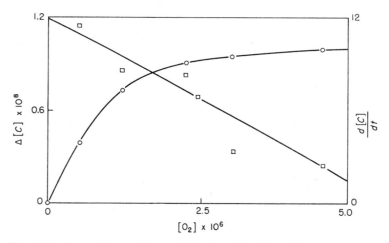

Fig. 35.2. Reversible and irreversible photobleaching of chlorophyll as a function of the molality of dissolved oxygen (after Livingston 1949): (O) Rate of irreversible bleaching (right scale); (□) extent of reversible bleaching (left scale).

reduced to almost zero. The low oxygen concentration sufficient to "saturate" the irreversible oxidation and to inhibit reversible bleaching can mean one of two things: either chlorophyll molecules associate with oxygen molecules, the association being practically complete when the concentration ratio is 1:1 (for evidence of such association, *cf.* Vol. I, page 460), or oxygen reacts with a long-lived active form of chlorophyll (such as tChl), which lives for a period of the order of 10^{-3} sec. Since, when irreversible bleaching is oxygen-saturated, its quantum yield is still very low, irreversible bleaching must be initiated by a reversible step, with the back reaction of the unstable intermediate competing very successfully with the permanently bleaching second step of oxidation. Livingston (1949) suggests the reaction sequence tChl + O_2 → tChlO$_2$; tChlO$_2$ → Chl + O_2; tChlO$_2$ + Chl → OChl + Chl, where OChl stands for *permanently* oxidized chlorophyll while oChl designated an unstable oxidation product, perhaps a free radical.

Irreversible bleaching not only fails to be accelerated, but is even somewhat slowed down by heating (by about 15% when the temperature increases from 16 to 36° C.). This indicates that the back reaction which reverses the first step of oxidation has a somewhat higher temperature coefficient than the forward reaction with which it competes.

In continuation of experiments by Rabinowitch and Weiss on the reversible decoloration of chlorophyll solutions by ferric and ceric salts and the accelerating effect of ferrous ions on the back reaction in reversible photobleaching (page 464, Vol. I), Knight and Livingston found that reversible bleaching of chlorophyll in methanol is enhanced by *cerous chloride, lanthanum chloride,* and *barium chloride* (in concentrations from 2 × 10^{-5} to 2 × 10^{-4} mole/liter). The back reactions become first-order reactions, with a half-period of 7–8 sec. in the presence of the cerium salt, and 20 sec. in the presence of the lanthanum salt. With repeated illumination, the absorption at 650 mμ *increased* irreversibly, indicating the gradual formation of a product absorbing red light even more strongly than chlorophyll itself. (In interpreting these results, one should recall the observations of Rabinowitch and Weiss on the effect of salts on the reversible reaction of chlorophyll with ferric chloride.)

When *iodine* was added to methanol, the back reaction was first order with a half-period of 25 sec. at 30° C.

With increased temperature (23 → 47° C.), the relative stationary bleaching in the presence of iodine increased by approximately 50%, despite the fact that the back reaction was accelerated by about a factor of 3 (still remaining a first-order reaction).

Under all conditions, the extent of steady bleaching remained proportional to the *square root* of light intensity. It was found to be proportional to [I_2] at concentrations up to 10^{-5} mole/liter; the half-life of the bleached state was, in this range, independent of [I_2]. A chlorophyll-sensitized reaction of iodine with methanol appeared to be the cause why the bleaching effects were found to decrease with repeated exposure to light.

In discussing these results, Livingston first reestimated, from figure 35.2, the quantum yield of irreversible bleaching in the oxygen-saturated state, and found $\gamma_{irr.}$ = 4.5 × 10^{-5} in agreement with the earlier estimates (*cf.* Vol. I, p. 497). Maximum quantum yield of *reversible* bleaching was calculated by extrapolation as $\gamma_{rev.} \geq$ 2.8 × 10^{-3}, *i. e.,* at least 6 times the value found in McBrady's work (table 35.I). In carbon tetrachloride, the quantum yield of irreversible bleaching was much higher—about 2.5 × 10^{-4}, but this is still a low value compared to the quantum yield of reversible bleaching. In the presence of iodine, the quantum yield of reversible bleaching was only 7.8×10^{-4}; in other words, the great enhancement of the stationary bleaching by iodine must be due entirely to a slowing down of the back reaction.

When stationary reversible bleaching is as strong as it can be in the presence of iodine (of the order of 10%), the bleaching effect of the *photometric light beam* cannot be neglected. Livingston showed that this influence was largely responsible for the observed deviations from the $\sqrt{I}$ law.

In summing up, Livingston pointed out that reversible bleaching apparently requires the presence of *polar molecules*. This parallels results obtained by the same investigator in the study of chlorophyll fluorescence (page 764); the latter, too, was found to require the association of chlorophyll with polar molecules (alcohols or amines).

Livingston and Ryan (1953) continued the study of reversible bleaching of chlorophyll in two directions. In the first place, they attempted to identify the spectrum of the "bleached" state (its only previously known feature being reduced absorption in the red). For this purpose, monochromatic scanning beams (isolated by interference filters) were sent through a methanolic chlorophyll solution, illuminated by an immediately adjoining 1000-watt incandescent lamp (through a Corning 3-66 filter) in a constant temperature bath. Experiments of this type permit calculation of the product (concentration of changed chlorophyll) $\times$ (difference between the absorption coefficients of changed and normal chlorophyll) for each scanning wave length; by assuming that the absorption coefficient, αP, of the photoproduct is zero at the wave length where the bleaching effect is strongest, a minimum value for the concentration of the bleached form can be calculated, and a consistent set of absorption coefficient obtained for all other wave lengths. (They will all be in error, by a constant factor, if the assumption $\alpha P = 0$ was wrong.)

The estimated absorption coefficients of the "phototrope" (as the "re-

TABLE 35.IA

AVERAGE SPECIFIC ABSORPTION COEFFICIENTS OF CHLOROPHYLL a AND b AND THEIR PHOTOTROPES, Chl a^* AND Chl b^*, IN METHANOL, DETERMINED FOR BANDS CENTERED AT λ_m (AFTER LIVINGSTON AND RYAN, 1953)

γ_m, mμ	Chl a	Chl a^*	Chl b	Chl b^*
403	69.3	50.8	12.7	26.4
439.5	62.7	80.0		
468.0	8.8	24.4	81.4	59.8
502	3.5	20.3		
524.5	3.1	13.5	3.4	21.8
528	10.4	(0.0)	9.0	(0.0)
645	30.6	10.4	20.7	7.6

versibly bleached" form was designated by Livingston) are shown in table 35.IA.

The *reduction* product of chlorophyll, observed by Krasnovsky *et al.* in the reaction with ascorbic acid (*cf.* section 4) and the *oxidation* product observed by Rabinowitch, and by Linschitz *et al.*, in reactions with ferric ions and quinone, respectively (*cf.* section 3), are similar to the phototrope observed in the reversible bleaching of chlorophyll in air-free methanol

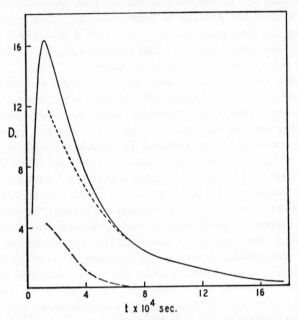

Fig. 35.2A. Decay of chlorophyll *b* absorption at 468 mμ after a flash (Livingston and Ryan 1953).   Solid line, uncorrected observations; dashed line, correction for scattering of flash light; dotted line, corrected decay curve.

which has (according to table 35.IA) a region of sharply increased absorption in the middle of the visible spectrum (439–525 mμ for *a*; 525 mμ for *b*), and sharply decreased absorption in the red (528–645 mμ); however, the spectrum of the phototrope does not appear to be identical with that of the two other unstable photoproducts (could it be a mixture of both?).

The second set of measurements by Livingston and Ryan (1953) was made with four photoflash lamps surrounding the chlorophyll solution; a scanning beam—photomultiplier—oscilloscope system permitted changes in absorption with a resolving time of 0.1 msec. to be registered.   Correction for scattered flash light was made by subtracting the results obtained in air-saturated solution (where no reversible bleaching occurs) from those obtained in air-free solution. Significant results were obtained mainly with chlorophyll b; figures 35.2A and 35.2B show the decay curves of its phototrope as determined at λ 468 and 524.5 mμ, respectively. The first curve is consistent with the assumption of a single phototrope (the same holds for 470.5 and 427.5 mμ); but the 524.5 mμ curve indicates the successive formation of two photoproducts—one with decreased, and one with

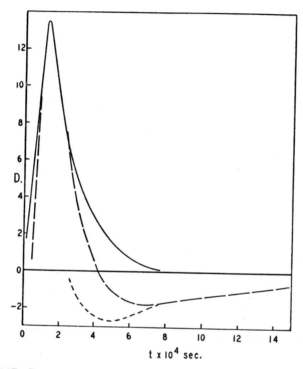

Fig. 35.2B. Decay of chlorophyll b absorption at 524.5 mμ after a flash (Livingston and Ryan 1953). Dashed line, uncorrected observations; solid line, correction for scattered flash light; dotted line, corrected decay curve.

increased absorption. The second, longer lived phototrope must be identical with that known from steady light experiments (table 35.IA). Previously described kinetic experiments indicated that this phototrope is a free radical, disappearing by a bimolecular reaction. Analysis of the decay curves in figure 35.2B makes it likely that the short-lived intermediary product, not observed in steady light—at least, not in the (relatively) weak light which had been used for this purpose—disappears by a first-order reaction (simple monomolecular decay, or—more likely—"self-quenching" by encounters with normal chlorophyll molecules). Livingston and Ryan suggested that this product is the often postulated chlorophyll molecule in a metastable electronic triplet state. (It could also be a tautomeric triplet form; for the difference between the two, see pages 790–795.)

The following set of reactions—most of which have been considered before—was stated to account satisfactorily for the flash measurements:

(35.12A a) $Chl \xrightarrow{+h\nu} Chl^*$ (excitation)

(35.12A b) $Chl^* \xrightarrow{-h\nu} Chl$ (fluorescence)

(35.12A c) $Chl^* \xrightarrow{k_t} tChl$ (conversion to metastable state)

(35.12A d) $tChl + Chl \longrightarrow 2\ Chl$ ("self-quenching" of metastable molecules)

(35.12A e) $tChl + S \longrightarrow oChl + rS$ (oxidation of tautomer to a radical)

(35.12A f) $rS + oChl \longrightarrow Chl + S$ (back reaction)
(35.12A g) $O_2 + tChl \longrightarrow tChlO_2$ (or $Chl \cdot O_2$)   (quenching of the metastable state by oxygen)
(35.12A h) $tChlO_2 + Chl \longrightarrow 2\ Chl + O_2$
(35.12A i) $Chl + tChlO_2 \longrightarrow Chl + OChl$ (irreversible oxidation)

Immediately after the flash, the solution was estimated to contain 65–70% of chlorophyll in the metastable form, tChl, and 15–20% in the oxidized, free radical form, oChl. The relation between tChl and oChl then shifted in favor of the radical, as indicated by figure 35.2B (the radical alone is supposed to absorb at 524.5 mμ).

It will be noted, that in reaction sequence (35.12A), Franck's mechanism of the oxygen effect (equations 35.2, 35.4) was adopted. The radical formation was interpreted as reversible *oxidation* of chlorophyll (by the solvent, or by an impurity, not as reversible *reduction* (as in 35.5 b, c). This was done without special justification. Whether the stationary photobleaching in air-free methanol is a reduction or an oxidation (or a combination of both?) remains open.

The "concentration quenching" of tChl (reaction d) was included in sequence (35.12A) because of Livingston and Knight's observations of the effect of chlorophyll concentration on stationary bleaching (*cf.* above); by themselves, the flash data could be accounted for also by a simple monomolecular deactivation, tChl → Chl.

Livingston, Porter and Windsor (1954) experimented with stronger flashes ($\sim$125 joule) and a synchronized flashing absorption beam, and found an almost complete transformation of the chlorophylls and pheophytins into the metastable form in (O_2-free) methanol, and even benzene; it decayed with a half-time of 2–5×10^{-4} sec.

Reversible photobleaching of oxygen-free chlorophyll solutions was observed also by Linschitz and Rennert (1952) in glassy ether-isopentane-ethanol mixtures, at $-190°$ C.; the change in spectrum (decrease of absorption in the red and blue peaks, increase at 480–590 and 700–740 mμ) was slight, and immediately reversible even at this low temperature, indicating that the photoproduct (metastable form of the chlorophyll molecule, or of a chlorophyll-solvent complex) reacts back monomolecularly without measurable activation energy. The light effect could be enhanced and stabilized by the presence of a quinone or imine (cf. next section).

Similar experiments were made by Kachan and Dain (1951), who froze chlorophyll solutions in ethanol or ethanol-ether (1:3) in liquid air and illuminated them with a 500-watt incandescent lamp, a mercury arc, or a spark. However, they found no effect of visible light; ultraviolet illumination caused the red absorption band to disappear in 20–30 min. The band returned upon melting; the reversible reaction was interpreted as an oxidation, with the electron detached by light and held by the solvent (and a proton transferred from chlorophyll to ether to form an oxonium ion, thus stabilizing the photoproduct). No effect was observed, even with ultraviolet irradiation, if methanol was used as solvent.

Uri (1952) used methyl methacrylate polymerization to indicate the formation of free radicals in illuminated chlorophyll solution. Polymerization was in fact observed in air-free $2 \times 10^{-4}\,M$ solutions of chlorophyll in methyl methacrylate, or 10% methyl methacrylate in ethanol or pyridine (but not in benzene or acetone) exposed to red light.

2. Photoxidation of Chlorophyll (Second Addendum to Section A2 of Chapter 18)

The reversible decoloration of chlorophyll (in methanol) by *ferric or ceric salts*, first observed by Rabinowitch and Weiss, was described on p. 464. Evidence was presented there for considering this reaction a reversible oxidation-reduction, leading to an equilibrium. This equilibrium could be shifted back and forth by light (cf. page 488). Among the difficulties of this interpretation mentioned on page 465 is the fact that the reversal of the color change could be produced not only by Fe^{++} ions but also by nonreducing salts, even by sodium chloride. However, the much faster rate of the restoration of green color with $FeCl_2$, the much lower ferrous salt concentration required for that purpose, the complete (immediate) reversibility of the reaction, and the possibility to repeat the light shift many times, were quoted there (and can again be quoted here) as supporting the hypothesis of reversible oxidation. The analogy with the chlorophyll-quinone reaction (to be described below) points in the same direction.

Ashkinazi, Glikman, and Dain (1950) opposed this interpretation because they found that reversible color changes of chlorophyll can be produced also by nonoxidizing salts. They suggested that metal complex formation is responsible for such changes in all cases, including that of iron.

Ashkinazi and Dain (1950) prepared a ferrous complex of chlorophyll by the action of ferrous acetate on pheophytin in acetic acid and found that in ethanol this compound is oxidized by air (presumably to a ferric complex) with a band shift from 645 to 610 mμ; upon illumination the band is shifted back to 645 mμ (presumably indicating reduction to the ferrous form).

The chlorophyll-ferric ion reaction and the possible formation of metal compounds of chlorophyll (with magnesium still in the center of the molecule and the metal ion attached elsewhere—perhaps to the enol group in ring V) remains in need of further study. As mentioned on pages 465 and 492, the similarity between the reaction of chlorophyll with Fe^{+++}, and the first, reversible stage of the "phase test" is suggestive; the first (reversible and light-sensitive) step in the conversion of chlorophyll to pheophytin (cf. page 493) also bears an outward similarity to these reactions.

Reversible photobleaching (probably photoxidation) of chlorophyll by quinones was described by Linschitz and Rennert (1952). To block the thermal back reaction they carried out the irradiation at $-190°$ in glassy solvent (8 parts ether + 3 parts isopentane + 5 parts ethanol, by volume). The bleaching effect in red and blue, and the enhancement of absorption in green (480–590 mμ) and far red (>700 mμ), noted upon illumination of the oxygen-free chlorophyll solution (cf. above, section 1) is strongly enhanced by the addition of 10^{-2} or 10^{-3} mole/l. of a quinone or imine; the bleached state survives in this case in the dark until the solvent is melted.

Evstigneev, Gavrilova and Krasnovsky (1950) measured the quenching of chlorophyll fluorescence by various organic reagents (cf. table 23.IIIC, and chapter 37C, section 4c) in pyridine and ethanol, and their influence on the red absorption peak of chlorophyll (cf. chapter 21, page 647 and chapter 37C, section 2). They inquired whether these effects occur together, and whether they are associated with accelerated photochemical bleaching of chlorophyll, but found no correlation. Thus, quinone, which is the strongest quencher of chlorophyll fluorescence in both ethanol and pyridine, has no effect on absorption and causes no photochemical bleaching in ethanol (and only a relatively slow one in pyridine). Ascorbic acid, which produces the fastest photochemical bleaching in pyridine (and is second only to oxygen in ethanol), has no effect on either fluorescence or absorption. Evstigneev et al. looked not only for the easily detectable progressive (slowly reversible or irreversible) photochemical bleaching of chlorophyll by quinone, but also for the more elusive rapidly reversible, stationary bleaching during the illumination (by sending a scanning beam through a strongly illuminated solution); but found no observable effect (compare, however, the above-described low temperature observations of Linschitz with the same system). They concluded that the reaction which leads to bleaching occurs not to the short lived, fluorescent chlorophyll molecules, but to the long lived, metastable ones (tChl), and therefore has no relation to the quenching of fluorescence (*cf.* scheme 19.II on page 546; also page 788, and scheme 23.II).

Calvin and Dorough (1948) and Huennekens and Calvin (1949) described the photochemical oxidation of certain chlorins to porphins by quinone, and reduction back to chlorins by phenylhydrazine.

Evstigneev and Gavrilova (1953[1]) found that *irreversible autoxidation* of chlorophyll *a* (in toluene) is accelerated by water and other polar molecules and slowed down by pyridine and other basic molecules (which favor the photo*reduction* of chlorophyll).

3. Reversible Photoxidation of Bacteriochlorophyll

Krasnovsky and Vojnovskaja (1951) noted that dissolved bacteriochlorophyll photoxidizes in air; the oxidation is faster in alcohol than in pyridine. The alcoholic solution gives, after oxidation, a strong peroxide test with ferrous thiocyanate. Adding ascorbic acid, or hydrogen sulfide, regenerates the pigment; after 10 hours standing in the oxidized state the greater part of the pigment could still be regenerated in this way. Oxidants other than molecular oxygen (*p*-quinone, nitrite, nitrate, hematin) and reductants other than ascorbate or hydrogen sulfide (malic, pyruvic, succinic acids; thiosinamine) were ineffective. *o*-Quinone oxidized bacteriochlorophyll, even in the dark, to a compound with a chlorin-type spectrum (with a strong band at 680 mμ), as mentioned by Schneider in 1934. Bacteriopheophytin is less easily oxidizable than bacteriochlorophyll; its photoxidation, too, is reversed by ascorbic acid.

The autoxidation of bacteriochlorophyll was interpreted by Krasnovsky as addition of oxygen to a photochemically produced biradical. As with chlorophyll, no *reversible* dehydrogenation could be observed (the reaction with *o*-quinone is irreversible).

4. Reversible Photoreduction of Chlorophyll and Its Derivatives (Addendum to Chapter 18, Section A5)

In chapter 16 (page 457) and 18 (page 505) we have discussed attempts to achieve reversible reduction of chlorophyll to a "leuco-chlorophyll." The conclusion was that no truly reversible reduction has as yet been achieved, and that chlorophyll, as it is known *in vitro*, appears to be more inclined to undergo reversible *oxidation*, than reversible reduction. The above-described experiments of Livingston and co-workers support (or, at least, do not contradict) the hypothesis that the reversible bleaching of chlorophyll is the result of reversible *oxidation*. Krasnovsky (1948[1]), on the other hand, has described experiments indicating a reversible photochemical *reduction* of chlorophyll, apparently to an unstable pink radical, by *ascorbic acid*. The reaction was observed in dry pyridine as solvent;

it did not occur in ethanol. In a mixture containing 5×10^{-6} mole/liter chlorophyll and up to 5×10^{-2} mole/liter ascorbic acid, illuminated by a 500-watt lamp through a red filter (and a layer of water), the chlorophyll fluorescence disappeared in 1–2 min. Phenylhydrazine also could be used as a reductant (instead of ascorbic acid). Some reversible reduction could be observed in alcoholic solution if a little pyridine or ammonia were added

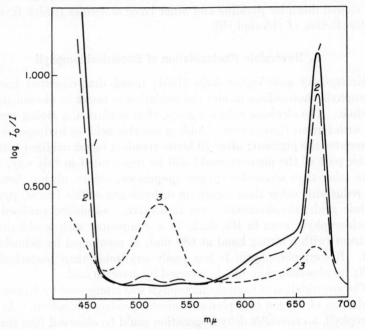

Fig. 35.3. Reversible reaction of chlorophyll a with ascorbic acid in pyridine in light (after Krasnovsky 1948): (1) spectrum before reaction; (2) spectrum after reaction; (3) approximate spectrum of the unstable reaction product (6 min. after darkening).

to alcohol. No reaction was observed (in pyridine) with pyruvic, oxalic, malic or citric acids, ethanol, or hydroquinone as reductants.

The dark back reaction required 2–3 hours. After complete recovery, the spectrum was very similar to that of original chlorophyll, especially when chlorophyll a was used. The chlorophyll b band at 470 mμ in an $(a + b)$ mixture was weakened after the cycle, indicating, in Krasnovsky's first surmise, irreversible reduction of the carbonyl group (which distinguishes chlorophyll b from chlorophyll a).

Figure 35.3 shows the spectrum of chlorophyll a before the reversible reaction with ascorbic acid in air-free pyridine (curve 1), and after this reaction (curve *2*).   The slightly increased absorption in the green may indicate the formation of a small amount of pheophytin.   Curve *3* is the approximate extinction curve of the unstable pink product.   Complete absorption curves of reduced chlorophyll (*cf.* fig. 37C.10) were determined by Evstigneev and Gavrilova (1953[2]).   They indicated two reduced species (perhaps an ion and a neutral semiquinone molecule).

In the discussion, Krasnovsky pointed out that the reversible reduction of chlorophyll apparently requires the presence of a basic compound (such as pyridine); he attributed this tentatively to the greater stability of an ionic form of the free radical "mono-dehydrochlorophyll" (which is the probable immediate product of the reaction between light-excited chlorophyll and ascorbic acid).   He suggested that this semiquinone is formed by hydrogenation of one of the conjugated double bonds in the "aromatic" porphin system.

The following scheme of reversible reduction was suggested:

(35.13) $\rangle C{=}C\langle + h\nu \longrightarrow \left(\rangle C{=}C\langle\right)^* \longrightarrow \rangle\overset{\uparrow}{C}{-}\overset{\uparrow}{C}\langle$

(Formation of a "biradical" by light absorption: the C=C bond is assumed to be part of the conjugated system.)

(35.14) $N\ldots\ HA + \rangle\overset{\uparrow}{C}{-}\overset{\uparrow}{C}\langle \longrightarrow NH^+ + A + \rangle\overset{\uparrow}{C}{-}C{-}\langle$

(Ascorbic acid, bound by a hydrogen bond to pyridine, cedes a proton to pyridine and an electron to the biradical of chlorophyll, thus forming monodehydroascorbic acid, and an anion of the monohydrochlorophyll radical.)

In a follow-up reaction, the anion could combine with an H^+ ion and the resulting neutral semiquinone dismutates into a quinone (chlorophyll) and a hydroquinone (didehydrochlorophyll = stable reduced product?);   but in a basic solvent, such as pyridine, the H^+ concentration may be so low as to make these steps improbable, and to limit the reversible reduction to the radical stage.

The absence of reversible reduction in alcoholic solution was attributed by Krasnovsky to the rapid reoxidation of the neutral form of the semiquinone, $\rangle\overset{\uparrow\ H}{C}{-}C\langle$ (which can be formed because of the presence of H^+ ions in ethanol).

Krasnovsky suggested that reversible photochemical reduction of chlorophyll by ascorbic acid (a compound that is present in all green plants) may be a step in photosynthesis.   If this were true, however, monodehydroascorbic acid should be able to liberate oxygen from water.

If the interpretation of Krasnovsky's results as proving the possibility of a *reversible photochemical reduction* of chlorophyll is confirmed, as well as the conclusion, based on observations of Rabinowitch, Porret, Weiss, Livingston, and Linschitz that chlorophyll can undergo *reversible photochemical oxidation*, the green plant pigment emerges as a compound capable of both reversible reduction and reversible oxidation in light, a combination which could be important for its function in photosynthesis, particularly if the latter involves two sets of photochemical reactions—"photoxidations" and "photoreductions," with chlorophyll as an intermediate (*cf.* chapter 7).

It appears that reversible oxidation of chlorophyll may require the presence of *polar molecules* (such as alcohol or water), while reversible reduction requires the presence of basic molecules (such as pyridine). According to Evstigneev and Gavrilova (1950), *presence of Mg* enhances the tendency for photoxidation, reduces that for photoreduction.

Krasnovsky and Brin (1949) suggested that chlorophyll attaches itself to pyridine in the same way as does hemochromogen to a protein—by a link between the metal atom and a nitrogen atom in an imidazole ring; a type of complexing known to affect the redox potential of hemins.

Krasnovsky, Brin and Voynovskaya (1949) investigated more systematically the influence of solvent on the photoreduction of chlorophyll *a* and *b* by ascorbic acid. They found that in *pyridine* the height of the red absorption peak was reduced in light by 90%, and that 80% of this bleaching was reversed in the dark. Dilution of pyridine with water decreased both the extent and the reversibility of bleaching. In *aniline* the red peak was reduced in light only by 22%, and only half of this bleaching was reversed in the dark. In *ethanol* the corresponding figures were 20 and 14%; in *acetone*, 29 and 19%. Addition of as little as 0.3% pyridine, imidazole, or histidine, to alcohol or acetone, increased the bleaching to 80%, with one-half of it being reversed in the dark. Twenty-six organic and two inorganic compounds were tried out as reducing agents in pyridine. Positive results were obtained with ascorbate, dihydroxymaleate, cysteine, phenylhydrazine, and hydrogen sulfide; pyruvic acid (previously mentioned by Krasnovsky as giving results similar to those produced by ascorbic acid) was now listed among nonreactive compounds.

Renewed investigation of chlorophyll *b* showed that its reduction by ascorbic acid in light, and reoxidation in dark, gives a product with absorption bands at 693 and 432 mμ, which is neither chlorophyll *a*, nor pheophytin *a* or *b*. (Conversion of chlorophyll *b* to chlorophyll *a* in this reaction was first suggested as a possibility, *cf.* above.)

Evstigneev and Gavrilova (1950) noted that chlorophyll and Mg-phthalocyanine were reduced by ascorbic acid in light in pyridine solution slower than the corresponding Mg-free compounds (but were photautoxidized faster than the latter in methanolic solution).

Krasnovsky and Voynovskaya (1952) found that chlorophyll can be reduced photochemically in pyridine also by *sodium sulfide*, but the reduction did not proceed beyond 25% (measured by the decline in the intensity of the red band).

Krasnovsky and Voynovskaya (1949) found that reversible reduction can be obtained also with *protochlorophyll* (from pumpkin seeds). A reversible *chemical* reduction of this compound was described (*cf.* chapter 37B) by Godnev and Kalishevich, who used Timiriazev's reagent (zinc + organic acid in pyridine). (For incomplete reversibility of this reaction, see chap. 18, p. 457, and chap. 37B, p. 1779.) *Photochemical* reduction (to a brown solution, with an absorption band at 470 mμ) was now obtained by illumination in the presence of ascorbic acid, at 8° C. The brown product was reoxidized after several hours in air, with (approximate) restoration of the original spectrum. If the illumination was prolonged (30 min.) and no red filter was used, a band at 675 mμ appeared after reoxidation, indicating partial conversion of the porphyrin, protochlorophyll, to a chlorin (chlorophyll ?); with chlorophyll *a*, no conversion to a bacteriochlorin was noted (which would have produced a band at 780 mμ).

Krasnovsky and Voynovskaya (1951) made similar reduction studies with *bacteriochlorophyll*. As with chlorophyll, the reaction goes best in pyridine, but was clearly observable also in alcohol. The reaction is rapidly reversed in the dark, even without air. Bacteriopheophytin is reduced faster and further than bacteriochlorophyll. The unstable reduction product of bacteriochlorophyll is green, with an absorption band at 640 mμ. No photoreduction was noted when malic, succinic, citric, or pyruvic acid, thiosinamine, or sodium thiosulfate was added instead of ascorbate.

The possibility of reversible hydrogenation of bacteriochlorophyll indicates that the photoreduction of chlorophyll (or protochlorophyll) does not occur in an isolated double bond in ring II (or II and IV); Krasnovsky suggested that in both pigments hydrogenation disrupts one of the conjugated double bonds, creating a free radical.

Krasnovsky and Gavrilova (1951) compared the photoreduction of chlorophyll (*a* + *b*) by ascorbic acid and other organic acids in different solvents. No significant reaction occurred in *acetone* or *ethanol*; in *pyridine*, ascorbic acid alone gave rapid photoreduction (as described before). In *dioxane*, too, ascorbic acid was the only one of the tested compounds to react with chlorophyll, but in this solvent the reaction was irreversible; it occurred even in the dark, but was accelerated by light; the product showed no characteristic absorption band at 525 mμ. The reaction did not occur in the presence of oxygen or quinone.   Hydrogen sulfide and cysteine also reduced chlorophyll in dioxane irreversibly.

Similar experiments with other dyestuffs (Mg-phthalocyanine, ribo-flavin, β-carotene, safranin T, neutral red, and phenol-indophenol) showed that many of them (but not β-carotene) also can be more or less reversibly reduced in light by ascorbic acid (some also by pyruvic acid); the photo-reduction depends on the solvent, being enhanced by the affinity of the lat-ter for protons.

Krasnovsky and Brin (1953) again discussed the question of why bases promote the photochemical reduction of chlorophyll.   Absorption studies (*cf.* chapter 37C, section 2) showed that some bases cause a new absorp-tion band at 640 mμ to appear in the chlorophyll spectrum (it becomes the dominant long-wave band in piperidine, *cf.* table 21.VII).   However, the appearance of this band (which occurs only in polar solvents and must be ascribed to polarization and ionization of an acid group, such as the enol group in position 10 in chlorophyll) does *not* parallel photochemical activa-tion.   The latter can be produced by a small amount of a base (such as phenylhydrazine) added to methanol solution without noticeable change in the absorption spectrum.   Krasnovsky and Brin concluded that activation must be attributed to a reaction between pigment and base which is differ-

TABLE 35.IB

INFLUENCE OF BASES ON PHOTOCHEMICAL REDUCTION (MEASURED BY DECLINE OF ABSORPTION IN RED) OF CHLOROPHYLL a AND PHEOPHYTIN a (AFTER KRASNOVSKY AND BRIN 1953)

Medium	Chl a, %		Pheo a, %	
	Un-reduced	Restored in dark	Unre-duced	Restored in dark
Pyridine..........................	6	87	15	68
Piperidine.........................	31	39	5	50
Nicotine...........................	61	81	—	—
Pyrrole............................	81	81	—	—
Quinoline..........................	93	94	72	86
Phenylhydrazine....................	4	62	—	—
Ethanol............................	82	85	73	76
+pyridine (50)*..................	42	52	43	59
+piperidine (50)*................	19	29	16	36
+nicotine (95)*..................	8	58	36	72
+urotropine (80)*................	49	29	—	—
+quinoline (90)*.................	98	98	61	90
+arginine (satur.)...............	94	93	—	—
+phenylhydrazine (100)*..........	52	85	—	—
+ammonia (satur.)................	9	26	—	—
+KOH (0.1–0.01 N)...............	98	99	—	—

* Number in parenthesis means milligrams of base in 7 ml. solution.

ent from the acid-base interaction, and which is without marked influence on the absorption spectrum—perhaps a coordinative binding of the base in the center of the molecule, reminiscent (as suggested by Krasnovsky and Brin 1949) of the hemochromogen-protein bond (known to change the oxidation potential of the hemochromogen). In chlorophyll the complexing may occur at the magnesium atom; it is not quite clear how a similar binding can occur in pheophytin (*cf.* table 35.IB).

Speculations concerning the activating effect of organic bases on the photoreducibility of chlorophyll obviously need to be related not only to the absorption data (chapter 21, pp. 647–649, and chapter 37C, section 2), but also to fluorescence measurements (chapter 23, pages 766–771, and chapter 37C, section 4) and chemical evidence. One obviously deals here with events in at least two—if not more—sensitive centers in the chlorophyll molecule which can be affected separately or simultaneously. One of them may be the cyclopentanone ring V with its keto-enol tautomerism; the other, the central magnesium atom. A correlation of all the pertinent evidence—derived from optical absorption spectra, infrared spectra, fluorescence, "allomerization," phase test, and photochemical activity—will be attempted in chapter 37C.

Krasnovsky and Brin (1948) compared the "photochemical activity" (capacity to react with ascorbic acid in light) of various types of chlorophyll preparations. They found reactivity in organic solvents, oils, lecithin, and emulsions of lipoid solvents in water; also in colloids obtained by dilution of alcoholic solutions by aqueous detergents (anionic, cationic, or neutral), in similarly prepared chlorophyll-protein colloids, and in chloroplasts and grana suspensions prepared with the same detergents. No photochemical activity could be found in colloidal solutions prepared by dilution of alcohol with water (before or after coagulation by electrolytes); or in chlorophyll adsorbates on the proteins, zein or gliadin, and their colloidal solutions (for the position of the absorption peaks in these preparations, see table 37C.IIIA).

5. Chlorophyll-Sensitized Oxidation-Reductions
(First Addendum to Chapter 18, Part C)

Capacity for reversible *photochemical* oxidation or reduction is important if a pigment is to serve as sensitizer for oxidation-reduction reactions—in the same way as capacity for reversible nonphotochemical oxidation or reduction is important for an oxidation-reduction catalyst. Only one chlorophyll-sensitized oxidation-reduction reaction *in vitro* was described in Volume I (page 513)—the oxidation of phenylhydrazine by methyl red. This reaction was discovered by Böhi in 1929, and studied quantitatively by Ghosh and Sengupta in 1934. They found that the quantum yield of methyl red bleaching can reach, or even exceed, unity. Livingston, Sickle and Uchigama (1947) pointed out that errors could have been caused, in Ghosh's and Böhi's work, by ill-defined nature of the chlorophyll preparations, and by changes in the absorption spectrum of methyl red (which is an acid-base indicator), which may be caused by the presence of the base, phenylhydrazine. (The quantum yield was determined by photometry of methyl red!) Furthermore, in Ghosh's experiment, an induction period of varying duration was noted, which affected unfavorably the reliability of the rate measurements.

Since light absorbed by methyl red could contribute to the reaction, Livingston used a red band $\lambda > 600$ mμ. (Ghosh and Sengupta worked in the green, at λ 435.8 mμ.) A green band (475–550 mμ) was used for the determination of methyl red. The initial concentrations of phenylhydrazine and methyl red (in methanol) were 5×10^{-2} and 1×10^{-4} mole/liter, respectively. The reaction was found to be of zero order (*i. e.*, the quantum yield remained constant) until about 80% of the dye was consumed. The concentration of chlorophyll was varied between 0.2 and 75 $\times 10^{-6}$ mole/liter (chlorophyll *a*), and 1 to 7.5 $\times 10^{-6}$ mole/liter (chlorophyll *b*). The observed quantum yields scattered over the range from 0.09 to 0.15, showing no clear dependence on nature or concentration of the chlorophyll used. The reason why Ghosh and Sengupta had found 6–7 times higher quantum yields could not be explained. Experiments with a manometer, using an acetonic solution of allyl thiourea (0.5 mole/liter), containing chlorophyll ($1–2 \times 10^{-5}$ mole/liter) and oxygen, indicated that the quantum yield of this reaction (for which values up to 1.0 had been found by Gaffron) was up to seven times higher than that of the methyl red-phenylhydrazine reaction—thus indirectly confirming the low quantum yield of the last-named reaction given above. The manometric experiments also showed that no gas was produced in the reduction of methyl red by phenylhydrazine (liberation of nitrogen could conceivably occur in this reaction).

Experiments showed that the occurrence of an induction period was entirely dependent on the presence of oxygen. From the amount of oxygen present in air-saturated methanol and the duration of the induction period, it appeared that the quantum yield of chlorophyll-sensitized autoxidation of phenylhydrazine (the reaction which probably takes place during the induction period) may be of the order of unity, similar to the quantum yield of the autoxidation of allylthiourea.

In the green, at 435.8 mμ, the quantum yield of the methyl red-phenylhydrazine reaction was found, in preliminary experiments, to be about 0.1, independently of changes in methyl red concentration; and despite the fact that, in this case, a varying proportion of light was absorbed by methyl red and not by chlorophyll. This indicates that the reaction can occur also by direct photochemical activation of the azo dye instead of by sensitization.

Attempts were made to substitute allylthiourea for phenylhydrazine as reductant in chlorophyll-sensitized reduction of methyl red, using acetone as solvent; but no bleaching of methyl red was noted under these conditions.

To check whether phenylhydrazine formed a complex with chlorophyll, the absorption spectra of chlorophyll a and b were measured in the presence of 0.05 M phenylhydrazine (in methanol). No change was noted in the spectrum of chlorophyll a; in chlorophyll b, the red band was somewhat broadened toward the longer waves. (Cf. Watson's data, given below and in chapter 37C.)

The views on the mechanism of the phenylhydrazine–methyl red reaction expressed in this paper were changed by Livingston and Pariser (1948), who studied more closely the dependence of the quantum yield on the concentrations of the reactants (phenylhydrazine and methyl red). Methyl red is known to occur in three colored forms, depending on acidity; it was concluded that only one of them—the intermediate one—takes direct part in the reaction. To determine the concentration of this form, extinction curves were obtained for methyl red solutions in methanol (2 $\times$ 10^{-5} M, containing from 0.4 to 10^{-5} M HCl; and from 10^{-6} to 10^{-3} M NaOCH$_3$). These curves were interpreted as due to the superposition, with varying relative intensities, of three absorption bands, with peaks at 406 (I), 491 (II), and 521 (III) mμ, respectively. The forms giving the bands (I) and (III), can be obtained in the pure state in strongly alkaline or strongly acid solution, respectively; but the intermediate form, which gives band (II), usually is present only in mixture with one of the other two forms. This intermediate form was interpreted by Thiel as a "zwitterion":

$$^{-}OOC\cdot C_6H_4 - \underset{H}{N}{}^{+}{=}N{-}C_6H_4N(CH_3)_2$$

However, this formula, with two opposite charges, may be correct for aqueous solutions only; in methanolic solution, Livingston and Pariser considered more likely the existence of a neutral molecule, with a hydrogen bond between the hydroxyl and nitrogen:

The absorption peaks of the acidic form (III) are situated not too far apart in aqueous and methanolic solution (517 and 521 mμ, respectively);

the bands of the other two forms are shifted strongly toward the red in methanol (from 406 to 447 mμ, and from 491 to 530 mμ), with the result that what was the "long wave band" in water, becomes the "central band" in methanol. Livingston and Pariser tried to relate the quantum yield to the total concentration of the dye, or to the concentration of any one of its three constituents. It transpired that the simplest relationships are obtained if form II alone is taken into consideration as a reactant.

The phenylhydrazine concentration (free base + hydrochloride) was varied between 0.02 and 1.0 mole/liter, the total methyl red concentration, from 0.24 to 6.10 $\times$ 10^{-4} mole/liter, and the (calculated) concentration of "form II" from 0.085 to 6.10 $\times$ 10^{-4} mole/liter. The quantum yields were found to vary between 0.10 and 0.49 mole/einstein. A maximum yield $\gamma = 0.5$ can be explained by assuming a reduction of the dye in two steps. A single light quantum can form, at best, one molecule of the intermediate semiquinone; two semiquinone molecules then dismute into one molecule of the dye and one molecule of the leuco dye.

From the effect of methyl red on the reversible bleaching of chlorophyll (section 1), Livingston concluded that the first step of the sensitized reaction possibly is the association of methyl red (in the form II) with the long-lived (tautomeric?) active form of chlorophyll, tChl,

35.15a)   Chl + hν $\longrightarrow$ Chl*   (absorption)

(35.15b)   Chl*$-\begin{array}{l}\xrightarrow{\ k_f\ }\text{Chl} + \text{h}\nu \\ \xrightarrow{\ k\ }\text{tChl}\end{array}$ (fluorescence, $\backsimeq 3\%$)
                                                    (tautomerization, $\backsimeq 97\%$)

(35.15c)   tChl $\xrightarrow{\ k_t\ }$ Chl   (detautomerization)

(35.15d)   tChl + MR" $\xrightarrow{\ k_1\ }$ tChlMR"   (complex formation)

(35.15e)   tChlMR" $\xrightarrow{\ k_1'\ }$ Chl + MR"   (complex decomposition + detautomerization)

The chlorophyll-MR" complex can be supposed to react with the reductant (phenylhydrazine, symbolized by PH$_2$), transferring one H atom:

(35.16)   PH$_2$ + tChlMR" $\xrightarrow{\ k_2\ }$ PH + Chl + MRH"

and forming two radicals, PH and MRH". These can be stabilized, either by dismutation, e. g.:

(35.17)   2 MRH" $\longrightarrow$ MRH$_2$" + MR" (leuco dye + dye)

or by dimerization:

(35.18)   2 PH $\longrightarrow$ HP·PH

If this scheme is compared with the various mechanisms discussed in chapter 18 (Vol. I), it appears as a variation of mechanism $A\beta1$ (page 515), exemplified in equations (18.33a–18.33d) for the case of molecular oxygen as oxidant. The alteration consists in the assumption that tChl associates with the oxidant in a complex, and in this form catalyzes the transfer of hydrogen from reductant to oxidant; while in its original form, scheme $A\beta1$ assumed that this catalysis occurs in two steps, tChl first transferring a hydrogen atom to the oxidant, and then recovering it from the reductant. The first mechanism is similar to an often postulated mechanism of enzymic catalysis, based on complex formation of enzyme and substrate; the second one is more in line with the known mechanisms of nonenzymic oxidation-reduction catalysis.

By permitting competition between the catalytic reaction (35.16) and the decomposition of the complex (35.15e), Livingston's scheme gives a possibility of explaining the dependence of the quantum yield on the *concentration of the reductant*, $[PH_2]$. To achieve a similar result in the original reaction scheme $A\beta1$, we would have to admit the possibility of a back reaction there, too. In scheme (18.33), *e. g.*, a reaction $oChl + HO_2 \rightarrow Chl + O_2$ would have to be postulated, reversing reaction (18.33b).

Livingston and Pariser derived, from the above reaction scheme, an expression showing the dependence of the average quantum yield, $\bar{\gamma}$, on the concentration of phenylhydrazine (which remains practically constant during a run) and the "logarithmic mean" of the (strongly changing) concentration of the reacting dyestuff:

$$(35.19) \qquad \overline{[MR'']} = \frac{[MR'']_0 - [MR'']}{\ln [MR'']_0 - \ln [MR'']}$$

$[MR'']_0$ is the initial, and $[MR'']$ the final concentration of the reactive form of the dye.

The equation obtained for the mean quantum yield has the form

$$(35.20) \qquad \bar{\gamma} = \frac{k_t}{2(k_t + k_f)} \times \frac{(k_2/k_1') [PH_2]}{1 + (k_2/k_1') [PH_2]} \times \frac{(k_1/k_t')[MR'']}{1 + (k_1/k_t') [MR'']}$$

With the below-determined constants, and applied to momentary concentrations of all components, this equation becomes

$$(35.21) \qquad \bar{\gamma} = 0.46 \times \frac{1 \times 10^{-2} [PH_2]}{1 + 1 \times 10^2 [PH_2]} \times \frac{5 \times 10^4 [MR'']}{1 + 5 \times 10^4 [MR'']}$$

The factor $1/2$ comes, as mentioned before, from the dismutation of the half-reduced dye; the factor $k_t/(k_t + k_f)$ from competition between fluorescence and tautomerization; the factor k_1/k_t' from competition between complex formation (35.15d), and the detautomerization of chlorophyll, (35.15c). As mentioned above, oxidation and reduction of tChl could be substituted for the complex formation and decomposition; the assumption of a back reaction reversing oxidation is needed in this case to make the over-all yield dependent on the concentration of phenylhydrazine, as represented in equation (35.21).

Livingston and Pariser extrapolated the observed quantum yields to $[PH_2] = \infty$ by means of the following equation:

$$(35.22) \qquad \gamma_{[PH_2]\,\infty} = \bar{\gamma}\left(1 + \frac{k_t'}{k_1[PH_2]}\right)$$

using for the ratio k_1/k_t' an empirically estimated value, 10^2 liters/mole. This extrapolation changed the values of $\bar{\gamma}$ significantly only for the lowest phenylhydrazine concentrations used—$[PH_2]$ from 0.02 to 0.05 mole/liter.

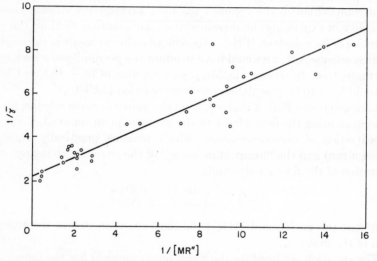

Fig. 35.4. Quantum efficiency of chlorophyll-sensitized reaction of methyl red and phenylhydrazine in relation to concentration of methyl red in form II (after Livingston and Pariser 1948).

The values of $1/\bar{\gamma}$ for $[PH_2] = \infty$ were plotted against $1/[MR'']$ and, in accordance with equation (35.22), an approximately straight line was obtained (although the individual values scattered considerably). From the slope and the intercept of this straight line (fig. 35.4), the following ratios could be derived:

$$(35.23) \qquad k_t/(k_f + k_t) = 0.92 \qquad k_1/k = 5.0 \times 10^4 \text{ liters/mole}$$

The first value means 8% fluorescence and 92% tautomerization (a plausible result as far as the yield of fluorescence is concerned), and thus an

"absolute" maximum quantum yield of $0.92/2 = 0.46$.   If a value for k_t'
is taken from earlier measurements of the life-time of the "long lived excited
state" (reversibly bleached state) of chlorophyll, we have:

(35.24) $k_t' = 2.5 \times 10^{-4} \text{ sec.}^{-1}$

(35.25) $k_1 \simeq 10^9 \text{ (liters/mole)}$

This high value for the constant of a bimolecular reaction indicates a reaction with only a very small, or vanishing activation energy.

In methyl red solutions, the life-time of the bleached state of chlorophyll
was estimated (*cf.* section 1) as ~ 1 sec.   This can be considered as the
life-time of the complex $\{tChl.MR''\}$ (or, alternatively, as the life-time of
chlorophyll oxidized by methyl red, oChl).   This leads to a value of the
order of 10^7 for the constant k_2, indicating that reaction (35.16) may require an activation energy.   Consequently, the quantum yield of the over-
all reaction can be expected to show strong temperature dependence when
$[PH_2]$ is low, and (35.16) is therefore the "bottleneck" reaction.

Watson (1952) in a subsequent paper (based on his work in Livingston's
laboratory) suggested a different interpretation of the mechanism of
chlorophyll-sensitized reduction of methyl red by phenylhydrazine.   His
experiments dealt with the quenching of fluorescence by phenylhydrazine
in a polar solvent (methanol), and its activation, by the same agent, in
nonpolar solvents (benzene or heptane) (*cf.* page 768; Watson's experimental results will be described in chapter 37C, section 4c).   From these
experiments, and the strong effect of phenylhydrazine (PH_2) on the absorption spectrum of chlorophyll *b* (*cf.* page 699 and chapter 37C, section
2), Watson concluded that phenylhydrazine forms two different complexes
with chlorophyll; its attachment to the chlorophyll molecule in one place
leaves the absorption spectrum of chlorophyll *a* unchanged and activates
fluorescence; its attachment in another place quenches the fluorescence
(independently of whether the first place is occupied by another phenylhydrazine molecule or not).   The calculated association constants were
1900 liters/mole for the fluorescence-promoting, and 16 liters/mole for the
fluorescence-quenching complexing (in benzene); the first constant was the
same, but the second was higher (58 liters/mole) in heptane.   Watson
pointed out that if these constants are correct then, under the conditions
of Pariser's experiments, a large part of chlorophyll must have been associated with phenylhydrazine.   The symmetry of equation (35.20) permits substitution of the assumption of a primary reaction between PH_2 and
excited Chl in a pre-formed complex for that of the primary formation of a
tChl-methyl red complex (*e. g.*, 35.15e), and subsequent reaction of this
complex with phenylhydrazine (*e. g.*, 35.16).

This mechanism, involving primary interaction of chlorophyll with the reductant, is in line with the observations of Krasnovsky and co-workers, which we will now describe.

According to the experiments of Krasnovsky which were described above (section 3), chlorophyll can be reversibly reduced in light by ascorbic acid. In the presence of riboflavin, or safranin T, the latter dyestuffs are reduced instead of chlorophyll—presumably by reacting with the photochemically reduced chlorophyll. Because of the relative positions of their reduction potentials, $E_0 = 0.22$ v. and 0.29 v., respectively (as compared with -0.05 v. for ascorbic acid), riboflavin and safranin T are not reduced by ascorbic acid in the dark. Reduction can be achieved by illumination

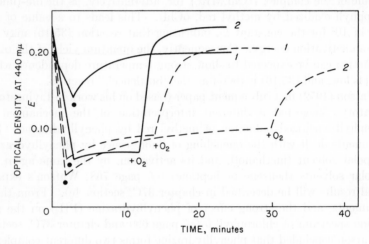

Fig. 35.5. Chlorophyll-sensitized reduction of riboflavin by ascorbic or pyruvic acid, and reoxidation in air (after Krasnovsky 1948). Curve 1, ascorbic acid; 2, pyruvic acid. Broken curves, in ethanol; solid curves, in pyridine. (●) Light off; (+O₂) air admitted.

with light absorbed by the dyes themselves, or, in the presence of chlorophyll, by illumination with red light absorbed by chlorophyll. In addition to ascorbic acid, pyruvic acid, too, can be oxidized in this manner.

The reactions were carried out in ethanol or pyridine as solvent; the concentrations were:

$$[dye] = 10^{-5} \text{ mole/liter} \qquad [reductant] = 6 \times 10^{-2} \text{ mole/liter}$$

The change in dyestuff concentration was determined photometrically. The solutions were boiled in vacuum to remove oxygen, and illuminated 1–3 min. by focussed light from a 500-watt lamp. Admission of air accelerated the back reaction. The following mechanism was assumed for the non-sensitized reaction:

$$(35.26) \quad 2\,D + 2\,AH_2 \underset{\text{dark}}{\overset{\text{light}}{\rightleftharpoons}} 2\,DH + 2\,AH \rightleftharpoons (DH_2 + D) + (AH_2 + A)$$

In the presence of sensitizer, the latter was assumed to serve as intermediate hydrogen acceptor.

Figure 35.5 illustrates Krasnovsky's results. It indicates that reversibility is more complete in pyridine than in methanol; Krasnovsky suggests as a possible reason the stabilization of the semiquinone DH by ionization

$$DH \rightleftharpoons D^- + H^+$$

encouraged by the proton affinity (basicity) of pyridine. The reaction with pyruvic acid in methanol is at least partially reversible.

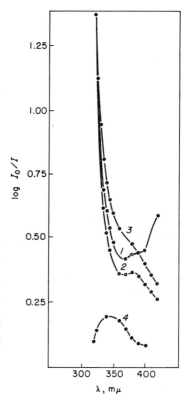

Fig. 35.6. Chlorophyll-sensitized reduction of coenzyme I (DPN) by ascorbic acid (after Krasnovsky and Brin 1949). Chlorophyll ($a +$ b) in pyridine with 10 mg. ascorbic acid and 1 mg. DPN; (*1*) spectrum before reaction; (*2*) spectrum after reaction (3 min. illumination in red light) without DPN; (*3*) spectrum after reaction (3 min. light) with DPN; (*4*) spectrum of reaction product ($DPNH_2$?) (obtained by subtraction of *2* from *3*).

Magnesium phthalocyanine also can be used as sensitizer, in the same concentration (10^{-5} mole/liter) as chlorophyll.

Krasnovsky pointed out that in the sensitized reduction of one mole of safranin T by ascorbic acid under standard conditions as much as 16 kcal of free energy must be accumulated, which is 40% of the energy of a red quantum, or 20% of the energy of two such quanta.

Later, Krasnovsky and Voynovskaya (1949) observed that the same reaction of ascorbic acid with safranin T can be obtained also with proto-chlorophyll (from pumpkin seeds) as sensitizer.

Krasnovsky and Brin (1949) described experiments which they inter-preted as indicating the sensitized reduction of the oxidized form of co-

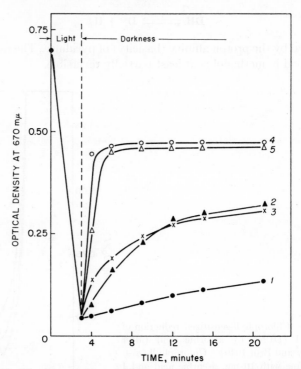

Fig. 35.7. Bleaching of chlorophyll ($a + b$) by ascorbic acid in red light and its regeneration by riboflavin (*5*), safranin T (*4*), oxygen (*2*), DPN (*3*), and without added oxidant (*1*) (after Krasnovsky and Brin 1949).

enzyme I (dipyridine nucleotide, DPN) by ascorbic acid, with chlorophyll as sensitizer. Here, again, aqueous pyridine must be used as solvent.

In these experiments, 1 cc. of a 5×10^{-4} M solution of DPN (a 60% pure preparation) and 10 mg. crystalline ascorbic acid were added to 5 cc. of a 7×10^{-6} M solution of chlorophyll ($a + b$) in a Thunberg tube. After evacuation by an oil pump, the spectrum was measured by means of a Beckman spectrophotometer. The tube was then illuminated for 3 min. at 8° C. and the spectrum re-examined. Comparison of this spectrum after illumination with the one obtained after similar treatment without DPN, showed a difference in the region 300–360 mμ, which indicated the formation of a compound with an absorption band at 345 mμ (fig. 35.6)—the well-known position of the absorption band of DPNH$_2$.

The band at 525 mμ, which appeared in illuminated chlorophyll-ascorbic acid mixtures in the absence of DPN and which was ascribed by Krasnovsky to reduced chlorophyll (HChl, or H$_2$Chl?), "sometimes" did not appear when DPN was present; this result was attributed to the high rate of the second reaction in the sequence (35.27a,b):

(35.27a) $Chl + AH_2 \xrightarrow{h\nu} H_2Chl + A \text{ (or HChl + AH)}$

(35.27b) $H_2Chl + DPN \text{ (or 2 HChl + DPN)} \longrightarrow DPNH_2 + Chl$

(AH$_2$ = ascorbic acid).

To prove the occurrence of reaction (35.27b) directly, a mixture of chlorophyll and ascorbic acid was illuminated alone in an evacuated Thunberg tube, and DPN (or other oxidants) was then added from a side tube. The disappearance of the absorption band at 675 mμ in light, and its reappearance in dark after the addition of oxidants, is illustrated by figure 35.7. This figure shows that recoloration was far from complete—the optical density, which had dropped in light from 0.7 to 0.1, was restored by the oxidants only to a value of 0.45. The figure also shows that safranin and riboflavin caused a much faster return of the color than did DPN, or air.

These results are suggestive, and Krasnovsky's conclusion that reduction of DPN by reduced chlorophyll is the link by which the photochemical process is tied, in photosynthesis, to the sequence of enzymatic reactions leading to fixation and reduction of CO$_2$, is plausible; it fits well into the picture of the reaction mechanism of photosynthesis derived from C(14) experiments (chapter 36). However, just because of this suggestiveness and the crucial importance of the conclusions, much more rigorous experiments will be needed than those described by Krasnovsky and Brin, before the capacity of chlorophyll to sensitize the reduction of the oxidized form of coenzyme II, by hydrogen donors such as ascorbic acid (thus overcoming an opposing normal potential difference of about 0.24 volt, at pH 7), can be considered as proved. Spectroscopic proof of the formation of DPNH$_2$ (based on a small difference between two high optical densities), as well as the proof of the reversible reduction of chlorophyll, may prove to be correct, but are as yet not quite convincing. The fact that the absorption at 675 mμ is restored to only one half its original value indicates a considerable irreversible change. Further development of these experiments, with better spectroscopic technique, supplemented by chemical separation and enzymatic tests, appears desirable.

Krasnovsky and Brin (1950) surveyed different oxidants for the reoxidation of photochemically reduced chlorophyll. The following compounds, all with negative oxidation potentials, were found to accelerate the return of absorption in the red peak (in order of decreasing efficiency): thionine ($5 \times 10^{-4} M$), quinone ($1 \times 10^{-2} M$), methylene blue ($5 \times 10^{-4} M$), phenol-indophenol ($5 \times 10^{-4} M$) and dehydroascorbic acid ($5 \times 10^{-2} M$). (The position of the latter in the series shows that the other enumerated oxidants, although they are known to react with ascorbic acid, reoxidize chlorophyll directly, and not through the intermediary of ascorbic acid.) Among compounds with positive potentials, not reacting with ascorbic acid in the dark, the order of effectiveness in the reoxidation of reduced chlorophyll was: hematin ($5 \times 10^{-4} M$), NO_3^-($10^{-2} M$), NO_2^-($10^{-2} M$), Fe^{+++}($10^{-2} M$), Cu^{++}($10^{-2} M$), and air. Among compounds with positive potentials, safranin T, neutral red, and Nile blue (all $5 \times 10^{-4} M$) accelerated reoxidation; also $5 \times 10^{-4} M$ riboflavin, and 1×10^{-3} or $5 \times 10^{-4} M$ DPN ($E_0 = +0.32$ volt) (cf. above). Since xanthin ($E_0 = +0.37$ volt) showed no influence, the authors concluded that the normal oxidation-reduction potential of the system chlorophyll-reduced chlorophyll is about $+0.35$ volt. (However, the potentials had been measured in water, while the observations of Krasnovsky and Brin were made in pyridine.) It is interesting to compare these results with those obtained with chloroplast suspensions; there, only oxidants with normal potentials below -0.1 volt were reduced with a good yield in air (cf. sections B4(d), (e) below); in the absence of oxygen, the reduction of compounds with normal potentials up to $+0.1$ volt could be observed; but compounds such as DPN, with $E'_0 > 0.3$ volt, were reduced only to a very slight degree, so that their reduction could be ascertained only by "trapping" with specific enzymatic systems (to be described in section B4(f)). Of course, in the Hill reaction of chloroplasts (as in photosynthesis) the reductant is water ($E'_0 = -0.8$ v.) and not ascorbic acid ($E'_0 = -0.0$ v.), making the (net) hydrogen transfer that much more difficult. Further studies are needed to find out whether a reduced form of chlorophyll, with the strong reducing power found by Krasnovsky in vitro, does play a role in photosynthesis, but is somehow prevented from displaying its full power in chloroplast suspensions. Perhaps, two types of reversible photochemical changes of chlorophyll occur in photosynthesis—one that permits it to acquire hydrogen from water (this capacity is preserved in chloroplast preparations) and one that permits it to transfer hydrogen to compounds with a normal potential >0.3 volt—this capacity being preserved in chlorophyll solutions in pyridine. This is, however, only a speculation, and one which calls for the minimum quantum requirement of photosynthesis to be 8 (cf. chapter 7). An alternative is that in vivo chlorophyll is able to transfer hydrogen directly from a system with a normal potential close to -0.8 volt, to a system with a normal potential > 0.3 volt, perhaps with the assistance of high energy phosphate produced by partial recombination of the primary oxidation and reduction products (Ruben, Kok, van der Veen, Warburg and Burk). In any case, the relation between the "Krasnovsky reaction" of chlorophyll in solution, the "Hill reaction" of chlorophyll in chloroplast suspensions, and photosynthesis is a most interesting photochemical problem.

Of seven fatty acids tested, in a study by Krasnovsky and Brin (1950), only 10^{-2} M malic acid produced marked acceleration of reoxidation. Temperature had little effect on the rate—a result taken as confirmation of the hypothesis that the pink reduced form of chlorophyll is a semiquinone, and, as such, able to react with a very small activation energy. (If this is the case, however, the low absolute rate of reoxidation becomes puzzling.)

As long as Krasnovsky's assumption of a reversible oxidation-reduction of chlorophyll rests only on the observation of a (sometimes far-reaching, but never complete) restoration of the extinction coefficient in the peak of the red band, some doubt remains whether this assumption is correct and whether the reaction does not leave an irreversible change in the chlorophyll molecule (in which case it could not serve as the basis for catalytic activity). It is of some interest, therefore, that Holt (1952) in checking Krasnovsky's experiments with ascorbic acid and quinone, was able to repeat the bleaching and recoloration cycle three or four times with the same sample. True, the restored red band became weaker with each cycle; nevertheless, the result seems incompatible with the assumption that after a cycle all chlorophyll molecules that took part in it are left with a permanent change in their structure. It seems more likely that the reaction is basically reversible, but that a certain proportion of chlorophyll molecules that take part in it undergo irreversible side reactions which lead to the loss of absorption. It would be important to find a way to suppress these irreversible reactions *in vitro* as effectively as they appear to be suppressed *in vivo*.

Krasnovsky and Voynovskaya (1952) compared the sensitization of oxidoreduction by chlorophyll, bacteriochlorophyll, and their pheophytins (in 10^{-5} M solutions), using ascorbic acid and sodium sulfide (about 10^{-2} M) as reductants, riboflavin or safranin T (about 10^{-4} M) as oxidant, in 85% aqueous pyridine (since sodium sulfide is more soluble in aqueous solvents). No changes were observed in the dark in binary systems pigment-reductant in pyridine (a slow pheophytinization occurred in alcohol in the presence of ascorbic acid); the pigment-oxidant binary systems and the mixtures oxidant-ascorbic acid also were stable, but sodium sulfide reduced safranin T and riboflavin in the dark, particularly in pyridine. Light had no effect on binary systems without the sensitizer. The binary system sensitizer-reductant reacted in pyridine in light as described in section 4.

In ternary systems absorption bands of the sensitizers were not affected to more than 5–10% by 3 minutes illumination, while those of the oxidants were strongly reduced in intensity.   The results are summarized in table 35.IC.

TABLE 35.IC

PERCENT REDUCTION OF DIFFERENT REDOX SYSTEMS BY 3 MINUTES OF ILLUMINATION WITH CHLOROPHYLL, BACTERIOCHLOROPHYLL OR THEIR PHEOPHYTINS AS SENSITIZERS (AFTER KRASNOVSKY AND VOYNOVSKAYA 1952)

Redox system	Chl a		Pheo a		BChl		BPheo	
	In EtOH	In C_5H_5N	In EtOH	In C_5H_5N	In EtOH	Ir-C_5H_5N	In EtOH	In C_5H_5N
Riboflavin + ascorbate	50		50		25		5	60
Riboflavin + Na₂S		60			*	70	40–60	70
Safranin T + ascorbate	25		25		25		5	25
Safranin T + Na₂S		80				70	40–60	50

* Complete bleaching of bacteriochlorophyll although the latter shows no reaction with Na₂S in absence of riboflavin.

A reduction of DPN could be observed with chlorophyll and ascorbic acid in pyridine (as described before) but not with bacteriochlorophyll.   (As in fig. 35.6, the reduction of DPN was derived from increase in the absorption of the illuminated solution around 340 mμ.)

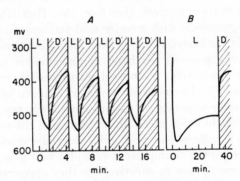

Fig. 35.7A. Changes of redox potential of chlorophyll and pheophytin in pyridine upon repeated illumination and darkening: (A) 10^{-4} mole/l. Chl $(a + b)$, 0.8×10^{-2} mole/l, ascorbic acid; (B) 10^{-4} mole/l. pheophytin, 0.6×10^{-2} mole/l. ascorbic acid (after Evstigneev and Gavrilova 1953[3]).

Although bacteriochlorophyll acts on the whole like chlorophyll, its reduced form reacts back so much faster that no determination of its absorption spectrum could be made.   Krasnovsky also noted that while bacteriochlorophyll can be photochemically reduced *in vitro* by sodium sulfide, it does not react with other reductants used by purple bacteria, such as malic acid or propanol; he suggested that these hydrogen donors must be acted upon by appropriate dehydrogenases before their hydrogen becomes available for photochemical transfer.

Evstigneev and Gavrilova (1953[3]) measured the *photogalvanic effect* in an illuminated solution of chlorophyll and ascorbic acid in pyridine. In the dark the oxidation-reduction potential of the solution is determined by the ascorbic acid-dehydroascorbic acid system. In light the potential rises, first rapidly, then more slowly, as shown in figure 35.7A; in the dark it returns almost to its initial value. (Here again we note that the reaction can be repeated several times with the same sample!) The widest potential change observed was about 0.29 volt with chlorophyll a (or $a + b$), 0.25 volt with chlorophyll b, 0.35 volt with pheophytin ($a + b$), 0.33 volt with Zn-pheophytin and 0.29 volt with Mg-phthalocyanine. Since the dilute (10^{-4} M) chlorophyll could not have oxidized more than about 1% of the 0.01 M ascorbic acid, and any change in potential caused by this oxidation must have been toward more negative values, the rise of potential actually observed in the illuminated solution indicates a high sensitivity of the electrode to the presence of a small amount of reduced chlorophyll. (The situation is similar to that in thionine-ferrous ion photogalvanic cells, described by Rabinowitch in 1940; there, too, a shift of the oxidation-reduction equilibrium in light leads to the electrode potential becoming more negative, *i. e.*, the electrode responds to the reduction of the dye-leucodye system more sensitively than to the oxidation of the Fe^{+2}/Fe^{+3} system.

The main potential-determining process in the illuminated chlorophyll-ascorbic acid solution must be the transfer of electrons from reduced chlorophyll to the positive electrode, and their return to dehydroascorbic acid via the negative electrode; *i. e.*, an electrode-catalyzed back reaction in the photochemically displaced chlorophyll-ascorbate equilibrium.

Evstigneev and Gavrilova pointed out that the value +0.35 volt (the maximum photogalvanic potential obtained in these experiments) is the same as was derived by Krasnovsky and Brin (1950) from the capacity of photoreduced chlorophyll solutions to reduce various oxidants (*cf.* above).

Evstigneev and Gavrilova noticed that after light has been switched off, the photogalvanic potential disappeared within a minute, while the red absorption band of chlorophyll was not fully restored until 30–40 minutes later; they concluded that the electrochemical effect is caused by a particularly unstable, intermediate form of reduced chlorophyll. This seems to call for a parallel experiment on the rate of disappearance in the dark of the bands at 518 mμ and 585 mμ, ascribed by the same authors (1953[2]) to the ionic and the neutral form of a semiquinone, respectively (*cf.* chapter 37C, section 2).

Evstigneev and Terenin (1951) made experiments on the photovoltaic effect (Becquerel effect) with electrodes (Pt, graphite) coated with chlorophyll, phthalocyanine or pheophytin. With chlorophyll in the presence of air they found a positive photoeffect (coated electrode became more positive in light) requiring about 1 min. of illumination to reach a stationary value and decaying in about 1 min. in darkness.   Reductants decreased the positive effect or even changed its sign.

If a rise of potential to a level 0.35 volt above the normal potential of ascorbic acid (about -0.04 volt at pH 7) could be maintained in the steady state of a photochemical reaction, chlorophyll-sensitized reduction by ascorbic acid of compounds with normal potentials of the order of $+0.3$ volt (as described by Krasnovsky and Brin, $cf.$ above) would be plausible. However, this low photogalvanic potential corresponds to a wide shift of the concentration ratio of a very dilute oxidation-reduction system, Chl/rChl; and as soon as the reductant in this system finds an oxidant with

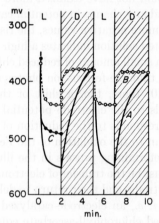

Fig. 35.7B. Changes in redox potential of chlorophyll in pyridine: (A) 10^{-4} mole/l. Chl $(a + b)$, 0.6×10^{-2} mole/l. ascorbic acid; (B) same $+$ 10^{-4} mole/l. safranin T; (C) same $+ 4 \times 10^{-4}$ mole/l. riboflavin (after Evstigneev and Gavrilova 1953).

which it can react, the concentration of the reductant must decline and the potential go up ("photogalvanic depolarization"); the reaction will be slowed down or stopped altogether.   This effect of hydrogen acceptors on the photogalvanic potential actually was noted by Evstigneev and Gavrilova.   Figure 35.7B shows that the presence of 4×10^{-4} mole/liter riboflavin reduces the potential drop to less than one-half of its original value. In other words, the photogalvanic potential cannot be taken as a measure of the effective reducing power of an illuminated redox system.   What oxidants can be reduced in light, and at what rate, is a problem of *kinetics*, and not, or only partly, of equilibrium (or pseudoequilibrium) *potentials*.

This may be a proper place for a general remark concerning the use of oxidation-reduction potentials in the discussion of photochemical mechanisms.   Let us assume that the action of light is to displace an oxidation-reduction equilibrium (say, between two intermediate redox catalysts, A/AH_2 and B/BH_2). What can be said about the secondary oxidations and reductions which can follow this displacement? In the first place, one has to remember that "reducing power" (say an accumulation of BH_2) arises simultaneously with "oxidizing power" (say, an accumulation of A), so that to speak of only one of them (one often hears of the "reducing power" of illuminated chloroplasts) means postulating that the systems A/AH_2 and B/BH_2 are either separated spatially immediately after the photochemical transfer of H from A to B; or else that, because of enzymatic specificity, the next system in the reduction sequence (say, C/CH_2) "sees," chemically speaking, only the reduced system B/BH_2 and *not* the simultaneously present oxidized system A/AH_2 (an analogous assumption must be made on the "oxidation side" of the primary photoprocess).

The specificity of enzymes and the heterogeneous structure of the photosynthetic apparatus make one—or both—of these important postulates not implausible.

The next question (selecting arbitrarily the "reducing power" rather than the "oxidizing power" for further consideration) is: what secondary reductions can be achieved by the system B/BH_2, in which the ratio $[BH_2]/[B]$ has been increased by light? Let us assume that the normal potential of the pair B/BH_2 is E_0^B; if the logarithm of the concentration ratio $[BH_2]/[B]$ has been shifted to δ ($\gg 1$), the redox potential of the pair becomes $E^B = E_0^B + 0.03 \, \delta$. On paper, by increasing δ, E^B can be increased indefinitely; e. g., with $\delta = 4$, $E^B = E_0^B + 0.12$ volt, and so on. In reality, however, the possible contribution of this concentration term to the reducing capacity of BH_2 in the steady state is very limited, because an extreme value of the concentration ratio (such as $10^4 : 1$) cannot be maintained when a reaction is in progress.

This is particularly true of a photochemical reaction with a high quantum efficiency. Such a reaction is only possible if no (or relatively few) quanta are wasted in the primary process; and if this process includes the transfer of hydrogen (or electrons) from AH_2 to B, there must be enough B present at all times to accept the proffered H atoms (or electrons). In other words, the steady-state concentration of B cannot drop low in light if this light is to be effectively used, and this means that no extremely high photostationary ratios $[BH_2]/[B]$ are permitted, and the oxidation-reduction potential of this system in light cannot be much different from E_0^B. To this consideration one must add a second one: to prevent exhaustion of B in light, the absolute rate of reaction of BH_2 with the next hydrogen (or electron) acceptor, C, must be sufficiently high. To use a concrete example, if B is called upon to accept one H atom every second, and if one-half of the total $B + BH_2$ must be available in the oxidized form to ensure that no photochemically supplied H will be wasted, BH_2 must react with C within one second to maintain the ratio $[BH_2]/[B]$ at the required level. This puts a limit on the admissible activation energy of the reaction $BH_2 + C \rightarrow B + CH_2$. If this reaction is endothermal, the minimum value of the activation energy is the heat of reaction, ΔH; and if the normal potential of the system C/CH_2 is significantly more negative than that of the system B/BH_2, the reaction $BH + C \rightarrow B + CH$ is likely to be endothermal by a similar amount. Furthermore, if this reaction has no activation energy in excess of ΔH, the back reaction, $CH_2 + B \rightarrow C + BH_2$ will be extremely rapid, and there will be little chance for any CH_2 formed to escape it by stabilizing processes. The net result of all these considerations is that only very limited help can be expected, in a photochemical reaction against the gradient of chemical potential, from the concentration term in the free energy relationship:

$$E = E_0 + \frac{0.06}{n} \log \frac{[\text{Red}]}{[\text{Ox}]}$$

What is needed for the success of the photochemical reaction is the capacity of the primarily light-activated molecule to utilize its energy for *direct* reduction of a compound with a potential negative enough for all subsequent steps in the reaction sequence to go "downhill" (on the ΔH scale). In more concrete terms, if there is a primary photochemical oxidant, B, its reduced form must be capable of carrying on the reduction of whatever has to be ultimately reduced—be it CO_2, RCOOH, or various Hill oxidants— by exothermal reactions. (These reactions may be made exothermal by cooperation of several BH_2 molecules, *i. e.*, by an "energy dismutation" mechanism—for example, with the aid of high-energy phosphates.)

Uri (1952) noted that the yield of polymerization of methyl methacrylate, photosensitized by chlorophyll (*cf.* above, section 1) increased enormously upon addition of ascorbic acid or urea, indicating a great increase in the photostationary concentration of free radicals. Reducing salts (ferrous sulfate, ferrocyanide) inhibited rather than stimulated polymerization.

Baur and Niggli (1943) in the last of the papers of the series reported in chapter 4 (section A4(*b*)) had claimed that chlorophyll, dissolved in geraniol or phytol, and emulsified in a solution of methylene blue in dry glycerol, could sensitize the reduction of circulating carbon dioxide to formaldehyde and liberate oxygen (from glycerol?). Linstead, Braude and Timmons (1950) were unable to confirm these results.

Gurevich (1948) described still another chlorophyll-sensitized oxidation-reduction: the reduction of *o-dinitrobenzene* by *phenylhydrazine*. (For his experiment on the use of *o*-dinitrobenzene as oxidant in Hill reaction, *cf.* part B, Sect. 4(*g*).) He used ethanolic extracts from nettle leaves. 5 cc. of "dark-green but transparent" extract were mixed with 0.5 cc. of phenylhydrazine (10% free base in ethanol) and 0.5 cc. *o*-dinitrobenzene. One half of this solution was illuminated, at 15–30°, 15 cm. from a 300-watt lamp, (H_2O filter) for 30 min.; the other half kept in darkness. The formation of *o*-nitrophenylhydroxylamine was proved by addition of concentrated ammonia, leading to dark-violet coloration. No nitrophenyl hydroxylamine was formed in controls without chlorophyll or phenylhydrazine. Ascorbic acid could be used as hydrogen donor instead of phenylhydrazine. (This reaction occurs spontaneously in alkaline medium, but *not* in neutral solution.) Similar results were obtained with eosin, erythrosin B and some other fluorescent dyes as sensitizers.

Gurevich (1949) later found that oxidation of phenylhydrazine by *o*-dinitrobenzene can be catalyzed in *the dark* by "chlorophyll hemin." The latter was obtained from an alcoholic leaf extract, by successive conversion to pheophytin and introduction of iron (by means of heating with ferric acetate). The green crystalline product, added to a saturated solution of *o*-dinitrobenzene in ethanol, also containing phenylhydrazine (free base), catalyzed the reduction of dinitrobenzene to *o*-nitrophenyl hydroxylamine, which can be recognized by its violet salts. The same result can be achieved with Fe_2O_3 as catalyst, but the catalytic effect of the "chlorophyll hemin" does not depend on contamination with inorganic iron salts.

Pariser (1950) and Weigl and Livingston (1952[2]) studied the chlorophyll-sensitized reduction of an azo dye (butter yellow) by ascorbic acid— a reaction of the same type as was studied by Krasnovsky and co-workers. According to Pariser, the maximum quantum yield of this reaction in methanol is about 0.5. Weigl and Livingston used *deuterated* ascorbic acid to see whether any deuterium could be found in chlorophyll after the reaction with butter yellow is over. To avoid isotopic exchange with the solvent, dioxane was used instead of methanol; this reduced the quantum yield to a very low value. After about ten deuterium atoms were transferred to the oxidant for each chlorophyll molecule present, analysis of chlorophyll for deuterium content revealed <4% of the amount to be expected if one D atom were to get stuck in chlorophyll in each reduction act. Experiments on deuterium exchange between chlorophyll and heavy water (Weigl and Livingston 1952[1]) showed that deuterium could not have been lost from chlorophyll during the chromatographic purification; it thus seems that, in this particular oxidation-reduction reaction, the primary photochemical process is *not* the transfer of hydrogen from excited chlorophyll to the oxidant (to be replaced later by hydrogen from the reductant). The primary act *can* be the transfer of hydrogen from the reductant to chlorophyll (as suggested by Krasnovsky's experiments)—at least, if one is permitted to assume that the *same* hydrogen is later transferred, by a thermal reaction, to the oxidant, without having been first pooled with other hydrogen atoms in the sensitizer.

6. Chlorophyll-Sensitized Autoxidations
(Second Addendum to Chapter 18, Part C)

In Volume I (chapter 18) a number of chlorophyll-sensitized autoxidations were described. Of these, only one was investigated quantitatively— the ethyl chlorophyllide-sensitized autoxidation of allyl thiourea (Gaffron

1927, 1933, *cf.* Table 18.II). This reaction appeared to have a limiting quantum yield of about 1, reached when the concentration of the oxidation substrate was sufficiently high and that of the sensitizer sufficiently low. Since one of the reagents—oxygen—is present only in small concentration in the liquid phase, shaking of the reaction vessel is needed to avoid yield deficiency due to local exhaustion of oxygen.

The autoxidation of thiourea (substituted for allyl thiourea since it shows a less pronounced dark reaction) with ethyl chlorophyllide as sensitizer was reinvestigated by Warburg and Schocken (1949), with a view on using this reaction in a manometric actinometer. Several solvents were tried out. Pyridine was found to be the most satisfactory, acetone (used in Gaffron's work) being too volatile, and dioxane producing complications (autoxidation quantum yields >1, with efficiency increased by traces of copper, and decreased by cyanide) conceivably caused by peroxide formation. Attempts to substitute other reductants, such as hydroquinone, for thiourea, gave no positive results. In addition to ethyl chlorophyllide, protoporphyrin could be used as sensitizer. The green pigment is suitable for the work in red and blue, the red one for the work in green and blue; mixed together, they give almost complete absorption throughout the visible spectrum.

A vessel 14 ml. in volume was used, containing 200 mg. thiourea and 2 mg. crystalline ethyl chlorophyllide (or 10 mg. crystalline protoporphyrin) in 5 cc. pyridine. It was illuminated for periods of the order of 15–30 min. through a flat bottom (area, 9 sq. cm.) with light from a large monochromator (beam cross section, 2 sq. cm.). The vessel communicated with a manometer filled with pure oxygen, and was shaken during illumination. Quantum yields of oxygen consumption obtained in this way are tabulated in Table 35.II.

TABLE 35.II

QUANTUM YIELDS OF OXYGEN CONSUMPTION IN SENSITIZED AUTOXIDATION OF THIOUREA
(AFTER WARBURG AND SCHOCKEN 1949)

λ, mμ	Absorption, microeinsteins	O_2, micromoles	γ, molecules O_2 per quantum
640–660	1.98	1.82	0.92
640–660	0.99	1.02	1.03
505–525	1.14	1.10	0.96
420–450	0.36	0.42	1.16
585–615	1.90	1.79	0.94
585–615	0.95	0.96	1.01
420–450	0.44	0.46	1.04
640–660	1.65	1.97	0.89
640–660	0.825	0.78	0.94
640–660	0.83	0.83	1.00
585–615	1.64	4.55	0.95
505–525	0.88	0.84	0.75

It will be noted that γ values show a decline with rising light intensity; Warburg and Schocken recommended not to use light intensities much in excess of 1×10^{-6} einstein absorbed per 15 min. in 5 cc. In part, the decrease can be due to oxygen exhaustion in the illuminated bottom layer, which may occur at higher light intensities despite shaking.

The nature and mechanism of the chemical change taking place in this actinometer remains uncertain. Up to 2.5 moles oxygen were consumed per mole thiourea after prolonged irradiation, while not more than 2 should be used if the reaction were:

$$(35.27) \qquad CS(NH_2)_2 + 2 O_2 \longrightarrow CNNH_2 + H_2SO_4$$

About 75% of the amount of sulfuric acid to be expected according to this equation was actually found; qualitative test for cyanamide formation was positive. 17% of the thiourea consumed was recoverable as urea, perhaps because of hydrolysis of the primarily produced cyanamide:

$$(35.28) \qquad CNNH_2 + H_2O \longrightarrow CO(NH_2)_2$$

While reacting with a quantum yield close to 1, the system continues to fluoresce strongly, which should account for the loss of probably not less than 10% of the absorbed quanta. That sensitization does not compete with fluorescence indicates (cf. Vol. 1, page 483) that it proceeds by the intermediary of a "long-lived active state" such as the "tautomer," tChl, which is formed in about 95% of all cases of excitation.

Warburg and Schocken, having observed that thiourea will react with oxygen in ultraviolet light without sensitizer, concluded that the most likely mechanism of sensitization is transfer of excitation energy from the chlorophyllide to thiourea. However, the mechanism of sensitized photochemical reactions is generally different from that of nonsensitized reactions because the reaction substrate (thiourea) has no way of accepting a "red quantum," either directly by light absorption or indirectly by transfer from an excited chlorophyllide molecule. The more likely mechanisms of sensitized autoxidation are, therefore, those involving intermediate reversible chemical changes of the sensitizer, such as were described in Volume I, pages 514–521 and in section 5 above. Whether the long-lived activated chlorophyllide molecule, tChl, reacts first with thiourea or with oxygen remains unknown.

It also remains a matter of speculation whether the chlorophyllide molecules enter into association with thiourea molecules (or oxygen molecules, or both) in the dark. According to table 23.IIID, thiourea does not quench the fluorescence of chlorophyll; and the same is probably true of chlorophyllide fluorescence. Association, if any, must therefore be of the type not affecting fluorescence; in other words, the photochemical reaction in the complex must be delayed until after the conversion of excited chlorophyllide into the metastable form, tChl. Another possible mechanism is analogous to that suggested by Livingston for the sensitized methyl red-phenylhydrazine reaction (cf. section 5 above); in this scheme no reaction occurs until the complex of tChl with one reactant encounters the other reactant (cf. equations 35.15c and d).

In any case, the reaction probably involves a one-step oxidation-reduction, followed by dismutation, or another short chain of elementary steps, bringing the quantum yield up to a value close to 1 (which implies the utilization of two oxygen atoms, i. e., the transfer of *four* electrons, or hydrogen atoms, by a single quantum). Because of the likelihood that the over-all reaction is composed of several successive elementary steps, involving intermediate free radicals or other unstable products, the quantum yield could be sensitive to factors such as the nature and purity of the solvent, concentration of the reactants, light intensity and temperature.

In some more recent papers, Burk and Warburg (1951) abandoned the quest for a quantum yield of 1.0 in the actinometer, since they found that in pyridine, with ethyl chlorophyllide as sensitizer, a quantum yield of close to 1 required not only in a relatively low light intensity, but also the presence of a certain amount of impurities (such as piperidine) in the solvent. In pure pyridine the newly observed quantum yields were between 0.86 (0.1 μeinstein per minute per vessel) and 0.69 (3 μeinsteins per minute per vessel). It was stated that by using crystallized pheophorbide (instead of chlorophyllide) and a large volume actinometric vessel (80 ml. instead of 7 ml. liquid), a constant quantum yield of 0.70 could be obtained for light absorptions up to 4 μeinsteins per minute.

Still more recently, Warburg and co-workers (1953) again assumed a quantum yield of 1.0 for a pheophorbide-thiourea actinometer of 120 ml., up to a light flux of 1 μeinstein/min.

Schenck (1953) found that an intermediate in the oxidation of thiourea in the actinometer—formed to an extent up to 81% of the oxidized thiourea—is the sulfinic acid $NH=C(HSO_2)—NH_2$.

Among new qualitative data of the photochemical action of chlorophyll we can mention Pepkowitz's (1943) observations of the photochemical destruction of carotene in the presence of chlorophyll. Because of the dependence of the rate of destruction on the amount of chlorophyll present, it is suggested that chlorophyll takes part in the reaction, and not merely sensitizes it.

B. Photochemistry of Chloroplast Preparations*

(Addendum to Chapter 4, Part A)

In chapter 4, Volume I (page 61) we have described in brief the production of oxygen by leaf macerates and dry leaf powders in light, first noted

* Bibliography, page 1627.

by Friedel, and later described by Molisch and by Inman; and the enhancement and stabilization of this phenomenon which Hill (1939, 1940) had achieved by providing an oxidant, such as ferric oxalate.

As anticipated in chapter 4, the study of the "Hill reaction" has proved one of the most promising approaches to the analysis of the mechanism of photosynthesis.

Little doubt now remains that the "Hill reaction" represents a part of photosynthesis which can be reproduced with nonliving material—although as yet only with complex colloidal systems obtained by mechanical disintegration of cells.

This part consists of photochemical oxidation of water leading to the liberation of oxygen, undoubtedly with the participation of an enzymatic system closely linked to, and surviving with, the photochemical apparatus. The part lost in the preparation of the chloroplasts is that concerned with the use of carbon dioxide as acceptor for the hydrogen taken away from water. Only relatively strong oxidants, such as ferric salts or quinones, can be used as hydrogen acceptors in the Hill reaction with a good quantum yield. True, it has been found possible to couple this reaction, through the intermediary of pyridine nucleotides, to enzymatic systems permitting the reduction of pyruvate to lactate, or its reductive carboxylation to malate, or (with the help of ATP), the reduction of phosphoglyceric acid to phosphoglyceraldehyde.

However, so far, this nearest approximation to photosynthesis outside the living cell could be achieved only with a very low quantum yield; therefore it remains an open question whether this reaction *in vitro* represents a significant approach to the reconstruction of the actual mechanism of photosynthesis *in vivo*.

The interpretation of the Hill reaction as oxidation of water is supported by oxygen isotope tracer studies.

In chapter 3 (Vol. I, page 54) we described tracer experiments with heavy oxygen which directly demonstrated that all oxygen evolved in normal photosynthesis originated in H_2O (and none in the oxidant, CO_2). In the case of the Hill reaction, many oxidants—such as $Fe[(CN)_6]^{+3}$— contain no oxygen at all; furthermore, the ratio of the amount of oxygen liberated to the amount of oxidant reduced agrees with the assumption that oxygen comes from the oxidation of water. An exception is chromate, where oxygen could conceivably come from the anion, and where the amount of liberated oxygen, as found in Holt and French's experiments, was much smaller than stoichiometrically expected. Holt and French (1948[2]) made a mass spectroscopic analysis of the oxygen evolved in the Hill reaction from normal water and from water enriched in O(18), using for comparison oxygen produced from the same water by electrolysis. The results are shown in Table 35.III; they confirm that in all studied cases of the Hill reaction—including that with chromate—the oxygen came from water. (In the experiment with chromate, pH 8.3 borate buffer was used to retard the isotopic exchange of oxygen between water and chromate.)

TABLE 35.III

ISOTOPIC COMPOSITION OF OXYGEN EVOLVED BY ILLUMINATED CHLOROPLASTS
(AFTER HOLT AND FRENCH, 1948[2])

| | | $100[O(18)O(16)]/[O(16)O(16)]$ oxygen produced by | |
| | | Hill reaction | Electrolysis of water |
Water used	Oxidant		
Normal	0.02 M ferricyanide	0.39	0.38
	0.02 M ferricyanide	0.39	0.38
Enriched	0.02 M ferricyanide	1.4	1.3
	0.02 M ferricyanide	0.84	0.83
	0.0067 M quinone	0.62	0.61
	0.0035 M dichlorophenol-indophenol	0.57	0.62
	0.00221 M K_2CrO_4	0.52	0.49

1. Can Carbon Dioxide Serve as Oxidant in Hill Reaction?

Claims of having obtained oxygen evolution from water by isolated chloroplasts, with simultaneous reduction of carbon dioxide, if not to a carbohydrate, at least to formic acid, have been made by Boichenko (1943, 1944). Since these investigations have only been published in Russian, we will describe them in some detail, despite the fact that techniques used were rather primitive and the results not too convincing.

Boichenko further claimed that chlorophyll preparations can reduce carbon dioxide not only in light, "photosynthetically," at the expense of water, but also in the dark, "chemosynthetically" (with hydrogen as reductant).

Boichenko thought (quoting Lubimenko) that under natural conditions the medium surrounding the chloroplasts has a very low value of rH—in other words, is strongly reducing. Since photosynthesis produces both oxidation products (O_2) and reduction products (carbohydrates), the reducing properties of the medium can be understood if the oxidation product (oxygen) is removed much more efficiently than the reduction products (sugars) ("removal" may mean translocation or a chemical change, such as polymerization of reducing sugars to sucrose or starch). The accumulation of reducing compounds around the chloroplasts is thus a *consequence* of photosynthesis, and, as such, more likely to *inhibit* than to stimulate it. Boichenko considered, to the contrary, that a low value of rH is a *prerequisite* for photosynthesis, and attempted to imitate nature by suspending chloroplasts in an artificial medium of low rH. To simulate natural conditions also in respect to pH and osmotic pressure, she followed the advice of Kuzin, and used as medium a solution of a reducing sugar (glucose, fructose) in saturated solution of basic magnesium acetate.

What she called "chloroplasts" was a preparation obtained simply by shredding leaves of clover with scissors, washing in a 0.5 mole/liter glucose or galactose solution, and passing the suspension through a paper filter under suction. The filter paper carrying the dark-green precipitate was cut into strips, and immersed into the above-mentioned reducing medium, to which bicarbonate was added. The pH of the solution was 7.5–8.5. Boichenko claimed that if the medium contained 0.1% reducing sugar, giving rH <9.9 (estimated by means of redox indicator dyes), oxygen was evolved, and carbon dioxide used up, upon illumination of the green strip. The results are summarized in Table 35.IV. The table shows that with fructose and, to a lesser extent, with glucose, the rH decreased and the pH increased upon exposure to light, and oxygen was liberated. With hydrosulfite and glycolaldehyde, the pH and rH changes were in the opposite direction, and no oxygen evolution was observed.

TABLE 35.IV

"PHOTOSYNTHESIS" WITH CHLOROPLAST FILMS ON FILTER PAPER
(AFTER BOICHENKO 1943, 1944)

Medium	rH		pH		O₂ evolution
	Before	After	Before	After	
No sugar	>14.4	14.4	8.0	8.0	None
0.1% maltose	<14.4	<9.9	8.0	8.0	None
0.1% glucose	9.9	5.2	8.0	8.3	Slight
0.1% fructose	<9.9	<5.2	8.0	8.5	Strong
0.1% glycolaldehyde	5.2	>14.4	8.0	7.5	None
0.1% hydrosulfite	<5.2	25.2	8.0	8.0	None

The fact that the rH of hexose solutions did *not* increase upon illumination was taken by Boichenko as proof that these sugars were not used up, and she concluded that they must have served as catalysts for the oxidation of water by carbon dioxide—which was also indicated by the increase in pH. She recalled in this connection the observation of van Niel and Gaffron that purple bacteria and "adapted" green algae can use organic hydrogen donors to reduce carbon dioxide. Inverting the reaction sequence suggested by them (which involved water as the primary, and organic compound as ultimate hydrogen donor), she suggested that organic H donors (such as fructose) serve as *primary* reductants (even in normal photosynthesis!), and that the oxidation of water (and liberation of oxygen) are caused by a secondary reaction between the oxidized sugars and water. It hardly needs pointing out that using carbohydrates as primary hydrogen donors to reduce carbon dioxide in the photochemical stage of photosynthesis leaves to dark stages a reaction which must require all the energy of photosynthesis, namely, the oxidation of water to oxygen by the oxidation product of a carbohydrate (such as a gluconic acid). The hypothesis is therefore utterly implausible.

Later, Boichenko (1947, 1948) described the "chemosynthetic" activity of the same chloroplast-impregnated filter paper strips: their capacity to catalyze carbon dioxide reduction by hydrogen *in the dark*. She found that these chloroplast preparations contain a "hydrogenase" capable of taking up molecular hydrogen and using it for the reduction of various substrates (O_2, CO_2, etc.—*cf.* the reactions of the hydrogen bacteria, Vol. I, page 116, and of "adapted" algae, Vol. I, page 130). The tests were made by observing the decoloration of methylene blue (*cf.* Vol. I, page 131) by the chloroplast-covered paper strip in an atmosphere of hydrogen; the uptake of hydrogen was confirmed by manometric measurements. The activity was highest with those species (*Trifolium repens, Chenopodium album*) whose chloroplasts did not easily disintegrate into grana.

Instead of methylene blue, *oxygen* could be used as hydrogen acceptor: with 0.6–0.67% O_2 in the air, from 75 to 288 mm.[3] of oxygen were taken up by 25 mg. of chloroplasts, together with from 0 to 200 mm.[3] hydrogen. At 0.6–1.5% O_2 in the atmosphere, the ratio $\Delta H_2/\Delta O_2$ was 1.06–1.17; at $[O_2] > 2\%$, the uptake of hydrogen declined rapidly. Boichenko interpreted this as evidence of deactivation of the hydrogenase by oxygen (*cf.* Gaffron's observations, Vol. I, page 132). When $[O_2]$ approached 10%, the uptake of oxygen also ceased.

The gas exchanges shown in Table 35.V were observed when carbon dioxide and hydrogen were offered to the chloroplast films in the dark. According to this table the uptake of CO_2 occurred without (or with only a slight) uptake of oxygen (without which no chemosynthesis had been observed in bacteria and algae!). Since the ratio $\Delta H_2/\Delta CO_2$ is close to 1.0 (rather than 2.0, as in Gaffron's adapted algae), the reaction reminds one not so much of "chemosynthesis" of carbohydrates, as of the synthesis of formic acid from H_2 and CO_2 by *E. coli* (Woods, *cf.* Volume I, pages 185, 208). The uptake of CO_2 and H_2 was noted even in the absence of oxygen, but was stimulated by its presence, even though only little oxygen was taken up. (It thus looks as if, when both CO_2 and O_2 are present, the former is used as oxidant in preference to the latter; a remarkable selection, considering the difference of oxidizing potential. However, a similar situation exists in photosynthesis, where, too, photoxidation gets under way only when the cells are deprived of carbon dioxide.)

TABLE 35.V
GAS UPTAKE BY 25 MG. CHLOROPLASTS ON FILTER PAPER IN DARKNESS, IN $H_2 + CO_2$
(AFTER BOICHENKO 1947, 1948)

CO_2 in atmosphere, %	Gas exchange			ΔH_2
	$-\Delta O_2$, mm.[3]	$-\Delta CO_2$, mm.[3]	$-\Delta H_2$, mm.[3]	$(\Delta O_2 + \Delta CO_2)$
2.0	0	250	238	0.99
2.7	0	338	413	1.22
3.0	0	375	388	1.03
0.6	25	75	100	1.00
1.6	13	200	200	0.99
3.0	0	375	263	0.70

Boichenko measured the effect of CO_2 concentration on the rate of gas uptake ($\Delta CO_2 + \Delta H_2$) and found that the uptake (by 25 mg. chloroplasts) increased from 12.5 mm.[3] in 5 min. at 0.6% CO_2 to 375 mm.[3] at 6% CO_2, but declined rapidly at the higher carbon dioxide pressures (*e. g.*, to 75 mm.[3] at 10% CO_2). The ratio $\Delta H_2/\Delta CO_2$ remained constant (1.0 to 1.1) up to 6% CO_2, but only carbon dioxide was taken up at 10% CO_2. The temperature coefficient of the gas uptake ($\Delta CO_2 + \Delta H_2$) was $Q_{10} \simeq 2$ between 20 and 35° C.; above 35° C., the hydrogenase was destroyed. The rate of the chloroplast-catalyzed reduction of methylene blue by hydrogen appeared to be independent of temperature. (Table 35.VI.)

TABLE 35.VI

TEMPERATURE EFFECT ON CO_2 REDUCTION AND METHYLENE BLUE REDUCTION BY
CHLOROPLASTS ON FILTER PAPER STRIPS (AFTER BOICHENKO 1947, 1948)

Temperature, ° C.	$\Delta(H_2 + CO_2)$, mm.[3]	Relative rate of MB reduction
20	125	15
25	175	16
30	250	16
35	363	17

A very peculiar observation was made: when the reaction was continued long enough, it reversed itself, and both hydrogen and carbon dioxide were rapidly liberated again! This occurred very early at temperatures above 35° C.; consequently at 35° (and even at 30° C.) no complete consumption of hydrogen or carbon dioxide could be achieved. At 25° C., only hydrogen came out again, and at <25° C., no reversal of the reaction took place at all. Boichenko associated these peculiar phenomena with the thermodynamic reversibility of the reaction $H_2 + CO_2 \rightleftarrows HCOOH$, but it is thermodynamically impossible for a reaction to proceed first in the one and then in the other direction.

That formic acid actually was formed in these experiments was confirmed by chemical tests (reduction of $AgNO_3$ and $HgCl_2$). The reducing power resided in the film, and not in the solution; the reductant (formic acid?) thus must have been present in "bound form." The amount of $HgCl_2$ reduced agreed with the (manometrically determined) amount of hydrogen taken up by the chloroplast film.

Boichenko saw in these experiments an imitation, with isolated chloroplasts, of the first step in the reduction of carbon dioxide in photosynthesis, but both the reliability of the experiments and their interpretation are doubtful.

Vinogradov, Boichenko and Baranov (1951) applied C^{14} tracer technique to the products of carbon dioxide fixation by Boichenko's chloroplast preparations in the dark, with H_2 as reductant, and found the tagged products entirely extractable by hot water, with up to 90% of it precipitable by barium chloride; about 75% of the precipitate consisted of uronic acids, the rest were highly carboxylated nonreducing acids.

Boichenko and Baranov (1953) studied C^{14} uptake by the same preparations in light under anaerobic conditions. In the presence of hydrogen the uptake was 0.01 relative units in the dark and 0.032 relative units in light (as against 0.067 and 0.015 relative units in the presence of 1.25% oxygen). In pure nitrogen the uptake was negligible (0.0003 relative units in light, 0.004 in dark). The authors saw in these results the indication that the dark "chemosynthetic" fixation of CO_2, which requires oxygen, is replaced in light by "photoreduction," similar to bacterial photosynthesis, which occurs only under anaerobic conditions. Only a fraction of C^*O_2 fixed in light was found in carboxylic groups—an observation which was considered evidence that carbon dioxide was actually reduced (and not merely taken up in a carboxyl).

Franck (1945) noted a stimulating effect of carbon dioxide on oxygen liberation by chloroplasts *in the absence of added oxidants* (*i. e.*, on the Friedel-Molisch phenomenon), and thought at first that this effect indicated the capacity of chloroplasts to use carbon dioxide as oxidant, albeit with a very low efficiency. Subsequent experiments with C(14) by Franck and Brown (1947) caused him to abandon this interpretation.

Franck (1945) determined small amounts of oxygen by the quenching of phosphorescence of dyes adsorbed on silica gel (page 851). Figure 35.8 shows the time course of oxygen liberation by a chloroplast preparation, both in the absence and in the presence of carbon dioxide. The oxygen liberation reaches a maximum immediately after the beginning of illumination; after about 0.5 minute, it begins to decline. After a few minutes of this decline, a steady level is reached, and the oxygen liberation remains at this

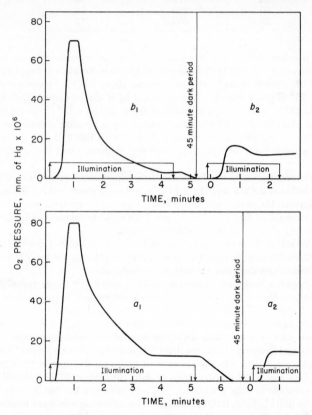

Fig. 35.8. Oxygen liberation by chloroplasts in light without added oxidant (after Franck 1945). Oxygen concentration in nitrogen, after passage through reaction vessel, determined by phosphorescence quenching method. Curves a, with CO_2; curves b, without CO_2.

level for an hour or more. Even the initial rate of oxygen liberation is only 1.5% of the rate of photosynthesis *in vivo*; the final, constant rate was only 0.3% of the latter. The maximum rate depended strongly on the way the sample was prepared, the age of the leaf, and other conditions.

The pairs of curves compared in fig. 35.8 (a_1,a_2 and b_1,b_2) were obtained with aliquot parts of the same chloroplast preparation, and the conditions differed only in the composition of the gas phase (pure N_2 in b_1,b_2, $N_2 + 20$ mm. CO_2 in a_1,a_2). CO_2 had no effect on the initial maximum rate, but a marked influence on the final, constant level; subsequent addition of CO_2 in the nitrogen atmosphere caused a marked increase in this rate. "Light saturation" of the steady oxygen production was reached, with isolated chloroplasts, much earlier than with intact leaves. In flashing light, too, the yield per flash was 50–100 times smaller with isolated chloroplasts than with whole leaves.

As mentioned above, Franck (1945) first interpreted these results as indicating an "oxygen burst" caused by photochemical utilization of a carbon dioxide derivative (RCOOH, or ACO_2, or $\{CO_2\}$ in our earlier designations) accumulated in the chloroplasts before the leaves were macerated, and a much lower, steady oxygen production which may be due to very slow renewed formation of the same compound in isolated chloroplasts. This hypothesis was revised by Franck when experiments with radiocarbon (Brown and Franck, 1947) produced no evidence of carbon dioxide fixation by chloroplasts (*i. e.*, of a CO_2 uptake not reversed by treatment with boiling acetic acid), either under anaerobic or under aerobic conditions. The sensitivity of the method was high enough to discover an uptake of CO_2 equivalent to the amount of oxygen liberated. The enhancing effect of carbon dioxide on oxygen liberation was therefore reinterpreted as a catalytic phenomenon.

Fager (1952[1]) attempted to obtain chloroplast suspensions retaining a capacity for the reduction of carbon dioxide by using low temperature ($<1°$ C.), anaerobic conditions (N_2 atmosphere) and only dim light during the preparation of chloroplasts (from spinach leaves). Crude juice, containing chloroplasts, grana, etc., but no whole cells, was obtained by pressing the macerate through a sintered filter plate. The uptake of radiocarbon from C^*O_2 by this juice was increased noticeably (by about 70%) in light; however, this increase corresponded to only 0.01 mole C^* taken up in 15 min. per mole chlorophyll—about 0.1% of photosynthetic fixation in intact cells. Centrifugation of the crude juice, and resuspension of the precipitate in buffer, gave a product without CO_2 fixing capacity; combining the precipitate with the supernatant restored it. Analysis showed that over 70% of the additional C^* fixation in light was in phosphoglyceric acid, PGA, (54%) and pyruvic acid, PA (18%). (Of the C^* fixed in the dark, 65% was in phosphoglyceric acid and 20% in pyruvic acid.) After only 1 min. of exposure, the ratio of extra tagged PGA to extra tagged PA was as high as 10:1, indicating that PGA was tagged first, in chloroplast preparation as in live cells (*cf.* chapter 36). Addition of various low molecular substances increased the extra fixation of C^* in light; among these were acetic acid (increase by 40%), acetaldehyde (by 90%), pyruvic acid (by 130%), glyoxal (by 140%), and 2-phosphoglycolaldehyde (by 40%). The same compounds, with the exception of glyoxal and phosphoglycoaldehyde, also increased the dark fixation. This seemed to indicate (see, however, below) the presence of an enzyme capable of fixing CO_2 in these C_2 compounds with the help of light energy—a result that could bear relation to the mechanism of formation of PGA in photosynthesis (*cf.* chapter 36, section 8). However, it now seems most likely (chapter 36, section 7) that PGA results from carboxylation and splitting of a pentose diphosphate.

The chloroplast preparations which showed the capacity to fix C^*O_2 in PGA and PA were found to be inactive as sensitizers of the Hill reaction with quinone as oxidant; while chloroplast preparations from the same plant material, made in the usual way, reduced quinone, but fixed no C^*O_2 in light. This striking difference could be demonstrated with two batches prepared from the same leaf material by the same procedure, except that one was frozen at $-190°$ C. and ground while frozen, while the other was cooled on ice and ground at $0°$ C.

In a second paper, Fager (1952[2]) described attempts to separate the protein responsible for the above-described effect of light on C^*O_2—fixation by cell free spinach juice. The material, prepared by powdering leaves at $-190°$ C., was subjected to fractional precipitation with acetone. The abundant precipitation obtained by adding up to 35% acetone fixed no C^*O_2; the precipitate brought down by 35–45% acetone took up C^*O_2 mostly in ether-extractable acids, but very little in PGA or PA; Fager suggested that this fraction contained the so-called "malic enzyme," and was responsible for the observations of Tolmach, Ochoa and Vishniac, and Arnon to be described in section 4(f) below. Over one-half of the C^*O_2 fixation in the fractions precipitated by 45–60% acetone was in PGA and PA. The C^*O_2 fixation in this fraction (in darkness and in light) could be increased 3–5 fold by $2 \times 10^{-3}\ M$ cysteine without changing the C^* distribution significantly.

The enhancing effect of glyoxal on C^* fixation, reported above for crude juice was not found with the separated protein fraction; instead, there was an inhibition (both in light and in the dark).

TPN ($1.3 \times 10^{-5}\ M$), or DPN ($5 \times 10^{-5}\ M$), had no effect on light induced C^*O_2 uptake by chloroplast preparations, but increased the fixation in the dark. "High energy phosphate" (ATP) caused inhibition instead of the anticipated enhancement. The strongest effect of ATP was on fixation in "neutral" products; this may indicate draining-off of PA (and, by equilibration, also of PGA) through accelerated conversion into malic acid, causing a decline in the reduction of PGA to triose. In agreement with this picture, arsenate (which is known to interfere with the utilization of high energy phosphate) had an effect on the C^*O_2 fixation which was opposite to that of ATP: it enhanced slightly the total fixation, and enhanced strongly the fixation of C^* in neutral compounds (sugars?).

The above-mentioned experiments by Tolmach, Vishniac and Ochoa and Arnon, in which carbon dioxide was drawn into the Hill reaction by supplying DPN or TPN as intermediate oxidants, will be dealt with in section 2(f) below.

More recently, Tolbert and Zill (1954) found that squeezed-out, plastide-bearing contents of giant *Chara* and *Nitella* cells can fix C^*O_2 in light in typical "photosynthetic" products (PGA, sugar phosphates, *cf.* chapter 36), to an amount of about 10% of that formed by whole cells. Conspicuous was the lack of tagged pentose and heptose phosphates, indicating that their formation may be the most easily disrupted link in the reaction cycle of photosynthesis.

Arnon, Allen and Whatley (1954) found that washed whole (but not fragmented!) spinach chloroplasts can fix C^*O_2 in light at a rate up to 160 times that of dark fixation. However, ascorbate had to be provided to achieve this rate, and as long as oxygen liberation has not been proved, it remains possible that ascorbate, rather than water, is used as reductant (Krasnovsky reaction, *cf.* p. 1583).

The same chloroplasts proved able to fix P^* from inorganic phosphate (more about this "photosynthetic phosphorylation" in chapter 36, part B). At high phosphate concentration, the C^*O_2 fixation was suppressed (as if the two processes were competitive). Since combination of photochemical H-transfer from H_2O (*e. g.*, to TPN) with carboxylation and ATP-formation seems to provide all the necessary "feed materials" for sugar synthesis, Arnon considered these experiments proof that the complete photochemical and enzymic apparatus of photosynthesis is present in the chloroplasts.

That whole chloroplasts behave differently from fragmented ones—in particular in that they tend to reduce preferentially weak oxidants—was derived by Punnett (1954) from analysis of published data.

Gerretsen (1951) noted, in studying the redox potential and the pH of crude chloroplast suspensions from *Avena sativa*, that under anaerobic conditions, the acidity, which grew slowly in darkness (probably because of CO_2 production by fermentation), grew more rapidly in light (at the same time the redox potential slowly changed). If, however, a small amount of carbon dioxide was introduced, the pH increased in l'ght and the redox potential changed much faster. Gerretsen interpreted these results as indicating participation of carbon dioxide as hydrogen acceptor in such crude preparations. The amount of CO_2 used up was about 2–3% of that consumed during the same time by an equal area of an illuminated leaf.

Boyle (1948) asserted that the Hill reaction (with quinone as oxidant) does not occur at all unless small quantities of carbon dioxide are present. However, this had not been confirmed by other investigators (Warburg, and others, unpublished; Clendenning and Gorham, 1950[1]).

2. Chloroplast Preparations from Different Plants

The original experiments by Hill (1937, 1939) and Hill and Scarisbrick (1940) were carried out with chloroplast preparations obtained by maceration of leaves from *Stellaria media*, *Lamium album*, and a few other plants. Since then, numerous species have been investigated; experiments have been made on preservation of the chloroplasts, the effects of various oxidants, and the methods for determining their reduction to supplement the measurement of liberated oxygen. Some kinetic studies have been made, including determinations of the quantum yield; but wide variations in the efficiency of individual preparations, and the rapid deterioration of the latter, have impeded systematic measurements.

Material for the preparation of chloroplast suspensions must fulfil the following requirements: It must be rich in chlorophyll; the plants must be easily macerated, with the destruction of cell walls and liberation of cell contents; the cell sap and plasma should not contain compounds which inhibit the Hill reaction, undergo dark reactions with the oxidant, or ferment, with the liberation of carbon dioxide, either in the dark, or in light.

"Crude" chloroplast preparations, $i.\ e.$, suspensions obtained from cell macerates simply by removing coarse debris (by filtration through cloth or by low-speed centrifugation) contain all the components of the plasma and cell sap. Such preparations show wide differences in the initial rate of oxygen liberation in light, the total amount of oxygen they can produce, and the extent of dark and photochemical side reactions. Their stability, $i.\ e.$, the rate of deterioration of the photochemical activity in dark storage or in light, also varies widely. Many of these differences probably are due to the presence of cell sap and plasma constituents. If these are removed, $e.\ g.$, by high-speed centrifugation, the precipitated and resuspended material, which now consists of whole and broken chloroplasts (with some plasma residues probably still clinging to them, $cf.$ chapter 14, page 369), shows fewer side reactions, but usually has a lower photochemical activity (related to unit mass of chlorophyll) than the crude suspension. The loss of activity is enhanced if the precipitate is washed to better remove the sap and plasma components. However, the activity lost can often be restored, at least partially, by the addition of salts, particularly of potassium chloride ($cf.$ below, section 3(c)).

The sap and plasma-free chloroplast preparations from different plants still exhibit considerable differences in efficiency. The latter depends not only on the species used but also on the season of the year and the time of the day when the leaves were gathered, their age, the intensity and duration of light exposure prior to collection, and preillumination (or dark storage) before maceration.

Hill and Scarisbrick (1940) noted that the efficiency of chloroplasts from *Stellaria media* depended strongly on the time of the day when the leaves were picked. French and Rabideau (1945), in comparing the quantum yields in chloroplast suspensions from *Spinacia* and *Tradescantia* (page 1129), found that pretreatment of the material (exposure of leaves to darkness or light) affected the yield much more strongly than the genetic difference between the two species.

Kumm and French (1945) compared the rates of oxygen evolution by chloroplast preparations from 22 species, using as oxidant Hill's mixture (0.5 M potassium oxalate, 0.01 M ferric ammonium sulfate, 0.02 M potassium ferricyanide, 0.2 M sucrose, 0.167 M borate buffer, pH 7.0). Many preparations gave no Hill reaction at all; inhibition by substances such as tannin, which bind Fe(III), was suggested as explanation. (This binding can often be recognized by the formation of highly colored complexes.)

The five species with which considerable oxygen liberation was observed were *Aster tatarica, Mirabilis jalapa, Impatiens biflora, Tradescantia fluminensis*, and *Spinacia oleracea.* They all showed rates of the same order of magnitude (related to equal amounts of chlorophyll); but considerable variations were found with leaves of each species in dependence on their history. Specifically, the efficiency was found to increase with the duration of preillumination. (In these experiments, detached leaves were kept for 2–3 days in the dark, then illuminated for 2–6 hours before maceration.) The rate of increase in efficiency was only about twice as high in light of 50 klux as in 115 klux; in general, the duration of the exposure appeared to be more important than its intensity. If, after 6-hr. illumination, the leaves were again darkened, the activity declined by about 50% in 1.6 hrs., and to almost zero in 6 hrs.

French concluded from these experiments that the Hill reaction is dependent on the presence of an accumulated product of photosynthesis which disappears in the dark, and that the maximum efficiency of the Hill reaction can be obtained only by using leaves which had been preilluminated for 10 hrs. or more. He suggested that insufficient preillumination might have been responsible for some low quantum yields found by French and Rabideau (Table 29.X).

Gurevich (1947) obtained evidence of photochemical reduction of *o*-dinitrobenzene with chloroplast suspensions from *Primula, Stellaria* and *Atriplex.* Andreeva and Zubkovich (1948), using quinone as oxidant, noted oxygen evolution with chloroplasts from *Primula obconica, Spinacia oleracea, Vicia faba, Phaseolus vulgaris, Nicotiana tabacum* and *Beta vulgaris.* They observed no parallelism between the capacities of these species for photosynthesis [5–15 mg. CO_2/(100 cm.^{2} × hr.), at 11 klux] and the efficiency of their chloroplasts in the Hill reaction with quinone [40–250 mm.^{3} O_2/(mg. chlorophyll × hr.) in light of the same intensity]. Older leaves of *Beta vulgaris* were more effective in the quinone reaction than the younger ones; leaves gathered in good weather were more effective than those collected in rain or cloudy weather. Preillumination of leaves collected in dim light with a 1000-watt lamp for 3 hrs. was found to improve their efficiency, in agreement with the observations of Kumm and French.

Holt *et al.* (1951) found pokeweed, *Phytolacca americana*, a particularly convenient source for the preparation of chlorophyll.

The most extensive comparative study of photochemical efficiency of chloroplasts from different plants was made by Clendenning and Gorham (1950^3). They measured the rate of liberation of oxygen in the first 5 min. of illumination with Hill's mixture as oxidant, using *p*H change (*cf.* under (*f*) below) as the rate of reaction measure. Tests were made with crude chloroplast preparations (obtained by grinding leaves and removing large debris by centrifuging at 2300 g.) from 80 species of unicellular and filamentous green algae, liverworts, horsetails, herbaceous monocotyledons and dicotyledons (all these gave positive results); and from mosses, ferns, gymnosperms and woody angiosperms (which showed no Hill activity at all). The suspensions from gymnosperms contained much oil, while those from broad leaf trees (*Acer, Populus, Quercus*) were so acid that the chloroplasts coagulated before the Hill solution was added. (Active chloroplasts from these leaves could probably be obtained by using more strongly buffered media.) With the 70 "active" species, the initial rate of acidification in Hill's mixture in light varied from an equivalent of 50 mm.^{3} O_2 to that of 2500 mm.^{3} O_2 per mg. chlorophyll per hr. The highest yields were obtained with material from millet, flax, Swiss chard, spinach, lettuce and lamb's quarters (*cf.* table 35.X). Chloroplast preparations from *Chlorella* (obtained by grinding chilled cells in a tissue homogenizer) gave initial rates of 200–500 mm.^{3}/hr., but the reaction stopped after about 5 minutes (compare the results of Punnett *et al.* below).

About 70 of the investigated crude suspensions produced acid *in the dark* in the presence of Hill's solution—in some cases (spruce, pine, arbor vitae), as much as an equivalent of 5000 mm.^{3} O_2/hr.! Millet, spinach and flax chloroplasts (as well as those of *Chlorella*) showed practically no such dark reaction, chloroplasts from Swiss chard and lamb's quarters only a very weak one. (These results show that the choice of spinach leaves as the most common experimental material for studying the Hill reaction has been a lucky one.) Crude suspension from *Lycopodium* and *Sedum* exhibited an alkaline instead of an acid "drift" after mixing with a neutral Hill solution—probably caused by precipitation of calcium oxalate (Clendenning and Gorham 1950[2]).

It was mentioned above that the inactivity of some chloroplast preparations was ascribed by Kumm and French to the presence of tannins forming colored complexes with iron. Clendenning and Gorham, too, observed a purplish brown coloration upon addition of Hill's mixture to some inactive chloroplasts, but the same change was noted also with some of the active preparations; furthermore, chloroplasts which were inactive with Hill's solution, were inactive also with quinone. By adding boiled cell sap from "inactive" species (*e. g.*, bean) to active chloroplast suspensions (*e. g.*, those from millet), it could be shown that this sap contained a heat-stable "inhibitor" of the Hill reaction.

With New Zealand spinach, chloroplasts from mature leaves were more active (with ferric oxalate as well as with quinone) than those from young leaves. This applied not only to crude suspensions, but also to chloroplasts separated by high-speed centrifugation from cells fluids and plasma. The activity decreased again in senescent leaves. The deficiency of certain minerals (N, Fe), which produced chlorotic leaves, caused the photochemical activity of the chloroplast preparations (related to unit chlorophyll weight) to decline by as much as 50%. Incipient wilting of wheat leaves increased the chloroplast activity by up to 40%; progressive wilting depressed it.

Leaves (of wheat or spinach) collected at various times of the day did not show the wide variations in activity previously described by Hill and Scarisbrick (1940) for chloroplasts from *Stellaria media*; checks with the latter plant also showed no strong variations.

Keeping leaves of New Zealand spinach in the dark for 48 hrs. did not affect significantly the activity of their chloroplasts—contrary to the observations of Kumm and French with *Tradescantia*; with the latter plant, too, Clendenning and Gorham could obtain no confirmation of Kumm and French's observations. Spinach showed complete loss of activity (with Hill solutions as oxidant) after only 6 hrs. in darkness; with quinone as oxidant the activity declined to $\frac{1}{4}$ of the original one after 4 days in darkness, but remained constant afterwards. No marked recovery followed upon renewed illumination for 6 hrs. These experiments do not support the hypothesis of Kumm and French that the Hill reaction involves a photosynthetic product, which slowly accumulates in light and disappears in darkness.

Punnett and Fabiyi (1953) and Hill, Northcote and Davenport (1953) described methods for the preparation of photochemically active chloroplast preparations from unicellular algae. Punnett and Fabiyi stirred the cells with alumina powder into a paste and squeezed it through a fine opening in a steel cylinder under high pressure, took up the product in 0.03 M phosphate buffer (pH 6.7) containing 0.3 M sucrose, and threw alumina and whole cells down by centrifugation. The suspensions of the chloroplast fragments obtained in this way produced oxygen in light, with ferricyanide as oxidant, at the same rate as chloroplast preparations from *Phytolacca americana*; the rate remained constant for at least 15 min. Such active suspensions were made successfully from *Chlorella* (*pyrenoidosa* or *vulgaris*) and *Bracteococcus*, but not from *Scenedesmus obliquus*, which did not break in the pressure cylinder. The blue-green *Anabaena variabilis* disintegrated easily, but neither the crude macerate (containing phycocyanin in solution) nor the precipitated and resuspended fragments gave Hill reaction in light.

Hill and co-workers (1953) obtained similar algal chloroplast preparations with the Mickle cell disintegrator. They noted that the green juice which remained after the precipitation of cell walls from disintegrated *Chlorella* had the capacity for indirect photochemical reduction of methemoglobin, indicative of the presence of an intermediate hydrogen acceptor first discovered in leaves (*cf.* below, section 4(*f*)). The same cytochromes Hill *et al.* had found in leaf plastids (*cf.* chapter 37A) appeared also in *Chlorella* chloroplasts.

The initial photochemical activity of Hill's suspensions of *Chlorella* chloroplasts was about one-half of that of a similar suspension from pea leaves; one-half of it was lost after 15 min. (at 15° C.).

Smith, French and Koski (1952) observed spectrophotometrically the development of photochemical activity of washed chloroplast suspensions during the greening of etiolated barley seedlings, and found that it increased proportionally with the chlorophyll content as the latter grew from 0.2 to 20 relative units. (The significance of this finding depends on whether the reaction was measured in limiting or saturating light; probably the second alternative prevailed and, if so, the result means that the content of the rate limiting enzyme remained, during the greening, proportional to the amount of chlorophyll.)

3. Preparation, Preservation and Activation of Chloroplast Material

(a) *Preparation of Chloroplast Suspensions*

The rapid loss of photochemical activity of chloroplast preparations has been noticed already by Hill and Scarisbrick (1940). This loss occurs not only during illumination but also in dark storage, even at 0° C. [*cf.* section (*c*)]. To obtain preparations of highest efficiency it is therefore important to work fast and at as low a temperature as possible.

It was described above that macerating at liquid air temperatures produced, in Fager's experiments, chloroplast preparations capable of fixing small amounts of C^*O_2 in light, but incapable of reducing quinone.

The usual way of preparing chloroplast suspensions is to grind leaves, with or without added liquid (such as an isotonic or hypertonic sugar solution and a buffer to maintain the desired pH) in a Waring Blendor, tissue homogenizer, or another macerator, under cooling (*e. g.*, by mixing the leaves with crushed ice). The cell wall debris, salt crystals and other coarse particles can be removed by filtration through cloth, and slow centrifuging, *e. g.*, at about 1000 g. The crude product obtained in this way can be used directly (Clendenning and Gorham's "crude suspensions"), or it can be freed from cell sap and soluble plasma proteins by faster and longer centrifuging (*e. g.*, 5 min. at 20,000 g.; or 30 min. at 2000 g.), precipitating whole and fragmented chloroplasts (Clendenning and Gorham's "separated chloroplasts") and leaving a yellow or yellow-green supernatant. All these operations should be carried out in the cold. The chloroplast material can be disintegrated still further, giving colloidal dispersions of various average particle size. For example, Warburg and Lüttgens (1946) obtained relatively uniform dispersions by grinding the mixture of whole and broken chloroplasts by means of a glass ball in a test tube. This product was thrice precipitated in the centrifuge at 2200 g., and reground in the test tube after each precipitation: its analysis showed 9% chlorophyll, 3% ash (1 mole P, 0.18 mole Fe, 0.02 mole Mn, 0.01 mole Zn per mole chlorophyll). Holt and French (1946) used ultrasonic waves to disintegrate spinach chloroplasts, while French and co-workers (1950) pressed chloroplast suspensions through a needle valve under high pressure. In view of the granular structure of leaf chloroplasts (cf. chapter 14 and 37A) suspensions containing relatively small chloroplast fragments have been sometimes described as "grana preparations" (Warburg and Lüttgens 1944, 1946; Aronoff 1946). There is, however, no positive evidence that these preparations consisted of pure grana, without admixture of the "stroma."

Furthermore, we now know (chapter 37A) that many chloroplasts, particularly in algae, contain no grana, but lamellae, running through their whole bodies.

According to Arnon, and Punnett (section 1), whole chloroplasts differ from fragments in affinity for certain oxidants, pH maximum, and other photochemical characteristics.

In dealing with unicellular algae (instead of leaves) short-cuts can be used. For example, disintegration and dispersion of unicellular algae can be carried out in one operation by pressing an algal suspension through a needle valve. Arnold and Oppenheimer (1950) found that certain blue-green algae (*Chroococcus*) can be disintegrated simply by squeezing their suspensions between the cylinder and the barrel of a hypodermic syringe. Some red algae disintegrate spontaneously when placed in distilled water. Punnett and Fabiyi's (1953) method of smashing *Chlorella* and other unicellular algae was mentioned in the preceding section.

French (1950) pointed out that any procedure adopted for the preparation of chloroplast suspensions, by necessity, must be a compromise between the desire to obtain a material of high activity, and the requirement of purity and uniformity. He recommended disintegrating 100 g. of leaves in 150 cc. water in a Waring Blendor for 0.5–1 min., filtering through cloth, and centrifuging 15 min. at 0° C. at 12,000 g. This throws down a white layer of starch and cell nuclei, and above it a green layer of chloroplastic material. The supernatant is brownish and contains very little chlorophyll. The green precipitate can be removed by a spatula and resuspended.

In section (*b*) we will describe stabilization of photochemical activity of chloroplasts by the addition of methanol. To minimize losses of activity during preparations, it has been suggested that leaf grinding and dispersion be carried out, from the beginning, in 15% methanol.

(b) Loss of Activity. Stabilization

Most troublesome in the quantitative study of the Hill reaction is the rapid deterioration of the active material in storage and in use.

The rate of deterioration depends on the nature of the preparation, and the results may vary with the type of oxidant used to measure it. Crude suspensions usually deteriorate faster than separated chloroplasts (Arnon and Whatley 1949), probably due to interaction with the constituents of the plasma or cell sap. On the other hand, fine dispersions of separated chloroplasts often prove less stable than preparation containing whole chloroplasts or large chloroplast fragments—perhaps because of increased contact with the medium. The same reason may explain why *shaking* of chloroplast preparations has been found to accelerate the loss of activity. This was reported by Hill and Scarisbrick (1940) and confirmed by Arnon and Whatley (1949), who found that chard chloroplasts, if shaken, in the absence of oxidants, at 15° C. (in an atmosphere of not especially purified nitrogen) lose as much as 50% of their activity in 20 min. Not unrelated may be the observation of Holt, Smith and French (1951) that activity is lost faster in dilute than in dense chloroplast suspensions.

The rate of "dark" deactivation is, as expected, a function of temperature. Thus, Warburg and Lüttgens (1946) found that heating for 10 min. to 40° C. reduced the rate of oxygen production by chloroplasts (with quinone as oxidant) by 50% and that heating for 10 min. to 50° C. brought it to a standstill. Chlorophyll appeared unchanged, and no coagulation of the grana was noticeable after heating. According to French, Anson and Holt (unpublished) deactivation is accompanied by a loss of fluorescence; however, the decay of fluorescence intensity is much slower than the loss of photochemical activity, *e. g.*, 30% loss after 15 min. at 35° C., at which time photochemical activity has declined by 80% (compare the results of Zubkovich *et al.* below).

The results of French, Anson and Holt indicated average temperature coefficient $Q_{10} = 6.4$—a very high value, which points to the denaturation of a protein as mechanism of deactivation. French and Holt (1946) had found a smaller temperature coefficient of deactivation—about 3.9 (3–15° C.).

Arnon and Whatley (1949) found that heating of chloroplasts to 55° for 5 min. inactivated them completely, and pointed out that the thermolability of the "Hill enzyme" appears much greater than that of the polyphenol oxidase, whose activity in chloroplasts also was studied by Arnon (*cf.* section 5(c) below, and chapter 37A); the latter activity remained unchanged, after 5 min., even at 75° C.

Although cooling of chloroplast suspensions slows down the deterioration, Milner, French *et al.* (1950) found freezing (of whole or dispersed chloroplasts) to reduce their activity; they also noted that frozen suspensions were difficult to resuspend. "Lyophilized" material (*i. e.*, material dried and preserved in vacuum in the cold) retained 90% of the original chloroplast activity after 48 hrs. (French, Holt, Powell and Anson, 1946). Dry powder, obtained from lyophilized leaves, and stored for a week, lost 20% of its activity at 5° C., and 60% at 25° C. Clendenning and Gorham

(1950[3]) reported that snap-freezing in dry ice in the presence of a molar sucrose solution and rapid thawing at room temperature led to preservation of the activity both in crude leaf macerates and in separated chloroplast suspensions. The chloroplasts treated in this way showed no decline in activity after storage at $-40°$ C. for 14 days; but at $-12°$ C. only 10% of the original activity was preserved after the same period. According to French and Milner (1951), lyophylized material resists attempts to disperse it into fine particles and is therefore unsuitable for the preparation of colloidal chloroplast dispersions.

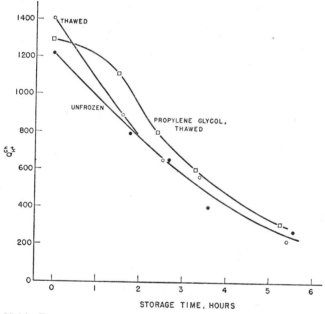

Fig. 35.8A. Deterioration of chloroplast material at $10°$ C. (Gorham and Clendenning 1950). 0.5 mg. Chl per vessel. (●) Fresh crude suspension in 0.5 M sucrose; (O) crude suspension, frozen and thawed, in 0.5 M sucrose; (□) same + 10% propylene glycol.

Gorham and Clendenning (1950) reported that chloroplasts stored for one year in 0.5 M sucrose at $-40°$ C. showed, upon thawing, the same activity (within 5%) as fresh preparations. Washed chloroplasts were preserved less well than nonwashed ones. Preservation was equally good with material from spinach, millet, flax, Swiss chard and other species; it was tested with Hill's mixture, ferricyanide, quinone and chromate. Preservation by vacuum drying ("lyophylizing") was less effective. Deterioration occurred mainly in the early stages of drying; once dry, the material could be stored at 5° C. (or lower temperature) without further loss of activity. It was noted that while snap freezing of fresh material at very low temperature (−75° C.) did not damage it, preparations which were first stored at −40° C. for a while lost some of their activity if they were cooled down to −75° C. before thawing. Figure 35.8A shows the loss of photochemical activity, at 10° C., of fresh and of snap frozen chloroplasts; propylene glycol is shown to slow down the deterioration in the first 1–2 hours after thawing.

Vereshchinsky (1951) described preservation of chloroplasts by snap freezing of a suspension in phosphate buffer (pH 6.5) at −183° C. Suspension drops were allowed to fall into liquid air (not liquid nitrogen, to avoid submerging).

Table 35.VII summarizes various observations on the deterioration of chloroplast preparations.

TABLE 35.VII

DETERIORATION OF CHLOROPLAST PREPARATIONS

Observer	Preparation	Oxidant	Temp., ° C.	Loss of efficiency in darkness
French, Anson and Holt (unpublished)	Chloroplast suspension from *Spinacia oleracea*	Fe(III) oxalate + ferricyanide	20 25 30 35	33% in 78 min. 33% in 26 min. 33% in 15 min. 33% in 4.5 min.
Warburg and Lüttgens (1946)	"Grana" (cf. section a) from spinach + 0.1 vol. 0.2 M phosphate + 0.1 vol. 0.5% KCl	Quinone	5	15% in 24 hrs.
Aronoff (1946)	"Grana" (cf. section a) (0.1 μ particles)	Quinone	2–3	50% in 11 hrs.[a]
Arnon and Whatley (1949)	Chloroplast fragments in phosphate buffer	Quinone	2	14% in 5 hrs.
Milner, French, Koenig, and Lawrence (1950)	Crude chloroplast preparation in water	Quinone	35 20 0	50% in "a few minutes" 50% in "a few hours" 50% in 24–36 hrs.

[a] Extrapolation indicates 25% loss during preparation.

Milner, French *et al.* (1950) found no difference in stability between chloroplast preparations stored in *air* or in *oxygen-free* atmosphere— indicating that deactivation was not the result of autoxidation. *Phosphate buffering* (pH 6.5) merely made the decay faster; however, Warburg and Lüttgens (1946) and Arnon and Whatley (1949) reported a faster deterioration in water, as compared to phosphate buffer. Holt, Smith and French (1951) found that in 0.02 M sodium sorbitol borate buffers of different pH, the photochemical activity of spinach chloroplasts (measured colorimetrically with phenol indophenol) was best preserved at pH 6.5 ($>90\%$ activity preserved after 2 hrs. at 0° C., about 25% after 10 min. at 35° C.). At pH 5.0 or 7.5 the losses were greater ($>35\%$ after 2 hrs. at 0° C. and $>80\%$ after 10 min. at 35° C.).

Kumm and French (1946) found that when leaves were preilluminated for several hours before maceration they not only showed a higher photochemical efficiency (as described in section 2 above), but also kept better in storage. However, Clendenning and Gorham (1950[3]) noticed no such stabilizing effect in experiments with chloroplasts from Swiss chard.

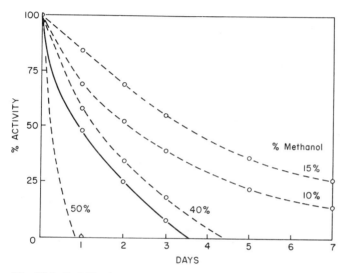

Fig. 35.9. Stabilization of chloroplast activity by methanol (after Milner, French, Koenig and Lawrence 1950).

Zubkovich and Andreeva (1949) looked for any parallelism between the decay of photochemical activity and changes in the absorption spectrum of chloroplasts, their fluorescence, the concentration of chlorophyll, and its association with proteins. As the activity of sugar beet chloroplasts decreased with time (e. g., from 43 mm.[3] O_2 per hour per milliliter of suspension to 9 mm.[3] after 2 days at 2–3° C.; or to 6 mm.[3] after 2 hours at 30° C.), the total chlorophyll content was found unchanged (0.49 mg. per cm.[3]); but the part of it extractable by 60% acetone (which is a measure of the chlorophyll attachment to protein), declined from 37% to 25 and 29%, respectively. The shape of the red absorption band was unchanged, and the suspension still fluoresced. With material from *Phaseolus vulgaris*, no change was noted also in the percentage of chlorophyll extractable with aqueous acetone, even after the photochemical activity had dropped, after storage, to 50 or 20% of the initial value.   The results show that the loss of activity must be due to the deterioration of enzymatic components and not to changes in the chlorophyll-protein complex.

Some success has been achieved with *chemical* stabilization.   Milner, French *et al.* (1950) noted a preserving effect of *sucrose* and of ethylene glycol, Holt, Smith and French (1950) studied the effect of various concentrations of *propylene glycol* at 0° C. and pH 6.5.   The best results were obtained with a 10% solution;   the activity loss in this medium was about

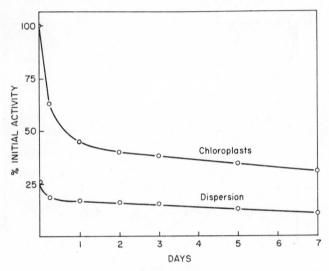

Fig. 35.10. Inactivation of chloroplast fragments and of their colloidal dispersions (after Milner, French, Koenig and Lawrence 1950).

one half of that without propylene glycol.   Diethylene glycol, *n*-propyl alcohol, isopropyl alcohol, glycerol (10%) and ethanol (10–50%) had only a weak effect, or no effect at all.   Strychnine, which stimulates the dye reduction by chloroplasts (Table 35.XI), had no preserving effect.

According to Arnon *et al.* (1954), whole chloroplasts prepared in ethylene glycol show no C^*O_2 fixation in light (in contrast to those prepared in 0.5 M glucose or 0.35 M NaCl).

A much stronger stabilizing effect than that of propylene glycol is produced by *methanol* (fig. 35.9).   This was noted by Milner, French *et al.* (1950) when studying fractional coagulation of colloidal chloroplast dispersions.   They observed that not only did these sols withstand considerable methanol concentrations without coagulating, but their photochemical efficiency was stabilized.

Colloidal chloroplast dispersions containing 15% methanol can be stored at $-5°$ C. without freezing; they then retain 50% of their initial activity after 10 days. Ethanol in equimolecular quantities had the same stabilizing effect at 5° C.; but a lesser one at higher temperatures.

The more concentrated dispersions kept better in 15% methanol than the dilute ones. The loss of activity is fastest in preparations the absolute efficiency of which is high (fig. 35.10); in line with this, the effect of methanol is much stronger in colloidal chloroplast dispersions than in crude suspensions of chloroplast fragments.

The most effective stabilization was achieved by macerating the leaves in 15% methanol, maintaining this composition of the medium in all subsequent operations, and keeping the temperature down to $-5°$. Hydrosols obtained in this way retained up to 50% of the activity of crude suspensions—a much smaller loss than is commonly suffered by dispersion in the absence of methanol.

A new, promising approach has been opened by McClendon (1944) and McClendon and Blinks (1952) with the finding that chloroplasts of red algae can be prevented from losing the phycobilins, and their Hill activity preserved, by preparing them in high-molecular solutions, e. g., containing 0.4–0.8 g./ml. of Carbowax 4000 (or 8000).

The deterioration of chloroplast material is accelerated by illumination, particularly in the absence of oxidants (Aronoff 1946[2]; Milner, French et al. 1950; Arnon and Whatley 1949[1,2]). To what extent photochemical deactivation is prevented when appropriate oxidants (such as ferricyanide or quinone) are present, so that the Hill reaction can take place, is not clear. A protective effect of a sensitization substrate on the sensitizer is a well-known phenomenon (cf. Vol. I, chapter 19). Warburg and Lüttgens (1946) noted it with chloroplasts and quinone, but Holt, Smith and French (1950) reported that the several chloroplast fractions obtained by fractional centrifugation of a colloidal suspension of chloroplastic matter, lost their photocatalytic capacity in light, in presence as well as in the absence of the ferric oxalate-ferricyanide mixture.

Spikes et al. (1950) gave a curve for the inactivation of spinach chloroplasts for the photoreduction of ferricyanide by prolonged illumination.

(c) Activation by Anions

Warburg and Lüttgens (1944[2]) first noted that after the capacity of spinach or beet chloroplast suspensions to evolve oxygen with quinone has been lost by dialysis, it could be restored by potassium chloride. They referred to the chloride ion as a "co-enzyme" of the Hill reaction, and found it to play a similar role also when ferric salts were used as oxidants instead of quinone. However, this stimulation is not specific for chloride. Warburg and Lüttgens (1946) themselves found that bromides had a similar, if slightly weaker, effect; iodide and nitrate had a small effect, while fluoride, rhodanide, sulfate and phosphate were without influence.

Arnon and Whatley (1949[1]) noted that the importance of chloride depended on the nature of the oxidant used. For example, the total oxygen yield obtainable from a certain quantity of quinone was reduced from 100% of the stoichiometric equivalent in the presence of 0.01 M KCl, to 36% without KCl; with ferricyanide, the reduction was from 100 to 19%; but

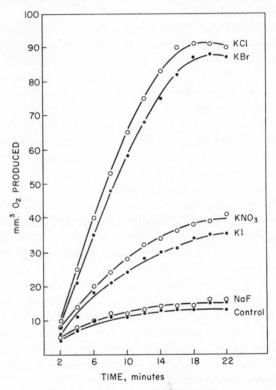

Fig. 35.11. Activation of Hill reaction in chloroplast preparations from chloride-free cells by salts (after Arnon and Whatley 1949[2]).

with phenol indophenol, the change was only from 100 to 90%. However, chloride proved equally important for obtaining a high initial rate of the reduction of all three oxidants.

Arnon and Whatley (1949[2]) pointed out that Cl^- is not a necessary plant nutrient; it is therefore unlikely that it is a natural component of the photosynthetic apparatus (as suggested by Warburg and Lüttgens). They grew sugar beet and Swiss chard in chloride-free nutrient solutions.

The plants grew well (and, implicitly, photosynthesized normally), but
the chloroplasts obtained by the disintegration of their leaves (which, as
expected, had no measureable Cl⁻ content) evolved only very little oxygen
upon illumination in the presence of quinone. Addition of protoplasmic
fluid from the same plants (which, too, was chloride-free) did not activate
them for the Hill reaction, but addition of potassium chloride brought it
under way. *Bromide* had the same effect, while effects of KNO_3 and KI
were much weaker, and NaF had no effect at all (fig. 35.11). Sulfate,
phosphate, thiocyanate and acetate also were without influence. The concentration of chloride required to fully activate chloride-free chloroplasts

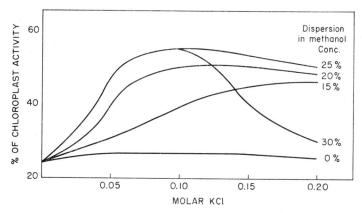

Fig. 35.12. Effect of chloride on photochemical activity of chloroplast dispersions
(after Milner, Koenig and Lawrence 1950).

was about 7×10^{-3} mole/liter—an amount which could not have been
left undiscovered in Cl⁻-starved plants, or lost in chloroplasts extraction.
Arnon concluded that chloride is not a natural component of the photosynthetic apparatus, but is required to prevent photochemical deactivation
of separated chloroplasts. The (almost) irreversible inactivation of chloroplasts caused by preillumination of chloride-free chloroplast suspension
in the absence of an oxidant could in fact be prevented by the addition of
chloride. The chloride exercised a certain protective effect also on the
deterioration of chloroplasts in the dark (see Warburg and Lüttgens
(1946); French and Milner (1951) were unable to stabilize disintegrated
chloroplasts by the addition of phosphate buffer and KCl, as recommended
by Warburg). Holt, Smith and French (1950) found that the deactivation
of chloroplast dispersions in light (which, in their experiments, occurred
in presence as well as in the absence of an oxidant) could not be reversed by
chloride.

Milner, Koenig and Lawrence (1950) investigated the effect of added salts on colloidal chloroplast dispersions; they found that *in the presence of methanol,* addition of certain salts markedly increased the photochemical efficiency of the material, but that no such activation was noticeable in the absence of methanol. Figure 35.12 shows that in water, quantities of KCl up to 0.2 mole/liter had no effect. (If [KCl] was >0.2 mole/liter, *deactivation* resulted; precipitation followed at about 1 mole/liter.) When

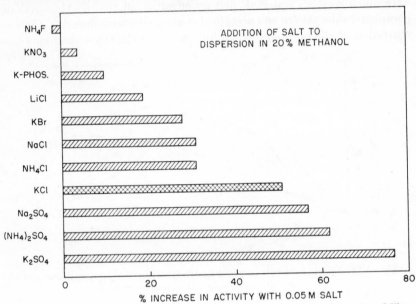

Fig. 35.13. Activation of chloroplast suspensions by different salts (after Milner, Koenig and Lawrence 1950).

25% methanol was present, addition of 0.1 M KCl doubled the photochemical efficiency. However, it must be taken into account that the chloroplast dispersion used had been only ¼ as active as the suspension from which it was prepared; thus, KCl merely restored a part of activity lost by dispersion. Reactivation was accompanied by turbidity; afterwards, the active material could be separated by mild centrifugation. In other words, activation was associated with visible coagulation of particles. The activation effect was strongest in the most concentrated dispersions. It was not permanent: after 24 hrs. the activity was back to the level it had before the addition of KCl. The loss of activation was even faster when NH₄Cl had been used instead of KCl. Phosphate buffer (0.01 M) produced a passing activation similar to that caused by other salts.

Fig. 35.13 shows that, according to Milner, Koenig *et al.* chloride is not the best "reactivator" of chloroplast dispersions; it is exceeded by sulfates (found inactive by Warburg and Lüttgens, and Arnon and Whatley). However, the activating effect of $(NH_4)_2SO_4$, for example, was extremely short-lived, and was soon replaced by inactivation.

Milner, French *et al.* also investigated the effect of some *cations*, with and without addition of "versene" (ethylene diamine tetra-acetic acid, a chelating agent). In these experiments, versene, which is an acid, was neutralized by KOH to pH 6.5. The potassium salt of versene alone had a marked reactivating effect—probably similar to that of other potassium salts. Addition of versene to a divalent salt solution, which in itself had an activating effect, produced no important changes; but its addition to a 5×10^{-4} M $CuSO_4$ solution (which, by itself, was strongly poisonous) leads to effective reactivation. (No reactivation was possible in 3×10^{-3} M $CuSO_4$.) Versene also reactivated dispersions inactivated by $HgCl_2$. Ferrous sulfate had no activating effect.

Gerretsen (1950[1]) described a strong enhancing effect of Mn^{++} ions on the change of redox potential, which occurs in crude chloroplast suspensions from *Avena* upon exposure to light (without added oxidants) under aerobic conditions. He suggested an interpretation in terms of manganous ions playing a role in the enzymatic mechanism of the liberation of oxygen.

Clendenning and Gorham (1950[1]) found that the initial rate of the Hill reaction with quinone was two or three times higher with crude suspensions than with separated chloroplasts, and that repeated washing reduced it still further; only about $\frac{1}{3}$ of the loss caused by washing could be restored by the addition of potassium chloride.

Gorham and Clendenning (1952) investigated the effect of anions on chloroplast activity in more detail, and arrived at conclusions which differed from those of both Warburg and Arnon. They grew spinach, Swiss chard, beet and millet in ordinary soil, and in chloride-containing and chloride-free nutrient solutions. Chloroplasts prepared from these plants were analyzed for chloride content, and their photochemical activity studied with various oxidants. The activity of crude suspensions was about the same in the three kinds of plants. Separation from cell sap and cytoplasm affected strongly the activity of preparations from plants grown in nutrient solutions—either with or without chloride—but material from soil grown plants could be washed extensively without inactivation. The activity lost by washing could be restored by anions, the order of effectiveness being $Cl^- > Br^- > CN^- >$ Hoagland's salt mixture (nitrate + sulfate + phosphate) $> NO_3^- > I^- > F^- > ClO_3^- > BrO_3^- > IO_3^- > SO_4^{--}$ (no effect). Ascorbate and thiocyanate caused inhibition. Maximum restoration could be achieved with $[Cl^-] \geq 3.3 \times 10^{-3}$ mole/l. Pre-illumination experiments did not confirm Arnon's hypothesis that chloride protects chloroplasts from light injury, since to restore the photochemical activity of chloride-free chloroplasts it proved enough to add chloride *after* the preillumination. The chloride thus acts directly on the photochemical reaction. Its effect was found to be proportionately the same at all light intensities. The pH optimum of the Hill reaction was found to shift in the presence of chloride to higher values (from pH 6.5 to 7.1 with Hill's mixture and 7.5 with quinone) (fig. 35.22E). Gorham and Clendenning emphasized the similarity of the anion effect on the Hill reaction with the effects observed in other enzymatic reactions, such as starch hydrolysis by dialyzed amylase or respiration of washed root discs, and suggested that the same explanation should apply to all of them.

The fact that chloride stimulation of chloroplast activity occurs only at $pH > 6$ (fig. 35.22E) may explain why no chloride influence could be found in the Hill reaction (as well as in photosynthesis) of whole *Chlorella* cells (*cf.* part C below).

To sum up, the nature of the salt effect on the Hill reaction is not yet clear; perhaps, at least in part, this effect is due to coagulation of smaller colloidal particles into larger ones which are more active photochemically (*cf.* next section) and less subject to deactivation (*cf.* section (*b*)).

(d) Fractionation of Chloroplast Material

Since the Hill reaction permits an important part of the photosynthetic apparatus to be separated from the living cell, biochemists would like to do with this part what they did so successfully with many other enzymatic systems—fractionate it by methods of protein chemistry and concentrate the photocatalytic principle in a small fraction; or, if the catalytic system is complex, separate it into its components. So far, this undertaking has not been successful. Several difficulties are responsible for the lack of progress.

In the first place, the chloroplast-protein material is not water-soluble. In other words, it does not fall apart, in contact with water, into more or less uniform building stones of macromolecular size. By mechanical fragmentation, chloroplastic matter can be converted into a water-born suspension; and the fragments can be disintegrated still further by one of the methods mentioned in section 3(*a*). Sols with colloidal particles of more or less uniform size can then be obtained by fractional centrifugation. However, there is no reason why such particles should consist of chemical or functional units; it is not even certain that they are identical in composition and structure (and not merely in size).

This difficulty is common to all work with water-insoluble proteins. The chloroplastic matter, in addition to containing insoluble proteins also includes a large amount—of the order of one third of the total—of lipoidic materials, including carotenoids and phospholipides (*cf.* Vol. I, chapter 14). It is likely—although it cannot be proved at present—that at least some of these materials are essential and that any fractionation which leaves them behind will lead to a loss of photocatalytic activity. The Hill reaction, although it must be simpler than complete photosynthesis, still is a complex process, partly photochemical and partly enzymatic. Its occurrence may be bound to the preservation of a definite pattern of pigments, prosthetic groups of one or several enzymes, proteins and lipoids.

The "photocatalytic activity" of chloroplastic material usually is defined as the (initial) rate of the Hill reaction with a given oxidant, related *to unit amount of chlorophyll*. This activity can only be increased if: (*a*) the activity of the preparation as measured before fractionation was limited by an enzymatic component (*i. e.*, if the measurement was made in *saturating light*, and with saturating concentration of the oxidant); and (*b*) if a fraction can be obtained in which this limiting enzyme is enriched *in relation to chlorophyll*.

If chlorophyll and the limiting enzyme are enriched together, activity tests related to unit chlorophyll content will show no change at all. It is, therefore, desirable to check the results of fractionation also by measuring the photochemical activity *per unit mass* (or per *unit amount of nitrogen*, if only protein fractionation is considered).

Following is a brief review of the chloroplast fractionation experiments.

French, Holt, Powell and Anson (1946) made a preliminary study of the effects of various treatments (freezing, lyophylizing, disintegration by supersonic waves, and centrifugation) on the photochemical activity of a chloroplast suspension. They considered the results as indicating the possibility of successful fractionation of the chloroplast material and concentration of active ingredients.

Holt, Smith and French (1950) (*cf.* Holt and French 1949) attempted fractionation by high-speed centrifugation, acid coagulation, salting-out, and adsorption and elution. They used a spinach chloroplast suspension in 10% propylene glycol; it was disintegrated by supersonic vibrations. When the resulting colloidal dispersion was fractionated by *centrifugation*, the first precipitate, obtained after 5 min. at 7600 g. and presumably composed of the largest particles, was found to contain one half of the total N present; its activity (*per unit weight of* N) was lower than the average, while that of the supernatant was twice as high. Centrifuging the supernatant for 10 min. at 8600 g. precipitated one half of the remaining nitrogen, the activity per unit N remaining the same in the precipitate and in the supernatant. The latter was centrifuged 30 min. at 3200 g., again precipitating about one half of the remaining N content. In this case, the sediment was 3.4 times more active per unit N weight than the original material, while the supernatant was only one half as active. The highest ratio of active material to total protein was thus found in the precipitate from the third centrifugation. However, an increase of specific activity by a factor of 3 or 4 is disappointing compared to the results obtained in experiments with water-soluble enzymes. Fractional coagulation by acid of the same (supersonically dispersed) chloroplast material produced, in the range pH 5.3–6.0, a series of precipitates which, when resuspended at pH 6.5, exhibited no marked difference in photochemical activity. Total precipitation at pH 4.6 led to complete loss of activity. *Salting-out*, e. g., with 30–40% Na_2SO_4, also produced no marked enrichment. *Detergents*, such as dupanol and vetanol, which are of help in solubilization and fractionation of some proteins, destroyed photochemical activity. French and Milner (1951) reported that addition of 1 volume saturated $(NH_4)_2SO_4$ to 4 volumes of a dispersion of chloroplast material precipitated nearly all green material, leaving in solution some colorless proteins—not more than $1/3$ of the total protein content. The resuspended precipitate showed only a slight photochemical activity, whether related to chlorophyll or to nitrogen content. A green precipitate could also be obtained by acidification, but its activity was similarly poor. Precipitates obtained by addition of salts to methanol-stabilized dispersions are more active than the starting material, but this appears to be due to *activation* by coagulation rather than to *enrichment* (*cf.* below).

Attempts to coagulate dispersed chloroplast material with *alcohols* were unsuccessful; even in 95% ethanol, precipitation occurred only after several hours; the alcoholic solution was photochemically inactive. Similar experiments with methanol later led French and co-workers to the discovery of the stabilizing influence of methanol on chloroplastic matter, which was described in section (*c*).

Adsorption of the chloroplast dispersion on a column (Supercel) at pH 5.5 gave, according to Holt, Smith and French (1950), a green band, which could be partially eluted in neutral buffer or distilled water. However, the easily eluted fraction had the same activity as the noneluted residue. According to French and Milner (1951), fractional adsorption on Fuller's earth or charcoal leaves, as the last, unadsorbed residue (a few % of the total) a dispersion that may be 2–3 times more active than the original material. Aronoff (1946) found that when "grana" from spinach chloroplasts were precipitated at 6700 g., the remaining *supernatant*, which was clear but showed a Tyndall cone, had a remarkably high photochemical activity with quinone (about ten times that of the precipitate, related to equal chlorophyll amounts); its activity remained almost constant for about 2 hrs. at 19 klux. Dried in a lyophylizer and redissolved, the product kept its activity;

in contrast to the precipitated chloroplast, this material could be stored for weeks in the dry state, in the cold, without losing its activity. The dialysis of this supernatant into distilled water precipitated additional green material, but the solution still showed the chlorophyll band. The yellow color appeared to be due to a protein with absorption bands at 337 and 270 mμ; the yellow "prosthetic group" of this protein was not separable by dialysis. Spectrally, it appeared to be a flavone, but it did not show the orange color upon reduction, which is characteristic of flavones.

The high activity of the supernatant, obtained according to Aronoff's procedure, was not confirmed by Clendenning and Gorham (1950[1]), using Hill's solution. With quinone, they noted an increase of efficiency (related to unit chlorophyll amount) compared to the green precipitate by not more than a factor of 2.

French and his co-workers (Milner et al. 1950, and Milner 1951) macerated leaves of Beta in a water-ice mixture in a Waring Blendor. The slurry was filtered through muslin and the filtrate centrifuged 1 min. at 12,000 g., all at a temperature not above 2° C. The sediment, which consisted of whole and broken chloroplasts, was resuspended in distilled water (2 mg. Chl/cm.[3]). Attempts to disperse this suspension by means of a colloid mill were unsuccessful. Ultrasonic wave generator (250 watt) was then used, with precautions to prevent the temperature from rising >5° C. The undispersed material was reprecipitated at 12,000 g.; the green supernatant was clear, but showed a strong Tyndall cone.

In this way, 5–10% of the original chloroplast material could be converted into a colloidal dispersion. Additional 10–15% could be dispersed by grinding the sediment from the last centrifugation with sand. The dispersion was about 50% less active photochemically (per unit chlorophyll amount) than the original material.

A more complete dispersion could be obtained by forcing the chloroplast suspension through a small opening (a needle valve from an ammonia cylinder) under high pressure. 40 cc. of suspension were placed in a precooled steel cylinder connected to the valve, and pressed through the valve by a 60-ton hydraulic press. Despite cooling with ice, the material came out at about 15° C. It was diluted to 0.5 mg. Chl/cm.[3], and centrifuged at 12,000 g.; the dark-green supernatant now contained as much as 60–70% of the total chlorophyll, but its photochemical activity was only 25% of that of the original material. This loss was found to decline with the pressure used and the duration of exposure to this pressure. At low pressure, less material is dispersed, and less activity is lost (fig. 35.14). The superiority of the dispersion obtained by the valve method over that obtained by supersonics is illustrated by figure 35.15.

Dispersions which were obtained by passage through the needle valve at 2000 psi sedimented slower than those obtained by ultrasonic waves; fractional sedimentation showed that the photochemical efficiency decreased with decreasing particle size. No evidence was obtained in sedi-

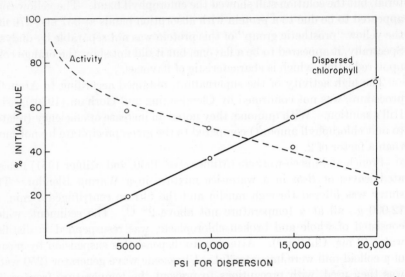

Fig. 35.14. Loss of activity (per unit chlorophyll amount) and efficiency of dispersion (percentage of chlorophyll dispersed by valving) as functions of pressure (after Milner, Lawrence and French 1950).

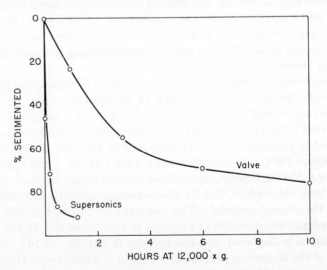

Fig. 35.15. Sedimentation of chloroplast dispersions obtained by supersonics and by the valve method (after French and Milner 1951).

mentation experiments of particles falling into discrete groups; rather the dispersion was completely heterogeneous, with random distribution of particles. About 25% sedimented in 15 min. at 20,000 g.; the rest in 10 min. at 60,000 g. About 90% had a molecular weight of 6–7 × 10^6, 10% seemed to be smaller. Under the electron microscope, most particles appeared to be <2 mμ in size; however, a number of particles 8 mμ in size were observed, and some agglomerates of the 8 mμ particles, about 25 mμ in size, also were noted. Such groups had not been noticeable in sedimentation experiments, which were, however, made with a different batch of chloroplasts.

Since the chlorophyll-bearing material of chloroplasts contains about 25% lipides, the effect of lipide-dissolving agents was studied by Milner et al. (1950). They shook a chloroplast dispersion with petroleum ether, extracting 2–3% of the total lipides. This caused the loss of up to one half of photochemical activity, which could not be restored by KCl. However, when the lipide extract was evaporated and the residue, dissolved in a little ether, returned to the depleted dispersion, the activity was restored, and the material could be still further activated by chloride. The same effect could be obtained more simply by adding a little ether to the aqueous phase after the petroleum ether extraction, and removing the ether again by evaporation in vacuum. It thus seems that the effect of petroleum ether (as well as that of salts) is associated with changes in the size and colloidal structure of the active particles rather than with the removal (or addition) of specific chemical constituents. After the larger and more active particles had been broken into smaller less active fragments, addition of salts causes them to coagulate again and thus restores activity. Petroleum ether, by removing some of the lipoid "glue," may cause the particle to fall apart into fragments. Addition and subsequent evaporation of ether may cause redistribution of the remaining lipides, bringing them from the interior to the surface, and thus cause renewed coagulation to larger units.

French and Milner (1951) mention that some detergents were found to split chloroplast particles into smaller fragments without destroying their photochemical activity, but this method has not proved useful for preparatory purposes.

All these experiments, however inconclusive, add to the impression that the photocatalytic activity of chloroplast preparations, as determined by the Hill reaction, is associated, not with one or two specific enzymatic components, but with a more or less complex structure which cannot be broken into small units without losing its activity. Perhaps this could be explained by the assumption—derived from kinetic experiments on photosynthesis and the Hill reaction in whole cells—that one of the enzymes involved in both reactions is present in a concentration of about 1 molecule per 200–2000 molecules of chlorophyll. If the particles in a chloroplast dispersion contain 0.05 g. chlorophyll in 1 g. dry weight, have a density of about 1, and contain 50% water, then one molecule chlorophyll is contained in about 7×10^{-8} μ^3, and one molecule of the limiting enzyme, in about 1.5–15×10^{-5} μ^3. In particles formed by disintegration of *grana*, the chlorophyll concentration will be higher. It was estimated as 0.2 mole/liter (or more) by Rabinowitch (1952); this corresponds to an average volume of 1×10^{-8} μ^3 (or less) per molecule of chlorophyll, or between 2 and $20 \times 10^{-6}\mu^3$ (or less) per molecule of the postulated limiting enzyme. Consequently, when particles in a grana dispersion become smaller than 10^{-6} μ^3 in volume, or $<0.01\mu$ (10 mμ) in linear dimensions, an increasing number of them will contain not even a single molecule of the limiting enzyme, and will thus be unable to contribute to the reaction at all. We have seen above that according to French, many of the particles in his dispersion appeared to be <2 mμ under the electron microscope!

The fact that chloroplast dispersions usually show a Tyndall cone in visible light merely indicates that the linear dimensions of some of the particles are >100 mμ; there may be enough smaller particles present to account for the drop in activity.

Thomas, Blaauw and Duysens (1953) made a direct comparison of particle size and photochemical activity of spinach chloroplasts, disintegrated by a magnetostriction oscillator. In air the disintegration led to the loss of about 50% of photochemical activity in 30 seconds, but in nitrogen the decrease in activity was only 5% after a whole minute of supersonic treatment. The active suspension, obtained in this way, was subjected to fractional centrifugation to obtain fractions of approximately uniform size. The distribution of particle sizes in each sample was observed under the electron microscope, and found to possess a sharp peak. Size measurements became unreliable below 3 mμ (limit of the resolving power of the electron microscope used), and above 15 mμ (where fractional centrifugation lost its effectiveness). Figure 35.15A shows photochemical activity (*i. e.*, rate of Hill reaction in the light-limited state, with quinone as oxidant) as function of (mean) particle volume. Characteristic is the sudden decline in activity of particles when their average volume declines below 1.5×10^{-7} μ^3. Thomas and co-workers estimated that the particles became inactive when they contained less than between 40 and 120 chlorophyll molecules (rather than between 200 and 2000 molecules, as predicted above).

The decline in activity with diminishing size is less sharp in saturating light [210 kerg/(cm.^{2} sec.)] than in limiting light. This is to be expected if particles below the "critical size" are not uniformly inactive but merely possessed of a statistical probability of being inactive, because some of them contain no enzyme; while the over-all ratio chlorophyll:enzyme (and thus, in theory, also the limiting rate in strong light) remain unchanged.

These results are suggestive, but will not be quantitatively convincing until more is known about the nature and composition of chloroplast fragments of different size. Are they pieces of protein lamellae with chlorophyll attached to them? Are they irregular chunks of grana, containing pieces of both proteidic and lipoidic phases? Do they contain any of the proteins (or lipoproteids) of the stroma? Even the average chlorophyll content of the chloroplast material is uncertain unless it has been determined in an aliquot of the same sample as that used for photochemical studies. The uncertainty becomes as great as a factor of ten when we deal with chloroplast fragments selected by fractional centrifugation, or another

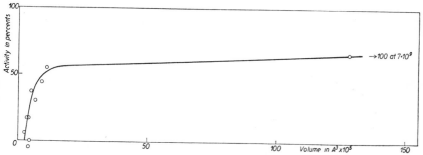

Fig. 35.15A. Oxygen evolution by suspension of chloroplast fragments as function of their average size, in the presence of quinone (after Thomas, Blaauw and Duysens 1953).

fractionation method. Particularly uncertain—and challenging—is the situation in the case of the chloroplast-free, phycocyanine-bearing blue-green algae, and of the chloroplast-containing, phycoerythrin-bearing red algae. What happens in the fragmentation of the chromoproteids? It seems that they are almost completely separated from the chlorophyll-bearing, insoluble fragments (*cf.* chapter 37A, section 3); the resulting suspension shows no Hill reaction (Van Norman *et al.*, 1948). McClendon and Blinks (1952) showed that the loss of phycobilins can be prevented by crushing the cells in a medium containing high-molecular compounds, such as Carbowaxes (*cf.* p. 1549); the material then shows well-sustained Hill activity (McClendon, 1954).

The results obtained by electron microscopy and ultracentrifugation of dispersed chloroplast material from the higher plants, blue-green algae, and purple bacteria will be presented in chapter 37A. We will see there that the morphological picture is as yet far from clear, particularly in respect to the submicroscopic localization of the various pigments. The correlation between the structure and the photochemical activity of the various dispersions is a matter for future exploration.

4. Different Oxidants

(a) Ferric Salts

It will be recalled that Hill first obtained sustained photochemical oxygen production from chloroplast preparations by adding cell extracts of indefinite composition, and later by adding complex ferric salts, such as *ferric oxalate*. Simple ferric salts, such as nitrate or perchlorate, are unsuitable because of their hydrolysis in the approximately neutral solution (needed for these experiments). Potassium *ferricyanide* was added by Hill to ferric oxalate in the assumption—based on his own observations—that $Fe(CN)_6^{-3}$ ions will not take direct part in the photochemical reaction, but will oxidize (in successful competition with oxygen) the ferrous oxalate, produced by the reaction, back to ferric oxalate, thus enabling the photochemical reaction to proceed until all ferricyanide is exhausted [since ferrocyanide ions—in contrast to ferrous ions—are not rapidly reoxidized to the Fe(III) level by molecular oxygen]:

$$(35.29a) \quad 2\ Fe^{+3}\ \text{oxalate} + H_2O \xrightleftharpoons[\text{dark}]{\text{light, chloroplasts}} 2\ Fe^{+2}\ \text{oxalate} + 2\ H^+ + \tfrac{1}{2}\ O_2$$

$$(35.29b) \quad 2\ Fe^{+2}\ \text{oxalate} + 2\ Fe(CN)_6^{-3} \xrightarrow{\text{dark}} 2\ Fe(CN)_6^{-4} + 2\ Fe^{+3}\ \text{oxalate}$$

$$(35.29) \qquad 2\ Fe(CN)_6^{-3} + H_2O \longrightarrow 2\ Fe(CN)_6^{-4} + \tfrac{1}{2}\ O_2 + 2\ H^+$$

Holt and French (1946), on the other hand, found that ferricyanide can take part in the Hill reaction also directly, without the addition of ferric oxalate. Figure 35.16 shows oxygen liberation curves recorded by them with the complete Hill solution, and with the same solution minus some of its constituents: (1) Hill's complete solution: 0.02 M $K_3Fe(CN)_6$, 0.01 M $FeNH_4(SO_4)_2$, 0.50 M $K_2C_2O_4$, 0.02 M sucrose, 0.17 M sodium sorbitol borate or 0.2 M phosphate, (2) same, minus $FeNH_4(SO_4)_2$; (3) same, minus $K_2C_2O_4$; and (4) same, minus both $FeNH_4(SO_4)_2$ and $K_2C_2O_4$.

The figure indicates that steady liberation of oxygen at about half the maximum rate observed with the complete Hill mixture can be obtained with ferricyanide alone. The rate maximum at pH 7–8 was there even when $FeNH_4(SO_4)_2$ was left out, indicating that it was not due to complexing of Fe^{+3} ions with OH^- ions (or some other initial step of hydrolysis).

Hill and Scarisbrick had worked with chloroplasts from *Stellaria* and *Chenopodium*; perhaps the spinach chloroplasts used by Holt and French contained enough ferric oxalate [or other organic salts of Fe(III)] to make their addition unnecessary. (Liebich found 0.05% Fe in the dry matter of spinach chloroplasts; *cf.* Vol. I, page 377; Kohman found as much as 9% oxalic acid in the dry matter of spinach leaves.)

A chloroplast-free Hill solution itself evolved some gas when illuminated with white light (250 f.-c.); to avoid errors due to this evolution, a nitrogen atmosphere and the presence of a 10% KOH solution in a side arm of the manometric vessel were used by Holt and French (1946). With these precautions, all pressure changes observed could be ascribed to oxygen. The addition of inactivated (boiled) chloroplasts to Hill's mixture had no effect.

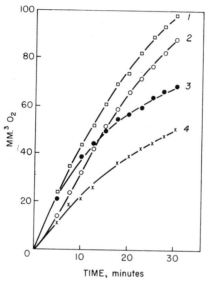

Fig. 35.16. Oxygen production by spinach chloroplasts immersed in various combinations of the constituents of Hill's mixture (after Holt and French 1946): (1) complete mixture; (2) 0.50 M $K_2C_2O_4$ + 0.02 M $K_3Fe(CN)_6$; (3) 0.01 M Fe-$(NH_4)(SO_4)_2$ + 0.02 M $K_3Fe(CN)_6$; (4) 0.02 M $K_3Fe(CN)_6$. 15° C., pH 6.8, all in 0.17 N sodium sorbitol borate buffer, 0.28 mg. of chlorophyll per vessel.

(b) Other Inorganic Oxidants

Holt and French (1948) investigated a variety of oxidizing agents They used spinach chloroplast fragments in a phosphate buffer in nitrogen atmosphere. Manometric evidence of gas production (and chemical proof that this gas was oxygen) was obtained with *chromate* [which was earlier found inactive with live *Chlorella* cells by Fan *et al.* (1943)] and with *m-vanadate* (too little O_2 for manometric study). Numerous other oxidants gave no oxygen at all, among them molybdate, bromate, chlorate, tetrathionate, tungstate, hypochlorite, permanganate, nitrate, periodate, bismuthate, iodine, arsenate, persulfate and perborate. An initial outburst of gas was obtained upon mixing chloroplasts with perborate or permanganate, but illumination led to no additional gas liberation.

The reaction with *chromate* was studied somewhat more closely. Oxygen was evolved only in light; this evolution was prevented if the chloroplasts were preheated to 50° C. for 15 min., showing that it involves an enzymatic reaction. The total amount of oxygen evolved was only about one

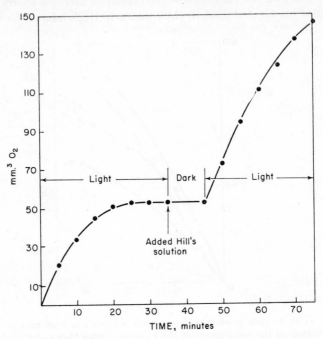

Fig. 35.17. Resumption of oxygen evolution by illuminated chloroplasts on addition of Hill's solution, following cessation of evolution from chromate (6.65×10^{-6} mole K_2CrO_4; O_2 equivalent; 111 mm.^{3}; pH 7.3; 0.1 M phosphate; 16° C.; nitrogen atmosphere; 0.25 mg. chlorophyll) (after Holt and French 1948).

half (45–75%) of that expected for the oxidation of water by Cr(VI), and the reduction of the latter to Cr(III):

$$(35.30) \qquad CrO_4^{-2} + 5\ H^+ \longrightarrow Cr^{+3} + 2\tfrac{1}{2}\ H_2O + \tfrac{3}{4}\ O_2$$

Figure 35.17 shows that the cessation of oxygen evolution, after about one half of the stoichiometric equivalent was produced, was not the result of damage to the photochemical system, since addition of Hill's mixture led to a resumption of oxygen liberation. On the other hand, oxygen liberation could not be renewed by the addition of fresh chloroplasts. Incubation of chloroplasts in $2 \times 10^{-3}\ M$ chromate solution for 30 min. in the dark did not inactivate them. The total fraction of chromate reduced was approximately the same for chromate concentrations between 1.5×10^{-3}

and 3.5×10^{-3} mole/l. (*e. g.*, in one set of experiments 70%); the initial rate also seemed to be independent of chromate concentration.

(c) Oxygen as Hill Oxidant

One of the puzzles of photosynthesis is how the photochemically transferred hydrogen manages to avoid the abundantly available strong oxidant, molecular oxygen, in favor of the sparse and extremely unwilling oxidant, carbon dioxide. Only under certain abnormal conditions—such as carbon dioxide starvation, or excessive illumination (*cf.* chapter 19)—does photautoxidation replace photosynthesis. It was suggested (*cf.* scheme 19.I, p. 544) that in these cases, oxygen acts as a "substitute hydrogen acceptor" replacing carbon dioxide, while the primary photochemical hydrogen transfer remains the same as in photosynthesis. However, as long as water is the reductant, the Hill reaction with oxygen as oxidant is a circular process, leading to no net chemical change, and therefore unrecognizable except by isotopic tracer experiments (photocatalysis of isotopic equilibration of free oxygen and water). For it to become observable by ordinary chemical methods, it has to lead to the oxidation of compounds other than water—such as benzidine (page 528) or chlorophyll itself (page 537). This may occur by direct substitution of these reductants for water in the photochemical process (as suggested in scheme 19.I), or indirectly by the action of hydrogen peroxide formed as intermediate in photochemical hydrogenation of oxygen (see below).

The isotopic tracer method was applied to the "hidden" Hill reaction (with oxygen as oxidant and water as reductant) by Brown (1953). Using water containing only O^{16} and oxygen gas enriched in O^{16} and O^{18}, he found that in light an exchange of the two isotopes took place at a rate comparable to that of the Hill reaction at the same light intensity. When chloroplasts deteriorated (by aging or phenanthroline poisoning) their capacity to photocatalyze the isotopic exchange of oxygen between H_2O and O_2 declined in the same proportion as their capacity for Hill reaction with quinone as oxidant.

An indirect but ingenious chemical proof that oxygen can serve as Hill oxidant with chloroplast suspensions was supplied by Mehler (1951[1,2], 1952). He used for this purpose the system ethanol-catalase, which can "trap" hydrogen peroxide (expected to arise as intermediate in the hydrogenation of oxygen). In the presence of ethanol, the oxidation-reduction reaction

(35.31) $$H_2O_2 + C_2H_4OH \xrightarrow{\text{catalase}} C_2H_4O + 2H_2O$$

in which catalase acts as a "peroxidase," competes with the more common "catalatic" dismutation of H_2O_2 to H_2O and O_2. First, Mehler had to show that when the Hill reaction is carried out with other oxidants—quinone, Hill's mixture, or cytochrome *c*—no hydrogen peroxide is formed as an intermediate *oxidation* product of water. He found, in fact, that no acetaldehyde is produced upon addition of ethanol and catalase to these common Hill reaction systems. This is the most convincing confirmation to date of the surmise—made in chapter 11, p. 286—that hydrogen peroxide is *not* an intermediate in the photochemical oxygen formation by plants.

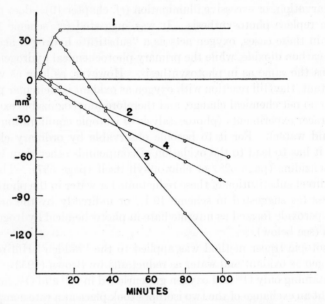

Fig. 35.17A. Evolution and absorption of O_2 by chloroplast material (300 μg. chlorophyll in 2 ml. phosphate buffer pH 6.8) (Mehler 1951). O_2 evolved in vessel 1 (5×10^{-6} mole quinone); O_2 consumed in vessel 2 (4 mg. catalase, 10^{-3} mole ethanol; O_2 first evolved, then consumed at double speed in vessel 3 (5 μmole quinone, 4 mg. catalase, 10^{-3} mole ethanol). Vessel 4; catalase, ethanol, and 5 μmole hydroquinone.

Mehler then could proceed with the demonstration that acetaldehyde does arise—as a *reduction* intermediate—if chloroplast suspensions containing ethanol and catalase are illuminated in the absence of added Hill oxidants, but in the presence of oxygen. Under these conditions, oxygen is *consumed* instead of being *liberated*, as in the usual versions of the Hill reaction (figure 35.17A). Two moles of acetaldehyde were found to be formed per mole of oxygen consumed, which is consistent with the reaction scheme (35.31A).

(35.31Aa) $$2\,H_2O \xrightarrow{h\nu} 2\,\{H\} + 2\,\{OH\}$$

(35.31Ab) $$2\,\{OH\} \longrightarrow H_2O + 1/2\,O_2$$

(35.31Ac) $$2\,\{H\} + O_2 \longrightarrow H_2O_2$$

(35.31Ad) $$H_2O_2 + C_2H_5OH \xrightarrow{catalase} C_2H_4O + H_2O$$

(35.31Ae) $$1/2 O_2 + C_2H_5OH \xrightarrow[catalase]{h\nu} C_2H_4O + H_2O$$

The normal redox potential of the system O_2/H_2O_2 is 0.27 volt (*cf.* table 11.I), well within the region of other efficient Hill oxidants. Aerated chloroplast suspensions contain about 10^{-4} mole/l. oxygen; quinone and other common Hill oxidants need to be present in concentrations of 2×10^{-3} mole/l. or higher (*cf.* section 5(*b*) below) to ensure high efficiency of oxygen liberation. This indicates that oxygen is a highly effective competitor of the other Hill oxidants, and emphasizes how remarkable is the fact that it is *not* an effective competitor of carbon dioxide in live, aerobically photosynthesizing cells.

Mehler suggested that photoxidations *in vivo* (described in chap. 19) may be based on a Hill reaction with oxygen as oxidant (as suggested in Vol. I, p. 544), in which some of the hydrogen peroxide, formed as reduction intermediate, is intercepted by peroxidases, causing it to react with the photoxidation substrates (in competition with its dismutation by catalase).

Mehler and Brown (1952) confirmed the above-suggested mechanism of the "Mehler reaction" by showing mass spectrographically that the *net consumption* of oxygen, according to equation (35.31A), is in fact the result of superposition of an oxygen *evolution* (eqs. 35.31Aa,b) upon a (twice as large) oxygen *consumption* (eq. 35.31Ac). For the purpose of this demonstration, the reaction was carried out in O^{18} and O^{16} enriched oxygen (in a helium atmosphere). The experimental system also contained quinone, in addition to catalase and alcohol. In light, quinone was reduced first, causing O_2^{32} to be evolved, while the O_2^{34} concentration remained constant. When practically all quinone was exhausted, the "Mehler reaction" got under way; both O_2^{32} and O_2^{34} were now consumed, but the second one much faster than the first. The curves showing the consumption of the two isotopic species were in quantitative agreement with predictions based on mechanism (35.31A).

Mehler (1951[2]) studied more closely the competition between quinone and oxygen as hydrogen acceptors in the Hill reaction. He found that in a chloroplast suspension containing both quinone and ethanol + catalase, quinone was hydrogenated at the usual rate until the reaction was 90% complete, at which time the oxygen consumption began; remarkably enough the latter was now 2–3 times faster than in a quinone-free system. (In the latter, the rate of oxygen consumption in light is only $1/2$ or $1/3$ of that of oxygen liberation with quinone; while in the mixed system, after quinone had been nearly exhausted, the rate of oxygen consumption is about equal to that of initial oxygen liberation.)   This stimulation of the photochemical alcohol oxidation by preceding quinone reduction was sustained even when an equivalent of five times the total amount of quinone present had been oxidized.   Checks showed that this catalytic effect is not due to the presence of hydroquinone.   The stimulation is still present if alcohol and catalase are added 10–20 minutes after the quinone reduction had been completed.   No similar stimulation follows the Hill reaction with ferricyanide;   but o- or p-naphthaquinone have the same effect as benzoquinone.   No stimulation is brought about by simply incubating chloroplasts in quinone solution in the dark.   Reducing quinone in the dark by *ascorbic acid* also caused no stimulation if the two reagents were mixed before adding the chloroplasts, but it produced the same stimulation as photochemical reduction if ethanol and catalase were first mixed with the chloroplasts and quinone and ascorbic acid added afterward.   The rate of oxygen uptake was enhanced by still another factor of two if more than the stoichiometric quantity of ascorbic acid was used.   (It is uncertain whether the thus quadrupled rate of oxygen consumption equalled, or exceeded, the rate of photosynthesis by the same amount of chlorophyll, *cf.* section 5(*b*) below.)   Only a slow photoxidation of ascorbic could be observed in illuminated chloroplast suspensions in the absence of quinone.   In the system (chloroplasts + quinone + ascorbic acid), one mole of oxygen was consumed in light.   Adding only catalase caused a 50% inhibition of this reaction, but adding both catalase and ethanol lead to the above-described maximum stimulation of oxygen consumption.   It continued until two moles of O_2 had been used up per mole ascorbic acid, after which the reaction rate dropped to the level characteristic of the (quinone + ethanol + catalase) system without ascorbate.   Similar effects were observed with glutathione; it, too, was photoxidized by chloroplasts slowly in the absence of quinone, and rapidly in its presence.   Because of Gerretsen's observations (*cf.* below), Mehler tried adding Mn^{++} salt to the above-described systems, and found that the only one on which it had an effect was (oxygen + ethanol + catalyse + chloroplasts);   the rate of oxygen consumption by this mixture in light was doubled by the addition of 10^{-3} mole/l. $MnCl_2$. The enhancing effects of quinone reduction and of Mn^{++} addition could not be superimposed upon each other.   The effect of manganous ions was catalytic;   ferrous ions did not produce it; instead, they themselves were rapidly photoxidized by chloroplasts in the presence of ethanol and catalase.

Gerretsen (1950[2]) observed that crude chloroplast preparations from *Avena*, which slowly absorbed oxygen in the dark (*cf.* below section 5(*c*)), *increased* this absorption 2–3 times in light (instead of replacing it by oxygen liberation, as noted by Hill and others with washed chloroplasts). Addition of glucose did not increase this photautoxidation; it was, however, stimulated by asparagine. Addition of manganese salts—which Gerretsen (1950[1]) had found to increase strongly the effect of light on the redox potential of the same material—often produces a marked temporary increase in the rate of oxygen uptake in light.

(*d*) *Quinones*

An important new group of oxidants capable of serving in the Hill reaction was found by Warburg and Lüttgens. They noted (1944) that chloroplasts isolated from spinach or sugar beet leaves can reduce *p-benzoquinone*—probably to hydroquinone—with the liberation of an equivalent amount of oxygen. A description of these experiments was given in a paper published in Russian (Warburg and Lüttgens, 1946) and later reprinted in Warburg's book *Heavy Metals as Prosthetic Groups* (1946; English edition, 1949). Warburg and Lüttgens discovered the quinone reaction while studying the "respiration" of juices obtained by maceration of spinach leaves. The oxygen consumption of these juices declined with time; in an attempt to maintain it, various oxidation substrates were added, and it was noted that with hydroquinone (or pyrocatechol) the respiration was sustained in the dark, but *markedly decreased in light*. This was attributed to photochemical reversal of the oxygen-consuming process—*i. e.*, to a (chloroplast-sensitized) photochemical oxidation of water by quinone:

$$(35.32) \qquad 2\ C_6H_4O_2 + 2H_2O \underset{\text{dark}}{\overset{\text{Chl, light}}{\rightleftharpoons}} 2\ C_6H_6O_2 + O_2 - 52\ \text{kcal./mole}$$

Similar observations were made with some naphthaquinones, *e. g.*, naphthaquinone sulfonic acid. No change in oxygen consumption was noted in light, neither in the liquid fraction from the maceration of spinach leaves (with or without pyrocatechol or hydroquinone) nor in the chloroplast-containing fraction without added polyphenol; but in the chloroplast fraction to which pyrocatechol was added, illumination caused 50% inhibition of the oxygen uptake (fig. 35.18); and if both pyrocatechol and hydroquinone were added, a complete inhibition of respiration or even a liberation of oxygen was observed in light.

After it was first noted that chloride may be needed as a "co-enzyme" for the quinone reaction (*cf.* above, sect. (*c*)), 0.05% KCl was added by Warburg and Lüttgens to all washed preparations. (If the centrifuged suspensions are not washed, natural chloride content is high enough to activate the photochemical reaction.)

Purity of the quinone used is important. Commercial pure benzoquinone was purified by distillation with water vapor and drying in vacuum. Dissolving the yellow crystals in pure water (even if carried out in the absence of air) gives a strongly colored solution; it contains an impurity which inhibits the photochemical activity. To avoid this, quinone was dissolved in 0.01 N sulfuric acid. Illumination of quinone solution in the absence of chloroplasts with the blue-violet light absorbed by quinone causes darkening; no reaction can be observed afterward upon the addition

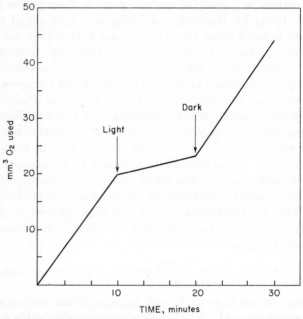

Fig. 35.18. Effect of light on oxygen consumption by chloroplast preparations in the presence of pyrocatechol (after Warburg and Lüttgens 1948).

of chloroplasts (Clendenning and Ehrmantraut, 1950). A chloroplast suspension to which a pure, acid quinone solution was added at pH 6.5 in the absence of oxygen showed in the experiments of Warburg and Lüttgens no gas exchange in the dark (except for occasional liberation of traces of CO_2); upon illumination, it produces oxygen until the volume of the latter reached 80–90% of that calculated for the oxidation of water by the available quinone, according to equation (35.32), thus confirming the validity of this equation (see figure 35.19).

That the liberated gas was oxygen was confirmed by absorption in phosphorus. Iodometric assay showed that when the photochemical gas liberation was ended, practically all quinone had disappeared from the solution.

Similar experiments with o-benzoquinone were unsuccessful because of the instability of this compound; but another orthoquinonoid compound, α-naphthaquinone sulfonic acid, could be reduced in the same way as p-benzoquinone. This, and the stimulation of the oxygen consumption in green extracts by the addition of pyrocatechol (section 5(c) below) makes it probable that o-quinones react similarly to p-quinones.

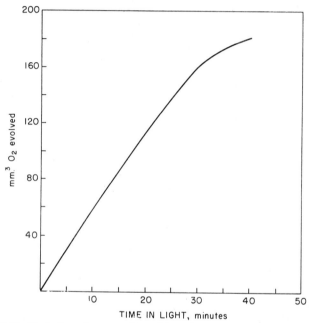

Fig. 35.19. Evolution of oxygen from chloroplast suspension in quinone solution in light (after Warburg and Lüttgens 1946). 2 ml. suspension in 0.05 M phosphate buffer, pH 6.5, 0.05% KCl, 1 μM chlorophyll in vessel, 20° C., argon atmosphere. 2 mg. quinone in 0.2 ml. 0.01 N H_2SO_4 added at time 0.

Since 18.5×10^{-6} mole quinone could be reduced by a suspension containing only 0.2×10^{-6} mole chlorophyll, the latter obviously could not have served as a reactant, but only as a catalyst; the same applies to all other components of the chloroplasts, none of which is available in such large quantities.

As shown in equation (35.32) the oxidation of water by quinone is endothermal to the extent of 52 kcal./mole oxygen—somewhat less than one half as much as the oxidation of water by carbon dioxide. This energy must be supplied by light.

Aronoff (1946) repeated Warburg's experiments with a variety of naphthaquinones and anthraquinones and found that they reacted at a rate roughly parallel to their oxidation-reduction potentials—in other words, stronger oxidants were reduced faster than the weaker ones. (This comparison refers to the saturation rate in strong light, not to quantum yield in weak light!) These results are in agreement with Holt and French's observations on dyestuffs (cf. Table 35.VIII).

Wessels and Havinga (1952, 1953; cf. also Wessels 1954) prepared and investigated 28 quinones with a range of normal potentials (measured at pH 6.5) from -0.444 volt (tetrachloro-o-benzoquinone), through -0.332 volt (p-benzoquinone), -0.181 volt (1,2 naphthaquinone), -0.086 volt (1,4 naphthoquinone), $+0.020$ volt (2-methyl-1,4-naphthoquinone), $+0.135$ volt (phthiocol), to $+0.21$ volt (chloranilic acid). They measured the effect of illumination on the redox potential of the chloroplast suspensions containing these quinones, and found, under aerobic conditions, a "photogalvanic effect" (change of redox potential in light) with all (17) quinones having normal potentials from -0.444 up to 0.058 volt (phenanthrene quinone); and no photogalvanic effect for all (11) quinones with potentials above 0.058 volt. Under anaerobic conditions, 7 quinones, with normal potentials from -0.444 to $+0.180$ volt were studied, and a photogalvanic effect was observed in six of them, with normal potentials up to $+0.090$ volt (2-hydroxy-1,4-naphthoquinone); no effect was observed only with sodium anthraquinone-2-sulfonate ($E_0' = +0.180$ volt). Similar results were obtained with quinonoid dyes (see below).

(e) Organic dyestuffs

Closely related to quinones are many organic dyestuffs that contain closed, conjugated double bond systems, and can be converted to "leucodyes" by the addition of two hydrogen atoms. In the leucodyes the conjugated system is either destroyed or, at least, reduced in length, with consequent weakening of absorption bands and their shift into the ultraviolet region. Many of these dyes form strong electrolytes, and their oxidation-reduction potentials can be easily determined.

Holt and French (1948) first observed that a number of reversibly reducible organic dyes can serve as photochemical oxidants of water in the presence of chloroplast suspensions. Attention must be given to photochemical effects produced by light absorption in the dye, and to the separation of this absorption and its chemical effects from those of chlorophyll (or other chloroplast pigments).

Quantitative experiments were made by Holt and French (1948) with the red dye *phenol indophenol*. No reaction could be observed in the dark, or with chloroplasts preheated to 50° C. Tests of the purity of the dye gave values as low as 55%; on this basis, the oxygen yields were 100 ± 4% of the theoretical value for the reaction (D = Dye):

$$(35.33) \qquad D + H_2O \longrightarrow H_2D + \tfrac{1}{2} O_2$$

The rate decreased with increasing dye concentration ($3.3 \times 10^{-4} \rightarrow 3.3 \times 10^{-3}$ mole/liter), probably because increased competition of the dye for light absorption brought the absorption by chlorophyll below the level needed for light saturation.

With *blue* dyes, such as *2,6-dichlorophenol-indophenol*, the absorption by the dye was so strong that the rate became too slow for manometric measurements. By using a very dilute solution, both in respect to the dye and in respect to chlorophyll (5×10^{-6} mole/liter), the occurrence of the dye reduction could be proved by observation of the decoloration of the dye in light. Experiments of this type were made with eight dyes at concentrations of the order of 5×10^{-6} mole/liter or less, at *p*H 6.6 and 8.0, with the results shown in Table 35.VIII.

TABLE 35.VIII

DYE REDUCTION BY CHLOROPLASTS (AFTER HOLT AND FRENCH, 1948)

	$-E_0'$ (volt)[a]	
	at *p*H 6.6	at *p*H 9.0
Positive results (at *p*H 6.6 and 9.0)		
Phenol-indophenol	0.254	0.083
2,6-Dichlorophenol-indophenol	0.247	0.089[b]
o-Cresol-indophenol	0.217	0.089
Positive results (at *p*H 6.6 only)		
Thionine[c]	0.074	(−0.001)
Negative results		
1-Naphthol-2-sulfoindophenol	0.147	0.003
Methylene blue	0.024	−0.050
Indigo tetrasulfonate	−0.027	−0.114
Indigo disulfonate	−0.104	−0.199

[a] Throughout this book, oxidation-reduction potentials are given on Lewis and Randall's scale on which strong oxidants have high negative potentials, *cf*. table 9.IV.

[b] Slow reaction.

[c] No oxygen evolution was found; reaction may thus be with a cellular hydrogen donor, such as ascorbic acid, rather than with water. The decolorization of thionine was incomplete, and reversed itself in the dark.

This table shows, in agreement with Aronoff's findings (*cf*. above), that the photochemical effectiveness of the several oxidants (saturation rate of oxygen liberation in strong light) increases generally with their oxidation potential. However, the parallelism is not strict, and specific effects seem to occur, as shown by the inactivity of the 1-naphthol-2-sulfoindophenol. It must be considered that the observed rate is the net balance of a photochemical forward reaction and a dark back reaction. The back reaction can involve either the final reduction product (such as the leuco dye), or a reduction intermediate (such as a semiquinone). The thermodynamic equilibrium lies practically always on the side of the dye and water, not on that of the leuco dye and oxygen. Therefore a back reaction is always possible—although it may be so slow as to be practically insignificant. The redox potential of the dye-leuco dye system is more likely to affect the rate of the dark back reaction than the quantum yield of the photochemical forward reaction. When the back reaction is fast, the Hill reaction becomes unobservable by ordinary methods. It may still be detectable by isotopic tracers, or by "trapping" the product chemically or physically, or by sensitive methods revealing a small shift of the oxidation-reduction equilibrium in light. We recall that in Hill's original experiments the rather fast reoxidation of ferrous oxalate by oxygen had necessitated the addition of ferricyanide as "stabilizer." Leucothionine or leucomethylene blue, if they are formed in the Hill reaction together with oxygen, will be reoxidized even more rapidly. Leucophenol indophenol, on the other hand, is reoxidized much more slowly, thus permitting practically complete decoloration in light. Only when the back reaction is negligible does the rate of decoloration provide a true measure of the photochemical reactivity of the suspension (*i. e.*, of the quantum yield of the photochemical reaction).

Additional quinonoid dyes were tried out by Holt, Smith and French (1951). Table 35.IX shows the results.

TABLE 35.IX

INDOPHENOL DYES REDUCED BY ILLUMINATED CHLOROPLASTS
(AFTER HOLT, SMITH AND FRENCH, 1951)

Dye (sodium salt)	Color at	
	pH 6.5	pH 8.0
2,6-Dibromobenzenone-indo-3'-carboxyphenol	Red-violet[a]	Blue[a]
2,6-Dibromobenzenone-indo-2'-bromophenol	Blue[a]	Blue[a]
2,6-Dibromobenzenone-indo-3'-methoxyphenol	Blue[a]	Blue[a]
2,6-Dibromo-2'-methyl-5'-isopropylindophenol	Blue[a]	Blue[c]
Benzenone-indo-2'-methyl-5'-isopropylphenol	Pink[b]	Blue[a]
2,6-Dibromobenzenone-indophenol	Blue[a]	Blue[a]
Benzenone-3'-methyl-6'-isopropylphenol	Red[b]	Olive green[a]

[a] Means strong decolorization.
[b] Means little decolorization.
[c] Means no decolorization.

Macdowall (1952) illuminated a suspension of washed Swiss chard chloroplasts in distilled water for $2^3/_4$ hours with light of about 2 klux in the presence of nine dyes, and determined the degree of reduction at the end of exposure either photometrically or potentiometrically. The potentials reached with five oxidants are listed in table 35.IXA.

The figures in table 35.IXA show that reduction was practically complete with the first three dyes, far-reaching with the fourth, and negligible

TABLE 35.IXA

NORMAL POTENTIALS OF FIVE DYES AND THE POTENTIALS MEASURED IN CHLOROPLAST
SUSPENSIONS CONTAINING THESE DYES BEFORE AND AFTER ILLUMINATION (AFTER
MACDOWALL 1952)

	2,6-Dichloro-phenol-indo-phenol	Toluylene blue	Cresyl blue	Methylene blue	Indigo disulfo-nate
E_0' (pH 6.5, 15° C.)	−0.283	−0.169	−0.116	−0.060	−0.067
E (before illumination)	−0.435	−0.448	−0.496	−0.471	−0.470
E (after illumination)	−0.071	−0.239	−0.046	−0.011	−0.009

with the fifth. The meaning of the potentials measured before the illumination is doubtful. The highest positive potential was reached with toluylene blue.

A similar but more extensive study was made by Wessels and Havinga (1952, 1953; cf. Wessels 1954), who observed the decolorization in light and the photogalvanic effect (change of redox potential in light) of fifteen quinonoid dyes with normal potentials (pH 6.5, 30° C.) from −0.255 volt (2,6-dichlorophenol-indophenol) through −0.137 volt (toluylene blue), −0.028 volt (methylene blue), +0.098 volt (indigo disulfonate) to +0.269 volt (safranin T). They found, in air, photogalvanic effects for all 9 dyes with E_0' values up to −0.028 volt, and none for all 6 dyes with more positive redox potentials. Decolorization was observed for 7 dyes with potentials up to −0.137 volt, and not for the 8 dyes with more positive potentials. Under anaerobic conditions 10 dyes were studied, and photogalvanic effects were observed with all but 3 of them, with a dividing line between +0.098 volt (indigo disulfonate) and +0.130 volt (indigo monosulfonate). Decolorization could be noted, however, only for dyes with potentials up to −0.137 volt (as under aerobic conditions). (The potentiometric test is more sensitive to small shifts in oxidation-reduction equilibrium than visual observation of color changes.)

The photostationary redox potentials, measured in illuminated solutions in which a photogalvanic effect could be observed, ranged from 0.00 volt to −0.10 volt, without obvious relationship to the E_0' of the dye (or quinone). (About the limited significance of such photostationary potentials, see p. 1522.)

A study was also made by Wessels of Hill reaction with a mixture of two oxidants (quinones or quinonoid dyes). If both components were "good" Hill oxidants, both were reduced; if one was a "borderline case" (such as thionine, $E_0' = -0.0777$ volt), it was hardly reduced at all. The presence in the mixture of an oxidant too positive for its own reduction did not affect the reduction of a "good" Hill reductant, except in the case of phthiocol (which is known to inhibit the Hill reaction).

These results, together with the earlier data of Holt and French (tables 35.VIII and 35.IX), and of Macdowall (table 35.IXA), establish rather clearly that, as far as electrode-active redox systems of the quinone-hydroquinone type are concerned, illuminated chloroplast suspensions can displace, by the transfer of hydrogen from water, the equilibrium of all of them whose normal redox potentials (at pH 6.5) are under -0.1 volt; if air is excluded (and the back reaction thus slowed down, because only the photochemically produced O_2, or its precursors, are available for reoxidation), the displacement of the equilibrium in light can be recognized potentiometrically for systems with normal potentials up to $+0.1$ volt.

The question whether *free radicals* are formed as intermediates in Hill reaction with quinones or quinonoid dyes was taken up by Uri (1952) and Wessels (1954) by inquiring whether this reaction has an effect on polymerization of methyl acrylate (Uri) or acrylonitrile (Wessels), or on the oxidation of benzene to phenol (Wessels). As mentioned in part A, Uri was able to confirm, by means of the polymerization test, the formation of free radicals in the photochemical reaction of dissolved chlorophyll with ascorbic acid; but neither he nor Wessels could obtain similar evidence for the presence of radicals in the quinone or dye reduction sensitized by chloroplast suspensions.

(f) Respiration Intermediates and Other Cellular Materials

The behavior in the Hill reaction of the compounds known to occur as intermediate oxidation-reduction catalysts in respiration is of particular interest, since these compounds could conceivably serve as links connecting the photochemical apparatus to an enzymatic system capable of reducing carbon dioxide in the dark. Among these intermediates, the most interesting ones are the well known "coenzymes" I and II (dipyridine nucleotide, DPN, and tripyridine nucleotide, TPN), and the more recently discovered "coenzyme A" ("thioctic" or "lipoic" acid). These catalysts have such high reduction potentials ($\simeq 0.3$ volt, *cf.* page 222) that their successful photochemical reduction would constitute a close approach—as far as energy utilization is concerned—to the reduction of carbon dioxide itself. More specifically, of the two steps in the reduction of carbon dioxide to the carbohydrate level (we imagine CO_2 to be first incorporated in a carboxyl, $RH + CO_2 \rightleftharpoons RCOOH$), the first one, the reduction of the carboxyl group to a carbonyl group, requires a normal potential of around 0.5 volt; but the second one, the reduction of a carbonyl group to a hydroxyl group, needs only about 0.25 volt (*cf.* table 9.IV). Reduced pyridine nucleotides are capable of bringing about the second step by themselves, but not the first reduction step. The first one becomes possible if the carboxyl is "activated" before reduction by conversion into a phosphate ester

(e. g., by a "transphosphorylation" reaction with adenosine triphosphate, ATP). Reduction then leads to the degradation of a "high energy" carboxyl phosphate to a "low energy" carbonyl phosphate, and the energy required for reduction is thus decreased by the energy difference between the two types of phosphate esters (about 10 kcal, corresponding to a shift of about 0.22 volt downward on the redox potential scale). We will return to these relationships below.

Attempts to use pyridine nucleotides as ultimate Hill oxidants were unsuccessful (Holt and French 1948; Mehler 1951).

Mehler found no reduction of DPN also when the dye dichlorophenol-indophenol (which reacts rapidly with $DPNH_2$) was supplied as intermediate, although the dye was reduced in light practically completely. (Considering the wide difference between the normal potentials of DPN and the dye, this is not astonishing, cf. considerations on p. 1522). Similar results were obtained by Wessels (1954) when he tried to use quinone, or dichlorophenol-indophenol, as intermediate catalyst to reduce oxidized glutathione, dehydroascorbic acid, dehydroxyphenylalanine, riboflavin or DPN.

The reason for the negative result of attempts to reduce pyridine nucleotides in the Hill reaction could be a rapid back reaction of reduced pyridine nucleotides with intermediates in the oxidation of water (or with the final oxidation product, molecular oxygen). The surmise that a small amount of $DPNH_2$ or $TPNH_2$ is present in the photostationary state was confirmed by "trapping" these compounds with one of the enzymatic systems which use them for the reduction of pyruvic acid or other respiration intermediates. This proof was given independently by Vishniac in Ochoa's laboratory in New York, by Tolmach in Franck and Gaffron's laboratory in Chicago and by Arnon in Berkeley.

Vishniac (see Ochoa 1950; Vishniac 1951; Ochoa and Vishniac 1951; Vishniac and Ochoa 1951) based his experiments on previous findings concerning reversible oxidative decarboxylation of malic acid (or d-isocitric acid) to pyruvic acid (or ketoglutaric acid) in the presence of "malic enzyme" (or isocitric dehydrogenase and aconitase), with TPN as specific hydrogen acceptor. These reactions normally proceed in the direction of decarboxylation and oxidation, but they can be reversed by the supply of excess $TPNH_2$ and CO_2, e. g.:

$$(35.34) \quad CO_2 + CH_3COCOOH + TPNH_2 \overset{\text{malic}}{\underset{\text{enzyme}}{\rightleftharpoons}} COOHCH_2CHOHCOOH + TPN$$
$$\text{pyruvate} \qquad\qquad\qquad\qquad\qquad\qquad \text{malate}$$

It was surmised by Ochoa, Veiga Solles and Ortiz (1950) that illuminated chloroplasts may be capable of converting TPN to $TPNH_2$ and thus driving reaction (35.34) from left to right. The first proof of this was obtained by Vishniac and Ochoa, who showed that if pyruvate and bicarbonate are added to a chloroplast suspension in the presence of TPN, malic enzyme (prepared from pigeon liver) and Mn^{++} ions (which this enzyme specifically requires), malic acid is formed. This formation can be demonstrated after exposure to light (but not in darkness) by means of a specific enzymatic test (liberation of CO_2 by malic decarboxylase). In a second test, tracer C^*O_2 was employed, and practically all of the C^{14} fixed in light was found in malate, with 75% of it localized in the β-carboxyl group.

Similar results were obtained with α-ketoglutaric acid and bicarbonate in the presence of chloroplasts, TPN and appropriate enzymes. Other pyridine nucleotide-specific reductions also could be carried out with the help of illuminated chloroplast preparations, including the reduction of pyruvate to lactate by DPN and lactic dehydrogenase:

$$(35.34Aa) \qquad DPN + H_2O \xrightarrow[\text{light}]{\text{chloroplasts}} DPNH_2 + {}^1/_2O_2$$

$$(35.34Ab) \quad \underset{\text{pyruvate}}{CH_3COCOOH} + DPNH_2 \longrightarrow \underset{\text{lactate}}{CH_3CHOHCOOH} + DPN$$

also reduction of oxalacetate to malate in the presence of DPN and malic dehydrogenase, reductive amination of α-ketoglutarate to glutamic acid by ammonia and DPN and reduction of fumaric acid to succinic acid in the presence of DPN and extracts from *Escherichia coli* (a reaction which can be brought about in the dark by molecular hydrogen).

All the above reductions (except that of fumarate) involve the hydrogenation of the *carbonyl* group, $C{=}O$ (a $C{=}C$ group is hydrogenated in fumarate). As stated above, these reductions can be achieved by pyridine nucleotides without the assistance of high energy phosphate. The reduction of a *carboxyl* group requires a stronger reducing agent than $TPNH_2$ or $DPNH_2$ (because, as mentioned on pages 215–219, C—O bonds are stabilized by accumulation at a single C atom). As was said before, in order to reduce a —COOH group by hydrogen available in reduced pyridine nucleotide, a high energy phosphate ester must be supplied, and its degradation to a "low energy" phosphate coupled with the reduction. (As an example, oxidation of glyceraldehyde to glyceric acid by DPN becomes reversible by oxidizing and phosphorylating a "low energy" triose monophosphate to "high energy" diphosphoglycerate.) By combining the reversal of this reaction with the (reversible) glycolytic reactions, it is possible to start with PGA, ATP and $DPNH_2$ (*i. e.*, DPN + chloroplasts in light), and end up with hexose diphosphate. Ochoa suggested (as did earlier Ruben, Kok, van der Veen and others, *cf.* pages 1116–1117) that the high energy phosphate needed for this synthesis of hexose from PGA can be supplied, in light, by reversal of a part of the photochemical reaction, *e. g.*, by allowing some of the $DPNH_2$ formed in light to be oxidized by molecular oxygen (perhaps *via* the cytochrome system) and storing the oxidation energy in phosphate bonds (a coupling demonstrated by Lehninger).

In the above-described experiments of Vishniac and Ochoa the proof of the assumed photochemical reduction of pyridine nucleotides by water consisted in the demonstration of *reduction* and *carboxylation* of pyruvate (or other metabolic acids) in light; a complete proof calls also for the demonstration of *oxygen liberation* in stoichiometric proportion. Furthermore, the relevance of these observations to the mechanism of photosynthesis depends on the *yield* of the reaction. As stated in chapter 4 in the discussion of earlier claims of photosynthesis *in vitro*, "everything is possible in photochemistry," provided one is satisfied with very small yields. Consequently, no reaction *in vitro* can be considered as a significant step in reconstructing photosynthesis outside the living cell unless its yield approaches that of natural photosynthesis.

Vishniac and Ochoa (1952) were able to demonstrate, using chromous chloride as reagent, that oxygen was in fact formed in the stoichiometrically expected amount (specifically, 0.5 mole O_2 were liberated per mole of lactic acid formed, in accordance with reactions (35.34Aa,b). The yield was, however, very low—corresponding to about one molecule oxygen per molecule chlorophyll every 3 hours or about 0.1% of the rate of photosynthesis in saturating light. Other above-enumerated enzymatic systems gave oxygen yields (calculated from the rate of formation of the reduction products) of one molecule oxygen per molecule chlorophyll between every 1.2 and every 60 hours. The light used was relatively weak—about 4 klux, but even with allowance for this fact, these rates are of different order of magnitude than those of photosynthesis.

Tolmach (1951[1,2]) came to a study similar to that of Vishniac and Ochoa from a different side. The evolution of oxygen by illuminated chloroplast suspensions in the absence of specially added oxidants (chapter 4, page 62) points to the presence in plants of a "natural Hill oxidant" (or oxidants). These may, or may not, serve as intermediates in Hill reaction, or photosynthesis, or both; in any case, it would be important to identify them. Hill had shown that the photochemical oxygen liberation by chloroplasts, without added oxidants, is very brief in washed chloroplasts, but lasts much longer if the chloroplasts are left suspended in the cell sap (or if a chloroplast–free leaf extract is added to washed chloroplasts). Figure 35.19A shows the course of oxygen liberation which Tolmach was able to demonstrate by suspending a drop of a suspension of spinach chloroplasts in an illumination chamber traversed by a stream of pure nitrogen, and analyzing the gas leaving the chamber for oxygen by the highly sensitive phosphorescence-quenching method of Pringsheim and Franck.

Tolmach inquired whether the oxygen evolution can be enhanced by known metabolic intermediates; he found, in fact, that the addition to the drop of 1×10^{-2} mole/l. phosphoglycerate (PGA) or pyruvate (PA) in-

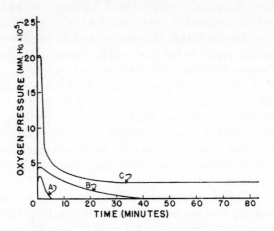

Fig. 35.19A. Photochemical O_2 evolution from 3 mm.³ of separated spinach chloroplasts (A) and from crude leaf juice (B,C), both containing 3 μg. Chl (Tolmach 1951). Phosphoroscopic determination of O_2 pressure in N_2 gas flow (9.6 cm.³ N_2/min.), 10–12° C.

creased the oxygen production by up to 16% of the stoichiometric equivalent of the amount added (assuming that each molecule of PGA or PA can consume 2 atoms hydrogen). Figure 35.19B shows the time curves of

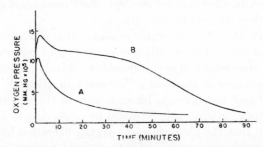

Fig. 35.19B. Photochemical O_2 evolution from 2.5 mm.³ crude spinach juice with addition of 2.5 mm.³ water (A); and 0.02 M PGA (B) at 15° C. (Tolmach 1951). 9.6 cm.³ N_2/min. Total O_2 yields: 0.026 mm.³ in (A), 0.095 mm.³ in (B).

oxygen consumption of chloroplasts suspended in cell sap, with and without added PGA. The shape of the curves and the total additional oxygen liberation varied widely, apparently in dependence of the physiological state of the sample.   This, and the failure of PGA to increase oxygen yield of chloroplasts which had been separated from the cell sap, indicate that PGA does not serve directly as a Hill oxidant, but contributes to the reaction in a more complex way—perhaps by dark reaction with the reduced form of a "natural" Hill oxidant.

Addition of adenosine triphosphate (ATP), glyceric acid or glucose to the chloroplast-bearing leaf juice did not increase the oxygen burst in light; but addition of TPN leads to strong stimulation of the oxygen production, as shown by figure 35.19C.   At low TPN concentrations (e. g., 2.5×10^{-5}

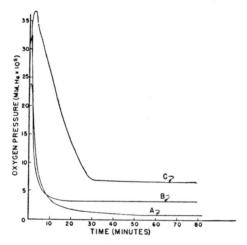

Fig. 35.19C. Photochemical O_2 evolution from 1.5 mm.³ chloroplast suspension (1.5 μg. Chl) to which were added: (A) 1.5 mm.³ water; (B) 1.5 mm.³ 1×10^{-3} M TPN; (C) 1.5 mm.³ 1×10^{-2} M TPN.   10–12° C.; 9.4 cm.³ N_2/ min. (Tolmach 1951).

M) the amount of extra oxygen evolved was up to 17 times the stoichiometric equivalent of the TPN added; at the higher concentrations (e. g., 5×10^{-4} M) this ratio declined to or below 1, but the initial rate of oxygen production continued to increase with [TPN] (e. g., from 41 mm.³ O_2 per milligram chlorophyll per hour in the absence of TPN, to 163 mm.³ at 2.5×10^{-5} mole/l. and 282 mm.³ at 5×10^{-4} mole/l. TPN.

Addition of TPN had no effect on oxygen liberation from washed chloroplasts, indicating that this compound, too, entered into secondary oxidation-reduction reactions between the "natural" Hill oxidant and some reducible substances present in cell sap, and did not act directly as Hill oxidant (in agreement with the earlier observations of Mehler, and Holt and French).   The above-suggested attribution of the incapacity of TPN to serve as such ultimate Hill oxidant, to rapid reoxidation of $TPNH_2$, was supported by Tolmach's observation of a rapid (nonphotochemical) oxidation of added $TPNH_2$ by spinach juice.

At this point (following a suggestion by Vennesland and Conn), Tolmach added to the chloroplast suspension the complete malic enzyme system (instead of TPN alone), to provide a "trap" for $TPNH_2$. In unseparated, chloroplast-bearing cell juice, the addition of TPN, pyruvate, carbonate, Mn^{++} salt and "malic enzyme" did not enhance the oxygen yield more than did TPN alone; but in precipitated, washed and resuspended chloroplast material, a small, but marked, stimulation was observed (figure 35.19D). If PGA was added together with the malic enzyme system, the extra oxygen burst was about double that with pyruvate alone.

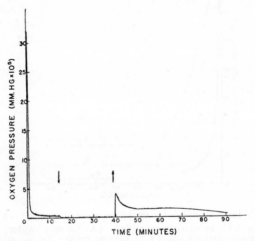

Fig. 35.19D. Stimulation of photochemical O_2 evolution from 3 mm.³ chloroplast suspension (1.8 μg Chl) containing 0.04 μmole $MnCl_2$, 0.17 μmole pyruvate, 0.4 μg. TPN, 0.08 μmole glycylglycine buffer (pH 7.0), by addition (at 21 min.) of 2 mm.³ malic enzyme, and switching on the light (at upward arrow) (Tolmach 1951). Gas: 4.2% CO_2 in N_2; flow 8.8 cm.³/min., 25° C.

To complement the demonstration of oxygen evolution from the malic enzyme system by a demonstration of concurrent CO_2 fixation, tracer C^*O_2 was used. Some C^*O_2 fixation could be observed in light even in the absence of malic enzyme; it was tentatively attributed to exchange reactions. Addition of malic enzyme increased the fixation by a factor of five, making it about equivalent to the extra oxygen production observed phosphorometrically under the same conditions.

The Chicago investigators did not attach to the pyruvate reduction, mediated by TPN in illuminated chloroplast suspensions, the same importance as did Ochoa and Vishniac, who saw in it evidence of the actual mechanism of photosynthesis. Tolmach was not certain whether the strong effect of TPN on oxygen liberation by crude leaf juice was due to intermediate reduction of TPN (as in the pyruvate-malic enzyme system), or to the conversion of some sap component into an effective Hill oxidant by TPN-mediated autoxidation (since he observed that addition of oxygen-saturated water to TPN containing juice also caused a new oxygen burst in light). The much greater volume of oxygen produced from crude leaf juice compared to washed chloroplast-pyruvate-bicarbonate-malic enzyme system indicated that only a small part of the former could be due to the reductive carboxylation of pyruvate. Tolmach also pointed out that the successful competition of carbon dioxide with oxygen as hydrogen acceptor in photosynthesis would be difficult to understand if the reduction of carbon dioxide were to be mediated by an intermediate (TPN) whose concentration in chloroplasts is very low (a value of 10^{-6} mole/l. was mentioned in Tolmach's paper; however, subsequent determinations in Vennesland's laboratory gave higher values).

According to Franck, efficient reduction in the presence of air would require TPN to displace the much more abundant O_2 (about 3×10^{-4} mole/l. in cell sap equilibrated with air) from contact with chlorophyll. In fact, if one assumes, as Franck does, that a molecule of the oxidant must be associated with each chlorophyll molecule, only a primary oxidant with a concentration of the order of 0.05 mole/l. (in the grana) can function with a high quantum yield. If one assumes that effective energy exchange between chlorophyll molecules reduces the number of centers in which oxidant molecules must stand ready to accept the H atoms, transferred in the primary photochemical process, by a factor of the order of 10^2 (or 10^3), then a concentration of $\sim 5 \times 10^{-4}$ (or $\sim 5 \times 10^{-5}$) mole/l. may be sufficient to keep the reaction centers occupied; this could possibly—but not very likely—make TPN a successful contender for these sites. On the other hand, the lack of discrimination, characteristic of photochemical processes (because of the excess activation energy usually available in a quantum), should warn us from reading too much significance into the reduction—with a small yield—of *any* reductant offered to the chloroplast system, particularly of a reductant whose reduced form we happen to know how to trap very efficiently.

Arnon (1951) also made experiments on the reductive carboxylation of pyruvic acid in the presence of malic enzyme and illuminated chloroplasts. He demonstrated that the malic enzyme is present in the cytoplasmic fluid left after the precipitation of chloroplast fragments by high-speed centrifugation, so that the complete photocatalytic system (except for TPN) can be obtained from one and the same plant. Figure 35.19E shows the photochemical evolution of oxygen from this system, whose detailed composition is given in the caption.   The reaction rate in this figure corresponds to about 8 molecules oxygen evolved per molecule chlorophyll per hour in light of about 28 klux—about 5% of the saturation rate of photosynthesis.   This yield, although considerably larger than that observed by Vishniac and Ochoa, is still quite small.   Furthermore, according to curve I, the oxygen formation stops after the evolution of only about 10^{-6} mole oxygen from 10^{-4} mole pyruvate.

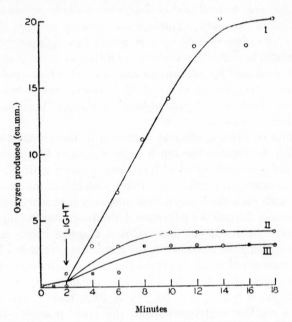

Fig. 35.19E. Curve I: O_2 evolution from chloroplast fragments (0.5 mg. Chl) in light in the presence of 2×10^{-6} mole KCl, 2×10^{-5} mole NaHCO₃, 2×10^{-6} mole MnCl₂, 1×10^{-5} mole li pyruvate, 6.5×10^{-7} mole TPN, and 0.2 ml. "malic enzyme" preparation from the same leaves.   Total volume 3 ml.; 15.1° C., 28 klux.   Curve II: same without malic enzyme.   Curve III: same without TPN. (Arnon 1951.)

Arnon and Heimburger (1952) added to the above-described study a chromato-graphic proof of the formation of tagged l-malate in the chloroplast-pyruvate-radiocar-bonate-malic enzyme system.   The estimate of C^*O_2 fixed in malate indicated a stoichio-metric equivalent of 4.5 mm.³ oxygen; manometric measurement showed, in this par-ticular case, an evolution of 18 mm.³ O_2 in the complete system and of 15 mm.³ O_2 in an aliquot from which malic enzyme was omitted, and in which practically no C^{14} was fixed. The difference (3 mm.³ O_2) is in satisfactory agreement with the value calculated from C^{14} fixation; but the very large O_2 evolution in the blank (not shown by curve II in figure 35.19E) makes the experiment somewhat unsatisfactory.

In evaluating the possible significance of these results for the mechanism of photosynthesis, Arnon referred to the tracer experiments of Calvin *et al.* (to be described in chapter 36), indicating that malate is not normally an intermediate in the main reaction sequence of photosynthesis.

Earlier in this section we mentioned the recently discovered "coenzyme A." Attempts to use this compound as ultimate Hill oxidant have not yet given positive results; whether it can serve as intermediate in the photochemical reduction of metabolites whose formation in respiration is coupled with the reduction of coenzyme A (such as the formation of acetate by oxidative decarboxylation of pyruvate) remains to be ascertained. An important role was ascribed to this compound in photosynthesis by Calvin; but since this hypothesis was not based on photochemical experiments with chloroplasts, we will consider it in chapter 36 when dealing with various suggested chemical mechanisms of photosynthesis.

More than halfway on the redox potential scale between the systems H_2O/O_2 ($E_0' = -0.81$ volt at pH 7) and H_2TPN/TPN ($E_0' = +0.282$ volt at pH 7) lies the system ferrocytochrome c/ferricytochrome c ($E_0' = -0.26$ volt at pH 7). Despite this favorable position, oxidized cytochrome c was found by Holt and French (1948) not to produce oxygen in light in the presence of chloroplast suspensions. Holt (1950) reinvestigated this system, using a photometric method to observe the reduction of cytochrome c. He found that oxidized cytochrome c was reduced by chloroplasts (from *Spinacia* or *Phytolacca americana*) in light, but that the reduction was rapidly reversed in the dark. Experiments with added reduced cytochrome c in the presence of oxygen showed that the chloroplasts contained an enzyme ("cytochrome oxidase") capable of transferring electrons from reduced cytochrome c to oxygen. The oxidation was inhibited by cyanide, azide and carbon monoxide. The inhibition by the latter, however, could not be reversed by light as is the case with cytochrome oxidase in respiration.

The presence of a cytochrome oxidase can explain the lack of oxygen production by illuminated chloroplast suspensions in the presence of oxidized cytochrome c; but it can not explain why practically complete reduction of cytochrome c could be observed spectroscopically—unless this reduction occurred not by hydrogen transfer from water, but by reaction with some cellular reductant.

Mehler (1951[2]) also found rapid autoxidation of cytochrome c to follow chloroplast-sensitized photochemical reduction (revealed by spectroscopic observation). He attributed the failure of cyanide to stimulate oxygen evolution from the cytochrome-chloroplast system (by poisoning the cytochrome oxidase) to a destructive effect on cyanide of concentrated spinach chloroplast suspensions (such as are used in manometric, in contrast to spectroscopic, observations of the Hill reaction). Mehler reported that Tolmach (working in the same laboratory) could observe photochemical oxygen liberation from the cytochrome-chloroplast mixture by using azide instead of cyanide as poison for the cytochrome oxidase.

In chapter 37A we will describe the finding, in chlorophyll bearing plant tissues, of a new iron-porphyrin-protein compound, designated as "cytochrome f" (Davenport and Hill 1952). It has a normal redox potential of -0.37 volt (at pH 6–8; E_0' increases at the higher pH values by 0.06 volt per pH unit). Compared with the normal redox potential of cytochrome c ($E_0' = -0.26$ volt), cytochrome f is a stronger oxidant. Hill (1951) and Davenport and Hill (1953) pointed out that the difference between the normal potentials of cytochrome f and of the oxygen electrode at pH 7 (-0.81 volt) is 0.44 volt, or 11.2 kcal/mole. The free energy of the reaction:

$$(35.34B) \quad 2\ H_2O + 4\ Cyt f\ Fe^{+++} \longrightarrow 4\ H^+ + 4\ Cyt f\ Fe^{++} + O_2$$

is therefore 44.8 kcal—or close to the energy of a red quantum. Davenport and Hill suggested that this reaction may represent the primary photochemical process in photosynthesis (with further increase in reduction potential achieved by an energy dismutation mechanism, as repeatedly discussed before). However, the transfer of four electrons by one quantum is an implausible mechanism. Furthermore, what matters for the possibility of a photochemical electron transfer is not the *free* energy change, ΔF, resulting from a similar transfer by the *"slow"* thermal mechanism, but the *total* energy change, ΔH^*, required for an *instantaneous* transfer (with all nuclei held more or less rigidly in position, in approximate accordance with the Franck-Condon principle). Since these reactions involve a change in ionic charges, the two energy values, ΔF and ΔH^*, may be quite different. (The ΔF of such reactions includes changes in the ion-dipole interaction with the medium—which are different for sudden and gradual transfer—and large entropy changes produced by liberation—or immobilization—of dipole molecules around the ions whose charges had been increased or decreased.) Not much significance could therefore be attached to the similarity between the standard free energy of the thermal reaction (35.34B), and the energy content of a red quantum, even if it were not for the improbability of an elementary photochemical process involving simultaneous transfer of 4 electrons. We conclude that if cytochrome f molecules do serve as intermediates in photosynthesis, they must do so by accepting single electrons transferred from single H_2O molecules by single quanta (which implies the loss of much more than one-half of the quantum energy); alternatively, they could play a role in the thermal back reaction (which may be essential for "energy dismutation," *e. g.*, *via* the formation of high energy phosphate esters, as repeatedly discussed above).

No oxygen liberation was observed in chloroplast suspensions with *glutathione* (Holt and French 1948), or with *dehydroascorbic acid* (Aronoff 1946, Holt and French 1948), or with *oxalacetic acid* and *riboflavin* (Mehler 1951[1]). (It will be recalled that the last named compound was used extensively by Krasnovsky for the dark reoxidation, in solution, of chlorophyll after its photoreduction by ascorbic acid, *cf.* part A of this chapter.)

This may be the place to mention attempts to use other intermediary metabolites, or miscellaneous biologically important substances, as Hill oxidants. Several of these compounds (including phosphoglyceric and pyruvic acid) were mentioned above as stimulating the photochemical oxygen evolution mediated by the "natural Hill oxidant" in crude leaf juices, but causing no oxygen liberation with washed chloroplast fragments. Another oxidant of the same type is *methemoglobin*. In studying the "natural" Hill oxidant (first described in Hill's 1939 work, *cf.* page 63), Davenport (1949) noted that the initial rate of methemoglobin reduction by chloroplast suspensions was as high in the presence of a chloroplast free leaf extract as in the presence of ferric oxalate. On the other hand, methemoglobin itself was not reduced photochemically by washed chloroplasts. Following this lead, Davenport, Hill and Whatley (1952) found that crude macerates of many leaves (cleared only by filtration through glass wool) reduced considerable amounts of methemoglobin in light. Results of this type were obtained with leaves of *Avena*, *Pisum sativum*, *Sambucus nigra*, *Chenopodium Bonns-Henricus* and *Strellaria media*. Similar preparations from *Calendula*, *Brassica* and *Tropaeolum* were only weakly active, and those from *Phaseolus multiflorus* and *Centranthus ruber* were inactive.

The activity (related to unit chlorophyll amount) decreased with dilution, *e. g.*, from about 0.5 cm.^{3} O_2 per mg. chlorophyll per hour at [Chl] $=$ 5.6 $\times$ 10^{-5} mole/l., to 0.15 cm.^{3} at [Chl] $=$ 1 $\times$ 10^{-5} mole/l.

Figure 35.19F shows the loss of methemoglobin reducing capacity of chloroplasts upon washing (by two centrifugations) and its restoration by the addition of the supernatant from the first centrifugation, or of an aqueous extract from previously acetone-extracted leaf powder (prepared as described on page 63). Similar aqueous extracts from acetone washed root material, or from (chlorophyll free) terminal bud material, were inactive. The bud extract inhibited the activity of the leaf extract, but the root extract contained no such inhibiting components. The "methemoglobin reducing" component of leaf extract was completely destroyed in 10 min. at 100° C., almost lost in 10 min. at 60° C., but remained almost unaffected after 10 min. at 50° C. It was gradually deactivated by exposure to air. It remained intact after overnight dialysis at 0° C., against

10^{-2} M phosphate buffer (pH 7.4). It stayed in solution after precipitation by acidification to pH 5, and its activity was found unchanged after the pH was adjusted back to 7.4; but acidification to pH 4.5, or alkalization to pH 9.3, destroyed the activity, which could not be brought back even by immediate neutralization. The rate of methemoglobin reaction in the presence of the extract had a maximum at pH 8.3 (a similar optimum, pH 8.0, was found earlier for whole *Stellaria* chloroplasts in ferric oxalate solution, while optimum pH values of about 6.5 were found with quinone

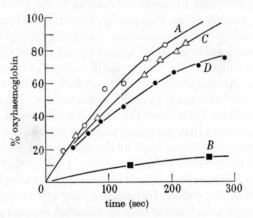

Fig. 35.19F. Photochemical methemoglobin reduction (measured by oxy-hemoglobin formation) by 0.4 ml. chloroplast suspension from *Chenopodium* (1.2 g. leaves in 6 ml. 6% glucose, 0.033 M phosphate buffer, pH 7.4) (Davenport, Hill, and Whatley 1952). Whale muscle hemoglobin: 0.78 × 10^{-4} mole/l. (*A*) crude suspension; (*B*) washed chloroplasts; (*C*) washed chloroplasts + 0.4 ml. first supernatant from washing; (*D*) washed chloroplasts + aqueous extract from acetone extracted leaf material, equivalent to 0.4 ml. supernatant.

or ferricyanide as oxidant, *cf.* section 5(b) below). The rate increased with methemoglobin concentration, reaching saturation >1.4 × 10^{-4} mole/l., it declined with increasing salt concentration in the extract (phosphate buffer or ammonium sulfate). Chloride ions appeared to have no effect on activity of the washed preparations. The reaction was inhibited by *o*-phenanthroline and urethan (*cf.* section 5(d)). Attempts to fractionate the —apparently proteidic—"methemoglobin-reduction-promoting" factor in leaf extracts, by fractional precipitation with phosphate buffer or ammonium sulfate, showed that activity was absent from the "globulin" fraction precipitated at half-saturation with the salts, and concentrated in the "albumin" fraction, precipitated only at complete saturation.

Gerretsen (1951) suggested that ascorbic acid can play in chloroplast suspensions (and in live cells as well) the role of a *substitute reductant* (replacing H_2O as hydrogen donor). He based this hypothesis on the finding of an "induction period" in the potentiometric observations of photochemical processes in crude suspensions of *Avena* chloroplasts. It could be ascertained that during this period the ascorbic acid content of the chloroplasts decreased. (Gerretsen suggested that photoxidation of ascorbic acid may be the cause of induction phenomena also in photosynthesis.) In agreement with this hypothesis, the "induction period" could be prolonged by the addition of extra ascorbic acid. This hypothesis is equivalent to the assumption that chloroplasts complete, in light, a "Krasnovsky reaction" before they begin to carry out the "Hill reaction" and liberate oxygen. However, it is also possible that the photoxidation of ascorbic acid occurs by a mechanism of the type suggested by Mehler, *i. e.*, *via* the formation of hydrogen peroxide by Hill reaction with molecular oxygen as oxidant, and secondary reaction of the peroxide with the substrate of photoxidation.

(g) *Miscellaneous Organic Compounds*

Some oxygen evolution was observed by Aronoff (1946) with salicylic aldehyde and benzaldehyde, but considerable chlorophyll bleaching occurred in this case. Some oxygen was also evolved with benzoyl peroxide; none with salicylic acid, fructose, methanol or butadiene monoxide.

Gurevich (1947) found that illuminated chloroplast suspensions (from *Primula, Stellaria* or *Atriplex*) can reduce *o*-dinitrobenzene, $NO_2C_6H_4NO_2$, first to $NO_2C_6H_4NHOH$, and then to $NO_2C_6H_4NH_2$. Since this reagent is a strong enzymatic poison, it was used in the form of a deposit on a filter paper strip suspended in the illuminated chloroplast suspension; in other words, it must have been reduced secondarily by products diffusing from the chloroplasts into the aqueous medium.

5. Kinetics

(a) *Methods for Measuring Reduction*

The common method for measuring the rate of the Hill reaction with any oxidants is the manometric (or chemical) determination of liberated oxygen. An advantage compared to photosynthesis is that only one gas is exchanged as a result of the photochemical reaction. The dark reactions also are less significant than respiration in living cells—at least with some chloroplast preparations and some oxidants. However, a correction for dark reactions, either consuming oxygen and liberating carbon dioxide ("respiration") or liberating CO_2 without consuming O_2 ("fermentation") often is needed (*cf.* section *c*).

With certain oxidants the determination of oxygen can be replaced or supplemented by convenient determinations of the oxidant. Physicochemical methods are more valuable than chemical assays because they permit the progress of the reaction to be followed without taking samples for titrimetric or gravimetric analysis.

The use of organic dyes as oxidants invites the application of *photometry*. French and Holt (1946) first used a visual method, determining the time needed for a given suspension to "completely decolorize" a certain quantity of dye. A complication arises when the absorption band of the dye overlaps that of chlorophyll; it is therefore most convenient to use dyes whose absorption peak is in the green.

Photoelectric spectrophotometry permits more precise measurements than visual colorimetry. In this case, a narrow band or line can be used to measure the concentration of the dye in a region where the plant pigments absorb only weakly or not at all. Apparatus of this type has been described by Holt, Smith and French (1951). They reported that, using the blue dye, 2,6-dichlorobenzenone-indophenol, the initial rate of the Hill reaction can be measured within 2 min., with as little as 0.05 mg. chloroplast material— a quantity which would yield only 0.1 mm.^{3} O_2 during the same period. Careful and repeatedly checked calibration (dye concentration *vs.* photoelectric current) is required for reliable absorption measurements with photoelectric cells in spectral bands isolated by filters; this calibration can be avoided by the use of monochromatic light.

Since some compounds may be reduced in light by chloroplast *without liberation of oxygen*, photometric measurements of the Hill reaction with untried oxidants must be checked to make certain that the reduction actually occurs at the expense of water. Washing of chloroplast material removes water-soluble reductants (such as ascorbic acid), and thus makes the photometric method less subject to errors.

Two *electrochemical methods* of measuring the Hill reaction are possible. One is applicable to oxidants whose reduction cause a change in acidity, for example:

$$(35.35) \qquad H_2O + 2 Fe(CN)_6{}^{-3} \longrightarrow 2 Fe(CN)_6{}^{-4} + \tfrac{1}{2} O_2 + 2 H^+$$

A *p*H meter can be used to follow the course of this reduction. This method was first applied by Holt and French (1946). They checked whether any *p*H changes occurred in light in *chloroplast-free* solution of Hill's reactants (ferric oxalate + ferricyanide + ferric ammonium sulfate) and found that in white light (4500 f. c.) this mixture did produce some acid—probably by direct photochemical reduction of ferric oxalate; however, this reaction could be prevented by the use of red light.

A similar method was also used by Clendenning and Gorham (1950) in their survey of the chloroplast preparations from different plants (section B2). With some species, strong acidification occurred *in the dark* (without liberation of oxygen). In a few cases, the *p*H drift in the dark was in the alkaline direction (*cf.* section (*c*) below). The absence of such drifts must be ascertained when the pH method is used to measure the rate of the Hill reaction.

Another potentiometric method for following the Hill reaction is the measurement of the *oxidation-reduction potential*. This is feasible whenever the system contains one—and only one—electrode-active oxidation-reduction couple (such as ferrous ion-ferric ion, ferrocyanide ion-ferricyanide ion, or dye-leuco dye). This method was described by Spikes, Lumry, Eyring and Wayrynen (1950[1,2]). They found it practicable with ferricyanide as oxidant. However, the oxidation-reduction potential often showed considerable drifts even in the absence of oxidant. For example, when crude suspensions of cell content from sunflower leaves were illuminated, the redox potential of the medium changed rapidly. The drift continued for 12 hours. This may indicate that the Hill reaction was proceeding at the cost of a natural oxidant present in the cell juice (as described in the early experiments of Hill). Macerated cell material from spinach showed no such prolonged drift.

Chloroplasts separated from the plasma and cell juice showed only a small change of potential with time during illumination without added oxidant. If the chloroplasts were boiled, the potential was not affected. even if ferricyanide was added.

If, however, the chloroplasts were "live," a change of potential was observed in light, when a complete Hill solution, or ferricyanide alone, or quinone were added to them. The strongest change was produced when ferricyanide was used in a buffered solution (to prevent complications due to changes in pH). With this system, phosphate-buffered at pH 6.85, potential *vs.* time curves could be determined under a variety of conditions.

Spikes *et al.* (1954) have developed a device to automatically record redox potentials in cell suspensions.

The same method was also used by Wessels and Havinga (1952, 1953; *cf.* Wessels 1954) in experiments with different quinones and quinonoid dyes as Hill oxidants, and by Gerretsen (1950[1,2], 1951), who combined the measurement of redox potential with that of pH changes in a study of light reactions in crude leaf juice.

It will be noted that the displacement of an oxidation-reduction equilibrium in light produces a nonequilibrium state in which one redox system (*e. g.*, quinone-hydroquinone) is in the reduced, and another one (*e. g.*, O_2/H_2O) in the oxidized state. Barring immediate effective spatial separation of the two couples, an electrode immersed into the illuminated mixture, will follow—entirely or preponderantly—the change in the composition of the component with the greater electrode activity. The situation is similar to that in the so-called "photogalvanic cells" (described by Rabinowitch) in which a platinum electrode, immersed into an illuminated mixture of thionine and ferrous sulfate, responds to the reduction of the dye more than to the oxidation of ferric salt (*cf.* part A, section 5 above). In following the Hill reaction with a redox electrode, one is actually measuring the photogalvanic effect in a system in which only one of the two components is definitely known, and assumes that the other has no effect on the potential at all (*e. g.*, because it remains confined in the chloroplasts and only escapes after the conversion of the oxidized form to molecular oxygen, which makes it "electrode inactive"). This is not necessarily true—some intermediates in oxygen liberation from water may diffuse into the medium, and may be electrode-active there. Another possible complicating factor is that in the presence of several Hill oxidants (*e. g.*, of the "natural" hydrogen acceptor together with the added one), the electrode may respond preferentially to one of them—and not necessarily to the one present in the highest concentration.

An elegant method for the study of the Hill reaction is the measurement of *isotopic oxygen exchange* by means of a mass spectrograph. This method alone permits measuring, simultaneously, oxygen-liberating and oxygen-consuming processes. Its application by Brown and co-workers to photosynthesis and respiration is described in chapter 37D (section 3); it was applied to the Hill reaction by Mehler and Brown (1952) and Brown (1953).

(b) Rate and Yield under Different Conditions

We include in this section a summary of measurements of the rate of the Hill reaction under different conditions even though the reproducibility of these measurements is not too well assured. In particular, it has not yet been possible to maintain a constant rate of reaction in chloroplast suspensions for more than a short period of time (of the order of an hour at best, and often much less). The comparison of the efficiencies of the Hill reaction with different preparations and different oxidants is therefore best based on measurements of the *initial* rate, made in the first few minutes of illumination of a fresh preparation (or a preparation preserved without loss of activity as described in section 3(*b*) above).

The most important kinetic constants of a reaction such as photosynthesis, or Hill reaction, are the *maximum quantum yield* as observed in weak light and the *saturation rate* in strong light. In studying the Hill reaction, attention has also been paid to the *total amount* of the added oxidant that can be utilized before the reaction comes to a standstill; however, this proportion has more to do with the chemical stability of the oxidant and its reactions with various components of the chloroplastic matter than with the efficiency of the photochemical apparatus.

Quantum Yield. French and Rabideau (1945) measured the *quantum yield* of the oxygen liberation by chloroplasts from *Spinacia* and *Tradescantia* (with ferric oxalate as oxidant), and obtained figures ranging from a minimum of 15, up to 50 or more quanta per mole oxygen (*cf.* chapter 29, Table 29.X). The variations must have been due to differences in the state of the chloroplasts; subsequent experiments (sec. 2 above) made it appear possible that duration of illumination prior to the grinding of the leaves has been the most important factor. The quantum yield was $\leq \frac{1}{2}$ of that obtained in a parallel set of experiments with live *Chlorella* cells in carbon dioxide.

In Chapter 29 we also tabulated the quantum yields found by Ehrmantraut and Rabinowitch (1952). Most of these were for whole *Chlorella* cells (*cf.* part C of this chapter). Measurements were made, however, also with chloroplasts from *Phytolacca*, using quinone, Hill's mixture and ferricyanide as oxidant. The results were close to those obtained with live cells ($1/\gamma = 9$ to 12, *cf.* table 29.XI). Since similar yields were obtained also for the oxygen production by *Chlorella* cells in carbonate buffers, they were considered as supporting the hypothesis that the primary photochemical process in the Hill reaction is the same as in photosynthesis.

Warburg (1952) arrived at entirely different conclusions. He measured the quantum yield of the Hill reaction in spinach chloroplasts with quinone as oxidant, at different wave lengths. His preparations (which he designated as "green grana," *cf.* section 2(*b*) above) gave $1/\gamma = 65, 73, 85$ and 101 quanta per O_2 molecule for $\lambda = 366, 436, 480$ and 644 mμ, respectively. Warburg noted that these quantum yields were proportional to wave lengths, so that the energy yields (ϵ on p. 1083) were constant (about 1%) throughout the spectrum (including the region of strong absorption by the carotenoids). He concluded that the Hill reaction is different from photosynthesis not only in that it has a very low photochemical efficiency, but also in that it has a λ-independent *energy* yield, ϵ, while photosynthesis has an extremely high efficiency and a λ-independent *quantum* yield, γ. It will be noted that the disagreement is in this case opposite to that obtained in the study of the quantum efficiency of photosynthesis, Warburg's efficiencies being much lower than those found by other observers. He seems to have used chloroplast preparations of low activity—as witnessed by their failure to give any reduction of Hill's mixture at all.

Light Curves. Hill and Scarisbrick (1940) gave the earliest light curve of the Hill reaction; it was reproduced in fig. 6 (p. 65, Vol. I), and showed saturation in the region of 20 klux. Aronoff (1946[2]) found that the rate of oxygen liberation from spinach "grana," with quinone as oxidant, was proportional to light intensity up to 13 klux; (*cf.* fig. 35.21). Spikes, Lumry, Eyring and Wayrynen (1950) reported that the light curve for spinach chloroplasts, with ferricyanide as oxidant, is a rectangular hyperbola.

Holt, Brooks and Arnold (1951) gave a light curve of the oxygen production by a chloroplast suspension from *Phytolacca americana* with an indophenol dye as oxidant.   Its shape is similar to that for photosynthesis (fig. 35.20).

Gilmour and co-workers (1953) measured light curves for the reduction of ferricyanide by beet chloroplasts and found them to be rectangular hyperbolas (*i. e.*, $1/H$ is a linear function of I).   Their saturation level was rather low (corresponding to about 800 mm.^{3} O_2 per milligram chlorophyll per hour, or a turnover time of 360 sec., *cf.* table 35.X).

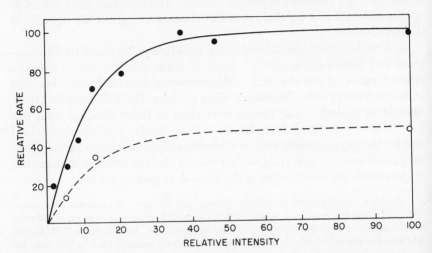

Fig. 35.20. Light curves of Hill reaction in chloroplast suspension: solid line, before irradiation; broken line, after irradiation with 253.7 mμ (after Holt, Brooks, and Arnold 1951).

Maximum Rate in Saturating Light. According to chapter 28 (section A5), the usual value of $P_{max.}^{max.}/Chl_0$—the saturating rate of photosynthesis in strong light with ample supply of carbon dioxide, related to unit amount of chlorophyll—corresponds to about one molecule O_2 liberated per molecule chlorophyll about every 20 sec. (much higher values have been found only with *aurea* leaves).   This corresponds to about 4000 mm.^{3} O_2 per mg. chlorophyll per hour.   Table 35.X gives in comparison some of the maximum (initial) rates of oxygen production by chloroplastic matter, as reported by several observers with different preparations and different oxidants.

With a given chloroplast preparation, the oxygen production in saturating light depends on the nature of the oxidant.   This can mean that the rate-limiting process involves the supply (or the preliminary transformation) of the specific oxidant prior to its participation in the photochemical reaction; or it may indicate a difference in the probability of back reac-

TABLE 35.X

MAXIMUM INITIAL RATE OF HILL REACTION, $H^{max.}$ (IN MM.^{3} O$_2$ PER MG. Chl PER HR.)

Observer	Preparation	Oxidant	Method	Temp., ° C.	$H^{max.}$
Arnon, Whatley (1949[1])	Chloroplast suspension from Swiss chard leaves; KCl added	Quinone	Manometric	2	1030
		Ferricyanide	"	"	800
		Phenol-indophenol	"	"	730
Clendenning, Gorham (1950[2])	Crude extracts from leaves and algae from 80 species[a]	Hill's mixture	Acidimetric	—	50–2500
Kumm, French (1945)	Chloroplast suspensions from *Tradescantia fluminensis*	Hill's mixture [K$_2$C$_2$O$_4$ 0.5 M, Fe (III)-NH$_4$-sulfate 0.01 M,	Manometric	5–10	320–1500
	Same, from *Spinacia*	K$_3$Fe(CN)$_6$ 0.02 M, sucrose 0.2 M, borate 0.167 M]	"		570
Holt, Brooks, Arnold (1951)	Chloroplast suspension from *Phytolacca americana*	2,6-Dichlorobenzenene	Colorimetric	—	2200

[a] Highest rates with lamb's quarters, millet, chard, lettuce, spinach, flax (*cf.* section B2 for details).
[b] *Cf.* section B2 for comparison of species.

tions between the (common) oxidation product (oxygen or a "photoperoxide") and the (individual) reduction products. Back reactions do not by themselves lead to light saturation, but if the maximum rate in strong light is determined by the deficiency of a "finishing" or "stabilizing" catalyst, then a difference in the reducing power of the various reduction products can affect the turnover of this catalyst, and thus influence the saturation level. Aronoff (1946[2]) found three different light curves (fig. 35.21), $H = f(I)$, for the rate of oxygen liberation by "grana" from spinach chloroplasts, as function of light intensity, for three different quinones. A different yield in weak light, as well as a different saturation level, could be attributed to differences in the reducing power of the three hydroquinones; but in this case the order of the curves should be the same in strong and in weak light. The crossing-over of these curves, shown in fig. 35.21, remains unexplained.

Effect of Concentration of the Oxidant. In photosynthesis, the effect of the factor [CO$_2$] on the rate (discussed in chapter 27) was represented by a saturation curve, with evidence of inhibition at very high concentrations. The initial increase in rate with [CO$_2$] appeared to be, to a considerable degree, the result of supply processes; we had to leave the question open whether supply effects can be eliminated, and an "intrinsic" CO$_2$ saturation curve of photosynthesis obtained, reflecting the *participation* of carbon dioxide in the first step of photosynthesis, rather than its *supply* to the locus of this reaction.

The same considerations apply to the Hill reaction; here, too, diffusion of oxidant may determine the shape of the function $H = f[\text{oxidant}]$. (In the case of Hill reaction in whole cells, the cell membrane is an important diffusion barrier.) High concentrations of oxidants produce inhibition similar to that caused by high concentrations of carbon dioxide; with some oxidants inhibition seems to occur even before saturation is reached.

Clendenning and Gorham (1950) investigated the effect of quinone concentration of the rate of Hill reaction in separated spinach and wheat

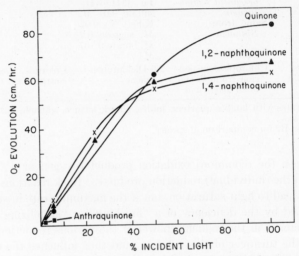

Fig. 35.21. Light curves of oxygen evolution by chloroplast fragments in light with different quinones (after Aronoff 1946).

chloroplast suspensions (fig. 35.22A). Maximum initial rate was observed at 0.5–1 mg. quinone in 2 cc. (2–4 × 10⁻² mole/liter). With 2 mg. quinone the initial rate was somewhat lower, but the total yield higher—the reaction proceeded steadily until about 90% of the stoichiometric oxygen amount was produced. With 4 or 8 mg. quinone the initial rate and the total yield both were much lower—an evidence of "self-inhibition" of the quinone reaction by excess quinone.

It will be seen in part C that similar observations were made by Clendenning and Ehrmantraut (1950) with live *Chlorella* cells.

Holt and French (1946), using Hill's mixture (ferricyanide and ferric oxalate), observed (acidimetrically) no effect of $[\text{FeCy}_6{}^{-3}]$ between 5 × 10⁻³ and 60 × 10⁻³ mole/liter on the initial rate of the Hill reaction. Spikes, Lumry, Eyring and Wayrynen (1950), on the other hand, who meas-

ured the rate of reduction of ferricyanide by the redox potential method
found that the initial rate declined with increasing [FeCy$_6$$^{-3}$], from 1.30
to 0.12 mole ferricyanide reduced per mole chlorophyll per minute.   Approximately, this initial rate was proportional to [FeCy$_6$$^{-3}$]$^{-1}$, indicating
a strong self-inhibition not found by Holt and French.   On the other hand,
the change in rate as the reaction proceeded followed closely the zero order
law.   Spikes *et al.* suggested, as possible explanation of this apparent con-

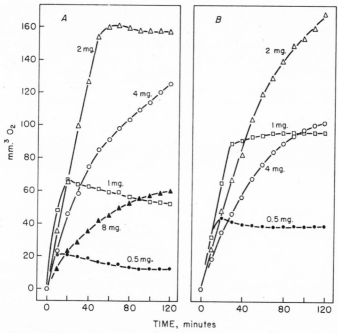

Fig. 35.22A. Effect of quinone concentration on oxygen production by chloroplast suspensions (after Clendenning and Gorham, 1950): (*A*) crude leaf macerate; (*B*) separated and resuspended chloroplast material.

tradiction, that the ferrocyanide produced the same inhibition as ferricyanide.   With quinone, where Clendenning and Gorham found clear evidence of self-inhibition, Spikes *et al.* observed a proportional *increase* of
initial rate with the concentration of the oxidant!

Wessels (1954) also found that the reduction (he used the dye DCPI
as oxidant) proceeds linearly with time, indicating no dependence of rate
on the concentration, [DCPI] (*cf.* figure 35.22B).

Maximum Yield and Back Reactions.   What proportion of the theoretical
amount of oxygen can be obtained in the Hill reaction with a given oxidant
depends (*a*) on the extent of side reactions which destroy the oxidant, *e. g.*,

by "dark" reduction or by photochemical reduction not involving water, and (b) on the rate of back reactions, which may lead to the establishment of a photostationary state short of complete reduction. Finally, deactivation of chloroplasts may cause the reaction to stop before all oxidant has been exhausted. In the latter case, addition of new oxidant will not revive the reaction.

With *quinone*, the main obstacle to 100% utilization of the oxidant seems to be its decomposition. Warburg and Lüttgens (1946) reported yields of the order of 85–90%; Arnon and Whatley (1949[1]) reported "100%" with added 0.01 M KCl, and 36% without it (chard chloroplasts); Aronoff (1946[2]) could obtain only 35% of the theoretical oxygen amount from quinone.

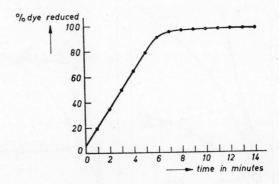

Fig. 35.22B. Percentage reduction of 2,6-dichlorophenol indophenol in illuminated chloroplast suspension as function of time (Wessels 1954). Straight ascending segment indicates zero order reaction.

With *Hill's mixture*, Holt and French (1946) obtained 93% of theoretical oxygen yield (calculated for the initial amount of ferricyanide) after 1 hr. in an atmosphere of nitrogen; upon longer illumination, oxygen was slowly *consumed*, probably through photoxidation. For the same reason, not more than 85% of theoretical yield could be reached in air, and the subsequent decline of oxygen pressure was much faster.

With *ferricyanide*, Arnon and Whatley (1949[1]) reported "100% yield" with 0.01 M KCl, and only 19% without added chloride.

With *phenol indophenol*, Arnon and Whatley (1949[1]) reported a "100% yield" in the presence of KCl, and as much as 90% without added KCl. Earlier, Holt and French (1948) had reported yields of the order of 85% of the stoichiometric amount; however, the calculation was uncertain because of the low content of the dye in the commercial product.

Clendenning and Gorham (1950[1]) found that, with both quinone or

Hill's mixture, 85–95% of the oxidant could be utilized for oxygen production in separated chloroplast fragments, and only 65–75% in crude suspensions containing plasma and cell sap, obviously reflecting oxidant
losses by reaction with cellular material.

Wessels (1954) considered more closely the second above-mentioned
factor in "maximum utilization" of the oxidant—the influence of back reactions. This influence must depend on whether the experiment is carried
out in an atmosphere of practically constant oxygen content in a closed
system where the photochemically produced oxygen is permitted to accumulate, or in a stream of oxygen-free gas. It was already noted in Hill's

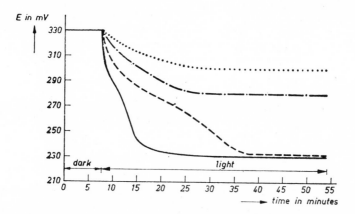

Fig. 35.22C. Effect of light intensity on change of redox potential in chloroplast suspensions containing 2,6-dichlorophenol indophenol ($E'_0 = -0.255$
volt): solid line, 15 and 12 klux; dashed line, 6 klux; dashed-dotted line, 2.3
klux; dotted line, 0.9 klux (Wessels 1954).

early experiments that the reduction of ferric oxalate stopped short of complete reduction, depending on the partial pressure of oxygen. Incomplete
decoloration of certain quinonoid dyestuffs also was observed before, and
we mentioned several times that the failure to observe Hill reaction with
many oxidants of low oxidizing power (such as the pyridine nucleotides)
probably was due to the photostationary state being almost entirely on the
side of reoxidation.

Wessels observed, beside some cases of incomplete decolorization (e. g.,
of toluylene blue), a large number of systems in which the photostationary
redox potential indicated incomplete reduction. Of course, the potential,
being a linear function of the logarithm of the ratio [reductant] [oxidant],
never shows complete reduction (or oxidation); but when it differs from the
normal potential by more than, say, 0.15 volt, its use for the calculation of

the degree of reduction becomes doubtful. The potential may now be affected by some minor component or an impurity; and even if it does reflect correctly the state of the main redox system, this state may be maintained not by the (photochemical) forward and (thermal) back reaction, but by some side reactions (such as the reoxidation of the reduced form by a minor component) which are difficult to avoid even in pure solutions, not to speak of complex biological systems. For this reason, the stationary "photogalvanic" potentials measured by Wessels in various quinones and quinononoid dye systems can be used for kinetic speculations only when the

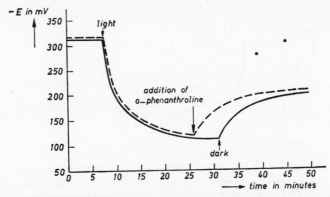

Fig. 35.22D. Back reaction induced by darkening or o-phenanthroline poisoning in chloroplast suspension in the presence of toluylene blue ($E'_0 = -0.137$ volt) (Wessels 1954).

concentrations of the two forms are not too different in order of magnitude. This is the case in the presence of oxygen, or in weak light, as illustrated by figure 35.22C. The normal potential of DCIP is -255 mvolt (on the "physicochemical" scale used in this book!); photostationary potentials of -285 mvolt and -225 mvolt thus correspond to 90% oxidation and 90% reduction, respectively.

That the photostationary potential is in fact determined by a back reaction is illustrated by figure 35.22D, which shows how the reduction of toluylene blue ($E_0 = -137$ mvolt) yields to reoxidation in darkness, or when o-phenanthroline is added, inhibiting the photochemical reaction.

pH Effect. The optimum pH for the Hill reaction depends on the oxidant (and, according to Punnett, 1954, on whether one works with whole or broken chloroplasts).

With *Hill's mixture* (ferric oxalate + ferricyanide) Holt and French (1946) found a maximum initial rate at pH 7.6 at 3° C., and at pH 7.0 at 10° C. Clendenning and Gorham (1950[1]) also found for this oxidant an optimum at pH 7.0; the rate depended, however, not only on the pH, but also on the chemical nature of the buffer. It was higher in 0.4 M sodium sorbitol borate buffer than in 0.04 M sodium or potassium phosphate buffer, although the pH was the same (7.0) in both cases.

Gorham and Clendenning (1952) found that the pH effect depends strongly on the presence of chloride (figure 35.22E).

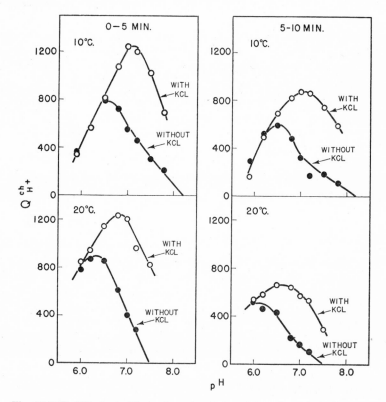

Fig. 35.22E. Effect of pH on photochemical activity of washed, frozen and thawed chloroplasts in Hill's mixture, with and without 10^{-2} M KCl (Gorham and Clendenning 1952). 0.78 mg. Chl per vessel.

With *ferricyanide* alone, Spikes, Lumry, Eyring and Wayrynen (1950) found (by redox potentiometry) an optimum at pH 6.85, with sharp decline of the rate to almost zero at pH <5 or >7.5.

With *quinone*, Warburg and Lüttgens (1946) gave pH 6.2–6.5 as optimum, the rate declining to zero at pH 7.0; Arnon and Whatley (1949), on the other hand, gave pH 7.0 at 10–15° C., and pH 7.6, at 3° C. as pH optima for the same oxidant.

Gorham and Clendenning (1952) found that the pH optimum lies at 5.0–6.5 without, and at 7.0–7.5 with added chloride.

For *chromate*, Holt and French (1948) found pH 7.3 as optimum acidity; the initial rate dropped by ⅓ of the maximum at pH 5.7, and by ½ of the maximum at pH 8.0.

Effect of Temperature. Increase in temperature probably increases the maximum rate, H^{max}, but since it also accelerates the deactivation of

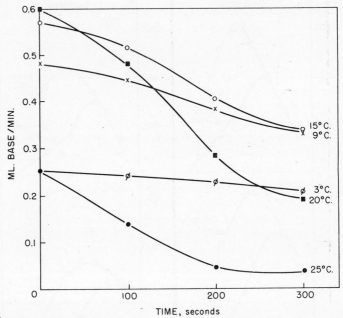

Fig. 35.23. Effect of temperature on the rate of acidification of chloroplast suspension in Hill's mixture in light; the chloroplasts had been in Hill's solution 3 minutes before illumination started (pH 6.8, 0.005 N KOH, 0.38 mg. chlorophyll) (after French and Holt 1946).

chloroplasts, the increase may be overcompensated by the fast decay even in the initial rate measurement. French and Holt (1946) found that the stimulating effect of increasing the temperature from 3° to 20° or 25° C. was over after only 5 minutes of illumination (fig. 35.23). The temperature coefficient of the initial rate (with Hill's mixture as oxidant) was $Q_{10} = 3.5$ (3–15° C.).

Arnon and Whatley (1949) found the highest rate of oxygen production at 15–20° C., dropping to equally low values at 10° C. and at 25° C. with all three oxidants used—quinone, ferricyanide and phenol indophenol. On the other hand, the *total obtainable yield* of oxygen was highest at

10° C.; the loss at 25° C. was particularly high in the absence of chloride (when the photochemical deactivation of the chloroplasts is particularly fast).

Gilmour *et al.* (1953) found a linear relation between log $P^{max.}$ and $1/T$ with ferricyanide as oxidant, for the range 6–23° C.; the slope corresponded to an activation energy of 7.4 kcal/mole. They reported that Bishop (1952) had observed, with the chloroplasts from the same species (*Beta vulgaris*) an activation energy of 10 kcal/mole.

Concentration of Chloroplasts. Variations in the concentration of chloroplasts in the suspension could influence the rate of the Hill reaction in two ways. One is trivial: with increased optical density the light absorption first increases almost proportionally with concentration, then rises more slowly, and finally approaches totality. The average absorption per chlorophyll molecule is at first almost constant and then decreases steadily. The same must be true of the yield per unit chlorophyll amount in the lower part of the light curve, where light supply is the rate-limiting process. In saturating light, the rate per unit chlorophyll amount should be independent of chloroplast concentration; but the higher this concentration, the more light will be needed to reach this saturation. (These relations have been discussed before, in chapters 25, 28 and 32.)

A second, more significant concentration effect could be caused by "poisoning" of the medium by products of respiration or fermentation of the chloroplast fragments; this inhibition (if it occurs at all) should be strongest in the most concentrated suspensions.

Observations on the rate of Hill reaction in suspension of different concentrations so far fall into the first, trivial category.

Spikes *et al.* (1950) found a proportional increase in the rate of ferricyanide reduction by spinach chloroplasts in a 0.25-cm. thick vessel at [Chl] values from 5 to 40 $\times$ 10^{-5} mole/liter in red light of "5000 lux" (this must mean intensity of white light before passing through a red filter, and seems to be too low a light for saturation, particularly in a concentrated suspension). Holt and French (1946) made the same observation in a much stronger light (4500 foot candles, or about 45,000 lux of white light before passing through a red filter) in a vessel about 0.5 cm. thick, and at chlorophyll concentrations up to but not in excess of 16 $\times$ 10^{-5} mole/liter.

Clendenning and Gorham (1950[1]) found the rate of the reaction with Hill's mixture to be proportional to [Chl] up to 7.5 $\times$ 10^{-5} mole/liter.

Wessels (1954) considered a different effect of chloroplast concentration —that on the final "photostationary" state (rather than on the rate of approach to this state). Figure 35.23A illustrates the finding that while the initial rate of reduction of DCPI increases, as expected, with the concentration of chloroplasts, the photostationary state (as measured by the

steady photogalvanic potential) remains the same. The kinetic significance attached to this result of Wessels, will be related below under "Kinetic
Theories."

Yield in Flashing Light. The data on the yield of the Hill reaction
is flashing light in relation to flash energy and duration of dark intervals
(Clendenning and Ehrmantraut 1951; Gilmour *et al.* 1953) were presented
in chapter 34, section B7.

Kinetic Theories. Kinetic analysis of the Hill reaction—of the type of
that attempted in chapters 27 and 28—is an even more uncertain undertaking than that of photosynthesis, because the deterioration of the activity of
chloroplasts with time makes quantitative reproducibility of the data

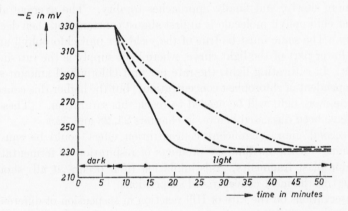

Fig. 35.23A. Influence of chloroplast concentration on change in redox potential
of suspension containing 2,6-dichlorophenol indophenol ($E'_0 = -0.255$ volt)
(Wessels 1954). Chloroplast concentrations: solid line, 4; dashed line, 2;
dashed-dotted line, 1.

questionable. In the case of live *Chlorella* cells (*cf.* part C below) there is
no equally rapid deterioration, but the only oxidant successfully used so
far, quinone, has a "self-poisoning" effect which complicates the kinetic
picture considerably.

A priori, the kinetic treatment of the Hill reaction should be simplified
by the elimination of the complex carbon dioxide factor. However, the diffusion of the oxidant to the chloroplasts may sometimes become the limiting factor. Supply barriers are, of course, reduced by the greater dispersion of the material and the absence of cell walls; but the necessity to use
some oxidants in a very dilute form (this applies to dyes because of their
strong light absorption; and to quinone—with live cells—because of its
poisonous effect) increases the possibility of "oxidant limitation."

Assuming the absence of such limitations, the parts of the discussion in chapters 27 and 28 applicable to the Hill reactions are those on pages 1020–1047, covering the effect of back reactions in the photochemical apparatus and the influence of "finishing" reactions of limited capacity, such as the enzymatic liberation of oxygen.

An additional factor, which can play an important role in the Hill reaction, is the back reaction between the two final products, molecular oxygen and the reduced oxidant (ferric salt, or hydroquinone, or leucodye). In photosynthesis this kind of back reaction is the cellular combustion of carbohydrates, an enzymatic reaction which is slow compared to photosynthesis, at least in strong light. In the Hill reaction many fully reduced oxidants are rapidly autoxidizable, so that a photostationary state is established in light (as described earlier in this section). The position of this state depends on light intensity, oxygen concentration, and the rate constants of the several forward and back reactions.

One of the few attempts to date at kinetic analysis of the photostationary state of the Hill reaction, is that of Wessels (1954). He postulated the simple sequence of three reactions:

(35.35Aa,a') $$H_2O + X \underset{\text{dark}}{\overset{\text{light}}{\rightleftharpoons}} XH_2 + \tfrac{1}{2}O_2$$

(35.35Ab,b') $$XH_2 + Q \rightleftharpoons QH_2 + X$$

(35.35Ac) $$QH_2 + \tfrac{1}{2}O_2 \longrightarrow Q + H_2O$$

where X is an intermediate redox catalyst common to all Hill systems (and probably to photosynthesis as well) and Q (for quinone or quinonoid dye) is a specific Hill oxidant. Comparison with reaction schemes such as 28.IB (page 1026) shows one important (and probably unjustified) omission—both back reactions, (35.35Ab') and (35.35Ac), are supposed to involve molecular oxygen, and no provision is made for reoxidation by oxygen precursors (systems Z/ZH_2 or $A'HO/A'OH_2$ in our earlier discussions, $cf.$ for example reaction 28.21d in scheme 28.IB).

The reaction sequence (35.35Aa,b,c) leads to expressions for the photostationary state which the reader can easily derive. These are of the form:

(35.35B) $$R = \frac{[\text{oxidant}]}{[\text{reductant}]} = \frac{a[X][O_2]^{1/2} + b[O_2] + c[\text{oxidant}][O_2]^{1/2}}{dI[\text{Chl}]}$$

Depending on whether the back reaction (35.35Ab') or (35.35Ac) predominates, either the first, or the second and the third term in the numerator can be neglected. In the second case (if one assumes the concentration of the intermediate X to be proportional to that of chlorophyll), R becomes independent of both chlorophyll concentration and the concentration of the oxidant, in agreement with Wessels' experimental results ($cf.$ $e.$ $g.$, figure 35.23A). In the second case, R depends on both [Chl] and [oxidant]. Wessels concludes that reoxidation occurs mainly by action of oxygen on the intermediate X, and not on the hydroquinone Q.

Among the uncertainties of this derivation are, in addition to the neglect of intermediate systems "on the oxidation side," also the use of the concentrations [X], [Chl], [ox.] and [red.] as if the system were homogeneous (while in fact, chlorophyll, and probably X as well, are structure-bound in the chloroplast fragments). Finally, the independence of R of [ox.] and [Chl] cannot be accepted as a general rule without more varied data.

For mathematical elaboration of the importance of the last point, we must refer to Horwitz (1954[2]). We can only mention here the more complex kinetic derivations of Gilmour *et al.*, intended primarily to account for observations in flashing light (*cf.* p. 1479).

(c)   Dark Reactions

It was mentioned before that cell macerates and chloroplast suspensions undergo various reactions in the dark, which may involve molecular oxygen or added oxidants, and complicate quantitative investigation of the Hill reaction.

Warburg and Lüttgens (1946) found that press juices from spinach or beet leaves "respire" (*i. e.*, consume oxygen in the dark); this oxygen consumption is not significantly affected by light.

The suspensions used in this stage of Warburg's work were prepared by grinding the leaves in a meat grinder, and pressing the mash through cloth. Whole cells and undissolved salts were precipitated from the suspension by centrifuging briefly at 1200 g. The supernatant was dark green, had a pH of about 6.5 and contained whole as well as broken chloroplasts. This green extract showed in a respirometer a rapidly declining oxygen uptake. Carbon monoxide (80%) reduced it by 50%. Since this inhibition was not light sensitive, it was considered indicative of oxygen transfer by a copper-containing oxidase (such as the cytochrome oxidase). This hypothesis was supported by the observation that the oxygen consumption increased upon the addition of the polyphenol, pyrocatechol. Even in the presence of this substrate, respiration declined with time; it could be further stabilized by the addition of excess hydroquinone. The oxidation-reduction chain, which is operative in the presence of both compounds, probably is

$$\left.\begin{array}{c} p\text{-hydroquinone} \\ + \\ o\text{-quinone} \\ + \\ Cu^+ \text{ oxidase} \\ + \\ \tfrac{1}{2} O_2 \end{array}\right\} \begin{array}{c} \longrightarrow \\ \longleftarrow \\ \longrightarrow \end{array} \left\{\begin{array}{c} p\text{-quinone} \\ + \\ \text{pyrocatechol} \\ + \\ Cu^{+2} \text{ oxidase} \\ + \\ H_2O \end{array}\right.$$

(35.36) $p\text{-hydroquinone} + \tfrac{1}{2} O_2 \longrightarrow p\text{-quinone} + H_2O$

The pyrocatechol thus serves as a catalyst; the accumulated oxidation product is p-quinone, which is less toxic than o-quinone. The oxygen uptake continues uniformly until all hydroquinone is used up (fig. 35.24). The production of carbon dioxide (which, without added substrate, is about equivalent to the consumption of oxygen) is reduced by about 50% by the presence of pyrocatechol, and is close to zero if both pyrocatechol and hydroquinone are added. This shows that hydroquinone has completely displaced the endogenous respiration substrate. When the suspended material was separated from the liquid by centrifuging (at pH 6.5), oxygen

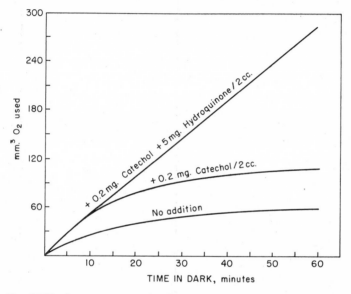

Fig. 35.24. Oxygen consumption by spinach chloroplast preparations in darkness (after Warburg and Lüttgens 1948).

consumption continued in both phases; but after centrifuging at pH 5 the "polyphenol oxidase" of the liquid phase was coprecipitated with the chloroplast material (since now only the precipitate showed autoxidation).

Arnon (1949) studied the polyphenol oxidase activity of leaf material. He found that chloroplastic matter, separated from the cytoplasmic fluid, retains all the polyphenol oxidase activity of the original cellular material.

Clendenning and Gorham (1950[1]) noted that in crude leaf macerates, freed only of heavy particles (by slow centrifugation), acid production upon addition of Hill's mixture occurs also in the dark. In some species the rate of this dark reaction was quite high—for example, in material from spruce and other gymnosperms it reached 4 moles acid per minute per mole chlorophyll. Leaf material from vegetables and cereals reacted much slower in the dark than leaf mash from trees, ferns and aquatics.

Clendenning and Gorham (1950[2]) later studied the dark reactions of chloroplast suspensions in more detail. *Acidification* was faster at pH 7.5 than at pH 6.0. It required Fe^{+3} as ferricyanide or oxalate and was non-enzymatic; it may involve reductants such as ascorbic acid, glutathione or tannins. Two other dark reactions also were observed: boiled sap from bean leaves *produced carbon dioxide* in the dark when mixed with Hill's solution—apparently by oxidative decarboxylation; crude chloroplast suspensions of the same species showed *oxygen absorption* on the dark (*cf.* the above-described observations of Warburg and Lüttgens). A similar but less rapid oxygen uptake occurred with chloroplasts of other species. The autoxidation was heat sensitive in some species and not in others, indicating that both enzymatic and nonenzymatic reactions are involved.

Gerretsen (1950[2]) also observed the "respiration" of crude *Avena* chloroplast suspension in the dark. It was cyanide-insensitive (up to 0.04% HCN), not stimulated by glucose, but enhanced by the amino acid asparagine; Gerretsen therefore concluded that the main cyanide-sensitive and glucose-stimulated respiration apparatus of the cells was destroyed in the maceration, while an accessory cyanide-insensitive mechanism, able to utilize amino acids, survived it. Mn^{++} ions had no influence on the rate of oxygen uptake by the chloroplasts in the dark (as contrasted to light). Gerretsen (1951) observed an increase in acidity of aerobic chloroplast suspensions in dark, which he ascribed to CO_2 formation by respiration; under anaerobic conditions a similar trend was observed and ascribed to fermentation.

(d) Inhibition and Stimulation

If Hill's reaction is brought about by a part of the photosynthetic apparatus salvaged after the mechanical destruction of the cells, it must contain intact the photochemical mechanism and the enzymatic components (designated by E_c and E_0 in chapters 7 and 9) involved in the liberation of oxygen from the primary photochemical oxidation product (designated there by Z, A'OH, or $\{O_2\}$). Whether any enzymes which ordinarily operate between the primary photochemical reduction product (designated as HX in chapter 7) and carbon dioxide are involved in the Hill reaction, we do not know. The substitute oxidants (such as quinone or Fe^{+3}) may react with the primary reduction product HX directly, without the help of an enzyme (or they may even take part in the photochemical reaction proper, without the intermediary of the system X/HX which we have assumed to be tied to chlorophyll). Certainly the Hill reaction does not need the carboxylating enzyme, E_A, which catalyzes the dark association of

CO_2 with an acceptor (A or RH) prior to reduction. The "stabilizing" catalyst, E_B, whose existence was postulated by Franck and Herzfeld in their interpretation of the kinetics of photosynthesis, and which they made responsible for the light saturation of photosynthesis under normal conditions in constant as well as in flashing light, should not be involved in Hill reaction if its function is to stabilize the intermediate reduction products of ACO_2 (symbolized by $AHCO_2$, AH_2CO_2...), but it should be required if it acts on oxidation intermediates (or on reduction intermediates not derived from carbon dioxide). In Franck and Herzfeld's scheme 7.VA (Vol. I, page 164) this catalyst was supposed to act on both the reduction and the oxidation intermediates; but we have argued that this is implausible because of the well-known specificity of enzymes. The experiments of Clendenning and Ehrmantraut on Hill reaction in live cells (cf. part C) indicate the probability that the same catalyst limits the rate in strong light of both photosynthesis and the Hill reaction; this makes it likely that this catalyst operates on the primary photochemical oxidation product (or a primary reduction product not derived from CO_2), and not on a reduction intermediate of carbon dioxide.

We expect the Hill reaction to be sensitive to inhibitors which affect the enzymes E_B, E_C, E_O, but not to inhibitors which act on enzymes, such as E_A, involved only in the transformation of carbon dioxide.

Cyanide was characterized in chapter 12 (Vol. I, page 309) as a specific poison of the "carboxylase," E_A. Hill and Scarisbrick (1940) found that the oxygen liberation of isolated chloroplasts in the presence of ferric salts is *not* inhibited by cyanide. Warburg and Lüttgens (1946) said that they were unable to study the effect of cyanide on the Hill reaction with quinone as oxidant because (at 20° C. and pH 6.5) quinone oxidized HCN directly in the dark, with liberation of carbon dioxide. Aronoff (1946) found no effect of cyanide on the photoreduction of quinone in "grana preparation" from spinach leaves. Ehrmantraut and Rabinowitch (1952) noted no inhibition of the quinone reaction *in live cells* at 10° C. and pH 6.5 when 0.005 M HCN was added immediately after the beginning of illumination (cf. part C below).

Macdowall (1949) found that >0.01 M KCN were needed to produce 50% inhibition of Hill reaction with phenol indophenol (Table 35.XI).

Wessels (1954) found no inhibition of potentiometrically recorded Hill reaction (with quinone as oxidant) by 0.01 M KCN.

Gorham and Clendenning (1952) noted that the presence of 10^{-3} mole/l. KCN affects the $H = f$ (pH) curves of the Hill reaction. It stimulated the activity of washed chloroplasts at pH 6.3–7.3, but inhibited it at other pH values. This influence is similar to that of other anions (cf. section 3(c)).

Azide. An inhibition of the Hill reaction by sodium azide was observed by French, Holt, Powell and Anson (1946), Macdowall (1949) (*cf.* Table 35.XI), and Arnon and Whatley (1949), but not by Hill and Scarisbrick (1940) and Aronoff (1946).

Clendenning and Gorham (1950) found that the effect of azide is different with quinone and with Hill's mixture as oxidants. Wessels (1954) noted that NaN₃ reacts with quinone. Low concentrations (<6.10⁻³ mole/l.) of azide caused only partial inhibition of oxygen liberation with quinone as oxidant. The strong inhibition, observed by Arnon and Whatley with quinone (50% inhibition at 6×10^{-4} mole/l.) must have been due to a reaction of the latter with the azide. With 2,6-dichlorophenol-indophenol (which does not react with NaN₃) Wessels found only partial inhibition by 6×10^{-3} mole/l. NaN₃, and complete inhibition by 6×10^{-2} mole/l., in approximate agreement with Macdowall's data.

Hydroxylamine. Hill and Scarisbrick (1940) reported that the Hill reaction is unaffected not only by cyanide but also by hydroxylamine—a result which seemed to disagree with the conclusion, reached in chapt. 12 (Vol. I, page 311) that hydroxylamine probably is a specific poison for the oxygen-liberating enzymatic system in photosynthesis. However, Hill's observations were confirmed by Aronoff (1946), who found no effect of hydroxylamine on photoreduction of quinone by fragmented chloroplasts from spinach leaves.

French, Holt, Powell, and Anson (1946), on the other hand, noted an inhibition of the photoreduction of Hill's mixture by hydroxylamine; and Macdowall (1949, *cf.* Table 35.XI) found that 3×10^{-4} M hydroxylamine inhibits the oxygen liberation by chloroplasts, with phenol-indophenol as oxidant, by 50%. The effect was about the same in strong and in weak light (see Vol. I, page 312 for similar observations in photosynthesis). Arnon and Whatley (1949) also found hydroxylamine to be a strong inhibitor for the photoreduction of quinone by chloroplasts.

Clendenning and Gorham (1950) found that 10⁻³ mole/l. NH₂OH inhibited the photoreduction of quinone but not of Hill's mixture. Wessels (1954) noted that, similarly to azide, hydroxylamine reacts with quinone (and also with 2,6-dichlorophenol-indophenol, probably reducing the dye to a leucodye). To be able to observe the true effect of NH₂OH on Hill's reaction, Wessels used toluylene blue, whose E_0' is too high for it to be reduced by hydroxylamine. He found a strong, albeit not complete, inhibition by 6×10^{-4} mole/l. NH₂OH; the surmise that hydroxylamine must inhibit the Hill reaction was thus confirmed. The controversial results obtained by other observers who used stronger oxidants, which react directly with NH₂OH, must have been due to differences in the relative amounts of the reactants (perhaps also in temperature and schedule of the experiments).

o-Phenanthroline. Warburg and Lüttgens (1946) found a strong inhibition of the photoreduction of quinone by *o*-phenanthroline, a compound that, similarly to cyanide, forms complexes with heavy metals, and also inhibits photosynthesis (*cf.* Vol. I, page 319) (50% inhibition by 4.3 × 10^{-6} mole/liter, 100% inhibition by 8.5 × 10^{-5} mole/liter). Since Zn^{+2} ions form complexes with phenanthroline, Warburg and Lüttgens suggested that an enzyme containing zinc as active metal may be involved in the Hill reaction, and thus probably also in photosynthesis. The phenanthroline inhibition could be cured by the addition of zinc sulfate. The effect of phenanthroline on the quinone reaction was confirmed by Aronoff (1946) and Arnon and Whatley (1949). The latter also confirmed (1949[3]) the reversal of the phenanthroline inhibition by zinc ions, but showed that the same effect could be produced by ferrous ions and copper ions (which are required micro nutrients), as well as by nickel and cobalt ions (which are not). Added in 1:1 stoichiometric relation to phenanthroline, nickel and cobalt produced a more effective reversal of inhibition than zinc; the latter, in turn, was more effective than copper or iron. The assumption that an enzyme with a zinc ion in its prosthetic groups participates in photosynthesis thus remains speculative.

Wessels (1954) noted a difference in the effect of phenanthroline on the Hill reaction with DCPI (almost complete inhibition by 6 × 10^{-5} mole/l.) and with quinone (6–10 times more poison needed for the same effect). He confirmed that the poisoning can be cured by Zn^{++}, Co^{++} or Ni^{++} ions, but not by Mn^{++}, Ca^{++} or Mg^{++}. The phenanthroline effect seems to be due to its attachment to a specific spot in an enzyme (rather than to a chelation of free zinc ions, as suggested by Warburg), because extracting the chloroplasts with phenanthroline does not leave an impairment of their activity after washing. Chelating agents, similar to phenanthroline (α,α'-dipyridyl, 3,3'-dimethyl-2,2'-dipyridyl), do not inhibit the Hill reaction, while the strong chelating agent "complexon" (ethylenediaminetetraacetic acid) even stimulate it.

o-Phenanthroline inhibits the methemoglobin reduction by crude chloroplast suspensions (50% inhibition at about 5 × 10^{-5} mole/l.).

Carbon Monoxide. Warburg and Lüttgens (1946) found that the quinone reaction is not inhibited by carbon monoxide (indicating the absence of iron-porphyrin enzymes in the enzymatic apparatus of the Hill reaction).

Narcotics. Hill and Scarisbrick (1941) and Warburg and Lüttgens (1946) noted the inhibition of the reduction of ferric oxalate or quinone by *phenylurethan* (50% inhibition by 0.1 mg. in 1 cc. according to Warburg and Lüttgens—approximately the same effect as on photosynthesis in *Chlorella*, *cf.* page 323, Vol. I). Aronoff (1946) obtained only 60% inhibition of the same reaction by a saturated phenylurethan solution; and

Macdowall (1949) found that 2×10^{-3} M phenylurethan are required for a 50% inhibition with quinone (table 35.XI). Arnon and Whatley (1949) found a higher sensitivity—nearer that observed by Hill and Warburg, than that observed by Aronoff and Macdowall.

Wessels (1954) found incomplete inhibition by 3×10^{-3} mole/l. phenylurethan of the photoreduction of benzoquinone, but a complete inhibition of that of 2,6-dichlorophenol-indophenol; the latter was 50% inhibited by 3×10^{-4} mole/l. Davenport *et al.* (1952) observed 50% inhibition at 1.2×10^{-3} mole/l. phenylurethan (or 0.35 mole/l. ethylurethan) of the methemoglobin reduction in crude chloroplast suspensions.

Warburg and Lüttgens (1946) observed that the quinone reaction is completely inhibited in a saturated solution of *octanol*.

Other Inhibitors. Macdowall (1949) made a study of the inhibition

TABLE 35.XI

INHIBITION OF HILL REACTION IN CHLOROPLASTS FROM SPINACH OR SWISS CHARD WITH PHENOL-INDOPHENOL AS OXIDANT (AFTER MACDOWALL, 1949)

Inhibitor	Concentration producing 50% inhibition, mole/liter	Inhibition occurs in strong or weak light
Poisons of Heavy Metal Prosthetic Groups		
Cyanide[a]	>0.01	—
Azide[a]	0.08	In strong light
Pyrophosphate	>0.1	—
Hydroxylamine[a]	3×10^{-4}	Equally in both
Resorcinol	0.09	Equally in both
o-Phenanthroline[a]	2.7×10^{-5}	In both, but more pronounced in weak light
Thiourea	0.15	—
Poisons of Sulfhydryl Groups[b]		
Dinitrophenol[a]	6×10^{-4}	In both, but more pronounced in weak light
Iodoacetate[b]	0.01	In strong light
Heavy Metal Ions		
Cu$^{+2 b}$	1×10^{-6}	Much stronger in weak light
Hg$^{+2 b}$	4×10^{-6}	More pronounced in strong light
Narcotics		
Phenylurethan	2×10^{-3}	Stronger in weak light
Thymol[b]	2×10^{-3}	Equally in both
Chloroform	0.03	Stronger in weak light
Ether	0.5	
Strychnine	>1.0	Stimulation in strong, inhibition in weak light

[a] *Cf.* other data above.
[b] *Cf.* Wessels' data below.

of the Hill reaction by a variety of agents; his results are summarized in Table 35.XI.

Wessels (1954) found partial inhibition of the photoreduction of quinone and DCPI by 6×10^{-4} mole/l., and full inhibition by 6×10^{-3} mole/l. *2,4-dinitrophenol*, in agreement with table 35.XI. In agreement with Aronoff (1948) and Clendenning and Gorham (1950), but contrary to French *et al.* (1946), he found no marked effect of *sodium fluoride* on the Hill reaction. *Thymol* inhibited quinone reduction by 50% in a concentration of 3×10^{-3} mole/l. In contrast to Macdowall's data, *iodoacetamide* (3×10^{-2} mole/l.), *p-chloromercuribenzoate* (6×10^{-4} mole/l.) and *p-aminophenyldichloroarsine* (6×10^{-4} mole/l.) (all three strong sulfhydryl inhibitors), were found without effect. Only slight inhibition was observed with 3×10^{-2} mole/l. *nitrite*. *Phthiocol* (6×10^{-5} mole/l.) inhibited the reduction of DCPI, but not that of quinone; 0.001 *M penicillin* or *chloromycetin* had no effect. *Sulfanilamide* and *nicotinic acid* were without effect even at 10^{-2} mole/l. Of the cations studied by Wessels (all 10^{-3} *M*), Zn^{++} was found to stimulate the reaction with quinone, but not that with DCPI; Mn^{++} stimulated both of them. Mg^{++} ions had no effect, while Ca^{++} ions accelerated only the reaction with quinone.

Cu^{++} ions inhibited strongly at 10^{-4} mole/l., Hg^{++} ions even at 10^{-5} or 10^{-6} mole/l. in agreement with table 35.XI.

No effect was caused by oxidized *glutathione*, *DPN* (*cf.* section 4(*f*) above) or *ATP* (6×10^{-4} mole/l.).

Figures in Table 35.XI and the inhibition experiments discussed before, support the view that the cyanide- and azide-sensitive component of the photosynthetic mechanism is not involved in the Hill reaction, and is probably concerned with the transformation of carbon dioxide. Hydroxylamine, *o*-phenanthrolin, and dinitrophenol are powerful inhibitors of the Hill reaction, affecting it either equally strongly in weak and strong light, or preferentially in weak light. Of the two heavy metals, cupric ions inhibit much stronger in weak light (*cf.* Vol. I, page 340 for a contrary observation by Greenfield on photosynthesis in *Chlorella*), mercuric ions in strong light. The narcotics act, as usual, at all light intensities; but phenylurethan and chloroform show a somewhat enhanced action in weak light.

Strychnine (5×10^{-3} *M*) strongly *stimulated* the Hill reaction in strong light (46 klux), but inhibited it slightly in weak light.

In addition to the specific inhibitors listed in Table 35.XI, Holt, Smith and French (1950) and Macdowall (1949) observed also the influence of various organic reagents: sucrose, formaldehyde, acetone, ethanol, methanol, carbitol, isopropanol, *n*-propyl glycol, propyleneglycol, glycerol, toluene, dioxane; and of salts, such as $MgSO_4$, $Na_2SO_4(NH_4)_2SO_4$ and $CaCl_2$. All had a more or less pronounced inhibiting effect. Complete inhibition was produced by 5% carbitol, 10% dioxane or 0.2 M $CaCl_2$; 50% inhibition was produced in strong light by 0.18 M formaldehyde, 0.4 M sodium sulfate, 0.7 M acetone, 1.4 M ethanol, etc. No stimulation by small quantities of formaldehyde (as reported by Bose for photosynthesis, cf. Vol. 1, page 343) was found at concentration down to 10^{-10}%.

The suspensions used in Macdowall's experiments contained between 2×10^{-5} and 4×10^{-6} mole/liter chlorophyll. In checks with o-phenanthroline (2×10^{-5} mole/liter) and thymol (2.5×10^{-3} mole/liter) the inhibition proved to be approximately independent of chlorophyll concentration in these limits.

Arnon et al. (1954) reported that with whole chloroplasts capable of (1) Hill reaction with quinone, (2) P* fixation as ATP* in light, and (3) C*O_2 fixation in light: 2,4-dinitrophenol (8×10^{-4} M) inhibits (3) and (2) much stronger than (1); iodoacetamide (2×10^{-2} M) inhibits (3) by 97% and has no effect on (2); and p-chloromercuribenzoate inhibits (3) strongly, (2) less strongly, and (1) hardly at all.

Ultraviolet Light. Irradiation by ultraviolet light (253.6 mμ) was found by Holt, Brooks and Arnold (1951) to inhibit the Hill reaction in chloroplast fragments in the same way, as it does the Hill reaction of whole cells (cf. part C below) and photosynthesis (page 344). In this case, too, the logarithm of the residual rate is a linear function of the duration of irradiation, indicating a "first order" deactivation process (i. e., deactivation by single quanta of ultraviolet light, and not by combined effect of two or more quanta on a single molecule). The fact that the Hill reaction—in chloroplasts or whole cells—is inhibited by ultraviolet light to about the same extent as photosynthesis is an argument against the hypothesis, made in chapter 13 (on the basis of observations of inhibition of C* uptake in the dark by ultraviolet light), that the 253.6 mμ sensitive factor in photosynthesis is the carbon dioxide fixing enzyme.

Activity was tested with the complete Hill's mixture and with ferricyanide alone, and the effect proved to be the same in both cases. This proves that photochemical decomposition of oxalate—which is known to occur in ultraviolet light—is not the cause of the inhibition of the reaction with Hill's mixture.

Similarly to whole *Chlorella* cells, the irradiation of chloroplast preparations with the line 253.6 mμ does not cause any significant changes in the absorption spectrum, even if it leads to complete deactivation. This has been checked spectrophotometrically for the region 220–400 mμ; no change of color was noticeable after irradiation.

The proportion of the photochemical activity which "survives" a certain irradiation dose is the same whether the activity is tested in strong or in weak light. Ultraviolet light thus belongs to the group of agents (including also hydroxylamine and narcotics) which affect photosynthesis more or less uniformly at all light intensities.

(e) Survival of Photochemical Reductant in the Dark

In the next chapter we will deal with the controversial question of whether illumination of live cells produces in the latter a strong reductant which survives long enough to permit the demonstration of its "reducing power" after the cessation of illumination. This controversy has extended also to the Hill reaction.

Mehler (1951[1]) attempted to find a surviving reductant in illuminated (crude) spinach leaf juice. From the data of Calvin, and Fager, on live cells (cf. chapter 36), coupled with estimates of the recovery of chlorophyll and other cell constituents in the preparation of this juice, he expected to find an amount of reductant equivalent to about 4% of that of chlorophyll. The suspension was illuminated in phosphate buffer in N_2 atmosphere, pipetted into a solution of dichlorophenol-indophenol (DCPI), and the absorption at 610 mμ measured about 15 seconds later. No difference could be noticed between the effect on the optical density of chloroplasts illuminated for $\frac{1}{2}$, 1 or 2 minutes, or not illuminated at all. The temperature of the experiment was not stated.

Krasnovsky and Kosobutskaya (1952), who made practically identical experiments with chloroplast suspensions from *Phaseolus*, arrived at the opposite conclusion. They illuminated the suspension for 3 minutes at 0° C. in a vacuum Thunberg tube, added DCPI from a side tube 1–5 seconds after the end of illumination, and found the optical density at 600 mμ, measured 20–40 sec. after the addition of DCPI, distinctly different from that measured in a similar experiment with not preilluminated suspension. This difference (ΔD) varied strongly, depending on the "physiological state" of the material; it was much smaller in a suspension of washed chloroplasts (≤ 0.05) than in the crude leaf juice (up to 0.15). The ΔD remained unchanged after $\frac{1}{2}$, 1 or 5 minutes, indicating that the "reducing power" survived for over 5 min. in the dark (at 0° C. and in the absence of O_2). Similar results were obtained with thionine, but ΔD was only one-half as large as with DCPI. A slow reduction of DCPI in the dark was found to be superimposed on the light reaction (or reaction of preilluminated chloroplasts); this dark reaction was attributed to the presence, in the juice, of dehydrogenases and hydrogen donors, such as ascorbic acid. Preillumination appeared to increase the quantity of the reductants in the chloroplast juice by 10–30%, equivalent to 5–8% of the amount of chlorophyll present. The light-activated reductant did not seem to be a reduced form of chlorophyll, since the absorption spectrum of the latter was not changed by preillumination. Krasnovsky suggested that Mehler's results were affected by high temperature and presence of air, which favored back reactions.

Gerretsen (1950[1]) believed he found potentiometric evidence that anaerobically preilluminated, crude chloroplast suspensions maintain in the dark, for more than an hour, a capacity to form a peroxide upon admission of oxygen or addition of Mn^{++} salt.

6. Mutations

Davis (1952) applied induced mutations to the study of the relation of Hill reaction to photosynthesis. He subjected *Chlorella* cells to ultraviolet irradiation and isolated three strains which differed from the wild type by being unable to grow in an inorganic nutrient solution in light. These strains grew well, however, if supplied with glucose. They were green and contained chlorophyll. Two strains (322 and 349) did not evolve oxygen in light when suspended in a carbonate bicarbonate buffer, and did not take up carbon dioxide. One strain (332) liberated oxygen in light, but did not take up carbon dioxide. Intact cells of strains 322 and 349 did not liberate oxygen when suspended in Hill's solution in the absence of external carbon dioxide and illuminated. They thus seemed to have a block in the oxygen-liberating mechanism. Strain 332 liberated oxygen in light in the absence of carbon dioxide, and in the presence as well as in absence of Hill's solution. In the latter case, hydrogen from water must have been donated to some cellular component. Strain 322, which is unable to photosynthesize, also has a subnormal respiration rate. Assuming single gene mutation, this correlation can be considered as indicative of the presence of two respiratory systems, one of which is associated with the chlorophyllous mechanism. With strains 322 and 349, the effect of light on respiration could be studied; experiments showed the absence of such an effect. The wild type was inhibited when grown in the presence of sufficient quantities of mutant cells. The inhibition could be caused either by chlorellin (*cf.*, page 880) being produced in greater quantities by the mutants than by the wild type, or by compounds which accumulate within the mutant cells as a result of the blocked reactions and diffuse into the medium.

C. Photochemistry of Live Cells[*]

The first observation that a "Hill reaction" (*i. e.*, sensitized oxidation of water to oxygen, with oxidant other than carbon dioxide) can occur in live cells was made by Fan, Stauffer and Umbreit in 1943 (Vol. I, page 541). They found that oxygen is liberated in light from carbon dioxide-free *Chlorella* suspensions supplied with *ferric phosphate* or other ferric salts.

[*] Bibliography, page 1629.

However, back reactions (reoxidation of ferrous salts by free oxygen) caused the oxygen production to come to an early stop. Better oxygen yields could be obtained with various organic compounds containing a carboxyl group, particularly *benzaldehyde* and *acetaldehyde*, as well as *parabanic acid* and *nitrourea*. Numerous other aldehydes, oximes, acids, quinonoid dyestuffs, carbohydrates, and urea and its derivatives (for a list, see Vol. I, page 542) were tried but gave negative results. The greatest oxygen production was observed with benzaldehyde, but the interpretation of this reaction was somewhat uncertain, since a considerable dark reaction was noted which produced carbon dioxide. Conceivably, this reaction could be accelerated in light, and benzaldehyde, instead of participating directly in the oxygen-liberating reaction, could be first photoxidized to carbon dioxide (or dismuted to reduced compounds, such as benzalcohol, and carbon dioxide) and the latter assimilated in the normal way. True, Fan *et al.* were unable to trap any free carbon dioxide by alkali; but this evidence is never completely convincing because rapid intercellular reutilization of carbon dioxide may make its trapping by extracellular absorbers impossible.

The highest observed rate of liberation of oxygen with benzaldehyde as oxidant was about 10% of the rate of photosynthesis.

Warburg and Lüttgens (1946; *cf.* Warburg, 1948) obtained the first reliable results with *o-benzoquinone*. In this case, too, a dark reaction occurred, which produced carbon dioxide; but its rate (about 0.02 cc. CO_2 per 1 cc. of cells in 5 min.) was only about 2% of the rate of liberation of oxygen in light (0.5 cc. O_2 per 1 cc. of cells in 5 min.).

Aronoff (1946[1]) repeated Warburg's experiments with *Scenedesmus* in a nitrogen atmosphere (0.1% O_2). He observed only slow oxygen evolution in light, and thought it to be limited by the rate of penetration of quinone into the cells.

Clendenning and Ehrmantraut (1951) made manometric studies of the oxygen production by *Chlorella* with *o*-benzoquinone or Hill's mixture as oxidants. (No oxygen liberation was obtained with ferricyanide alone or with phenol-indophenol.)

The manometer vessel, containing CO_2-free cells and the substitute oxidant, could be placed in homogeneous light side by side with a similar vessel containing identical cells in carbonate buffer; or the two vessels could be used alternately in the same position. In this way the yield of the Hill reaction could be measured in relation to the yield of photosynthesis under the same conditions (except for the difference in pH). Several conclusions emerged from this comparison:

Constancy of Rate, and Total Yield. With 10 mm.[3] of cells and 1 mg. of quinone in 3 cc. (about 3×10^{-3} mole/liter), the initial rate of oxygen evolution in continuous light was maintained for 30–40 min.; a total oxygen amount was obtained which corresponded to 75 ± 5% of the theoretical equivalent of the amount of quinone added. Since white light was used, this low yield might have been caused by direct photochemical decomposition of quinone. An increase in the amount of cells did not change the yield. At the lower *concentration of quinone* (0.25 mg. or 0.5 mg. in 3 cc.), the initial rate and the final yield were the same as with 1.0 mg. and exhaustion was reached correspondingly sooner—in 30 min. and 15 min.,

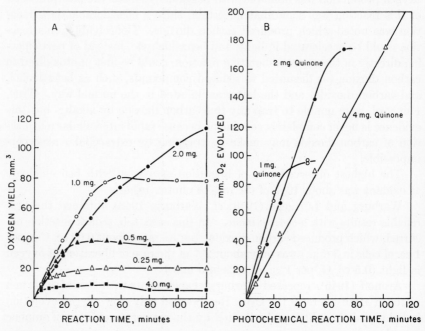

Fig. 35.25. Effect of quinone concentration on photochemical oxygen production by *Chlorella* (concentrations in milligrams in 3 cc.) (after Clendenning and Ehrmantraut, 1951). (A) In white light (fluorescent light); (B) in red-orange light ($\lambda > 520$ mμ).

respectively. With 2 mg. quinone the initial rate and the total yield were markedly smaller, and with 4 mg. only very little oxygen was produced (fig. 35.25A). Two phenomena seem to be involved in the failure to obtain a stoichiometric oxygen equivalent of the added quinone. One is the *destruction of quinone* (by reactions with cell constituents; in blue-violet light, quinone is decomposed even in the absence of cells). That quinone actually is lost is indicated by the observation that if the reaction with 0.5 mg. quinone is continued until all oxygen production ceases, the addition of another 0.5 mg. revives it, and approximately the same oxygen amount (equivalent to ~75% of the extra quinone added) can be produced again. The results were improved by using red-orange light, only slightly absorbed

by quinone (figure 35.25B).   However, even in this case, very little oxygen
was produced when 4 mg. quinone were added.   This cannot be explained
by direct photolysis of quinone, and indicates the occurrence of a second
phenomenon—"self-inhibition" of the Hill reaction by quinone (also noted
with isolated chloroplasts, *cf.* section 4(d) above.

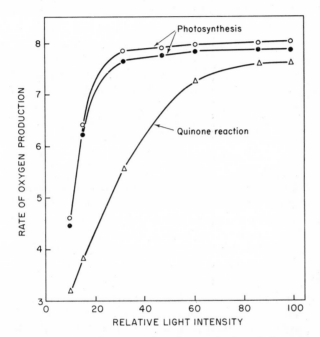

Fig. 35.26. Light saturation curves for photosynthesis and the quinone reaction in whole *Chlorella* cells (after Clendenning and Ehrmantraut 1951).   (●) net
photosynthesis; (○) photosynthesis corrected for respiration.

Maximum Rate in Strong Light.   Figure 35.26 shows the light curves of
photosynthesis and of the Hill reaction (with quinone as oxidant) for two
aliquots of the same cell suspension.   (10 mm.³ cells in 3.0 cc. and 3×10^{-3}
M quinone.)   *The two curves approach the same saturation level in strong
light,* although more light is needed to saturate the Hill reaction.   The rates
were measured in the first 30 min. of illumination, following a 20-min. dark
period after the addition of quinone.   (We will see below that even brief
preillumination of cells without quinone produced an inhibition.)
  Clendenning (1954) found that at low temperatures (0–15° C.) O_2
evolution with quinone as oxidant far exceeds that by photosynthesis.
This supports Franck's view (chapter 31) that at these temperatures carboxylation becomes the rate-limiting reaction in photosynthesis.

Quantum Yield. Figure 35.26 shows a lower yield of quinone reduction compared to photosynthesis in *Chlorella* in subsaturating light. This seemed to point to a lower maximum quantum yield of the former reaction; Clendenning and Ehrmantraut (1951) found, in fact, about a 70% lower efficiency in the weakest light used. However, the percentual difference between the rates of the two reactions seems to have a maximum in the region of half-saturation, and to decline in stronger and in weaker light. Ehrmantraut and Rabinowitch (1952) found that this difference disappears in both limiting cases—that of light saturation as well as that of light limitation. Their quantum yield measurements, carried out partly with filtered neon light and a Warburg-Schocken actinometer and partly with a monochromator and bolometer, were summarized on pages 1130–1131. The second method, which is more precise, gave an average quantum efficiency of $\gamma = 10 \pm 1$, practically identical with that found in parallel experiments for the quantum efficiency of the photosynthesis of the same cells in carbonate buffer No. 9. The actinometric data were slightly, but not significantly higher (*cf.* table 29.XI).

These results, together with those obtained with chloroplast suspensions, support strongly the hypothesis that the primary photochemical process is the same in photosynthesis and Hill reaction and requires the same number of quanta for the transfer of one hydrogen atom, despite the fact that much less energy is needed to transfer it to a typical Hill oxidant, than to carbon dioxide.

The relation between the light curves of photosynthesis and those of the Hill reaction in *Chlorella*—convergence in two limits, divergence in the middle—is peculiar, and cannot be explained by a simple kinetic model. It is probably related to the "self-poisoning" of the Hill reaction by quinone, which may leave the saturation rate unchanged, and the effect of which on the rate in subsaturating light may depend on the duration and intensity of illumination (so that in measurements in weak light, self-poisoning has no time to develop itself).

Yield in Flashing Light. The experiments on the oxygen liberation by *Chlorella* cells in quinone in flashing light already were described in chapter 34 (section B7). As illustrated by figure 34.26 (Clendenning and Ehrmantraut 1951), the *dark intervals* needed to obtain the maximum yield per flash (with "instantaneous" discharge flashes) were found to be the same for quinone reduction and for photosynthesis of the same cells in bicarbonate. Experiments with increased flash energy by Ehrmantraut and Rabinowitch (1952) indicated (figure 34.27) that the *maximum yield* per flash also is the same for both reactions, although it requires a higher flash energy in the case of quinone as oxidant (the same relation was noted also in continuous light, *cf.* figure 35.26). The significance of these findings—

which seem to support the concept of a common rate-limiting enzymatic process in Hill reaction and photosynthesis—was discussed in chapter 34C.

Induction. Under the conditions when photosynthesis in continuous as well as in flashing light had the often observed induction period of about 5 min., fully developed after about 5 min. of darkness (*cf.* chapter 33), oxygen liberation with quinone was found to begin instantaneously. This finding of Clendenning and Ehrmantraut (1951) already was described in chapter 33 (section A8) and its possible implications for the theory of the induction phenomena were discussed there (section C4).

The same difference between induction in photosynthesis and quinone reduction by *Chlorella* was found also in flashing light.

Inhibition. The Hill reaction with quinone in whole *Chlorella* cells is not inhibited by *cyanide* (0.0005 mole/liter)—a result that agrees with previously reported observations on chloroplast preparations (section B5(*d*) above), but which is nevertheless important because it proves that the Hill reaction in live cells does not proceed via the formation of free carbon dioxide, followed by normal photosynthesis.

With Hill's mixture, oxygen evolution by *Chlorella* cells in dark was inhibited by cyanide as effectively as photosynthesis—a confirmation of the suggestion (*cf.* below) that this evolution results from photosynthesis at the cost of carbon dioxide produced by photolysis of oxalate.

The Hill reaction in live cells was found by Clendenning and Ehrmantraut to be inhibited by *hydroxylamine* ($3 \times 10^{-4} M$ gave 100% inhibition), *fluoride* (0.02 M, 65% inhibition), *ethylurethan* (1% solution gave 33% inhibition), *iodoacetate* (0.02 M, 100% inhibition) and—rather unexpectedly—*malonate* (35% inhibition at $6 \times 10^{-3} M$). No *chloride* effect was noted by comparing the Hill reaction in *Chlorella* cells grown with or without potassium chloride, or by adding chloride to the reaction mixture.

Preillumination Effect. The quinone reduction by *Chlorella* is inhibited by preillumination of cells in the absence of oxidant (Fig. 35.27). The inhibition occurs in red light as well as in light of shorter wave lengths, indicating that it is a chlorophyll-sensitized process. (It is not a direct photochemical transformation of chlorophyll—or, at least, does not reveal itself as such by a change in color.)

The preillumination effect reminds one of a similar phenomenon observed by Warburg and Lüttgens (1946) and Arnon and Whatley (1949) with isolated chloroplast preparations. (We recall, however, that no inhibition by preillumination of chloroplasts was found by Holt and French, 1948.) It also makes one think of the observation reported in chapter 19 (Vol. I) that photoxidation can be induced in cells by illumination in the absence of carbon dioxide. However, inhibition by preillumination was observed by Clendenning and Ehrmantraut in nitrogen as well as in air.

Clendenning and Ehrmantraut noted that preillumination of *Chlorella*, which reduced the *rate* of quinone reduction by 50%, did not affect the

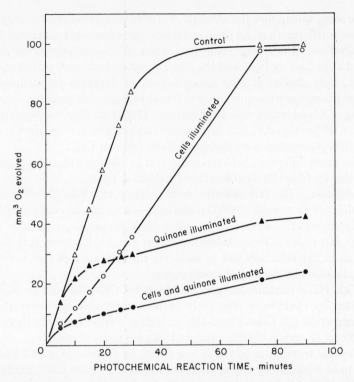

Fig. 35.27. Effect of preilluminating *Chlorella* cells and quinone on subsequent photochemical oxygen production by *Chlorella* (after Clendenning and Ehrmantraut 1951).

total yield of oxygen liberated from a given amount of quinone.

It would be interesting to know whether inhibition by preillumination affects equally the maximum rate of the Hill reaction in strong light and its quantum efficiency on weak light; no such observations have been made

The Hill reaction with quinone also is inhibited by the preillumination of quinone without the cells (using the blue-violet light absorbed by quinone). This illumination causes a darkening of the quinone solution, and apparently produces a strongly poisonous substance that inhibits the Hill reaction. The two preillumination effects, one due to the deactivation of cells, and the other caused by photochemical decomposition of quinone, are independent and additive.

When the Hill reaction is measured with quinone as oxidant, in light from which blue-violet rays have not been excluded, one must expect that the decomposition of quinone and the production of the poison will proceed simultaneously with the main reaction (unless all quinone added is taken up by the cells and bound there in such a way as to be protected from photodecomposition). Available evidence does not show to what extent and how rapidly quinone—or any of the other oxidants used in the study of Hill reaction—are taken up by cells (or by colloidal chloroplast dispersions). Perhaps the drop in the rate and in total yield of the Hill reaction, which occurred when the amount of quinone was increased above 3×10^{-3} mole/liter, could be due to the incapacity of the cells to take up so much quinone and protect it from photochemical decomposition.

Quinone is not only a self-inhibitor of the Hill reaction but it also inhibits photosynthesis and respiration. *Chlorella* cells which have once been used for the study of Hill reaction are permanently incapable of photosynthesis (at least in carbonate buffer—no experiments were made in phosphate buffer). Exposure to quinone (1 hr. in 0.08% solution) in darkness also destroys the capacity for photosynthesis. Respiration, too, is strongly but not completely inhibited by incubation with quinone.

It thus seems that despite unchanged appearance the term "intact cells" should be used with caution in application to cells which have been exposed to quinone.

The Hill reaction in *Chlorella* cells with quinone as oxidant also is inhibited by ultraviolet irradiation ($\lambda = 253.6$ mμ). According to Holt, Brooks and Arnold (1951) the kinetics of this inactivation is similar to that observed in the study of photosynthesis or of the Hill reaction in chloroplast preparations. The absolute rate of inactivation also seems to be the same as in the case of photosynthesis.

Different Algae. The Hill reaction, with quinone or ferricyanide-ferric oxalate mixture as oxidant, can be observed also with blue-green algae *Cylindrospermum* (Clendenning and Ehrmantraut, unpublished). The yield appeared to be considerably lower than with *Chlorella*. No experiments have as yet been reported on the possibility of carrying out the Hill reaction with live higher plants.

Different Oxidants. From the oxidants tested so far, *o*-benzoquinone appears to be the only effective one for whole cells; yet its photochemical instability makes its use desirable only in light with $\lambda > 500$ mμ, and its poisonous properties preclude its use in any but very low concentrations.

Because of these drawbacks, it would be useful to find another oxidant capable of penetrating into live cells which would be more stable and less poisonous. Clendenning and Ehrmantraut tried some of the dyestuffs that gave good results with chloroplast suspensions, such as phenol indophenol, but obtained no oxygen liberation with whole *Chlorella* cells; perhaps these dyes could not penetrate through the cell membrane. No positive results were obtained also with chromate.

Clendenning and Ehrmantraut (1951) reported oxygen evolution by *Chlorella* cells from Hill's mixture in light; but Ehrmantraut and Rabinowitch (1952) found that ferric oxalate underwent direct photolysis in cell-free solution (in the white light used by Clendenning and Ehrmantraut) at about the rate at which oxygen is liberated by cells in Hill's mixture. This indicates that the latter reaction is photosynthesis utilizing the carbon

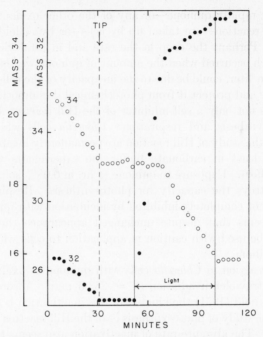

Fig. 35.28. Isotopic tracer study of Hill reaction with quinone and oxygen in *Chlorella* cells (Brown 1953). 1 mg. quinone tipped into cell suspension in phosphate buffer as shown. Respiration poisoned at once. Only $O_2(32)$ evolved in light (18 klux) until 87% of quinone reduced; $O_2(34)$ taken up and $O_2(32)$ evolved afterwards in light as expected for Hill reaction with O_2 as oxidant.

dioxide produced by the decomposition of oxalate. This surmise is confirmed by the absence of oxygen liberation in red light, and by the inhibition of oxygen liberation by cyanide.

Ehrmantraut and Rabinowitch (1952) also could not confirm the liberation of oxygen by *Chlorella* in the presence of benzaldehyde; the findings of Fan, Stauffer and Umbreit, mentioned at the beginning of Part C, must therefore be considered as in need of renewed study.

Isotopic oxygen tracer experiments by Brown (1953) seem to indicate that *oxygen* can act as Hill oxidant in *Chlorella* cells—in other words, these cells function as photocatalysts for the exchange of O^{18} between O_2 and H_2O (*cf.* section B4 (*c*)). In the presence of quinone (*cf.* figure 35.28) this isotopic equilibration in light does not begin until practically all quinone has been reduced (similar observations were described in part B for chloroplast preparations).   In the absence of quinone, one has the problem of distinguishing between (light-stimulated) respiration and the "Mehler reaction," as possible mechanisms of isotopic equilibration.   The best evidence is obtained with species such as *Anabaena*, or *Scenedesmus*, in which respiration can be poisoned by cyanide without affecting the isotopic exchange in

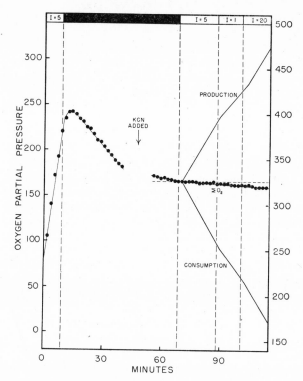

Fig. 35.29. Isotopic tracer evidence of closed-circle Hill reaction in live *Anabaena* cells in carbonate buffer No. 11. Respiration (1.73 mm.^{3}/min.) and CO_2 reduction poisoned by cyanide (0.01 mole/l.). The only effect of light (6.5, 1.5, 26 klux) is 1:1 isotopic exchange of O between O_2 and H_2O (after Brown 1953).

light (whose rate remains considerably higher than that of unpoisoned dark respiration, *cf.* figure 35.29). It seems most likely that the photochemical exchange mechanism is in these cells—and by inference, in other species as well—the one suggested by Mehler for chloroplasts: a Hill reaction leading to hydrogen transfer from H_2O to O_2, converting the latter to H_2O_2, followed by the catalatic decomposition of the peroxide.

Horwitz (1954[1]) found that substitution of *deuterium oxide* for ordinary water reduces the rate of quinone reduction by *Chlorella* at all light intensities, and not only in the light-saturated state, as is the case with photosynthesis (*cf.* p. 296).

Bibliography to Chapter 35

A. *Photochemistry of Chlorophyll Solutions*

1943   Pepkowitz, L. P., J. *Biol. Chem.*, **149,** 465.
Baur, E., and Niggli, F., *Helv. Chim. Acta*, **26,** 251, 994.

1947   Livingston, R., Sickle, D. and Uchiyama, A., *J. Phys. & Coll. Chem.*, **51**, 775.

1948   McBrady, J. J., and Livingston, R., *ibid.*, **52**, 662.

Livingston, R., and Pariser, R. L., *J. Am. Chem. Soc.*, **70**, 1510.

Krasnovsky, A. A., *Compt. rend. (Doklady) Acad. Sci. U.S.S.R.*, **60**, 421.

Krasnovsky, A. A., *ibid.*, **61**, 91.

Gurevich, A. A., *ibid.*, **59**, 937.

Gurevich, A. A., *ibid.*, **64**, 369.

Krasnovsky, A. A., and Brin, G. P., *Compt. rend. (Doklady) Acad. Sci. U.S.S.R.*, **63**, 163.

Calvin, M., and Dorough, G., *J. Am. Chem. Soc.*, **70**, 699.

1949   Warburg, O., and Schocken, V., *Arch. Biochem.*, **21**, 363.

Livingston, R., "Photochemistry of Chlorophyll" in *Photosynthesis in Plants*, Iowa State College Press, Ames, Iowa, 1949.

Krasnovsky, A. A., and Voynovskaya, K. K., *Compt. rend. (Doklady) Acad. Sci., U.S.S.R.*, **66**, 663.

Krasnovsky, A. A., and Brin, G. P., *ibid.*, **67**, 325.

Krasnovsky, A. A., Brin, G. P., and Voynovskaya, K. K., *ibid.*, **69**, 393.

Huennekens, F. M., and Calvin, M., *J. Am. Chem. Soc.*, **71**, 4024, 4031.

1950   Knight, J., and Livingston, R., *J. Phys. & Coll. Chem.*, **54**, 703.

Pariser, R., Thesis, Univ. of Minnesota.

Linstead, R. P., Braude, E. A., and Timmons, C. J., *Nature*, **166**, 557.

Krasnovsky, A. A., and Brin, G. P., *Compt. rend. (Doklady) Acad. Sci. U.S.S.R.*, **73**, 1239.

Ashkinazi, M. S., Glikman, T. S., and Dain, B. J., *ibid.*, **73**, 743.

Evstigneev, V. B., Gavrilova, V. A., and Krasnovsky, A. A., *ibid.*, **74**, 315.

Evstigneev, V. B., and Gavrilova, V. A., *ibid.*, **74**, 781.

1951   Krasnovsky, A. A., and Voynovskaya, K. K., *ibid.*, **81**, 879.

Evstigneev, V. B., and Terenin, A. N., *ibid.*, **81**, 223.

Krasnovsky, A. A., and Gavrilova, V. A., *ibid.*, **81**, 1105.

Kachan, A. A., and Dain, B. J., *ibid.*, **80**, 619.

Burk, D., and Warburg, O., *Z. Naturforsch.*, **6b**, 12.

1952   Weigl, J. W., and Livingston, R., *J. Am. Chem. Soc.*, **74**, 4160.

Uri, N., *ibid.*, **74**, 5808.

Weigl, J. W., and Livingston, R., *ibid.*, **74**, 4211.

Watson, W. F., *Trans. Faraday Soc.*, **48**, 526.

Linschitz, H., and Rennert, J., *Nature*, **169**, 193.

Krasnovsky, A. A., and Voynovskaya, K. K., *Compt. rend. (Doklady) Acad. Sci. U.S.S.R.*, **87**, 109.

Krasnovsky, A. A., Evstigneev, V. B., Brin, G. P., and Gavrilova, V. A., *ibid.*, **82**, 947.

Holt, A. S., Paper at Gatlinburg Conference on Photosynthesis, October, 1952.

1953   Krasnovsky, A. A., and Brin, G. P., *Compt. rend. (Doklady) Acad. Sci. U.S.S.R.*, **89**, 527.

Evstigneev, V. B., and Gavrilova, V. A., *ibid.*, **89**, 523.

Evstigneev, V. B., and Gavrilova, V. A., *ibid.*, **91**, 899.

Warburg, O., Krippahl, G., Buchholz, W., and Schröder, W., *Z. Natur-forsch.*, **8b**, 675.

Schenk, G. O., Personal communication.

Livingston, R., and Ryan, V. A., *J. Am. Chem. Soc.*, **75**, 2176.

Evstigneev, V. B., and Gavrilova, V. A., *Compt. rend. (Doklady) Acad. Sci. U.S.S.R.*, **92**, 381.

1954   Livingston, R., Porter, G., and Windsor, M., *Nature*, **173**, 485.

B. Photochemistry of Chloroplasts

1939   Hill, R., *Proc. Roy. Soc.*, **B127**, 192.

1940   Hill, R., and Scarisbrick, R., *Nature*, **146**, 61; *Proc. Roy. Soc. London*, **B129**, 238.

1942   French, C. S., Newcomb, E., and Anson, M. L., *Am. J. Botany*, **29**, 85.

1943   Fan, C. S., Stauffer, J. F., and Umbreit, W. W., *J. Gen. Physiol.*, **27**, 15.

Boichenko, E. A., *Compt. rend. (Doklady) Acad. Sci. U.S.S.R.*, **38**, 181.

1944   Boichenko, E. A., *ibid.*, **42**, 345.

Warburg, O., and Lüttgens, W., *Naturwissenschaften*, **32**, 161, 301.

1945   French, C. S., and Rabideau, G. S., *J. Gen. Physiol.*, **28**, 329.

Franck, J., *Rev. Modern Phys.*, **17**, 112.

Kumm, J., and French, C. S., *Am. J. Botany*, **32**, 291.

1946   Holt, A. S., and French, C. S., *Arch. Biochem.*, **9**, 25.

Warburg, O., and Lüttgens, W., *Biokhimiya (Russ.)*, **11**, 303; reprinted in *Schwermetalle als Wirkungsgruppen von Fermenten*, Berlin, 1946, and *Heavy Metal Prosthetic Groups and Enzyme Action*, Clarendon Press, Oxford, 1949.

French, C. S., Holt, A. S., Powell, R. D., and Anson, M. L., *Science*, **103**, 505.

Aronoff, S., *Plant Physiol.*, **21**, 393.

French, C. S., and Holt, A. S., *Am. J. Botany*, **33**, 19a.

1947   Boichenko, E. A., *Biokhimiya (Russ.)*, **12**, 196.

Gurevich, A. A., *Compt. rend. (Doklady) Acad. Sci. U.S.S.R.*, **55**, 263.

Holt, A. S., and Macdowall, F. D., A.A.A.S. Symposium, Chicago, Dec. 1947.

1948   Brown, A. H., and Franck, J., *Arch. Biochem.*, **16**, 55.

Holt, A. S., and French, C. S., *Arch. Biochem.*, **19**, 368.

Holt, A. S., and French, C. S., *ibid.*, **19**, 429.

Boyle, F. P., *Science*, **108**, 359.

Boichenko, E. A., *Biokhimiya (Russ.)*, **13**, 219.

Andreeva, T. F., and Zubkovich, L. E., *Compt. rend. (Doklady) Acad. Sci. U.S.S.R.*, **60**, 681.

Van Norman, R. W., French, C. S., and Macdowall, F. D. H., *Plant Physiol.*, **23**, 455.

1949   Holt, A. S., and French, C. S., "The Photochemical Liberation of Oxygen from Water by Isolated Chloroplasts" in *Photosynthesis in Plants*, Iowa State College Press, Ames, Iowa, 1949.

Zubkovich, L. E., and Andreeva, T. F., *Compt., rend. (Doklady) Acad. Sci. U.S.S.R.*, **67**, 165.

Davenport, H. E., *Proc. Roy Soc. (London)* **B136**, 281.

Macdowall, F. D. H., *Plant Physiol.*, **24**, 462.

Arnon, D. I., *Plant Physiol.*, **24, 1**.

Arnon, D. I., and Whatley, F. R., *Arch. Biochem.*, **23**, 141.

Arnon, D. I., and Whatley, F. R., *Science*, **110, 554**.

Arnon, D. I., and Whatley, F. R., *Am. Assoc. Plant Physiol.*, New York Meeting, Dec. 1949.

1950   Arnold, W., and Oppenheimer, J. R., *J. Gen. Physiol.*, **33**, 423.

Clendenning, K. A., and Gorham, P. R., *Can. J. Research*, **C28**, 78.

Clendenning, K. A., and Gorham, P. R., *ibid.*, **28**, 102.

Clendenning, K. A., and Gorham, P. R., *ibid.*, **28**, 114.

Gorham, P. R., and Clendenning, K. A., *ibid.*, **28**, 513.

Spikes, J. D., Lumry, R., Eyring, H., and Wayrynen, R. E., *Proc. Nat. Acad. Sci., U.S.*, **36**, 455.

Spikes, J. D., Lumry, R., Eyring, H., and Wayrynen, R. E., *Arch. Biochem.*, **28**, 48.

Milner, H. W., French, C. S., Koenig, M. L. G., and Lawrence, N. S., *ibid.*, **28**, 193.

Milner, H. W., Koenig, M. L. G., and Lawrence, N. S., *ibid.*, **28**, 185.

Milner, H. W., Lawrence, N. S., and French, C. S., *Science*, **111**, 633.

Gerretsen, F. C., *Plant and Soil*, **2**, 159.

Gerretsen, F. C., *ibid.*, **2**, 323.

Ochoa, S., Veiga Solles, J. B., and Ortiz, P. J., *J. Biol. Chem.*, **187**, 863.

1951   Vereshchinsky, I. V., *Biokhimiya*, **16**, 350.

Holt, A. S., Smith, R. F., and French, C. S., *Plant Physiol.*, **26**, 164.

French, C. S., and Milner, H. W., *Symposia Soc. Exptl. Biol.*, **5**, 232.

Hill, R., *ibid.*, **5**, 222.

Gerretsen, F. C., *Plant and Soil*, **3**, 1.

Arnon, D. I., *Nature*, **167**, 1008.

Mehler, A. H., *Arch. Biochem. and Biophys.*, **33**, 65.

Mehler, A. H., *ibid.*, **34**, 339.

Vishniac, W., and Ochoa, S., *Nature*, **167**, 768.

Tolmach, L. J., *ibid.*, **167**, 946.

Tolmach, L. J., *Arch. Biochem. and Biophys.*, **33**, 120.

Vishniac, W., *Federation Proc.*, **10**, 265.

Holt, A. S., Brooks, I. A., and Arnold, W. A., *J. Gen. Physiol.*, **34**, 627.

Vinogradov, A. P., Boichenko, E. A. and Baranov, V. I., *Compt. rend. (Doklady) Acad. Sci., U.S.S.R.*, **78**, 327.

Clendenning, K. A., and Ehrmantraut, H. C., *Arch. Biochem.*, **29**, 387.

1952   Ehrmantraut, H. C., and Rabinowitch, E., *Arch. Biochem. and Biophys.*, **38**, 67.

Smith, J. H. C., French, C. S., and Koski, V. M., *Plant Physiol.*, **27**, 212.

Davis, E. A., *Am. J. Botany*, **39**, 535.

Bishop, N. I., Thesis, Univ. of Utah.

Ochoa, S., and Vishniac, W., *Science*, **115**, 297.

Vishniac, W., and Ochoa, S., *J. Biol. Chem.*, **195**, 75.

Davenport, H. E., Hill, R., and Whatley, F. R., *Proc. Roy. Soc. London*, **B139**, 346.

Davenport, H. E., and Hill, R., *ibid.*, **B139**, 327.

Wessels, J. S. C., and Havinga, E., *Rec. trav. chim.*, **71**, 809.

Krasnovsky, A. A., and Kosobutskaya, L. M., *Compt. rend. (Doklady) Acad. Sci., U.S.S.R.*, **82**, 761.

Warburg, O., *Z. Naturforsch.*, **7b**, 443.

Fager, E. W., *Arch. Biochem. and Biophys.*, **37**, 5.

Gorham, P. R., and Clendenning, K. A., *ibid.*, **37**, 199.

Mehler, A. H., and Brown, A. H., *ibid.*, **38**, 365.

Macdowall, F. D. H., *Science*, **116**, 398.

Rabinowitch, E., *Ann. Rev. Plant Physiol.*, **3**, 229.

Uri, N., *J. Am. Chem. Soc.*, **74**, 5808.

McClendon, J. H., and Blinks, L. R., *Nature*, **170**, 577.

1953   Thomas, J. B., Blaauw, O. H., and Duysens, L. N. M., *Biochem. et Biophys. Acta*, **10**, 230.

Wessels, J. S. C., and Havinga, E., *Rec. trav. chim.*, **72**, 1076.

Gilmour, H. S. A., Lumry, R., Spikes, J. D., and Eyring, H., AEC Technical Report No. 11, Contract No. AT (11-1)-82.

Brown, A. H., Personal communication.

Boichenko, E. A., and Baranov, V. I., *Compt. rend. (Doklady) Acad. Sci. U.S.S.R.*, **91**, 339.

Hill, R., Northcote, D. H., and Davenport, H. E., *Nature*, **172**, 948.

Punnett, T., and Fabiyi, A., *ibid.*, **172**, 947.

1954   Spikes, J. D., Lumry, R., Rieske, J. S., and Marcus, R. J., *Plant Physiol.*, **29**, 161.

Horwitz, L., *ibid.*, **29**, 215.

Punnett, T., Thesis, Univ. of Illinois.

Tolbert, N. E., and Zill, I. P., *J. Gen. Physiol.*, **37**, 575.

Arnon, D. I., Allen, M. B., and Whatley, F. R., *Nature*, **174**, 39.

Arnon, D. I., Whatley, F. R., and Allen, M. B., *J. Am. Chem. Soc.*, **76**, 6324.

McClendon, J. H., *Plant Physiol.*, **29**, 448.

Horwitz, L., *Bull. Math. Biophys.*, **16**, 45.

Wessels, J. S. C., Thesis, Univ. Leyden.

C. Photochemistry of Cells

1943   Fan, C. S., Stauffer, J. F., and Umbreit, W. W., *J. Gen. Physiol.*, **27**, 15.

1946   Warburg, O., and Lüttgens, W., *Biokhimiya (Russ.)*, **11**, 303; *Schwermetalle als Wirkungsgruppen von Fermenten*, Berlin. 1946; *Heavy Metal Prosthetic Groups and Enzyme Action*, Clarendon Press, Oxford, 1949.

Aronoff, S., *Plant Physiol.*, **21**, 393.

1951   Clendenning, K. A., and Ehrmantraut, H. C., *Arch. Biochem.*, **29**, 387.

Holt, A. S., Arnold, W., and Brooks, I. A., *J. Gen. Physiol.*, **34**, 627.

1952   Ehrmantraut, H. C., and Rabinowitch, E., *Arch. Biochem. and Biophys.*, **38**, 67.

1953   Brown, A. H., Personal communication.

1954   Clendenning, K. A., Personal communication.

CHAPTER 36

CHEMICAL PATH OF CARBON DIOXIDE REDUCTION*

(ADDENDA TO CHAPTERS 3, 8 AND 9)

A. ISOTOPIC CARBON TRACER STUDIES*

Abbreviations used in this chapter: GA, glyceric acid; PGA, phosphoglyceric acid; PA, pyruvic acid; PPA, phosphopyruvic acid; MA, malic acid; and OOA, oxalacetic acid.

TP, triose phosphate; DHAP, dihydroxyacetone phosphate; GMP, glucose monophosphate; FMP, fructose monophosphate; FDP, fructose diphosphate; RDP, ribulose diphosphate; and SMP, sedoheptulose monophosphate.

Also DPN and TPN, diphospho- and triphosphopyridine nucleotides (coenzymes I and II, hydrogen carriers); coA, coenzyme A ("acetyl carrier"); LA, lipoic (or thioctic) acid (hydrogen carrier); and ADP and ATP, adenosine diphosphate and triphosphate (high-energy phosphate acceptor and donor, respectively).

The experiments and speculations described in this chapter are concerned with the primary fixation of carbon dioxide in photosynthesis and its subsequent reduction—topics that have been discussed in chapter 8 (sections 3 and 4) and chapter 9 (section 10) of Vol. I, respectively. Also included are observations that throw some light on the sequence in which different sugars, amino acids and other synthesized products appear in photosynthesis—a matter discussed in chapter 3.

Some data will have to be included in this chapter concerning the effect of poisons on photosynthesis—a subject dealt with in chapter 12, and again in chapter 37D (section 2a).

1. Photosynthetic and Respiratory Fixation of C^*O_2

It was hoped at first that the application of tracer carbon would rapidly lead to clarification of the hitherto mysterious chemical mechanism of carbon dioxide reduction. The task proved to be more difficult than was anticipated for two reasons. In the first place, it has become apparent that, whatever the intermediates and primary products of carbon dioxide transformation in photosynthesis may be, they are very rapidly changed into a variety of other compounds; or, at least, the tracer carbon incorporated in them is rapidly redistributed through a multitude of metabolites. Within a few minutes, C(14) makes its appearance in compounds of differ-

* Bibliography, page 1710.

ent types, including sugars, proteins and even fats. It seems that this redistribution of assimilated radiocarbon begins even before carbon dioxide has been reduced to the carbohydrate level, by side reactions of intermediate reduction products (such as amination of C_3 or C_4 acids), or their involvement in respiratory reactions.

Aronoff, Benson, Hassid and Calvin (1947) investigated the active constituents of barley seedlings exposed to light for one hour in C(14)-tagged carbon dioxide. Radiocarbon was found in all fractions, with the largest accumulation in sugars (Table 36.I).

TABLE 36.I

TRACER DISTRIBUTION IN BARLEY SEEDLINGS AFTER ONE HOUR OF PHOTOSYNTHESIS IN TAGGED CARBON DIOXIDE (AFTER ARONOFF, BENSON, et al., 1947)

Fraction	Per cent of total C*	
	Plants with roots	Plants without roots
Ether-extractable acids (fatty acids)............	12.5	2.9
Lipids (including pigments).................	6.1[a]	3.6[b]
Amino acids...............................	7.2	5.6
Acids.....................................	11.3	7.7
Sugars....................................	25.8	35.0
Soluble proteins...........................	0.7	6.9
Other water-soluble components.............	3.5	—
Cellulose..................................	2.8	3.6
Lignin, etc................................	8.3	9.4
Unaccounted..............................	18.8	20.3

[a] 0.9% in carotenoids.   [b] 0.8% in chlorins, 0.9% in phytol.

Aronoff, Barker and Calvin (1947) subjected the sugar fraction in table 36.I to fermentation (by yeast, or by *Lactobacillus casei*), and from the activity of the various products determined the relative amount of C* in the different positions in the C chain. The results are summarized in table 36.II; they indicate that even after a full hour of photosynthesis, the tagging of hexoses was still far from uniform, and C* was preferentially found in positions 3 and 4.

TABLE 36.II

TRACER DISTRIBUTION IN SUGARS PHOTOSYNTHESIZED IN ONE HOUR BY BARLEY SEEDLINGS (ARONOFF, BARKER AND CALVIN, 1947)

Material	Product	Fermented by	C* in positions		
			1,6	2,5	3,4
Plants with roots.....	Hydrolyzed sugar	Yeast	—		1.96
	Crystalline glucose	*L. casei*	0.83	taken as	1.60
Plants without roots..	Nonhydrolyzed sugar	" "	0.41	1.00	2.95
	Crystalline glucose	" "	0.68		2.61

Similar results were obtained by Calvin and Benson (1948). After one hour of photosynthesis, tagged glucose contained 61% of its C* in positions 3 and 4, 24% in positions 2 and 5, and 15% in positions 1 and 6; after 2 hours of photosynthesis, the distribution was 37, 36, 27%—obviously approaching equilibrium. A similar spread of C(14) from position 1 (carboxyl) to positions 2 and 3 could be observed in alanine.

Gibbs (1949) reported results quite different from those of Calvin and Benson. After 1 hour photosynthesis in C(14)-labelled CO_2, he found glucose to be labelled preferentially in positions 1 and 6.

All these early results appear to be in some contradiction to the more recent degradation experiments in Berkeley, where all preferential tagging (up to 90% C* in glucose in positions 3 and 4 after 30 seconds exposure, cf. table 36.VII) was found to yield to practically uniform tagging in a matter of minutes, not hours.

In the first Russian experiments with C(14) as tracer, reported by Nezgovorova (1951, 1952[1]), long exposures to $C*O_2$ in light (of the order of one hour) were used, and the tracer was found largely in proteins. Doman, Kuzin, Mamul and Khudjakova (1952) went over to exposures of 1–2 seconds, following them by 0–300 seconds of photosynthesis in nontagged carbon dioxide. They used young leaves of 17 species, and obtained, by a ionophoretic method of fractionation, a large variety of results. For example, *Phaseolus* was found to fix C*, after 1 second exposure, only in anionic substances; with other plants, it was found also in cathionic substances, with still others, in neutral substances.

Nezgovorova (1952[2]) observed the dark uptake of $C*O_2$ by leaves, and found no effect of preillumination.

The insoluble tagged compounds synthesized by barley in 5-minutes exposure to $C*O_2$ are 95% *polysaccharides*; in *Scenedesmus*, they are 50% polysaccharides and 50% proteins, the latter containing mainly tagged alanine and aspartic acid (Calvin *et al.* 1951).

This result may have some bearing on the observations of Smith *et al.* (Vol. I, page 36) that the product of photosynthesis in sunflower is almost 100% carbohydrates, and on the failure of other observers to obtain similar simple results with other plants, particularly with algae.

The second complication is due to the fact that, as we now know, there occurs (in dark as well as in light), in addition to C* assimilation by photosynthesis, also a C* uptake by exchange of $C*O_2$ with the carboxyl groups of certain respiration (and fermentation) intermediates.

We mentioned in Vol. I (page 208) that, since 1936, many observations had revealed the capacity of bacteria (and of certain animal tissues) to assimilate carbon dioxide in the dark. This fixation often can be attributed to the reversibility of certain respiratory decarboxylations, such as:

(36.1) $COOHCH_2COCOOH$ (oxalacetate) $\rightleftharpoons$

$CH_3COCOOH + CO_2$ (pyruvate + carbon dioxide)

or of decarboxylations coupled with oxidation-reductions, such as

(36.2) $CH_3COCOOH + A + H_2O$ (pyruvate + oxidant) $\rightleftharpoons$

$CH_3COOH + CO_2 + AH_2$ (acetate + carbon dioxide + reductant)

The oxidant in (36.2) is, *in vivo*, phosphopyridine nucleotide.

Some irreversible reactions of the latter type become reversible if accompanied by conversion of "low energy" into "high energy" phosphate. (For this, the oxidant and the reductant must be in the form of phosphate esters, and the ester of the reductant must release less energy on hydrolysis than that of the oxidant; this is the case, *e. g.*, when the reductant contains a carbonyl and the oxidant a carboxyl group.)

More recently, it has been found that the capacity for taking up radioactive carbon from carbon dioxide and distributing the tagged carbon atoms through a variety of metabolites is common to many animal and plant cells. It may perhaps be considered an inevitable concomitant of cellular respiration (and fermentation), since both processes involve reversible decarboxylations such as (36.1) or (36.2) and associated reactions, which, too, are either reversible in themselves, or can be reversed by coupling with degradation or high-energy phosphates. More specifically, all partial processes of glycolysis leading from sucrose to pyruvic acid, as well as the "Krebs cycle," by which pyruvic acid is decarboxylated and dehydrogenated, are of this character. Therefore, what we observe as the net production of carbon dioxide in respiration (or fermentation) is the excess of reactions running in the direction of chain fission (and hydrogen transfer to oxidized pyridine nucleotides) over reactions by which the carbon chain is built up (and hydrogenated with hydrogen supplied by reduced pyridine nucleotides). The presence of $C*O_2$ in the atmosphere in which respiration or fermentation takes place must then lead to some C* atoms "creeping back," first into the intermediates of the decarboxylation cycle, and thence into those of glycolysis. Simultaneously, the C* atoms may also penetrate into compounds (such as certain amino acids), whose respiratory breakdown is coupled with that of carbohydrates.

Because of the existence of a C* uptake from $C*O_2$ which is unrelated to photosynthesis, it is not permissible to conclude that a certain compound is an intermediate (or an early product) of photosynthesis merely because it appears C* tagged soon after the exposure of the plant to $C*O_2$. Rather, specific evidence is needed to justify such a conclusion. In strong light, when photosynthesis far exceeds respiration, C* uptake determined by radioactive method can be compared with the net CO_2 uptake determined by manometry (or other analytical methods), and if the former does not exceed markedly the latter, the *bulk* of the C*-tagged compounds must have been produced by photosynthesis. Even in this case, however, the tagged compounds which are present in relatively small amounts could be due to the reversal of respirative (or fermentative) decarboxylations, and have no relation to photosynthesis.

The existence of these complications was not known when the first carbon tracer studies of photosynthesis were made by Ruben and co-workers with the short-lived carbon isotope, C(11). It is therefore difficult to decide which of their observations (described in Vol. I, pages 201 and 241) remain significant from the point of view of the mechanism of photosynthesis.

Ruben, Kamen and co-workers found (1939, 1940) that *in the dark*, $C^{11}O_2$ was incorporated, by an enzymatic reaction, into a water-soluble molecule, with a molecular weight of about 1000, forming a carboxyl group. *After brief illumination*, they found most of the active carbon in a similar (perhaps, the same) large molecule, but by now not, or not exclusively, in a carboxyl group. The active material was, however, still soluble in water and precipitable by barium. It was later observed, with some surprise, by Frenkel (1941) (also at Berkeley) that in the dark, the C* uptake was localized in the cytoplasm. After brief illumination, however, the radioactivity was found predominantly in the chloroplasts.

The amount of C(11) taken up after several hours of exposure to C^*O_2 *in the dark* was about 0.05 mole/liter of cell volume—roughly equivalent to the amount of chlorophyll present; however, the tagged product was *not* bound to chlorophyll. (We noted above that it could be extracted with water.)

It seemed natural at that time to identify the C^*O_2 acceptor compound, whose formation in the dark was indicated by these experiments, with the often postulated substrate of photochemical reduction (which we have variously symbolized by {CO_2}, ACO_2 or RCOOH). However, this identification presented certain difficulties. One of them was the slowness with which C(11) was taken up: about an *hour* was needed to "saturate" the cells with radiocarbon in the dark (*cf.* fig. 21, Vol. I); the same amount of carbon can be absorbed in about 20 seconds, either by photosynthesis in strong light, or by "pick-up" after intense photosynthesis in the dark (Vol. I, p. 206).

Two explanations of the slowness of the observed C* uptake could be suggested. One is that this uptake is slow when it has to proceed through isotopic *exchange*:

$$(36.3) \qquad C^*O_2 + RCOOH \rightleftharpoons CO_2 + RC^*OOH$$

but becomes *fast* when it can occur by C^*O_2 *addition to free acceptor*:

$$(36.4) \qquad C^*O_2 + RH \rightleftharpoons RC^*OOH$$

(However, on page 203, the "one hour uptake" itself was tentatively attributed to reaction with free acceptor—in order to be able to explain the occurrence of additional CO_2 uptake after evacuation.)

During intense photosynthesis, in a medium which is low in carbon dioxide, the acceptor may be present in the photostationary state predominantly in the decarboxylated state, RH. When illumination is stopped, CO_2 rushes in, in a rapid gulp, as observed in "pick-up" experiments. In the experiments of Ruben and Kamen, on the other hand, the acceptor could have been present mainly in the carboxylated form, RCOOH, and C(11) could enter it only by the slow exchange reaction (36.3).

A second possible reason for the observed slowness of the C* uptake in the dark has become apparent after it had been established that C^*O_2 can be taken up by mechanisms unrelated to photosynthesis. The acceptor responsible for the slow uptake of C(11) in the dark could be altogether different from that active in photosynthesis.

Frenkel's observation that the C* uptake in the dark takes place in the cytoplasm, and not in chloroplasts, has been related on page 66 (Vol. I) to the incapacity of isolated chloroplasts to use carbon dioxide as hydrogen acceptor in light. This seems suggestive. but since the early products of carbon dioxide fixation in photosynthesis are water-soluble, it is possible for them to be primarily formed in the chloroplasts and yet to diffuse (or be eluted) into the cell sap cytoplasm fraction during the maceration and fractionation of the cell material. Clendenning and Gorham (1952) found that in multicellular algae (Nitella—the organism used by Frenkel—Chara and Riccia), most of the (C14) taken up in brief periods of photosynthesis—down to 5 seconds—was found in the cell sap; in unicellular algae—Chlorella and Scenedesmus—a larger fraction could be located in insoluble lipoid and proteinaceous materials from the chloroplast fraction. The question of whether the enzymatic transformations of carbon dioxide in photosynthesis occur inside the chloroplasts, or outside these bodies (in which case they must be mediated by a reductant produced photochemically inside the chloroplasts and diffusing out of them), has not been definitely answered by these experiments. The observation of Arnon et. al. (1954), that intact chloroplasts take up C* in light, was described on pp. 1537 and 1615.

Ruben and Kamen's observation that $C(11)O_2$ is taken up by carboxylation, with the formation of a water-soluble carboxylic acid, has been confirmed by all the subsequent investigations with C(14); it is true for photosynthetic as well as for respiratory C* fixation. On the other hand, the conclusion that this acid has a molecular weight of about 1000 appears to be inaccurate for both types of fixation, since the first product of photochemical fixation seems to be phosphoglyceric acid (molecular weight 187), while respiratory fixation is likely to lead to products such as pyruvic or oxalacetic acid, which, too, have low molecular weights.

The possibility of "respiratory" C* fixation was not fully taken into account also in the early stages of work with the long-lived isotope C(14) by Benson, Calvin and co-workers at Berkeley (1947). It was first emphasized by Allen, Gest and Kamen (1947), and by Brown, Fager and Gaffron (1948), and subsequently recognized also by the Berkeley group.

Allen, Gest and Kamen (1947) attempted to distinguish between the two types of C* absorption by recalling an early observation of Ruben, Kamen and Hassid with C(11) (Vol. I, page 242). The latter had found that in Chlorella the cyanide inhibition of the C* uptake in the dark resembles that of photosynthesis, rather than that of respiration (for example 10^{-2} M KCN reduced the rate of both photosynthesis and dark C* fixation to 0.3% of the normal value, but left respiration almost unchanged). Allen, Gest and Kamen repeated these experiments, using C(14), with both Chlorella and Scenedesmus. (In the second species, respiration is more sensitive to cyanide than photosynthesis, cf. Vol. 1, page 305.) They found that, by the criterion of cyanide sensitivity, dark C* fixation in Scenedesmus appears to be related to photosynthesis rather than to respiration, while in Chlorella (in disagreement with earlier observation) the effect of cyanide on dark C* fixation was intermediate between those on photosynthesis and respiration. With Scenedesmus cells starved for 24 hours in darkness, the results were erratic, but with similarly starved Chlorella cells, the effect of cyanide on dark C* fixation was definitely similar to its effect on respiration and quite different from that on photosynthesis.

Kamen concluded that one part of dark C* fixation is "photosynthetic" and another part is "respiratory" in origin, and that the latter part is particularly large in starved *Chlorella* cells.

Subsequently, Calvin and co-workers achieved substantial progress by distinguishing clearly between three types of C^*O_2 uptake: in the dark without preillumination, in the dark immediately after preillumination, and in light. (A further distinction is indicated by the work of Gaffron, Fager *et al.*—between preillumination in the absence of CO_2, and that in the presence of CO_2.)

Most revealing are the results obtained by first illuminating cells in ordinary carbon dioxide with strong light long enough to establish a steady state of photosynthesis, then rapidly supplying them with tagged C^*O_2, and killing them as quickly as possible after a very brief continuation of the light exposure. In some experiments of Calvin and co-workers, photosynthesis in tagged C^*O_2 lasted only 0.4 second.

The results obtained at Berkeley in this study—which is being continued—have been presented, between 1948 and 1954, in about twenty papers under the general title "Path of Carbon Dioxide in Photosynthesis," and in several reviews, *e. g.*, by Benson and Calvin (1948, 1950) and Calvin (1952[1,2]), *cf.* also the reviews by Gaffron and Fager (1951), Brown and Frenkel (1953), and Hölzer (1954).

Brown and Frenkel paid particular attention to the question of whether all the Berkeley results were obtained in a steady state of photosynthesis, as was assumed in their interpretation. A source of uncertainty in this respect was the flushing of the vessel with air prior to the introduction of the tracer. The criterion of the steady state is the linearity of the C^* uptake with time, which was observed in many, but not in all, of the Berkeley experiments.

2. C^*O_2 Fixation in Darkness with and without Preillumination. A Surviving Reductant?

Benson and Calvin (1947) began by resuming Ruben and Kamen's study of the C^*O_2 uptake *in darkness*. They used two *Chlorella* suspensions; suspension I was kept in the dark for eight hours in 4% carbon dioxide, while suspension II was strongly illuminated for one hour in CO_2-free nitrogen. Both were then exposed to C^*O_2 in the dark for 5 min. and the cells killed by acid (HCl + CH_3COOH). The purpose was to see whether preillumination of cells in the absence of carbon dioxide creates in them a chemical agent ("reducing power") able to cause subsequent uptake (which Calvin and Benson presumed must mean *reduction*), of carbon dioxide in the dark. The C^* uptake was found to be five times greater in the preilluminated algae. The chemical distribution of radiocarbon also was different in the two samples: as much as 70% of total activity in sample I was found in *succinic acid* (about 85% of it in the two carboxyl groups), 15% in amino acids, and 9% in "anionic substances" (*i. e.*, substances whose active component could be adsorbed on anion-exchange resins), while in (preilluminated) sample II, the largest fraction of total activity (30%) was found in amino acids (mostly alanine), 25% in an unidentified fraction (described as extractable from water by ether at pH 1), and 10% in anionic substances; only small amounts were found in succinic acid (6%), malic acid (6%), and fumaric acid (1%); and 1.5% in sugars.

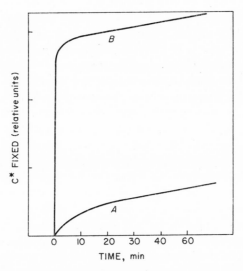

Fig. 36.1. Rate of dark fixation of radiocarbon by *Scenedesmus*. Curve *A*, one-day-old *Scenedesmus* cultures after one hour dark incubation in 4% CO_2 in nitrogen. Curve *B*, same cells immediately after 10 min. preillumination (after Calvin and Benson 1947).

Calvin and Benson (1947) gave the curves (reproduced in fig. 36.1) for the time course of the C* uptake in the dark without preliminary illumination (curve *A*), and with 10-min. preillumination (curve *B*). In answer to suggestions that much if not all of the dark C*O₂ uptake previously reported by them, may have been due to the reversal of decarboxylations in the respiratory system (and thus bear no direct relation to photosynthesis), Calvin and Benson pointed out that figure 36.1 indicates the superposition of two processes: a *slow* uptake (curve *A*, and second part of curve *B*), which admittedly may be due to reversible reactions in the respiratory system, and a *fast* uptake (initial part of curve *B*), which occurs only after preillumination and which (it was argued) must be related to photosynthesis. (This uptake could be considered as radiometric equivalent of the manometrically observed fast CO₂ "pick-up.")

This hypothesis is plausible; however, a period of intense illumination in the absence of external CO_2 supply (the pretreatment used in these experiments) could lead to extensive decarboxylation not only of the carbon dioxide acceptor in photosynthesis but also of respiratory intermediates. Consequently, the fact that a "CO_2-gulp" was observed after such a period is not in itself convincing evidence that the C*, taken up in this gulp, enters the photosynthetic reaction sequence. Calvin and co-workers saw an additional proof of their hypothesis in the distribution of tracer carbon among different compounds. This distribution was qualitatively similar, after the fast dark uptake by preilluminated cells, to that after a short period of photosynthesis in C*O_2, but quite different after the slow dark uptake without preillumination (cf. fig. 36.2).

Tables 36.III and 36.IV show the fractionation of the tagged material obtained under different conditions. We note (table 36.III) that *without preillumination* a large part of total activity was in ether-soluble organic acids. (Only 5% of total C* was now found in succinic acid—as against 70% reported in 1947—16% in malic acid, and 31% in other ether-soluble carboxylic acids; 31% in amino acids, and only 16% in "anionic groups not extractable with ether.")

In *preilluminated* cells, the proportion of tagged carbon present in ether-soluble fatty acids was much smaller. It decreased with the duration of preillumination, while the relative activity of amino acids and of ether-insoluble, anionically tagged substances increased. The distribution was similar to that obtained after brief photosynthesis in C*O_2 (table 36.IV).

Tables 36.III and 36.IV are thus in agreement with the hypothesis

TABLE 36.III

C(14) TRACER DISTRIBUTION IN *Chlorella pyrenoidosa*[a]
AFTER A DARK FIXATION TIME OF FIVE MINUTES (CALVIN AND BENSON, 1947)

Fraction	No preillumination (total fixation, 1 rel. unit)	Preillumination (total fixation, 10 rel. units)		
		5 min.	60 min.	120 min.
I. Carboxylic acids in ether extract[b]	52%	21%	14%	11%
Including malic acid[c]	16	11.5	7.4	—
Including succinic acid[c]	5.2	3.1	0.5	—
II. Amino acids[d] (adsorbed on cation resin)	31	41	64	74
III. Anionic substances[e] (adsorbed on anion resin)	16	29	21	—
IV. Sugars (nonionized compounds)[f]	0.45	1.0	0.96	1.0

[a] One-day-old cultures. [b] Rapid, continuous 15-hr. extraction. [c] Separated by partition chromatography on silica gel column. [d] Eluted from Duolite C-3 resin with 2.5 N HCl. [e] Eluted from Duolite A-3 resin with 1.5 N NaOH. [f] Effluate from both resins.

that the two kinetically different mechanisms of dark C* uptake lead to different tagged compounds. The slow mechanism, which is the only one operative in starved, not preilluminated cells, produces predominantly tagged fatty acids (whether succinic, malic, or others, is a secondary question) and also some tagged amino acids. The fast mechanism, active after preillumination in absence of carbon dioxide, leads to large amounts of tagged anions of ether-insoluble organic acids (*e. g.*, glyceric acid or other polyhydroxy acids which are much more hydrophilic than simple fatty acids, such as succinic, and the monohydroxy acids, such as malic acid).

TABLE 36.IV

C(14) TRACER DISTRIBUTION IN *Chlorella* AND *Scenedesmus* AFTER EXPOSURE TO C*O₂ IN DARK AND IN LIGHT (CALVIN AND BENSON, 1947)

	C* fixation in darkness		C* fixation in light[c]	
	Chlorella[a]	*Scenedesmus*[b]	*Chlorella*[a]	*Scenedesmus*[b]
Preillumination time..............	60 min.	10 min.[f]	—	—
Fixation time....................	1 min.	1 min.	30 sec.	30 sec.
Total C¹⁴ fixed (millions c.p.m.)......	0.97	0.98	3.1	6.2
Proportion of C(14) in:				
I. Ether-extractable acids........	13%	12%	2.5%	10%
II. Cationic groups (amino acids)..	53%	39%	14%	11%
III. A. Anionic groups, ammonia elutable[d]	2.4%	4.2%	38%	44%
III. B. Anionic groups, not ammonia elutable[e]..........	31%	42%	36%	27%
IV. Nonionic compounds (sugars)..	0.3%	0.1%	4.5%	4.7%

[a] *Chlorella pyrenoidosa*, one day old.   [b] *Scenedesmus* D-3, two day old.   [c] Cells, rapidly photosynthesizing, given HC*O₃⁻ and shaken, then killed.   [d] Adsorbed on Duolite A-3, eluted with 1.5 N NH₄OH.   [e] Eluted with NaOH following ammonia elution.   [f] "Time needed to ensure maximum C*O₂ uptake" (Calvin and Benson).

These conclusions are confirmed by Figure 36.2, taken from a subsequent paper by Benson, Bassham *et al.* (1950). It shows the distribution of tagged compounds obtained in the dark (with and without preillumination), and in brief photosynthesis, as revealed by paper chromatography and radioautography. We note the prevalence of C₃ and C₄ acids in the first radiogram (dark uptake without preillumination), and the absence in it of tagged phosphate esters. The other two radiograms show the prevalence of phosphate esters of glyceric acid (PGA), of hexoses (HMP and HDP), and of pyruvic acid (PPA); they also have in common the appearance of tagged sucrose and of large amounts of tagged alanine. Malic acid and alanine contain considerable quantities of tracer carbon after all three tagging procedures.

As mentioned above, Calvin and co-workers considered the similarity

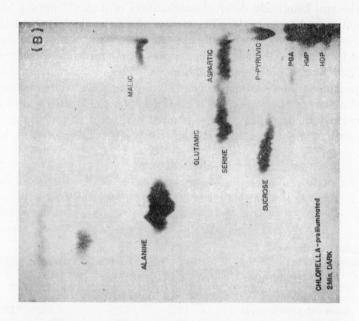

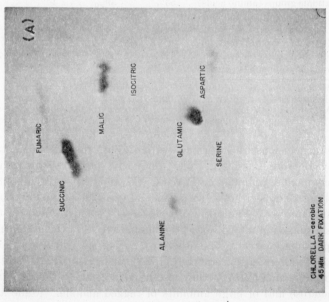

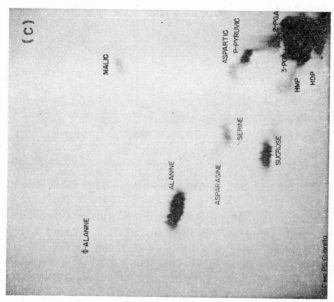

Fig. 36.2. Radiograms of radiocarbon-tagged products of C*O$_2$ fixation by algae in darkness. (A) 45 min. of dark fixation in CO$_2$; (B) 2 min. dark fixation after 5 min. preillumination in the absence of CO$_2$; (C) 30 sec. photosynthesis. Note similarity of (B) and (C) (after Benson, Bassham, Calvin et al. (1950)).

between the C* distribution obtained by the "fast" dark fixation after preillumination, and that obtained by fixation in light, as argument for the assumption of a "photosynthetic" rather than "respiratory" nature of the initial dark C^*O_2 fixation by preilluminated cells. They further assumed that the occurrence of "photosynthetic" carbon fixation in preilluminated algae means that illumination leaves in the cells, in addition to a carbon dioxide acceptor, also a strong reductant ("reducing power") capable of reducing carbon dioxide in the dark; this reductant survives for a period of several minutes. An alternative hypothesis (Gaffron *et al.*, *cf.* section 4)

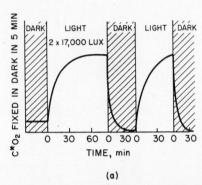 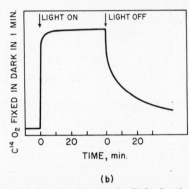

(a)   (b)

Fig. 36.3. Effect of duration of preillumination. (a) On five min. dark C^*O_2 fixation by *Chlorella;* (b) on one min. dark fixation in *Scenedesmus* (after Calvin *et al.* 1948).

is that preillumination leads merely to the accumulation of a carbon dioxide acceptor, capable of being carboxylated in the dark, without reduction, forming phosphoglyceric acid or substances of a similar reduction level. The presence in Calvin's radiograms of preilluminated cells of tagged sucrose and hexose phosphates (fig. 36.2(B)) cannot be explained in this way; but Gaffron *et al.* found practically nothing but phosphoglyceric and phosphopyruvic acids among the tagged compounds produced by dark fixation after preillumination. This disagreement remains to be resolved.

Calvin and Benson (1947) measured C^*O_2 fixation by preilluminated algae, as function of the duration of preillumination. The cells (in a thin, lollipop-shaped vessel in CO_2-free atmosphere) were illuminated from two sides with 17 klux, then dropped into a darkened $HC^*O_3{}^-$ solution, and killed 1 or 5 min. later. The resulting curves (fig. 36.3) indicate gradual saturation of cells with a C^*O_2 acceptor (and a reductant?) in light, and their disappearance in the dark. Calvin and Benson stated that the build-up was 80–100% complete after 20 *seconds* of preillumination, but figure 36.3a indicates that in *Chlorella*, at least, it may require as much as one hour. In *Scenedesmus* (fig. 36.3b), saturation was reached sooner, but even for this species, table 36.IV indicates ten *minutes* as "preillumination time needed to ensure maximum C^*O_2 uptake in the dark."

The illumination time required to accumulate the maximum capacity for C^*O_2 uptake in the dark is significant for the interpretation of this uptake. If this time is 10–60 min., a "photosynthetic" origin of the CO_2 gulp after preillumination is less likely than if this time is of the order of 20 sec. (as suggested by Calvin and Benson). The reasons are as follows:

If the maximum accumulation of the carbon dioxide acceptor in photosynthesis is of the order of magnitude of that of chlorophyll (as indicated, *e. g.*, by the volume of the "pick-up") then we can expect this peak concentration to be reached in the absence of

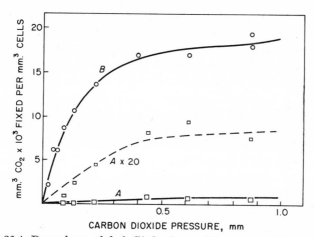

Fig. 36.4. Dependence of dark C* fixation on CO_2 pressure: *A*, non-preilluminated algae; *B*, preilluminated algae (after Calvin and Benson 1948[2]).

carbon dioxide after a time of the order of magnitude of that required for each chlorophyll molecule to reduce one carbon dioxide molecule ("assimilation time"—which according to chapter 28, is about 20 sec. in saturating light). If saturation of the cells with the acceptor requires a much longer time, it is unlikely to be due to the main reaction sequence of photosynthesis (since the rate of any partial process in this sequence cannot be slower than that of photosynthesis as a whole). This consideration applies also to the accumulation of "reducing power." It does not apply to side effects, such as decarboxylation of respiratory intermediates (in consequence of CO_2 withdrawal into the photosynthetic system), since the yield of these processes could be much smaller than that of photosynthesis itself.

The origin of the "C^*O_2-gulp" by cells which have been preilluminated in the absence of carbon dioxide and then exposed to C^*O_2 in the dark, has been further discussed by Calvin and Benson (1948). They argued that if the gulp were due to C^*O_2 uptake by the respiratory intermediates decarboxylated during the illumination period, the difference between the initial slopes of the curves showing C* fixation as function of [CO_2] (fig. 36.4) would indicate that the partial pressure of CO_2 inside the cells has been reduced, by preillumination, from ≃0.1 mm. to as little as 0.001 mm., and this, they said, light cannot do. (In support of this assertion they recalled the known falling-off of photosynthesis when external carbon dioxide pressure drops below 1.0 mm.—a phenomenon which, however, may be due only to slow penetration of carbon dioxide into the cells, *cf.* chapter 27, section A7.)

Calvin and Benson also noted that the "carbon dioxide curves" of dark fixation in preilluminated cells (fig. 36.4) are similar to those of photosynthesis (*cf.*, for example, fig. 27.4), and asserted—without further elaboration—that this similarity can best be explained by the assumption that fixation is caused by the formation, during the preillumination period and subsequent survival in the dark, of both a reductant *and* a carbon dioxide acceptor.

Stepka, Benson, and Calvin (1948) found by paper chromatography that in the material from preilluminated *Scenedesmus*, exposed to C^*O_2 in the dark, the predominant tagged amino acid was aspartic acid, while *Chlorella* yielded mainly tagged alanine. The most abundant—but entirely untagged—amino acid was, in both cases, glutamic acid.

The question of the "surviving reductant" is important for the interpretation of the primary photochemical process in photosynthesis. It was mentioned in chapter 28 (p. 941) that Franck considered the effect of $[CO_2]$ on chlorophyll fluorescence as proof of a direct association of the oxidant (be it CO_2 itself, or a carboxylation product such as PGA) with the sensitizing pigment. Other arguments—*e. g.*, the nonphotochemical reduction of carbon dioxide by chemosynthetic organisms—have been adduced in favor of the reduction process being coupled to the primary photochemical process by the intermediary of a kinetically independent "primary reduction product" (designated by X in many of our schemes); X could be the same in true photosynthesis, Hill reaction, bacterial photosynthesis, and perhaps even chemosynthesis. (Reduced pyridine nucleotide is one such possible mediator between the photochemical apparatus and the enzymatic reduction system.)

The second view is the more generally accepted one at the present time; and if the observations of Benson, Calvin *et al.* of the survival of the reducing power in preilluminated cells could be definitely confirmed, a strong argument would be won against Franck's hypothesis.

Apart, however, from the uncertain "survival of the reductant," none of the tracer observations is altogether irreconcilable with the hypothesis that the reduction of carbon dioxide, from the formation of the acceptor to triose synthesis, or even beyond this stage, takes place in molecular association with chlorophyll, so that H atoms for reduction can be supplied to the acceptor (phosphoglyceric acid) *directly by the photochemical process*.

On p. 1615 we reported the divergent findings of Mehler and of Krasnovsky concerning the survival of a reductant in preilluminated chloroplast suspensions.

3. C^*O_2 Fixation in Light: Phosphoglyceric Acid as First Intermediate

More conclusive proved the observations which Calvin and Benson (1947) made on the tracer distribution in cell material obtained by exposure to C^*O_2 *in light.* Plants which have been engaged in steady photosynthesis in ordinary carbon dioxide were briefly exposed to C^*O_2 and then killed by acid. The results of one of these experiments were shown above, in the second part of Table 36.IV. This table indicates, first of all, that the total C* fixation after 30-sec. exposure to C^*O_2 in light is 3–6 times larger than the total uptake in 1 min. darkness after "saturating" preillumination. The distribution of the tracer, while again showing its presence in practically all fractions (including ether-extractable fatty acids, as well as in a large amount of amino acids), was characterized by a marked increase of C* in the sugar fraction (from <1% to 5% of the total tracer), and by *strong accumulation of the tracer in the ether-insoluble anionic fraction* (specifically, in its sub-fraction elutable by ammonia from A-3 duolite resin). Together, the two anionic sub-fractions (the second one contained substances elutable by NaOH, and not by NH₄OH), accounted for as much as 74% of total tracer in the material obtained from *Chlorella* and for 71% of that obtained from *Scenedesmus.*

The *ether-soluble fraction* of these materials (obtained after 1 min. exposure to C^*O_2 in the dark, as well as after 30-sec. exposure in light), was found to contain mainly *malic acid* (75% of the total activity of this fraction). The *cationic fraction* from dark C^*O_2 fixation by *Chlorella* contained up to 50% alanine; less than 15% alanine were found in the material obtained by dark fixation in *Scenedesmus,* or by fixation in light by either of the two species.

A most significant finding was the identification by Calvin and Benson (1947) of the bulk of the ammonia-elutable, anionically tagged compounds (in other words, of the main part of tagged material formed in 30 sec. exposure to C^*O_2 in light), as *phosphoglyceric acid.* It was identified as such by preparation of crystallized *p*-bromophenacylglycerate after hydrolysis by 1 *N* HCl. Up to 90% of the anionic subfraction *not* elutable with ammonia was found to be convertible to phosphoglyceric acid by oxidation in air, and it was suggested that it may be *phosphoglyceric aldehyde.*

Calvin and Benson (1948) further fractionated the last-named fraction (obtained from *Scenedesmus* by 30–60 sec. photosynthesis in C^*O_2). It accounted for 44% of total C* in the 30-sec. material, and 59% in the 60-sec. material. Its chemical behavior showed that it could have contained hexose phosphates and triose phosphates, and perhaps also gluconic and mucic acids. The eluted material was divided into subfractions by vacuum concentration and readsorption. One subfraction was not readsorbable; another, when readsorbed, could not be eluted again by ammonia. The second subfraction could be interpreted as phosphoglyceric acid, formed by air oxidation of phosphoglyceraldehyde, while the nonreadsorbable subfraction could have originally consisted of easily hydrolyzable hexose phosphates (*e. g.,* glucose-6-phosphate).

Calvin and Benson (1947) found no tagged intermediates or by-products of the *tricarboxylic acid cycle* (citric, isocitric, glutamic acids) in cells killed *immediately* after a brief period of photosynthesis in C^*O_2; the activity appeared, however, in these compounds if the cells were allowed to stand in the dark for a few minutes before killing.

Utter and Wood (1951) criticized the identification of PGA as first photosynthetic intermediate, suggesting that its tagging may be the result of an exchange, and not of a net carboxylation. Fager and Rosenberg (1952) pointed out, in answer, that the quantitative correspondence between manometrically determined CO_2 uptake and the amount of C^* found in PGA does not admit of such an interpretation.

We will have to return to this finding, and the conclusions derived from it as to the interaction between photosynthesis and respiration, later in this chapter, and also in chapter 37D.

4. The Experiments of the Chicago Group

Before proceeding with a description of the further findings by the Calvin group, made possible by paper chromatography (*cf.* sections 5–10), we will describe work carried out in 1948–49 by Gaffron, Brown, Fager and

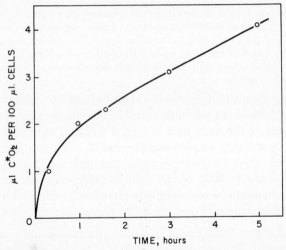

Fig. 36.5. Dark fixation of C^* by 105 μl. cells in 5 ml. phosphate buffer. CO_2 exhausted by preillumination. No significant uptake of CO_2 observed manometrically (after Brown, Fager, and Gaffron 1949).

Rosenberg in Chicago in which, like the above-described earlier Berkeley studies, more common methods of chemical separation were used. Their first results (1948, 1949) contrasted sharply with the Berkeley findings; in particular, they found only insignificant amounts of phosphoglyceric acid among the early products of photosynthesis. Subsequently, however (1950[1], 1951), the role of phosphoglyceric acid as the most important early product of photosynthetic C^* fixation was confirmed at Chicago.

The earlier, contradictory results have not been satisfactorily explained. It was, however, suggested that they might have been due to the pretreatment of the algae. To exhaust all $C(12)O_2$, prior to exposure to $C(14)O_2$, the cells were made to photosynthesize for a long time without renewed supply of carbon dioxide; this could have depleted them of all photosynthetic intermediates, and caused $C(14)$ to spread practically instantaneously beyond the first fixation product (phosphoglyceric acid). It may be noted here that Calvin could find no satisfactory explanation also for the failure of Ruben, Kamen, and co-workers to identify any of the known respiration intermediates among the product of brief photosynthesis in $C(11)O_2$ (*cf*. Vol. I, page 242).

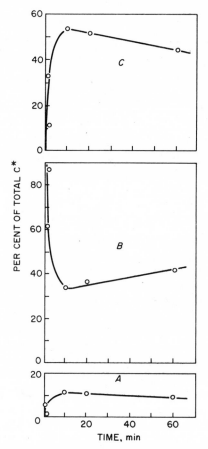

Fig. 36.6. Distribution of C^* fixed aerobically in the dark over fractions *A*, soluble in aqueous alcohol and benzene; *B*, soluble in aqueous alcohol, insoluble in benzene; and *C*, insoluble in aqueous alcohol, as function of time (after Brown, Fager, and Gaffron 1949).

Brown, Fager and Gaffron (1948, 1949) were aware of the complications which may be caused by "respiratory" C^*O_2 fixation. They therefore made only a few measurements of the C^*O_2 uptake in darkness, and studied mainly the tracer uptake in brief periods of illumination.

The C^* fixation *in the dark* was found by them to be fastest in the first hour of exposure to C^*O_2, and to settle to an approximately constant rate (0.01 to 0.02 cc./C^*O_2, per cc. of cells per hour), after the second hour (fig. 36.5). No significant disappearance of carbon dioxide from the medium could be observed during this period: C^* uptake appeared therefore to be due entirely to an exchange of CO_2 and C^*O_2 (Fig. 36.5 is to be compared with Calvin's Fig. 36.1).

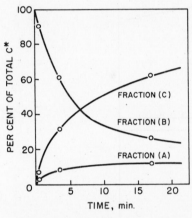

Fig. 36.7. Time change of tracer distribution between fractions (A), (B), and (C) during photosynthesis (after Brown, Fager, and Gaffron 1949).

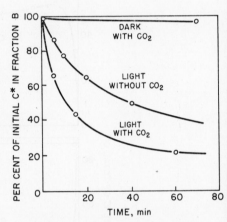

Fig. 36.8. Effect of light and CO_2 on transfer of tracer from fraction (B) (after Brown, Fager, and Gaffron 1949).

Under *anaerobic conditions*, the C^*O_2 fixation by *Scenedesmus* in the dark was only about one-half of that in air, indicating that the capacity for reversible carboxylation is smaller for the intermediates of anaerobic than for those of aerobic metabolism. Furthermore, the tagged products of anaerobic fixation were found only in the fraction "B" (soluble in aqueous alcohol, insoluble in benzene), while the products of aerobic fixation were scattered over all three fractions (A, B and C) into which the cell material was divided (*cf.* below). It seems likely (*cf.* fig. 36.6) that under aerobic conditions, too, all C^* was *initially* taken up in fraction B, but passed rapidly into the other fractions (while under anaerobic conditions it stayed in fraction B). If, after a period of dark fixation, C^*O_2 was removed from the medium, the tracer content of fraction B declined, confirming that this fraction contained carbon in a reversibly bound form (*e. g.*, that of a dissociable carboxyl group). The transfer of C^* from the water-soluble fraction B

into the two other fractions could be stopped by the removal of air, showing that it is associated with respiration.

When algae were exposed to C^*O_2 *in light*, the amounts of tracer fixed were much larger than those taken up in the dark; furthermore, they corresponded to the manometrically observed carbon dioxide uptakes, indicating that isotopic exchange reactions could be disregarded, at least in the explanation of the origin of the *main* tagged products.

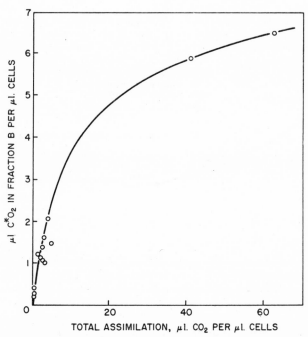

Fig. 36.9. Relation between C^* in fraction B and CO_2 uptake by photosynthesis (after Brown, Fager, and Gaffron 1949).

As mentioned above, the tagged products were divided into three fractions: one fraction (C), insoluble in aqueous alcohol, formed 78% of the total dry weight, and contained chiefly proteins and polysaccharides. Of the two fractions soluble in aqueous alcohol, one—fraction A, 21% of dry weight—was soluble also in benzene; it contained pigments and other lipophilic constituents. The second one—fraction B—was insoluble in benzene; it formed only about 1% of dry weight. As in dark fixation, *all* C^* was first taken up in fraction B, and subsequently distributed over all three fractions (fig. 36.7). However, while the redistribution of C^* taken up (aerobically) in the dark occurred rapidly in the dark, the redistribution of C* taken up in light was fast only in light. It occurred faster in presence than in absence of CO_2 (fig. 36.8). It was therefore concluded that fraction B contained one or several *intermediates of photosynthesis* formed only in light, and requiring light for their further transformation. This intermediate did *not* exchange its C* with ordinary CO_2 in the dark.

Since the tracer entered fraction B in light and moved out of it also in light, a steady C* content of this fraction was established after a certain illumination period—about one hour in saturating light (fig. 36.9). (As pointed out before, this seems too long a time to be required for a main-line intermediate of photosynthesis to reach stationary state in strong light.)

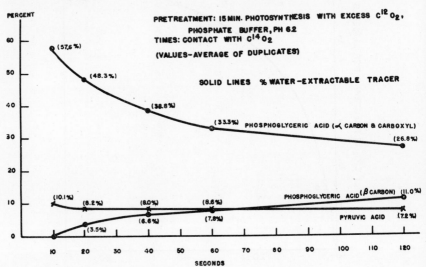

Fig. 36.10. Percentage of tracer fixed in water soluble compounds contained in phosphoglyceric and pyruvic acid, as function of length of exposure to $C*O_2$ in light (after Gaffron *et al.* 1951).

When fraction B was saturated with radiocarbon in light, as much as 50% of it was derived from tagged $C*O_2$. Fager (1949) conjectured from chemical evidence that C* was present in at least two compounds in this fraction; one was three or four times more abundant than the other.

Attempts to identify these compounds with known organic substances, in particular with any common respiration intermediates, were unsuccessful. A special search was made for polyhydroxy acids (of which the simplest is glyceric acid) by isolation of barium salts of phosphate esters and oxidation by periodic acid after hydrolysis. Both methods gave no evidence of the presence of an active polyhydroxy acid or of a phosphate ester of such an acid.

Clendenning (1950) made a closer study of the composition of the benzene-soluble fraction A.   After 20-sec. exposure, C* was found to be present in this fraction in water-insoluble, nonvolatile compounds.   The chlorophylls (a and b) were not tagged, and could be isolated free of C* by purification on sugar columns.   After saponification of the A fraction, C* was

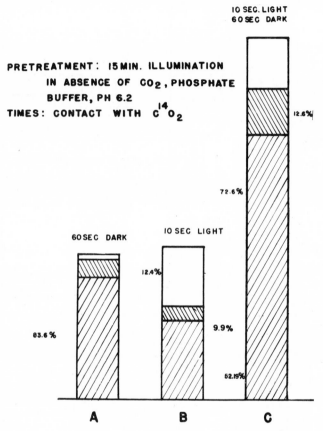

Fig. 36.11. C(14) fixation by *Scenedesmus* after 15 min. preillumination in the absence of CO_2 and O_2.   Light-shaded areas, phosphoglyceric acid; dark-shaded areas, pyruvic acid; unshaded areas, other tagged compounds (after Gaffron *et al.* 1951).

found in the nonsaponified part, in fatty acids (saturated as well as unsaturated), and in water-soluble products of saponification.

These experiments showed that some C* enters lipoid products already in the first minute of exposure to C^*O_2.

In revision of their earlier results, Fager, Rosenberg and Gaffron (1950)

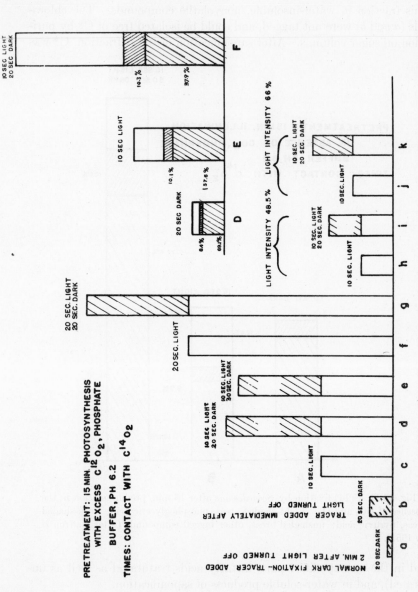

Fig. 36.12. C(14) fixation by *Scenedesmus* after 15 min. preillumination in the presence of CO_2. Shaded areas, C*-uptake in dark. Inset: Distribution of C* between phosphoglyceric acid (light-shaded areas), pyruvic acid (dark-shaded

and Fager and Rosenberg (1950) described the isolation of phosphoglyceric acid from tagged products of photosynthesis in *Scenedesmus*. An analytically pure sample of barium glycerate was prepared from this material by an ion exchange separation method. The proportion of total activity found in phosphoglycerate decreased with increased length of an exposure (10 to 120 sec.) from 58 to 38%; while that in pyruvic acid (a second tagged compound also identified in these experiments) declined from 10 to 7%. Within the phosphoglyceric acid molecule, the amount of tagging in the α position grew from 0 to 11% (of the *total* C^* taken up); probably, that of tagged β-carbon increased in the same way (fig. 36.10). After 2-min. exposure, activity was more or less uniform in all three carbon atoms (compare table 36.V).

The ratio of C^* in phosphoglyceric acid to that in pyruvic acid remained the same (5–6) over the whole range of exposures; it dropped to 4 if after exposure the cells were left in the dark for 20 sec., before killing. This was interpreted as an indication that if pyruvic acid is involved in the carbon dioxide reduction in photosynthesis, its place in the reaction sequence is *after* and not before the phosphoglyceric acid.

Most of the above results were in good agreement with observations of the Berkeley group. Gaffron *et al.* (1950, 1951) disagreed, however, with Calvin's interpretation of C^* uptake in the dark after preillumination. As mentioned in section 2 Calvin saw in this uptake proof of photochemical formation of both a CO_2 acceptor ("C_2 compound"), and of a comparatively long-lived, powerful reductant ("reducing power"). Fager and Gaffron doubted the second conclusion, referring to the observation of Mehler (chapter 35, page 1615) that adding dyes (known to act as Hill oxidants in light) to preilluminated chloroplasts produces no reduction, indicating that no "reducing power" survives the illumination period.*

In further support of the assumption that what survives in the dark after illumination is only the CO_2 acceptor, Gaffron and co-workers quoted their observation (fig. 36.11) that practically only phosphoglyceric acid and pyruvic acid were tagged in 60-sec. exposure to C^*O_2 in the dark after 15 min. preillumination in CO_2 and O_2 free gas (bar A); absence of O_2 is required to avoid CO_2 formation by respiration. (In other words, they found, under these conditions, no tagged products whose formation would require both carboxylation *and reduction*.) If preilluminated cells were exposed to C^*O_2 *in light* for 10 sec., the percentage of C^* fixed in phosphoglyceric and pyruvic acid was found by Gaffron *et al.* to be much smaller than without preillumination (bar B), indicating that much of the tracer has pene-

---

* This conclusion is supported, to some degree, by Spruit's (1953) measurements of the redox potential in *Chlorella* suspensions. We can merely refer here to this interesting study, as well as to the earlier one by Wassink (1947) on suspensions of *Chromatium*.

trated into the reduction products of phosphoglyceric acid. When preilluminated cells were tagged for 60 sec. in the dark, freed from C^*O_2 by washing, and then illuminated for 40 sec., the total amount of C^* in the cells was found to be the same as before washing, but only 35% of the original quantity of phosphoglyceric acid was found; this, too, indicated that, in light, phosphoglyceric acid underwent further transformation (reduction). When cells preilluminated in absence of CO_2 and then exposed to CO_2 in light for 10 sec. were left in the dark in C^*O_2 for 60 sec. before killing, an additional tracer uptake was observed, again concentrated practically exclusively in PGA and PA (bar C).

These results are in disagreement with the paper chromatograms obtained at Berkeley (see, e. g., fig. 36.2b), which indicated the formation in preilluminated algae of tagged products (such as sucrose) that could not be obtained from phosphoglyceric acid without further reduction.

In the Berkeley and Chicago experiments, preillumination was carried out in an atmosphere of N_2, H_2, or He_2, free of CO_2 or O_2 (the latter to avoid CO_2-production by respiration). *Chlorella* was used in Berkeley, *Scenedesmus* in Chicago; but it is unlikely that the survival of the "reducing power" after illumination should occur only in certain species.

Gaffron, Fager, and Rosenberg (1951) described also the "pick-up" of C^*O_2 carbon after a period of illumination in abundant carbon dioxide. It differs, in several respects, from the C^*O_2 uptake after preillumination without CO_2. Fig. 36.12 illustrates the findings. Bar *a* indicates the residual "dark fixation" as it occurs after the effect of preillumination has worn out (*i. e.*, after 2 minutes in darkness); bar *b* shows the much larger C^* fixation after a period of photosynthesis in ordinary CO_2; bars *e* and *f* show the fixation during 10 and 20 sec. photosynthesis in C^*O_2, respectively; bars *d*, *e*, and *g*, the "pick-up" of C^* after these pretreatments. It is seen that the pick-up is completely developed after 10 sec. photosynthesis in saturating light, and is then equivalent to CO_2-consumption in 10 sec. of photosynthesis. The pick-up is completed in less than 10 sec. (while the dark C^*O_2 uptake after illumination in CO_2-free medium requires several minutes for completion according to both the Berkeley and the Chicago measurements).

The much larger shaded area in *d*, compared to that in *b*, could perhaps be taken as an indication of slow penetration of C^*O_2 to the site of the pick-up. An alternative explanation, suggested by Gaffron *et al.*, is that after photosynthesis with ample CO_2, all acceptor is present in the cells in the form of a loose complex (corresponding to $A.CO_2$ in Franck and Herzfeld's theory). If the last ten seconds of illumination had been carried out in tagged C^*O_2, this loose complex is tagged, and its transformation into the stable complex, ACO_2 (which is supposed to follow in the dark), will be registered as a "C^*O_2 pick-up." (It being assumed that without time allowance for a dark stabilization period, the loose complex $A.C^*O_2$ will dissociate when the cells are killed.)   If C^*O_2 is added only at the moment when the light is switched off, the loose complex $A.CO_2$ is *not* tagged, and C^*O_2 can be taken up into this complex, in the subsequent dark period, only by exchange, in competition with the stabilization reaction $A.CO_2 \rightarrow ACO_2$; the uptake is correspondingly smaller.

This interpretation implies that the C^*O_2 "pick-up" in fig. 36.12 means no true (*i. e.*, manometrically measurable) absorption of carbon dioxide. In Volume I, chapter 8 (section B4) and in chapter 33 (section A3), evidence of a *net* pick-up of CO_2-gas after the end of photosynthesis has been presented (McAlister, Aufdemgarten, van der Veen).   Its volume (about one molecule CO_2 per molecule chlorophyll, equivalent to about 20 sec. of maximum photosynthetic CO_2-uptake) and its time requirement (about 20 sec.) were about the same as described by Gaffron *et al.* for the radiometrically determined C^*O_2 pick-up.   True, McAlister and Myers found no measurable pick-up when the CO_2 concentration was high (as it has been in Gaffron's experiments); nevertheless, the apparent equality in the rate of the two processes seems to argue against the assumption that one of them represents a combination of free acceptor A with CO_2, and the other, stabilization of $A.CO_2$ to ACO_2.

At subsaturating light intensities, the amount of postphotosynthetic C^*O_2 pick-up is reduced proportionally, remaining approximately equivalent to the CO_2 uptake in 10 sec. in light (*cf.* bars *h–k* in fig. 36.12).

Bars D and F in the fig. 36.12 insert show that the postphotosynthetic C^*O_2 pick-up leads to a distribution which is markedly different from that observed by Gaffron *et al.* after preillumination without CO_2 (fig. 36.11): 25% of the tracer in D, and >50% of it in F, are located in compounds other than PGA and PA.   This observation, too, remains in need of interpretation.   Perhaps an explanation could be based on the difference between cells filled with abundant intermediates of photosynthesis and cells bare of such intermediates.

Observations of the type shown in fig. 36.22, revealing changes in the distribution of C^* within the cells immediately after the end of illumination, are obviously relevant to the pick-up phenomena, whether observed analytically (chapters 8 and 33) or noted radiometrically.

5. Early Intermediates Other Than PGA; Paper Chromatography

A most important step forward was made in 1948 by application, to the problem of carbon dioxide reduction intermediates, of a new chromatographic technique: paper chromatography.   To combine this method (developed by Consden, Gordon and Martin in England in 1944) with the radioactive tracer technique in the study of photosynthesis was first suggested by Fink and Fink (1947).   Calvin and co-workers found this combination particularly suitable for rapid fractionation and identification of the numerous tagged compounds obtained in their experiments with C(14). The procedure consists in placing a drop of the cell extract (in aqueous alcohol or acid) in one corner of a sheet of filter paper, letting it

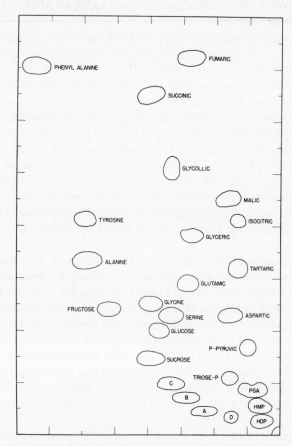

Fig. 36.13. Scheme of paper chromatography of photosynthetic products (after Calvin 1950). The coordinates, taken from a large number of radiograms, were plotted by using serine and alanine as reference points. PGA, phosphoglyceric acids; HMP, hexose monophosphates; HDP, hexose diphosphates; A, B, C, unidentified sugar phosphates (for subsequent identification, see section 7); D, unidentified compound containing glucose and a glucose phosphate (for subsequent identification, see section 10).

dry and then allowing a solvent to pass slowly through the paper (which, for this purpose, is suspended vertically from a trough containing the solvent). The solvent moves the various constituents out of the original spot for different distances down the sheet. The sheet can then be dried, and a second fractionation made with another solvent, moving under right angle to the first one, thus producing a two-dimensional pattern. The resulting spots, usually invisible to the eye, can be "developed" by color reagents (such as ninhydrin for amino acids or molybdate for phosphoric acid); radioactive spots are easily detected by "radioautography"—for this purpose, the filter paper is pressed against an x-ray film, and the latter developed.

Individual spots can be identified from the known solubilities of the compounds, whose presence appears likely, and the identification can be confirmed by coincidence checks with known compounds. If a spot contains sufficient material it can be cut out, eluted and investigated by the usual chemical methods.

This technique was first applied by Stepka, Benson and Calvin (1948) to the C^*-tagged amino acids from *Chlorella* and *Scenedesmus*.

After 30-sec. photosynthesis in the presence of C^*O_2, the material from *Scenedesmus* showed activity predominantly in aspartic acid, somewhat less in alanine. Radioautographs revealed some activity also in asparagine, serine, alanine and phenylalanine. In similar material from *Chlorella*, there were about equal amounts of active aspartic acid and alanine.

Calvin and Benson (1948), and Benson, Bassham, Calvin, Goodale, Haas and Stepka (1949) extended the chromatographic method to tagged products other than the amino acids.

Figure 36.13 shows the location on the paper chromatogram of a number of compounds which may be of interest in connection with the work on photosynthesis. Water-saturated phenol is the one (basic) solvent; a mixture of butanol with propionic acid and water the second (acidic) solvent. Cationic substances are moved toward the left, anionic toward the top of the figure. Lipids and lipophilic compounds are moved into the upper left corner, farthest from the origin; while sugars, phosphate esters, and other neutral, hydrophilic compounds stay near the original spot, in the right bottom corner. A mixture containing acetic (instead of propionic) acid was used when it was desirable to move phosphate esters more effectively.

In these experiments, algae (or leaves) were killed by dropping them, after exposure to C^*O_2, into hot 80% aqueous ethanol (instead of acid, as before). The extract was concentrated to 2 cc. and 0.01–0.2 cc. were applied to a 1.5-cm. circle in the corner of the sheet. Amounts varying between a few microgram (acids) and 1–2 mg. (sugars) could be separated in this way.

Radiograms were made from cells exposed to C^*O_2 for between 5 and 90 sec. in light, after having been engaged in steady photosynthesis in 1–4%

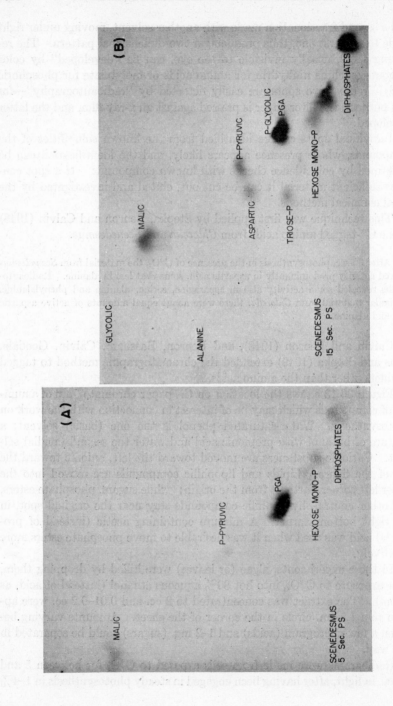

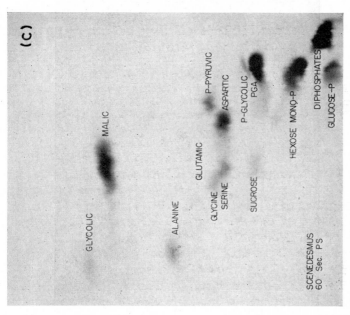

Fig. 36.14. Radiograms of products photosynthesized by *Scenedesmus* in C^*O_2: (*A*) in 5 sec.; (*B*) in 15 sec.; (*C*) in 60 sec. (after Benson, Calvin *et al.* 1951).

inactive carbonate for 0.5 to 1 hr. During this exposure time, no activity entered any compounds insoluble in aqueous alcohol.

In the *carboxylic acid* field (upper right), a number of spots appeared which were identified as malic, succinic, glycolic and fumaric acids. In similar radiograms from dark-exposed (nonpreilluminated) cells ("respiratory C* uptake"), iso-citric, succinic, fumaric, and malic acids were found. Each of these identifications was checked by "co-chromatographing" with the corresponding pure acids.

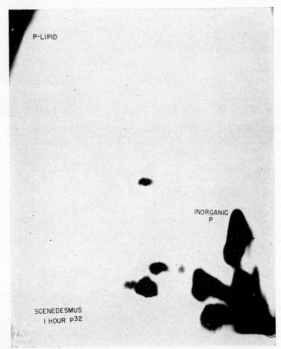

Fig. 36.15. Radiophosphorus-containing products of 1 hour photosynthesis in *Scenedesmus* (after Benson, Calvin *et al.* 1951).

The shorter the exposure, the greater was the proportion of activity which stayed near the original spot (fig. 36.14). After an exposure of 15 sec. or 1 min., three or four dark areas could be distinguished there (fig. 36.14B,C), but after five-seconds exposure or less, only the uppermost of them was significant (fig. 36.14A). This spot was therefore considered as containing the earliest identifiable product of the fixation of carbon dioxide in light. From the general position of the spots, it could be surmised that the compounds in all three spots were phosphate esters; to test this hypothesis, radiograms were made of algae which had been allowed to photosynthesize for an hour in normal carbon dioxide in the presence of *radioactive phosphate*. Active spots were found in the same region near the origin of the radiogram (fig. 36.15). A similar pattern could be produced also by using P(32)-labelled phosphorylated intermediates from the fermentation of glucose by yeast. By separating the several phosphate esters from the fermentation product (by selective elution from an anion exchange resin) and chromatographing them in one dimension, it was ascertained that the *phosphoglyceric acid* moves ahead of fructose-6-phosphate, and the latter moves ahead of fructose-1,6-diphosphate. The three above-mentioned spots in C(14) radiograms from photosynthesizing cells were therefore identified, from the bottom upward, as "hexose diphosphate," "hexose monophosphate" and "phosphoglyceric acid."

Since the third spot was the earliest to appear, and therefore commanded the greatest interest, experiments were made to support its identification as phosphoglyceric acid. P(32)-labelled material from algae which had been exposed for 1 hr. to ordinary CO_2 in active phosphate was coprecipitated with synthetic barium phosphoglycerate, and the precipitate, after conversion to free acid, was cochromatographed with the extract obtained from algae after 90 sec. photosynthesis in C^*O_2. The perimeters of the P* and C* activities in the region of the "third spot" were found to coincide, thus indicating that the C*-labelled compound must be identical with the P*-labelled compound (whose barium salt was proved before to be coprecipitable with barium phosphoglycerate).

From products of 5 sec. exposure of *Scenedesmus* cells to C^*O_2 (which, we recall, gave one strong radioactive spot only), phosphoglyceric acid was isolated and identified by the following procedure: 1-g. batches of cells, exposed for 5 sec. to C^*O_2 in intense light, were added to 18 g. normal algae (to provide bulk for isolation). The algae were killed by acid (4CH₃-COOH, glacial + 1 HCl, conc.), all activity going into aqueous extract. (This method was again used, instead of killing with 80% alcohol, to remove as much protein, cellulose and lipids as possible at the very beginning of the process.)

Fractionation of the extract by precipitation at *p*H 7 and leaching out at *p*H 10, repeated precipitation with $BaCl_2$ from 50% ethanol, and dissolution in 0.05 *N* HCl, led to a crystalline precipitate whose P content and specific rotation were close to those of barium-3-phosphoglycerate. Oxidation by periodate led to products (formaldehyde, formic acid, carbon dioxide) found also with glyceric acid. The somewhat lower rotation of the photosynthetic product was taken as indicating the presence of a small amount of 2-phosphoglyceric acid of higher specific activity than the main amount of 3-phosphoglyceric acid. On some of the radiograms, the PGA spot was in fact double; the "right half" could be changed into the "left half" by heating in 0.1 N HCl for 1 hr. It was suggested that the right half is 2-phosphoglyceric acid and the left one, 3-phosphoglyceric acid. The proportion of the 2-substituted acid was much higher in strong than in weak light. When the temperature during the C^*O_2 exposure was lowered to 4° C., only the right half of the spot appeared. It thus seems that the 2-phosphoglyceric acid is the first formed, but less stable isomer.

The crystalline product which thus had many properties of authentic phosphoglyceric acid weighed 10 mg. and accounted for one-third of total C^* fixed in 5-sec. exposure. The last washings and supernatants from this preparation accounted for another 30%; when chromatographed, they, too, deposited their activities in the PGA spot.

Easily hydrolyzable phosphate esters could be identified in the paper chromatograms by spraying with molybdate to form molybdenum blue. In this way, glucose-1-phosphate, phosphopyruvic acid, and triose phosphate (apparently, both 3-phosphoglyceraldehyde, and phosphodihydroxyacetone) were identified in positions shown in figure 36.13. *Phosphopyruvic acid* is one of the earliest of these compounds to appear in photosynthesis, as illustrated by figure 36.6a. According to Calvin *et al.* (1950), free *glyceric acid* often appears, together with malic acid and phosphopyruvic acid, as the earliest companions of phosphoglyceric acid in the radiograms from briefly photosynthesizing cells. In one experiment, after 5-sec. photosynthesis, 87% of the tracer was found in PGA, 10% in PPA and 3% in malic acid. These results agree with Gaffron and Fager's observations (Fig. 36.10), except that the latter listed PA rather than PPA as the main companion of PGA in the first seconds of photosynthesis. In all probability, both PGA and PPA may undergo hydrolysis in the extraction and separation processes; free acids, GA and PA, will then be found instead of the originally present phosphate esters.

The identification and order of appearance of *amino acids* was mentioned above. It is significant that some of them—those with C_3 and C_4 chains—appear very early, even before tagged sugars or their phosphate esters.

With these paper-chromatographic observations, the previous results, obtained with ordinary analytical methods and summarized in tables 36.III and 36.IV, were largely confirmed and greatly enlarged. The role of phosphoglyceric acid as the first compound which becomes tagged in photosynthesis was established much more firmly than before. The early appearance of phosphopyruvic acid and of the phosphates of trioses and hexoses was clarified. (In previous experiments, all these compounds must have been hidden in the second anionically tagged, "non ammoniaelutable," subfraction.) The early appearance of tagged amino acids was confirmed, and their specific nature established.   Seldom has the application of a new method of analysis brought such sudden light into the darkness and permitted the identification of so many compounds present in a complex mixture only in microgram amounts.   This work undoubtedly constitutes one of the greatest successes so far of the isotopic tracer technique in chemical analysis; but it could only be achieved by combination of this method with chromatography, an analytical method which, although almost fifty years old, has only recently been extended beyond its original narrow field of application to organic pigments.

The distribution of tracer carbon within the carbon chain of PGA, hexoses (*cf.* section 1), and of other early products also was reinvestigated. Typical results of these "degradation experiments" are shown in table 36.V.   It shows the initial preferential (or exclusive) labelling of the carboxyl group in PGA, malic acid and alanine, and gradual approach to equidistribution, already noted before.   This approach to isotopic equilibrium occurs in a closely parallel way in PGA, alanine and hexose.

TABLE 36.V

DISTRIBUTION OF CARBON 14 WITHIN THE CARBON CHAIN IN THE PRODUCTS OF PHOTOSYNTHESIS (10,000 F. C.) (AFTER CALVIN *et al.* 1950)

		Barley			*Chlorella* 5 sec.
	Position	2 sec.	15 sec.	60 sec.	
Phosphoglyceric acid	COOH	85	56	44	95
	CHOH		21	30	3
	CH₂OH	15	23	25	2
Alanine	COOH	—	67	48	—
	CHNH₂	—	30	44	—
	CH₃	—	30	<5	—
					Scenedesmus 30 sec.
Sucrose	$C_{3,4}$	—	52	37	87
	$C_{2,5}$	—	25	34	7
	$C_{1,6}$	—	24	32	6
					Scenedesmus 10 sec.
Malic acid	COOH	—	—	—	93.5
	rest	—	—	—	6.5

It will be noted that approximate equidistribution of C* in the sucrose molecule is reached, according to table 36.V, already after 60 sec. exposure.

In the 1947 experiments (table 36.I), the distribution of C(14) in glucose was far from uniform even after a whole hour of photosynthesis; in 1948 experiments (also mentioned in section 1), uniform distribution was approached, in glucose, only after about two hours. The reason for this difference is not clear.

Gibbs (1949, 1950) studied the distribution of C*(14) in glucose, fructose, dextrin, starch, alanine, and malic acid, in material from sunflower leaves exposed to C^*O_2 for 1.5, 2, and 4 minutes, with rather confusing and irreproducible results. In fructose, for example, the distribution was nonuniform after 1.5 and 2 minutes, but uniform after 4 minutes; in starch, on the other hand, the 3,4 positions were strongly favored even after 4 minutes; in malic acid, three quarters of total C* were found in the carboxyl both after 1.5 and after 4 minutes of exposure. When sunflower plants were exposed to C^*O_2 in darkness, C* was found to >90% in the carboxyl groups in alanine and malic acid, and in 3,4 positions in sucrose, dextrin, and starch, after 16 or 27 hours of exposure.

The rapid appearance of C* in the α and β positions in PGA is very significant. It proves—almost beyond doubt—*that photosynthesis involves a cyclic process.* An "acceptor" molecule, A, first takes up CO_2 to form PGA; the newly added carbon is located entirely in the carboxyl group. The carboxyl-tagged PGA then undergoes reduction and condensation, at some stage of which the products divide into two parts; one is transformed into permanent photosynthates (polysaccharides, proteins), the other is reconverted into the carbon dioxide acceptor, A. The latter now contains labelled carbon; it therefore gives, upon carboxylation, PGA molecules with the tracer not only in the carboxyl group (γ, or 3-position), but also in the two other positions(α and β, or 1 and 2).

A cyclic process of this type was anticipated by biochemists, who saw the mechanism of photosynthesis, almost *a priori*, as a reversal of that of respiration, and therefore expected it to include a cycle in which hydrogen atoms (supplied by donors identical with, or analogous to, reduced coenzymes I and II) and carbon dioxide molecules (supplied by appropriate carboxylases) are first "grafted" on a "stock" (a C_3 or C_4 compound); the C atoms in the product are then shuffled around (and H atoms thrown in) until a triose molecule is synthesized and the "stock" regenerated. Taking this type of mechanism for granted, the biochemists asked whether the "catabolic" cycle will prove to be simply the known anabolic cycle (Krebs cycle) run in reverse (which seemed to be the simplest hypothesis), or different from it. The above-described early findings with C(14) proved that the biochemists' main hunch was correct—a cyclic mechanism of the postulated type does exist in photosynthesis; but it seems to be different from any known respiratory cycle (*e. g.*, it contains no tricarboxylic acids as intermediates).

It is useful to realize that a cyclic mechanism was not an *a priori* necessity for photosynthesis (as it had not been an *a priori* necessity for respiration).   Even leaving aside, as biochemically implausible, the once popular Baeyer's mechanism, which envisaged a straight reduction of C_1 compounds $(CO_2 \rightarrow HCOOH \rightarrow CH_2O)$ followed by condensation of formaldehyde to glucose, one could imagine other mechanisms in which C_1 fragments were grafted onto a large carrier molecule, then reduced to the carbohydrate level, and the reduction product split off from the carrier without the latter having been directly involved in the reduction process.   This, in fact, was the model used in most chemical and kinetic speculations concerning photosynthesis, such as the kinetic theories reviewed in chapters 27 and 28.   The symbols ACO_2 or $\{CO_2\}$ were used there to designate a CO_2 molecule "grafted" onto an acceptor molecule prior to being photochemically reduced; the acceptor, A, was assumed to be regenerated at some stage of the process, without change, and returned into the cycle.   True, some evidence was found, even prior to the radiocarbon studies, that the CO_2 acceptor itself is a product of photosynthesis.   (For example, certain induction phenomena could be attributed, in chap. 33, sect. C3, to the disappearance of the CO_2 acceptor in the dark and its regeneration in light); but even this did not prove that the acceptor molecule undergoes a continuous, cyclic transformation in light.   Radiocarbon studies first proved that the carbon skeleton of the acceptor molecule is assembled anew at the end of each cycle from carbon atoms derived, in part, from the carbon dioxide molecules it has taken up in the preceding turns of the cycle.   (Without this throwing of the new and the old carbon atoms into a common reservoir, the labelling of the α and β carbons in PGA would not occur at all, or would occur much slower than it actually does.)

One consequence of this finding is that in any future analysis of the kinetics of photosynthesis, one will have to consider the concentration of the acceptor, not as a constant (A_0 in chapter 27), but as a function of the rate (and perhaps also of certain special conditions) of photosynthesis.   A further complication will arise if the acceptor (or its carboxylation product) is produced also as intermediate (or by-product) of respiration (as seems to be the case with PGA; *cf.* chapter 37D, section 3).

The proof of regeneration of the carbon dioxide acceptor by a rapid cyclic process can be considered as the second important result of the application of carbon tracer to the study of photosynthesis (the first one having been the identification of phosphoglyceric acid as the first intermediate).

The study of the intramolecular distribution of labelled carbon was continued by Bassham, Benson, and Calvin (1950).

Degradation experiments with labelled phosphoglycerate showed that α and β carbon atoms have approximately the same activity (*e. g.*, in one experiment, after 60-sec. photosynthesis in C^*O_2, 55% of all C^* present in phosphoglyceric acid was located in the carboxyl, 25% in α, and 27% in

β carbon). This indicates that at some point in the regenerative cycle a symmetric intermediate must be formed (e. g., oxalic acid, succinic acid, or glycol)—a compound in which two equivalent groups have equal chance to contribute α or β atoms for the formation of phosphoglyceric acid.

Calvin (1949) confirmed the previously mentioned observation that, while tagged C_5 and C_6 acids are absent among the products of brief photosynthesis, they appear within minutes after photosynthesis is stopped. In these experiments, cells were allowed to photosynthesize in C^*O_2, and the vessel was then swept by helium for 90 sec. before killing the cells. If, during the sweep, the cells were left in light, no tagged citric, isocitric or glutamic acid was found. These three acids appeared, however, if during the sweep the cells were left in darkness. It thus seemed that the intermediate products of photosynthesis were drawn, immediately after the cessation of illumination (but *not* before), into the respiration process, yielding C_5 and C_6 acids of the Krebs cycle (and related amino acids) (compare fig. 36.23).

From observations of this type, and also from kinetic studies with $C(14)$ by Weigl, Warrington and Calvin (1950), it was concluded that normal respiration of the cells is largely inhibited during photosynthesis. However, this generalization is not supported by other experiments, e. g., those with isotopic oxygen. An alternative explanation of the tagging experiments by Steward and Thompson (1950) will be mentioned in Chapter 37D, (section 3), where the whole question of the relations between photosynthesis and respiration will be reviewed.

Another interesting result of the study by Weigl *et al.*—the strong isotopic discrimination in photosynthesis between $C(12)$ and $C(14)$—also will be discussed in chapter 37D.

6. The Role of Malic Acid : One or Two Carboxylations in Photosynthesis?

Malic acid has been found, in all experiments of Calvin and co-workers (as well as those of Stutz, and Gibbs), to be a major early tagged product (*cf.* fig. 36.14); but its true role in photosynthesis is still uncertain.

At first it appeared likely that malic acid is another "first product" of photosynthesis, possibly arising by reaction (36.1), followed by reduction of oxalacetic acid to malic acid; or by direct reductive carboxylation of pyruvic acid, as observed in chloroplast preparations by Vishniac and Ochoa, Tolmach, and Arnon (*cf.* chapter 35, equation 35.34), catalyzed by the so-called "malic enzyme." One could imagine, for example, that the formation of PGA (by carboxylation of an unknown C_2 acceptor) is followed by dehydration to pyruvic acid, and reductive carboxylation of the latter to malic acid.

However, subsequent experiments did not square with the assumption that malic acid is an intermediate in the main reaction sequence of photosynthesis.

Bassham, Benson and Calvin (1950) found that *malonate* inhibits, by as much as 70–97%, the formation of tagged malic acid in light, without inhibiting photosynthesis as a whole by more than 15–35%. Malonate had no effect either on the *amount* of tagged phosphoglyceric acid or on the *distribution* of tracer between the carboxyl and the α- and β-carbon atoms in this compound. These experiments indicate that malic acid is *not* a link in the direct sequence of reactions leading from carbon dioxide via phosphoglyceric acid to sugars. Since, however, it is one of the first compounds to be labelled in light even when the labelling of fumaric acid and succinic acid is negligible, as well as in darkness (where the latter acids form the bulk of the tagged compounds), it appears that tagged malic acid is produced not only by the respiratory but also by the photosynthetic C^*O_2 uptake mechanism. It was suggested that in the second case, malic acid is not an intermediate in the carboxylation cycle, but a side product, a "storage reservoir" of C^*, isotopically equilibrated with a C_4 product in the main reaction sequence (such as oxalacetic acid, OAA). The early appearance of phosphopyruvic acid (PPA) suggested the scheme:

$$(36.4A) \quad PGA \xrightarrow{-H_2O} \underset{\text{(enol)}}{PPA} \xrightarrow{+C^*O_2} OAA \underset{-2[H]}{\overset{+2[H]}{\rightleftarrows}} \begin{array}{l} \longrightarrow \text{main sequence to sugars} \\ \\ \text{malic acid} \end{array}$$

This equilibration could conceivably be interrupted by malonate, while the main reaction sequence remains unaffected.

Badin and Calvin (1950) chromatographed the products of C^*O_2 fixation in *Scenedesmus* obtained by photosynthesis in very low light. The most interesting finding was that in low light the first identifiable C^*-tagged product was *malic acid* (30% of total C^* uptake, if extrapolated to zero time). Organic phosphates (including phosphoglyceric acid) accounted, in such low light, for less than 30% of total C^* (as against the 90% found in phosphoglyceric acid alone after 5 sec. photosynthesis in *strong light*).

From these experiments, Calvin *et al.* concluded that two primary C^*O_2 uptake reactions occur in photosynthesis: one leading directly to the formation of phosphoglyceric acid, the other, indirectly, to malic acid. The separate formation of these two products was supported by the observation that the percentages of total C^* present in organic phosphates and malic acid extrapolated to finite values at time zero. Calvin and co-workers suggested that the primary uptake of C^*O_2 in photosynthesis involves the two reactions:

(36.5) C_2 acceptor $+ C^*O_2 \longrightarrow$ (phospho)glyceric acid

(36.6) C_3 acceptor $+ C^*O_2 \longrightarrow$ (oxalacetic acid) $\rightleftharpoons$ malic acid

the first reaction being predominant in strong light, and the second one in weak light.

Gaffron and co-workers (1951) disagreed with this hypothesis and suggested that (36.5) is the *only* carboxylation reaction directly related to

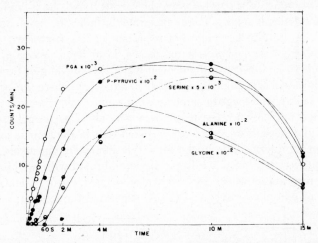

Fig. 36.16. C^*O_2 fixation in C_2 and C_3 compounds as function of time in *Scenedesmus* at 15° C. The cells (10 μl.) were supplied with an amount of C^*O_2 sufficient for only 4 min. of photosynthesis; this explains the decline of activity at longer times (after Benson *et al.* 1952).

photosynthesis. They argued that the assumption of two different carboxylations will require five different photochemically induced reduction steps (*cf.* section 12 below), which they considered theoretically implausible. The evidence for an independent carboxylation leading to malic acid they found inconclusive, even the low-light findings of Badin and Calvin (1950) (since in very weak light, dark catabolic processes occur at rates comparable with those of light-induced reactions). More recently (Bassham *et al.* 1954) this point of view was accepted also by Calvin and his group. This meant the abandonment of the argument that any intermediate whose tagging curve approaches the zero point on the time axis under a finite angle, must be tagged by the uptake of external C^*O_2, without any sizable reservoirs of intermediates interposed between it and the medium. Malic and phosphoglyceric acids consistently showed this behavior (*cf.* figs. 36.16 and 36.18); but so did several other compounds, including some sugar phosphates (*cf.* fig. 36.17), which certainly could not be the direct products of carboxylation. Bassham *et al.* (1954) discussed two mechanisms that could possibly account for the immediate appearance of tagged carbon atoms in compounds not connected directly with the external C^*O_2 reservoir. One of them is the possibility that some rapid enzymatic reactions

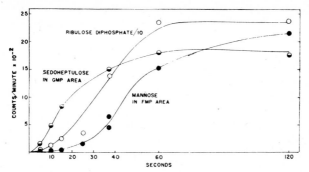

Fig. 36.17. C^*O_2 fixation in sedoheptulose phosphate, ribulose diphosphate, and mannose phosphate as function of time. 10 μl. *Scenedesmus* cells, 20° C. The separation of sedoheptulose and mannose is imperfect (both occurring in the same general monophosphate area) (after Benson *et al.* 1952).

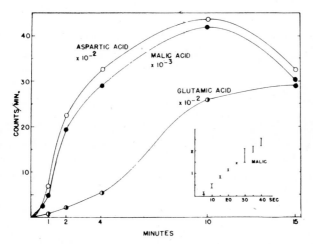

Fig. 36.18. C^*O_2 incorporation in some C_4 compounds as function of time (10 μl. *Scenedesmus*, 15° C.). Insert shows the initial slope of the malic acid tagging curve (after Benson *et al.* 1952).

could occur during (or after) the supposedly instantaneous and complete stoppage of life processes by boiling alcohol, and could transfer some C^* atoms from the primary into the "secondary" products. The second (rather vaguely described) possibility is that of labelled C^* "skipping" from enzyme to enzyme without undergoing full isotopic equilibration with the interenzymatic reservoirs. No suggestion was made as to whether the early tagging of malic acid could be ascribed to one of these two causes; but it was implied that some such mechanism, rather than the previously postulated more or less direct equilibration with the external tagged carbon dioxide, must be responsible for it.

The mechanism of formation and the function of C_4 bodies in the reaction sequence of photosynthesis remains, at this writing, one of the uncertain parts in the interpretation of the radiocarbon experiments.

7. The C_5 and C_7 Sugars as Intermediates in Photosynthesis

Benson, Bassham, Calvin, Hall, Hirsch, Kawaguchi, Lynch and Tolbert (1952) described the identification (first announced by Benson, Bassham and Calvin 1951, and Benson 1951) of two new photosynthetic intermediates—a pentose and a heptose sugar or, more precisely, their phosphate esters. These compounds were found to appear in tracer quantities after a few seconds of steady-state photosynthesis in unicellular algae, higher plants, and purple bacteria (cf. figs. 36.17 and 36.21). Their identification resulted from a further development of the area of the paper chromatograms containing the phosphate esters—lower right corner in Figs. 36.13 and 36.15. This area contained, in addition to spots attributable to phosphoenolpyruvic, phosphoglyceric, and phosphoglycolic acids, to triose (dihydroxyacetone) phosphate, and to several hexose phosphates, also two previously unidentified major spots whose relative importance increased with decreasing exposure to C^*O_2, thus indicating that they were due to early intermediates of photosynthesis. The sugar obtained by hydrolysis of one of the unknown phosphate esters was found to form reversibly an anhydride with the equilibrium constant characteristic of sedoheptulose. After the oxidation of this sugar by periodic acid, 15% of its tracer was found in formaldehyde, 55% in formic acid, and 28% in glycolic acid, in agreement with expectations for a C_7 ketose. Periodic acid treatment of the polyalcohol derived from the same sugar gave one molecule of tagged formaldehyde per three molecules of tagged formic acid. Assuming equal labelling of all carbon atoms in the chain (a permissible assumption for carbohydrates found after 5 min. of steady photosynthesis in saturating light, cf. table 36.V), the theoretical ratio is 1 : 2 for a hexitol, and 1 : 2.5 for a heptitol. The empirical value of 3 thus confirmed that the chain was longer than C_6. Co-chromatographing of the unknown sugar (or its anhydride) with chemically pure sedoheptulose (or its anhydride) led to a definite identification.

The second unknown sugar was identified as a pentose by reduction, and more specifically, as ribulose, by co-chromatographing with the pure compound.

Table 36.VI shows the relative amounts of the several tagged sugar phosphates found after 1 to 20 min. photosynthesis in C^*O_2 in different organisms.

TABLE 36.VI

RELATIVE AMOUNTS OF DIFFERENT PHOSPHORYLATED SUGARS AFTER SHORT PERIOD OF STEADY-STATE PHOTOSYNTHESIS IN C^*O_2 (AFTER BENSON et al. 1952)

Organism	Duration of PS in C^*O_2 (min.)	Percent C^* in			
		Glucose	Fructose	Sedo-heptulose	Ribulose
Rhodospirillum rubrum......	20	50	20	15	15
Scenedesmus (1 day old)....	5	40	10	16	34
Chlorella.................	1	40	14	40	6
Barley seedling leaves......	1	53	16	17	13
Soy bean leaves..........	5	39	24	36	1

In discussing these findings, Benson et al. noted that sedoheptulose accumulation is known to occur during the photosynthesis of certain succulents. The same sugar (or its phosphate) was also identified in many other plants. Ribulose, on the other hand, is not known as a constituent of plants, although the corresponding aldose (ribose) is known to occur in them. Ribulose phosphate has been previously observed in bacteria, but not in photosynthesizing organisms.

Bassham, Benson, Kay, Harris, Wilson and Calvin (1954) inquired into the distribution of labelled carbon in the ribulose and sedoheptulose skeleton after brief periods of steady photosynthesis in C^*O_2; exposures as short as 0.4 sec. were used in this work. A suspension of Scenedesmus obliquus was placed in a rectangular reservoir traversed by a stream of air charged with 4% CO_2. The steadily photosynthesizing suspension was pumped out of this reservoir through a transparent tube. At a certain point in the tube, a solution of C^*O_2 was injected into the suspension. The mixture was then discharged into boiling methanol. The time of exposure to C^*O_2 in light (between injection and discharge) could be varied by changing the rate of pumping; the illumination was about 40 klux from each side.

Table 36.VII shows the distribution of $C(14)$ in C_3, C_6, C_7 and C_5 chains formed after 5.4 sec. or steady-state photosynthesis of Scenedesmus in C^*O_2.

Table 36.VII indicates clearly that the C_6 chain is formed by head-to-head condensation of two C_3 chains. The mechanism of formation of the C_7 and C_5 sugars is less obvious; the suggested interpretation will be discussed in section 12 below.

TABLE 36.VII

C(14) DISTRIBUTION IN PRODUCTS FORMED BY 5.4 SEC. EXPOSURE OF *Scenedesmus* TO C*O$_2$ DURING STEADY-STATE PHOTOSYNTHESIS (AFTER BASSHAM *et al.* 1954)

Carbon no.	C$_3$ (glyceric acid)	C$_6$ (fructose)	C$_7$ (sedoheptu-lose)	C$_5$ (ribulose)
1	6	3	2	3
2	6	3	2	5
3	82	42	28	69
4		43	24	10
5		3	27	11
6		3	2	
7			2	

Sedoheptulose and ribulose have similar configurations (at the C-5 and C-6 atoms of the former and the C-3 and C-4 atoms of the latter). Cleavage of an aldoheptose into a "biose" (glycolaldehyde) and a pentose appears a likely reaction from recent chemical studies of this type of compound by Horecker (*cf.* below); in the case of sedoheptulose the product of this splitting will be ribose, which could isomerize to ribulose; a similar cleavage of ribulose must lead to a "biose" and a triose. Benson *et al.* therefore suggested that the function of sedoheptulose and ribulose in photosynthesis is to serve as sources of the C$_2$ body (whose carboxylation leads to PGA).

The location on the chromatogram suggests that ribulose is formed as a diphosphate, and sedoheptulose as a monophosphate. This identification of the esters was further supported (Benson, 1952) by a determination of the ratio C(14):P(32) in the products of prolonged photosynthesis in doubly tagged medium. This ratio was 0.9 in the fraction suspected to be pentose diphosphate, as against 1.35 in the fraction containing PGA, 2.3 in that identified as glucose monophosphate, and 2.6 in that containing fructose and sedoheptulose. The theoretical values for the first three compounds (assuming complete isotopic equilibration with the medium) were 2.5, 3.0 and 6.0, respectively. Since all values were smaller than expected, the saturation with C* must have been incomplete, but the order of the ratios clearly points to the first-named fraction as the one containing more phosphate residues than all the others.

As mentioned above, when the C$_5$ and C$_7$ intermediates were first found it was suggested that they are the source of the then postulated "C$_2$ acceptor" in photosynthesis. Subsequently, a simpler hypothesis was suggested—that the C$_5$ sugar phosphate itself serves as the carbon dioxide acceptor, giving rise to two molecules of phosphoglycerate by hydrolytic splitting:

$$(36.7) \qquad\qquad C_5 + C_1 \xrightarrow{\ +H_2O\ } 2\ C_3$$

It is easy to see that a pentose has the correct "reduction level" ($L = 1.0$, *cf.* p. 109) to give glyceric acid ($L = 0.833$) after dilution with one molecule CO_2 ($L = 0$): $5/(5 + 1) = 0.833$. The mechanism of reaction (36.7) involves a not implausible internal dismutation-conversion of two neighboring keto groups into a carboxyl and a hydroxyl group (*cf.* second arrow in equation 36.8):

(36.8)

$$
\begin{array}{c}
CH_2O\circledP \\
| \\
CHOH \\
| \\
CHOH \\
| \\
C=O \\
| \\
CH_2O\circledP
\end{array}
\xrightarrow[+H_2O]{+CO_2}
\begin{array}{c}
COOH \\
| \\
CHO\circledP \\
| \\
CH_2OH \\
+ \\
CH(OH)_2 \\
| \\
C=O \\
| \\
CH_2O\circledP
\end{array}
\longrightarrow
2\begin{array}{c}
COOH \\
| \\
CHOH \\
| \\
CH_2O\circledP
\end{array}
$$

where $\circledP$ is a phosphate residue, H_2PO_3.

Reaction (36.8) recently was observed *in vitro* by Weissbach, Smyrniotis and Horecker (1954) with a leaf extract, and by Quayle, Fuller, Benson and Calvin (1954) with a *Chlorella* extract as catalyst, making its inclusion in the hypothetical reaction sequence of photosynthesis very plausible. In spinach extracts, reaction (36.8) is stimulated by TPN and ATP, suggesting that it may include a reversible oxidation-reduction stage.

It will be noted that it is due to its occurrence as a diphosphate that ribulose can be split into two molecules of PGA (in reaction 36.8 the products are one molecule of α-PGA and one molecule of β-PGA).

As discussed in chapter 8 (section A4), carboxylation of RH to RCOOH is, under standard conditions, a reaction with a total energy close to zero, and a positive standard free energy of several kcal/mole (table 8. VIII); consequently, the equilibrium usually lies on the side of decarboxylation. The kinetics of CO_2 fixation in photosynthesis, on the other hand, points to CO_2 fixation reaction with an equilibrium far on the side of synthesis, even at 0.03% CO_2 (*cf.* chapter 27). Even known reversible carboxylations, such as that of pyruvic to oxalacetic acid, do not satisfy this requirement.

Bassham *et al.* (1954) attempted to estimate the free energy of reaction (36.8). Assuming pH 7, and concentrations of 5×10^{-4} M for the pentose, 10^{-2} M for carbon dioxide, and 1.9×10^{-3} M for glycerate (for justification of these values, see section 9 below), they obtained $\Delta F = -7$ kcal./mole, a value which would place the equilibrium far on the side of carboxylation.

Using standard bond energies (table 9.II) one notes that the dismutation reaction (second arrow in reaction 36.8) which is, in essence:

$$2C=O \longrightarrow C-O + O-C=O$$

should have a ΔH of -29 kcal.   Empirically, the energies of this type of reactions ("Cannizzaro reaction") are not quite as large, but they *are* negative; a coupling with dismutation could therefore reduce the carboxylation energy markedly—*e. g.*, bring it from the standard value of close to zero (table 8.VII) to as low as -20 kcal.   This should shift the free energy of carboxylation (which, in table 8.VIII, differs by about 15 kcal from the total energy) to about -5 kcal, or close to the above estimate.

This estimate of ΔH and ΔF is very crude, but it points to one important relationship.

It has been repeatedly emphasized in this book that photosynthesis involves two reduction steps of different types: carboxyl to carbonyl, and carbonyl to hydroxyl.   Because of the stabilization of carbon-oxygen bonds by accumulation at a single carbon atom, the first step requires considerably more energy than the second one.   (According to table 9.IV, the normal potentials of transitions of the first type are about $+0.5$ volt, those of the second type, about $+0.2$ volt; the difference of 0.3 volt corresponds to a free energy of dismutation of about $-2 \times 0.3 \times 23 = -14$ kcal.)   In schemes 36.IIIB and 36.V, light energy is used in one step only (conversion of PGA to TP) which is the more difficult of the two required reduction steps.   By converting six carboxyl groups into six carbonyl groups—twice as many as are needed for the final carbohydrate synthesis—we acquire the possibility to dismute the three extra carbonyls, and to use the energy of their dismutation to drive forward an otherwise difficult reaction—fixation of CO_2 in a carboxyl.   This is achieved in the coupled reaction (36.8) which can thus be considered as a chemical mechanism for indirect use of stored light energy to facilitate carboxylation.   A further "assist" may be provided (as first suggested by Ruben, *cf.* p. 201) by a "high energy phosphate"; specifically, such a phosphate may be involved in the introduction of a second phosphate residue in ribulose diphosphate.   However, the amount of energy stored in this way is likely to be considerably below the 10–12 kcal available in carboxyl phosphates.

The assumption that sedoheptulose and ribulose phosphates are not involved in the synthesis of hexoses in photosynthesis is supported by the observation (*cf.* table 36.VII) that the distribution of tracer carbon in them bears no similarity to that in hexoses.   (One does not see how a hexose with preferential C labelling in position 3,4 could be derived from a ribulose with preferential labelling in C atom 3, or a sedoheptulose with equal labelling of atoms 3, 4, 5.)   If it were not for this argument, one would be tempted to consider the formation of the C_5 and C_7 sugars as related to the "alternative path" of respiration, first suggested by Warburg, and more recently established by Horecker (*cf.* Horecker 1951 and later), in which glucose phosphate is oxidized to phosphogluconate, decarboxylated in ribose, and the latter split into a triose and a C_2 compound.

8. The C$_2$ Fragment

The appearance of a C$_3$ compound (PGA) as the first carboxylation product in photosynthesis naturally pointed to a C$_2$ compound as carbon dioxide acceptor. If the carboxylation were not coupled with reduction, or phosphorylation (or both), the acceptor would have to be phosphoglycol:

(36.9) $H_2PO_3CHOHCH_2OH + CO_2 \longrightarrow H_2PO_3CHOHCHOHCOOH$

In the case of reductive carboxylation, the acceptor could be phospho-glycol aldehyde.

Although C$_2$ compounds have been found among the early tagged photosynthesis products, none of them could be identified as the CO$_2$ acceptor, and the hypothesis arose that this acceptor does not occur in the free state at all, its formation by splitting of a long-chain compound being coupled with carboxylation. The findings described in section 7 support this hypothesis.

Nevertheless, the study of the early tagged C$_2$ products remains of interest, because even in a reaction of the type (36.7), fleeting appearance of free C$_2$ fragments remains possible. The actually found labelled C$_2$ compounds may be, if not identical, at least related to an evasive C$_2$ intermediate in the main reaction chain.

Labelled phosphoglycolic acid, glycolic acid, and glycine are the main C$_2$ compounds appearing on the chromatograms (cf. for example, fig. 36.14c). Glycolic acid has a reduction level ($L = 0.75$) too low to produce GA by carboxylation (which would require, according to equation 36.9, glycol with $L = 1.50$); however, glycolic acid could be a by-product of oxidation of the acceptor.

Calvin and co-workers (1951) observed that if plants are illuminated in C*O$_2$ until labelled C$_3$ and C$_4$ compounds appear, and illumination then continued in absence of CO$_2$, the C*$_3$ and C*$_4$ compounds disappear, and labelled *glycolic acid* (CH$_2$OH·COOH) and *glycine* (NH$_2$CH$_2$·COOH) increase on the radiograms. The two compounds may be related to the C$_2$ acceptor, and accumulate whenever this acceptor is prevented from being converted to PGA by the absence of carbon dioxide. It is further of importance that glycolic acid is found to be labelled symmetrically in both carbon positions. This shows that it is derived from a symmetric precursor, such as glycol, OHCH$_2$CH$_2$OH.

The appearance of glycolic acid was studied in more detail by Shou, Benson, Bassham and Calvin (1950). They confirmed that even after very short exposure the two carbons in glycolic acid are uniformly labelled (similarly to the α and β carbons in PGA). Shou *et al.* fed *Scenedesmus* C(14)-labelled glycolic acid at pH 2.8 (to suppress ionization) and found an appreciable assimilation. In the dark, under anaerobic conditions, the label was incorporated in glycine and serine. In light, tagged products similar to those obtained from $C*O_2$ were observed. The PGA obtained in this way was labelled uniformly in α and β positions, irrespective of the position of the label in glycolic acid.

In section 12, we will refer to Calvin and Benson's speculations (1949) that the C_2 acceptor in photosynthesis may be vinyl phosphate, $CH=CHOPO_3H_2$, a dehydration product of glycol phosphate (*cf.* equation 36.9). These speculations have been superseded by the above-mentioned hypothesis of direct carboxylation of a C_5 sugar diphosphate to form two molecules of PGA.

9. Kinetic Studies

Most conclusions presented so far in this chapter are based on qualitative kinetic information—the sequence in which different tagged compounds appear when photosynthesizing cells are offered tagged carbon dioxide. On a few occasions, we have referred to more quantitative data,

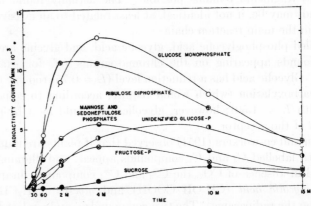

Fig. 36.19. $C*O_2$ incorporation in hexose phosphates as function of time of photosynthesis. 15° C., 10 μl. *Scenedesmus* cells. "Unidentified glucose phosphate" later identified as uridine diphosphate glucose + related compounds (after Benson *et al.* 1952).

e. g., to the changes in the ratio of labels in phosphoglyceric and pyruvic acid with time (*cf.* fig. 36.10).

More recently, the absolute and relative amounts of labelling on different compounds as function of time have been studied more systematically by Calvin and co-workers (Benson, Kawaguchi, Hayes and Calvin 1952; Calvin and Massini 1952; Benson *et al.* 1954).

Figures 36.16 to 36.20, taken from the first-named paper, show time curves of the tagging of several compounds in *Scenedesmus* cells exposed to C*O₂ during steady photosynthesis in saturating light, at 15–20° C. (The ordinates are the radioactivities *eluted* from the paper chromatogram— about ⅓ of those measured by direct plating.)

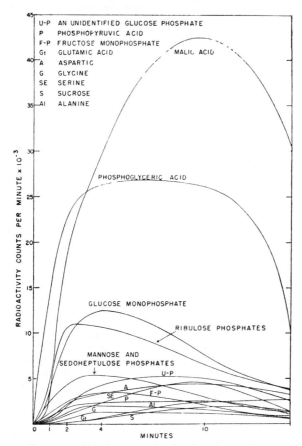

Fig. 36.20. Course of C*O₂ incorporation in *Scenedesmus* in most important early tagged compounds presented on common time and activity scales (*Scenedesmus*, 15° C., 10 μl. cells) (after Benson *et al.* 1952).

Figures 36.16 and 36.20 show clearly that no appreciable "reservoir" exists between C*O₂ and PGA. Figure 36.16 does not preclude a similar, direct C*O₂ incorporation in PPA. We have mentioned before arguments against such an assumption, presented particularly by the Chicago investigators (Fig. 36.10), and suggesting that PPA is a secondary product, rapidly equilibrated isotopically with PGA.

The malic acid tagging curve also appears, in fig. 36.18, to have a finite slope at $t = 0$, indicating the possibility of its formation by uptake of external CO_2 without sizable accumulation of the label in a "reservoir" (such as oxalacetic acid). However, here, as in the case of pyruvic acid, the conclusion is not binding. Peculiar in the case of malic acid is the sharp increase in the slope of the curve about one minute after the beginning of exposure. The steeper slope is equal to that of PGA, (fig. 36.20); it can be taken as indicative of the formation of malic acid, at this stage, by carboxylation of compounds derived from phosphoglyceric acid.

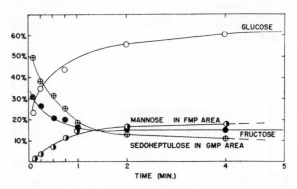

Fig. 36.21. Distribution of C(14) label between several sugars as function of time of photosynthesis (*Scenedesmus*, 15° C.) (after Benson *et al.* 1952).

The finite initial rate of tagging of MA was still considered by Benson *et al.* (1952) as evidence of an independent "second carboxylation" leading to malic acid, probably through rapid isotopic equilibration with a C_4 compound in the main photosynthetic sequence (oxalacetic acid?). A tagging curve obtained at 2° C. also indicated a finite initial rate of C* incorporation in malic acid. From the shape of the curve showing the over-all rate of tagging as function of time (which, after a single addition of $C*O_2$, must mean a function of decreasing CO_2 concentration), it was conjectured that the $C_1 + C_2 \rightarrow C_3$ carboxylation required a higher CO_2 concentration to maintain its saturation rate than the $C_1 + C_3 \rightarrow C_4$ carboxylation.

Among the sugars monophosphates (figs. 36.17 and 36.19), those of fructose and seduheptulose also appeared to be tagged at a finite rate at zero time, while tagged mannose and glucose came up later (*cf.* also fig. 36.21).

After the single "shot" of labelled C* begins to get exhausted in the medium, the tagged metabolic intermediates are used up by equilibration with the major carbon storage reservoirs in the plant. Figures 36.19 and 36.20 show that glucose monophosphate is the first tagged compound to show a decline in activity; PGA seems to be the last one (figs. 36.16 and 36.20). The order of disappearance of the label may be taken as indication of the relative distance from the various compounds to the final, stable products of photosynthesis.

Calvin and Massini (1952) described tagging experiments at 24° C., in a large vessel (2 ml. wet algae in 200 ml. water), from which successive 20 ml. samples could be withdrawn, first as photosynthesis in C^*O_2 proceeded, and then after the light had been switched off. The results were rather erratic, but several compounds (or types of compounds) were clearly shown to be saturated with C^* after illumination periods of the order of 5 min.; these could be assumed to be intermediates in the direct path of photosynthesis (rather than its by-products, or final products). By assuming that in the saturated state the reservoirs of these intermediates are fully equilibrated isotopically with the external C^*O_2, the concentrations of these intermediates in the photostationary state could be calculated from the amount of radioactivity found in them in the chromatograms. Table 36.VIII shows the results.

TABLE 36.VIII

PHOTOSTATIONARY CONCENTRATION OF PHOTOSYNTHETIC INTERMEDIATES IN *Scenedesmus* ILLUMINATED BY WHITE FLUORESCENT LIGHT (10 KERG./CM.² SEC.) AT 24° C. 1% CO_2, 2 ML. CELLS IN 200 ML. WATER (AFTER CALVIN AND MASSINI 1952, AND BENSON 1952)

Compound	Concentration, millimole/l. (wet cell volume)	
	from C*	from P*
Phosphoglyceric acid	1.4	5.7
Triose (dihydroxyacetone) phosphate	0.17	
Fructose phosphate	0.12	
Glucose phosphate	0.4	1.2
Mannose phosphate	0.05 ⎱	0.6
Sedoheptulose phosphate	0.18 ⎰	
Ribulose diphosphate	0.5	1.0
Alanine	0.2	

However uncertain the numbers in table 36.VIII probably are, they represent the first estimate of the concentration of intermediates in photosynthesizing cells, and are as such of the greatest interest. It will be noted that the photostationary concentration of PGA (1.4×10^{-3} mole/l.) is about one order of magnitude lower than that of chlorophyll in algal cells (*cf.* chapter 15, section B7). The amount of activity in most of the compounds listed in table 36.VIII continued to increase slowly after "saturation" has been reached, indicating that they were also "fed" from the growing reservoir of labelled final products of photosynthesis (polysaccharides).

In contrast to the compounds listed in table 36.VIII, the reservoirs of malic acid, glutamic acid, and sucrose showed constant growth of activity during photosynthesis over periods of the order of 30 min. (fig. 36.22). These compounds must therefore form large, slowly labelled reservoirs.

Figure 36.22 shows peculiar changes in the "postphotosynthesis" period, including a sudden "wave" of [PGA] (which reaches a peak in about one minute, and then subsides), and an almost instantaneous depletion of diphosphate esters. Analysis of the monophosphate area indicated also a

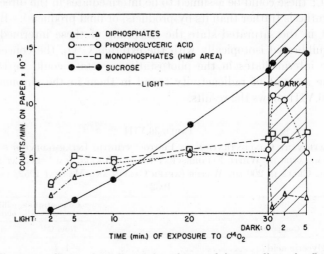

Fig. 36.22. Change in radioactivity of several intermediates in *Scenedesmus* with time during photosynthesis and after cessation of illumination (after Calvin and Massini 1952).

depletion of sedoheptulose phosphate, while the reservoirs of tagged hexoses (and of sucrose) increased. The malic acid reservoir dropped in darkness, while that of glutamic acid increased rapidly. The citric acid reservoir, negligible in light, increased suddenly to a low, but measurable steady value (fig. 36.23).

In another run, the concentration of ribulose diphosphate was much smaller in light, and the increase in PGA, after light had been switched off, was much less pronounced. While the reasons for the difference between the two experiments are unknown, the parallelism of the two changes may be significant (confirming that the C_5 sugar is the precursor of PGA).

If light was switched on again after 10 min. of darkness, the stores of diphosphates, PGA, and malic acid grew again.

These results bear obvious relation to the manometric (and other) observations of transient gas exchange phenomena at the beginning and at the

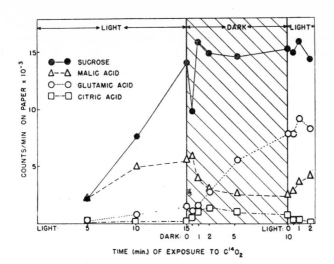

Fig. 36.23. Change in radioactivity of several compounds with time during photosynthesis and afterwards (after Calvin and Massini 1952). Note steady increase in darkness of tagged glutamic acid, appearance of tagged citric acid, and decline in tagged malic acid.

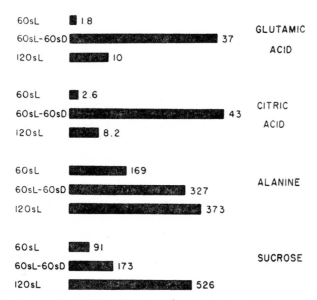

Fig. 36.24. Effect of 1 min. strong light, 1 min. dark sequence on amounts of tagged glutamic acid, citric acid, alanine, and sucrose in *Chlorella* (after Calvin and Massini 1952).

end of illumination, described in chapters 8 and 33. Changes in the cell composition, observed by radiography, undoubtedly are correlated with the liberation of CO_2 or O_2 into the medium (or their uptake from the medium).

Figure 36.24 summarizes the results of another experiment in which 0.2 ml. of wet *Chlorella* cells were exposed to 1 min. strong light (160 kerg/cm.^{2} sec., infrared-free) + 1 min. dark sequence. Controls were exposed to light for 1 or 2 min. This figure again illustrates the appearance of C* in citric and glutamic acids after the light had been switched off.

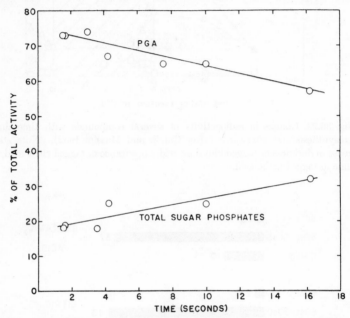

Fig. 36.25. Extrapolation of tagging in *Scenedesmus* to zero time (after Bassham *et al.* 1954).

Benson (1952) described an independent determination of the photostationary concentration of various phosphate esters in steadily photosynthesizing *Scenedesmus*. It consisted in "saturating" the plants with radiophosphorus by 20 hours photosynthesis at 30 klux, in a nutrient solution containing 2 mc. P(32), in 4% CO_2, killing them with boiling ethanol in light, extracting with hot ethanol and water, chromatographing, and counting the several radioactive spots. Table 36.VIII showed the results in the last column. Considering the difference in conditions between the two experiments, the agreement with the data obtained by C(14) saturation is satisfying.

Bassham, Benson *et al.* (1954) gave some additional kinetic data pertinent to the problem of initial fixation. Figure 36.25 shows that extrapolating the percentage of fixed C* to zero time, gives 75% for PGA and 17% for sugar phosphates, thus leaving 8% unaccounted for by compounds of these two types. This residue was distributed between malic acid (3%), free GA (2%) and phosphopyruvic acid (3%). In the sugar phosphate fraction, no single component shows a trend to become predominant at zero time (*cf.* fig. 36.21).

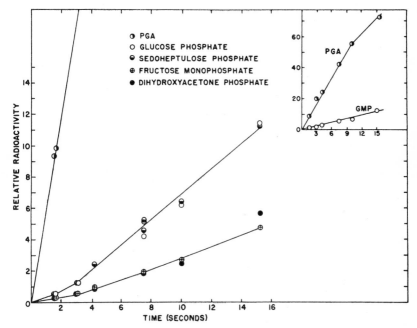

Fig. 36.26. Tagging of several compounds in the first seconds of exposure to C*O₂ of steadily photosynthesizing *Scenedesmus* (after Bassham *et al.* 1954). This figure corresponds to an enlargement of the left corner of Fig. 36.20.

Using the estimates of photostationary concentrations given in table 36.VIII, the rate of increase in specific activity of the several intermediates could be calculated from curves of the type of those in figs. 36.21 and 36.26. (Figure 36.26 is an enlarged representation of the first seconds of tagging.) For the period between $t = 2$ and $t = 10$ sec., these rates are 0.3 for glucose monophosphate and 1.0 for PGA, with the values for FMP, DHAP, RDP and SMP falling between these two limits (after division by 2 for PGA and DHAP, and by 3 for SMP, to account for the 2 or 3 equally labelled C* atoms in these compounds). This illustrates well the rapidity with which the C(14) spreads over a multitude of cellular "reservoirs."

In one set of experiments, the volumes of the several C* reservoirs during steady photosynthesis in 1% CO_2 were compared with those after a sudden decrease of carbon dioxide pressure to 3×10^{-3} %. Figure 36.27 shows the result (which is opposite of that caused by darkening, *cf.* Fig. 36.22). The RDP reservoir increased sharply, reached a peak, and then settled to a new, higher steady level; the PGA reservoir, to the contrary, decreased, within 2 min. to a much lower steady level. The change in

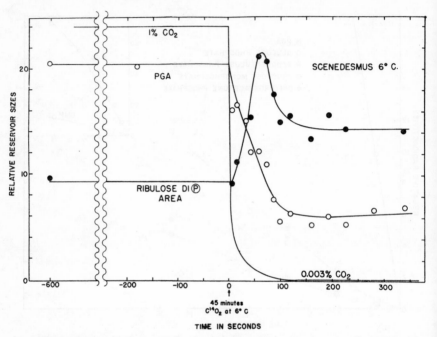

Fig. 36.27. Effect of a sudden decline in CO_2 concentration from 1 to 3×10^{-3}% on the volume of tagged reservoirs in *Scenedesmus* (after Bassham *et al.* 1954).

steady levels is in agreement with the concept that PGA is a product of carboxylation of RDP; but the transient peak of [RDP] requires interpretation (as do all the peaks and troughs observed in the transitional states).

10. The Sequence of Sugars

In chapter 3 (p. 44) we discussed the evidence concerning the "first sugar" derived from chemical analysis of the products of photosynthesis. Some of this evidence favored the disaccharide, sucrose, as a precursor of free monosaccharides, glucose and fructose; other observations contradicted this hypothesis. Knowing now from tracer studies how brief must be the exposures to lead to reliable discrimination between primary and secondary products of photosynthesis, this earlier chemical evidence cannot be considered as very significant.

The C(14) work, described in the preceding section, proved that the first products on the reduction level of carbohydrates ($L = 1.0$) are phosphate esters. These include mono- and diphosphates of trioses, pentoses, hexoses and heptoses. The heptose and pentose phosphates seem to function as intermediates in the regeneration of PGA, rather than in the formation of the stable products of photosynthesis—sugars and proteins. The path to the latter leads from triose phosphates to hexose phosphates, and from these to sucrose; while free glucose and free fructose appear only later, as hydrolysis products of sucrose, or of their own phosphate esters. This sequence represents an approximate, but not exact, reversal of the common mechanism of glycolysis, which begins with free glucose and proceeds via glucose diphosphate to fructose diphosphate, and thence to triose monophosphates.

Following are the successive observations of Calvin and coworkers on the chemical mechanism of sugar transformations in photosynthesis.

On their first paper chromatograms, Calvin and Benson (1949) noted that, of the three nonesterified sugars, sucrose was the first to appear; they suggested that it was formed directly from glucose monophosphate and fructose monophosphates (which—as well as hexose diphosphate—regularly appeared earlier than the free sugars); and that free hexoses were formed afterwards by hydrolysis of sucrose. Of the two hexose monophosphates, the fructose-6-phosphate appeared to precede the glucose-1-phosphate; in agreement with this, sucrose at first contained more activity (after 30 sec., twice as much) in the fructose moiety than in the glucose moiety.

Aronoff and Vernon (1950) made similar experiments with soybean leaves, and confirmed most of the findings of Calvin and Benson; they found, however, that glucose-1-phosphate appeared before the fructose-6-phosphate and suggested that the reactions leading to these relatively late products of photosynthesis do not need to proceed in exactly the same way in different plants. They also noted that tagged glyceric acid was more abundant than tagged phosphoglyceric acid after several minutes of photosynthesis, but that PGA was predominant in the first seconds of photosynthesis.

Bean and Hassid (cf. Hassid 1951) found that leaves (of barley, sugar beet or soybean) killed by being dropped into boiling ethanol, after exposure to CO_2, confirmed Calvin's conclusions: the tagging of sucrose precedes that of free hexoses. Extraction methods not leading to equally rapid inactivation of enzymes resulted in tagged hexoses being found before the tagged sucrose. It could be proved, however, that these free hexoses were the product of decomposition of phosphate esters. For example, if the cells were dropped into liquid nitrogen, ground in the cold, and extracted with ethanol at 20° C., the radioactivity was found predominantly in nonphosphorylated compounds—including glyceric acid and glucose; but if extraction was done with *boiling* ethanol, all activity was found in the phosphate esters.

Similar experiments had been described earlier by Benson (1950). According to him, higher plants (barley) and purple bacteria (*Rhodospirillum*) contain a phosphatase which has considerable resistance to heat. Immediate killing of leaves with boiling alcohol produces no free hexoses or trioses and very little free glyceric acid; but freezing in liquid air, grinding and extraction with boiling ethanol gives considerable amounts of free sugars and acids.

Buchanan, Lynch, Benson, Bradley and Calvin (1953) called attention to a previously unidentified spot on the paper chromatogram, which appears after about 30 sec. of steady photosynthesis in C^*O_2, and is situated in the same general area as the known sugar phosphates. This material very easily produced glucose by hydrolysis. More extensive chromatographic study revealed that it also contained galactose and mannose. It was surmised that the spot may contain *uridine diphosphates* of these and other hexoses (compounds described by Leloir). This surmise was confirmed by co-chromatography with pure compounds and other chromatographic tests. The hexoses contained in esters of this type constitute a large fraction of labelled, nonpolymerized hexoses present after several minutes of steady photosynthesis in C^*O_2. Adenine phosphate, adenosine-5'-phosphate and uridine-5'-phosphate also were found in the hydrolysate from this radioactive spot.

Benson, Kawaguchi, Hayes and Calvin (1952) gave fig. 36.21 for the course of tagging of several sugar phosphates, showing that fructose is labelled ahead of glucose (and mannose). Calvin and Massini (1952) suggested that the synthesis of sucrose occurs by the interaction of fructose phosphate with the above-described glucose phosphate-uridine complex (uridine diphosphoglucose). The first product could be *sucrose monophosphate*. By treating the material from the hexose monophosphate area of the chromatogram by a phosphatase free of invertase, Buchanan (1954; cf. Buchanan, Bassham *et al*. 1953) was able to demonstrate the actual presence of sucrose monophosphate, lending considerable support to the hypothesis. Calvin and Massini suggested that compounds of the type of uridine diphosphoglucose may serve as "glucose donors" also in the subsequent formation of polysaccharides.

11. Effect of Poisons and pH on CO_2 Fixation

It was mentioned in section 6 that *malonate* was found to inhibit the tagging of malic acid, without much effect on the yield of sugar synthesis. Following are observations on the effect of some other poisons, according to Calvin *et al*. (1951) (based on the experiments of Stepka 1951).

In the presence of 1.5×10^{-4} M *iodoacetamide*, the total uptake of C^* was reduced by 90%, but the formation of labelled sucrose was not affected at all. (At lower concentrations of the inhibitor, it was even increased.) In glycolysis, iodoacetamide is known to inhibit the reaction by which triose phosphate is oxidized to phosphopyruvate; it thus could be expected to block the synthesis of sugars if it occurred by the reversal of this reaction. The actually observed effect of iodoacetamide on the *total* C^*O_2 fixation can be attributed to this source. However, the lack of effect on sucrose synthesis has then to be explained by the *ad hoc* assumption of another partial reaction beyond the triose stage which, too, is affected by iodoacetamide in such a way that the flow of intermediates through some channel by-passing sucrose is slowed down, and ten times more than the usual proportion of intermediates are converted into sucrose.

The evidence concerning the effect of iodoacetamide on the *respiration* of green cells also was contradictory until lately, when Arnon (1952, 1953) and Hölzer (*cf.* Hölzer 1954) proved definitely that an iodoacetamide-sensitive respiration path does exist in green plants. This was taken as proof that their respiration, like that of animal tissues or yeast, proceeds, at least in large part, via the triose-pyruvate step, with triose dehydrogenase as catalyst, a pyridine nucleotide as hydrogen acceptor, and ADP as "energy acceptor." It seems, however, that in green cells this reaction is not DPN-specific, as usual, but can use either DPN or TPN.

Because of the probable spatial separation of the sites of the main catabolic and anabolic processes, the proof of the presence of a triose dehydrogenase in green cells is not a very strong argument for the participation of this enzyme in photosynthesis. More convincing are the observations on the inhibition of photosynthesis itself by iodoacetate (chapter 12, section 5, and chapter 37D, section 2). In conjunction with the data of Stepka *et al.* on the effect of iodoacetamide on the uptake of radiocarbon, these observations can be considered as lending support to the—anyhow plausible—assumption that the next step in photosynthesis after the formation of PGA is its reduction to triose by an iodoacetamide-sensitive hydrogenase. To a certain extent, these observations also make it plausible that the hydrogen donor in this reduction is a pyridine nucleotide ($DPNH_2$ or $TPNH_2$) and that consequently a high energy phosphate, such as ATP, must be supplied to make the reduction possible; however, these conclusions are by no means certain.

A number of previous observations (*cf.* Vol. I, pages 301–311) led to the conclusion that *cyanide* is a specific poison for the carboxylation reaction in photosynthesis. Calvin and co-workers illuminated *Scenedesmus* for 30 min. in CO_2-free air to build up the CO_2 acceptor, then added 3 $\times$ 10^{-4} M KCN, and one minute later exposed the cells to C^*O_2. The tracer fixation was inhibited by 95%, but the compounds whose tagging was least inhibited were alanine, malic acid and phosphoglyceric acid—supposedly the immediate (or near-immediate) products of carboxylation!

The tagging of triose and hexose phosphates was inhibited much more strongly. It thus seems that cyanide establishes blocks not, or not only, in the carboxylation reaction, but also, or mainly, in the subsequent transformation of the carboxylated compounds. (This, of course, does not affect the conclusion that cyanide affects the participation of carbon dioxide in photosynthesis, and has little influence on the parts of the photosynthetic process which do not involve carbon dioxide—such as the primary photochemical process, and the reactions which lead to the liberation of oxygen from water.)

$5 \times 10^{-3} M$ *hydroxylamine*, added under similar conditions, produced a 75% inhibition of total C^* uptake. The tagging of malic acid was least affected by this poison; the tagging of glutamic, succinic, fumaric and citric acids was even enhanced. Calvin interpreted this as an indication that hydroxylamine removes a block that normally prevents, in light, the utilization of photosynthetic intermediates as material for respiration (*cf.* section 12).

Gaffron, Fager and Rosenberg (1951) found *cyanide* to inhibit the postillumination C^*O_2 fixation strongly, whether it was added during the illumination or after the light had been turned off. The inhibition affected particularly the water-soluble fraction, indicating (in some contrast to the data of Calvin *et al.*) an inhibition of the PGA formation. *Hydroxylamine*, on the other hand, inhibited the postillumination fixation of C^*O_2 only if given during the illumination period, but had no effect if given together with the tracer after the return to darkness.

One-minute photosynthetic C^* fixation in *Scenedesmus* was constant, according to Calvin *et al.* (1951), between pH 4 and 9; the rate declined by about 50% at pH 2 and 10, and dropped abruptly to zero at pH 10.5. The rate-depressing effects of excess acidity (pH 2) or alkalinity (pH 10) did not increase with time; cells could be kept at these extreme pH values for 30 minutes, and the full rate of C^* fixation restored upon return to pH 7.

The main changes in C^* distribution caused by variations in pH were an increase in the proportion of tracer found in malic acid (*e. g.*, from 5% at pH 1.6 to 25% at pH 11.4) and a drop in its proportion in sucrose, from 7 to 0%. The absolute amounts of tagged malic acid and phosphopyruvic acid showed sharp maxima at pH 9.

12. Evolution of the CO_2 Reduction Mechanism

Between 1946, when the C(14) tracer was first used systematically for the study of photosynthesis, and mid-1954 (the time of the final revision of this chapter), our knowledge of the chemical mechanism of carbon dioxide reduction has undergone rapid development.   Chemical mechanisms based on almost pure speculation (such as Baeyer's formaldehyde theory), or on plausible analogy (such as Thimann's 1938 surmise that photosynthesis involves a reversal of glycolysis, *cf.* p. 183), which had been current before the new approach (and extensively used in the preceding parts of this monograph), have been replaced by schemes based primarily on experimental evidence, although still strongly influenced by analogies with other better known metabolic mechanisms.   The Berkeley group (Benson, Calvin *et al.*) in particular, has proposed many such schemes.   They were primarily heuristic hypotheses, repeatedly altered to fit the growing body of data.   At this writing, some of the originally controversial questions have been settled, and several steps in the reaction sequence have been firmly established; others, while still speculative, have become at least highly plausible.   As this section was revised in 1954, it seemed tempting to discard the chronological presentation of the several hypotheses adopted at its first writing in 1950, and use only the picture suggested in the most recent papers.   However, retelling the gradual emergence of this picture may not be useless, even if somewhat confusing.   It is an interesting record of gradual emergence of a landscape from the fog, through which at first only one or two disconnected landmarks were visible.   Furthermore, this kind of presentation serves to underline the incompleteness and uncertainty of the current mechanism—instead of making it appear final and unalterable.

Since much of the study of the chemical mechanism of carbon dioxide *fixation* in photosynthesis has been guided, consciously or subconsciously, by what is known of the mechanism of carbon dioxide *liberation* in respiration, it is useful to begin by saying a few words about the latter process.

In Volume I (p. 224, scheme 9.II) we reproduced an early version of the respiratory decarboxylation cycle.   Since that chapter was first written, this cycle has been amended and enlarged, and has acquired a more or less definitive shape known as the "tricarboxylic acid cycle," the "citric acid cycle," or—most commonly—the "Krebs cycle."   It is reproduced in scheme 36.I.

The main difference between this scheme and the earlier scheme 9.II is the insertion, between pyruvate and succinate, of a sequence of C_6 and C_5 tricarboxylic acids.   Furthermore, the present cycle differs from the earlier one in the mechanism by which pyruvate is fed into the cycle.   Instead of a simple $C_3 + C_3$ condensation (pyruvate + pyruvate) starting a new turn of the wheel, as assumed in 9.II, we now postulate a $C_4 + C_2$ condensation (oxalacetate + "active" acetyl, *i. e.*, acetyle + coenzyme A complex).   Pyruvic acid now functions, in the steady state, only as source of the acetyl (being converted into it by oxidative decarboxylation, with

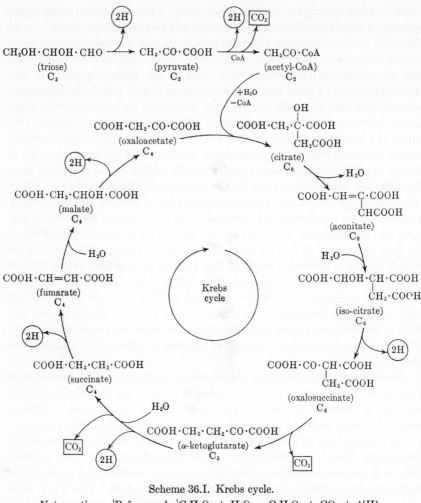

Scheme 36.I. Krebs cycle.

Net reaction:	Before cycle	$C_3H_6O_3 + H_2O \rightarrow C_2H_4O_2 + CO_2 + 4[H]$
	In cycle	$C_2H_4O_2 + 2H_2O \rightarrow 2CO_2 + 8[H]$
	Total	$C_3H_6O_3 + 3H_2O \rightarrow 3CO_2 + 12[H]$

lipoic acid as hydrogen acceptor).   The fact that pyruvate and oxalacetate are in a reversible carboxylation-decarboxylation equilibrium does not alter the fact that the Krebs cycle revolves upon oxalacetate rather than upon pyruvate as a pivot.   It is the oxalacetate that takes up the acetyl group, merges with it in citrate, loses CO_2 molecules and H atoms to decarboxylases and dehydrogenases, and is regenerated at the end of the cycle.

We now turn to the mechanism of carbon dioxide reduction.

Calvin and Benson assumed, when beginning their studies (1947), that carbon dioxide and a hydrogen donor ("reducing power") must be drawn into a cycle similar—but opposite in sense—to the known decarboxylation and dehydrogenation cycles in respiration. At first, when they made no distinction between "photosynthetic" and "respiratory" tracer uptake, the occurrence of tagged succinic, malic, and fumaric acids, and the absence of tagged C_5 and C_6 acids, led them to suggest that the carboxylation cycle in photosynthesis is the reversal of the short C_3-C_4 decarboxylation cycle shown in scheme 9.II (Vol. I, page 224)—rather than of the complete Krebs cycle, illustrated by scheme 36.I above. The early appearance of the tracer in certain amino acids caused them to postulate side reactions of C_3 and C_4 acids in the cycle (such as pyruvic and oxalacetic acids, whose reductive amination leads to alanine and aspartic acid, respectively). This scheme contained two primary carboxylation reactions—the Wood-Werkman reaction:

(36.10) $C^*O_2 + CH_3COCOOH \rightleftharpoons C^*OOHCH_2COCOOH$

and the Lipmann reaction:

(36.11) $C^*O_2 + CH_3COOH + 2[H] \rightleftharpoons CH_3COC^*OOH + H_2O$

(*cf.* equations 36.1 and 36.2).

Later (1948, 1949), when succinic acid faded out of the picture as a likely intermediate of photosynthesis, and phosphoglyceric acid was found to be the main primary carboxylation product, the specific cycle postulated in 1947 had to be altered. The initial C(14) fixation in carboxyl group of phosphoglyceric acid, and its subsequent penetration into the two other positions (Table 36.V) was taken as evidence that phosphoglyceric acid is the pivot of the anabolic cycle—the role assumed in the catabolic cycle, as represented in scheme 9.II, by pyruvic acid. (It will be noted that enol pyruvic acid is a dehydration product of glyceric acid, and that the two acids have the same reduction level.) In the catabolic cycle, 9.II, one molecule of pyruvic acid accepts a second similar molecule and carries it through a series of reactions, as a result of which it is completely torn apart (all carbon being accepted by decarboxylases and later released as free CO_2 gas, and all hydrogen transferred to dehydrogenases and thence, through a series of intermediate catalysts, to oxygen). The other molecule of pyruvic acid is regenerated at the end of the cycle, so that the same series of reactions can be repeated.

Calvin and co-workers thought (1948) that a similar cyclical mechanism, running in the reverse sense, can start with one molecule of phosphoglyceric acid and end with two such molecules, having assembled the second one from carbon dioxide (via one or several carboxylases) and from hydrogen atoms donated by water (via an unknown series of reactions, including at

least one photochemical step).   Of the two phosphoglyceric acid molecules
present at the end of the reaction cycle, one could be reduced to triose and
thence dimerized to hexose (reversal of glycolysis), while the other could
be returned into the cycle.

The two reaction systems are presented in scheme 36.II, which omit
phosphorylations and leave open the specific nature of intermediates in the
two cycles.   Calvin and co-workers did, however, speculate in some detail
on the nature of these intermediates.   The first fact relevant to these speculations was that after very brief photosynthesis in strong light, when
>95% of total tracer taken up was contained in phosphoglyceric acid,
practically all of it was located in the carboxyl group of this acid.   This
made it likely that PGA is a direct product of carboxylation, and since it
is a C_3 acid, leads to the assumption of a C_2 carbon dioxide acceptor.

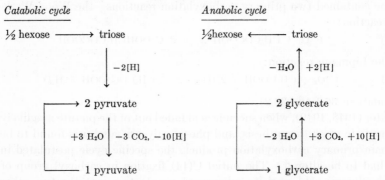

Catabolic cycle

½ hexose ⟶ triose

        −2[H]

2 pyruvate

+3 H_2O | −3 CO_2, −10[H]

1 pyruvate

Anabolic cycle

½hexose ⟵ triose

−H_2O | +2[H]

2 glycerate

−2 H_2O | +3 CO_2, +10[H]

1 glycerate

Scheme 36.II.   The catabolic cycle in respiration and the anabolic cycle in photosynthesis, according to Calvin, Benson and co-workers (1948).

Retaining, at first, the remainder of the originally postulated cycle,
Calvin and Benson (1949) suggested the interpolation between the last
C_4 acid in this cycle (succinic acid) and pyruvic acid, of the following reaction steps:

$$CH_3C{\overset{O}{\underset{OPO_3H_2}{<}}} \xrightarrow{+2[H]} CH_3-\underset{OPO_3H_2}{\overset{OH}{C}}-H \xrightarrow{-H_2O}$$

acetyl phosphate   phosphoacetaldehyde

(36.12) $CH_2{=}CHOPO_3H_2 \xrightarrow[+H_2O]{+CO_2} \underset{OH\ \ OPO_3H_2}{CH_2{-}CH{-}COOH} \xrightarrow{-H_2O} \underset{OPO_3H_2}{CH_2{=}C{-}COOH}$

vinyl phosphate   2-phosphoglyceric   2-phospho-enol-
(C_2-acceptor)   acid   pyruvic acid

This sequence was to replace a reversal of Lipmann's reaction (reductive carboxylation of acetate to pyruvate) in the original cycle; the other

carboxylation reaction—pyruvic to oxalacetic acid—was retained. In support of the hypothesis that *vinyl phosphate* serves as carbon dioxide acceptor in photosynthesis, Calvin quoted the observation that some C(14) can be volatilized from *Chlorella* material obtained after about 1 min. of photosynthesis, in the form of acetaldehyde, by 10 min. hydrolysis with N HCl at 80°C.; the presence of a tagged vinyl ester offered a plausible explanation of this observation.

Later (1950), Calvin and Benson became doubtful also of the correctness of the oxalacetate-malate-fumarate-succinate segment of the original cycle. The absence from the radiograms of active oxalacetic acid could be attributed to its instability, and the appearance of active aspartic acid (derivable from oxalacetic acid by reductive amination) could be considered as indirect evidence of the occurrence of the latter. The scarcity of active succinic acid was, however, difficult to explain. In some experiments, glyceric acid, labelled in all three positions, as well as labelled hexose, have been obtained in complete absence of labelled succinic acid. Furthermore it was necessary to account for the early appearance of radioactive glycolic acid (fig. 35.14) and glycine (probably derived from glyoxylic acid). Malonate, which is known to inhibit the succinic acid–fumaric acid conversion, was found not to interfere with photosynthetic carbon dioxide reduction—not only with the production of active sugar but also with the appearance of active glycolic acid and glycine. (Only the formation of active malate was totally eliminated by malonate, *cf.* above, section 6.) This proved that a different path, avoiding the malate-succinate-fumarate series, must exist, leading—it was still assumed—from oxalacetate to acetyl phosphate or another C₂ compound.

Calvin and co-workers (1950) discussed the possibility that a C^*_1 compound could serve as precursor of the C^*_2 acceptor (a hypothesis which is *a priori* implausible because of the poisonous nature of both formaldehyde and formic acid). Experimentally, only traces of labelled formaldehyde or formic acid were found. Assuming complete isotopic equilibration of these traces with the C^*O_2 used, the quantities of C^* found in C_1 compounds corresponded to 2×10^{-10} mole H_2CO, and 12×10^{-10} mole HCOOH in 1 g. of wet cells. In all likelihood these small quantities were artifacts (*cf.* Vol. I, chapter 10.C).

If the C_2 acceptor is not formed via a C_1 compound, the most likely mechanism of its formation is splitting in two of a C_4 compound, as assumed in scheme 9.II. Calvin and co-workers proceeded to discuss the most likely mechanism of this splitting.

With succinic and fumaric acids eliminated as possible intermediates between oxalacetic acid and the C_2 compound (their appearance in tagged form being now attributed to respiratory CO_2 fixation), and with malic acid also excluded as main line intermediate by malonate inhibition experiments, a mechanism had to be invented by which oxalacetic acid could be converted into C_2 fragments without being first reduced to malic acid. Glycolic or glyoxylic acid, for example, could be formed by hydrolysis of oxalacetic acid, either directly or via tartaric acid:

(36.12a) $COOH \cdot CH_2CO \cdot COOH + H_2O$ ($\longrightarrow$ $COOH \cdot CHOH \cdot CHOH \cdot COOH$)
              oxalacetic acid   tartaric acid

                     $\longrightarrow COOH \cdot CH_2OH + COOH \cdot CHO$
                           glycolic acid   glyoxylic acid

However, no labelled tartaric acid has been observed in radiograms of products of short-time photosynthesis.

Intermediate formation of dihydroxymaleic acid (to be split into two molecules of glyoxylic acid) or of diketo succinic acid (to be split into oxalic acid and glyoxylic acid) also were mentioned as possibilities by Calvin and co-workers. However, the formation of these C_4 acids would mean *oxidation* of oxalacetic acid, while the cycle as a whole must be reductive.

Another alternative discussed by Calvin *et al.* (1950) was the reduction of the dicarboxylic C_4 acid to dialdehyde level before its splitting into C_2 compounds. The cleavage of (diphospho)tartaric dialdehyde into (phospho)glycolaldehyde and (phospho)glyoxal is a plausible reaction, bearing resemblance to the splitting of fructose diphosphate by aldolase.

The assumption of two primary carboxylations—(36.10) and (36.11)—was retained by Calvin and co-workers at that time for the reasons already explained in sections 6 and 9. The tagging of malic acid immediately at the beginning of the exposure to C^*O_2 in light seemed to call for a more direct mechanism of its equilibration with C^*O_2 in the medium than could be provided by secondary transformations of PGA. Reaction (36.10) offered itself as a possibility, even if the reduction of OOA to MA had now to be treated as a side reaction rather than as a step in the main reaction sequence of photosynthesis. The experiments of Badin and Calvin (1950), mentioned in section 6, which indicated that in weak light, tagged malic acid appears even earlier than tagged PGA, were considered by Calvin *et al.* as supporting the hypothesis of a "second CO_2 acceptor"—a C_3 compound, as contrasted to the "first CO_2 acceptor," which had to be assigned a C_2 structure.

It was suggested that in strong light the photochemically produced "C_2" acceptor is the more abundant of the two; while in darkness, this acceptor may disappear altogether. The "C_3 acceptor," on the other hand, was assumed to be regenerated by glycolysis. At the beginning of illumination, C_2 acceptor must first be built up to a steady level, which is higher the stronger the illumination. In weak light, the C^*O_2 taken up by the C_3 acceptor will be largely stored as tagged malic acid. In the steady state, whether in weak or in strong light, both carboxylations must proceed at the same rate (more exactly, *two* CO_2 molecules must be taken up by the C_2 acceptor for each CO_2 molecule taken up by one C_3 acceptor, *cf.* scheme 36.III*A*). However, in very weak light, the establishment of this steady state may require a measurable time, during which the tagging of malic acid will outrun that of all other compounds, including PGA. Another possibility to be taken into consideration is that of tagged malic acid being involved in respiratory, catabolic processes, *i. e.*, serving as a "bridge" between photosynthesis and respiration. We will return to this important possibility when discussing the interaction of respiration and photosynthesis (chapter 37D, section 3), and its possible effect on quantum yield measurements (same chapter, section 3). Here, we will continue the evolution of the carbon dioxide reduction mechanism.

It was reported in section 6 that the postulate of two different primary carboxylations, both essential for photosynthesis, was opposed by Gaffron, Fager and co-workers, who suggested that even Badin and Calvin's finding of a preferential tagging of malic acid in very weak light can be explained by transformations of the only primary tagged product, PGA (leading to a marked storage of the tracer in a C_4 side product when the main sequence proceeds very slowly).

The only way in which the C_3 carboxylation could run steadily at a rate higher than one half of that of the C_2 carboxylation, without causing malic acid to accumulate indefinitely, is for this acid to be drawn into catabolic reaction by which it is again decarboxylated. This would be in agreement with Calvin and Benson's conception of malic acid as a half-way "bridge" between photosynthesis and respiration.

Fager, Rosenberg, and Gaffron (1951) suggested a reaction scheme making use of only one CO_2 acceptor. The C_2 acceptor was assumed to be regenerated from the final product—hexose sugar—by splitting of the latter into three C_2 molecules (which must then be reduced to the level required for an acceptor able to produce glyceric acid by carboxylation):

$$(36.13a) \quad C_2H_4O_3 + CO_2 \underset{(+H_2O)}{\rightleftarrows} C_3H_6O_4 \qquad \text{Carboxylation of } C_2 \text{ acceptor (glycol?) to PGA}$$

$$(36.13b) \quad C_3H_6O_4 + 2[H] \longrightarrow C_3H_6O_3 + H_2O \qquad \text{Reduction of PGA to triose}$$

$$(36.13c) \quad C_3H_6O_3 \longrightarrow \tfrac{1}{2}C_6H_{12}O_6 \qquad \text{Dimerization to hexose}$$

$$(36.13d) \quad \tfrac{1}{3} C_6H_{12}O_6 \longrightarrow C_2H_4O_2 \qquad \text{Dissociation of hexose to biose, glycolaldehyde}$$

$$(36.13e) \quad C_2H_4O_2 + 2[H] \longrightarrow C_2H_4O_3 \qquad \text{Reduction of glycolaldehyde to glycol}$$

$$(36.13) \quad CO_2 + 4[H] \longrightarrow \tfrac{1}{6} C_6H_{12}O_6 + H_2O$$

The relation of the Chicago model (36.13) to that preferred in Berkeley in 1950 is best illustrated by schemes 36.IIIA and B.

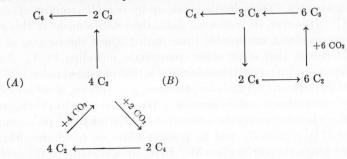

Scheme 36.III. Transformation of the carbon chain in the carboxylation cycles.
(A) Calvin, Bassham et al. (1950). (B) Fager, Rosenberg and Gaffron (1950).

Calvin and co-workers sustained until 1953 the belief in the "second carboxylation" because of the kinetic evidence detailed in section 9. While the question of the C_3 acceptor (and, more generally, of the role of C_4 compounds in the reaction sequence of photosynthesis), thus remained in dispute, a new important experimental finding was added by the Berkeley group—the identification of sedoheptulose and ribulose phosphates as early tagged products in photosynthesis (described in section 7 above). These observations, and the indications that the C_7 and C_5 compounds may serve as precursors of the C_2 acceptor (rather than as intermediates in the formation of the final products of photosynthesis), led Calvin and co-workers to a new scheme for the transformation of the carbon chain in photosynthesis. This mechanism is shown in scheme 36.IV. In this scheme, the unknown acceptor C_2 is regenerated in two successive reactions —one half of it in the reductive splitting of a heptose, producing a pentose, and the other half in a similar splitting of the pentose. The heptose is supposed to be produced by reductive condensation of a triose and a C_4 compound (oxalacetate?). The malate still appears as a by-product (and a possible "bridge" to the respiratory system).

The essential difference between scheme 36.IV and Calvin's earlier schemes is the replacement of the direct split $C_4 \rightarrow 2\ C_2$ by a roundabout mechanism $C_4 + C_3 \rightarrow C_7 \rightarrow C_2 + C_5 \rightarrow 2\ C_2 + C_3$, with a C_3 (triose) molecule acting as a catalyst and being regenerated at the end.

When Bassham et al. (1954) finally decided—as mentioned in section 6— to follow Gaffron et al. in postulating only one carboxylation, scheme 36.IV had to be changed, and evolved into scheme 36.V. Eliminating one carboxylation permitted reduction of the number of hydrogenations from four to one—the reduction of glyceric acid to glyceraldehyde. The rest of the

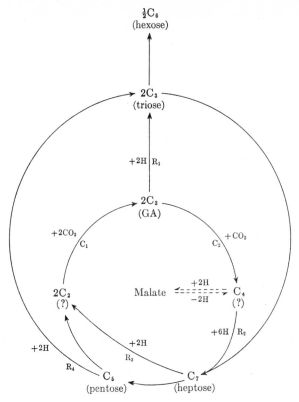

Scheme 36.IV. CO_2 reduction mechanism with regeneration of C_2 acceptor via C_7 and C_5 sugars (two carboxylations, C_1 and C_2, four reductions, R_1, R_2, R_3, R_4) (Calvin *et al.* 1951).

reactions in scheme 36.V are disproportionations or condensations of sugars (more precisely, sugar phosphates) without changes in the reduction level: $C_3 + C_4 \rightarrow C_7$; $C_3 + C_7 \rightarrow 2 C_5$; $C_6 + C_3 \rightarrow C_4 + C_5$. Malic acid must be derived in scheme 36.V from an as yet unidentified C_4 sugar (tetrose). The C_2-acceptor formation had been eliminated in passing from scheme 36.IV to scheme 36.V in favor of a direct carboxylation of pentose coupled with splitting into two C_3 fragments. (An unstable intermediate C_6 compound—on the reduction level of a uronic acid— could be postulated here.)

The simplification of the scheme to a single carboxylation and a single hydrogenation makes it fundamentally similar to Gaffron, Fager and Rosenberg's scheme 36.III*B*, with the important elaboration of the mechanism by which $5/6$ of the primarily formed triose is converted back into phosphoglyceric acid.

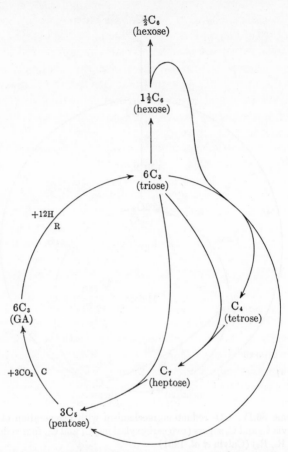

Scheme 36.V. Mechanism of carbon dioxide reduction (single carboxylation C, single reduction R, all other reactions are disproportionations of sugars) (Bassham *et al.* 1954).

The sugar transformations postulated in this scheme have been made plausible by recent investigations of the chemistry of pentoses and heptoses by Horecker and co-workers (*cf.*, for example, Horecker 1952).

13. The Lipoic Acid Hypothesis

Calvin and Barltrop (1952) (*cf.* Calvin 1952[2]) suggested that the inhibition of respiration in light—or at least, the failure of fresh photosynthates to be involved in respiration as long as illumination continues (which they deduced from the lack of tagging in tricarboxylic acid in light)—can be explained by the assumption that a catalyst, needed for the respiration cycle, is involved also in photosynthesis, and is kept in the reduced state as long as photosynthesis is going on, thus preventing it from catalyzing the oxidation process. (Another way to state the same fact is to say that the competition between the photochemical and the thermal supply of H atoms to the oxidizing catalyst is won by the former in practically every case.) Specifically, Calvin (1952[2]) suggested that this catalyst is lipoic acid (LA), which is needed, in accord with scheme 36.I, as hydrogen acceptor for the conversion of pyruvate into "active acetyl" (acetyl-CoA). This suggestion formed part of a hypothesis ascribing to lipoid acid a key role in photosynthesis (Calvin 1952[2]; Calvin and Barltrop 1952; Barltrop, Hayes and Calvin 1954). This compound, whose presence in green plants and blue-green algae has been demonstrated by Cayle, Holt, and Punnett (1953), contains a ring of three carbon and two sulfur atoms. Calvin $et\ al.$ suggested that this ring is under such a strain that it can be opened, and lipoic acid thus converted into a biradical (a dithiyl) by an energy quantum of $\sim$40 kcal ($i.\ e.$, by a single photon of red light), although the standard value for the energy of a S—S bond is (according to Pauling's tables) > 60 kcal.

Calvin and Barltrop (1952) argued that the shift of the absorption peak in the series: straight-chain disulfide – 4,8-thioctic acid – 5,8-thioctic acid – 6,8-thioctic (lipoic) acid, from 250 to 330 mμ, indicates that the dissociation energy of the ground state is decreased, from the open chain to the five-membered ring, by someting like 10,000 cm.$^{-1}$, or $\sim$20 kcal. However, this estimate is based on the assumption of an approximately unchanged energy of the excited state—while it seems more likely that the latter changes even more strongly than the former.

From stereochemical considerations, Barltrop, Hayes, and Calvin (1954) estimated a strain of about 10 kcal/mole in the 5-membered ring.

Postulating that the strain in the five-membered ring is sufficient to reduce the S—S dissociation energy to below 40 kcal, Barltrop and Calvin suggested that the photochemical formation of the dithiyl biradical:

is followed by a dark reaction with water:

(36.14)

(36.15)

The addition product was assumed to dismute, liberating O_2 (perhaps with H_2O_2 as intermediate):

(36.16)

(Arguments in favor of such a dismutation reaction of a sulfenic acid were presented by Barltrop *et al.* 1954.) The result of the reaction (36.16) is the utilization of *two* quanta for the oxidation of *one* molecule of water, and reduction of one molecule of lipoic acid.

The normal redox potential of the couple:

$$(36.17) \qquad \overset{-S}{\underset{-S}{\diagdown}}\Big/\overset{-SH}{\underset{-SH}{\diagup}}$$

was assumed by Calvin *et al.* (1954) to be close to that of the pyridine nucleotides (*i. e.*, about $+0.3$ volt), so that the standard free energy of reaction (36.18):

$$(36.18) \qquad \overset{-S}{\underset{-S}{\diagdown}} + H_2O \longrightarrow \overset{-SH}{\underset{-SH}{\diagdown}} + \tfrac{1}{2} O_2$$

—which is the sum of (36.14), (36.15) and (36.16)—became, at pH 7:

$$(36.19) \qquad \Delta F = 2 \times 23.0 \,(0.8 + 0.3) = 50.6 \text{ kcal/mole}$$

(where 0.8 volt is the potential of the oxygen electrode at pH 7).

It was suggested that the dithiol:

$$\overset{-SH}{\underset{-SH}{\diagdown}}$$

reduces DPN (or TPN) in the dark, and the reduction of PGA to triose is then achieved by DPNH$_2$ (or TPNH$_2$) with the assistance of ATP, as repeatedly suggested before. The high energy phosphate, of course, has to be also produced by light, *e. g.*, by an "energy dismutation" of the type repeatedly discussed before (*cf.* also section B below).

According to Lehninger, three high energy phosphates can be produced by autoxidation of one molecule of DPNH$_2$. The supply of the one ATP molecule needed to reduce PGA would thus increase the quantum requirement from 2 to $2^2/_3$ per two H atoms transferred; if this were all the energy needed for the synthesis of a triose, and if no additional energy (*e. g.*, in the form of more ATP) were required to convert triose to hexose, the overall quantum requirement of photosynthesis would be $5^1/_3$. Calvin *et al.* suggested, however, that one additional ATP molecule may be needed to phosphorylate ribulose monophosphate to ribulose diphosphate; this would raise the over-all quantum requirement to 6.0.

We will return to these estimates in chapter 37D (section 4e). Here we must point out that the theory of lipoic acid as the key catalyst in photosynthesis is at this writing unsupported by evidence. Calvin *et al.* (1954) found that under special conditions the rate of the Hill reaction (with quinone as oxidant) can be accelerated by lipoic acid. Barltrop, Hayes and Calvin (1954) made interesting photochemical experiments on sensitized photoxidation of model compounds, such as trimethylene disulfide, but as yet the findings do not seem to bear much relation to the suggested function of lipoic acid in photosynthesis.

One argument against Calvin's hypothesis that lipoic acid is the "quantum acceptor" in photosynthesis is as follows: If it is assumed that the S—S bond in lipoic acid is looser by 20 kcal (or more) than the standard S—S bond, then the reducing power of the couple (36.17) should be correspondingly weaker (since there is no reason why S—H bonds in the dithiol:

should not have the normal strength). Assuming approximate parallelism of free energies and total energies of reduction for the different disulfides, the redox potential of the couple (36.17) should be $1/2 \times 20:23$ or about 0.45 volt less positive than that of a similar "standard" system (such as cystine/cysteine). The normal potential of the latter pair is about $+0.35$ volt (close to that of pyridine nucleotides); that of the couple (36.17) should then be *negative,* and thus quite insufficient to reduce TPN or DPN.

14. Tracer Studies of Special Forms of Photosynthesis

The observation of Tobert and Zill (1954) on the C^*O_2 fixation and tracer distribution in squeezed-out material from the giant Chara and Nitella cells were described in chapter 35 (p. 1536). In the same chapter we briefly reported also the findings of Arnon, Bell and Whatley (1954, *cf.* p. 1615) of the fixation of C^*O_2 and ATP* formation by whole chloroplasts, and the apparently competitive character of these two processes.

Some carbon tracer measurements have been made with *hydrogen adapted algae* Gaffron, Fager and Rosenberg (1951) "stabilized" adapted *Scenedesmus* cells with phthiocol (*cf.* chapter 6) to be able to observe photoreduction in relatively strong light. They noted that under these conditions, the scattering of C* over the three fraction A, B, C (*cf.* section 4) was almost as rapid as in true photosynthesis. The tagged primary products thus could be converted into various metabolites, including fats and proteins under strictly anaerobic conditions, *i. e.,* without any help of respiratory energy. Badin and Calvin (1950) made similar experiments, but did not inhibit "de-adaptation"; they had therefore to work at very low light intensities and use very long exposures; the same kind of tagged compounds was found after photoreduction as after prolonged photosynthesis in weak light.

Comparatively little C* was found, by Badin and Calvin (1950), to be fixed in the *oxyhydrogen-carbon dioxide reaction* of hydrogen adapted *Scenedesmus* (*cf.* chapter 6, section 3); apparently none of the tracer passed into the insoluble fraction (polysaccharides, proteins).

Benson (1950) stated that *purple bacteria (Rhodospirillum rubrum)* produced a greater variety of tagged compounds in 5 min. photoreduction in $H_2 + C^*O_2$ than did barley leaves in equal period of photosynthesis. Unicellular algae were found to stand midway between higher plants and bacteria in respect to the complexity of tagged products. Benson also noted that *Rhodospirillum* produced no sucrose, but formed a polysaccharide, "probably starch."

This may be the place to mention the study, by means of the C(14) tracer, of the *de-acidification of succulents* in light—a phenomenon described in chapter 10 (section D2). The two alternative interpretations suggested there, were: (*1*) "photosynthesis" with malic (or citric) acid as "substitute oxidant" (replacing CO_2 as hydrogen acceptor), and (*2*) photoxidation of these acids to carbon dioxide, followed by normal photosynthesis. Tracer experiments could perhaps permit a choice between these two hypotheses.

Thurlow and Bonner (1948) and Varner and Burrell (1950) found that, in darkness, acidification in tagged C^*O_2 produced, in *Bryophyllum calycinum*, malic acid tagged preferentially in the carboxyl group, indicating its probable formation by the Wood-Werkman reaction (*i. e.*, carboxylation of pyruvic to oxalacetic acid followed by reduction of the latter to malic acid. It will be recalled that the same mechanism has been discussed —but more recently abandoned—by Calvin and co-workers also as explanation of the tagging of malic acid in photosynthesis.)

In light, the hexoses which are formed in the succulent when malic acid disappears, were tagged preferentially in the 3,4 position (as in ordinary photosynthesis, *cf.* table 36.VII). This indicates that the C_4 dicarboxylic acid is either photoxidized completely to CO_2, or, at least, decarboxylated to a C_3 acid (with the remaining carboxyl still tagged) before it is used for the synthesis of sugars by the reduction of the C_3 acid to triose and head-on condensation of two triose molecules to a hexose (leading to the accumulation of labelled carbon in the two middle atoms of the C_6 chain).

If malic acid were to take direct part in C_6 synthesis, *e. g.*, in the way postulated by Benson, Calvin *et al.* in 1949–1950 (*i. e.*, splitting of the C_4 chain into two C_2 fragments, and their carboxylation), this would lead to a C_3 acid with labelled carbon in the β-position, rather than in the carboxyl; reduction of the product to triose and condensation of the latter to hexose would then place the labels on carbon atoms 2 and 3 in the C_6 chain.

Stutz (1950) exposed *Bryophyllum calycinum* to labelled carbon dioxide for several hours in light and chromatographed the synthesized organic acids on a column; activity was found in succinic, oxalic, malic, citric, and iso-citric acid. After 12 hours in light and 12 hours in darkness, almost 90% of C* was found in malic acid, with only 58% in iso-citric acid and 4% in citric acid (although the absolute amount of iso-citric acid present was larger than that of malic acid). Similar preferential labelling of malic acid was noted after $1/2$, 2 or 4 hours in light without a subsequent dark period. When *Calicynum* leaves, exposed to C^*O_2 for 15 min. in light, were left in darkness (without C^*O_2) for 4 hours (to observe the shift in the relative concentration of the different acids, *cf.* p. 269), the specific activity of all acids was found to increase (obviously at the cost of some nonacid C* reservoir formed in light), despite a strong increase in the absolute quantity of all acids. (Malic acid increased, in the dark period, by a factor of 5 in absolute amount and a factor of 2 in specific activity, citric acid by a factor of 3 in quantity and 6 in specific activity, iso-citric acid by a factor of 2.8 in quantity and 2.4 in specific activity.) Similar experiments were carried out with tobacco leaves (which also store malic and citric acid, *cf.* p. 264). There, too, C* was fixed predominantly in malic acid. It was shown that 100 mg. quantities of heavily labelled malic and citric acid can be prepared by growing *Bryophyllum* or tobacco seedlings in $C^*(14)O_2$.

B. Photosynthesis and Phosphate Metabolism*

As described in part A, most reactions in the reduction of carbon dioxide in photosynthesis involve *phosphate esters* rather than free organic com-

* Bibliography, page 1712.

pounds. Phosphoglyceric acid, phosphopyruvic acid, phosphoglycolic acid, triose phosphates, pentose phosphate, hexose phosphates, heptose phosphate and sucrose phosphate have all been found among the early tagged products of photosynthesis. (For a review of phosphates identified in tracer experiments with C(14) and P(32), see Buchanan *et al.* 1952.)

Some of the observed phosphate esters contain one, some two phosphoric acid residues; none of them—except phosphoenolpyruvate, whose function in photosynthesis is not clear—are true "high energy phosphates." If it is true, however, that the main reduction step in photosynthesis is (as postulated in the "one-carboxylation, one-reduction" mechanism in section A,12) the reduction of PGacid to PGaldehyde by reduced pyridine nucleotide, then the cooperation of a high-energy phosphate is indispensable; *i. e.*, PGA has to be phosphorylated to DPGA (with one H_2PO_3 residue attached to the carboxyl group, forming a "high energy" ester) before it can be reduced. It has been suggested that the needed high-energy phosphate (ATP) is produced by partial reoxidation of an intermediate, such as $TPNH_2$. If this is correct (and as of this writing it appears a plausible hypothesis), then the beginning of photosynthesis in a cell should lead to an increase in the concentration of high energy phosphate (and a corresponding consumption of orthophosphate, or of a "low-energy" phosphate ester). The steady progress of photosynthesis beyond the reduction level of PGA will require a certain steady concentration, [ATP], which must be higher the higher the light intensity (at least up to saturation). In the dark, this concentration will decline again as the cell uses up its energy reserves (*cf.* Lynen 1941, 1942).

In chapter 9, section 5, we reported some experiments by Emerson, Stauffer and Umbreit (1944) indicating an effect of photosynthesis on the phosphate household of *Chlorella*. (A more direct, but quantitatively not very convincing evidence of storage of energy in high-energy phosphates was obtained by Vogler and Umbreit (1943) with chemosynthetic bacteria, *cf.* p. 114.) More recently, more significant evidence has been supplied.

Wassink, Tjia, and Wintermans (1949) observed shifts in the phosphate content of a medium containing the purple bacterium *Chromatium* D upon transfer from light to darkness. The uptake of inorganic phosphate occurred in light in N_2, H_2, and—to a smaller extent—in $N_2 + CO_2$; shift to darkness caused a small release of phosphate if the gas phase remained unchanged, and a marked release if $N_2 + CO_2$ was substituted for H_2. These results were interpreted as supporting the hypothesis of Vogler and Umbreit that, in the energy-storing period (oxidation of sulfur in chemosynthetic bacteria, illumination in H_2 in photosynthetic bacteria), high-energy phosphate bonds are built up, while in the energy-utilizing period (CO_2 supply in the absence of O_2 in chemosynthetic bacteria, CO_2 supply in darkness in photosynthetic bacteria) the energy of these bonds is used up for the fixation and reduction of carbon dioxide.

Wassink, Wintermans and Tjia (1951[1]) made similar experiments with *Chlorella*. In addition to measuring the inorganic phosphate in the medium, the amount of phosphate in the cells extractable with trichloroacetic acid (TCA) also was determined. In the absence of carbon dioxide, phosphate was taken up from the medium in light, and up to 30% of the TCA-soluble phosphorus in cells was converted into TCA-insoluble form. The shifts were much smaller in the presence of carbon dioxide.

Wassink, Wintermans and Tjia (1951[2]) found that glucose had the same effect on the phosphate transformation in *Chlorella* as carbon dioxide.

Wintermans and Tjia (1951) described the liberation of the largest part of the phosphate, made insoluble in TCA by illumination in the absence of carbon dioxide, by hydrolysis in 1 N HCl. The (much smaller) amount of TCA-insoluble phosphate, synthesized in the presence of carbon dioxide, is divided about equally between a labile (*i. e.*, HCl hydrolyzable) fraction and a fraction that is stable in 1 N HCl at 100° C.

Kandler (1950) also made experiments on the "phosphate level" of *Chlorella pyrenoidosa* in darkness and in light. He determined the diffusible "inorganic" phosphate and the "TCA-soluble" organic phosphate. The former declined by 20% in the first $1/2$ min. of exposure to light, rose to a peak at 1 min., and, after a second shallow minimum at about 3 min., settled to a constant level, about 10% below that in darkness. Upon switching the light off, the level of TCA-soluble phosphate rose in about 2 min., to a maximum about 30% above the steady value in light, then declined again and assumed a constant level about 10% above that in light. These "transients" show remarkable similarity to those observed in gas exchange and chlorophyll fluorescence (chapter 33) and C* incorporation in certain intermediates (this chapter, section 9).

Kandler interpreted these variations in phosphorus content as evidence of the participation in photosynthesis of high-energy phosphate (ATP) and discussed two alternative mechanisms for its formation and utilization in the photochemical process (*cf.* below).

Simonis and Grube (1952) and Grube (1953) took up the study, first attempted by Aronoff and Calvin (1948), of the incorporation of P(32) tracer in different fractions of green cells in darkness and in light. Aronoff and Calvin could find no uptake of P in the TCA-soluble fraction of *Chlorella* in light (which would be a sign of increased concentration of organic phosphates, such as ATP). Kamen, Gest and Spiegelmann (*cf.* Gest and Kamen 1948, Kamen and Spiegelmann 1948) observed, in light, mainly a change in the TCA-insoluble P* fraction; the effect was decreased by HCN poisoning. Simonis and Grube resumed this study using

Elodea densa leaves instead of unicellular algae. They suggested that leaf pieces can be freed from adsorbed radiophosphorus, by rapid rinsing before killing, much more effectively than unicellular algae. After killing in 10% TCA at 5° C., the leaves were extracted three times with TCA, and the P* activity determined in the total extract; the inorganic orthophosphate (including perhaps some phosphate from very easily hydrolyzable organic esters) was precipitated by magnesium, with inactive orthophosphate as carrier, and its activity measured; so was the P* activity of the remaining TCA-soluble organic material and of the TCA-insoluble residue.

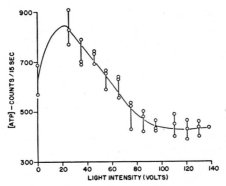

Fig. 36.28. The effect of light on the steady ATP level in *Chlorella* (in the presence of CO_2, after 2–3 hours of anaerobic incubation). Measured by the firefly extract luminescence method (after Strehler 1952).

The experiments indicated a decrease in inorganic orthophosphate and an increase in TCA-soluble organic phosphate in light; the effect was stronger in the presence than in the absence of carbon dioxide (but was definitely present also in the CO_2 free system). The change could be observed after 1–10 min. of illumination. An increase in TCA-insoluble P* (observed before by Kamen and Spiegelmann) was noted only after about 1 hour. The P* uptake in TCA-soluble fraction increased at first (and that in an organic phosphate decreased) with light intensity, but reached a constant level at about 2.5 klux.

Strehler and Totter (1952) and Strehler (1953) (*cf.* also Strehler 1952) applied to the problem of phosphate metabolism in photosynthesis the sensitive technique (discovered by McElroy) based on the stimulation of chemiluminescence of firefly extracts by ATP. They estimated that in the steady state of photosynthesis in *Chlorella* about one molecule ATP is added to the cellular pool for every six molecules of liberated oxygen. If one assumes that one (or two) ATP molecules are degraded to ADP to make the liberation of one molecule of oxygen possible, the observed net increase in ATP indicates an excess of 7.5% (or 15%) of the photochemically produced over the simultaneously consumed ATP.

Figure 36.28 illustrates the relation of the ATP concentration to light intensity. Contrary to expectation, this concentration has a maximum at a certain relatively low light intensity; at the higher light intensities it settles to a steady level, which is still markedly higher than in darkness. A further peculiarity is illustrated by fig. 36.29: the ATP value *increases* in the dark immediately after the cessation of illumination. This concentration shows a characteristic transient fluctuation also at the beginning of the illumination period (fig. 36.30) which should be considered in conjunction with the induction curves of gas exchange and fluorescence, described in chapter 33, and with the transients in the concentration of tagged compounds, observed by the Berkeley group (figs. 36.22 and 36.23).

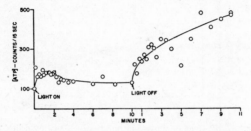

Fig. 36.29. Changes in ATP level in *Chlorella* during and after 10 min. illumination in the absence of CO_2 (after Strehler 1952).

The concentration of ATP in *Chlorella* can be enhanced also by the admission of oxygen to anaerobically incubated cells (*i. e.*, by stimulation of respiration). The photochemical enhancement is much less sensitive to a lowering of temperature than the respiratory enhancement, which seems to indicate a direct relation of ATP formation to the primary photochemical act, rather than to the enzymatic stages of photosynthesis.

Strehler interpreted these results as supporting the hypothesis that formation and utilization of ATP is a part of photosynthesis. Rather than thinking of ATP as merely an "assistant" in the reduction of RCOOH to RCHO, he suggested that direct photochemical hydrogen transfer from water occurs only to an acceptor with a potential not higher than 0.0 volt (*cf.* chapter 35, section B4 for evidence which could be adduced in support of this postulate), and that the further enhancement of reducing power ("energy dismutation") is brought about by reoxidation of some of the reduced products and storage of their oxidation energy as phosphate bond energy.

It may be useful to juxtapose here the different variants of the theory of phosphate bond energy storage in photosynthesis. The "extreme" variant (suggested, *e.g.*, in the paper by Emerson, Stauffer and Umbreit 1944) is that *all* light energy utilized in photosynthesis is first converted to phosphate bond energy; our objections, based on the undesirability of splitting 43 kcal energy quanta into 10 kcal portions before accumulating them again (chapter 9, p. 228), were directed against this extreme theory. An "intermediate" suggestion is that one quantum of light is used to lift hydrogen from water ($E_0' \simeq 0.8$ volt) to an intermediate redox catalyst with a potential around 0.0 volt, and that high energy phosphates (created by partial

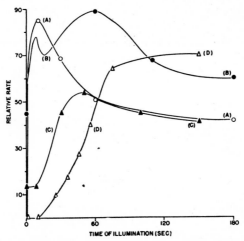

Fig. 36.30. Transient changes in ATP concentration (E) at the beginning of illumination of *Chlorella*, compared with those of fluorescence (A), chemiluminescence (B), and CO_2-uptake (D) (after Strehler 1952).

reoxidation of this intermediate) take over from there (Kandler 1950, Strehler 1952). Finally, there is the "modest" suggestion (Ruben 1943, Calvin *et al.* 1954), which assigns to phosphate energy only the bridging of the final gap between $E_0 \simeq 0.3$ volt (pyridine nucleotides) and the energy needed to reduce a carboxyl to a carbonyl ($E_0 \simeq 0.5$ volt).

All the above-discussed hypotheses suggested partial reoxidation of *intermediates* as source of ATP energy. Burk and Warburg postulated instead (*cf.* chapter 37D, section 3), partial reoxidation of the *final products* of photosynthesis (carbohydrates). To complete the review of alternatives, the oxidant in the back reaction need not be molecular oxygen—as postulated by most of the above-enumerated authors—but could be an intermediate oxidation product ("oxygen precursor") formed by the photochemical process. (This assumption becomes particularly plausible if one wants to apply the same general concept to photosynthesizing bacteria and "hydrogen adapted" algae, which do not produce free oxygen, but nevertheless reduce CO_2 to the carbohydrate level.)   By encompassing all these alternatives, one is brought to the most general picture—that of "energy dismutation" (chapter 7, section 6 and chapter 9, section 7) by back reactions between intermediate or final oxidation products and intermediate or final reduction products of photosynthesis, with the one specific suggestion that the energy of these back reactions is temporarily stored as phosphate bond energy.   Energy storage in phosphate bonds is, however, not the only conceivable mechanism of energy dismutation; and though the available experimental indications of the participation of ATP in photosynthesis are suggestive, they are not yet conclusive.

TABLE 36.IX

RELATIVE SIZE OF PHOSPHATE RESERVOIRS IN THE STEADY STATE OF PHOTOSYNTHESIS IN *Scenedesmus* (AFTER GOODMAN *et al.* 1953)

Compound	1 hr. light	1 hr. light + 15 min dark	1 hr dark	1 hr. dark + 15 min. light
Phosphoglycerate.............	33	30	29	39
Hexose monophosphate........	7	6	7	7
Uridine diphosphoglucose......	14	11	7	10
Sugar diphosphates...........	19	14	17	9
ADP......................	9	10	7	10
ATP...	18	30	28	25

Goodman, Bradley, and Calvin (1953) initiated a systematic quantitative study of the incorporation of P(32) tracer in different compounds by dark and photochemical metabolism of *Scenedesmus obliquus*, using paper chromatography to separate and identify the labelled compounds.   After about 30 sec. exposure to radiophosphate *in the dark*, 72% of incorporated P* were found in ATP and 9% in ADP, with 11% in sugar diphosphates, 5% in the hexose monophosphate area, and 3% in PGA.   After 30 sec. *in light*, the P* distribution was much more uniform (39% in sugar diphosphates, 19% in hexose monophosphates, 17% in PGA, 15% in ADP, and 10% in ATP).   This means that even 30 sec. is too long a time, in strong light, to identify the port of entry of P*.   The early P* labelling of PGA in light suggests a close relation between photosynthesis and the organic binding of mineral phosphate (which is indicated also by the above-described analytical experiments).   The considerable labelling of ADP is worth noting, because the terminal phosphate in ADP is not usually considered as contributing to metabolic transformations.

By longer exposures to $P^*O_4^{3-}$, enough labelled compounds could be obtained to permit more detailed fractionation of the tagged compounds. The P* distribution between glucose-6-phosphate, fructose-6-phosphate, and mannose-6(sedoheptulose)-phosphate corresponded to the equilibrium concentrations of these three esters, after exposures of from 1 to 25 min. in dark or in light. Still longer experiments (1 hour exposure), permitted a first estimation of the volumes of the various phosphate reservoirs in the cell (on the assumption that after this time, a steady state has been reached in respect to these volumes, and all reservoirs have been uniformly labelled). Table 36.IX shows the relative reservoir volumes computed on this basis.

It is interesting to note the smaller proportion of P contained in ATP in light (compensated by a greater proportion in sugar phosphates).

Frenkel (1954) described the formation of ATP from ADP + orthophosphate in light by sonically disintegrated *Rhodospirillum rubrum*. Arnon *et al.* made similar observations on whole chloroplasts. At first (Arnon, Bell and Whatley 1954) oxygen was reported to interfere with "photosynthetic phosphorylation"; but later (Arnon, Whatley and Bell 1954) it was reported to occur also under aerobic conditions. Mg^{++} ions, the vitamins C (ascorbic acid) and K, and certain other compounds, were found to act as "co-factors," stimulating the ATP formation.

C. Nitrate Metabolism and Photosynthesis*

This chapter would be the place to discuss also the relation of photosynthesis to the *nitrate* metabolism of plants. It, too, is affected by illumination, and affects photosynthesis, *e. g.*, by changing the photosynthetic ratio $\Delta CO_2/\Delta O_2$ from about 1.0 in solutions containing no nitrogen or only ammonia nitrogen, to much lower values in solutions containing nitrate, in consequence of partial substitution of HNO_3 for CO_2 as ultimate hydrogen acceptor. Early experiments on the photochemical reduction of nitrate by *Chlorella* by Warburg and Negelein have been described in chapter 19, section B1. It was stated there that "unfortunately, the subject has received no further attention since 1920." Since this was written, some new studies have appeared in this field. Space limitations prevent us from entering here into their description; we can only refer to the series of papers by Burström (1942–1945), Myers and co-workers (1948, 1949), Davis (1952) and Kessler (1953), and to the discussion by Kandler (1950).

The radiocarbon tracer experiments, described in part A of this chapter, have indicated how early the reduction of carbon dioxide in photosynthesis can branch out into various side reactions, including transaminations leading to simple aminoacids (and perhaps from there to proteins) before the reduction stage of the carbohydrates has been reached. At some stage

* Bibliography, page 1713.

(or stages) of the reduction mechanism of photosynthesis, HNO_3 may become substituted for CO_2 as hydrogen acceptor whenever photosynthesis is carried out in a nitrate-containing medium. Various possibilities of this coupling can be envisaged, such as nitrate serving as Hill oxidant in competition with carbon dioxide (as oxygen competes with quinone according to Mehler, *cf.* chapter 35, section B4). Another possibility is that of nitrate substituting for oxygen as oxidant in the often postulated partial reversal of the primary photochemical process.

Bibliography to Chapter 36

Chemical Path of Carbon Dioxide Reduction

A. Isotopic Tracer Studies

1939   Ruben, S., Hassid, W. Z., and Kamen, M. D., *J. Am. Chem. Soc.*, **61**, 661.

1940   Ruben, S., Kamen, M. D., and Hassid, W. Z., *ibid.*, **62**, 3443.

Ruben, S., Kamen, M. D., and Perry, L. H., *ibid.*, **62**, 3450.

Ruben, S., and Kamen, M. D., *ibid.*, **62**, 3451.

1941   Frenkel, A. W., *Plant Physiol.*, **16**, 654.

1947   Benson, A. A., and Calvin, M., *Science*, **105**, 648.

Aronoff, S., Barker, H. A., and Calvin, M., *J. Biol. Chem.*, **169**, 459.

Aronoff, S., Benson, A. A., Hassid, W. Z., and Calvin M., *Science*, **105**, 664.

Allen, M. B., Gest, H., and Kamen, M. D., *Arch. Biochem.*, **14**, 335.

Wassink, E. C., *Antonie van Leeuwenhoek*, **12**, 281.

Calvin, M., and Benson, A. A., *Science*, **107**, 476.

Fink, R. M., and Fink, K., *Science*, **107**, 253.

1948   Stepka, W., Benson, A. A., and Calvin, M., *Science*, **108**, 304.

Brown, A. H., Fager, E. W., and Gaffron, H., *Arch. Biochem.*, **19**, 407.

Benson, A. A., and Calvin, M., *Proc. Cold Spring Harbor Symp. Quant. Biol.*, **13**, 6.

Thurlow, J., and Bonner, J., *Arch. Biochem.*, **19**, 509.

Kamen, M. D., in *Photosynthesis in Plants.* Iowa State College Press, Ames, Ia., 1949, p. 365.

Brown, A. H., Fager, E. W. and Gaffron, H., *ibid.*, p. 403.

Fager, E. W., *ibid.*, p. 423.

Benson, A. A., Calvin, M., Haas, V. A., Aronoff, S., Hall, A. G., Bassham, J. A., and Weigl, J. W., *ibid.*, p. 381.

Weigl, J. W., and Calvin, M., *J. Chem. Phys.*, **17**, 210.

Calvin, M., and Benson, A. A., *Science*, **109**, 140.

1949   Gibbs, M., *J. Biol. Chem.*, **179**, 499.

1950   Benson, A. A., Bassham, J. A., Calvin, M., Goodale, T. C., Haas, V. A., and Stepka, W., *J. Am. Chem. Soc.*, **72**, 1710.

Benson, A. A., and Calvin, M., *J. Exptl. Botany*, **1**, 63.

Bassham, J. A., Benson, A. A., and Calvin, M., *J. Biol. Chem.*, **185**, 781.

Calvin, M., Bassham, J. A., and Benson, A. A., *Federation Proc.*, **9**, 524.

Badin, E. F., and Calvin, M., *J. Am. Chem. Soc.*, **72**, 5266.

Shou, L., Benson, A. A., Bassham, J. A., and Calvin, M., *Physiol. Plantarum*, **3**, 487.

Stutz, R. E., CO_2 *Assimilation in Biological Systems*, Brookhaven Conference Report, Assoc. Univ. Inc., Upton, N. Y., pp. 77–96.

Benson, A. A., *ibid.*, pp. 119–138.

Gibbs, M., *ibid.*, pp. 139–145.

Fager, E. W., Rosenberg, J. L., and Gaffron, H., *Federation Proc.*, **9**, 525.

Fager, E. W., and Rosenberg, J. L., *Science*, **112**, 617.

Benson, A. A., and Calvin, M., *Ann. Rev. Plant Physiol.*, **1**, 25.

Clendenning, K. A., *Arch. Biochem.*, **27**, 75.

Aronoff, S., and Vernon, L., *ibid.*, **27**, 239.

Varner, J. E., and Burrell, R. C., *ibid.*, **25**, 280.

Steward, F. C., and Thompson, J. F., *Nature*, **166**, 593.

1951   Calvin, M., Bassham, J. A., Benson, A. A., Lynch, V. H., Ouellet, C., Schou, L., Stepka, W., and Tolbert, N. E., *Symposia Soc. Exptl. Biol.*, **5**, 284.

Gaffron, H., Fager, E. W., and Rosenberg, J. L., *ibid.*, **5**, 262.

Gaffron, H., and Fager, E. W., *Ann. Rev. Plant Physiol.*, **2**, 87.

Hassid, W. Z., in *Phosphorus Metabolism*. Vol. I, John Hopkins University Press, Baltimore, pp. 11–66.

Horecker, B. L., *ibid.*, pp. 117–144.

Nezgovorova, L. A., *Compt. rend. (Doklady) acad. sci. USSR*, **79**, 537.

Benson, A. A., *J. Am. Chem. Soc.*, **73**, 2971.

Benson, A. A., Bassham, J. A., and Calvin, M., *ibid.*, **73**, 2970.

Weigl, J. W., Warrington, P. M., and Calvin, M., *ibid.*, **73**, 5058.

Utter, M. F., and Wood, H. G., in *Advances in Enzymology*. Vol. 12, Interscience, New York-London, p. 41.

Stepka, W., Thesis, Univ. of California.

1952   Benson, A. A., Bassham, J. A., Calvin, M., Hall, A. G., Hirsch, H. E., Kawaguchi, S., Lynch, V. H., and Tolbert, N. E., *J. Biol. Chem.*, **196**, 703.

Benson, A. A., Kawaguchi, S., Hayes, P. M., and Calvin, M., *J. Am. Chem. Soc.*, **74**, 4477.

Calvin, M., *Harvey Lectures*, Ser. **46**, pp. 218–251.

Calvin, M., *Harrison Howe Lecture, UCRL, Report No.* **2040**.

Calvin, M., and Massini, P., *Experientia*, **VIII 12**, 445.

Calvin, M., Bassham, J. A., Benson, A. A., and Massini, P., *Ann. Rev. Phys. Chem.*, **3**, 215.

Calvin, M., and Barltrop, J. A., *J. Am. Chem. Soc.*, **74**, 6153.

Benson, A. A., *Z. Elektrochem.*, **56**, 848.

Clendenning, K. A., and Gorham, P. R., *Arch. Biochem. and Biophys.*, **37**, 56.

Fager, E. W., and Rosenberg, J. L., *Arch. Biochem. and Biophys.*, **37**, 1.

Horecker, B. L., *J. Cellular Comp. Physiol.*, **41**, Supplement 1, pp. 137–164.

Arnon, D. I., *Science*, **116**, 635.

Nezgovorova, L. A., *Compt. rend. (Doklady) acad. sci. USSR*, **85**, 385.

Nezgovorova, L. A., *ibid.*, **86**, 853.

Doman, N. G., Kuzin, A. M., Mamul, T. V., and Khudjakova, R. I., *ibid.*, **86,** 369.

Buchanan, J. G., Bassham, J. A., Benson, A. A., Bradley, D. F., Calvin, M., Davis, L. L., Goodman, M., Hayes, P. M., Lynch, V. H., Norris, L. T., and Wilson, A. T., in *Phosphorus Metabolism.* Vol. II, Johns Hopkins University Press, Baltimore, pp. 440–459.

1953   Buchanan, J. G., Lynch, V. H., Benson, A. A., Bradley, D. F., and Calvin, M., *J. Biol. Chem.*, **203,** 935.

Spruit, C. J. P., *Acta Botanica Neérl.*, **1,** 551.

Arnon, D. I., *ibid.*, 67–81.

Cayle, T., Holt, A. S., and Punnett, T., unpublished.

Brown, H. A., and Frenkel, A., *Ann. Rev. Plant Physiol.*, **4,** 23.

1954   Bassham, J. A., Benson, A. A., Kay, L. D., Harris, A. Z., Wilson, A. T., and Calvin, M., *J. Am. Chem. Soc.*, **76,** 1760.

Barltrop, J. A., Hayes, P. M., and Calvin, M., *J. Am. Chem. Soc.*, **76,** 4348.

Buchanan, J. G., unpublished.

Hölzer, H., *Angew. Chem.*, **66,** 65.

Weissbach, A., Smyrniotis, P. Z., and Horecker, B. L., *J. Am. Chem. Soc.*, **76,** 3611.

Tolbert, N. E., and Zill, I. P., *J, Gen. Physiol.*, **37,** 575.

Arnon, D. I., Allen, M. B., and Whatley, F. R., *Nature*, **174,** 394.

Quayle, J. R., Fuller, R. C., Benson, A. A., and Calvin, M., *J. Am. Chem. Soc.*, **76,** 3610.

B. Phosphate Metabolism and Photosynthesis

1941   Lynen, F., *Ann.*, **546,** 120.

1942   Lynen, F., *Naturwissenshaften*, **30,** 398.

1943   Vogler, K. G., and Umbreit, W. W., *J. Gen. Physiol.*, **26,** 157.

Ruben, S., *J. Am. Chem. Soc.*, **65,** 279.

1944   Emerson, R. L., Stauffer, J. F., and Umbreit, W. W., *Am. J. Botany*, **31,** 107.

1948   Kamen, M. D., and Spiegelmann, S., *Cold Spring Harbor Symposia Quant. Biol.*, **13,** 151.

Gest, H., and Kamen, M. D., *J. Biol. Chem.*, **176,** 299.

Aronoff, S., and Calvin, M., *Plant Physiol.*, **23,** 351.

1949   Wassink, E. C., Tjia, J. E., and Wintermans, J. F. G. M., *Proc. Acad. Sci. Amsterdam*, **52,** 412.

1950   Kandler, O., *Z. Naturforsch.*, **5b,** 423.

1951   Wassink, E. C., Wintermans, J. F. G. M., and Tjia, J. E., *Proc. Acad. Sci. Amsterdam*, **54,** 41.

Wassink, E. C., Wintermans, J. F. G. M., and Tjia, J. E., *ibid.*, **54,** 496.

Wintermans, J. F. G. M., and Tjia, J. E., *ibid.*, **55,** 34.

1952   Simonis, W., and Grube, K. H., *Z. Naturforsch.*, **7b,** 194.

Strehler, B. L., in *Phosphate Metabolism.* Vol. II, Johns Hopkins University Press, Baltimore, pp. 491–501.

Buchanan, J. G., Bassham, J. A., Benson, A. A., Bradley, D. F., Calvin, M., Daus, L. L., Goodman, M., Hayes, P. M., Lynch, V. H., Norris, L. T., and Wilson, A. T., *ibid.*, 440–459.

Strehler, B. L., and Totter, J. R., *Arch. Biochem. and Biophys.*, **40**, 28.

Arnon, D. I., in *Phosphate Metabolism.* Vol. II, Johns Hopkins University Press, Baltimore, p. 69.

1953   Grube, K. H., *Planta*, **42**, 279.

Arnon, D. I., in *Soil and Fertilizer Phosphorus in Crop Nutrition.* Academic Press, New York.

1954   Goodman, M., Bradley, D. F., and Calvin, M., *J. Am. Chem. Soc.*, **75**, 1962.

Arnon, D. I., Allen, M. B., and Whatley, F. R., *Nature*, **174**, 394.

Arnon, D. I., Whatley, F. R., and Allen, M. B., *J. Am. Chem, Soc.*, **76**, 6324.

Frenkel, A. *ibid.*, **76**, 5568.

C. Nitrate Metabolism and Photosynthesis

1942   Burström, H., *Naturwissenschaften*, **30**, 645.

1943   Burström, H., *Ann. Agr. Coll. Sweden*, **11**, 1.

Burström, H., *Arkiv. Botanik*, **3013**, No. 8, 1.

1945   Burström, H., *Ann. Agr. Coll. Sweden*, **13**, 1.

1947   Myers, J., and Cramer, M. L., *Science*, **105**, 552.

1948   Cramer, M., and Myers, J., *J. Gen. Physiol.*, **32**, 93.

1949   Myers, J., and Johnston, J. A., *Plant Physiol.*, **24**, 111.

Cramer, M., and Myers, J., *Plant Physiol.*, **24**, 255.

Myers, J., in *Photosynthesis in Plants.* Iowa State College Press, Ames, Iowa, pp. 349–364.

1950   Kandler, O., *Z. Naturforsch.*, **5b**, 423.

1952   Davis, E. A., *Plant Physiol.*, **28**, 539.

1953   Kessler, E., *Flora*, **140**, 1.

Kessler, E., *Arch. Mikrobiol.*, **19**, 438.

Chapter 37

MISCELLANEOUS ADDITIONS TO VOLUMES I AND II,1

When this chapter was first planned, it was intended to described in it the various new developments, in the fields covered in Volumes I and II, 1, which were not extensive enough to warrant treatment in separate chapters (as did the two topics discussed in chapters 35 and 36). By the time of the final revision of the text, however, some of these subjects had grown so much that devoting a separate chapter to them would have been quite appropriate, but cross references in previous volumes made rearrangement impossible.

Since parts A and B below are more in the nature of independent chapters than subdivisions of a single one, the bibliography follows each part, instead of being collected at the end as in the other chapters.

A. Structure and Composition of Chloroplasts, Chromoplasts and the Chromatoplasm*

(Addendum to Chapter 14)

1. Light Microscopy

Despite its much lower magnification, light microscopy retains one advantage over electron microscopy—the possibility of observing the cell in its natural state, without maceration, desiccation, or chemical treatments unavoidable in the preparation of objects for electron microscopy.

In chapter 14 (pp. 358–363), it was reported that microscopic observations of chloroplasts, in visible and ultraviolet light, have revealed the presence, in most of them, of round, flattened dark bodies designated as grana, about 0.5μ in diameter (Heitz, fig. 39a). In some cells, however the chloroplasts seemed to consist of continuous bands—designated as *lamellae*—without clear evidence of granular structure (Menke, fig. 41a). Menke suggested that the grana may be, quite generally, only bulbous parts of the lamellae, as illustrated by schematic figure 41b.

We will see in the next section that for a while electron microscopy has centered all attention on the grana and the stacks of thin lamellae or discs of which these bodies appear to be constructed. More recently, however, several observers have obtained electron micrographs, of sec-

* Bibliography, page 1775.

tioned chloroplasts of certain species showing a laminated structure extending through the whole chloroplast, without grana, similar to Menke's ultraviolet micrograph of the *Anthoceros* chloroplast in figure 41a. This attracts new interest to the observation of chloroplasts under the light microscope, where the relationship between granulated and laminated structure can be studied under more nearly natural conditions and on a much wider scale.

The first question is whether it is true that the grana in granular chloroplasts are arranged in several planes parallel to the large cross section of the chloroplast? If this is the case, is there evidence that the individual grana are not independent bodies, but hang together as parts of a continuous layer (which could be conceivably destroyed in the preparation of objects for electron microscopy)? Heitz, the discoverer (or more properly, rediscoverer) of the grana, saw them arranged in layers, giving the chloroplasts a laminated appearance when looked upon from the side (fig. 39c). Similar layers are easily recognizable on some electron micrographs, *cf.* fig. 37A.18.

Strugger (1950) saw, in the exceptionally large chloroplasts of *Dracaena*, that the grana, in addition to belonging to several distinct layers in the "horizontal" plane, were also arrayed in "vertical" columns, one above the other. This arrangement was confirmed, in a renewed study, in isolated chloroplasts from the same plant (1951). Plastids were suspended in 0.2 M sucrose solution to prevent swelling; they could then be seen clearly, under the light microscope, to contain green grana amidst a colorless stroma. Strugger noted that moving the depth of the focus did not change the position of the green spots—indicating that they formed vertical columns continued through the whole depth of the chloroplast. The same arrangement was directly visible in chloroplasts lying on their side; selective staining of the grana with rhodamin B made the picture even clearer. (It may be asked, however, whether the columnar arrangement of the grana is a general rule; conceivably, it may be a response to intense illumination, similar to the phototactic redistribution of whole chloroplasts in the cell.) When, in Strugger's experiments, water was substituted for 0.2 M sucrose solution as the suspension medium, chloroplasts as were seen to swell in the direction of the short axis, the columnar arrangement of the grana was disturbed, and the plastids disintegrated into lamellae which seemed to carry the grana in them. Upon still further swelling, the grana ceased to be visible.

The same type of structure could be observed also in leaf sections containing undamaged cells, with various *Lilleiflorae*, as well as with about 60 species from 59 other families. The "carrier lamellae" in which the grana are imbedded, according to Strugger (like pills in cellophane sheets in certain pharmaceutical preparations), cannot be recognized *in vivo*, but the columnar arrangement of the grana in living chloroplasts is clearly visible in side view. Large starch grains sometimes push the grana-carrying layers apart, thus disrupting the columns (fig. 37A.1).

Fig. 37A.1. Microscopic view of the chloroplasts of *Glecoma heder-acea* from the top (at left) and from the side (at right), showing starch bodies pushing apart layers of grana and thus interrupting their columnar arrangement (after Strugger 1951).

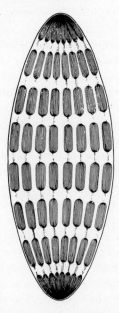

Fig. 37A.2. Chloroplast model, showing grana arranged in layers and supported by thin, colorless lamellae. Grana in all layers from vertical columns (after Strugger 1951).

Strugger made experiments on chloroplast fixation, and confirmed earlier findings (Meyer, Heitz) that 2% OsO_4 is a satisfactory reagent for the preservation of chloroplast structure (better than picric acid and other commonly used fixatives). Such jellied preparations could not be stained directly, but only after slight preliminary swelling with KOH (1%); after this pretreatment the grana, stained with neutral red at pH 7, appeared dark red; they were then seen still forming columns (if viewed sideways), but the distance between the grana in each column appeared wider the more prolonged the swelling.

From these experiments, Strugger derived the hypothetical model of a chloroplast reproduced in figure 37A.2, showing carrier lamellae, grana imbedded in them, and columnar arrangement of the latter. He was certain that each chloroplast is surrounded by a proteinaceous membrane, quoting, in support of this view, the observed formation of vacuoles inside the chloroplasts, and the separation of the membrane from the chloroplast content in some pathological conditions.

In connection with this model of the chloroplast, Strugger (1950, 1951) developed a theory of the morphogenesis of the chloroplasts and grana, according to which they develop from amoeboid "proplastides," containing a single "plastidogen disc"; the chloroplasts arise by division of this "gene-like" body, which is followed by the division of the stroma. In the metamorphosis of the protoplastid into a mature chloroplast, the "plastidogen" disc divides into grana, which fill up the chloroplast body.

Strugger believes that the grana-carrying laminae, although colorless, are distinct from the—also colorless—stroma, and that the photosynthesis proper is associated with the laminae, while the starch synthesis takes place in the stroma; he referred in this connection to the work of Schmidt (1951), showing that photosynthesis can continue even when the stroma is swollen by osmotic pressure, and the lamellae separated from each other.

Rezende-Pinto (1948, 1949, 1952[1,2,3]) developed, also from light microscopic observations, a different picture of chloroplast structure: he placed all grana in a single band—a "chloroplastoneme" winding, as a spiral, around the inner core of the chloroplast containing the stroma and starch grains. Several such bands were postulated to exist in elongated chloroplasts (e. g., those of Spirogyra). These pictures were said to interpret satisfactorily the observed birefringence of the chloroplasts.

However, electron microscopic evidence clearly shows that grana are distributed throughout the whole body of the chloroplast. One question which seems to have been clarified by the above described (and other) microscopic observations is the distribution of chlorophyll between the grana and the stroma. In Chapter 14 (section A2) we mentioned that microscopic observations indicated the concentration of chlorophyll in the grana, but that sometime the stroma also appeared colored—perhaps by scattering. Jungers and Doutreligne (1943) observed that in faintly green, starch-filled chloroplasts, with only a single layer of grana visible against the background of starch, green coloration was clearly restricted to the grana. We mentioned above the finding of Strugger (1950, 1951) that when the grana are arranged in columns the areas between the columns appear colorless. Fluorescence-microscopic observations of Strugger (1951) and Düvel and Mevins (1952) confirmed the report of Metzner (*cf.* p. 362) that (contrary to some earlier findings of Lloyd) the chlorophyll fluorescence is restricted to the grana. We will see in section 2 that electron microscopy supplies an indirect support for the assumption that all chlorophyll is located in the grana.

2. Electron Microscopy

While light microscopy permits observation of the chloroplast structure under more nearly natural conditions than electron microscopy, it pushes the capacity for visual discrimination to its limit, where interpretations tend to become subjective and generalizations uncertain. Electron microscopy, on the other hand, gives objectively precise shapes of even much smaller structural elements, but does it only after the cell has been destroyed mechanically and subjected to drying in vacuum.

(*a*) *Structure*

In Volume I on pages 363–364 are two early pictures of chloroplasts under the electron microscope—a photograph of the edge of a chloroplast from a mosaic-diseased tobacco leaf, by Kausche and Ruska (1940), showing the presence of large, thin lamellae (thickness 0.1 μ, diameter $\sim$1 μ); and a photograph by Roberts (1944) of a single chloroplast disintegrated into a conglomerate of grana of various size, from 0.02 to 0.5 μ in diameter.

Much more detailed and revealing studies of chloroplast structure have been made since. Granick and Porter (1947) used spinach. Its saucer-shaped chloroplasts were found to swell in distilled water, their content became clearly granular, and flat protrusions or "blebs"—probably related to Kausche and Ruska's "lamellae"—appeared on their surface, the larger ones on the concave side of the saucer. No swelling occurred in 0.5 M sucrose, suggesting that the chloroplasts were enclosed in a membrane. Material most clearly showing the grana could be prepared by macerating turgid leaves in a Waring Blendor in 0.05 M phosphate solution (pH 6.5), at 5° C. The suspension was filtered through cheesecloth, and the filtrate centrifuged at 200 g. to remove whole cells, crystals, and other heavy material. Sedimentation at higher speed was then used to precipitate chloroplasts and their fragments, containing grana.

It was noted that, when chloroplasts were separated from the plasma by this procedure, the absorption peak of chlorophyll shifted from 681 to 679 mμ, and fluorescence intensity increased. This may indicate that a change in the pigment-protein-lipide complex had occurred during separation; however, the product was "intact" to the extent of still giving a strong Hill reaction (reduction of ferric oxalate with the liberation of oxygen in light).

Fig. 37A.3. Electron micrograph of a maize chloroplast (unshadowed). The darker circular areas are the grana (after Vatter 1952).

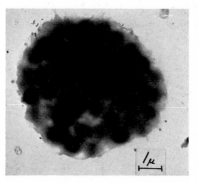

Fig. 37A.4. Electron micrograph of a maize chloroplast showing grana (shadowed). From fifty to two hundred grana may be present in one plastid (after Vatter 1952).

Fig. 37A.5. Electron micrograph of the edge of a maize chloroplast exposed to OsO_4 vapor after isolation prior to drying. Folded "blebs" or "vesicles" are common in materials prepared by this method (after Vatter 1952).

Perhaps the band shift was only an apparent one, caused by diminished scattering.

A drop of the chloroplast suspension was placed on a plastic film spread over a fine wire mesh and dried. Under the electron microscope (without metal shadowing), the residue presented a picture similar to that shown in figure 37A.3. The darker grana (about 40–60 of them are present in spinach chloroplasts, about 50–200 in maize chloroplasts, used in fig. 37A.3) are rather uniform in shape and size; they are embedded in a less dense "stroma." Shadowing (deposition of a thin film from a parallel stream of heavy metal atoms impinging on the specimen under an angle) clearly shows the greater thickness of the grana as compared to the matrix (see fig. 37A.4).

Fig. 37A.6. Electron micrograph of grana of maize (shadowed). Note the different thicknesses of the grana, which seem to bear no relation to their diameter. (Perhaps the thinner bodies are residues from partially scattered grana.) (After Vatter 1952.)

From the angle of shadow cast and the length of the shadow, the height of the grana can be estimated as being of the order of 0.1 μ (0.05–0.30 μ); their average diameter is about 0.6 μ. (It should be kept in mind that these are dimensions determined in the dried, and therefore more or less shrunken, state.)

Granick and Porter's photomicrographs showed, in addition to grana, also round or oval, partly folded "blebs," which they thought consisted of vacuolated and collapsed stroma material. Figure 37A.5 shows these forms in maize chloroplasts.

Washing a chloroplast film with methanol visibly leaches out the pigments—and probably other lipophilic materials as well. Under the electron microscope, leached grana appeared to Granick and Porter to have lost much of their density and to have shrunk considerably, thus confirming

Weier's conclusion (Vol. I, chapter 14) that they contain much lipide material. In Granick's shadowed preparations, the leached grana were scarcely distinguishable from the matrix. What remains of the grana after leaching probably consists of proteins, about as dense as those which form the matrix. Granick and Porter estimated, from these observations, that less than one-half of the grana material is proteidic.

Fig. 37A.7. Electron micrograph of macromolecules in stroma of a maize chloroplast isolated in methanol. The size of the macromolecules varies from less than 10 mμ to more than 50 mμ depending on the solvent or buffer in which the plastids were isolated (after Vatter 1952).

So-called "grana" preparations, obtained by Granick and Porter, according to Aronoff's prescriptions (cf. Chapter 35, page 1556), showed, under the electron microscope, mostly fragmented chloroplasts in which clusters of grana were still embedded in matrix material. Whether the presence of the latter—which is difficult to remove altogether—is essential for the Hill reaction, is an interesting question.

Algera, Beijer, van Iterson, Karstens and Thung (1947) obtained microphotographs very similar to those of Granick and Porter, and showing some details in greater clarity. They used tulip leaves, ground in a mincer while sodium carbonate solution was added dropwise to a pH of 6.0. After passing through cheesecloth, the opalescent suspension was centrifuged at 3000 r.p.m. By resuspending in 10% sucrose solution and precipitating several times in a slow-speed centrifuge, a material consisting of intact, whole chloroplasts could be obtained. Figure 37A.4 (Vatter 1952) is similar to those of Algera *et al.*, showing shadowed grana in a whole chloroplast. Figure 37A.6 is a shadow-cast preparation of a disintegrated chloroplast, showing grana—flat cylinders about 0.6 μ in diameter. Figure 37A.7 represents the stroma ("matrix") material, photographed with a higher magnification, and revealing, in the "blebs" and scattered all over the film, small spherical granules about 0.025 μ in diameter. According to Vatter (1952), these globular molecules vary in size from 10 to 50 mμ, depending on the solvent used in the extraction of lipides.

Algera *et al.* suggested that the "lamellae" or "blebs" are similar to, or identical with, the "myelin tubes" observed under the light microscope in whole chloroplasts and illustrated in figure 47 in Volume I (p. 375); the latter had been interpreted as swollen phosphatides. Algera *et al.* pointed out that the "blebs" often are larger in diameter than the original chloroplast, and thus must be artefacts.

However, one has to be careful and distinguish between the many different thin objects seen in the electron micrographs of chloroplasts. Some of these objects are folded, others smooth; some granular, others uniform; some large and varied in size and shape (usually round or oval, but sometimes streaky or fibrous), others small and uniform in size. The only thing they have in common is that they are thin compared to the grana.

The *very large, folded objects* may be chloroplast membranes, from which the content has leaked out. Frey-Wyssling and Mühlethaler (1949) published electron micrographs (of tobacco chloroplasts) showing all grana enclosed in a large, folded membrane bag. They pointed out that, to form folds, this membrane must be half-solid, *i. e.*, a gel. It may be formed by fibrous proteins; Thomas, Bustraan and Paris (1952) noted that chloroplast membrane bags remain whole after extraction with benzene, and that fragments of them are visible after digestion with lipase. They suggested that the chloroplast membrane—similar to the erythrocyte membrane— consists of a "skeleton" of fibrous proteins supporting a delicate lipide "epilemma."

However, Vatter (1952) could obtain folded membranes only in preparations fixed with osmic acid (fig. 37A.5), or exposed to concentrated buffers, and suggested that they are precipitation artifacts.

The same opinion was expressed by Leyon (1953[1], *cf.* below) and later also by Frey-Wyssling and Steinmann (1953). The latter pointed out that even if the folded bags, which on some micrographs seem to enclose all grana, prove to be artifacts formed when the outer layer of the stroma comes in contact with a changed medium (such as distilled water), this does not mean that in the natural state chloroplasts do *not* have a membrane; but merely that it has not yet been possible to demonstrate its existence.

A second type of thin structure, repeatedly observed in electron micrographs of disintegrated chloroplasts, are *small round discs*, with a diameter

Fig. 37A.8. Electron micrograph of a maize granum that has become dissociated into discs (after Vatter 1952).

Fig. 37A.9. Electron micrographs howing the not-folded blebs that surrounded a maize chloroplast isolated in distilled water and then dried (after Vatter 1952). Compare with fig. 37A.5.

about equal to that of a single granum. They often appear in groups of 15 to 50, looking like a scattered money roll. These rolls are very clearly visible in pictures of maize chloroplasts taken by Vatter (1952), of which fig. 37A.8 is a good example, but were first noted by Frey-Wyssling and Mühlethaler, (1949), who used tobacco leaves. Frey-Wyssling interpreted them as protein lamellae, which he assumed to be stacked in the intact granum, like layers in a cake, held together by interlarded layers of lipide material.   When the latter is extracted by solvents, or oozes out in the drying process, the discs become loosened, the granum sags, and occasionally overturns, scattering the protein discs over the film.

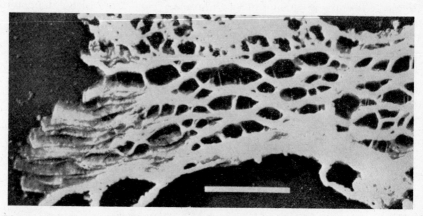

Fig. 37A.10. Cross section through *Spirogyra* chloroplast fixed for 10 min. in 1% OsO_4, showing disintegration into band-shaped laminae (after Steinmann 1952[1]).

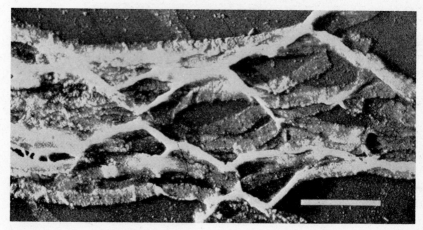

Fig. 37A.11. Cross section through *Mougeotia* chloroplast, fixed for 45 min. in 1% OsO_4, showing disintegration into band-shaped laminae (after Steinmann 1952[1]).

The much *larger*, also thin, *non-folded structures*, usually round or oval, but occasionally streaky or fibrous (Vatter 1952, and Thomas *et al.* 1952, *cf.* fig. 37A.9), were interpreted by Frey-Wyssling as dried-out residues of lipide drops. Most of these large myelin "pancakes" lie free on the film, but some seem to protrude from grana, like ham slices from a sandwich. This supports Frey-Wyssling's suggestion that some "myelin" material originates in the grana. However, estimates of the total amount of lipide in grana and in the stroma (*cf.* below) convinced Frey-Wyssling that this cannot be true of *all* myelin; rather, a large part of it must come from the stroma. The above-mentioned small granules, embedded in the "myelin" masses, or scattered on the supporting film, are, according to Frey-Wyssling, globular protein molecules, originally associated with the lipides in the lipoproteinaceous stroma.

The grana and the discs, into which they disintegrate, appeared as the most striking—and potentially significant—structures in the photosynthetic apparatus. It was therefore important to establish whether they occur in all photosynthesizing organisms.

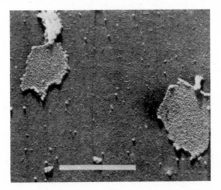

Fig. 37A.12. Irregularly shaped patches obtained by sonic disintegration of laminar chloroplasts of *Spirogyra*, fixed for 15 min. in 1% OsO₄ (*cf.* Figure 37A.13) (after Steinmann 1952[1]).

Thomas (1952) published electron micrographs showing the presence of grana in higher plants (*Spinacia oleracea*), green algae (*Chlorella vulgaris*), blue-green algae (*Synochoccus* spp.), red algae (*Porphyridium cruentum*), diatoms (*Nitzchia*), purple bacteria (*Chromatium* D, *Rhodospirillum rubrum*), and green sulfur bacteria. The diameter of the grana reproduced in his paper ranges from 1.3 μ (*Nitzschia*), through 0.7 μ (*Porphyridium*), 0.6 μ (*Chlorella, Syncechococcus*), and 0.4 μ (*Spinacia*), to about 0.15 μ in bacteria. Another set of electron micrographs of material obtained from the same organisms shows thinner, round bodies of the same diameter. These are interpreted by Thomas as single protein discs from disintegrated grana; however, on some photographs (in particular, those of purple and green bacteria), the distinction in thickness between the "grana" and the "discs" is not very great, at least in the reproductions.

Colorless bacteria showed no grana, but small grana were found in the colorless alga, *Prototheca zopfii*.

These electron microscope observations were supported by ultracentrifuge studies (to be described in section 3), also indicating the presence of grana in blue-green algae and purple bacteria. However, just when one may have become inclined to postulate that the grana are universal (and therefore probably indispensable) elements of the photosynthetic apparatus, complications appeared.

Steinmann (1952[1]) found in the large, spiral band-shaped chloroplasts of the algae *Spirogyra* and *Mougeotia*, fixed in 1% OsO₄, a lamellar structure extending through the whole chloroplast, without evidence of grana.

Fig. 37A.13. A circular lamella ("disc") from the granum of a tulip chlorplast, fixed 25 min. in 1% OsO₄ and disintegrated by sonic oscillations (after Steinmann 1952[2]). Note granulated surface. Compare with Fig. 37A.12.

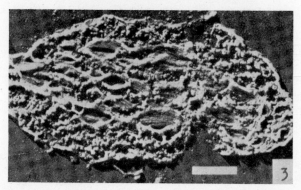

Fig. 37A.14. Cross section of a tulip chloroplast fixed for 15 min. in 1% OsO₄, showing laminated grana imbedded in granulated stroma (after Steinmann 1952[2]).

The lamellar structure is clearly visible on longitudinal sections of such fixed *Spirogyra* chloroplasts (fig. 37A.10). *Mougeotia* chloroplasts easily disintegrated into long, narrow bands (fig. 37A.11). By sonic vibrations, these bands could be further disrupted into irregular-shaped patches (fig. 37A.12), the thinnest of which were about 7 mμ thick, *i. e.*, of the same thickness as the "discs" in the grana.

Albertson and Leyon (1954) reproduced a very interesting electron micrograph of a fixed and sectioned *Chlorella* cell, showing that the cup-shaped chloroplast consists of 4–6 dark shells, each about 35 mμ thick, separated by lighter layers of about the same thickness. Each dark shell seems, in its turn, to consist of several (usually four) thinner shells each about 5 mμ thick. No grana are visible in the picture.

On the other hand, stacks of disc-shaped lamellae (of the type of those shown in fig. 37A.8) were obtained, in the same study by Steinmann, from

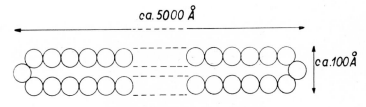

Fig. 37A.15. Idealized cross section of a granum disc, consisting of two monolayers of macromolecules (after Frey-Wyssling and Steinmann 1953). As observed under the electron microscope, the discs are only 50–70 Å. thick because of shrinkage.

Aspidistra chloroplasts; they contained up to 40 thin discs of uniform diameter. Figures 37A.18a and 37A.18b show the cross section of lamellae in fixed and sectioned chloroplasts of a higher plant according to Palade (1953).

Steinmann drew attention to the occurrence of lamellar structure in visual rods, and suggested that this similarity may have something to do with the common purpose of the two cellular structures—utilization of light energy.

In another note, Steinmann (1952[2]) showed that single thin round protein discs can be obtained from granular chloroplasts (*e. g.*, those of tulip, or *Aspidistra*) by sonic disintegration (fig. 37A.13). Electron micrographs of sections through fixed tulip chloroplasts clearly showed that such discs are the structural elements of intact grana. Incidentally, these electromicrographs—*cf.* fig. 37A.14—also confirmed the layered arrangement of the grana in each chloroplast, first noted by Heitz on ultraviolet micrographs (*cf.* fig. 39c in Vol. I).

No carrier lamellae which support the grana in a layer, according to Strugger (1951), are visible on fig. 37A.13. Leyon (1954[1]) noted, however, that in *Aspidistra elatior*, the lamellae within the grana extend from it into the surrounding stroma, the grana being merely regions of accentuated lamination.

Frey-Wyssling and Steinmann (1953) suggested that the discs (thickness, 7–10 mμ) obtained by disintegration of grana from the chloroplasts of

Aspidistra, consist of only two layers of macromolecules, as represented schematically in fig. 37A.15. (The same structure can be suggested also for the bands or shells of approximately the same thickness, observed in *Mougeotia* and *Chlorella*, respectively.)

This conclusion was drawn from the observation of the transformation of the grana, suspended in 1 *M* sucrose solution, caused by dilution with water. Under the phase contrast microscope the grana could be seen swelling, flaking off, and growing into long strands; the fluorescence microscope

Fig. 37A.16. Chains of collapsed bags, obtained from a granum of *Aspidistra* by treatment in distilled water (after Frey-Wyssling and Steinmann 1953). Fixed in 1% OsO₄, chromium shadowed. It is suggested that this is a "money roll" (Fig. 37A.8) in which each protein "coin" has swelled up by penetration of water between two monolayers (Fig. 37A.15), precipitation membrane has formed on the outside, and the bags have collapsed.

showed that the latter still carried the chlorophyll. Under the electron microscope the strands appeared to consist of round, collapsed, and folded bags, about 1 μ in diameter (fig. 37A.16). These bags were interpreted as the protein "discs," similar to those shown in fig. 37A.8, which had swollen into bubbles in water and then collapsed. The growth and collapse of the grana bags was considered by Frey-Wyssling and Steinmann as an indication that the grana had originally consisted of two layers of macromolecules (as shown in fig. 37A.15) which have been pushed apart by the osmotic pressure of water penetrating into the space between them. The fine granulation, observed on the best electron micrographs of the grana surface, suggests that these macromolecules are spherical; they could not yet be measured exactly, but certainly are under 0.01 μ in diameter, and must therefore have a molecular weight of <400,000.

The "laminated" chloroplast structure again appeared in Wolken and Palade's (1952, 1953) investigation of two flagellates—protozoans which become autotrophically active when exposed to light, but switch to heterotrophic metabolism in darkness. The organisms used were *Euglena gracilis*, which, in the active state, measures about $70 \times 20 \ \mu$ and contains 8–12 chloroplasts, and *Poteriochromonas stipitata*, a much smaller, round cell, with usually only two chloroplasts.

The cells were fixed with 1% OsO_4 at pH 7–8, swelling being prevented by the addition of sucrose. The preparations were embedded in plastic and sectioned to 0.1 μ thickness, or thinner. The chloroplasts of active

Fig. 37A.17. Section of an *Aspidistra* chloroplast fixed in formaldehyde solution showing continuous laminar structure interrupted by starch grains (Leyon 1953[1]).

Euglena appeared as cylindrical bodies, 0.5–1.5 μ by 5–10 μ in longitudinal cross section. They showed faint lamination under the phase contrast microscope, and double refraction in the polarization microscope. Electron microscopy showed a laminated structure of the chloroplasts *as a whole*, without subdivision into grana. The lamina were 18–32 $m\mu$ thick—considerably thicker than the "discs" into which grana-bearing chloroplasts disintegrate ($< 10 \ m\mu$). The lamina were separated by interstitial spaces 30–50 $m\mu$ in width. The layers were even thicker in *Poteriochromonas;* an indication of a further substructure (a central layer of lighter material, and two denser outside layers) could be discerned in them.

After 7 days dark growth, the *Euglena* chloroplasts vanished altogether, while those of *Poteriochromonas* appeared to have shrunk and lost their structure. Laminated structure reappeared after 4 hours exposure to light.   At first, the laminae were thinner and wider-spaced than in fully light-adapted cells; the original structure was restored only after 72 hours in light.   Spectroscopic observations showed that some chlorophyll remained in the cells after complete dark adaptation; the pigment content declined during the first few hours in light, and only then began to grow, particularly rapidly on the second day of the exposure.   This shows that the formation of the laminae is not related to the synthesis of chlorophyll.

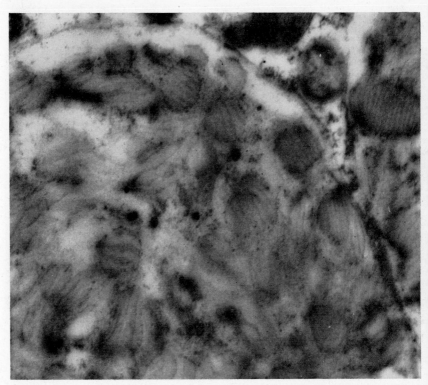

Fig. 37A.18a. Layered structure of grana in chloroplasts of a higher plant.   Sectioned parallel to the large cross-section of the chloroplasts (Palade 1953).

Leyon (1953[1]) showed that the same species may exhibit both granular and laminated chloroplasts.   He investigated chloroplasts from *Beta saccharifera* and *Aspidistra elatior*, fixed, embedded in plastic, and sectioned.   On cross sections normal to the large plane of the chloroplast, the layers sometimes appeared continuous, interrupted only by starch deposits (fig. 37A.17).   Yet, the same plant produced also typical "money rolls" of disc-shaped lamellae, consisting of 50 or 60 discs of equal diameter, apparently originating from a granum.   This suggested that a change from granular to laminated structure (or *vice versa*) may be the result of aging,

or other changes in the physiological conditions in the cell. This led Leyon
(1953[2]) to an electron micrographic study of the development of the
chloroplasts. He used leaves of *Vallota speciosa* growing in light, and
Taraxacum grown in darkness—the former containing much, the latter
little assimilation products. In young leaves he found "proplastids"

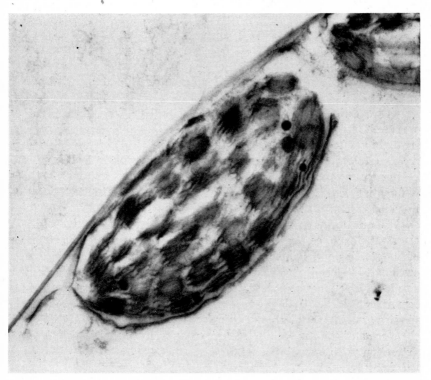

Fig. 37A.18b. Same as in fig. 37A.18a, but sectioned normal to the large plane.

showing a laminated structure. The continuous stratification was interrupted, in these proplastids, only by irregularly occurring, unstructured
bodies of assimilates. The grana appeared in mature leaves. Menke, as
well as Strugger (*cf.* Strugger 1950), had suggested that grana first arise as
nodules in continuous laminae (figs. 40b and 37A.2), and remain suspended
in the latter, even when mature; but Leyon, similarly to Steinmann, could
see no evidence of the existence of supporting laminae in mature granulated chloroplasts. He suggested that, in a certain stage of development,
continuous laminae break up into packages of stacked discs—perhaps torn
apart by the pressure of the accumulated assimilates.

Further studies of the development of the chloroplasts by Leyon (1954), this time on *Aspidistra elatior*, produced a very beautiful sequence of pictures, showing first a few folded lamellae which rapidly multiply into a packed group and finally fill the whole chloroplast, which then appears like a carefully combed wig. The grana appear in these chloroplasts only as more or less clearly outlined areas, of circular cross-section, in which the striation is accentuated by greater thickness of the lamellae and greater regularity of their parallel arrangement. The lamellae continue into the intergranular space, where single lamellae often become paired into double sheets.*

Thomas (1954) suggested that "grana free" chloroplasts should be considered as single, giant grana.

The question of the origin of grana—as well as of the chloroplast as a whole—is in need of more study; the surmise that "chloroplasts arise only by division of chloroplasts, and grana only by division of grana," is by no means established (and in the case of grana, most likely incorrect). We cannot enter here into these problems of cytogenetics and morphological differentiation (*cf.*, for example, their review in the article by Weier and Stocking, 1952).

We must now say a few words on the so far rather neglected subject of the structure of the *stroma*. It was stated above that it seems to consist of lipoproteids, not stainable by lipide-soluble dyes, and to give rise, upon swelling to "blebs," "pancakes," and "myelin figures," of widely varying size in which numerous spherical macromolecules (probably, lipoproteids) remain imbedded. Under certain conditions, the stroma can produce also fibrillar proteinaceous structures, first observed by Thomas *et al.* (1952) in the stroma of spinach chloroplasts after the removal of lipoids by acetone extraction or digestion by lipase.

Bustraan, Goedheer and Thomas (1952) found that these structures—similar to those observed in certain cytoplasmic preparations—consist of beads ("chromidia") about 0.12 μ in diameter, strung together on threads ("interchromidia"). Bustraan *et al.* measured the optical density of the "chromidia" and "interchormidia" on non-shadowed micrographs, and their thickness on metal-shadowed micrographs, and concluded that the material of the chromidia is denser by about $1/3$ (after acetone treatment) or $1/2$ (after lipase treatment) than that of the interchromidia.

In Frey-Wyssling and Steinmann's (1953) electron micrograph of a cross section of a fixed tulip chloroplast, laminar grana are seen imbedded in a granular stroma. (As mentioned above, no carrier laminae, postulated by Strugger, are noticeable on this photograph, and the arrangement of the grana does not suggest their existence.)

Frey-Wyssling and Steinmann noted that the stroma has a much

* Results obtained with new methods of fixation and sectioning, and clearly showing the relation of granular to laminar structures, are briefly reported on p. 1986, *cf.* Figs. 38.1–38.4.

greater tendency for swelling than the grana; round protrusions on the chloroplast surface can be noticed even in 0.5 M sucrose. This is not due to myelin formation, since the latter requires a separation of lipides from the proteins, and does not occur in neutral sugar solutions; rather, the lipoproteids swell as a whole. This swelling produces bubbles of widely varying size; after their surface had solidified, the bubbles collapse, and appear as folded membranes. When such a large collapsed bubble covers the whole chloroplast, it appears as a chloroplast membrane.

Unlike the collapsed bubbles, the myelin figures (*cf.* fig. 32A.5) do not fold on the object holder.

As the swelling proceeds, the grana join in it, and after some time may cease to be visible as such, their proteins having been incorporated in the bubbles and the collapsed precipitation membranes.

(b) *Shape, Dimensions and Composition*

Several estimates have been made of the total volume occupied by the grana and the stroma, and the absolute amounts of proteinaceous and lipide material in these two parts of the chloroplast. The conclusions varied rather widely, an important source of uncertainty being the fact that size estimates made by measuring out electron micrographs apply to dry material, in which the different parts of the chloroplast had shrunk by unknown (and undoubtedly different) factors.

In making these estimates, one also has to keep in mind the above-described variations in the size of grana from species to species, and their change with the physiological state of the cell. The following calculations (Rabinowitch 1952) apply primarily to chloroplasts of the higher plants.

Typical mature chloroplasts of higher plants contain from 20 to more than 200 cylindrical grana, 0.5–1 μ in diameter and 0.1–0.2 μ in height (measured in the dry state!). The average volume of such a dry granum is about 0.05 μ^3; that of one hundred of them 5 μ^3. This is about 15% of the volume of a fresh chloroplast (about 30 μ^3). However, the grana dimensions—the height, in particular—undoubtedly are larger in "live" grana, because of the loss of water (and probably also of fluid lipides) during the drying in vacuum. Therefore, the part of the chloroplast volume occupied by the grana in the living cell undoubtedly is larger than 15%—but how much larger we do not know. Frey-Wyssling and Mühlethaler (1949) used a figure of 50% by weight—which means <50% by volume, because of the higher density of the grana compared to the stroma. In a later paper, Frey-Wyssling (1949) used a much lower estimate (only 6% of the total chloroplast volume occupied by the grana); but this figure seems to be incompatible with the large amount of chlorophyll that has to find place in the grana (*cf.* below).

All these calculations have a wide range of uncertainty, particularly if they combine chloroplast *numbers*, counted by one observer in one plant, with chloroplast *dimensions*, determined by someone else on another plant, and *grana dimensions*, measured by a third person with still different plant material. For example, values between 20 and 50 μ^3 can be used for the chloroplast volume, those between 50 and 200 for the number of grana in a chloroplast, and those between 0.03 and 0.1 μ^3 for the volume of a granum

Starch-free chloroplasts are known to contain, under normal conditions of nutrition, 50–60% of "proteinaceous" and 30–44% of "lipide" material (*cf.* below). The "lipides"—*i. e.*, compounds soluble in ether or alcohol, including chlorophylls and the carotenoids—appear to be more abundant in the grana than in the stroma. However, it was mentioned above that the grana cannot be purely lipide and the stroma purely proteinaceous (as one may be tempted to suggest), for two reasons: First, the total content of lipides in the chloroplasts is so high that all of them cannot find place in the grana; second, grana are still visible after treatment with lipophilic solvents, indicating that they contain a proteinaceous "skeleton." Certain lipophilic stains, such as Sudan red, color only the grana (*cf.* Vol. I, p. 361) this does not prove, according to Frey-Wyssling, that the stroma is lipide free, but can be explained by the assumption that the stroma lipides are tied up in lipoproteins.

Dispersion and fractionation of chloroplast material has never yet produced a purely lipide or a purely proteinaceous pigment-bearing fraction The "chloroplastin" of Stoll (*cf.* Vol. 1, p. 385 and section 6(*a*) below) contained proteins, pigments, and lipophilic materials in approximately the same proportion as whole chloroplasts. Similarly, no significant shifts in the [nitrogen] : [chlorophyll] ratio could be observed in the fractionation of dispersed chloroplast material by French, Holt and others (*cf.* Chapter 35 pages 1555–1556).

It was postulated by Hubert (1936) and Frey-Wyssling (1938) that grana contain proteinaceous and lipide material in the form of alternate layers, with chlorophyll molecules attached to protein layers by their chlorophyllin "heads" (made polar by the presence of magnesium and of carbonyl groups), and to lipide layer by their non-polar phytol "tails."

Granick and Porter pointed out that, if less than one-half of the grana material is proteinaceous, and all pigments are concentrated in the grana the ratio [protein] : [chlorophyll] in the grana must be less than one-half of the average—in itself very low—ratio of these two components in the chloroplasts as a whole. (For the discussion of this ratio, see Vol. 1, p. 389.) Frey-Wyssling (1953) estimated that grana contain 9 chlorophyll molecules per "Svedberg unit" of protein (table 14.IX shows other estimates, ranging from 1 to 22).

Fully green chloroplasts contain, on the average, 10–15% chlorophyll and other pigments (in relation to dry weight). This corresponds to about 1–2 $\times$ 10⁹ pigment molecules per chloroplast, or an average pigment concentration of 0.05–0.1 mole/liter.

In a single granum, the number of pigment molecules should be of the order of 1–2 $\times$ 10⁷, and the chlorophyll concentration in them must be 0.2–0.4 mole/liter. Grana probably are denser and contain less water than the predominantly proteinaceous phases of the cell (the stroma and the cytoplasm); nevertheless, for the chlorophyll concentration in them to reach 0.2–0.4 M, the proportion of chlorophyll by weight in the dry matter of the grana must be very high—perhaps as high as 20 or 30%.

With a concentration of chlorophyll in the granum of the order of 0.2–0.4 mole/liter, the distance between the centers of two nearest chlorophyll molecules (and also the average distance from a molecule of a carotenoid, or phycobilin, to the nearest chlorophyll molecule) should be about 20 Å—if these molecules are distributed at random. Because the pigment molecules probably are arranged in layers, the distance between the centers of two nearest chlorophyll molecules in a layer probably is much shorter than 20 Å.

If one considers the granum as a disc 0.6 μ in diameter, its two large surfaces have a total area of 0.5 μ^2. According to surface film measurements of Hanson (Vol. 1, p. 449), chlorophyll molecules, stacked like books on a half-filled shelf, require an area of about 1 mμ^2 apiece. That means that not more than 5 $\times$ 10⁵ chlorophyll molecules could find place in the two surface layers of the granum, and that at least 20 parallel layers of these molecules must be present in each of them. The thin discs into which grana have been observed to disintegrate, might then contain one or two layers of chlorophyll molecules each—perhaps one layer on each side of the disc (as suggested in Frey-Wyssling's and Steinmann's model, cf. fig. 37A.15).

Wolken (1954) made similar estimates for the continuous laminae in the non-granulated chloroplast of *Euglena* and *Poteriochromonas*. Each *Euglena* chloroplast contained 18–24 bands, 18–25 mμ thick, separated by layers of "stroma" 30–50 mμ thick. The chlorophyll content of a chloroplast was estimated by Wolken as 0.88–1.23 $\times$ 10⁹ molecules (average chlorophyll concentration in *Euglena*, 0.025 mole/liter). In *Poteriochromonas*, the number of bands was 9–11 per chloroplast, the band thickness 21–50 mμ, their separation 25–51 mμ, and the chlorophyll concentration 2.2 $\times$ 10⁸ molecules per chloroplast, or 0.016 mole/liter for the cell as a whole. (In both flagellates, the average chlorophyll concentration is considerably lower than in green plant cells.)

From the average length and width of the lamina, Wolken estimated that a surface area of 222 Å^2 is available per chlorophyll molecule in

Euglena, and one of 246 Å² in *Poteriochromonas*. This, he suggested, is just enough for a monomolecular layer of chlorophyll molecules, assuming that their porphyrin ring systems *lie flat on the surface*.

The smaller surface area of the lamellae in flagellates, compared to that of the discs in granular chloroplasts, caused by the greater thickness of the laminae, is more than compensated, in the calculation of the area per molecule, by the much smaller number of chlorophyll molecules to be accommodated per unit chloroplast volume.

These estimates can be compared with the observations of chlorophyll monolayers on water (Chapter 16, p. 449), and Chapter 32, section 5). As noted in Chapter 32, chlorophyll layers of "crystalline" type cannot be present in the living cell, because their absorption band lies at or beyond 725 mμ. Monomolecular layers of the "compressed gas" type, on the other hand, have—similarly to chlorophyll *in vivo*—an absorption peak at about 670 mμ. The surface requirements of chlorophyll molecules in such layers (about 1.1 mμ²) is not incompatible with the above calculations for the grana discs, and more than ample for Wolken's calculations for layered chloroplasts. (In these monolayers, chlorophyll molecules do not lie flat, but stand on edge like books on a half-filled shelf.) The possible significance of a dense two-dimensional arrangement of chlorophyll molecules for the excitation energy migration *in vivo* was discussed in Chapter 32.

(c) *Location of Chlorophyll*

In section 1, we described light-microscopic and fluorescence-microscopic evidence indicating the concentration of chlorophyll in the grana and its absence in the stroma. Electron microscopy cannot answer the question of chlorophyll location directly, but an ingenious indirect method can be used. It has been described in Chapter 14 that silver nitrate is reduced by chloroplasts to metallic silver even in strongly acid solution ("*Molisch reaction*"), and that this reaction is accelerated by light. If this silver precipitation is a photochemical process sensitized by chlorophyll, silver should be deposited in the vicinity of the pigment, and could be used as its "tracer" on electron micrographs. The "silver grana" observed in some experiments (*cf.* fig. 40) would then be silver-coated chloroplast grana.

More recently, the silver precipitation by chloroplasts was studied by several authors using histochemical methods. Some of them addressed themselves to the old question of the probable nature of the reductant, not always clearly distinguishing between the reduction in the dark and the additional (and perhaps chemically different) photochemical reduction.

Nagai (1950) found the silver precipitates formed in light to be clearly associated with the chloroplasts, but those formed in darkness to be distributed irregularly in the cell. The selective chloroplast staining with silver nitrate could be observed only a pH 4.5, not at pH >7. Nagai suggested that this selective silver deposition is the result of migration and adsorption of silver atoms on the chloroplast surface, rather than evidence of the presence of a reducing agent directly in the latter. In a second paper, Nagai (1951) noted that several plant substances—particularly ascorbic acid and di-oxyphenylalanine (to a lesser extent, also tannings and flavone derivatives)—can reduce silver nitrate under the conditions of the Molisch test.

Later (1952) Nagai observed the Molisch reaction in many marine and fresh water algae, and concluded that the only appropriate reducing compound found in all of them is ascorbic acid. Algae which showed a negative Molisch test also gave no evidence of ascorbic acid in chromatographic separation. In sorrel and similar "oxalate plants" the Molisch test gave no clear positive results, despite the presence of ascorbate, but this could be attributed to the interference of oxalic acid.

The effect of light was considered by Nagai in still another paper (1952[2]). He found that the Molisch test was negative in etiolated seedlings, but became positive after 2 hours exposure to light, simultaneously with the visible formation of chlorophyll. Nagai suggested that the photochemical effect consists in attracting to the chloroplast the silver formed elsewhere by a non-photochemical reaction of ascorbic acid with silver nitrate, and consequent formation of localized black deposits instead of a diffuse, plasmatic precipitate. This seems a much less plausible explanation than sensitized photochemical reduction of silver ions (or photochemical reduction of chlorophyll by ascorbic acid, followed by re-oxidation of reduced chlorophyll by silver ions).

Hagène and Goas had noted (1945) that the disintegration of chloroplast structure (e. g., by heat) is accompanied by a cessation of fluorescence, and inquired (1949) whether the capacity of chloroplasts for the reduction of silver nitrate shows a parallelism with their fluorescence. They found this to be true, but not under all conditions: fluorescence is preserved, e. g., after freezing chloroplasts in liquid air, while the reducing capacity disappears. No general parallelism exists between the capacity for silver nitrate reduction and for photosynthesis. It is not clear whether in these experiments the *photochemical* component of the silver nitrate reduction was considered rather than the—perhaps quite unrelated—thermochemical reduction.

Metzner (1952[1]) observed the distribution of silver deposits in sections from the lower surface of leaves of *Agapanthus umbellatus* and cotyledons of *Impatiens parviflora*. Blackening was found to occur in the cytoplasm as well as in plastides and nuclei. Within the chloroplasts, the reaction occurred preferentially in the grana and at the surface (perhaps at a membrane). The chloroplast reaction becomes predominant at pH 3, that in the cytoplasm at pH 7–8. Both reactions occurred in the dark; light accelerated the reduction. The action spectrum of $AgNO_3$ reduction by (initially) living *Agapanthus* cells showed peaks in the red and in the violet, indicating sensitization by chlorophyll and suggesting that direct photochemical decomposition of unstable silver salts (precipitated in the cells) does not contribute much to the blackening. In cells killed by several minutes immersion into silver nitrate solution in the dark, the action spectrum (for silver deposition in a following light period) was quite different, showing no peaks in the chlorophyll bands—except for the reaction in the grana. Cells killed by lead acetate still reduced $AgNO_3$, but only in the plastides; cells killed by brief boiling were completely inactive. Metzner (1952[2]) tried to sensitize the photochemical silver nitrate reduction in chloroplasts by vital staining with Rhodamin B, but the action spectrum of stained cells still showed the "green gap" characteristic of sensitization by chlorophyll.

Thomas, Post and Vertregt (1954) first used the electron microscope to study the distribution of silver in chloroplasts and their fragments. They showed that suspensions of chloroplast fragments (consisting predominantly of grana), suspended in a silver nitrate solution, liberate silver in light. Whereas, according to Metzner, the photochemical reduction of $AgNO_3$ in "living" chloroplasts is best observed at pH 3, the same reaction in "grana suspensions" was fastest in neutral solution. The rate increased with light intensity slower than linearly, but without definite indication of saturation, which would indicate the participation of an enzyme—

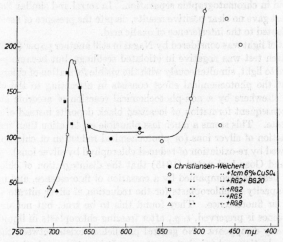

Fig. 37A.19. Three sections of the action spectrum of Molisch reaction (Ag precipitation from $AgNO_3$ in acid solution) in a suspension of chloroplasts from *Hibiscus rosa sinensis*, obtained with different sets of filters (after Thomas, Post and Vertregt 1954). Abscissae: relative rates, measured by increase of opacity with time (rate in Na light = 100). Light filters as indicated in figure.

in agreement with Metzner's observations that it can occur also in cells killed by silver nitrate; Thomas *et al.* found that 10 minutes boiling of the suspension also did not stop the reaction.

Experiments with colloidal suspensions of pure chlorophyll in silver nitrate solution indicated that chlorophyll in itself has the capacity to reduce $AgNO_3$ in light, without the aid of other cellular components; the chlorophyll-free alga, *Prototheca zopfii*, showed no increase in the rate of $AgNO_3$ reduction in light. These observations suggest that, even while ascorbic acid appears essential for the silver nitrate reduction by chloroplasts in the dark, it may not be required for the photochemical reduction. The latter may occur at the cost of chlorophyll itself (although it will then have to stop soon), or at the cost of other cellular hydrogen donors. Reduction at the cost of water (Hill reaction with Ag^+ ion as oxidant) seems unlikely because of the apparently non-enzymatic kinetics, and also be-

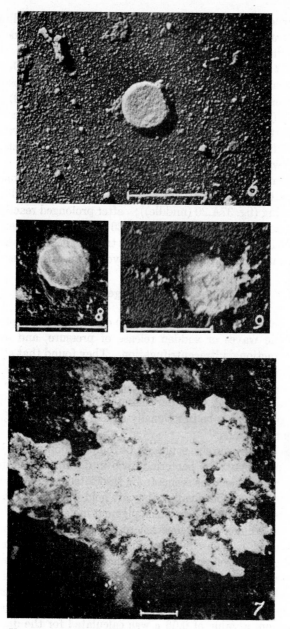

Fig. 37A.20. Uncoated *Hibiscus* chloroplast granum (marked 6), and grana first smoothly coated (marked 8), and then deformed (marked 9) by silver deposits from AgNO₃ (after Thomas, Post and Vertregt 1954). Micrograph marked 7 shows a heap of grana overgrown with silver deposit.

cause of the continuation of the reaction in killed cells. Addition of ascorbic acid to grana suspensions considerably increases the yield—perhaps by reducing again the chlorophyll oxidized by Ag^+ ions.

Thomas et al. also measured the action spectrum of $AgNO_3$ reduction by grana suspension, and found it to be quite similar to this absorption spectrum, and essentially determined by chlorophyll (fig. 37A.19).

Electron diffraction study of the grana after the Molisch reaction showed a strong scattering pattern, indicating the presence of crystalline silver deposits (no diffraction rings were visible in the scattering pattern of grana not covered with silver).

Electron-microscopic observations of grana after the Molisch reaction showed uncoated (fig. 37A.20 (top)) grana as well as grana in different stages of silver coating (fig. 37A.20 (middle)); after prolonged reaction, silver deposits grew and hid the grana (fig. 37A.20 (bottom)). When grana were disintegrated into single discs by ultrasonic treatment, and the latter exposed to silver nitrate in light, they, too, were overgrown with silver deposits.

3. Ultracentrifuge Study

Pardee, Schachman and Stanier (1952) disintegrated purple bacteria by grinding, sonic waves or sudden release of pressure, and subjected the products to fractional ultracentrifugation. They found that all pigments—the bacteriochlorophylls as well as the carotenoids—came down in a single fraction, consisting of large particles, and called the latter "chromatophores." It seems that these particles, though smaller than the grana of the higher plants, may be functionally similar to them; we will therefore refer to them as "grana."

Particles of the same size could not be found in non-photosynthetic bacteria, or in photosynthetic bacteria grown in dark and containing no pigment. Their presence thus seems to be associated with that of the photosynthetic pigments—conceivably, they are held together by the strong resonance attraction that exists between pigment molecules.

From the sedimentation constant of the colored fraction of bacteria, Schachman et al. calculated—assuming spherical shape—a particle diameter of $0.04~\mu$. Electron micrographs of the same fraction showed the presence of flattened ellipsoids, or low cylinders, with a diameter of $0.11~\mu$. The authors suggested that these particles originally had been spherical, but became flattened in the preparation of samples for electron microscopy. On this assumption, a value of $0.06~\mu$ was calculated for the diameter of the original spheres—in fair agreement with the value derived from sedimentation experiments. However, agreement can be achieved also by assuming that the bacterial grana have the approximately cylindrical shape observed under the electron microscope, but that their thickness is such that, in sedimenting edgewise, they have a cross-section similar to that of a 0.04 μ sphere. For a diameter of 0.11 μ, this thickness is 0.05 μ. These dimensions are small, but not so small as to make implausible the assumption of functional identity of the bacterial "chromatophores" with the grana of the higher plants and algae. More recently grana of approximately this size have been in fact found in bacteria by electron microscopy (Thomas 1952; *cf.* section 2 above).

Schachman *et al.* estimated that a single bacterial cell contains about 5,000 colored particles; but this estimate involved several rather uncertain premises.

In a suspension prepared by grinding blue-green algae, fractional ultracentrifugation also showed the presence of a single chlorophyll-bearing fraction. The colored particles were even larger than in bacteria. Electron microscopy indicates the presence in blue-green algae of grana of the same, or even somewhat larger, size than in higher plants—about 0.8 μ across (Vatter 1952, Thomas 1952). The large-particle fraction of blue-green algae contained all chlorophyll, but phycocyanin was found mainly in a slow-sedimenting fraction. However, the occurrence of phycobilin-sensitized chlorophyll fluorescence in algae (*cf.* Chapter 24), argues against spatial separation of the two pigments in the living chromatoplasm, and for this separation having been effected in the grinding of the cells. This is supported by the observations of McClendon (1952, 1954), *cf.* section 6 below.

4. Optical Evidence of Chloroplast Structure

In Volume I (p. 365), measurements of double refraction and dichroism of chloroplasts were described. Frey-Wyssling's (1938) interpretation of these observations given there, was that the "positive" double refraction of chloroplasts in the natural state is a "morphic" birefringence, caused by lamellar structure, while the "negative" double refraction, found after imbibition of chloroplasts with glycerol, is an "intrinsic" birefringence caused by the presence in the chloroplasts of an orderly array of long rod-shaped hydrocarbon chains, such as exist in lipides and phospholipides. However, Frey-Wyssling noted that the intrinsic double refraction of chloroplasts is weak, and suggested an imperfect alignment.

Frey-Wyssling and Steinmann (1948), in a more precise study of the double refraction of *Mougeotia* chloroplasts, used different fixatives, and imbibed the chloroplasts with varying amounts of different liquids. They obtained in this way a set of hyperbolic curves showing double refraction as a function of refractive index. For all fixating solutions, the hyperbolas had a peak at $n = 1.58$ (which is close to the refractive index of protein).

With osmic acid as fixative, the peak corresponded to a weak positive double refraction; with Zenker's solution, to no double refraction at all (fig. 37A.21). The authors suggested that osmic acid fixes both proteins and lipides, while Zenker's fluid fixes proteins only. If the negative morphic

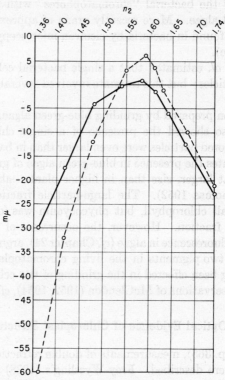

Fig. 37A.21. Double refraction of *Mougeotia* chloroplasts as a function of imbibition (after Frey-Wyssling and Steinmann 1948): (—) fixed with Zenker fluid, imbibed with acetone + CH_2I_2; (- -) fixed with OsO_4 + $HgCl_2$, imbibed with acetone + CH_2I_2. Ordinate, retardation (Γ) in mμ; abscissa, refractive index, n_2, of the imbibing fluid.

double refraction is due to protein lamellae, and the negative intrinsic double refraction to an array of lipides in the lipide layers, the different effect of the two fixatives is easily explained.

5. Composition of Chloroplasts

(a) *Proteins, Lipids and Nucleotides*

Timm (1943) obtained some additional data concerning the *protein* content of the chloroplast and the cytoplasm in leaves (*cf.* Vol. I, p. 371).

He found 13.8% N in proteins from chloroplast matter, against 14.5% in those from the cytoplasm. The chloroplast matter contained 4.6% ash, 0.5% P, and 1.13% S; the cytoplasmic matter, 3.1% ash, no P, and 1.03% S. The amino acids were nearly the same in proteins from both sources, the cytoplasm containing slightly more lysine and glutamic acid, and slightly less histidine (*cf.* table 14.IV).

Sisakyan, Bezinger and Kuvaeva (1950) used paper chromatography to identify sixteen amino acids in chloroplast proteins. Osipova and Timofeeva (1950[1]) found that chloroplast proteins reduce more ferricyanide than cytoplasmic proteins, and that their capacity to absorb chlorophyll from alcoholic solution parallels their reducing capacity. After oxidation with ferricyanide, chloroplast proteins lost about three-fourths of this capacity and their reducing power became the same as that of proteins from the cytoplasm. When chloroplast proteins absorb chlorophyll, their capacity to be oxidized by ferricyanide is largely lost, indicating that chlorophyll blocks their reducing groups.

Osipova and Timofeeva (1950[2]) observed changes in chloroplast composition caused by nitrogen deficiency. With nitrogen supply reduced to one-quarter of the normal, protein concentration went down from 70 to 26%, while the amount of starch rose from 3 to 30%.

Godnev, Shlyk and Tretjak (1952) determined, using P (32) as tracer, the *phosphorus* content in chloroplasts in relation to the total phosphorus content in the leaf, and found 6, 15 and 22% in oats, rye and lettuce, respectively. Of the total phosphorus found in chloroplasts, about 3% were contained in phospholipids; the mass ratio chlorophyll : phospholipide was 5.5 in rye and 2.5 in lettuce—much higher than required by Hubert's model (fig. 46); this discrepancy was noted before (Vol. I, p. 375) in the analysis of Chibnall's data.

Menke (*cf.* p. 384) suggested the possible presence in chloroplast material of *nucleoproteids*. Euler, Bracco and co-workers (1948, 1949) first found ribonucleic acid in the products of precipitation of isolated chloroplast material by lanthanum salts. Metzner (1952[1,2]) confirmed the presence of nucleic acids in chloroplasts from *Agapanthus umbellatus* by cytochemical tests. He noted that the staining of grana with basic dyes can be prevented by extraction with agents which dissolve nucleic acid, and that the digestion of chloroplast proteins by trypsin can be prevented by precipitation of nucleic acid with lanthanum salts, or with streptomycin. Metzner surmised that the stroma—which contains phosphatides, as indicated by its capacity to form myelin figures (*cf.* section 2)—contains ribonucleic acid (often associated with phosphatides); while staining evidence indicates that the grana may contain both the ribonucleic and the desoxyribonucleic acid. McClendon (1953) noted that in the fractionation of homogenates from tobacco leaves, the distribution of desoxyribonucleic acid followed, in general, that of chlorophyll. Metzner considered the probable presence of desoxyribonucleic acid in the grana as important in connection with Strugger's hypothesis that chloroplast propagation is initiated and directed by a "plastidogen" (cf. section 1).

Sisakyan and Chernyak (1952) obtained nucleic acid, from the chloroplast material of sugar beet leaves, by alkaline extraction and acetic acid precipitation; color reaction with orcin was used to identify ribose. A cytochemical test (formation of a fluorescent complex with acridine, which is selectively absorbed by nucleoproteids), showed mostly red fluorescence (typical of ribonucleic acid), and only in spots, green fluorescence (characteristic of desoxyribonucleic acid).

In connection with the projects to grow large amounts of algae for food or fuel, considerable study has been devoted to the possibility of directing their metabolism toward the synthesis of increased quantities of proteins or fats. It was found possible to vary the composition of algal cells very widely by variation in culture conditions; but no studies have as yet been made concerning the distribution of the accumulated fats and proteins between the cytoplasm and the plastides.

Reviews of this subject by Milner, by Fogg and Collyer, and by others are found in the monograph "Algal Culture, from Laboratory to Pilot Plant" (1953), which also contains an extensive bibliography.

(b) Enzymes

From the point of view of photosynthesis one is most interested in the presence in chloroplasts of *enzymes* whose activity could conceivably be involved in the fixation and reduction of carbon dioxide, or in the liberation of oxygen from water.

Among the carbon dioxide-binding enzymes, we can first inquire about *carbonic anhydrase;* we recall (Vol. I, p. 198) that the hydration of carbon dioxide to H_2CO_3 has been considered a possible "bottleneck" in photosynthesis. It was mentioned in Volume I (p. 380) that no carbonic anhydrase was found in leaves by Burr and Mommaerts; but that it was identified there by Neish. Neish's results have since been confirmed by Day and Franklin (1945), Bradfield (1947), Steemann-Nielsen and Kristiansen (1949), and Waygood and Clendenning (1950). They all found that chloroplast material has an accelerating effect on the hydration of carbon dioxide. Steemann-Nielsen and Kristiansen noted that carbonic anhydrase appears to be present in *Elodea* as well as in *Fontinalis*, although the first of these aquatic plants (according to Steemann-Nielsen) can use HCO_3^- ions for photosynthesis, while the second one uses CO_2 molecules only (cf. Vol. II, part 1, p. 888). According to Waygood and Clendenning, the carbonic anhydrase is located in the cytoplasm rather than in the chloroplast.

It is generally assumed that carbon dioxide enters photosynthesis through carboxylation of an organic molecule. Vennesland and co-workers (1947, 1949, 1950) have identified a number of *carboxylases* in plants, using mostly wheat germ and other nonchlorophyllous tissues. However, oxalacetic carboxylase was identified also in spinach leaves.

Waygood and Clendenning (1950) found that, in leaves, the carboxylases (pyruvic, oxalacetic, oxalsuccinic, ketoglutaric, and glutamic) were present in cytoplasmic rather than in chloroplastic material.

The so-called *malic enzyme*, which simultaneously carboxylates and reduces pyruvic acid, also was found in non-chlorophyllous plant tissues (and, in smaller amounts, in spinach leaves) by Conn, Vennesland and Kraemer (1949) and Ceithaml and Vennesland (1949); *cf.* also Vennesland (1950). Arnon (1951) extracted the same enzyme from beet leaves (it could be obtained from leaf mash from which chloroplasts had been removed, and thus seemed to be located in the cytoplasm). Combining the extract with a chloroplast suspension from the same plant, Arnon was able to photosynthesize malate and oxygen from carbon dioxide, pyruvate and water, with only TPN and Mn^{++} added from non-plant sources. He described this as an "extracellular photosynthetic reaction"; the limitations of this analogy have been pointed out in Chapter 35 (section B.4f).

Clendenning, Waygood and Weinberger (1952) inquired into the existence in leaves of a carboxylase abundant enough to "bear the traffic" of photosynthesis, and sensitive to cyanide (since it has been suggested that the carboxylation reaction is the main locus of cyanide sensitivity in photosynthesis, *cf.* Chapter 12, p. 307, and Chapter 37D, section 2). In *Chlorella* extracts, they found only a low activity of oxalacetic and α-ketoglutaric carboxylases, and practically none of pyruvic and glutamic carboxylases; also no evidence of malic enzyme or hydrogen lyase. In wheat leaf extracts, the glutamic carboxylase content was high (Weinberger and Clendenning, 1952); of the known carboxylases (leaving aside the hydrogen lyase), it alone is cyanide sensitive. However, this carboxylase is found in only few species, and the reaction it catalyzes is practically irreversible and therefore unsuitable for photosynthesis. Oxalacetic carboxylase and malic enzyme were found by Clendenning and co-workers to be more concentrated in the extract from parsley leaves than in the extract from the roots of the same plant. They estimated that the malic enzyme concentration in parsley leaf macerate was sufficient to maintain the high rate of carboxylation needed to keep up with the Hill reaction as observed in the same material. Although—according to Clendenning *et al.*—this enzyme is cyanide-sensitive "only at very low enzyme concentrations," it was suggested by them, that in consideration of the observations of Ochoa and Vishniac, Tolmach, and Arnon (described in section

B.4, Chapter 35), malic enzyme must be looked upon as the port of entry of carbon dioxide into photosynthesis. However, this conclusion is not supported by other evidence, in particular by the more recent radiocarbon studies described in Chapter 36. These studies have rather conclusively eliminated malic acid as the primary carboxylation product in photosynthesis. Ribulose diphosphate has emerged as the most likely primary carbon dioxide acceptor (*cf.* Chapter 36, section A7). Its carboxylation, combined with hydrolytic splitting of the carbon chain, leads to two molecules of phosphoglyceric acid (eq. 36.8). Weissbach, Smyrniotis and Horecker (1954) found that an enzyme catalyzing this reaction can be extracted from spinach leaves; Quayle, Fuller, Benson and Calvin (1954) found it also in *Chlorella*. Thermochemical calculations (*cf.* Chapter 36, Section A12) made it plausible that the equilibrium lies, in this case, far on the side of carboxylation, as required by the kinetics of photosynthesis. It will be interesting to know whether this enzyme is cyanide sensitive.

To sum up, it seems unlikely, at present, that any of the common decarboxylases found in plants are directly involved in photosynthesis; and the same probably is true of malic enzyme.

Boichenko (1948) asserted that clover-leaf chloroplasts contain an enzyme (formic dehydrogenase or hydrogenlyase) capable of combining CO_2 with H_2 to formic acid; it was mentioned above that this enzyme was not found in *Chlorella* cells by Clendenning and co-workers.

Coming now to enzymes engaged in the transfer of hydrogen from organic substrates to oxygen (which conceivably could also be useful in the reverse process), we note that *cytochrome c* was repeatedly reported in plants, but first successfully extracted from them by Hill and Scarisbrick (1951) using both chlorophyllous and nonchlorophyllous plant tissues. They also discovered two new plant hemoporphyrins, which they designated as *cytochrome b_3* and *cytochrome f*. The second of these new cytochromes was found in chlorophyllous tissues only, not alone in leaves, but also in some species of algae. One molecule of cytochrome *f* was present per about 400 molecules of chlorophyll. Cytochrome *f* was found by Davenport and Hill (1951) to have a more negative potential than cytochrome *c* ($E = -0.365$ volt *vs.* -0.260 volt).

Hill, Northcote and Davenport (1953) observed the characteristic cytochrome *f* absorption band at 555 mμ also in acetone-extraction residue from *Chlorella* cells. The ratio (chlorophyll):(cytochrome *f*) seemed to be of the order of 500.

Cytochrome oxidase, which mediates between cytochrome *c* and molecular oxygen, was reported as present in chloroplasts by Rosenberg and Ducet (1949) and Sisakyan and Filipovich (1949). Baghvat and Hill (1951) demonstrated the occurrence of the complete cytochrome system, including cytochrome oxidase, in seeds, bulbs, roots, and tubers of many plant species, indicating the general capacity of plants for the (cyanide-sensitive) cytochrome-mediated respiration. Webster (1952) found cyto-chrome oxidase in leaf material from 19 species and in many other plant tissues. McClendon (1953) fractionated homogenized tobacco leaves and separated the product into four fractions containing, respectively, whole chloroplasts, chloroplast fragments of different size, and no chloroplastic material at all. Cytochrome oxidase activity was found in all fractions, but in approximately inverse relation to the chlorophyll content, in con-tradiction to the conclusions of Rosenberg and Ducet, and of Sisakyan and Filipovich. (Chlorophyll precipitated preferentially with the largest particles, cytochrome oxidase with the smallest ones; as mentioned above, desoxyribonucleic acid followed chlorophyll in this fractionation.) At-tempts to prepare a chloroplast fraction quite free of cytochrome oxidase, however, did not succeed. McClendon suggested that most, if not all, of the cytochrome oxidase in leaves is associated with mitochondria, as in animal tissues. No cytochrome f oxidase was found by Hill and co-workers.

Daly and Brown (1954) demonstrated cytochrome oxidase action by ob-serving the reversal, in light, of CO_2 inhibition of the $O(18)O(16)$ uptake by live leaves.

An alternative mechanism of hydrogen transfer to oxygen in respira-tion involves the copper-containing *polyphenoloxidase* (=tyrosinase, or catecholase) instead of the cytochrome oxidase. This oxidase is widely distributed in plants, although Holt (1950) found no evidence of it in *Phytolacca americana*. This respiration mechanism is not inhibited by cyanide and could conceivably account for the low cyanide sensitivity of respiration in many plants, *e. g.* in *Chlorella* (*cf.* Chapter 12, section A1).

Arnon (1948, 1949) reported that, in beet leaves, the polyphenol oxidase is localized in the chloroplasts. Leaves were mashed in a Blendor, and chloroplast fragments separated by high-speed centrifugation. The oxidase was assayed in both fractions, using ascorbic acid as oxidation substrate and catechol as intermediate catalyst, and found to be concen-trated to more than 80% in the chloroplast fraction.

According to Arnon, disintegration of *Beta* chloroplasts by grinding with glass beads on a Nickle tissue-grinding machine and repeated high-speed centrifugation (a procedure by which the more proteinaceous or lipopro-teinaceous stroma of the chloroplasts presumably is separated from the more strongly lipoidic grana) fails to separate the oxidase activity from the green precipitate.

These results do not agree with the observations of Warburg and Lütt-gens (1946), who noted that at pH 6.5, the larger part of the oxidase responsible for the "respiration" of mashed spinach leaves remained, after centrifugation, in the cytoplasmic fluid; only at pH 5 was the enzyme precipitated with the chloroplast fragments. Similarly, Bonner and Wildmann (1947) noted that, after grinding spinach leaves in a colloid mill all polyphenoloxidase stayed in the colorless fluid, and none was precipitated with the chloroplast fragments.

In a later paper, Wildmann and Bonner (1947) described fractionation of cytoplasmic proteins from spinach leaves (probably including some of the chloroplast stroma proteins) into two main fractions. A large electrophoretically homogeneous fraction (70–80% of the total) was found to contain auxin and a phosphatase, while a smaller, inhomogeneous fraction, contained polyphenoloxidase, as well as four different dehydrogenases, a peroxidase and a catalase.

McClendon (1953) measured the polyphenol oxidase activity of the several fractions he obtained from homogenized tobacco leaves (*cf.* above), and found no significant concentration in any one of the three precipitates; about one-half of the enzyme was left in the colorless supernatant. Much of the enzyme could be easily washed out of the chloroplast fragments, but some seemed to be bound to these fragments more tightly.

Smirnov and Pshenova (1941) described a special kind of polyphenol oxidase they found in tobacco leaves which oxidized hydroquinone. Laties (1950) observed a new cyanide-insensitive oxidation enzyme in spinach chloroplasts.

Catalase can be considered as an oxidase because it, too, catalyzes a reaction which involves molecular oxygen (usually as a product rather than as a reactant, because of the irreversibility of the dismutation of hydrogen peroxide). In Chapter 14 (page 379) we noted that, according to Neish, all leaf catalase is present in chloroplasts; but Krossing found it also in the cytoplasm. In the four fractions obtained by McClendon (1953) by centrifugation of tobacco leaf homogenates, about one-half of the enzyme was in the chlorophyll-free supernatant, the other half in the three precipitates, its amount being about proportional to that of total protein in each fraction. However, since washing the precipitates by centrifugation extracted a large part of catalase, it is quite possible that before fractionation much more than one-half of catalase was associated with the plastides.

Glycolytic enzymes are responsible for phosphorylation and cleavage of hexoses, and hydrogen transfer from trioses and the acids of the Krebs cycle, to TPN, DPN (co-enzymes I and II) and lipoic acid (which in turn transfer them to flavins, cytochromes, and ultimately to oxygen). Since many of the partial reactions in glycolysis are reversible, the same enzymes could conceivably participate also in the reverse process of sugar formation in photosynthesis; their occurrence in green plant cells—in particular that of triose phosphate dehydrogenase—has been touched upon in chapter 36. In respiration, this enzyme oxidizes phosphoglyceraldehyde to phosphoglyceric acid, transferring hydrogen to a pyridine nucleotide; it could conceivably catalyze the reverse process in photosynthesis.

A controversy has arisen about the presence of triose dehydrogenase in green plants in connection with observations of the lack of inhibition of their respiration by iodoacetate; however, as described in chapters 36, page 1687, and 37D (section 2), Arnon was able to demonstrate this inhibition, and thus to confirm the occurrence in plants of the respiration path via triose and glycerate. More recently, Arnon, Rosenberg and Whatley (1954) described a new kind of TPN—specific triose phosphate dehydrogenase in green cells, not requiring inorganic phosphate as co-factor.

Sisakyan and Shamova (1949) identified several known *dehydrogenases* in chloroplast material. Sisakyan and Kobjakova (1949) found *phosphoglucomutase*. Holzer and Holzer (1952) (*cf.* also Holzer 1954) demonstrated the presence, in plasmolyzed *Chlorella* cells and in acetone powder extracts from these cells, of *hexokinase, phosphofructo-kinase, aldolase,* and *triose phosphate dehydrogenase*. Inhibition of the latter with iodoacetic acid produced, in glucose medium, the same accumulation of fructosediphosphate in *Chlorella* as it did in yeast.

Chloroplasts must also be the sites of carbohydrate transformations by which hexose are converted to sucrose and starch. Nezgovorov (1940, 1941) found in chloroplasts small amounts of free *amylase;* Sisakyan and Kobjakova (1949), *invertase* and *amylase.*

For more detailed compilations of the enzymatic components of chloroplasts (and other plant cell structures) we must refer here to the reviews by Sisakyan (1951), Van Fleet (1952) and Weier and Stocking (1952).

(c) Heavy Metals

The paper by Liebich (1941) on the *iron content* of chloroplasts was summarized in Volume I (p. 378) on the basis of an earlier note by Noack and Liebich. A new study of mineral components of chloroplast ash was made by Vecher (1947), who added a few new elements to those identified earlier by Neish and Menke (Vol. I, p. 376). Whatley, Ordin and Arnon (1951) found that, of the elements Fe, Cu, Mn, Zn and Mo, the first two are present in chloroplasts in higher concentrations than in the (sugar beet) leaves as a whole.

(d) Ascorbic Acid

In chapters 10 (part E) and 14, we summarized briefly the evidence for the occurrence of ascorbic acid in the chloroplasts, and in the cytoplasm of green leaves, and for the increase of its concentration in light. A participation of ascorbic acid as intermediate hydrogen carrier in photosynthesis has repeatedly been suggested (*cf.* Chapter 10, section E2). Experiments of Krasnovsky (Chapter 35, section A4) on photochemical chlorophyll reduction by ascorbic acid *in vitro* have added some new interest to these suggestions. We cannot review here the considerable new literature on the ascorbic acid content of green cells, and its variability, but will mention a few relevant investigations. Åberg (1946) has studied the effect of light and temperature on the ascorbic acid content of tomato and kale leaves, and found on approximate proportionality of this content with light intensity up to about 80 cal./cm.² min.; he noted a rapid decrease of this content in darkness. Later (1945) he made similar studies also with parsley and spinach leaves, and noted that the decrease of ascorbate concentration in dark could be largely prevented by feeding with sugar.

Matuyama and Hirano (1944) determined the ascorbic acid content of *Chlorella*, and found 2–3 mg. in 1 g. dry weight; 60–70% of it were in the reduced form. In the dark, the ascorbate concentration went down, and the percentage of the reduced form decreased, both increased markedly after three hours exposure to light in the presence of carbon dioxide. The percentage of the reduced form (but not the total content) could be raised also by a supply of 5% CO_2 in the dark. Iron-deficient, chlorotic algae were found to contain more ascorbate than the normal ones, while Mg or N-deficient cells showed a subnormal ascorbate content.

The role of ascorbate in the Hill reaction and in Arnon's *et al.* (1954) "photosynthesis with whole chloroplasts" was described in Chapter 35, sections 1 and 4.

6.   State of Pigments in Chloroplasts

(a) *Chloroplastin*

In section 2, it was tentatively suggested that chlorophyll may be located on the protein-lipide interfaces in the grana discs (or lamina). This picture, however plausible, is still speculative; and even if correct, leaves open the question of the nature of the association between the protein, the pigment, and the lipoid constituents. Even less certain is the location and state, *in vivo*, of the accessory pigments, in particular, of the hydrophylic phycobilins.

In Chapter 14 (sections C2 and C3), we reviewed the evidence for (and, mainly, against) the assumption of a stoichiometric chlorophyll-protein compound in chloroplasts. Since then some new experiments have been published dealing with the pigment-protein-lipoid complex as obtained from green cells.

Stoll and Wiedemann (1947) gave some additional data on the properties of "chloroplastin" prepared as described in their earlier papers (*cf.* Vol. I, p. 385). The ether extract from salt-induced cleavage of *Aspidistra* chloroplastin was analyzed and found to consist of 49% insoluble proteins,

20% soluble proteins, 10% saponifiable lipides and 20% nonsaponifiable lipides (including the pigments). The pigments were: 7.5% chlorophyll, 0.4% carotene, 0.2% carotenoles (xanthophyll). Electrophoretic measurements showed that well purified chloroplastin from a given species (or two closely related species) moved with a single boundary, while chloroplastins from two nonrelated species (e. g., spinach and nettle) formed two separate moving boundaries. The anodic velocity was relatively high: $u = 12 \times 10^{-5}$ cm.^{2}/(volt sec.) (at pH 7). The stability range was narrow, pH 5.5–8.5; the velocity increased from 10.6 at pH 6 to 13.3×10^{-5} cm.^{2}/(volt sec.) at pH 8.3. Sedimentation measurements showed that the suspensions were not as uniform as the electrophoresis seemed to indicate. Several distinct sedimentation boundaries could be observed, showing that the variation in size was not continuous. Three sizes of particles appeared to be present in the *Aspidistra* chloroplastin. Even the smallest of them had molecular weights of several million. In other words, chloroplastin particles were much larger and much more complex than those of hemoglobin.

Wassink (1948) suggested the term "chromophyllin" for the general type of photosynthetic protein-pigment complexes, and "chlorophyllin" for the protein-chlorophyll complex in green plants. (The second term is, however, generally used for the large, acid moiety of the chlorophyll molecule, *cf.* Vol. I, p. 439.)

(b) Crystallized Lipoprotein-Chlorophyll

In support of the concept of a stoichiometric protein-chlorophyll compound, Takashima (1952) described the preparation of a crystalline chlorophyll protein from clover leaves. The procedure consisted in clarifying a suspension of whole and broken chloroplasts with β-picoline (or pyridine), washing it by dialysis through cellophane into a 50–55% aqueous solution of the same base, and filtering the green solution remaining in the cellophane bag from the carotenoid crystals formed in it. The peak of the red absorption band of the filtrate was at 668 mμ, as compared to 678 mμ in the original suspension. Addition of dioxane until the solution contained 20% dioxane, 43% α-picoline (or pyridine), and 37% phosphate buffer (pH 7.0) led—after standing for 4–7 days in the ice box—to the precipitation of clusters of needle-like green crystals. The presence of protein in these crystals was confirmed by ninhydrin, xanthoprotein and biuret reactions; its molecular weight (in 55% α-pycoline) was estimated osmometrically as about 19,000. It contained 0.61% P, indicating the possible presence of phospholipides. Spectrophotometric estimates indicated the presence of between 1.3 and 2.4 molecules of chlorophyll per protein unit of 19,000, corresponding to 7–12% by weight. It may be asked, however, whether the crystal contained intact chlorophyll, or a derivative such as that known to be formed by interaction of chlorophyll with piperidine *in vitro, cf.* p. 642 and chapter 37C, section 2a.

Chiba (1954) obtained similar crystals from centrifuged chloroplast material (consisting mainly of grana) rather than from whole cell macerates, thus reducing the chance of participation of proteins not connected with chlorophyll in the natural state. He separated the crystalline material chromatographically into a blue-green and a yellow-green fraction (both separately crystallizable), which he considered as containing the *a* and *b* component of chlorophyll, respectively.

(c) Is All Chlorophyll in the Cell in the Same State?

In Chapter 14 (pp. 392–393) and Chapter 23 (p. 818) we mentioned Seybold and Egle's suggestion that chlorophyll is present in the cell in two different phases—a non-fluorescent (adsorbed?) phase responsible for most of the light absorption, and a strongly fluorescent (dissolved) phase responsible for the weak average fluorescence. It was argued there that the mutual position of the fluorescence and the absorption peaks *in vivo* makes this hypothesis implausible. To this, it was suggested that the fluorescence band *in vivo* may be distorted by reabsorption, shifting its peak toward the longer waves; but in this case, dilute cell suspensions should show a shift of the fluorescence band back toward its position in solution, which does not seem to be the case.

Suggestions that chlorophyll (meaning chlorophyll *a*) may be present in cells in at least two different forms, have since been renewed. Duysens (unpublished) saw an analogy between the absorption spectrum of chlorophyll in algae and that of bacteriochlorophyll in bacteria. Nothing like the two or three separate infrared peaks shown by bacteria appears in the spectra of green cells; but the main absorption band of chlorophyll *a* in the red is broadened more than the corresponding fluorescence band—too much to be accounted for by the "sieve" and "agglomeration" effects analyzed in Chapters 22 (p. 672) and 37C, section 6a. This can be considered as evidence of overlapping of two absorption bands—provided it is assumed that the potential curves of the ground state and of the lowest excited state of chlorophyll are equally affected by association with proteins and the dense packing of pigment molecules (causing the shapes of the absorption and the fluorescence band to be changed in the same way). The resonance between closely packed pigment molecule should affect the potential curves of the excited state stronger than that of the ground state; the absorption band can be therefore affected differently from the fluorescence band.

Krasnovsky and Kosobutskaya (1953) observed a shift in the absorption peak, during the greening of etiolated leaves, from 670 to 678 mμ, and a simultaneous decrease in the sensitivity of chlorophyll to bleaching, and concluded that chlorophyll exists in the cells in two forms. They assumed one to be a monomeric, "photoactive," fluorescent form, with an absorption peak at 670 mμ; the other, a polymeric, "photo-inactive," non-fluorescent form, with a band at 678 mμ. After 16 hours of greening, the absorption peak moved from 670 to 678 mμ, indicating that the proportion of "photoactive" or "bleachable" chlorophyll declined sharply. (The total amount of chlorophyll grew, while that of the "photoactive" component remained almost constant.)

This interpretation of the chlorophyll spectrum *in vivo* was analogous to that suggested by Krasnovsky *et al.* for the two main absorption peaks of bacteriochlorophyll in the living cell (*cf.* Chapter 37C, section 6c).

Whether the postulate of the two forms of chlorophyll is correct or not, it is certainly implausible (and in the case of bacteriochlorophyll, incorrect) to attribute (as Krasnovsky suggests) the fluorescence (and photochemical activity) to the form with the absorption band at the shorter waves. Experiments on energy transfer, described in Chapter 32, clearly proved that excitation energy moves toward the pigment with the lowest excitation level, and that this pigment (or this pigment form) is responsible for both the fluorescence and the photochemical activity of the whole system.

It remains to be proved that the band shift from 670 to 678 mμ with increasing pigment density is not due to changes in scattering. It may also be caused by "organization" of molecularly dispersed chlorophyll into coherent monolayers (*cf.* chapter 37C, section 3).

The position of the red absorption band of chlorophyll in the living cell (between 670 and 680 mμ, as compared to 650–660 mμ in organic solvents) has been for a long time used as the basis for speculations (and experiments) concerning the nature of the "chlorophyll complex" *in vivo*. This matter was discussed in Chapter 21, without arriving at a definite conclusion; and the problem must still be considered as open at this writing ten years later. The alternative—but not mutually exclusive—interpretations of the "red band shift" *in vivo* are pigment association with a protein, and resonance interaction between closely packed chlorophyll molecules.

Rodrigo (1953) prepared a number of artificial protein-chlorophyll complexes, and found that one of them, a protein extracted from white leaves of *Pelargonium zonale*, had an absorption peak at 680 mμ.

In Chapter 37C we will describe experiments on chlorophyll crystals and monolayers, showing a red resonance shift depending on the density of the packing (and, to a certain extent, on the resonance volume). The concentration of the chlorophyll molecules *in vivo* (assuming they form monomolecular layers on grana discs or chloroplast laminae) is such that a resonance shift is to be expected, although its extent cannot be estimated without much better knowledge of the packing density.

Another criterion of the state of chlorophyll *in vivo* is its fluorescence—assuming that it is not due to a small fraction of the pigment present in a special state. Rodrigo's protein-chlorophyll complex was fluorescent, while artificial monomolecular layers of chlorophyll, as well as chlorophyll crystals, do not fluoresce. However, fluorescence may perhaps be activated by a protective coating of chlorophyll monolayers with lipide materials (which probably exists in the chloroplasts), so that new model experiments are needed before it can be asserted that the fluorescence of chlorophyll *in vivo* proves that chlorophyll molecules are attached individually to protein molecules and do not form monomolecular layers with a resonance interaction within them. (See, in this connection, Krasnovsky's data in table 37C.IIIB.)

(d) Location of Accessory Pigments

Not much, if any, new information has been developed on the location of accessory pigments, carotenes and phycobilins, in relation to chlorophyll and other cell constituents, since Hubert's scheme (Vol. I, fig. 46) tentatively placed the carotenoids between the phytol chains in the lipoid layers of the chloroplasts.

Particularly in need of clarification is the question of the location of the phycobilins. Several sets of observations seem to be difficult to reconcile. Microscopic observations (of some red algae, at least) seems to indicate that the red pigment is spread over the whole chloroplast while chlorophyll is concentrated in small "grana"; in ultracentrifugation experiments with blue-green algae, described in section 3 of this chapter, chlorophyll has been observed to precipitate in a large-particle fraction, while the phycobilins precipitated much later (*cf.* also Calvin and Lynch, 1952).

These experiments seem to indicate a spatial separation of green from the red (or blue) pigments in the natural state.

Experiments on sensitized fluorescence and action spectra of photosynthesis (Chapters 24 and 32) indicates on the other hand, a close association between the phycobilins and the chlorophylls, permitting a highly efficient energy transfer.

The ultracentrifuge experiments could perhaps be explained by a leaching out of the chromoproteids during the maceration of the cells. McClendon and Blinks (1952, 1954) found that chloroplasts of red alga *Griffithsia pacifica* easily loose their phycoerythrin when the plants are crushed in a distilled water, highly saline solution (up to 1.5 M) or sucrose solution (up to 2 M). In polyethylene glycol (Carbowax 4000, molecular weight 2,400) and other equally high-molecular solvents, on the other hand, the plastids do not swell and retain their red pigment. It seems that sol-

ents with a molecular weight >1500 do not penetrate into the plastides of
these algae and thus do not cause the phycobilins to dissolve and ooze out
into the medium.   (Their separation from chlorophyll is accompanied by a
sudden increase in fluorescence yield, noted in Chapter 32.)

The Hill reaction of the plastids of *Griffithsia, Antithamnion* and *Coral-
ina* is quite strong in Carbowax 4000, but drops greatly in buffer solution.

Bibliography to Chapter 37A
Morphology and Composition of Choroplasts

936   Heitz, E., *Ber. deut. botan. Ges.*, **54**, 362; *Planta*, **26**, 134.

Hubert, B., *Rec. trav. botan. neérland.*, **32**, 323.

937   Geitler, L., *Planta*, **26**, 463.

938   Frey-Wyssling, A., *Submikroskopische Morphologie des Protoplasmas und
seiner Derivate.* Springer, Berlin. English edition: *Submicroscopic
Morphology of Protoplasm and Its Derivatives*, Elsevier, New York,
1948.

939   Hanson, E. A., *Rec. trav. botan. neérland.*, **36**, 183.

940   Kausche, G. A., and Ruska, H., *Naturwiss.*, **28**, 303.

Nezgovorov, L., *Compt. rend. (Doklady) Acad. Sci. USSR*, **29**, 60.

941   Liebich, H., *Z. Botanik*, **37**, 129.

Smirnov, A. I., and Pshennova, K. V., *Biokhimiya*, **6**, 29.

Nezgovorov, L., *Compt. rend. (Doklady) Acad. Sci. USSR*, **30**, 258.

943   Jungers, V., and Doutreligne, Soeur J., *La Cellule*, **49**, 409.

Timm, E., *Z. Botanik*, **38**, 1.

944   Roberts, E. A., *Am. J. Botany*, **29**, 10.

Matuzamo, H., and Hirano, Z., *Acta Phytochem. Japan*, **14**, 131.

945   Hagène, M., and Goas, L., *Compt. rend. soc. biol.*, **139**, 159.

Day, R., and Franklin, J., *Science*, **104**, 363.

946   Bonner, J., and Wildmann, S. G., *Arch. Biochem.*, **10**, 497.

Warburg, O., and Lüttgens, W., *Biokhimiya*, **11**, 303.

Åberg, B., *Ann. Agr. Coll. Sweden*, **13**, 241.

Gollub, M., and Vennesland, B., *J. Biol. Chem.* **169**, 233.

947   Granick, S., and Porter, K. R., *Am. J. Botany*, **34**, 545.

Algera, L., Beijer, J. J., van Iterson, W., Karstens, W. K. H., and Thung,
T. H., *Biochim. et Biophys. Acta*, **1**, 517.

Wildmann, S. G., and Bonner, J., *Arch. Biochem.*, **14**, 381.

Bradfield, J. R. G., *Nature*, **159**, 467.

Vecher, A. S., *Biokhimiya*, **12**, 156.

Boichenko, E. A., *ibid.*, **12**, 153.

Vennesland, B., Ceithaml, J., and Gollub, M., *ibid.*, **171**, 445.

Stoll, A., and Wiedemann, E., *Schweiz. Medizin. Wochenschr.*, **77**, 664.

948   Bracco, M., and Euler, H. v., *Kem. Arbeten (Univ. Stockholm)*, New Series
No. 10, March 1948.

Arnon, D. I., *Plant Physiol.*, **24**, 1.

Boichenko, E. A., *Biokhimiya*, **13**, 88.

Euler, H. v. and Hahn, L., *Ark. Kem. Miner. Geol.*, **25B**, No. 1.

Sisakyan, N. M., and Kobjakova, A. M., *Biokhimiya* **13**, 88.

Wassink, E. C., *Enzymologia*, **12**, 362.

Euler, H. v., *Deut. med. Wochschr.*, **73**, 265.

Frey-Wyssling, A., and Steinmann, E., *Biochim. et Biophys. Acta*, **2**, 254.

Frey-Wyssling, A., *Submicroscopic Morphology of Protoplasm and Its Derivatives*, Elsevier, New York.

Rezende-Pinto, M. C. de, *Protug. Acta Biol.* (**A**)2, 111.

1949   Frey-Wyssling, A., *Faraday Soc. Discussions*, No. 5, p. 130.

Frey-Wyssling, A., and Mühlethaler, K., *Vierteljahrsschrift naturforsch. Ges. Zürich*, **94**, No. 3.

Rezende-Pinto, M. C. de, *Portug. Acta Biol.*, **A**(2), 367.

Hagène, M., and Goas, L., *Compt. rend. soc. biol.* **143**, 147.

Arnon, D. I., *Nature*, **162**, 341.

Vennesland, B., Gollub, M. C., and Speck, J. F., *J. Biol. Chem.*, **178**, 301.

Steemann-Nielsen, E., and Kristiansen, J., *Physiol. plantarum*, **2**, 325.

Euler, H. v., and Hahn, L., *Ark. Kem. Miner. Geol.*, **26A**, No. 11.

Rosenberg, A. Y., and Ducet, G., *Compt. rend.*, **229**, 331.

Conn, E. E., Vennesland, B., and Kraemer, L. M., *Arch. Biochem.*, **23**, 179

Sisakyan, N. M., and Shamova, K. G., *Compt. rend.* (*Doklady*) *Acad. Sci USSR*, **67**, 377.

Sisakyan, N. M., and Kobjakova, A. M., *ibid.*, **67**, 703.

Sisakyan, N. M., and Filipovich, I. I., *ibid.*, **67**, 517.

Godnev, T. I., Kalishevich, S. V., and Zakharich, G. F., *ibid.*, 66, 957.

Åberg, B., *Physiol. Plantarum*, **2**, 164.

Vennesland, B., *J. Biol. Chem.*, **178**, 591.

Ceithaml, J., and Vennesland, B., *ibid.*, **178**, 133.

1950   Strugger, S. *Naturwiss.*, **37**, 166.

Nagai, S., *J. Inst. Polytech. Osaka City Univ.*, **1**, 33.

Sisakyan, N. M., Bezinger, E. N., and Kuvaeva, E. B., *Compt. rend* (*Doklady*) *Acad. Sci. USSR*, **74**, 385.

Osipova, O. P., and Timofeeva, I. V., *ibid.*, **74**, 979.

Holt, A. S., *Oak Ridge Natl. Lab. Rept.* ORNL 752.

Osipova, O. P., and Timofeeva, I. V., *Compt. rend.* (*Doklady*) *Acad. Sci USSR*, **80**, 449.

Waygood, E. R., and Clendenning, K. A., *Can. J. Research*, **C28**, 673.

Conn, E. E., and Vennesland, B., in "Brookhaven Conference Report," Assoc. Univ., Upton, N. Y., pp. 64–76.

Laties, G. G., *Arch. Biochem.*, **27**, 404.

1951   Strugger, S., *Ber. deut. botan. Ges.*, **64**, 69.

Nagai, S., *J. Inst. Polytech. Osaka City Univ.*, **2**, 7.

Arnon, D. T., *Nature*, **162**, 341.

Hill, R., and Scarisbrick, R., *New Phytol.*, **50**, 98.

Davenport, H. E., and Hill, R., *Proc. Roy. Soc. London*, **B139**, 327.

Hill, R., *Symp. Soc. Exptl. Biol.*, **5**, 222.

Whatley, F. R., Ordin, L., and Arnon, D. I., *Plant Physiol.*, **26**, 414.

Sisakyan, N. M., "Enzymatic Activity of Protoplasma Structures" (in Russian) Moscow, Acad. Sci. USSR.

Bhagvat, K., and Hill, R., *New Phytol.*, **50,** 112.

Whatley, F. R., Ordin, L., and Arnon, D. I., *Plant Physiol.*, **26,** 414.

Arnon, D. I., *Nature*, **167,** 1008.

1952   Pardee, A. B., Schachman, H. K., and Stanier, R. Y., *Nature*, **169,** 282.

Takashima, S., *Nature*, **169,** 182.

Thomas, J. B., Bustraan, M., and Paris, C. H., *Biochim. et Biophys. Acta,* **8,** 90.

Vatter, A. (personal communication).

Düvel, D., and Mevius, W., Jr., *Naturwiss.*, **39,** 23.

Schmidt, H., *Protoplasma*, **41,** 336.

Rezende-Pinto, M. C. de, *Protoplasma*, **41,** 336.

Rezende-Pinto, M. C. de, *Portug. Acta Biol.*, (**A**)**3,** 281.

Thomas, J. B., *Proc. Roy. Acad. Amsterdam*, **C55,** 207.

Bustraan, M., Goedheer, J. C., and Thomas, J. B., *Biochim. et Biophys. Acta,* **8,** 477; **9,** 499.

Metzner, H., *Protoplasma*, **41,** 129.

Metzner, H., *Nachr. Akad. Wiss. Göttingen, Math. physik. Kl. IIc. Biol. physiol. chem. Abt., No. 1.*

Steinmann, E., *Exptl. Cell Research*, **3,** 367.

Steinmann, E., *Experentia*, **VIII/8,** 300.

Weier, T. E., and Stocking, C. R., *Botan. Rev.*, **18,** 14–75.

Wolken, J. J., and Palade, G. E., *Nature*, **170,** 114.

Nagai, S., and Ogata, E., *J. Inst. Polytech. Osaka City Univ.*, **3,** 37.

McClendon, J. H., and Blinks, L. R., *Nature*, **170,** 577.

Weier, E., and Stocking, C. R., *Botan. Rev.*, **18,** 14–75.

Van Fleet, D. S., *Botan. Rev.*, **18,** 354.

Godnev, T. B., Shlyk, A. A., and Tretyak, N. K., *Compt. rend. (Doklady) Acad. Sci. USSR*, **87,** 493.

Clendenning, K. A., Waygood, E. R., and Weinberger, P., *Can. J. Botany*, **30,** 395.

McClendon, J. H., *Am. J. Botany*, **39,** 275.

Metzner, H., *Naturwiss.*, **39,** 64, *Biol. Zentr.*, **71,** 17.

Weinberger, P., and Clendenning, K. A., *Can. J. Botany.* **30,** 755.

Holzer, H., and Holzer, E., *Chem. Ber.*, **85,** 655.

Sisakyan, N. M., and Chernyak, M. S., *Compt. rend. (Doklady) Acad. Sci. USSR*, **87,** 469.

Calvin, M., and Lynch, V., *Nature*, **169,** 455.

1953   Wolken, J. J., and Palade, G. E., *Ann. N. Y. Acad. Sci.*, **56,** 873.

Leyon, H., *Exptl. Cell Research*, **4,** 371.

Leyon, H., *ibid.*, **5,** 520.

Frey-Wyssling, A., *Fortschritte der Botanik*, **14,** 66.

Frey-Wyssling, A., and Steinmann, E., *Vierteljahresshu. naturforsch. Ges. Zürich*, **98,** 20.

Heitz, E., and Maly, R., *Z. Naturforsch.*, **8b,** 243.

Rabinowitch, E., *Ann. Rev. Plant Physiol.*, **3**, 229–264.

McClendon, J. H., *Am. J. Botany*, **40**, 260.

Krasnovsky, A. A., and Kosobutskaya, L. M., *Compt. rend. (Doklady Acad. Sci. USSR*, **91**, 343.

Hill, R., Northcote, D. H., and Davenport, H. E., *Nature*, **172**, 947.

Algal Culture, from Laboratory to Pilot Plant, J. S. Burlew, Editor, Car negie Institution Publication No. 600, Washington, 1953; in particula Fogg, G. E., and Collyer, D. M., "The Documentation of Lipides by Algal," pp. 177–181; Milner, H. W., "The Chemical Compositio of Algal," pp. 285–302.

Rodrigo, F. A., *Biochim. et Biophys. Acta*, **10**, 342.

1954   Wolken, J. J., *J. Gen. Physiol.*, **37**, 111–120.

Thomas, J. B., Post, L. C., and Vertregt, N., *Biochem. et Biophys. Acta*, **13** 20.

Chiba, Y., *Arch. Biochem. and Biophys.*, **54**, 83.

Leyon, H., *Exptl. Cell Research*, **7**, 265.

Albertson, P. A., and Leyon, H., *ibid.*, **7**, 288.

Leyon, H., and Wettstein, D. v., *Z. Naturforsch.*, **9b**, 472.

Thomas, J. C., *Rapp. Comm. 8me Congr. Botanique*, Paris, Section 11, p 28.

Holzer, H., *Angew. Chemie*, **66**, 65.

Weissbach, A., Smyrniotis, P. Z., and Horecker, B. L., *J. Am. Chem. Soc.*, **76**, 3611.

Quayle, J. R., Fuller, R. C., Benson, A. A., and Calvin, M., *ibid.*, **76**, 3610.

McClendon, J. H., *Plant Physiol.* **29**, 448.

Arnon, D. I., Rosenberg, L. L., and Whatley, F. R., *Nature*, **173**, 1132.

Daly, J. M., and Brown, A. H., *Arch. Biochem. Biophys.*, **52**, 380.

B. CHEMISTRY OF CHLOROPLAST PIGMENTS*
(EXCLUDING PHOTOCHEMISTRY)

(ADDENDA TO CHAPTERS 15 AND 16)

No important progress has been achieved, since the publication of Volume I in 1945, in the synthesis of chlorophyll or in further elucidation of its structure. Important observations have been made, however, concerning the biogenesis of chlorophyll and its oxidation–reduction reactions.

1. Biosynthesis of Chlorophyll; The Protochlorophyll

(Addendum to Chapter 15, section B2)

In Vol. I (p. 405), after the description of protochlorophyll and its possible function as chlorophyll precursor in plants, the remark was made that "the whole problem of chlorophyll development in seedlings is in need of renewed study."

Since then, the subject has been taken up by Smith and co-workers at the Stanford Laboratory of the Carnegie Institution. Through quantitative determination of protochlorophyll, chlorophyll a and chlorophyll b in etiolated seedlings after exposure to light, they proved that up to 90% of the protochlorophyll, accumulated in the dark, are quantitatively converted, within a minute or less of moderately strong illumination, into chlorophyll a. After this initial period, the formation of chlorophyll a continues (and that of chlorophyll b gets under way) at a much slower rate, to reach saturation in a day or two; during this second stage, the rate is governed by thermal reactions, involving other precursors besides protochlorophyll—$e.g.$, those containing no magnesium in ether-soluble form. Whether this slow synthesis goes through protochlorophyll as intermediate, or by-passes this compound (as was assumed in Lubimenko's scheme, illustrated on p. 405), remains an open question. The presence of small amounts of protochlorophyll in fully green barley plants, noted by Koski and Smith (1948[2]), could be explained by protochlorophyll's being a side product, as well as by its being a necessary intermediate in chlorophyll synthesis.

Following is a brief summary of the studies of Smith and co-workers.

Smith (1947) determined the changes in the total magnesium content, ether-soluble magnesium, and chlorophyll magnesium, caused by exposure to light of etiolated barley seedling, in attached as well as in excised leaves. The results are summarized in Table 37B.I.

* Bibliography, page 1790.

TABLE 37B.I

SYNTHESIS OF ORGANIC MAGNESIUM COMPOUNDS BY ETIOLATED
BARLEY SEEDLINGS IN LIGHT (AFTER SMITH 1947)

| | Total Mg | | Total ether-sol. Mg | | Chl Mg |
Leaves	Before	After	Before	After	After
Attached (71 hr. exposure)....	0.16	0.22	5.2×10^{-4}	2×10^{-2}	1.8×10^{-2}
Detached (46 hr. exposure)...	0.19	0.216	5.4×10^{-4}	1.2×10^{-2}	1.11×10^{-2}

Weight per cent of dry matter before and after exposure

The fastest increase in ether-soluble magnesium was noted in the first
two hours of exposure to light; during this time, the total formation of
ether-soluble magnesium compounds ran considerably ahead of that of
chlorophyll, indicating the accumulation of other magnesium-containing
organic molecules—perhaps chlorophyll precursors (*cf.* section 2 below).
After a day or two, chlorophyll formation caught up with that of total
organic magnesium compounds; in attached leaves, in particular, over
90% of the total ether-extractable magnesium was found, at that time,
to be present in chlorophyll.

Leaves left in the dark as controls formed no more ether-soluble magnesium compounds after germination, indicating that light is needed not
only for the formation of chlorophyll, but also for the accumulation of the
other magnesium-containing organic compounds.

Smith (1949) gave time curves for the formation of total ether-soluble
magnesium and chlorophyll magnesium in etiolated barley seedlings at
three different temperatures.

At $0°$ C., the maximum amount of ether-soluble magnesium compounds
formed was only 6% of that formed at $19°$ C.; the synthesis reached saturation in a few hours, after which the concentration of ether-soluble magnesium began to decline. The chlorophyll synthesis fared even worse—
the amount synthesized never exceeded 15% of total ether-soluble magnesium, and started to decline already after two hours of exposure.

At $7°$ C., a fast initial formation of a small amount of chlorophyll was
noticeable in the first hour (without much change in the total ether-soluble magnesium); a delay ensued in the next few hours, after which the
formation of ether-soluble magnesium compounds got under way and continued steadily even after 40 hours' exposure. The formation of chlorophyll
followed, and gradually caught up with, that of the total ether-soluble
magnesium compounds; after 40 hours, 70% of total ether-soluble magnesium was in chlorophyll.

At $19°$ C., the chlorophyll formation, after a slight initial lag, caught up
in a few hours with the total formation of ether-soluble magnesium compounds (in agreement with the results shown in Table 37B.I for attached

leaves). The concentration of organic magnesium reached saturation after about 40 hours' exposure, after which the amount of chlorophyll began to decline slightly, probably because of photoxidation.

These experiments, particularly that at 7° C., clearly pointed to a two-stage process of chlorophyll formation—a fast photochemical reaction and a relatively slow thermal reaction, brought almost to a standstill at 0° C.

The formation of ether-soluble phosphorus compounds was found to follow a course parallel to that of the formation of ether-soluble magnesium compounds.

The isolation of sizable quantities of pure protochlorophyll by Koski and Smith (1948[1]), and the absolute determination of its absorption coefficients (cf. fig. 21.8 in Vol. II,1, page 618) made it possible to correlate quantitatively the formation of chlorophyll with the disappearance of protochlorophyll.

Smith (1948) made the first such comparison by determining the amount of chlorophyll formed in the first two hours of illumination at 0° C. and the amount of protochlorophyll present at the beginning of the exposure. He found an approximate proportionality between the two magnitudes, with the proportionality constant <1. In fact, the amount of synthesized chlorophyll corresponded, under these conditions, to little more than one-half of the available protochlorophyll.

A more precise study was carried out by Koski (1950), by restricting the measurements to the first few minutes of illumination. This allowed working at room temperature, without the slow thermal reactions interfering significantly with the fast photochemical transformation.

Corn seedlings were used. They were germinated for 15 days in the dark and then exposed to fluorescent light (150 foot-candles) at room temperature. Protochlorophyll, chlorophyll a and chlorophyll b were determined spectrophotometrically at different times after the beginning of illumination, using the following specific absorption coefficients:

λ	$\alpha_{sp.}$(Chl. a)	$\alpha_{sp.}$(Chl. b)	$\alpha_{sp.}$(protochlorophyll)[a]
663 mμ	95	5.1	0.19
644 mμ	15.4	57.5	1.15
624 mμ	13.9	9.9	39.9

[a] Contrary to the observations of Seybold and Egle on pumpkin seeds (Vol. I, p. 404 and Vol. II.1, p. 619), no evidence of the presence of a protochlorophyll b was obtained by Smith and Koski.

Fig. 37.B1 shows the rapid formation of chlorophyll a in the first minute of exposure, and an exactly equivalent decrease in protochlorophyll content. After the first minute, the amount of chlorophyll formed begins to trail somewhat, but not significantly, behind the amount of protochlorophyll lost, so that the total pigment concentration drops very slightly. After about one hour of illumination, chlorophyll b appears, and

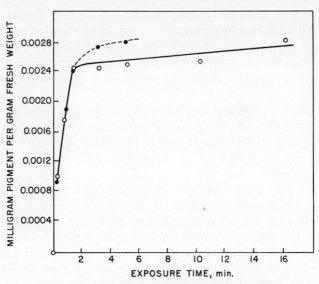

Fig. 37B.1. Quantity of chlorophyll formed (O) and of protochlorophyll used up (●) in etiolated corn seedlings (after Koski 1950).

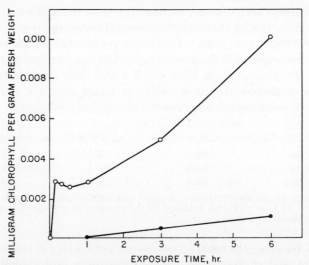

Fig. 37B.2. Formation of chlorophyll a (O) and b (●) at 12° C. in etiolated corn seedlings (after Koski 1950). Original protochlorophyll content of the seedlings was 0.003 mg./g. fresh weight.

the amount of chlorophyll a begins to rise above the almost stationary level that was established after the first few minutes of illumination (fig. 37.B2).   This slow, but steady, increase continues for hours; it must be determined by the rate of replenishment of the pool of chlorophyll precursors by slow thermal reactions.   The initial fast pigment formation undoubtedly is the result of photochemical conversion of pre-existent protochlorophyll into chlorophyll.   Only the a component is formed in this way.

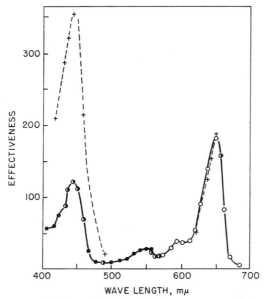

Fig. 37B.3. Action spectrum of transformation of protochlorophyll to chlorophyll a in etiolated corn leaves: (O) normal, (+) albino (Koski, French and Smith 1951).

The sharp absorption band in the violet, noted by Koski and Smith (1948) in the spectrum of protochlorophyll, has an analogue in the *action spectrum* of chlorophyll formation, first noted by Frank (1946) in experiments on oat seedlings in filtered light.   The finding of this band invalidated a previously used argument against identification of the precursor which produces chlorophyll in light, with protochlorophyll.

Frank's study left the question of carotenoid contribution to the action spectrum peak in the blue-violet unsettled; an "auto-photocatalysis" by chlorophyll (*cf*. Vol. I, p. 430) seemed to be indicated, but could not be definitely proved.

The action spectrum of chlorophyll formation was re-investigated by

Koski, French and Smith (1951) using a powerful monochromator with normal and albino corn. The albino mutant (*cf.* Koski and Smith 1951) formed, in the dark, more protochlorophyll than the normal strain; it converted it into chlorophyll in light, but this chlorophyll was rapidly destroyed by further illumination, indicating that albinism was due to lack of protection of chlorophyll against photoxidation. Other, "virescent," mutants, described by Smith and Koski 1948, produced only very little protochlorophyll in the dark, but kept forming chlorophyll slowly upon prolonged illumination, and once formed, did not lose it easily.

The albino seedlings had the great experimental advantage of containing almost no carotenoids.

The action spectra for chlorophyll synthesis of the two strains are shown in fig. 37.B3. The ordinate is inversely proportional to the number of quanta needed to transform 20% of the total available protochlorophyll into chlorophyll; the peak at 650 mμ corresponds to this transformation being completed in 18.4 sec., in a flux of 80 erg/(cm.^{2} $\times$ sec.). The absorption peaks are situated, in both cases, at 445 and 650 mμ. The ratio of the ordinates in the two peaks is 1.89 in albino and 0.66 in normal plants, clearly indicating the relative (or complete) inefficiency of the carotenoids. (Frank, 1946, had found a ratio of 1.47. This result may indicate either a lower content, or a higher efficiency of carotenoids in oat seedlings. A more trivial explanation also is possible—a smearing-out of the action spectrum, caused by the use of light filters.)

The red action peak in fig. 37.B3 is shifted by 21 mμ, and the violet peak, by 11 mμ, toward the longer waves, compared to the absorption peaks of protochlorophyll in methanol solution; both figures correspond to a shift of about 500 cm.$^{-1}$ on the wave-number scale. It seems plausible that the absorption bands of protochlorophyll *in vivo* are shifted by that amount toward the red from their position *in vitro*. A transmission minimum was in fact noted in the spectrum of squash seeds at 650 mμ (*cf.* Chapter 37C, section 2e).

When plants in which one-half of protochlorophyll had been converted to chlorophyll, were illuminated with a monochromatic band centered at 680 mμ (a wave length only slightly absorbed by protochlorophyll, but strongly absorbed by chlorophyll *a in vivo*), very little additional chlorophyll formation was observed, indicating the practical absence of "auto-photocatalysis."

Smith (1951, 1954) used Franck and Pringsheim's phosphorescence quenching method (Vol. II,1, p. 851) to determine whether any *oxygen* was produced during the photochemical reduction of protochlorophyll to chlorophyll. The conversion was not inhibited by an atmosphere of pure hydrogen ($<10^{-5}$ per cent O_2) needed for the application of this method. The observed oxygen liberation was $\leq 2.5\%$ of that calculated on the assumption that the reduction occurs at the expense of water (protochlorophyll $+$ $H_2O \rightarrow Chl + O_2$).   Under similar conditions, in leaves which contained some chlorophyll, oxygen evolution from photosynthesis could be easily observed; this shows that the lack of oxygen production in etiolated leaves was not due to immediate re-utilization of this gas by the cells.   The conclusion is thus justified that the photochemical conversion of protochlorophyll into chlorophyll is *not* coupled with the oxidation of water.   (It therefore cannot represent the oxygen-liberating step in photosynthesis, as has been occasionally suggested.)

Smith and Benitez (1954) inquired into the *temperature dependence* of the initial protochlorophyll $\rightarrow$ chlorophyll conversion in light, over a wide range, from $-175°$ to $+55°$ C.   They noted that heating above 40° C. progressively destroyed the capacity for conversion and suggested that this indicates the denaturation of a protein (to which protochlorophyll can be assumed to be attached *in vivo*, and which may be essential for the transformation; dissolved protochlorophyll is not converted to chlorophyll by illumination).

Cooling below 40° C. slowed down the photochemical conversion. This, and the fact that the reaction followed a bimolecular law (strictly at 589, 579 and 546 mμ; less strictly at 436 mμ) indicated interaction between an excited and a normal protochlorophyll molecule.   (Proportionality of the rate with the first power of light intensity excludes a reaction between two excited molecules.)   Perhaps the reaction is a dismutation with one protochlorophyll molecule being reduced and one oxidized, but no oxidation product has yet been observed.

The temperature curve can be followed down to $-80°$ C., at which temperature the conversion is still appreciable in both rate and total amount.   It becomes unobservable at $-195°$ C.   Thawing after freezing destroys the capacity for conversion; slow passage through the freezing zone damages it.   In order to measure the rate at $-10°$ or $-20°$ C., the leaves must be snap-frozen at $-80°$ C. and then warmed up.

Some experiments were made by Smith and co-workers on the rate of protochlorophyll formation by barley seedlings *in the dark*.   A sigmoid curve was obtained, almost no protochlorophyll being formed in the first three days of germination, an accelerated formation occurring between the third and the sixth day, and the synthesis slowing down after the sixth day.   The development of carotenoids followed a similar course.

Godnev and Terentjeva (1953) found that the conversion of protochlorophyll to chlorophyll can be achieved, in etiolated corn seedlings, instead of by exposure to light, also by infiltration with an extract from pine seedlings (conifers, like algae, can form chlorophyll in darkness).

Krasnovsky and Kosobutskaya (1953) observed that when etiolated leaves (or plastid fragments from them) were exposed to light the formation of chlorophyll occurred in two stages. In the first 2–3 hours, the absorption peak was at 670 mμ, and most of the chlorophyll formed was easily bleachable by strong light. Later, the band peak gradually shifted to 678 mμ, and most of chlorophyll became photostable.

As mentioned above, the development of *chlorophyll b* in etiolated barley occurs, according to Smith, only in the second, slow stage that follows the initial rapid conversion of preformed protochlorophyll into chlorophyll *a*. It is possible, but not certain, that the synthesis of the *b* component involves a "protochlorophyll *b*." Such a compound does not accumulate in etiolated seedlings; but according to Seybold and Egle (*cf.* pp. 404 and 619) it is present in pumpkin seeds. It is very unlikely that chlorophyll *b* is formed by oxidation of chlorophyll *a*.

The delayed formation of chlorophyll *b* was noted also by Goodwin and Owens (1947) in oat seedlings.

The appearance of chlorophyll *b* is not essential for the beginning of photosynthesis, according to Smith (1954).

Some x-ray mutants of barley were found to be permanently deficient in chlorophyll *b* (Highkin 1950), but capable of photosynthesis. In some mutants of corn, chlorophyll *b* was formed only after a delay of from 4 to 14 days, depending on temperature (Schwartz 1949).

Certain x-ray mutants of *Chlorella*, obtained by Granick (1951), produced chlorophyll only in light (similarly to the higher plants, but unlike normal algae). Granick suggested that the enzymatic system capable of reducing protochlorophyll to chlorophyll in the dark was absent in these mutants.

The effect of *narcotics* and of *colchicine* on the synthesis of chlorophyll in etiolated wheat seedlings was studied by Brebion (1948, 1950). Ether, acetone, benzene and phenol vapors were found to delay the greening in high concentrations and to stimulate it in low concentrations (with phenol, as low as $1 \times 10^{-5}\%$).

Among new observations of the influence of different external factors on the development of chlorophyll, we can mention the specific effect of *streptomycin*, first noted by von Euler, Bracco and Heller (1948). Seeds germinating on paper wetted with streptomycin solution developed completely colorless coleoptiles and first leaves. Streptomycin had no effect on leaves already containing chlorophyll. Provasoli and co-workers (1948, 1951) found that streptomycin causes *Euglena gracilis* cells to lose their capacity for forming chloroplasts; this deficiency was inherited by their offspring.

Bogorad (1950) noted that the cotyledons of a pine (*Pinus Jeffryi*), which normally can form chlorophyll in the dark, will do it only in light if the seeds had been germinated in the presence of streptomycin. This antibiotic seems to prevent the formation of the enzyme that converts protochlorophyll into chlorophyll.

It must be kept in mind, however, that this interpretation (whether applied to x-ray mutants, or to the action of streptomycin) takes it for granted that *all* chlorophyll formation occurs via protochlorophyll—a question which we have left open.

The relation between the appearance of chlorophyll and the *beginning of photosynthesis* was mentioned in Chapter 32 (section 3). Additional observations have been since reported by Blaauw-Jansen, Komen and Thomas (1950), and Smith (1954). Blaauw Jansen *et al.* found that etiolated oat leaves had only a slight capacity for photosynthesis when first illuminated. This capacity increased, upon exposure to light, faster than the chlorophyll content; and it was noted that it grew parallel with the increase in the $[b]:[a]$ ratio, until the latter attained its normal value. Smith (1954) found, by the phosphorescence-quenching method, that even after 85% of the protochlorophyll present in etiolated barley leaves had been converted into chlorophyll a by illumination in pure hydrogen, the leaves were still incapable of photosynthetic oxygen production. If such leaves (containing only chlorophyll derived from the original reservoir of protochlorophyll) were exposed to air in the dark, they acquired a slight capacity for photosynthesis. This capacity was greatly increased by brief illumination—the increase being out of all proportion with the accumulation of new chlorophyll. It thus seems that the chlorophyll formed from protochlorophyll in the first minute or two of exposure of etiolated leaves to light is photosynthetically inactive. This inactivity should be due to difference, either in chemical structure, or in the composition of the pigment complex, or in the arrangement of the pigment molecules. (For example, activity may require the formation of monomolecular layers of the pigment on protein discs, as suggested in Chapter 37A.)

Alternatively, the delay in the acquisition of photosynthetic capacity could be caused by deficiency of a catalytic component other than chlorophyll. (This component must be rapidly formed in the cycle: brief anaerobic irradiation—exposure to air in the dark—brief aerobic irradiation; and only more slowly in continuous light.)

As mentioned above, Krasnovsky and Kosobutskaya (1953) found that the first chlorophyll formed has an absorption peak at 670 mμ while the main mass of the pigment, formed later, has a peak at 678 mμ. They suggested that the (more easily photoxidized) first batch ("Chl 670") is the only "photoactive" part of the pigment; while the subsequently formed bulk ("Chl 678"), is in an inactive, polymeric form, and contributes to photosynthesis only by energy transfer to the "active" form. The above-described observations by Smith and Koski suggest the reverse hypothesis—that only "Chl 678" is photosynthetically active. (The capacity for photoxidation may well be antiparallel, rather than parallel, to photosynthetic activity.) In Chapter 37C (section 6b) we will quote another argument, pointing to the same conclusion: Resonance energy transfer always is directed toward the pigment with the lower excited state (while Krasnovsky's hypothesis calls for energy transfer in the opposite direction). The 670 mμ absorption band may belong to as yet "unorganized" (but already protein-bound) chlorophyll, while the 678 mμ band may be that of chlorophyll arranged in monomolecular layers; the shift may then be due to the electrostatic interaction of the pigment molecules in a regular array, to be discussed in section 3 of Chapter 37C.

Yocum (1946) observed the inhibition of chlorophyll formation in excised, etiolated bean leaves by poisons. *Carbon monoxide* reduced both respiration and chlorophyll formation in red light, in approximately the same ratio; strong blue light reversed the inhibition in both cases. *Cyanide* (10^{-3} M) reduced the formation of protochlorophyll in the dark, but did not affect the conversion of protochlorophyll to chlorophyll.

The *biodecomposition* of chlorophyll was discussed by Noack (1943), who attributed the destruction of the green pigment in autumn to the action of hydrogen peroxide, not decomposed by the, now inactivated, catalase, on water-soluble chlorophyllides formed by the action of chlorophyllase.

2. Biogenesis of Chlorophyll; Earlier Precursors

If one wants to speculate on the mechanism of chlorophyll synthesis in the living cell beyond the experimentally established photochemical conversion of protochlorophyll to chlorophyll, one must take recourse to indirect evidence.

Granick (1948,[1,2] 1950,[1,2] 1951, 1954) obtained such evidence from experiments in which *Chlorella* cells were exposed to x-rays, producing a variety of mutants. Several of these—viable in glucose solution but incapable of photosynthesis—were found to contain no chlorophyll: instead, some of them carried pigments of the porphin type not normally encountered in algae. One mutant, in particular, dark brown in color, contained globules of *protoporphyrin 9*. In another mutant, which, when grown on a solid nutrient medium, developed an orange-brown color, small amounts of the *magnesium derivative* of the same protoporphyrin could be identified (in addition to the protoporphyrin itself). A third, yellow mutant yielded magnesium-vinyl pheoporphyrin a_5, i. e., protochlorophyll without the phytol chain.

Granick postulated that the appearance of these pigments signifies that the development of chlorophyll has been interrupted at an intermediate stage by lack of a specific enzyme (caused by damage to a gene).   He derived from these observations the scheme of the biosynthesis of chlorophyll, which is represented in the right side of fig. 37B.4.

Protoporphyrin 9 is the porphyrin most closely related to hemoglobin (in fact, it is the heme minus iron).   According to Granick, this porphyrin is the common precursor of both the red blood pigment and the green plant pigment.

Granick speculated further on the probable mechanism of synthesis of protoporphyrin 9 from ultimate, small building blocks—assumed to be glycine and acetate.   The first synthesized pyrrole derivative he assumed to be (I) in fig. 37B.4.   Uroporphyrin (II) was assumed to be the first tetrapyrrole formed from this monopyrrole derivative, and coproporphyrin (III), the intermediate between uroporphyrin and protoporphyrin 9.

Additional results were reported by Bogorad and Granick (1952). They found new *Chlorella* mutants, containing porphyrins with 2, 3, 4, 5 and 8 carboxyl groups.   One of them, the monovinyl hydroxy dicarboxylporphyrin, was suggested as a likely immediate precursor of protoporphyrin; its own precursor could be hematoporphyrin, also found in these mutants.

The role of glycine in supplying nitrogen for the synthesis of porphin derivatives was first demonstrated by Shemin and Rittenberg in 1946, by experiments on human erythrocytes with N^{15} tracer.   The (indirect) acetate origin of the carbon atoms (other than those supplied by the α-carbons of glycine), also was supported by isotope tracer studies of Rittenberg and co-workers.   Salomon, Altman and Rosa (1950) showed that the α-carbons of acetic acid and of glycine are used in the synthesis of chlorophyll in the plant cell; this lends support to Granick's hypothesis that the formation of chlorophyll follows—up to a certain point—the same path as the synthesis of heme.

Granick suggested, as a further hypothesis, that biosynthesis, as it occurs in plants now, repeats the path of evolution.   In other words, he postulated that organisms synthesizing uroporphyrin, coproporphyrin, protoporphyrin and, finally, protochlorophyll and chlorophyll, have evolved in this order.   He assumed that, at the time when any one of these compounds represented the final product of synthesis, it was used for some metabolic process by the organism; this particular process fell into disuse as the synthesis advanced another step.   More specifically, Granick suggested that all porphin pigments presently encountered in cells have been used, at some stage of evolution, as photochemical sensitizers.   He saw a confirmation of this view in the capacity of "vestigial" pigments, such as chlorophyll c, to sensitize photosynthesis. (He had found chlorophyll c to be a porphin, rather than a chlorin, *cf.* section 5

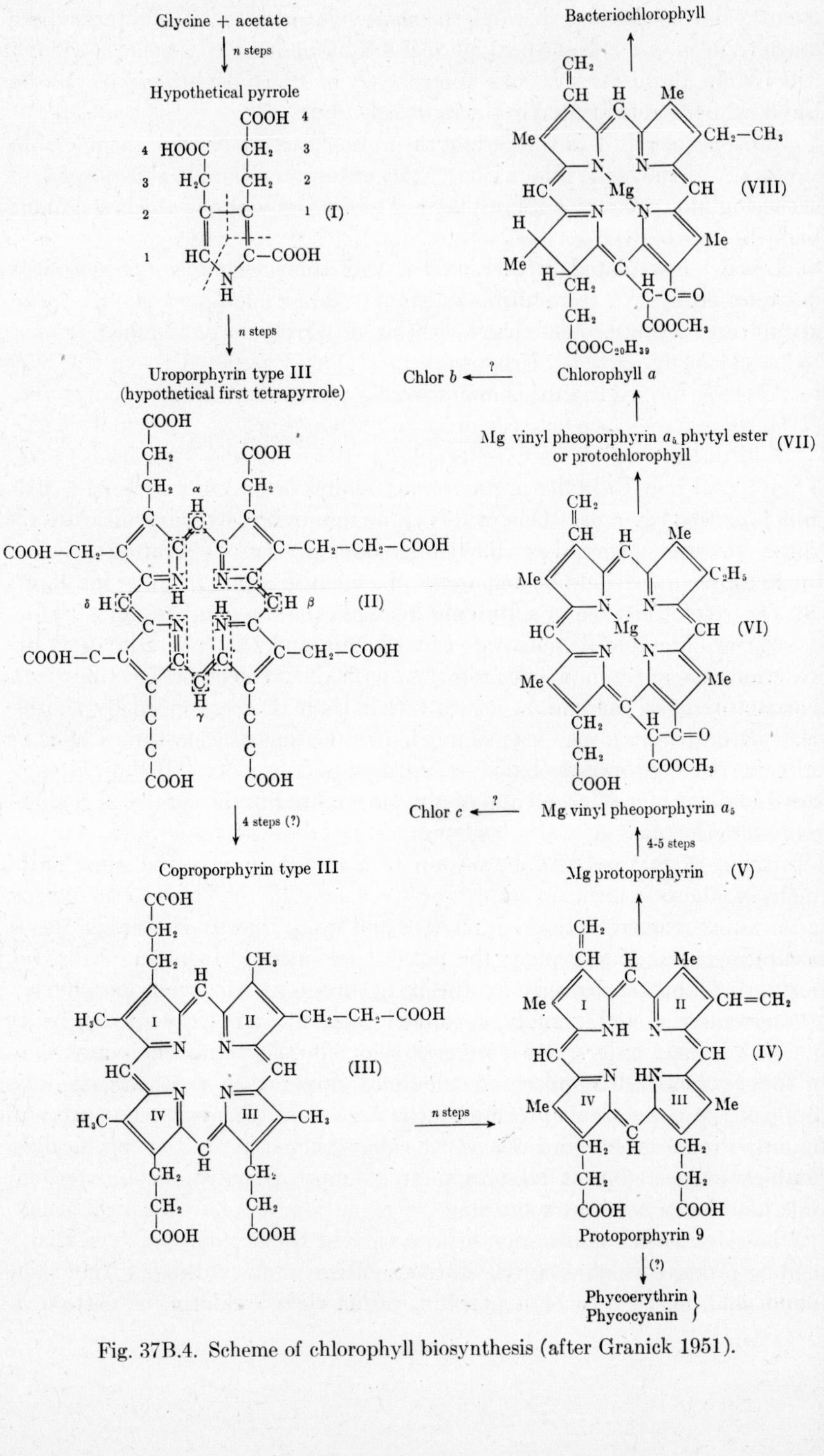

Fig. 37B.4. Scheme of chlorophyll biosynthesis (after Granick 1951).

below, and considered it a side product of evolution of Mg vinyl pheo-porphyrin a_5, as indicated in fig. 37B.4.) Granick saw in the same light the role in photosynthesis of the phycobilins, which he considered another survival from an early stage of evolution.

This approach differs, in its general tendency, from the theories that consider organic evolution as having been accompanied by a *loss* of syn-thesizing abilities rather than by their gradual *aquisition*. Also, Granick sees the role of accessory pigments in somewhat different light than the—presently most plausible—hypothesis that these pigments serve as sup-pliers of energy, by resonance, to the one pigment adapted for the photo-catalytic function proper—chlorophyll *a* (*cf.* Chapters 30 and 32).

3. Isomers and Solvates of Chlorophyll

(Addendum to Chapter 15, section B1)

In Vol. I, page 403, we mentioned that Strain and Manning (1942) had observed the reversible conversion of chlorophylls *a* and *b* into slightly different forms, which they called *a'* and *b'*. (It will be recalled that four such forms: *d*, iso-*d*, *d'* and iso-*d'* were observed with chlorophyll *d*.) Strain (1949, 1953) gave additional details on these compounds.

When chlorophyll is extracted from leaves, hydrolytic and oxidative reactions are apt to occur, leading to a multiplicity of colored bands in the chromatographic column. The relative rates of these reactions depend on the plant species used, and on incidental factors such as the method of mincing (for example, chopping causes less oxidation than grinding or crushing). Light is to be avoided during preparation and storage of the minced leaf material.

Rapid extraction of chopped mallow or barley leaves by grinding in methanol or acetone, to which some petroleum ether had been added, gives, according to Strain, only chlorophylls *a* and *b*. If, however, chopped leaves are placed into boiling water for 1–2 minutes before extraction, *a'* and *b'* are also found in the extract. (Plants with acid sap, such as *Opuntia*, *Pelargonium*, and *Bryophyllum*, rapidly form pheophytin when heated in air.) Chopped leaves, dried in air for 24 hours, yield small amounts of *a'* and *b'*; heating to 100° C. in air for 15 minutes after drying increases the quantity of these isomers considerably. No new pigments are produced, in either mallow or barley leaves, by freezing and thawing, or by standing with saturated ammonium sulfate for 20 hours and washing (by dialysis into distilled water) for 20 hours.

Isomerizations similar to those occurring with chlorophylls *a* and *b* can be produced also with the chlorophyllides, *e. g.*, by heating their pro-panol solutions, or permitting them to stand for several days at room temperature. The isomeric chlorophyllides are less adsorbable than the original chlorophyllides a and b. Separated on the column and redissolved in propanol, they can be (at least partially) reconverted to a and b by heating. The isomerization equilibrium of the ethyl and methyl chlorophyllides seems to correspond, at room temperature, to $[a]:[a'] = [b]:[b'] = 3:1$.

Isomerization is not affected by the presence of air or dimethyl-aniline (which, respectively, bring about and prevent allomerization). It is accelerated by alkali: 0.2% KOH produces isomeric equilibration in 1–5 minutes, followed by a slower oxidation.

In discussing the possible mechanism of isomerization, Strain pointed out that its absence after allomerization points to a role of the C(10) atom, and suggested that the isomers differ only by the spatial arrangement of the two groups ($COOCH_3$ and H) attached to C(10); they could then be converted into each other via their common enol, in which the H-atom is transferred from C(10) to C(9) to form a hydroxyl group there. This could account for the catalytic effect of alkalis on the isomerization.

Freed and Sancier (1951) noticed a variability of the spectrum of chlorophyll b preparations—particularly of the small peak at 481.5 mμ.

Subsequently, Freed, Sancier and Sporer (1954) isolated from such preparations a fraction which they called *chlorophyll* b''. It had a spectrum very similar to that of b, but gave no phase test. Freed suggested that b, b' and b'' may be the three isomers anticipated on page 444, differing only in the routing of the conjugated bond system. On the other hand, Freed's b'' appears similar to Holt's "fraction 3" of allomerized chlorophyll a (*cf.* page 1775).

The main subject of the studies of Freed and Sancier (1951, 1952, 1953, 1954) was the transformation of the chlorophylls and their derivatives *at low temperatures*. At first (1951) the observed reversible spectroscopic changes were interpreted as evidence of the formation of new isomers. Because of the analogy between these spectral changes and those caused by various solvents, it was suggested that the solvent effect, too, may be caused by isomerization. After the experiments of Livingston and co-workers, Evstigneev, and others (*cf.* Chapter 21, section B1; Chapter 23, sections 4–6, and Chapter 37C, section 2) had revealed that chlorophyll forms complexes with water and other solvents which differ in their absorption spectrum and capacity for fluorescence, Freed and Sancier (1954) reinterpreted the temperature changes of the absorption spectra as also resulting from the formation and dissociation of solvates. However, the two types of transformation—isomerization and solvation—may be coupled; *e. g.*, association with a protophilic solvent is likely to favor enolization.

It is a matter of arbitrary choice whether to discuss the solvent effects and temperature effects on the chlorophyll spectrum in the present chapter (as isomerization or solvation phenomena), or in Chapter 37C under the heading of "Solvent Effects on Absorption Spectra." Since the latter arrangement had been adopted in Chapter 20 we will adhere to it; the description of Freed's low temperature studies will be therefore found in Chapter 37C, section 2a. Only the part of these experiments related to the mechanism of certain irreversible reactions of chlorophyll (with alkalis and amines) will be described in section 4 below.

4. Oxidation, Allomerization and Reduction of Chlorophyll

(Addendum to Chapter 16, section B3)

In Chapter 16 (p. 459) the so-called *allomerization* of chlorophyll was discussed—a transformation that occurs upon standing in alcoholic solution, involves the uptake of oxygen, and can be brought about also by addition of oxidants such as quinone. It was interpreted as oxidation of the "lone" hydrogen atom at C(10). The allomerized chlorophyll differs from the intact compound by its incapacity to give the "brown phase" in alkalysis, and by its spectrum. A significant feature of this spectrum (fig. 21.4A) is the apparently complete absence of the short-wave satellite of the main blue-violet band, that is present, with varying intensity, in the spectra of all chlorophylls, chlorophyllides, pheophorbides, etc. (*cf.* figs. 21.1 and 21.26). This satellite could be due to a vibration (of the order of 750 cm.$^{-1}$), or to the doublet structure of the excited electronic term (perhaps, corresponding to charge oscillations in two mutually perpendicular directions in the porphin plane, *cf.* Chapter 37C, section 1); or to a tautomeric form (as suggested tentatively on p. 627, Vol. II,1). Whatever the correct interpretation of the satellite band may be, its disappearance upon allomerization must be significant.

It has long been known that upon extraction from leaves and standing in solution, homogeneous chlorophyll preparations very soon form several fractions which are adsorbed in separate bands on the chromatographic column. Some study was devoted to these changes by Strain (1949), who placed mallow or barley leaves in methanol for over 24 hours, and studied the products formed in the presence and in the absence of air. Prolonged treatment with methanol turned chopped mallow leaves yellow; crystals of the methyl chlorophyllides *a* and *b*, and a small amount of acidic chlorophyllides (*i. e.*, free chlorophyllins) *a* and *b* (extractable with 0.01 *N* KOH), were formed in them. In addition, new green and yellow-green pigments were produced, the spectra of which were similar to those of the chlorophylls *a* and *b*, but which gave no positive phase test and could thus be presumed to be oxidation products. They were not formed in the absence of air, or in dried leaves moistened with water and then immersed into methanol (even in the presence of air). Formation of the methyl chlorophyllides as well as of the colored oxidation products could be prevented by preliminary exposure of leaves to boiling water or steam, or to a temperature of 100° C. in a sealed tube—presumably because heat destroyed both the chlorophyllase and the enzymes catalyzing oxidation.

Sometimes pheophytins also were formed during the treatment of leaves with methanol; this could be prevented by the addition of a base, such as dimethylaniline. The formation of the chlorophyllides was faster when a smaller volume of methanol was used, or aqueous methanol (50–75%) was employed instead of pure solvent.

In barley leaves, no chlorophyllase action occurred upon standing in methanol; if air was absent, they yielded mainly the original chlorophylls a and b; in air, the two above-mentioned, nonacidic oxidation products. The oxidation enzymes resisted freezing but not dehydration. They were most active in young seedlings.

Strain analyzed products formed by standing in methanol also in leaves of seventeen other species, and in isolated chloroplasts of Swiss chard. Some gave mainly unaltered chlorophylls, and others chlorophyllides, pheophytins or oxidized chlorophylls.

A 10–20 hour treatment with acetone or methyl acetate caused chlorophyll in freshly chopped, or dried and moistened, mallow leaves to be converted largely to chlorophyllin. Heating of dried leaves to 100° for 10 minutes did not prevent this conversion, but it could be avoided by a 1–2 minute immersion into boiling water.

When chopped mallow leaves were permitted to stand in acetone in air (but not in vacuum) for 24 hours, very strongly adsorbable pigments—presumably oxidation products of the chlorophyllins—were formed.

Barley leaves treated with acetone in air yielded primarily the same oxidation products, which were also observed in treatment with alcohols.

The green pigments formed from chlorophyll a by enzymatic oxidation were found to differ from those formed by allomerization in solution. Allomerized chlorophyll a is blue-green; absorption peaks lie (*cf.* fig. 21.4A) at 650 and 420 mμ (in methanol); on a sugar column, it forms a band well above chlorophyll a. No trace of this band is visible in the chromatograph of enzymatic oxidation products from chopped barley leaves left standing in methanol. On the other hand, the most strongly adsorbed of the several minor green products formed in allomerization of chlorophyll a in methanol, appeared to be identical with the main enzymatic oxidation product formed in leaves. Its band maximum lies at 662 mμ

in petroleum ether (blue-green solution) and at 667 mμ in methanol (green solution).

Allomerization of chlorophyll a' in methanol yielded the same series of pigments as that of chlorophyll a.

Chlorophyll b also produced, by allomerization in methanol, several products, with the principal one having absorption bands shifted toward the shorter waves (to 631 and about 442 mμ in petroleum ether, 636 and about 458 mμ in methanol).

Experiments with etiolated barley plants, immersed into chlorophyll solution in methanol, showed that the chlorophyll entering the tissues is rapidly deposited there in the form of green "crystals," which upon re-dissolving give no brown phase and therefore must be considered as oxidation product.

Once plants had become green, the assortment of chlorophyll pigments in the leaves remains remarkably constant—in darkness as well as in light, in air, oxygen, carbon dioxide or hydrogen. In the disappearance of chlorophyll in ripening fruit or autumn leaves, no *colored* transformation products of the natural chlorophylls could be observed.

Holt and Jacobs (1954) also found that allomerized chlorophyll (or chlorophyllide) a, formed by standing in air in methanolic solution, can be separated by chromatography into several components. In addition to the main fraction, with the spectrum of the type illustrated by Fig. 21.4A ("fraction 2"), there was one more readily absorbed fraction ("fraction 3") with a spectrum practically identical with that of "native" chlorophyll a, and a smaller, less readily absorbed "fraction 1," with a red peak further toward the longer waves (*cf.* Fig. 37.C.3). All three fractions gave no "brown phase" with alkali. All of them could be reduced in light by ascorbic acid ("Krasnovsky reaction," *cf.* Chapter 35). All three fractions could be reversibly decolorized (oxidized?) by ferric chloride ("Rabinowitch-Weiss reaction," *cf.* Chapter 16, section B3, and this section, further below). Infrared spectroscopy (*cf.* Chapter 37C, section 2e) indicated that fraction 3 alone contains the C=O group in position 9. If negative phase test is attributed to incapacity for enolization of this group, this incapacity must be attributed, in fraction 3, to an oxidative substitution of the H-atom in position 10, *e. g.*, by a methoxy group:

$$(37A.1) \qquad \underset{\overset{|}{\underset{O}{\|}}}{\overset{V}{\overset{|}{HC}}}\underset{9}{\overset{10}{-}}\overset{III}{\overset{|}{C}}-\overset{|}{C}= \xrightarrow[+1/2 O_2]{+ CH_3OH} \overset{V}{\overset{|}{CH_3OC}}-\overset{III}{\overset{|}{\underset{\overset{\|}{O}}{C}}}-\overset{|}{C}= + H_2O$$

In fractions 2, allomerization must involve a more drastic change—probably disruption of ring V, with the formation of a lactone (as suggested by Fischer and Pfeiffer, 1944):

$$(37A.2) \qquad \underset{O}{\overset{V \quad III}{HC-C-C=}} \xrightarrow[+1^{1}/_{2}O_{2}]{+CH_{3}OH} \underset{O}{\overset{III}{CH_{3}OC-O-O-C-C=}} + H_{2}O$$

The difference between the fractions 2 and the (small) fraction 1 remains to be interpreted.

The chlorophyll reaction with *ferric chloride*, described by Rabinowitch and Weiss and interpreted by them as oxidation (Vol. I, p. 464), also was studied by Strain (1949). He noted that extraction of the yellow product with water and petroleum ether led to regeneration of chlorophyll *a*, and that addition of dimethylaniline prevented the formation of the yellow product. He concluded from these observations that the reaction in question is *not* an oxidation. However, the interpretation of Rabinowitch and Weiss was based on the assumption of an equilibrium between the reduced and the oxidized form—and in this form their hypothesis is not contradicted by Strain's observations.

Strain confirmed that the decoloration reaction with ferric chloride occurred also in allomerized chlorophyll *a*, and in the above-described green product of enzymatic oxidation in chopped leaves.

Objections against the interpretation of the reaction of chlorophyll with ferric salt as reversible oxidation were raised also by Ashkinazi, Glikman, and Dain (1950). They noted that bleaching of the red absorption band of chlorophyll in methanol can be caused not only by Fe^{+3} salts, but also by the salts of Al^{+3} and Sn^{+2} (while Cu^{+2} and Zn^{+2} caused an enhancement of the red band, and K^+, Ca^{+2}, Pb^{+2} and Mn^{+2} had little or no effect). The authors suggested that the bleaching effects of Al^{+3}, Sn^{+2} and Fe^{+3} are caused primarily by the acidity of these salts, which leads to pheophytinization of chlorophyll (and consequent weakening of the red band and increase in absorption in the green). The ions Fe^{+2}, Cu^{+2} and Zn^{+2} (but *not* Sn^{+2} and Al^{+3}) react with pheophytin, replacing hydrogen and forming metal complexes; in these complexes, the red band is restored to the same (or even greater) intensity it had in chlorophyll. Ashkinazi *et al.* suggested that a similar complex, but with a much weaker red band, is formed also by pheophytin with Fe^{+3} ions; the Rabinowitch-Weiss "reversible oxidation" was thus reinterpreted by them as conversion of Mg-pheophytin (chlorophyll) into olive-green pheophytin, followed by formation of greenish-yellow ferripheophytin complex, or a bright green ferropheophytin complex. Ashkinazi and Dain (1951) prepared a pheophytin-ferrous iron complex by heating ferrous acetate with pheophytin $(a + b)$ solution in acetic acid, extracting with chloroform, evaporating to dryness, washing out the iron salt and dissolving in ethanol. Exposure to air caused oxidation of the complex, with a band shift from 645 to 610 mμ; in strong light, the process was reversed and the band returned to 645 mμ.

Reactions of this type had been observed also by Rabinowitch and Weiss; however, these reactions are quite different from the instantaneous and completely reversible transformation to which the hypothesis of reversible oxidation was applied. Ashkinazi et al. left chlorophyll and ferric chloride to react in the dark for 24 *hours* before observing the spectral change; according to Rabinowitch and Weiss, reversibility is lost after a few *minutes*. It is quite likely that a chlorophyll solution left standing for several hours with ferric chloride will be converted to pheophytin. This conversion is essentially *irreversible* (except via the Grignard reaction). Green pheophytin complexes of different divalent ions, Zn^{++}, Cu^{++}, etc., are well known; they can be formed by direct substitution, but not instantaneously; and their absorption spectra differ markedly between themselves, and from that of the Mg^{++} derivative (chlorophyll).

Watson (1953) confirmed the finding of Rabinowitch and Weiss that the decoloration of chlorophyll a in methanol by ferric chloride is spectroscopically fully reversible by *immediate* addition of reducing salts, such as Cu_2Cl_2, and therefore must be attributed to regeneration of the original pigment rather than to the formation of new green compounds (such as the metal complexes of pheophytin, suggested by Ashkinazi et al.). On the other hand, the much slower restoration of the green color upon standing, or upon the addition of non-reducing salts, such as NaCl, leads to "allomerized" chlorophyll, with its distinct spectrum; regeneration by hydroquinone results in a still different, unknown green compound. Interpretation of the reversible reaction with $FeCl_3$ as oxidation is supported, according to Watson, by analogy with the transitory bleaching of chlorophyll observed upon addition of bromine or iodine, and by the formation of allomerized (*i. e.*, oxidized) chlorophyll upon standing of the decolorized solution. The acceleration of the transformation by non-oxidizing salts may be similar to the known acceleration of allomerization by $LaCl_2$; dissolved oxygen is needed in the latter case as oxidant.

Duniez, Thomas, Van Pee and Livingston (1951) built a flow system to study spectroscopically the intermediates of chlorophyll reaction with alcoholic alkali (*"phase test"*). They found that the brown intermediate [an ether, ionized either at C(10) or at the enol at C(9)] is formed without the participation of oxygen, and is converted into a green chlorine by reaction with oxygen. In the absence of oxygen, a slow irreversible reaction ensues. Weller (1954) measured the absorption spectrum of the phase test intermediate with much better precision than Duniez et al. Its bands were located (in pyridine) at 683, *524*, 486, 428 and 375 mμ for chlorophyll a, and at 630, *558*, 560, 505 and 444 mμ for chlorophyll b (main bands itali-

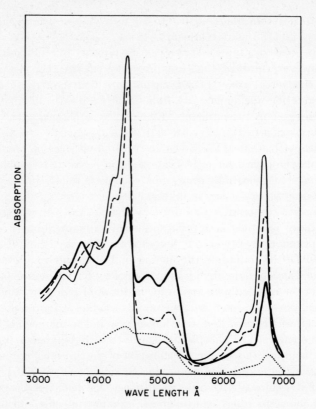

Fig. 37B.5. Absorption spectra of the "brown phase." Chlorophyll *a* in 10% mono-isopropyl amine, 10% isopropyl benzene and 80% 1:1 propane-propene: (———) 190° K., (– – –) 170° K., (———) 160° K. (after Freed and Sancier 1953). Curve (...) has been derived by Dunicz *et al.* (1951) for the transient intermediate of chlorophyll *a* at 300° K

cized). Weller suggested that the brown intermediate is a triplet (diradical) form of the anion formed by enolization and acid dissociation in position 9. This diradical is stabilized by resonance between several structures, with free valencies in different positions in the—normally conjugated—ring system. The striking similarity of the absorption spectra of the phase test intermediate, the anaerobically bleached chlorophyll (in steady or flashing light), the reversibly reduced chlorophyll and the reversibly oxidized chlorophyll (in rigid solvent) can be understood if all these products have a similar radical or biradical structure, with interrupted all-round conjugation.

The brown intermediate of the "phase test" was studied by Freed and and Sancier (1953) by low-temperature spectroscopy. They found that if chlorophyll a (or b, or b') is dissolved at low temperature in a base (isopropylamine), a brown (or red) solution is formed, which becomes green upon warming and again brown (or red) upon (immediate) cooling. The reaction becomes irreversible if the solution in pure amine is allowed to stand after warming; but if the amine is diluted (e. g., 10% amine in 45% propane + 45% propene; or 10% amine in 40% propane + 40% propene + 10% isopropyl benzene), the reversibility is preserved. The absorption spectrum of the brown (or red) solution is very similar to that given by Dunicz et al. (1951) for the "brown phase" (Fig. 37B.5). The green color of the solution in amine-containing solvent can be "frozen in" by sudden cooling from room temperature to $-190°$ C.; upon warming up, the "brown phase" reappears in a certain interval of temperatures. It is thus confirmed that the brown product exists in equilibrium with green chlorophyll, and that its formation (by enolization?) requires an activation energy. The suggested identification of the brown (or red) low-temperature products of the reaction with amines, with the similarly-colored intermediates of the phase test, is supported by the observation that no such products are obtained with allomerized chlorophyll. No red compound could be obtained from chlorophyll b in the presence of diisopropylamine, indicating that basic reaction alone is not sufficient for its formation.

The *reversible* chemical *reduction* of chlorophyll to a leuco compound by zinc and organic acid, claimed by Timiriazev, and Kuhn and Winterstein, but found to result in irreversible changes by Albers, Knorr, and Rothemund (cf. Vol. I, p. 457), was again studied by Kosobutskaya and Krasnovsky (1950). They used chlorophyll ($a + b$, a, b), pheophytin, the complexes of pheophytin with zinc and copper, and magnesium phthalocyanide. The addition, to 3 ml. of 10^{-4} M pigment solution in pyridine, of 0.3 g. zinc powder in 0.06 ml. glacial acetic acid, under vacuum, caused brownish discoloration of all pigments; phthalocyanin became entirely colorless. Re-admission of air restored the green color in every case; however, only with two compounds—Mg phthalocyanin and Zn pheophytin—were both the red and the blue-violet peak restored exactly to their original positions. In compounds of the a-series, the bands of the final product lay at 661 and 431 mμ—the positions they have in Zn pheophytin. With chlorophyll b, the bands were at 656 and 470 mμ before, and at 644 and 459 mμ after the "cycle." When very concentrated solutions of chlorophyll b were used, a weak band in the region 510–530 mμ was noticeable in the reduced state (cf. Chapter 35 for the presence of this band in *photochemically* reduced chlorophyll).

With the nonfluorescent Cu pheophytin, the "cycle" leads to the anpearance of fluorescence; the shape of the final absorption spectrum could be explained by assuming the presence of a mixture of Zn pheophytin with unchanged Cu pheophytin.

In all cases, the "cycle" led to the destruction of a considerable fraction of the pigment (50% in the case of chlorophyll a, 80% in that of phthalocyanin).

The order of increasing velocities of reduction was phthalocyanin, chlorophyll a, chlorophyll b, Zn pheophytin, pheophytin. Reoxidation required 1.5–2 hours at room temperature with chlorophyll a, and up to 10 hours with phthalocyanin.

The general conclusion was that Timiriazev's reaction is irreversible because it leads to the replacement of magnesium by zinc, and not because it causes hydrogenation of the vinyl group in ring I (as tentatively suggested in Vol. I, p. 457).

Godnev (1939) applied Timiriazev's method to protochlorophyll, and found similar results—decoloration with zinc and acetic acid, restoration of green color upon admission of air. Marked differences between the absorption spectra before and after the experiment were noted by Godnev and Kalishevish (1944).

The experiments of Linschitz and co-workers on *photochemical oxidation*, and of Krasnovsky and co-workers on *photochemical reduction* of chlorophyll and its analogues, and the reversals of these reactions in the dark, have been described in chapter 35.

The abnormal position of chlorophyll a band in *piperidine* was noted on p. 642. More recent studies (Weigl and Livingston 1952; Holt, unpublished) showed that this band shift is caused by an irreversible reaction of the pigment with this strongly basic solvent. Similar reactions occur with other strong bases, *e. g.*, parabenzoyl amine (*cf.* Chapter 37C, section 2a). A peculiar behavior was noted by Freed and Sancier (1954) also when chlorophyll b was dissolved in a solvent containing a secondary amine (*e. g.*, diisopropylamine). At $-188°$ C. this solution showed a sharp double band (430 and 480 mμ) in place of the single band (at 450 mμ) which characterizes chlorophyll b solutions at room temperature; in other solvents only a broad absorption at 450–480 mμ appeared at low temperatures, indicating the formation of solvates. Upon warming of the solution of diisopropylamine, an irreversible transformation of chlorophyll b took place.

Weller and Livingston (1954) pointed out that a cleavage of ring V by amines was observed in 1936 by Fischer and Göbel in methyl pheophorbide, and that the product was identified by them as chlorin-6-acetamide. The bond between the C-atoms 9 and 10 is broken in this reaction, the H-atom being added in position 10 and the amide residue in position 9.

(37B.3) $HC\!-\!C$ (V, 9, 10) O $+ RNH_2 \longrightarrow$ $H_2C \quad CRNH$ O

Weller and Livingston measured the rate constants of this reaction spectroscopically with seven different amines. They ranged, in the case of chlorophyll a at 26° C., from $\log k' = -1.88$ sec.$^{-1}$ with piperidine, to $\log k' = -5.38$ sec.$^{-1}$ for phenylhydrazine, and < -8.0 sec.$^{-1}$ for aniline. The order of rate constants parallels (for both chlorophylls a and b) the order of basicity of the amines (as measured by pK_a in water). *Allomerized* chlorophyll a in isobutylamine showed no reaction even after 3 days. Temperature effect on the rate of reaction of Chl a with isobutylamine indicated a very small activation energy (<6 kcal); the (negative) entropy of activation must therefore be large (to account for the relatively low absolute rate at room temperature).

In weekly basic amines the reaction is so slow that the reversible formation of an amine + pigment complex can be observed, as described by Krasnovsky and Brin (*cf.* Chapter 37C, section 2a).

The phase test reaction with alkali differs from the reaction of chlorophyll with amines in several respects: (*1*) It goes via a brown intermediate, which is formed at room temperature within less than 1 sec., and disappears within 20–30 sec. (in the system chlorophyll a in pyridine + methanolic KOH); (*2*) the energy of activation is ≥ 20 kcal, and (*3*) the presence of at least a small amount of alcohol is needed for the reaction. The allomerization process has characteristics similar to those of the phase test.

In analogy with the accepted mechanism of aminolysis of esters, Weller and Livingston suggested the following mechanism of cleavage of ring V, in its keto form, by amines:

(37B.4) $HC\!-\!C$ (V, 10, 9) O $+ RNH_2 \rightleftharpoons$ Transient addition product $\longrightarrow$

$HC^- \quad CNH_2{}^+R$ (V, 10, 9) O $\longrightarrow$ $H_2C \quad CNHR$ (10, 9) O

The basicity of the amine is determined by the charge accumulation on the nitrogen, and the same factor also determines the tendency of the amine to attach itself to the electrophilic carbon atom (9).

According to Holt (1954) the brown "phase test intermediate" can be obtained instantaneously by the action of sodium methanolate on chlorophyll or other solvents (and is then comparatively long-lived at room temperature).

Weigl and Livingston (1952) could observe no *isotopic exchange* of hydrogen and deuterium between water and chlorophyll *a* (or pheophylin *a*) in neutral organic solvents (ether, dioxane, acetone, benzene); similar negative results, obtained by Norris, Ruben and Allen with tritium, were described on p. 557.

5. Crystallization and Stability of Chlorophyll and Bacteriochlorophyll

(Addendum to Chapter 16, section A5)

Despite occasional reporting of microcrystalline chlorophyll preparations, it seems that all previously recommended methods lead to amorphous, more or less wax-like products. In particular, the procedure by which Willstätter and Stoll had obtained a product described as "microcrystalline," was found by Hanson (*cf.* p. 448) to yield a preparation without a sharp x-ray diffraction pattern (Fig. 37B.7)—which is decisive proof of the absence of a regular molecular arrangement.

Jacobs, Vatter and Holt (1953, 1954) were able to obtain crystalline chlorophylls *a* and *b*, as well as crystalline bacteriochlorophyll, by using as guide the shift of the absorption band upon crystallization, first noted with alkyl chlorophyllides (*cf.* Chapter 37C, section 3). The several methods they found to produce crystalline chlorophyll preparations had in common the presence of water during the precipitation, although this presence alone is not sufficient for the purpose. Thus, chlorophyll precipitated from acetonic solution by dilution with water remains amorphous unless a small amount (≥ 100 p.p.m.) of Ca^{++} ions is present. (Calcium is not incorporated in the precipitate; its effect must be an electric one, destroying the stability of the amorphous colloid.) Other and better methods to prepare crystalline chlorophyll are: (*1*) adding water to a chlorophyll solution in ether, and slowly evaporating the ether in vacuum; (*2*) adding pentane to water-saturated ethereal solution of chlorophyll and removing the ether by repeated washing with water; and (*3*) adding hexane to the ether-water solution and removing ether by evaporation. In contrast to the chlorophylls (and bacteriochlorophyll), the pheophytins can be crystallized by evaporation of their ethereal solutions also in apparently complete absence of water. The difficulty of crystallizing chlorophyll is thus caused by the presence, in the same molecule, of the long hydrophobic phytol chain, and the polar magnesium atom.

Fig. 37B.6 is an electron micrograph of crystalline chlorophyll *a*. It shows that the crystallization extends mainly in two dimensions; the material forms sheets only a few molecules thick, which have the tendency of rolling into cylinders upon drying. The extreme thinness of the crystals explains why their diffraction patterns (Fig. 37B.7) are less sharp than those of crystalline ethyl chlorophyllide, in which the crystals (although, they, too, have the tendency to grow mainly in two dimensions) reach much

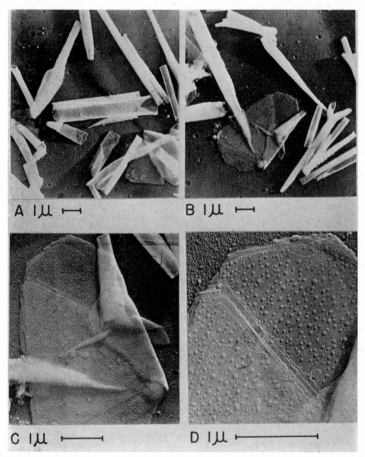

Fig. 37B.6. Electron micrograph of crystalline chlorophyll *a* (after Jacobs, Vatter and Holt 1954).

greater thickness. Fig. 37B.8 shows microcrystals of ethyl chlorophyllide *a* of different size. Fig. 37B.9 is a model of their crystal structure, as suggested by Hanson (*cf.* Chapter 16, p. 448).

The difference in the x-ray diffraction patterns indicates that Hanson's chlorophyllide model does not apply to chlorophyll, but no definite structure can yet be proposed for the latter. The diffraction pattern of methyl bacteriochlorophyllide shows no evidence of a three-fold screw axis, suggesting that the successive layers may be oriented in parallel (or rotated by 90°, instead of by 120°, as in chlorophyllide; compare the shapes of the conjugated ring systems in Fig. 37C.1!). The diffraction pattern of the

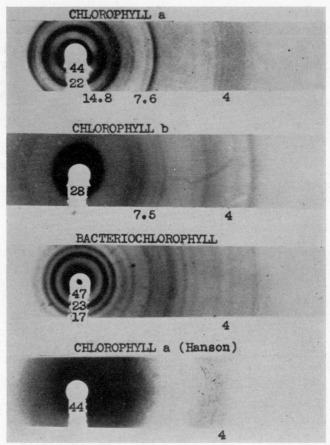

Fig. 37B.7.   X-ray diffraction patterns of microcrystals of chlorophyll *a* and *b* and of bacteriochlorophyll (after Jacobs, Vatter and Holt 1954).

pheophorbides shows a spacing of 16 Å, instead of 12.8 Å as in the chlorophyllides, suggesting that the molecules in each layer may be standing up vertically, instead of being inclined by 55° (16 = 12.8/sin 55°) (Jacobs 1954).

The absorption spectrum of crystalline chlorophyll will be described in Chapter 37C, together with that of the crystalline chlorophyllides (*cf.* Figs. 37C.16 to 18).

In contrast to the often reported instability of amorphous chlorophyll preparations, crystalline powders of chlorophyll and bacteriochlorophyll were found unchanged after six months storage at room temperature, at

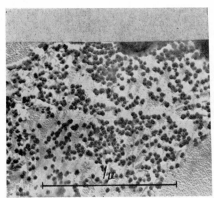

Fig. 37B.8. Microcrystals of the chlorophyllides (after Jacobs and Holt 1954)

least as judged by the criterion of a high ratio between the absorption coefficients in the two main peaks and in the trough between them. (These spectroscopic "purity ratios," suggested by Zscheile, are particularly sensitive to loss of magnesium.)

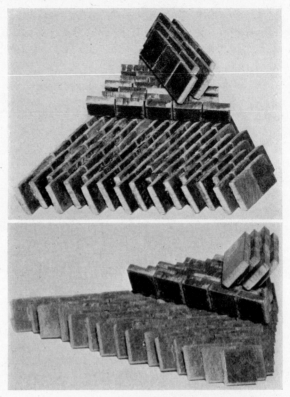

Fig. 37B.9.   Model of the crystal structure of chlorophyllides (after Hanson).

6. Nature of Chlorophyll *c*

(Addendum to Chapter 15, section B3)

The chemical nature of chlorophyll *c* was investigated for the first time by Granick (1949). The absorption spectrum of this faintly green pigment (*cf.* insert in Fig. 21.5*C*, p. 615) is quite similar to that of proto-chlorophyll (Fig. 21.8). By analogy, it can be surmised that chlorophyll *c* is a porphyrin and not a chlorin. Granick's tests indicated that chlorophyll *c* contains magnesium (bound more strongly than in chlorophyll) but no phytol. Positive phase test indicates the presence of the cyclopentanone ring.

7. Chemistry of Bacteriochlorophyll and Bacterioviridin

(Addendum to Chapter 16, section A3)

Holt and Jacobs (1954[2]) found that bacteriochlorophyll is not as unstable as it has been described. A green oxidation product, which is easily formed during the extraction, can be separated from the bulk of the blue pigment by chromatography; after bacteriochlorophyll has been so purified it proves quite stable, not only in crystalline form (*cf.* section 5 above), but also in ethereal solution.

The green oxidation product, obtained in the preparation of bacteriochlorophyll, probably has the oxidation level of dihydroporphin, and may be identical with the green compound obtained by Schneider (*cf.* p. 445) by oxidation of bacteriochlorophyll with ferric salts, iodine, quinone and other mild oxidants, and by Krasnovsky and Voynovskaya (1951) by the action of quinone on a bacteriochlorophyll solution in toluene. The latter observers reported that the oxidation can be reversed by ascorbic acid—an interesting suggestion which needs confirmation. The oxidation product has a chlorophyll-type spectrum, with the main absorption bands at 432 and 677 mμ (as measured by Holt and Jacobs in ether); it fluoresces with red light. Fischer (p. 445) suggested that it may differ from bacteriochlorophyll only by the absence of two H atoms in ring II, and also that the "bacterioviridin" of green sulfur bacteria may be identical with it.

Seybold and Hirsch (1954) reported that the azure-blue, non-fluorescent (more correctly: infrared fluorescent!) bacteriochlorophyll (which they called "bacteriochlorophyll *a*") is, *in vitro*, "extraordinarily unstable," and is converted "in a few minutes" into a green "bacteriochlorophyll *b*" (obviously the above-mentioned green oxidation product!).

The question of the chemical identity of *bacterioviridin* remains to be settled. Barer and Butt (1954) found, in pigment extract from green bacteria, two main absorption bands, at 664 and 434 mμ, respectively. The first one is markedly different from the red band of the oxidation product of bacteriochlorophyll (677 mμ); both bands are almost coincident with the peaks of chlorophyll *a*. Barer asked whether "bacterioviridin" could not be identical with chlorophyll *a*; but noted differences in the position of the minor bands and in the chromatographic behavior, which argued against this identity (*cf.* also Katz and Wassink's curves in Fig. 21.7!).

Seybold and Hirsch's absorption curve of an extract from *Microchloris* showed *three* peaks, including, in addition to Barer's "red" and "violet" peaks, also a peak in the far red, at 770 mμ, just where the bacteriochlorophyll band is usually found. Seybold and Hirsch interpreted this as evidence that green bacteria contain, *in vivo*, the same "bacteriochlorophyll *a*" as the purple ones, but that this pigment is rapidly converted (oxidized) into "bacteriochlorophyll *b*" (= bacterioviridin) upon extraction. An alternative explanation is, however, that Seybold and Hirsch's culture of *Microchloris*, when used for pigment extraction, was contaminated with purple bacteria. (The absorption curve given by them for live *Microchloris* cells shows a weak but unmistakable band at 850 mμ, typical of purple bacteria!)

We will see in Chapter 37C (section 6c) that the absorption spectra of live green (and purple) bacteria, given by Seybold and Hirsch, also disagree with those found by other observers, and suggest contamination of the green cells with purple ones, and of the purple cells with green ones.

8. Molecular Structure and Properties of Phycobilins

(Addendum to Chapter 17, part B)

Lemberg and Legge (1949) reviewed the data on bile pigments, including the phycobilins. Structural formulae of phycoerythrobilin and phycocyanobilin, suggested by Seidel (1935), are represented below in a form which emphasizes their similarity to porphyrins and chlorins.

(I) Seidel's mesobiliviolin
(= phycocyanobilin?)

(II) Seidel's mesobilirhodin
(= phycoerythrobilin?)

(III) Lemberg and Legge's suggested
formula for phycoerythrobilin

The two formulae, I and II, differ only by the position of one imino hydrogen, and consequent alteration in the path of the (seven-membered) conjugated double bond system. The question was raised in Vol. I (p. 443) whether, in the case of porphin derivatives, arrangements of this type would be stable isomers, tautomers or mesomers. In the case of bilan derivatives, mesomery or tautomery is less likely, because of the openness of the whole structure. Their isomers could therefore be stable; the considerable spectroscopic difference between the two pigments makes it unlikely that they are isomers containing conjugated double bond systems of the same length, as implied in the formulae (I) and (II). Lemberg and

Legge suggested, for phycoerythrobilin, the structure III, with only five conjugated double bonds.   This seems, however, too short for a compound with a strong absorption band in the green.   (Lemberg and Legge said that the spectroscopic properties of erythrobilin are similar to those of mesobilin b—a compound with a structure of type III—but mesobilin b is yellow and its first absorption band lies at 452 mμ in dioxane, and at 450 mμ in HCl + alcohol, while those of the red-violet erythrobilin lie at about 530 and 560 mμ, respectively.)   (Only one band, at 498 mμ, was listed in our table on p. 665; but Lemberg and Legge give, for erythrobilin in 5% HCl, two bands—at 560 and 495 mμ, respectively.)

Lemberg and Legge refer to one difficulty, pointed out on p. 666 (Vol. II, 1): the implausibly high absolute values (3×10^5) calculated for the molar extinction coefficients of the phycobilins.   They suggest that the estimate of 8 chromophores ($M = 536$) per chromoproteid molecule ($M =$ about 200,000) used in this calculation (about 2% phycobilin by weight!) has been too low, and that the number of chromophores per chromoproteid molecule may be as high as 16; the previously calculated molar extinction coefficients will then have to be halved.

The phycocyanin of *Oscillatoria* was hydrolyzed at 100° C. in 6 N HCl, and subjected to fractionation by paper chromatography by Wassink and Ragetli (1952).   Sixteen amino acids were found, and 13 of them identified, one of the "unknowns" was a major component.   Non-occurrence of arginine is the only notable difference of the phycocyanin protein from the proteins of *Chlorella*, or leaf chloroplasts, or hemoglobin.

Swingle and Tiselius (1951) developed a chromatographic method for the separation of phycochromoproteins.   Its application led to the discovery of several new pigments of this class.

Koch (1953) found a new *phycoerythrin* (in addition to the two or three varieties encountered in *Rhodophyceae* and *Cyanophyceae*) in one of the *Bangiales*, a rather primitive red algal group; it is characterized by the absence of the 495 mμ absorption peak (*cf*. Fig. 21.39).

A new *phycocyanin* was isolated chromatographically, from both blue-green and red algae, by Haxo, O'hEocha and Strout (1954), and tentatively named "P-phycocyanin."   It has a single absorption peak at 650 mμ, as contrasted to the "R-phycocyanin" from red algae (which has peaks at 555 and 617 mμ), and the "C-phycocyanin" from blue-green algae (which has a single peak at 615 mμ, *cf*. Fig. 21.40).

Blinks (1954) suggested that "R-phycocyanin" may be a complex of C-phycocyanin ($\lambda_{max.}$ 617 mμ) with phycoerythrin ($\lambda_{max.}$ 555 mμ).   The evidence is electrophoretic and chromatographic; in both types of experiments, a mixture of the two pigments is observed to behave, under certain conditions, as a single, anionic entity.

Haxo, O'hEocha and Strout (1954) found typical "P-phycoerythrin," with peaks at 497, 537 and 566 mμ, in *Rhodymenia palmata* and *Polyneura latissima*, and typical "C-phycoerythrin," with a single peak at 560 mμ, in *Phormidium persicinum*, *Ph. fragile*, and *Nostoc*. On the other hand, *Ph. ectocarpi* yielded a phycoerythrin with only two peaks, at 542 and 566 mμ. In *Bangiales*, such as *Prophyra tenera* or *P. perforata*, they found a phyco-erythrin with peaks at 497 and 566 mμ, but with no definite middle peak. Phycoerythrin from another of the *Bangiales*, *Porphyridium cruentum*, had only one broad band, at 545 mμ, and three bands in the ultraviolet, at 368, 306 and 276 mμ, the second of which is not present in R-phycoery-thrin.

Krasnovsky, Evstigneev, Brin and Gavrilova (1952) found that phy-coerythrin can be extracted from *Callithamnion rybosum* more conveniently than from *Ceramium*. They purified the extracted pigment by chromatog-raphy on a tricalcium phosphate column. Developing with 0.15 M di-sodium phosphate permitted complete separation from phycocyanin. The product, extracted into 0.15 M Na_2HPO_4, showed two protein fractions in the ultracentrifuge, with $M = 300,000$ and $M \simeq 50,000$, respectively. The phycoerythrin solution was found to be photochemically stable against oxidation by air, as well as against reduction by ascorbic acid. It therefore did not sensitize the reduction of riboflavin or safranin by ascorbic acid. (These results, belonging in Chapter 35, were not mentioned there.) Pho-toxidation was accelerated by dioxane or pyridine, and seemed to involve a partial separation of the chromophore from the protein (drop of absorption at 565 and 540 mμ, preservation of the 495 mμ peak).

This observation may be interesting from the point of view of a search for better methods of separation of erythrobilin from its associated protein —a most important hurdle in the study of these pigments. The methods in use at present—hydrolysis with hot hydrochloric acid or alkaline hy-drolysis (Bannister 1954)—destroy a large part of the chromophore while prying it off the protein.

Bibliography to Chapter 37B

Chemistry of Chloroplast Pigments

1939   Godnev, T. N., *Uchenyje Zapiski Beloruss. Univ. (Chem. Ser.)*, **1939,** No. 1, 15.

1943   Noack, K., *Biochem. Z.*, **316,** 166.

1944   Fischer, H., and Pfeiffer, H., *Ann. Chem. Justus Liebigs*, **555,** 94.
         Godnev, T. N., and Kalishevish, S. V., *Trudy Inst. Fisiol. Rastenij.*, **1944,** No. 2, 160.

1946   Frank, S. R., *J. Gen. Physiol.*, **29**, 157.
        Yocum, C. S., Paper at Boston Meeting of Am. Botan. Soc., December, 1946.
1947   Goodwin, R. H., and Owens, O. H., *Plant Physiol.*, **22**, 197.
        Smith, J. H. C., *J. Am. Chem. Soc.*, **69**, 1492.
1948   Koski, V. M., and Smith, J. H. C., *ibid.*, **70**, 3558.
        Smith, J. H. C., and Koski, V. M., *Carnegie Inst. Wash. Yearbook*, **47**, 95.
        Granick, S., *J. Biol. Chem.*, **172**, 717; **175**, 333.
        Smith, J. H. C., *Arch. Biochem.*, **19**, 449.
        Euler, H. von, Bracco, M., and Heller, L., *Compt. rend.*, **227**, 16.
        Provasoli, L., Hutner, S. H., and Schatz, A., *Proc. Soc. Exptl. Biol. Med.*, **69**, 219.
        Brebion, G., *Galliga Biolog Acta*, **1**, 24, 124.
1949   Smith, J. H. C., "Processes Accompanying Chlorophyll Formation," in *Photosynthesis in Plants*, Iowa State College Press, Ames, Iowa, 1949, pp. 209–217.
        Strain, H. M., "Functions and Properties of the Chloroplast Pigments," *ibid.*, pp. 133–178; and private communication.
        Schwartz, D., *Botan. Gaz.*, **111**, 123.
        Lemberg, R., and Legge, J. W., *Hematin Compounds and Bile Pigments*, Interscience, New York-London.
        Granick, S., *J. Biol. Chem.*, **179**, 505.
1950   Granick, S., *ibid.*, **183**, 713.
        Blaauw-Jansen, G., Komen, J. G., and Thomas J., B., *Biochim. et Biophys' Acta*, **5**, 179.
        Koski, V. M., *Arch. Biochem.*, **29**, 339.
        Highkin, H. R., *Plant Physiol.*, **25**, 294.
        Kosobutskaya, L. M., and Krasnovsky, A. A., *Compt. rend. (Doklady) Acad. Sci. USSR*, **74**, 103.
        Bogorad, L., *Abstr. Botan. Soc. of America*, Sept. 1950.
        Granick, S., *Harvey Lectures*, **44** (1948–49), C. C Thomas, Springfield, Illinois, 1950, pp. 220–244.
        Salomon, K., Altman, K. I., and Rosa, R. D., *Federation Proc.*, **9**, 222.
        Ashkinazi, M. S., Glikman, T. S., and Dain, M. Y., *Compt. rend. (Doklady) Acad. Sci. USSR*, **73**, 743.
1951   Koski, V. M., French, C. S., and Smith, J. H. C., *Arch. Biochem.*, **31**, 1.
        Smith, J. H. C., *Carnegie Inst., Dept. Plant Biol. Ann. Repts.*, **50**, 123.
        Granick, S., *Ann. Rev. Plant Physiol.*, **2**, 115–144.
        Ashkinazi, M. S., and Dain, M. Y., *Compt. rend. (Doklady) Acad. Sci. USSR*, **80**, 385.
        Provasoli, L., Hutner, S. M. and Pintner, I. J., *Cold Spring Harbor Symp. Quant. Biol.*, **16**, 113.
        Freed, S., and Sancier, K. M., *Science*, **114**, 275.
        Krasnovsky, A. A., and Voynovskaya, K. K., *Compt. rend. (Doklady) Acad. Sci. USSR*, **81**, 879.

Dunicz, B., Thomas, T., Van Pee, M., and Livingston, R., *J. Am. Chem. Soc.*, **73**, 3388.

Swingle, S. M., and Tiselius, A., *Biochem. J. London*, **48**, 171.

Koski, V. M., and Smith, J. H. C., *Arch. Biochem. and Biophys.*, **34**, 189.

1952   Bogorad, L., and Granick, S., *Am. Soc. Plant Physiol. Abstr.*, Cornell Univ. Meeting, Sept. 1952.

Weigl, J. W., and Livingston, R., *J. Am. Chem. Soc.*, **74**, 3452.

Weigl, J. W., and Livingston, R., *ibid.*, **74**, 4160.

Freed, S. and Sancier, K. M., *Science*, **116**, 175.

Wassink, E. C., and Ragetli, W. J., *Proc. Roy. Acad. Amsterdam* (6), **55**, 462.

Krasnovsky, A. A., Evstigneev, V. B., Brin, G. P., and Gavrilova, V. A., *Compt. rend. (Doklady) acad. sci. USSR*, **82**, 947.

1953   Jacobs, E. E., Vatter, A. E., and Holt, A. S., *J. Chem. Phys.*, **21**, 2246.

Godnev, T. N., and Terentjeva, M. V., *Compt. rend. (Doklady) acad. sci. USSR*, **88**, 725.

Krasnovsky, A. A., and Kosobutskaya, L. M., *ibid.*, **91**, 343.

Koch, W., *Arch. Mikrobiol.*, **18**, 232.

Freed, S., and Sancier, K. M., *Science*, **117**, 655.

Strain, H. H., *ibid.*, **117**, 654.

Watson, W. F., *J. Am. Chem. Soc.*, **75**, 2522.

1954   Smith, J. H. C., and Benitez, A., *Plant Physiol.*, **29**, 135.

Smith, J. H. C., *ibid.*, **29**, 143.

Freed, S. and Sancier, K. M., *J. Am. Chem. Soc.*, **76**, 198.

Weller, A., and Livingston, R., *ibid.*, **76**, 1575.

Haxo, F., O'hEocha, C., and Strout, P. M., *Rapports Commun., Section 17, 8th Congr. Botany*, Paris, July 1954.

Blinks, L. R., "The Role of Accessory Pigments in Photosynthesis," in *Symposia Soc. Gen. Microbiol.*, **4**, 224, Cambridge Univ. Press, Cambridge.

Granick, S., "Metabolism of Heme and Chlorophyll," in *Chemical Pathways of Metabolism*, Vol. II, Chapter 16, Academic Press, N. Y.

Bannister, T. T., *Arch. Biochem. and Biophys.*, **49**, 222.

Jacobs, E. E., Vatter, A. E., and Holt, A. S., *Arch. Biochem. and Biophys*, **53**, 228.

Weller, A. and Livingston, R., *J. Am. Chem. Soc.*, **76**, 1575.

Weller, A., *ibid.*, **76**, 5819.

Freed, S., Sancier, K. M., and Sporer, A. H., *ibid.*, **76**, 6006.

Holt, A. S. and Jacobs, E. E., unpublished.

Jacobs, E. E., unpublished.

Holt, A. S., unpublished.

C. Spectroscopy and Fluorescence of Pigments[*]

(Addenda to Chapters 21-24)

1. Theory of Chlorophyll Spectrum

(Addendum to Chapter 21, Section A4)

In Vol. II, Part 1 (pp. 619–635), a purely empirical discussion of regularities in the spectra of porphin derivatives was given. Since then, several papers have appeared dealing with the theoretical analysis of the spectra of large conjugated bond systems in general, and of porphin and its derivatives in particular.

Simpson (1949), Kuhn (1949), and Nakajima and Kon (1952) used the free-electron model; Platt (1950[1,2]) and Longuet-Higgins, Rector and Platt (1950), the one-electron LCAO model (LCAO = linear combination of atomic orbitals). They arrived, in general, at similar results concerning the sequence of low excited states of porphin and tetrahydroporphin. (These two molecules were treated, in preference to dihydroporphin, because of their simpler symmetry—D_{4h} in porphin and D_{2h} in tetrahydroporphin.)

The basis of all theoretical considerations in this field is the well-founded postulate that ring systems such as porphin, containing a closed sequence of conjugated double bonds, are, similarly to benzene, naphthalene, etc., rigid planar structures. Their chromophoric properties are due to the excitation of the so called "π-electrons" in the conjugated ring system—electrons which can be considered as belonging to this system as a whole, rather than to an individual atom. In the more nearly circular porphin structure (fig. 37C.1A), the electric dipole oscillations corresponding to the combination of the ground state with the low excited states, while confined to the plane of the ring system, are not further restricted ("polarized") in respect to any special direction in this plane. An electron in a round potential box therefore provides an appropriate first approximation for the analysis of the term system of porphin and its derivatives, such as protochlorophyll—although the side chains, particularly such containing double bonds conjugated with the main ring system, may strongly affect the closeness of the approximation. In the more elongated tetrahydroporphin

[*] Bibliography, page 1882.

structure, which can be treated, in first approximation, as a rectangular—rather than circular—potential box (fig. 37C.1C), oscillations ∥ and ⊥ to the long axis of symmetry should have different frequencies and intensities; the corresponding absorption and emission bands should therefore consist of two components, differing in wave length and strength, polarized in two mutually perpendicular directions.

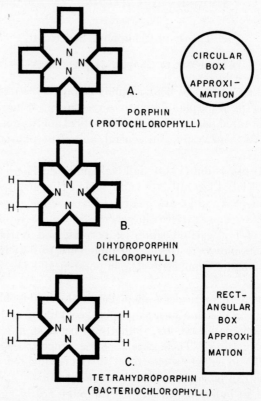

Fig. 37C.1. Porphin ("round field"), dihydroporphin and tetra-hydroporphin ("long field") conjugated ring systems.

Table 37C.I summarizes the term estimates, made by the two methods, for the two lowest excited terms of porphin, and the four lowest excited terms of tetrahydroporphin, and their attempted correlation with the empirical absorption bands.

All these bands arise by transfer of the electron in the filled shell which has the highest angular momentum, 4, into the lowest empty shell. The combination of the angular momentum, 5, of this excited electron, with the angular momentum, 4, of its partner left behind after excitation, produces two states, with the angular momenta of 1 and 9, respectively. The second state lies below the first one; its excitation gives rise to the red band, while transition to the state with angular momentum 1 must be responsible for the blue-violet band.

Each of the two main levels is split in two, when the D_{4h} symmetry of porphin is destroyed by substitutions, or partial hydrogenation of the double bonds.

TABLE 37C.I

CALCULATED AND OBSERVED ENERGY LEVELS OF PORPHIN AND TETRAHYDROPORPHIN (AFTER PLATT 1950)

Transition type	Polariza- tion (relative to long axis)	Estimated level in cm.$^{-1}$ (center of gravity, singlet + triplet)				Observed singlet transition (band peak in ether)	
		Free electron model		LCAO model			
		Uncorr. for N atoms	Corr. for N atoms	Uncorr. for N atoms	Corr. for N atoms	ν, cm.$^{-1}$	λ, mμ
PORPHIN							
$A_{2u} \rightarrow E_g$	None	9300	15600	9000	14500	16100	621[a]
$A_{1u} \rightarrow E_g$	None	20200	20200	21300	16500	23200	420[b]
TETRAHYDROPORPHIN							
$B_{1u} \rightarrow B_{3g}$	⊥	8900	13300	8700	13200	13000	772[c]
$A_u \rightarrow B_{3g}$	∥	16200	16400	16100	10300	17400	575[d]
$B_{1u} \rightarrow B_{3g}$	⊥	24100	29700	22200	21000	(25300)	(395[e,f])
$B_{1u} \rightarrow B_{2g}$	∥	23000	24100	23000	27200	27800	360[g]

[a] 613 mμ in porphin in dioxane, cf. fig. 21.9; 621 mμ in protochlorophyll in ether, cf. fig. 21.8.
[b] "Soret band," 430 mμ in porphin in dioxane, cf. fig. 21.9; same wave length in protochlorophyll in ether, cf. fig. 21.8.
[c] 772 mμ in bacteriochlorophyll in ether, 771 mμ in methanol (Weigl 1952).
[d] 575 mμ in bacteriochlorophyll in ether, 609 mμ in methanol (Weigl 1952); in Platt's table a value of 613 mμ was used.
[e] A weak band at 513 mμ, noted by Weigl in impure bacteriochlorophyll preparations, belongs to spirilloxanthin (Holt and Jacobs 1954[2]).
[f] A "satellite" of the 360 mμ band, cf. section 2, below.
[g] "Soret band" of bacteriochlorophyll; the different value (417 mμ) in Platt's original table was based on French's curve (fig. 21.6) that did not extend below 400 mμ.

The spectrum of dihydroporphin (chlorin) which has only one short two-fold axis of symmetry, cf. fig. 37C.1, has not yet been analyzed; but we can expect it to resemble that of tetrahydroporphin more than that of porphin, because the circular symmetry of the conjugated system is destroyed by the hydrogenation of a single pyrrole ring. It can therefore be expected that the absorption bands of dihydroporphin derivatives— similarly to those of tetrahydroporphin derivatives—will be split into components polarized in the direction of the symmetry axis of the conjugated bond system and normal to this direction, respectively. One can expect, however, to find this split less wide than in tetrahydroporphin.

The spectrum of chlorophyll (and other dihydroporphin derivatives) shows, instead of the two widely separated long-wave bands of bacterio-chlorophyll (located, in ether, at 772 and 575 mμ, respectively), only one main band (at 660 mμ in chlorophyll *a* in ether, *cf.* fig. 21.1). However, the relatively weak "orange" band (located at 613 mμ in ethereal solution),

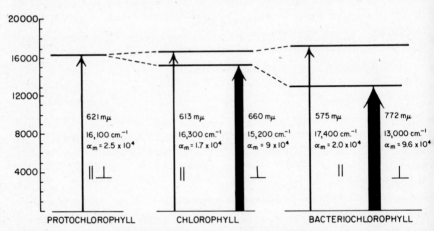

Fig. 37C.2.   Low frequency bands of protochlorophyll, chlorophyll *a*, and bacterio-chlorophyll (in ether).   The symbols ∥ and ⊥ refer to the long axis in bacteriochloro-phyll and the corresponding direction in chlorophyll (which is not a symmetry axis).

which was interpreted in table 21.VI as the first vibrational sub-band of the red band, could be due partially, or even mainly, to an independent electronic transition.   (This was suggested, as an alternative, on p. 631 in Part 1 of Vol. II.)   The bands at 660 and 613 mμ would then correspond to the long-wave band pair of bacteriochlorophyll, but with narrower separation.   This hypothesis is illustrated in fig. 37C.2.   An alternative is to assume that one component of the doublet is "prohibited" in dihydro-porphin.

Stupp and Kuhn (1952) concluded, from fluorescence polarization measurements (*cf.* below section 4b) that the weak "green" band near 530 mμ (527.5 mμ in table 21.VI), rather than the "orange" band at 613 mμ, must be attributed to a separate electronic transition with an electrical momentum normal to that of the main red band.   If this conclusion is accepted, values of the constants of the "∥ band" of chlorophyll *a*, given in figure 37C.2, must be changed to 530 mμ, 18,900 cm.$^{-1}$, and $\alpha_m = 0.4 \times 10^4$, respectively.   The separation between the ∥ and the ⊥ component would thus be increased to 3700 cm.$^{-1}$—approaching that assumed for bacteriochlorophyll (4400 cm.$^{-1}$). However, the experimental results of Stupp and Kuhn are in need of confirmation (*cf.* section 4b).

The attribution of the long-wave (red) band in chlorophyll, as well as in bacteriochlorophyll, to a vibration parallel to the symmetry axis, and of the short-wave (orange) component to a vibration perpendicular to this axis, is plausible because the molecular structure changes, in the series porphin-dihydroporphin-tetrahydroporphin, much less strongly in the direction normal to this axis than parallel to it (*cf.* fig. 37C.1). Of the two bands interpreted above as components of the red doublet, the short-wave (orange) band changes comparatively little, in position or intensity, in the transition from porphin to tetrahydroporphin (*i. e.*, from proto-chlorophyll to bacteriochlorophyll); while the long-wave (red) band is strongly shifted and enhanced by this transition (fig. 37C.2).

This difference becomes less pronounced if the constants of the "‖ band" in chloro-phyll are changed, as suggested above, to account for the polarization experiments of Stupp and Kuhn.

The blue-violet band is a doublet, in chlorophyll as well as in most of its derivatives. (Allomerized chlorophyll appears to be an exception, *cf.* fig. 21.4A.) The relative intensities of the main "blue" peak and of its "violet" satellite change strongly from preparation to preparation (*cf.* p. 607). Whenever the violet satellite appears particularly prominent, suspicion arises that pheophytin is present as an impurity; however, careful chro-matographic purification never eliminates the satellite band entirely, but only reduces its prominence. The separation and relative intensity of the violet satellite band depends considerably on the solvent (*cf.* fig. 21.26). Its interpretation is at present uncertain. A vibrational sub-band could occur on the short-wave side of the blue peak. Isomerism (or tautomerism) could account for a doublet structure. A final possibility is that the two bands correspond to the two theoretically expected electronic transitions. In the last case the blue band of chlorophyll *a* (at 429 mμ in ether) and its violet satellite (at 410 mμ in ether) are to be considered as components of an electronic doublet, the first one polarized ‖, and the second one ⊥ to the short axis of the molecule. They are then analogous to the two ultra-violet bacteriochlorophyll bands (395 and 360 mμ, respectively); but the "satellite" is located at the short-wave side of the main component in chlorophyll, and on the long-wave side of it in bacteriochlorophyll.

According to Stupp and Kuhn (1952), the polarization of chlorophyll fluorescence, excited by absorption in the blue-violet region, can be interpreted by a superposition of two bands, with electric momenta in two mutually perpendicular directions (*cf.* fig. 37C.21).

The wide error margin of the calculations, which is obvious from table 37C.I, the arbitrariness in the selection of weak bands interpreted as inde-pendent electronic transitions, and the uncertain isomeric homogeneity of chlorophyll and bacteriochlorophyll preparations, combine to make the suggested interpretation of the spectra uncertain. It provides, however, a better starting point for further investigation than the purely empirical suggestion, made on p. 622, that the addition of a pair of hydrogen atoms to the porphin system generates a new low electronic state, and pushes all the old levels upward. According to the present hypothesis, the homologous bands are 621 mμ in protochlorophyll, 660 mμ in chlorophyll, and 775 mμ in bacteriochlorophyll; in other words, the shift with increasing hydrogeneration is toward the *longer* waves.

In Part 1 of Vol. II it was argued—by analogy with polyene chains, or with the benzene-naphthalene-anthracene series—that addition of new links to a conjugated double bond system (which occurs in the series tetrahydroporphin-dihydroporphin-porphin) should lower, rather than raise, the first excited level (*i. e.*, produce a "red" rather than "blue" shift of the first absorption band). Longuet-Higgins and Platt (1950) pointed out, however, that a shift of the absorption band toward shorter waves with increasing number of conjugated bonds has been noted also in other ring structures, in which this addition *broadened*, rather than *elongated* the conjugated system.

To make the theoretical treatment of the spectra of porphin pigments more precise and reliable, both better calculations and better experimentation are needed. In particular, spectroscopic measurements on oriented molecules (in flowing solutions, monolayers, or single crystals) could be helpful, by providing direct evidence of the polarization of the several bands in respect to the symmetry axes of the molecule. Further development of the above-mentioned studies of fluorescence polarization also is desirable.

The *life-time* of the lowest excited state of chlorophyll *a* and *b* in solution, first estimated by Prins (p. 633), was re-estimated by Livingston (personal communication) for ethereal solutions and by Jacobs (1952, 1954) for acetonic solution. They used a quantum-mechanical equation given by Lewis and Kasha (1945), instead of the classical relation used by Prins, to calculate the "oscillator strength," f, and the mean life time of excitation, τ, from the integral under the absorption band. The results of the two calculations do not agree well:

	Livingston	Jacobs	
Chl *a:*	$\tau = 1.8 \times 10^{-8}$ sec.	1.27×10^{-8} sec.	$(f = 0.38)$
Chl *b:*	$\tau = 4.4 \times 10^{-8}$ sec.	1.62×10^{-8} sec.	$(f = 0.28)$

Perrin (1929) and Stupp and Kuhn (1952) estimated the life time of chlorophyll *a* excitation in solution from the relative polarization of fluorescence in two solvents, one of these (castor oil) so viscous as to practically suppress Brownian rotational movement. The calculated (actual) excitation time was $\tau_a = 3 \times 10^{-9}$ sec. (Perrin) and $\tau_a = 1.5 \times$

10^{-8} sec. (Stupp and Kuhn); the *natural* life time must be $\tau = \tau_a/\varphi$ sec., where φ, the quantum yield of fluorescence, is about 0.25 (*cf.* table 37C.IV).

2. New Measurements of Absorption Spectra of Pigments in Solution

(Addendum to Chapter 21, Sections A1, 2)

(a) Chlorophyll, Chlorophyllides and Pheophorbides.

Holt and Jacobs (1954[1]) made absolute extinction measurements on the *ethyl chlorophyllides* a and b in ethyl ether, in the visible and the ultra-violet (figs. 37C.3 and 4), from 220 to 780 mμ.

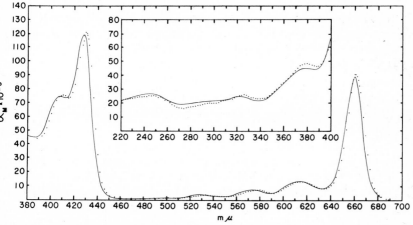

Fig. 37C.3. Absorption spectrum of ethyl chlorophyllide a in ether (after Holt and Jacobs 1954).   Dots represent Zscheile's data for chlorophyll a.

Similar measurements were made also with the two *ethyl pheophorbides* (figs. 37C.5 and 6).

According to these studies, the molar absorption curves of chlorophyll a and ethyl chlorophyllide a in ether are almost identical (within $\pm 3\%$ in respect to *intensity*, and ± 0.5 mμ in respect to the *position* of the band peaks between 250 and 700 mμ, *cf.* fig. 37C.3).   In the case of the b component, the main peaks of the chlorophyllide appear shifted towards the shorter waves by 1.5–2 mμ from their position in chlorophyll, without noticeable change in intensity.   This corrects our earlier statement (p. 626), which was based on Stern's absorption curves (fig. 21.16), that the absorption peaks of porphin derivatives become sharper when a short-chain alcohol is substituted for phytol.

Weigl and Livingston (1952) confirmed the finding of Katz and Wassink (Vol. II, Part 1, p. 642) that in *piperidine*, the absorption peak of chloro-

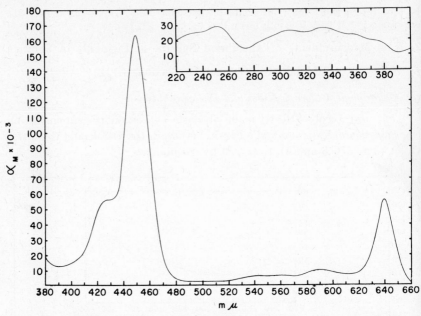

Fig. 37C.4. Absorption spectrum of ethyl chlorophyllide b in ether (after Holt and Jacobs 1954).

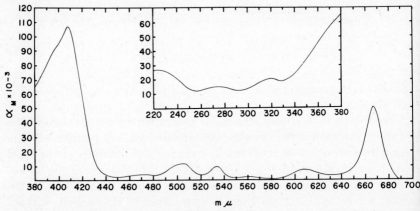

Fig. 37C.5. Absorption spectrum of ethyl pheophorbide a in ether (after Holt and Jacobs 1954).

phyll a is located at much shorter waves than in any other solvent. They found it at 642.5 mμ; it was 35% lower than in ether, while the blue peak was 65% higher. Evaporating and re-dissolving in ether did not bring the band back to its normal position, indicating an irreversible chemical

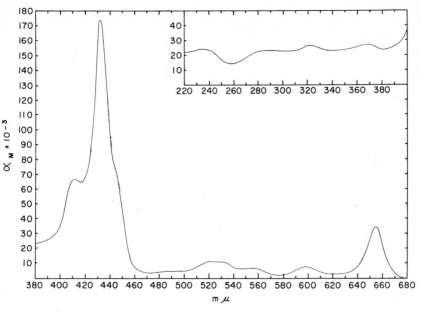

Fig. 37C.6. Absorption spectrum of ethyl pheophorbide *b* in ether (after Holt and Jacobs 1954).

change. A similar spectral shift is caused by dissolving chlorophyll in *parabenzoylamine* (Livingston, Watson and McArdle 1949).

The observations of Freed and Sancier (1951), concerning the irreversible transformation of spectra of chlorophyll solutions in *secondary amines,* belong to the same category. All these results were mentioned in chapter 37B (section 4) as evidence of irreversible aminolysis of the cyclopentanone ring in chlorophyll, which proceeds faster the more basic the amine.

Freed and Sancier (1951–54) studied the absorption spectra of the chlorophylls and their derivatives at *low temperatures.* As stated in chapter 37B (section 4), they first attributed the observed changes to a reversible isomerization of the pigment; later (1954) it was suggested that they are caused by a reversible formation of *solvates.* (That the two phenomena may be coupled was also mentioned in chapter 37B.)

Freed and Sancier (1951) measured the spectra of the chlorophylls *a*, *b*, and *b'* in a mixture of *n*-propyl ether (20 p.), propane (60 p.) and propene (60 p.), from −198° to −63° C.; and in a mixture of *n*-propyl ether (20 p.) and *n*-hexane (80 p.) from −63° C. to room temperature. Figs. 37C.7 and 8 show the observed transformations. They indicate

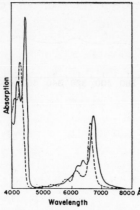

Fig. 37C.7. Visible absorption spectra of solutions of chlorophyll a at 230° K (dashed line) and at 75° K (solid line) (Freed and Sancier 1951). Concentrations are different at the two temperatures.

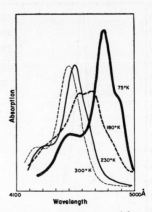

Fig. 37C.8. Changes with temperature of the absorption spectrum of the mixture of isomers of chlorophyll b in solution (Freed and Sancier 1951).

the replacement of "room temperature bands" by "low temperature bands," generally situated at somewhat longer wave lengths (*cf.* particularly fig. 37C.8).

The changes shown in figs. 37C.7 and 8 are completely reversible. The same spectra could be obtained by approaching a certain temperature from below or from above; they are therefore to be considered as belonging to equilibrium mixtures of different solvates, formed practically without any activation energy. The chlorophylls a and b are half-converted into their low-temperature, solvated forms at −93° C., chlorophyll b', at −43°C. Linschitz and co-workers (1952) noted that spectral changes similar to those described by Freed and Sancier for the chlorophylls occurred also upon cooling of ethyl chlorophyllide solutions (a or b) in EPA (ether + pentane + ethanol, 8:5:3) to −193° C. The rigidity of the solvent over a part of this temperature range did not interfere with the completion of the changes. As noted also by Freed and Sancier, allomerization does not prevent the transformation, which thus cannot depend on the keto-enol isomerism in the cyclopentanon ring.

Strain (1952) suggested that the effects observed by Freed and Sancier could be due to the formation of colloidal (amorphous or crystalline) particles. Freed and Sancier (1952) argued against this interpretation, pointing out that what they had observed was substitution of new bands for the original ones, and not a gradual shift of the latter. However, we will see below in section 3, fig. 37C.16–18, that the formation of crystalline particles also produces new bands, which then shift with the growth of the particles. A more convincing argument against Strain's suggestion is that phase changes are not likely to be reversible or lead to an equilibrium.

In the same paper, Freed and Sancier (1952) described the low-temperature transformation of the spectrum of chlorophyll b' in diisopropyl amine (10%) + propane (45%) + propene (45%); the red band, located at 645 mμ at $-43°$ C., was replaced, at $-103°$ C., by one at 662 mμ. (The transformations in the blue-violet region indicate that in this system, irreversible aminolysis is superimposed on solvation.)

Freed and Sancier (1954) based the above-mentioned reinterpretation of the temperature effect on its similarity with the effects caused by changes in solvent. Cooling of chlorophyll b solution in (not specially dried) hydrocarbons enhanced the long-wave band components, attributable to complexes with water, at the cost of the short-wave components, attributable to water-free pigment.

This, however, is only a partial explanation, since a similar transformation was found also in dry (nonfluorescent) solutions. It had to be attributed there to thermal excitation of a vibration ($\Delta H = 1.4 \pm 0.2$ kcal/m.). A similar ΔH value (1.32 kcal m., corresponding to 460 cm.$^{-1}$) was derived from the width of the band split in the red; the split of the blue band gave $\Delta H = 1.42$ kcal/m. In wet solvent (n-propyl benzene), on the other hand, the temperature dependence indicated a ΔH of only 2.5 kcal/m.; this lower value suggested that, in this case, vibrational excitation was coupled with the dissociation of a hydrate. Thermally excitable vibrational states were noted, in addition to chlorophyll a, also in chlorophyll b, and possibly in bacteriochlorophyll, but not in the pheophytins, allomerized chlorophylls, or metal porphyrins. By varying the concentration of a polar admixture (water, propyl ether, pyridine, diisopropylamine) in a nonpolar solvent, spectroscopic evidence of the formation of both mono and disolvates could be obtained. With pyridine as admixture, and chlorophyll b as solute, an equilibrium constant $K = [\text{ChlPy}_2]/([\text{ChlPy}][\text{Py}]) = 10$ was calculated (at 2° C.).

Solvations of this type occur also with allomerized chlorophyll, the pheophytins, and metal porphyrins. With isopropylamine as admixture, a second type of solvation can be observed, leading to brown compounds (phase test intermediates, *cf.* chapter 37B, section 4). If this phenomenon is attributed to interaction of the amine with the enol group in position 9, the first type of solvation could be interpreted as involving the polar group in the center of the molecule (magnesium-nitrogen bonds in chlorophyll, imino groups in pheophytine, metal-nitrogen bonds in metal porphyrins).

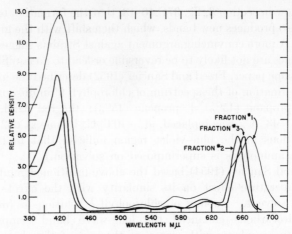

Fig. 37C.9. Absorption spectra of three fractions of allomerized chlorophyll in ether (after Holt and Jacobs 1954). Red peaks arbitrarily matched in height.

Livingston, Pariser, Thompson and Weller (1953) measured the absorption spectrum of pheophytin *a* in methanol in the presence of acids or bases. In acid solution, a reversible conversion of the "neutral" into an "acidic" form was revealed by spectroscopy; in basic solutions, an irreversible conversion into a "basic" form took place. In dilute solutions of strong bases, or in solutions containing weak bases (*e. g.*, aliphatic amines), the conversion into the basic form was gradual. Neutralization of the base changed the spectrum of the basic form, but did not convert it back into that of the neutral (or acidic) form.

Neuberger and Scott (1952) interpreted the spectral changes, obtained in several porphyrins by *p*H variation, as evidence of transformation of the free base, P, first into a monovalent cation, PH^+ (often around *p*H 7) and then into a divalent cation, PH_2^{++} (often at about *p*H 4). This would mean that porphyrins are stronger bases than pyridine; the authors attributed this increased proton affinity to additional resonating structures that become possible when one or two H^+ ions are added to the pyrrole nitrogens. Scott (1952) suggested that a similar addition of H^+ ions to ring nitrogens accounts for the effect of acidity on tetraphenylporphin spectrum (*cf.* fig. 21.14), with the peculiarity that the addition of the second H^+ ion to the ring causes, in this particular case, the appearance of a "chlorin type" spectrum. (The spectrum of the intermediate, low-acidity form seems to be similar to that of the monocations of other porphyrins.)

Holt and Jacobs (1953) also measured the absorption curve of *allomerized chlorophyll a* in ether, and found it very similar to that given by Livingston for the same material in methanol (fig. 21.4A). The main peaks are at 420 mμ (Soret band) and 650 mμ, with minor peaks at 610, 567 and 520 mμ. The most notable feature of this spectrum is the absence of the "satellite" band on the short-wave side of the Soret band.

Closer investigation by Holt and Jacobs (1953) confirmed the findings of Strain (*cf.* chapter 37B, section 4), that "allomerized chlorophyll" is not a single compound, but can be separated chromatographically into at least three fractions. Fig. 37C.9 shows the visible absorption spectra, in ether, of the three fractions of allomerized ethyl chlorophyllide *a*. The most abundant one of them (No. 2) has the spectrum shown in fig. 21.4A; another (No. 3) a spectrum very similar to that of chlorophyllide itself; the third one (No. 1) an absorption band further to the red, near 680 mμ.

Evstigneev and Gavrilova (1953) made the first quantitative study of the absorption spectrum of *photochemically reduced chlorophylls a* and *b*.

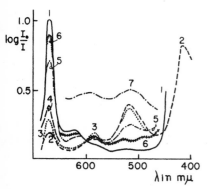

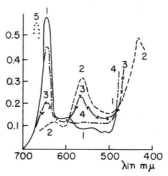

Fig. 37C.10. Absorption spectra of reduced chlorophyll *a* (after Evstigneev and Gavrilova 1953). Curve 1: before reduction. Curve 2: after reduction. Curves 3, 4: same after 30 and 160 min. of reoxidation in darkness without air. Curves 5, 6: same after 100 additional min. and 1 day in air. Curve 7: absorption curve of reduced pheophytin *a* (larger scale).

Fig. 37C.11. Absorption spectra of reduced chlorophyll *b* (after Evstigneev and Gavrilova 1953). Curve 1: before reduction. Curve 2: after reduction. Curves 3 and 4: different stages of re-oxidation, 25 min. in darkness without air and same plus 60 min. in air. Curve 5: shift of red peak after 24 hr.

As described in chapter 35 (part A), chlorophyll can be reduced by illumination in the presence of ascorbic acid in basic medium ("Krasnovsky reaction"). The product has been described as "pink," with an absorption band at about 530 mμ (fig. 35.3); but its rapid re-oxidation after the cessation of illumination had prevented a quantitative study of the spectrum. Evstigneev and Gavrilova found that if the reaction is carried out in toluene (instead of pyridine), and with phenyl hydrazine serving as both the reductant and the basic ingredient, the back reaction is slowed down so much that a comparatively concentrated chlorophyll solution can be completely reduced, and the absorption spectrum of the product can be measured before re-oxidation occurs. Figs. 37C.10 and 11 show the results for the chlorophylls *a* and *b*, respectively. The different behavior of the bands at 518 and 585 mμ (in a), and at 565 and 635 mμ (in b), indicates that they belong to two different forms of reduced chlorophyll; Evstigneev and Gavrilova suggested that the "long-wave" bands belong to nondissociated semiquinones (derived from the chlorophylls by one-step reduction, cf. Krasnovsky's hypothesis on p. 1503), and the "short-wave" bands to their ions.

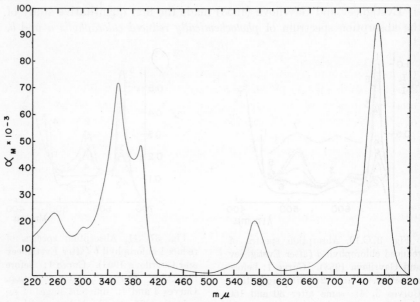

Fig. 37C.12. Absorption spectrum of methyl bacteriochlorophyllide in ether (after Holt and Jacobs 1954).

(b) Bacteriochlorophyll and Derivatives

New measurements have been made in the absorption spectrum of bacteriochlorophyll, by Manten (1948), Krasnovsky and Vojnovskaja (1951), Weigl (1952) and Holt and Jacobs (1954[2]). Fig. 37C.12 shows the absorption spectrum of methyl bacteriochlorophyllide in ether. The main red peak is located, according to Weigl, at 772 mμ in ether, 771 mμ in acetone and methanol, and 782 mμ in benzene; and according to Holt and Jacobs, at 769 mμ in ether, all in satisfactory agreement with fig. 21.25. Weigl noted a striking effect of polar solvents on the "orange" band: it is found at 575 mμ (577 mμ according to Holt and Jacobs) in ether, 580 mμ in acetone, and 581 mμ in benzene, but is shifted to 609 mμ in methanol. (French, as well as Manten, reported a similar position— 605 mμ.) Weigl converted bacteriochlorophyll to bacteriopheophytin, calculated the concentration of the latter from French's absorption data (*cf.* fig. 21.21) and derived in this way a value for the maximum (decadic) absorption coefficient ($\alpha_{max.}$ = 9.6 × 10^4 l. mole^{-1} cm.$^{-1}$) in the peak of infrared band of bacteriochlorophyll. Absolute measurement by Holt and Jacobs confirmed this calculation. (They found $\alpha_{max.}$ = 9.5 × 10^4 l. mole^{-1} cm.$^{-1}$.)

The position of the peak of the main short-wave band of bacteriochlorophyll, which we assume to be analogous to the "Soret band" of chlorophyll, could be given previously only as ≤400 mμ (*cf.* fig. 21.6). It has since been determined by Manten (1948) as 362 mμ (in methanol), by Weigl (1953) as 358 mμ (in ether or acetone), 362.5 mμ (in benzene), or 364 mμ (in methanol) and by Holt and Jacobs (1954[2]) as 356 mμ (in ether). A satellite band appears at 390–400 mμ (392 mμ in ether). The variable relative intensity of this *long-wave* satellite reminds one of the behavior of the *short-wave* satellite of the main blue-violet band in chlorophyll (*cf.* Part 1 of Vol. II, p. 646).

According to Weigl (1953) the absorption peaks of *bacteriopheophytin* lie, in ether, at 750 mμ ($\alpha_{max.}$ = 6.3 × 10^4 l. mole^{-1} cm.$^{-1}$), 680 mμ, 620 mμ, 525 mμ, 384.5 mμ and 357 mμ.

Barer and Butt (1954) confirmed the earlier observations (*cf.* pp. 618–619) that the red absorption band of *bacterioviridin*, extracted from green sulfur bacteria, lies at 664 mμ—quite close to that of chlorophyll *a;* they found the same to be true of the main violet band, at 434 mμ. Nevertheless, on the basis of chromatographic behavior and minor spectroscopic characteristics, Barer and Butt agreed with the suggestion (p. 619) that bacterioviridin is *not* identical with chlorophyll *a*. Larsen (1953) gave an absorption curve of an acetonic extract from *Chlorobium thiosulfatophilum*, showing two sharp main peaks, at 435 and 660 mμ, respectively; and minor bands at 770 (very weak), 625, 496, 467, 412, 392 (shoulder), and 338 mμ; those at 496 and 467 probably indicate the presence of carotenoids. Again, the main bands almost coincide with those of chlorophyll *a*, but the minor bands have different positions.

Whether the much wider shift of the red band toward the longer waves, found in green bacteria (as compared to algae), is due to a difference in the chemical structure of the two pigments, or to a different state of aggregation (or binding to a different protein-lipoid complex), remains to be established. The shift is similar to that found for bacteriochlorophyll in purple bacteria.

The divergent results of Seybold and Hirsch (1954) already were noted in chapter 37.B. These observers found, in extracts from what they called "purple spirillae," as well as in those from green bacteria (*Microchloris*), absorption bands at both 770 and 660 mμ, and contended that green and purple cells carry one and the same pigment, which they called "bacteriochlorophyll a" (characterized by the 770 mμ band); they suggested that upon extraction this pigment is very rapidly converted into "bacteriochlorophyll b" (= bacterioviridin), characterized by a band at 660 mμ. The finding with purple bacteria could be related to the observations of Schneider; Holt and Jacobs; and others, who also noted the oxidation of bacteriochlorophyll in vitro to a green product (cf. chapter 37B); but since the absorption curve of live purple bacteria, given by Seybold and Hirsch, indicated the presence of green cells (cf. below, section 6(c)), this contamination may have been the main reason also for their results in vitro. Their finding with green bacteria similarly suggests a contamination of green cultures by purple cells.

(c) Protochlorophyll and Other Porphin Derivatives

The absorption spectrum of protochlorophyll, reproduced in Vol. II, Part 1 (fig. 21.8), from Rudolph (1933) and Koski and Smith (1948), was re-determined by Krasnovsky and Vojnovskaja (1949). Absorption peaks were found at 623, 571, 533 and 433 mμ in ether, and at 633, 588, 550 and 453 mμ in pyridine (cf. table 21.IV). The transmission minimum of protochlorophyll in coats of winter squash seeds was observed at 645–650 mμ (cf. p. 705).

Krasnovsky, Kosobutkaya and Voynovskaya (1953) noted that in etiolated leaves the corresponding transmission minimum was located at 635 mμ, and considered this as evidence that protochlorophyll can be present, in vivo, in two forms—an "active" form, "Pchl 635," capable of conversion into chlorophyll in light, and an "inactive" (polymeric ?) storage form, "Pchl 645." (Protochlorophyll in seed coats is not converted to chlorophyll by illumination.) This suggestion is analogous to Krasnovsky's hypothesis of the existence of two states of chlorophyll and bacteriochlorophyll in vivo (cf. below, section 6b).

In extension of the observations of Livingston and co-workers, and of Evstigneev et al., on the effect of complexing (with water or organic bases) upon the absorption spectrum of chlorophyll, Livingston and Weil (1952)

TABLE 37C.IA

COMPLEXING CONSTANTS (K_1) CALCULATED FROM ABSORPTION CHANGES
(AFTER LIVINGSTON AND WEIL 1952)

	Pigment			
Activator	Mg-porphyrin	Zn-porphyrin	Mg-Chlorophyll (= Chl a)	Zn-Chlorophyll
Aniline.............	41	—	46	—
Benzyl alcohol.......	1.120	—	2.900	—
Quinoline..........	8.300	1800	13.300[a]	15.200
Heptylamine........	110.000	—	160.000	—

[a] Similar value obtained from fluorescence measurements.

measured the absorption spectra of *miscellaneous porphin derivatives*, (Mg-, Zn- and Ca-complexed mesoporphyrin dimethyl ester; Mg-complexed tetraphenylchlorin, and Zn- or Ca-substituted chlorophylls) in pure, nonpolar solvents, and in the presence of alcohols or organic bases. The association constants in table 37C.IA (to be compared with constants calculated from fluorescence and listed on p. 768 in table 23.IIIA!) were calculated from absorption measurements.

Imino compounds (in which the metal is replaced by two hydrogen atoms), such as pheophytin, showed no tendency at all for complexing with bases. This, and the unchanged complexing tendency of allomerized chlorophyll, supports the hypothesis of Evstigneev *et al.*, attributing complexing to the central metal atom, in preference to Livingston's initial hypothesis of complexing through enol formation in ring V.

In section 2a above, we have noted Freed and Sancier's evidence for the occurrence of both types of association with bases, the association in the cyclopentanon ring leading to "discolored" compounds (brown in the case of chlorophyll *a*).

(d) Spectra of Accessory Pigments

A few new measurements of the absorption spectra of plant *carotenoids*, particularly of those of purple bacteria, have been added to those summarized in chapter 21 (part C). Polgar, van Niel and Zechmeister (1944) gave absorption data for *spirilloxanthin* from *Rhodospirillum rubrum* (peaks at 540.5, 503.5 and 473 mμ in dioxane; 548.5, 510 and 479 mμ in benzene; 571.5, 532 and 495 mμ in carbon disulfide). Comparison with the absorption spectrum of Karrer and Solmssen's *rhodoviolascin* from *Rhodovibrio* (table 21.IX, p. 659, and fig. 37C.13) indicates the probable identity of the two pigments. Two methoxyl groups have been identified in both of them, and their most likely formula is therefore that suggested by Karrer, $C_{40}H_{50}(OCH_3)_2$. Natural spirilloxanthin is the all-*trans* isomer; partial conversion to *cis* form produces a new peak at 495 mμ.

Some new absorption measurements on *phycobilins* also must be mentioned. According to Lemberg and Legge (1949), the phycoerythrin from *Rhodophyceae* ("R-phycoerythrin") has three absorption bands, while that from *Cyanophyceae* ("C-phycoerythrin") has only one. However, fig. 21.39 shows considerable variations in the relative intensities of the different bands in phycoerythrin from different red algae, and it is not impossible that these variations may occasionally lead to spectrum with only one prominent peak. From this point of view, the absorption spectrum of phycoerythrin from *Porphyridium cruentum*, measured by Koch (1953), is of interest—it shows only one main peak at 535 mμ, but a satellite at 565 mμ and a shoulder at 500 mμ also are noticeable. Blinks (1954) suggested (*cf.* chapter 37B, section 8) that this shows the presence, in *Bangiales,* of a third type of phycoerythrin ("B-phycoerythrin"); alternatively, the same chromophore can be associated with different proteins (or other molecules), or present in different forms (as an adsorbed monolayer, a colloid, or a solution). The situation is quite analogous to that in purple bacteria, where bacteriochlorophyll exhibits, in *Thiorhodaceae,* three infrared peaks of varying relative intensity and in *Athiorhodaceae* only one major (and one minor) peak (*cf.* chapter 22, p. 702).

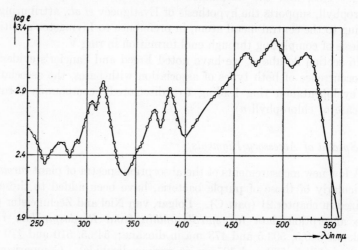

Fig. 37C.13. Absorption spectrum of *rhodoviolasin* (after Karrer and Jucker 1948). $\epsilon(= 2.30\alpha) = \log_e (I_0/I)/cd.$

For phycocyanin, Lemberg and Legge (1949) distinguished two varieties—"phycocyanin R" (from *Rhodophyceae*), with two absorption bands (*e. g.,* at 614 and 551 mμ), and "phycocyanin C" (from *Cyanophyceae*) with a single band (*e. g.,* at 615 mμ). Blinks (1954) suggested (*cf.* chapter 37B, section 8) that "phycocyanin R" may be a complex of phycocyanin C with phycoerythrin (with the 551 mμ band due to the latter).

Haxo, O'hEocha and Strout (1954) extracted a new variety of phycocyanin from several red and one blue-green alga; it had an absorption peak at 645–650 mμ (halfway between those of phycocyanin C and chlorophyll).

A review of the absorption and fluorescence spectra of chlorophyll, carotenoids and phycobilins, with all curves replotted in a unified way, has been prepared by French and Young (1953).

(e) Infrared Spectra of Chlorophyll and Its Derivatives

The early infrared absorption curves, reproduced in fig. 21.4, obtained with solid deposits of unknown density, can be now replaced by better data, obtained with solutions of known concentration by Weigl and Livingston and by Holt and Jacobs.

Weigl and Livingston (1953) published absorption curves for chlorophyll a, chlorophyll b, pheophytin a, bacteriochlorophyll, and allomerized chlorophyll a. They gave a list of bands (a) common to all five compounds, (b) common to several compounds and (c) unique to single compounds, and suggested (in addition to several rocking and bending frequencies) the following identifications of bond-stretching vibration frequencies:

ν (cm.$^{-1}$) (in CCl$_4$ or dry films)		Assignment	
3400	(pheophytin a)	N—H	
2862–2956	(all compounds)	C—H	
1740	(all compounds)	$\overset{\displaystyle O}{\underset{\displaystyle \diagdown}{\overset{\diagup\!\diagup}{C}}}$	(ester)
		OR	
1700	(all compounds)	C=O	(ketone)
1660	(all phytol-containing compounds)	C=C	(phytol)
1610	(all but bacteriochlorophyll)	C=C	(in ring)
1380	(all phytol-containing compounds)	C—CH$_3$	

No O—H band was noted in any of the five compounds, including chlorophyll a (where it could be produced by enolization), and allomerized chlorophyll (where it would be present if oxidation in position 10 were to lead to an $H\overset{|}{\underset{|}{C}}(10)OH$, rather than to an $H\overset{|}{\underset{|}{C}}(10)OCH_3$ group). More remarkably, no "aldehyde" C=O band could be noted in chlorophyll b.

Holt and Jacobs (1954) obtained the infrared spectra of the same compounds, as well as of several other chlorophyll derivatives, dissolved in chloroform, carbon tetrachloride and pyridine. Some of the results are represented in fig. 37D.14. Most interesting are the changes in the C=O and O—H bands, indicating transformations in the cyclopentanone ring (enolization, chelation, allomerization), which characterize this ring as the most reactive center in the molecule. These transformations are sensitive to changes in solvent (for example, a basic solvent stabilizes the enol group, and prevents its chelation with the adjoining ester group); they are characteristically affected by the presence of the magnesium atom in the molecule (which favors enolization):

Ketone   Enol   Chelated enol
(stabilized by the   (stabilized by base)
absence of Mg)

In pheophytins, no enolization (with or without chelation) is noticeable in CCl$_4$ solution.

In contrast to Livingston and Weigl's observation, Holt and Jacobs' curves show the expected extra "aldehyde" C=O band in compounds of the b series.

Fig. 37C.15 shows the effect of allomerization (by exposure to air in methanol) on the infrared absorption spectrum of ethyl chlorophyllide a in chloroform. In the curve set (a), most striking is the practical disappearance of the (ketone) C=O band at 1680 cm.$^{-1}$ in the main allomerized fraction, No. 2. This is in agreement with Fischer and Pfeiffer's hypothesis of lactone formation (as indicated under the top curve in set (b)); this transformation increases the frequency, since CO bonds generally are stabilized by accumulation at one C atom ($cf.$ p. 215). The band at 1720 cm.$^{-1}$ can therefore be attributed to the lactone (the ester band at 1740 cm.$^{-1}$ showing only as a shoulder). The two bands are similarly merged also in pyridine. In CCl$_4$, the ketone C=O band seems to reappear (at 1675 mμ), suggesting a dismutation equilibrium between the lactone, CH$_3$—O—C(10)—O—C(9), and the ketoester, O=C(10)+

CH$_3$O—C(9) (analogous to the equilibrium suggested by Fischer for the
   ‖
   O

corresponding alcohol, HO—C(10)—O—C(9); $cf.$ Fischer and Stern 1940, p. 88).

In CCl$_4$ or CHCl$_3$, none of the allomerized forms shows an OH-band, confirming Fischer's view that allomerization ordinarily leads to an OCH$_3$ (rather than an OH) group in position 10 (except when no alcohol is present, as in the allomerization of methyl pheophorbide by dilute KOH in pyridine).

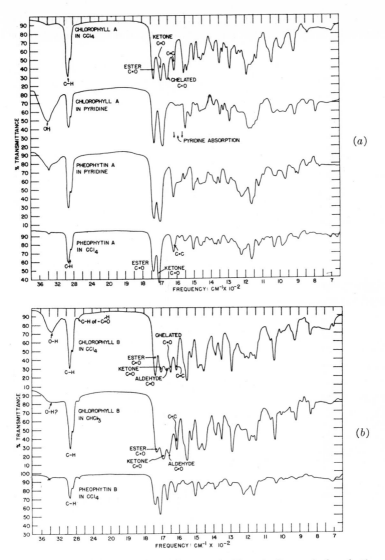

Fig. 37C.14. Infrared absorption spectra: (a) of chlorophyll a and pheophytin a, in CCl₄ and C₅H₅N; (b) of chlorophyll b, in CCl₄ and CHCl₃, and of pheophytin b in CCl₄ (after Holt and Jacobs 1954). Note (1) additional "aldehyde" C=O band in b-compound; (2) bands of "chelated" C=O in chlorophylls a and b in CCl₄* (absent in C₅H₅N and CHCl₃!); (3) absence of "chelated" C=O band in pheophytins; (4) presence of OH band—indicating enolization—in chlorophyll a and pheophytin a in pyridine, and its practical absence in CCl₄; (5) presence of OH band in chlorophyll b in CCl₄, and its absence in pheophytin b in the same solvent.*

* Experiments with fresh chlorophyll b preparations showed no evidence of chelation in CCl₄. Also, the OH—band seen before in chlorophyll b in CCl₄ was weakened by prolonged evacuation, indicating that it may be due to traces of water.

The OH group re-appears in fraction No. 2 in pyridine.   This is remarkable since, with the bond between C_9 and C_{10} assumed to be broken

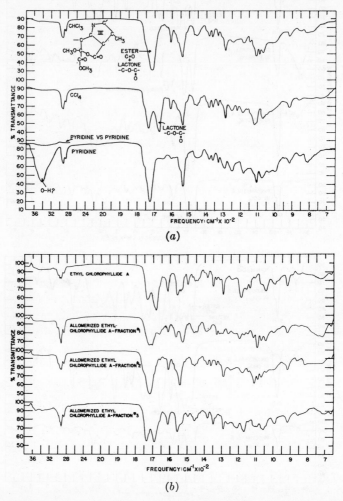

(a)

(b)

Fig. 37C.15. Infrared absorption spectra of allomerized ethyl chlorophyllide a. (a) Intact chlorophyllide, and three fractions of its allomerization product, all in $CHCl_3$. Note differences in the C=O band region (1600–1800 cm.$^{-1}$). (b) Main allomerization product ("fraction No. 2") in $CHCl_3$, CCl_4 and C_5H_5N (after Holt and Jacobs 1954). Note evidence of a lactone structure in CCl_4 (and probably also in $CHCl_3$), and of an OH group in pyridine.

in the allomerized state, where can the H-atom needed for enolization come from? Shall perhaps this result be taken as an argument for returning to Fischer's original concept of ring III (rather than ring IV) as site of the two extra H-atoms? (This would mean interchanging the "short" and the "long" axes in the chlorin and bacteriochlorin systems!)

Fraction No. 3 may be simply the C(10)-methoxy derivative, without lactone formation. In the optical spectra of several preparations of this fraction, considerable variations (from 1.33 to 1.59) in the intensity ratios of the blue and the red peak were noted; but all of them gave essentially the same infrared spectrum.

3. Spectra of Crystalline and Colloidal Chlorophyll Derivatives

(Addenda to Chapter 21, Section B2)

The scanty data on the absorption spectra of solid chlorophyll and chlorophyll derivatives (summarized in Part 1 of Vol. II, p. 649) have been considerably augmented by a study by Jacobs et al. (cf. Jacobs 1952, Kromhout 1952, Rabinowitch, Jacobs, Holt and Kromhout 1952, Jacobs, Vatter and Holt 1953, 1954, Jacobs, Holt and Rabinowitch 1954, Jacobs and Holt, 1954, Jacobs, Holt, Kromhout, Rabinowitch and Vatter 1954) of the properties of chlorophylls, alkyl chlorophyllides, pheophorbides, and bacteriochlorophyllide, in the form of microcrystals, colloids and monolayers. The solid preparations were obtained by diluting acetone solutions of the pigments with water (occasionally, gum arabic, or water-soluble cellulose, was added to slow down crystal growth). Immediately upon dilution (within 0.1 sec.) the red transmission minimum of the suspension was observed to move (in compounds of type a) from 660 to 670 mμ; fluorescence disappeared at the same time. When chlorophyll a was used (in Ca^{++}-free solvent) the band remained at 670 mμ indefinitely, and no crystal formation could be observed at all. With chlorophyllide, on the other hand, the transmission minimum continued to move further towards the infrared; after a few seconds (or minutes), depending on temperature, viscosity and concentration, it reached a final position in the region of 735–745 mμ. Kromhout (1952) (cf. Rabinowitch, Jacobs, Holt and Kromhout 1952) was able to follow this transformation of the red band by means of a rapid-action, rotating mirror spectrophotometer, in which the visible spectrum was scanned within 0.01 sec. at 0.1 sec. intervals by a synchronized photomultiplier–cathode ray oscilloscope–photographic camera system.

Later, similar sequences of spectra could be obtained also by ordinary spectroscopy, by conducting the crystallization at 0° C. (Jacobs, Holt, et al., 1954). Fig. 37C.16 shows, in graphs a and b, a sequence of transmission spectra of growing chlorophyllide a microcrystals. Graph c

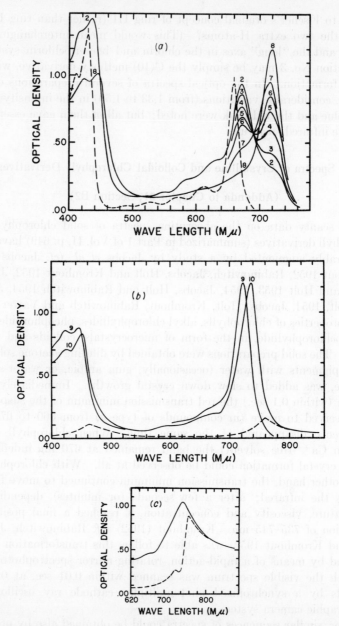

Fig. 37C.16(a), (b), (c). Absorption spectra of ethyl chlorophyllide a crystals of different size (after Jacobs et al. 1954). Curve 1, solution; curves 2–10, small microcrystals at consecutive stages of growth; (c), large microcrystals. Dashed lines: scattering correction.

represents the transmission spectrum of still larger microcrystals, obtained by using a more concentrated pigment solution.

Electron microphotographs of some of these crystalline preparations were reproduced in fig. 37B.8. In the case of the b-compound, only relatively large microcrystals could be obtained.

The spectrum of the microcrystals was measured in the collimated transmitted beam, in aqueous suspension. The presence of a Tyndall cone indicated that all suspensions produced marked scattering. For crystals with dimensions small compared to the wave length of light, this scattering is not too disturbing, as shown by the dotted line in fig. 37C.16b. Although the

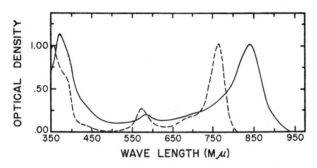

Fig. 37C.17. Spectrum of methyl bacteriochlorophyllide in solution (dashed line) and in large microcrystals (solid line). (Jacobs *et al.* 1953.)

scattering is predominantly of the "selective" type, with peaks on the red side of the transmission minima, it is not strong enough to shift the peaks; nor does it affect significantly the shape of the bands.

For crystals with linear dimensions >0.5μ, (*cf.* figs. 37B.8 and 37C.16c), the shape of the transmission curves is more strongly influenced by scattering. The experimental scattering curve of a suspension of such crystals is shown by the dashed line in fig. 37C.16c. It has a sharp peak at 765 mμ—considerably on the long-wave side of the transmission minimum at 745 mμ—and a minor peak at 715 mμ. The scattering declines only slowly in the infrared; this must be largely responsible for the similar behavior of the transmission curves of the larger microcrystals. With such crystals, correcting the transmission curve for scattering—to transform it into true absorption curve—does change the position of the peak significantly, shifting it by about 5 mμ and making its slope on the long-wave side much steeper.

Fig. 37C.17 shows the effect of crystallization on the spectrum of methyl bacteriochlorophyllide.

As described in chapter 37B, section 5, similar spectroscopic shifts were observed with chlorophyll itself, and showed the way to reliable preparation of crystalline chlorophylls *a* and *b*, and of crystalline bacterio-chlorophyll (figs. 37B.6 and 7). Fig. 37C.18 gives a comparison of the spectra of chlorophyll *a* in acetonic solution and in microcrystalline form (the latter corrected for scattering!).

Monolayers of chlorophyll, chlorophyllide and bacteriochlorophyllide were obtained by Jacobs (1952, *cf.* Jacobs, Holt and Rabinowitch 1954) by spreading on water a drop of a solution of these pigments in petroleum ether. (The solubility of these pigments in pure petroleum ether is very

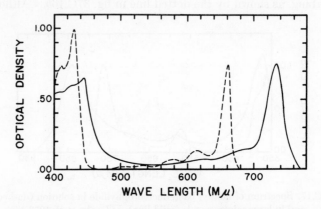

Fig. 37C.18. Absorption spectrum of chlorophyll *a* micro-crystals, corrected for scattering (after Jacobs and Holt 1954). Dashed line, solution; solid line, crystals.

small; but it can be made adequate by first dissolving the pigment in a small amount of pyridine, and then adding a large amount of petroleum ether.)

The absorption spectra were obtained by picking up the monolayers on glass plates. Even a single monolayer absorbs enough to permit the localization of the main absorption peaks; a stack of 5–10 glass plates, each carrying a single monolayer, can be used to obtain a complete spectrum. (Attempts to collect several monolayers on a single plate were not successful.)

Figs. 37C.19 and 20 show the absorption spectra of monolayers of chlorophyll *a*, and ethyl chlorophyllide *a*. It will be noted that in chloro-phyllide (and bacteriochlorophyllide) monolayers, the red band is shifted toward the longer waves almost—but not quite—as far as in "large" microcrystals (*cf.* table 37C.II).

With chlorophyll itself, two kinds of monolayers were observed, as illustrated in fig. 37C.20. One kind—obtained from solutions containing

$\geq 10^{-6}$ mole/l. Ca^{++}—has a very high optical density, and a red band shifted as far as 735 mμ. The red band of monolayers obtained from

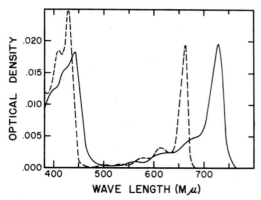

Fig. 37C.19. Absorption spectrum of ethyl chlorophyllide a monolayer on water (after Jacobs, Holt and Rabinowitch 1954). Dashed line, solution; solid line, monolayer. Ordinate: optical density of a single monolayer.

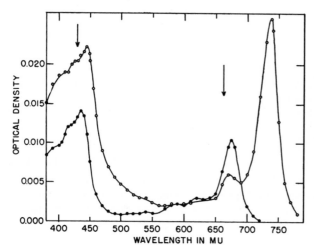

Fig. 37C.20. Absorption spectra of chlorophyll a monolayers (after Jacobs *et al.* 1953). Dots, "compressed gas" or "colloidal" type monolayer (prepared without Ca^{++} ions); circles, "crystalline" monolayer (prepared in the presence of Ca^{++} ions). Ordinate, optical density of a single monolayer; arrows, location of absorption peaks in solution.

Ca^{++}-free solutions is located at 670 mμ; their optical density in this band is much lower (*cf.* table 37C.III).

According to Hanson (*cf.* Vol. I, p. 448), chlorophyllide crystals consist

TABLE 37C.II

RED ABSORPTION BAND OF CHLOROPHYLL DERIVATIVES IN DIFFERENT STATES OF AGGREGATION (AFTER JACOBS)

Pigment	Position of red peak (λ in mμ)					Shift in 1000 cm.$^{-1}$ (observed)	
	Soln. in acetone	Gas (extrapol.)	Microcrystals		Monolayer	Gas to large crystal^a	Gas to monolayer
			Small	Large^a			
EtChl. a.......	660	648	718	740	730	1.9	1.7
EtChl. b.......	645	632	—	710	—	1.7	—
EtPheo. a......	665	652	690	715	—	1.3	—
EtPheo. b......	655	642	680	690	—	1.1	—
MeBact........	760	740	840	860	845	1.9	1.5
			Colloid	Crystal	Monolayer		
Chlorophyll a..	660	648	670	735	675, 735	1.8	0.43, 1.8
Chlorophyll b..	645	632	655	695	—	1.4	—
Bacteriochlorophyll........	760	740	—	($\geq$860)	—	($\geq$1.9)	—

^{a} Corrected for scattering.

TABLE 37C.III

OPTICAL DENSITY OF SINGLE MONOLAYERS (AT RED PEAK)

Pigment	$\log (I_0/I)$	Shift gas → monolayer $\Delta \nu$ 1000 cm.$^{-1}$
Et chlorophyllide a............	0.019 ± 0.03	1.69
Me bacteriochlorophyllide......	0.019 "	1.64
Chlorophyll a (Ca^{++} present)...	0.026 "	1.81
" (no Ca^{++})........	0.011 "	0.43

of layers built and arranged as shown in fig. 49 (Vol. I). Fig. 37B.9 represents a model of this structure. Monolayers of chlorophyllide on water have, according to Hanson, the same structure as the layers in the crystal, with the plane of the porphin ring inclined by 55° to the water-air interface—perhaps, because of the affinity of the magnesium atom for water. The surface density is one molecule per 0.69 mμ^2.

In *colloidal* chlorophyll *monolayers*, each molecule occupies 1.06 mμ^2. The additional 0.37 mμ^2 (compared to the surface requirement of ethyl chlorophyllide) is needed to accommodate the phytol chain. More precisely, the presence of phytol prevents the orderly arrangement characteristic of chlorophyllide monolayers, and leaves the pigment molecules more or less randomly oriented—except that their symmetry axes seem to prefer the orientation parallel to the water surface also in this "compressed gas type" monolayer; this is indicated by the fact that, as shown in table 37C.III, the absolute optical density of the chlorophyll monolayers of this type (in the peak of the red band), is smaller than that of the chlorophyllide monolayers, in the ratio of $11:19 = 0.58$—which is not much less than the ratio of molecular surface densities ($70:106 = 0.66$).

The optical density of the chlorophyll monolayers of *crystalline* type is about 2.4 times that of colloidal ones, and 1.4 times that of ethyl chlorophyllide monolayers. It seems probable (but needs experimental confirmation) that its *molecular* surface density is correspondingly higher. The "red shifts" of the absorption band—which may be considered as indices of the closeness of the chromophore packing—follow the same trend (table 37C.II). That it should be possible to rearrange a monolayer of the type shown in fig. 37B.9, into a 30% denser pattern would be startling enough even if we were dealing with chlorophyllide itself; it is even less likely if we are, at the same time, substituting, for chlorophyllide, chlorophyll, whose phytol "tail" must interfere with close packing.

One could suggest that an increase in *optical* density could be achieved without a proportional increase in *molecular* density. For this, the vibration planes of the optical electrons should be re-oriented so as to enhance the absorption of light passing through the monolayer normal to its plane. However, in Hanson's model of the monolayer, the short axis of the porphin ring is oriented parallel to the water surface; and, according to Platt (table 37C.I), this is the plane of vibration of the main red absorption band. If these assignments are correct, one does not see how any re-orientation of molecules could enhance the optical density of the monolayer in the red band.

A more plausible interpretation of the high density surface layer of chlorophyll is that it is a *two-molecular layer*. If this is so, the shift of the red absorption band to 735 mμ may be due either to an increased interaction within each layer, or to interaction between the adjacent pigment molecules in the two layers.

The blue-violet absorption band also shifts toward the longer waves in crystals and monolayers, but its behavior is more complex, because of its double structure. According to Kromhout (1952) the observed changes in this band can be explained by taking into account the different polarizations of the two components (*cf.* table 37C.I) and the preferential growth of the microcrystals in one plane: when crystal particles grow mainly in one plane, transmitted light consists increasingly of rays that have passed through the crystals under the right angle to this plane.

The strong scattering of light by the larger crystals—already mentioned in connection with the red band—adds complication to the shape of the blue-violet doublet. According to fig. 37C.16c, the selective scattering of large microcrystals has its peak at 485 mμ, on the long-wave side of the

450–470 mμ peak; it thus increases the apparent absorption in the blue component of the doublet much more strongly than in the violet one.

The curves in Fig. 37C.16a–c were drawn so as to equalize the heights of the red peaks. Estimates indicate that crystallization causes no large change in the area under the red band. The area under the blue-violet band, on the other hand, seems to be substantially reduced by crystallization. (In the case of ethyl pheophorbide b, the optical density in the peak of the blue band is seven times that in the peak of the red band in solution, but about equal to it in small microcrystals!)

In part, at least, the explanation may be the same as suggested above for mono-layers: the light transmitted through thin plate-shaped crystals consists mainly of beams that have passed through the crystals normally to their planes; the oscillation dipole of the red band lies in this plane, while that of the "Soret band" is mainly (or entirely) normal to it.

Probably the formation of a high-density solid chlorophyll phase accounts for the observations of Strain (1952). He dissolved chlorophyll (a, a', b, or b') in petroleum ether + 5% methanol; upon extraction of methanol with water, the chlorophyll solution in petroleum ether became "colloidal" and the red band moved to 710 mμ (in a and a') and to 690 mμ (in b and b').

A theoretical interpretation of the band shift in crystals and mono-layers can be obtained (cf. Jacobs, Holt et al. 1954) by considering the interaction of an orderly array of resonating "virtual" dipoles (which are associated, in quantum theory, with the transition between two stationary states, and determine the "oscillator strength" of the transition). Each molecule in the array has the same average probability of being excited by an incident light wave. Heller and Marcus (1951) showed that the excitation energy of an *infinite* isotropic lattice of such virtual dipoles differs from that of an individual dipole by a term equal to the "classical" interaction energy of a system of *actual* oscillating dipoles of the same average magnitude, having a phase difference of $e^{i2\pi \vec{k} \cdot \vec{R}}$ (where $\vec{k}$ is the wave number vector of the incident wave, and $\vec{R}$ the distance vector between two lattice points). Jacobs applied Heller and Marcus' equations to a *finite* isotropic crystal, and obtained an expression for E_R''', the energy of the excited state as a function of the radius R of the crystal. Because of the mutual cancellation of the effects of dipoles with "unfavorable" phase differences, this function grows only very slowly, until the crystal dimensions reach the order of magnitude of a wave length, after which the increase becomes more rapid; in other words, the contribution to the interaction energy of spherical shells closest to the center is smaller than that of the shells with $R \geq 100$ mμ.

The sigmoid-shaped $E_R''' = f(R)$ curve reaches saturation at

$$(37C.1) \qquad E_\infty''' = E_0 + \Delta E_\infty''' = E_0 - (4\pi\mu^2/3R_0^3)$$

where E_0 is the energy of an isolated molecule, and $\Delta E_\infty'''$ the change in energy caused by an infinite cubic lattice with a lattice constant R_0 and a virtual dipole μ in each lattice point.

For a *monomolecular layer* traversed by light perpendicular to its plane, the phase difference is zero for all molecules in the plane, and the interaction energy is therefore a rapidly converging function of the radius of the monolayer. For a circular, isotropic array of dipoles, with a radius R, the interaction energy in the excited state is:

$$(37C.2) \qquad \Delta E_R'' = -\frac{\pi\mu^2}{R_0^3}\left(1 - \frac{R_0}{R}\right)$$

The saturation energy at $R = \infty$ is:

$$(37C.2A) \qquad \Delta E_\infty'' = -\pi\mu^2/R_0^3$$

The value of $\Delta E_\infty''$ is equal to $^3/_4$ of that of $\Delta E_\infty'''$ given in (37C.1) for an infinite cubic crystal with the same lattice constant.

The dipole moments of the transitions can be estimated from the intensity of absorption (*i. e.*, the total area under the absorption band), and the lattice constant, from x-ray diffraction studies. Using these data, Jacobs obtained table 37C.IIIA for the crystals whose structure is known or can be surmised (no such surmise is as yet possible for chlorophyll, *cf.* chapter 37B, section 5). The table shows that the "limiting" shifts, found in three-dimensional crystals of the two chlorophyllides and their pheophorbides, are close to the theoretical estimates.

TABLE 37C.IIIA

Crystal	Red absorption peak in crystals, mμ	Red absorption peak in isolated molecules (extrapolated as in fig. 21.25), mμ	Molecular density in crystals (molecules per cc.) $\times 10^{-21}$	Oscillator strength of "red" transition, f	Band shift $\Delta\nu$ (cm.$^{-1}$) Theoretical (for 2-dimensional crystals) $\times 10^{-3}$	Band shift $\Delta\nu$ (cm.$^{-1}$) Experimental (table 37C.II) $\times 10^{-3}$
Ethyl chlorophyllide a.	740	648	1.1	0.38	1.9	1.9
Ethyl chlorophyllide b.	710	632	1.1	0.28	1.4	1.7
Methyl bacteriochlorophyllide............	860	740	1.1	0.79	4.4	1.9
Ethyl pheophorbide a..	715	652	0.89	0.31	1.2	1.3
Ethyl pheophorbide b..	690	642	0.89	0.27	1.1	1.1

The experimentally observed dependence of the band shift on crystal size, illustrated in fig. 37C.16, indicates rapid rise to saturation at $R \ll 100$ mμ, as expected theoretically for a two-dimensional system, and not the sigmoid shape predicted for a three-dimensional lattice. It follows that crystals of these pigments behave, in the first approximation, like stacks of monomolecular layers, with interactions restricted in the first approximation to molecules in a single layer. However, the final stage of the approach to saturation seems to be slower than predicted for a monolayer, and the saturation position of the band in crystals is somewhat beyond that found in monolayers (table 37C.II). This indicates that a final contribution to the total interaction energy comes from molecules belonging to different layers.

The band shifts observed in the two chlorophylls and the two pheophytins follow, as expected, the order of their oscillator strengths; but the band shift observed in bacteriochlorophyll is much smaller than could be expected from its higher oscillator strength. An explanation could be sought in a different orientation of the transition dipole in respect to the crystal plane, or the superposition of several electronic transitions.

It will be noted that the band shift was interpreted above without recourse to overlapping of electron clouds of the individual molecules, *i. e.* without the assumption of any quantum mechanical resonance phenomena. The shift therefore gives no information as to the probability of *energy migration* between molecules in the crystal or monolayer (as was first suggested by Rabinowitch *et al.* 1953). Information about the latter point must be derived from observations of *fluorescence* and *band width*, the first of which indicates the actual lifetime of excitation, and the second the extent of its coupling with molecular vibrations.

No fluorescence of the chlorophyllide crystals could be detected by Jacobs *et al.*, indicating that it is either extremely weak ($\ll 0.1\%$), or located beyond 1 mμ (where the sensitivity of the detector used drops rapidly). In the first case, the actual life time of the excited state is $\tau_a = \tau\varphi = 1.2 \times 10^{-8}\varphi \ll 1.2 \times 10^{-11}$ sec. (*cf.* section 1 of this chapter). The red band in crystals has about twice the half-width of the corresponding band in solutions; this shows that the coupling of electronic excitation with intramolecular vibrations is not destroyed by crystallization, and probably supplemented by coupling with lattice vibrations. The excitation must therefore stay in the absorbing molecule for a time $>10^{-13}$ sec. (the period of an intermolecular vibration). This permits $\ll 120$ excitation transfers during the life time. In the (less likely) alternative case of an as yet undiscovered fluorescence band above 1 mμ, the latter does not overlap with the absorption band at 740 mμ, and no resonance excitation energy transfer is possible at all. We therefore conclude that despite the closeness of identical pigment molecules in a crystal lattice the quantum is "trapped" in the absorbing molecule and only a few (if any) resonance transfers occur before it is dissipated into vibrations. The situation is quite different from that found by Scheibe in one-dimen sional crystals (mesophases) of isocyanin and similar dyes (chapter 32, section 5, cf. fig. 32.7), where an electronic excitation, polarized in the direction of the thread, is practically uncoupled from molecular vibrations, and rapidly sweeps through the whole thread; the absorption band is in this case extremely narrow, and exhibits intense resonance fluorescence.

Krasnovsky and Brin (1948) measured the absorption spectra of a number of colloidal preparations and adsorbates of chlorophyll ($a + b$?) and also observed their fluorescence and photochemical activity, the latter "mostly" by determination of chlorophyll-sensitized autoxidation of ascorbic acid ("Krasnovsky reaction," cf. chapter 35). The results did not

TABLE 37C.IIIB

TRANSMISSION MINIMA, FLUORESCENCE AND PHOTOCHEMICAL ACTIVITY OF CHLORO-PHYLL ($a + b$?) COLLOIDS AND ADSORBATES (AFTER KRASNOVSKY AND BRIN 1948)

State	$\lambda_{max.}$, mμ	Fluorescence	"Activity"
1. *True solutions*, in:			
(a) Low-molecular org. solvents......	660–670	+++	Active
(b) Fatty acids, oils, lecithin, aq. emulsions of lipoids............	668–670	+++	"
2. *Colloidal solutions*, obtained by:			
(a) Dilution of alc. with water.......	670	−	Inactive
(b) Dilution of alc. with aq. detergents......................	668–670	+++	Active
(c) As (a), but coagulated by electrolytes......................	670–690[a]	−	Inactive
3. *Adsorbates* on:			
(a) Paraffin, palmitic acid, MgO.....	668–670	++	Not measured
(b) Al_2O_3, TiO_2, ZnO, SiO_2..........	668–670	−	" "
(c) Alc.-sol. proteins (zein, gliadin); obtained in colloidal solution, by diluting alc. solns. of chlorophyll and protein by water......................	668–670	−	Inactive
(d) Other proteins (egg albumen, keratin, fibroin, edestin)........	670	−	Not measured
(e) As (c), but obtained by dilution with aq. detergents........	668–670	+++	Active
4. *Films* left, after evaporation on glass or filter paper..............	670	−	Not measured
5. *Leaves*			
(a) Living leaves, chloroplasts, grana......................	677–678	+	Low sensitizing activity
(b) Leaves killed by boiling........	670	+	" " "
(c) Leaves killed by freezing in liquid air....................	678	+	" " "
(d) Chloroplasts and grana in aq. detergents....................	668–670	+++	Active

[a] Depending on degree of coagulation; shift may be due, at least in part, to scattering.

go very far beyond what was already described in chapter 21 (part B2); they are summarized in table 37C.IIIB.

The one remarkable result in table 37C.IIIB is the fluorescence and photochemical activity of chlorophyll colloids prepared with the help of aqueous (cathionic, anionic or neutral) *detergents*. Presumably they contain chlorophyll molecules adsorbed on detergent micelles. Such preparations have absorption bands at 668–670 mμ, as compared to 678 mμ for the main peak in living leaves. (*Cf.* section 6(*a*) below for Krasnovsky's hypothesis that leaves contain chlorophyll in two forms, one fluorescent and photochemically active, with an absorption band at 665–670 mμ, and one nonfluorescent and photochemically inactive, with an absorption band at 677–678 mμ.)

Krasnovsky, Voynovskaya and Kosobutskaya (1952) studied, in a similar manner, the spectra of different preparations of *bacteriochlorophyll* and *bacteriopheophytin*. Solid films, obtained by evaporation of ethereal, acetonic or alcoholic solution of these pigments, showed two absorption peaks—at 800 and 850 ($\pm$10) mμ, respectively. Heating to 60° C. caused a weakening of the second and enhancement of the first peak; the original relation was restored upon cooling. Condensing water vapor on the film shifted the peak from 850–860 to 870 mμ; when a trace of urea was added to the solution before film formation, condensation of water upon the film sometime shifted the peak to as far as 890 mμ. In some cases, "hydrated" films showed three peaks—at 800, 850 and 890 mμ.

Various organic compounds (sugar, palmitic acid, glycocoll, yeast, nucleic acid, sulfur, etc.,) introduced into the ethereal solution of bacteriochlorophyll before evaporation, had no effect on the film spectrum; other additions (lipoids, imidazole, cetyl alcohol) reduced the absorption peak at 850 mμ—which Krasnovsky attributed to a state of higher aggregation— while preserving that at 790 ($\pm$10) mμ.

The observation that films obtained from raw methanolic extract of bacteriochlorophyll (transferred into ether and then evaporated) had only one absorption peak (at 780–790 mμ) was attributed to a lipoid impurity carried over from the cell material.

Bacteriopheophytin films showed a single peak at 850 ($\pm$5) mμ; it was not affected by heating to 100° C.

Colloidal solutions of bacteriochlorophyll were obtained by direct dissolution in water of the pigment adsorbed on sugar, and by dilution with water of pigment solutions in alcohol, acetone, dioxane or pyridine (usually, 7 cc. of solution were diluted by 8 cc. distilled water, and 0.5 cc. of 10% $MgCl_2$ solution was added to stimulate coagulation). Freshly prepared colloidal solutions generally had two peaks (at 800 and 850 $\pm$ 10 mμ); only one peak (at 800 mμ) was present when pyridine was used as solvent.

Coagulation by magnesium chloride caused a shift of the absorption intensity toward the longer waves (and a sharp increase in scattering). Colloidal solutions of crude bacteriochlorophyll exhibited only one peak.

These observations show obvious similarity to the above-described findings of Jacobs *et al.* Krasnovsky's interpretation was somewhat different; he did not inquire into crystallization, and considered the two absorption peaks of the films at 800 and 850 mμ (and the possible third peak at 890 mμ) (as well as the several peaks in bacteria located at approximately the same wave lengths, *cf.* below, section 6(*c*)), as belonging to different "states of aggregation" of bacteriochlorophyll. (*In vitro*, the several bands obviously cannot be attributed to association with different proteins—or other foreign molecules—as was suggested by Katz and Wassink for the three bacteriochlorophyll bands *in vivo*, *cf.* Vol. II, 1, p. 704, and below, section 6(*c*).)

The band at 790–800 mμ, nearest to the "monomer" band (located in organic solvents, at 750–770 mμ), corresponds, according to Krasnovsky and co-workers, to a relatively low state of aggregation, while the bands at 850 and 890 mμ are attributed by them to states of higher aggregation. The three states may differ not only in the size of the particles but also in nature of their bonding. (It was suggested, for example, that in "BChl 800," association occurs *via* the magnesium atom, while, in "BChl 850," it occurs through some other group—because only the "850" form was observed in bacteriopheophytin.)

Comparison with the results of Jacobs on methyl bacteriochlorophyllide and bacteriochlorophyll (table 37C.II) leads to the suggestion that the 840–850 mμ band may belong to a crystalline phase, and that at 790–800 mμ to a noncrystalline, "colloidal" phase. The relation between the bacteriochlorophyll peaks at 750–770 mμ (solution), 790–800 mμ (colloid) and 840–850 mμ (crystal) would then be analogous to that between the chlorophyll peaks at 660 mμ (solution), 670 mμ (colloid) and 735–740 mμ (crystalline precipitates and monolayers). The nature of the "890" form remains open, but one could think of analogy with the "high density" forms of chlorophyll.

Whether the several bands of bacteriochlorophyll *in vivo* can be interpreted in the same way as the several bands *in vitro* will be discussed in section 6(*c*) below.

4. Fluorescence of Chlorophyll *in vitro*

(Addendum to Chapter 23)

French (1954) described the fluorescence spectra of several photosynthetic pigments *in vitro* and *in vivo*, obtained with a highly sensitive recording spectrophotometer. With chlorophyll b in ether, a curve very similar to that in fig. 23.2 was obtained; but with chlorophyll a the whole fluorescence spectrum was displaced by about 7 mμ towards the longer waves compared to Zscheile and Harris' curve ($\lambda_{max.}$ = 672 mμ, as compared to 665 mμ in fig. 23.2).

(a) Quantum Yield

In improvement of the measurements reported in Part 1 of Vol. II (p. 752), Forster and Livingston (1952) re-determined the quantum yield of fluorescence of the chlorophylls a and b, in different solvents and with different exciting light. They used an integrating sphere, thus avoiding errors that could be caused by polarized emission. Table 37C.IV summarizes the results obtained in different solvents. In each case, the yield was determined as function of chlorophyll concentration and extrapolated to infinite dilution, to eliminate the effects of self-absorption (all concentrations used were too low for marked self-quenching, $cf.$ section 4(c) below, and chapter 23, p. 775).

Table 37C.IV shows for chlorophyll a no differences in yield in the several fluorescence-supporting solvents; at [Chl] $\to$ 0, the values of φ become practically the same (0.24 to 0.26) for methanol, ether, acetone, benzene and cyclohexanol.

The quantum yield is lower and solvent-dependent with chlorophyll b (φ_0 = 0.06 in methanol, 0.11 in ether). With pheophytin a, the yield in 10^{-5} M solution is about equal to that of chlorophyll a of the same concentration; but it fails to increase in the same proportion as that of chlorophyll when the concentration is reduced, because the re-absorption of pheophytin fluorescence is relatively weak. (The same applies to mesoporphyrin.)

Table 37C.V compares the yields of fluorescence produced by excitation in the blue band (λ 436 mμ), with those produced by excitation in the red band (627.5, 644, 662 and 698 mμ). Contrary to the earlier results shown in table 23.IIC, (Vol. II, 1, p. 762), identical values were now found for φ, whether the excitation was in the blue or in the red band. Clearly confirmed was the (as yet not adequately theoretically understood, $cf.$ chapter 30) sharp drop of the fluorescence yield in the far red ($cf.$ point at 698 mμ).

It will be noted in table 37C.V that measurements have been made only in the main blue-violet band (436 mμ) and the main red band (628–698 mμ) of chlorophyll $a;$ and in the minor blue-violet band (436 mμ) and the main red band (644 mμ) of chlorophyll b. In consideration of theoretical expectations (section 1) and experimental observations of different polarizations of the several chlorophyll bands (section 4(b)), more systematic measurements of the action spectrum of fluorescence of chlorophyll (and bacteriochlorophyll) appear desirable. One would like to know (for example)

TABLE 37C.IV

QUANTUM YIELD OF FLUORESCENCE OF CHLOROPHYLL AND RELATED COMPOUNDS
(AFTER FORSTER AND LIVINGSTON 1952)

Pigment	Solvent	[Chl] molarity $\times 10^6$	$\dfrac{\varphi \text{ quanta emitted}}{\text{quanta absorbed}}$
Chlorophyll *a*.........	Methanol	20.0	0.15 ± 0.02
	"	14.0	0.14 ± 0.02
	"	11.0	0.17 ± 0.02
	"	10.0	0.18 ± 0.02
	"	8.6	0.17 ± 0.02
	"	6.2	0.18 ± 0.02
	"	5.5	0.21 ± 0.02
	"	2.7	0.21 ± 0.02
	"	(0)	0.24 ± 0.02^a
	Ethyl ether	21.0	0.15 ± 0.02
	" "	7.2	0.20 ± 0.02
	" "	5.0	0.20 ± 0.02
	" "	2.3	0.22 ± 0.02
	" "	(0)	0.24 ± 0.02^a
	Acetone	9.7	0.21 ± 0.02
	"	3.3	0.24 ± 0.02
	"	(0)	0.26 ± 0.04^a
	Benzene (wet)^b	5.5	0.23 ± 0.02
	" "	(0)	0.26 ± 0.04^a
	Cyclohexanol	5.0	0.20 ± 0.02
	"	(0)	0.26 ± 0.04^a
Chlorophyll *b*...	Methanol	15.0	0.043 ± 0.005
	"	6.5	0.048 ± 0.007
	"	(0)	0.06 ± 0.01^a
	Ethyl ether	12.0	0.090 ± 0.010
	" "	9.0	0.074 ± 0.007
	" "	(0)	0.11 ± 0.01^a
Pheophytin *a*..........	Methanol	10.0	0.14 ± 0.02
	"	2.5	0.13 ± 0.03
Mesoporphyrin.........	Benzene	20.0	0.10 ± 0.03
	"	10.0	0.10 ± 0.03

^{a} Extrapolated values, φ_0, for infinite dilution.
Fluorescence is very weak in *dry* benzene (p. 766).

whether the yield of fluorescence is independent of the mutual orientation of the dipole
oscillations in the absorption and the emission band.

The absolute fluorescence yield, found by Forster and Livingston for
chlorophyll *a* (24%), is considerably higher than that previously estimated
by Prins (about 10%). Re-absorption of fluorescence light, which is
much stronger for chlorophyll than for most other dyes, is the most probable reason for Prins's low value.

EFFECT OF THE WAVE LENGTH OF THE EXCITING LIGHT ON THE QUANTUM YIELD OF
FLUORESCENCE, φ (AFTER FORSTER AND LIVINGSTON 1952)

Pigment	Solvent	Exciting λ, mμ	φ
Chlorophyll a........	Methanol	436	0.24 ± 0.02
	"	627.5	0.24 ± 0.03
	"	644	0.25 ± 0.04
	"	662	0.26 ± 0.03
	"	698	0.11 ± 0.04
	Ethyl ether	436	0.24 ± 0.02
	" "	627.5	0.21 ± 0.03
	" "	644	0.24 ± 0.03
	" "	662	0.24 ± 0.03
Chlorophyll b........	Ethyl ether	436	0.11 ± 0.01
	" "	644	0.11 ± 0.02

This re-absorption, and the consequent reduction in the fraction of absorbed energy that escapes the solution as fluorescent light, may explain, according to a suggestion by Forster and Livingston, how some chlorophyll-sensitized photochemical reactions can have quantum yield close to 1.0 (cf. chapter 18, Vol. I, and chapter 35, sections A5 and A6).

(b) Polarization

The polarization of chlorophyll fluorescence was first measured by Perrin (1929), in four solvents of different viscosity, from petroleum ether ($\eta = 0.003$) to castor oil ($\eta = 8.32$). The degree of polarization of fluorescence, excited by linearly polarized light, ranged in these four solvents from 0.01 to 0.42 with excitation by red light (660 mμ); from 0.000 to 0.105 with excitation by violet light (430 mμ), and from 0.000 to 0.22 with excitation by ultraviolet light (380 mμ). These results were used to calculate, by means of simple assumptions concerning the rotational relaxation time, the (actual) mean excitation time of chlorophyll (cf. section 1 of this chapter). The dependence of polarization on wave length of the exciting light indicated that some absorption bands correspond to electric dipole oscillations along an axis different from that in which the emission band oscillation occurs. This dependence was studied more systematically by Stupp and Kuhn (1952). Fig. 37C.21 shows their results for chlorophyll a in castor oil. Perrin's three points fit well Stupp and Kuhn's curve. According to Perrin's theory, when the relaxation time is long compared to the excitation life time, the degree of polarization can vary between +0.50 for parallel oscillations in absorption and emission and −0.33 for mutually perpendicular oscillations. Fig. 37C.21 indicates that the condition $t(\text{relax}) \gg t(\text{excit.})$ is fulfilled for chlorophyll in the—highly viscous—castor oil. The excitation dipole appears to be parallel to the emission dipole in the orange and red (580 mμ), and perpendicular to it at 540 mμ; below 520 mμ the two types of excitation seem to be combined, with the "parallel type" becoming more prevalent below 430 mμ. Calculation shows that a polarization degree of $+0.2$ results if the contribution of the "parallel type" excitation is 1.8 times that of the "perpendicular type."

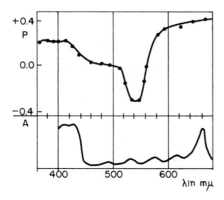

Fig. 37C.21. Polarization (P) of chlorophyll a fluorescence as function of wavelength of (polarized) exciting light (after Kuhn and Stupp 1952). Lower curve: absorption spectrum (A) of chlorophyll a in castor oil.

The significance of these findings for the theoretical interpretation of the chlorophyll bands, and the estimation of the life time of the excited state, was mentioned in section 1 above. It seems, however, that the matter is in need of further experimental study. Jacobs and Coleman (unpublished) could find no reversal of polarization in the 540 mμ band of either chlorophyll or chlorophyllide, but did note such an effect in pheophorbide. Since the pheophytin absorption in this region is much stronger than that of chlorophyll, even a small content of Mg-free product in the chlorophyll preparation used could perhaps account for Kuhn and Stupp's results.

(c) *Quenching*

Watson and Livingston (1950) continued the study of *self-quenching* ("concentration quenching") of chlorophyll fluorescence, described in chapter 23 (*cf.* fig. 23.7). Measurements with chlorophyll a in ether, methanol and acetone confirmed the absence of concentration quenching below 2×10^{-3} M, and supported the interpretation (offered on p. 774) of the observations of Weiss and Weil-Malherbe as an artefact caused by re-absorption.

Above 2×10^{-3} M, self-quenching was found to be about the same for the two chlorophylls, a and b, with blue or red exciting light, in ether or in

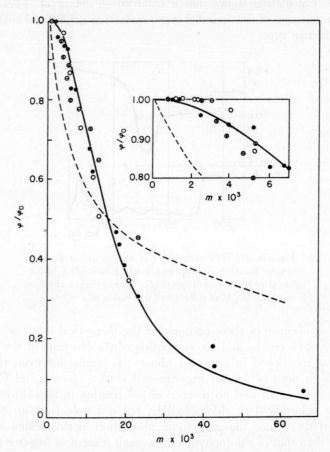

Fig. 37C.22. Concentration quenching of the fluorescence of chlorophyll solutions: (●) chlorophyll a (in ether) excited with 435.8 mμ;   (○) chlorophyll b (in ether) excited with 435.8 mμ;   (⊗) chlorophyll b (in acetone) excited with 642.5 mμ;   (⊖) chlorophyll b (in acetone) excited with 435.8 mμ (after Watson and Livingston (1950)).   Solid line is from eq. (37C.3); dashed line from an equation based on the assumption that dimerization (to non-fluorescent dimers) is the reason for concentration quenching.

acetone (fig. 37C.22). The results fitted the one-constant equation (solid curve):

$$(37C.3) \qquad \varphi_0/\varphi = 1 + 4300[\text{Chl}]^2$$

where φ_0 is the maximum yield of fluorescence at high dilution, φ the yield in concentrated solution, and [Chl] the concentration in mole/l.

The temperature effect on the yield of fluorescence appears to be somewhat stronger in the quenched state than in dilute solution ($d\varphi/dt = 0.83$, 13–49° C., in $1.2 \times 10^{-2}\ M$ solution of chlorophyll b in acetone, where $\varphi/\varphi_0 = 0.64$ at 30° C.).

The absorption spectrum of chlorophyll a (in diethyl ether) was found to be the same in 0.02 M as in 0.001 M solution, despite an over 50% effective quenching of fluorescence in the first-named solution. This, and the form of the concentration dependence of φ, argue against dimerization as the cause of self-quenching. Neither does quenching appear to be due to encounters of excited with normal dye molecules, because it cannot be represented by the Stern-Volmer equation ($\varphi_0/\varphi = 1 + \text{Const.}[\text{Chl}]$). The experimental results, although they can be expressed approximately by the one-constant equation (37C.3), are not inconsistent with Vavilov's three-constant equation, which is based on the assumption of a constant probability of dissipation in every energy transfer between two molecules:

(37C.4) $$\varphi_0/\varphi = (1 + \alpha + \beta - \beta e^{-\Omega_0[\text{Chl}]})e^{\Omega_0[\text{Chl}]}$$

The data are, however, insufficient to calculate the three constants α, β and Ω_0 separately. If the assumption is made that $\alpha \ll \Omega_0$, the two constants Ω_0 and β can be derived from the empirical data, and the results ($\Omega_0 = 8.3 \times 10^{-21}$ and $\beta = 1.32 \times 10^{-18}$ cc. per molecule) are of the same order of magnitude as the constants derived by Vavilov and co-workers for other dyes in glycerol-water mixtures.

According to p. 760 (*cf.* also chapter 32, section 5), the probability of energy dissipation by resonance transfer may depend on concentration more strongly than is postulated in Vavilov's model (*e. g.*, if dissipation is caused by dimers encountered in the resonance chain, as suggested by Forster); it may also depend on temperature (if dissipation occurs in "hot" chain links as suggested by Franck).

The study of the *quenching* of chlorophyll fluorescence by different *admixtures*, described in chapter 23 (section 6) was extended by Livingston, Thompson and Ramarao (1952) to mesoporphyrin and protoporphyrin. Fourteen admixtures were tested, and the only significant difference between the porphyrins and chlorophyll was found in sensitivity to oxygen— the quenching constant (K_1 in the equation $\varphi_0/\varphi = 1 + K_1[Q] + K_2[Q]^2$, *cf.* p. 785) was ten times higher ($K_1 = 335$ l./mole) for the oxygen effect on porphyrins than for its effect on chlorophyll ($K_1 = 35$). The porphyrin value is similar to that found for many aromatic hydrocarbons; chlorophyll fluorescence is thus exceptionally insensitive to oxygen—a fact that reminds one of the low quantum yield of photoxidation of chlorophyll (*cf.* chapter 18).

The quenching effect of quinone (and other oxidants) on chlorophyll fluorescence is shown by these experiments to be unrelated to the presence of the two extra ring hydrogens in the chlorin system (since it is equally strong in porphyrins, which contain no such hydrogen atoms).

In continuation of the work of Livingston and Ke on quenching of chlorophyll fluorescence (Vol. II, Part 1, chapter 23, pp. 781, 787), and of Livingston, Watson and McArdle on its activation (chapter 23, p. 766), Watson (1952) described in more detail the effect of phenylhydrazine. With chlorophyll *a* in a *polar* solvent (such as methanol), a quenching was found that followed the Stern-Volmer equation, with a constant $K_1 = 3.2$ liter/mole (table 23.IIIC gave $K_1 = 3.7$ l./mole). Phenylhydrazine has no noticeable effect on the absorption spectrum of chlorophyll *a* in methanol; nevertheless, quenching seems to be due to complex formation (rather than to kinetic encounters), because it develops only several minutes after the addition of the quencher. This complex formation is reversible; at least, a gradual return of fluorescence with time was noted when acetone was used as solvent (instead of methanol), and this could be attributed to disappearance of phenylhydrazine by the formation of hydrazone.

With chlorophyll *b* in methanol, the previously described change in absorption spectrum upon addition of phenylhydrazine (*cf.* pp. 649, 786) was confirmed. The absorption peak moves from 652 to 672 mμ.

When chlorophyll *a* is dissolved in a *nonpolar* solvent (benzene, or *n*-pentane), small quantities of phenylhydrazine (up to 0.05 mole/l.) *activate* fluorescence (*cf.* table 23.IIIA), while larger quantities produce quenching (as stated on p. 768); the absorption spectrum is changed significantly only in the activating stage. An expression was proposed for the intensity of fluorescence as a function of phenylhydrazine concentration that assumed two independent associations of chlorophyll with phenylhydrazine (P)—one causing activation and the other quenching:

$$(37C.5) \quad \varphi/\varphi_{\text{max.}} = K_1[P] + K_3[A]/\{1 + K_3[A] + (K_1 + K_2)[P] + K_1K_2[P]^2\}$$

where K_1 and K_2 are the two association constants for Chl and P, and K_3 is the association constant for Chl and an "adventitious" activator, A, which is supposed to account for residual fluorescence in nonpolar solvents. The empirical data fit this equation with $K_1 = 1900$ (for benzene or *n*-heptane), $K_2 = 16$ (benzene) or 58 (*n*-pentane), and $K_3[A] = 0.27$ (benzene) or 0.16 (*n*-heptane).

(For application of these results to photosensitization of the phenyl-hydrazine-methyl red reaction, see chapter 35, section 5.)

Evstigneev, Gavrilova and Krasnovsky (1950) pointed out that the rate of photobleaching of chlorophyll in solutions containing various admixtures does not parallel the quenching effect of these admixtures on chlorophyll fluorescence. The strongest quenchers, such as nitrophenol, dinitrophenol, quinone and nitrosobenzene, do not enhance bleaching, while ascorbic acid, which causes strong reversible bleaching, does not quench fluorescence.

(d) Activation

The equilibrium between fluorescent and nonfluorescent forms of chlorophyll in mixed solvents (*cf.* Vol. II, Part 1, pp. 767–770) was farther studied by Livingston and Weil (1952). They confirmed the observation of Evstigneev, Gavrilova and Krasnovsky (p. 771) that pheophytin fluoresces equally strongly in dry and in wet toluene, but not their observation that the fluorescence of magnesium phthalocyanine is activated by moisture similarly to that of chlorophyll. However, the first experiment alone is sufficient to justify ascribing the activating complex formation to the magnesium atom, rather than to the keto group in ring V (Livingston's original hypothesis).

Absorption measurements (described in section 2(*c*) above) confirmed this surmise by showing approximately equal complexing tendency for several metal porphyrins and chlorins. Strangely, the magnesium-chlorin complex (chlorophyll) seems to be the only compound that requires complexing with a base to be able to fluoresce; with Mg and Zn complexes of porphyrin, there was no effect of base at all, while Zn-chlorin showed only an increase of 20%. (In chlorophyll *a* or *b*, complexing with bases increases the yield at least by a factor of 25!)

The *phosphorescence* of chlorophyll solutions in isoamylamine (*cf.* p. 754), not observed in other solvents, must be associated, according to the experiments of Weller (chapter 37B, section 4) with the products of aminolysis, rather than with chlorophyll itself.

(e) Sensitization

The sensitization of chlorophyll *a* fluorescence by chlorophyll *b* in solution was observed by Watson and Livingston (1950) and Duysens (1952). (For description of the same phenomenon *in vivo*, see next section.)

Watson and Livingston (1950) used excitation with a band at λ 475 mμ, absorbed mainly by chlorophyll *b*, and observed fluorescence through a filter (Wratten 88) that transmits the fluorescence of chlorophyll *a* much better than that of chlorophyll *b*. The total transmitted fluorescence in equimolar mixtures of *a* and *b* solutions proved to be markedly in excess of that calculated under the assumption of independent absorption and re-emission by each pigment (by 10–30%, dependent on concentration, which was varied from 0.35 to 19.4×10^{-4} mole/l.).   The interpretation of the results is complicated by the fact that sensitization, self-quenching and $a \longleftrightarrow b$ "cross-quenching" all grow with increasing concentration. An approximate kinetic analysis led to the following tentative conclusions. (1) Energy transfer from Chl$b$ to Chl$a$ becomes significant above 2×10^{-4} mole/l.—an order of magnitude earlier than self-quenching of either a or b

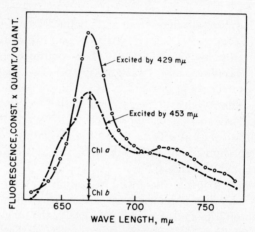

Fig. 37C.23. Fluorescence spectra of chlorophyll $a + b$ in ether (1.2×10^{-3} M) excited by $\lambda = 429$ (70% absorbed by chlorophyll a) and by $\lambda = 453$ mμ (5% absorbed by chlorophyll a).   Corrected for self-absorption.   Fluorescence in (quanta emitted)/-(quanta absorbed), multiplied by arbitrary factor.   The peak at 670 mμ is due to chlorophyll a, the hump at 650 mμ to chlorophyll b.   Vertical arrow shows large contribution of chlorophyll a to fluorescence at 670 mμ excited by λ 453 mμ, where the absorption of chlorophyll a is small; it indicates energy transfer from chlorophyll b to chlorophyll a (after Duysens 1952).

(this may be attributed to stronger overlapping of the absorption band of a with the fluorescence band of b, as compared to the overlapping of the absorption band of each pigment and its own fluorescence band).   (2) The quenching of chlorophyll b fluorescence by chlorophyll a is highly efficient; that of a fluorescence by b is negligible.   (3) The quenching of b by a increases with concentration faster than the sensitization of a.   (It appears as if the first effect may be proportional to the square, the second one to the first power, of concentration.)   Above 10^{-3} mole/l., quenching begins to reduce markedly the yield of sensitization, and the latter drops to zero above 10^{-2} mole/l.

Duysens (1952) determined the ratio of the intensities of fluorescence excited in an ethereal solution, 1.2×10^{-3} M in both chlorophyll a and chlorophyll b, by λ 429 and 453 mμ, respectively. Chlorophyll a absorbs fourteen times more quanta at 429 than at 453 mμ; nevertheless, the intensity ratio was only 1.7. Since the spectrum of fluorescence excited at 453 mμ indicates that only a minor part of it was due to the emission by chlorophyll b (fig. 37C.23), the intensity measurements indicate that the energy absorbed by chlorophyll b is made available for fluorescence of chlorophyll a; the efficiency of this transfer could be estimated as 40–50%.

At lower concentrations (5 $\times$ 10^{-4} M, and 1.2 $\times$ 10^{-4} M in each component), the effectiveness of the transfer declined to 30–40% and 20%, respectively.

(f) Fluorescence of Colloidal Chlorophyll Solutions

Table 37C.IIIB shows that Krasnovsky and Brin (1948), while confirming the nonfluorescence of most colloids and adsorbates of chlorophyll, found some fluorescence in adsorbates on paraffin, palmitic acid and magnesia, and strong fluorescence in colloidal solutions containing detergents, whether prepared by dilution of alcoholic chlorophyll solutions with aqueous detergents (2b), or by similar dilution of alcoholic solutions containing alcohol-soluble proteins (3e), or by treatment of chloroplast or grana suspensions with aqueous detergents (5d) (*cf.* pp. 775–777 for earlier observations of weak fluorescence in some colloidal chlorophyll preparations). The non-fluorescence of *microcrystalline* chlorophyll suspensions was noted above in section 3.

(g) Fluorescence of Bacteriochlorophyll and Protochlorophyll

The presence of two fluorescence bands, at 695 and 810 mμ, respectively, in the fluorescence spectrum of *bacteriochlorophyll*, was noted in Part 1 of Vol. II (p. 748, fig. 23.4). An interpretation of this phenomenon—if it were real—could be sought in the theory of the tetraporphin spectrum (*cf.* table 37C.I), according to which the "orange" absorption band of bacteriochlorophyll corresponds to a dipole oscillation parallel to the long axis of the conjugated double bond system, while the red absorption band corresponds to an oscillation perpendicular to this axis. Internal conversion of the "parallel" into the "perpendicular" oscillation could be difficult; the orange band of bacteriochlorophyll (in contrast to the blue-violet bands of both chlorophyll and bacteriochlorophyll) could then have a fluorescence band of its own associated with it.

However, it seems more likely that the two-band fluorescence spectrum in fig. 23.4 was obtained not with pure bacteriochlorophyll, but with a mixture of bacteriochlorophyll and a green oxidation product (described in chapter 37B, section 6). Purified bacteriochlorophyll has no visible fluorescence, while the green oxidation product fluoresces red.

French (1954) made similar observations: A two-band fluorescence spectrum was found in a "crude" bacteriochlorophyll preparation; after chromatography a green fraction was separated which gave only one fluorescence band, at 687 mμ. However, the main blue fraction still showed, in French's experiments, the two original bands. Their relative intensity depended on the wave length of the exciting light, confirming the surmise that they belonged to two different compounds, in other words, that the blue fraction still was a mixture rather than a pure pigment.

French (1954) gave also a spectral curve for the fluorescence of *proto-chlorophyll* in acetone. It showed a main peak at 630 mμ and a secondary peak at 685 mμ.

(h) Fluorescence of Phycobilins

Bannister (1954) found that the quantum yield of fluorescence of the purest phycocyanin preparations (*i. e.*, preparations freed as much as possible from adventitious proteins), excited with monochromatic ultraviolet light, was constant (within 10%) from 250 to 400 mμ, including the region around 275 mμ, where a considerable fraction of the absorbed light must be assigned to the protein moiety of the chromoprotein molecule, more specifically, to tryptophane and tyrosine residues. (Crude estimates indicated the protein share of the absorption in this region to be of the order of 50%.) This indicates an efficient excitation energy transfer from the protein to the chromophore—a type of energy transfer suggested before as explanation of CO-removal from hemoproteins by light absorbed in their protein moiety. In the latter case, however, an alternative to transfer of electronic excitation is conceivable: the conversion of electronic excitation into vibrations, and accumulation of enough vibrational energy in the iron-carbon monoxide bond to dissociate it; no such alternative explanation seems to be possible in the case of protein-sensitized fluorescence of phycobilins.

5. Chemiluminescence of Chlorophyll *in vitro* and *in vivo*

The only evidence of chemiluminescence of chlorophyll, described in Part 1 of Vol. II, was the light emitted, upon heating, by solutions of chlorophyll in tetralin (p. 751). Since then, two studies have been developed in this field. One deals with a system *in vitro*, the other with photosythesizing cells.

Linschitz and co-workers (1952) found that chlorophyll (and other metalloporphyrin dyes) chemiluminesce when reacting with organic peroxides (at $t > 100°$ C.). The kinetics of luminescence decay (studied with Zn-tetraphenyl porphin and tetralin hydroperoxide) indicated that the over-all process includes: (1) a second-order reaction of peroxide, P, with the dye, DH_2; (2) an approximately second-order catalytic decomposition of the peroxide; and (3) a slow first-order, noncatalyzed decomposition of the peroxide. Between 20 and 60 peroxide molecules are decomposed for each permanently destroyed dye molecule. The decay of chemilumines-cence follows the second-order law, $I \cong [P][DH_2]$. The following free-radical reaction mechanism (of the type first proposed by J. Weiss for the chemiluminescence of luminol) is suggested for the main catalytic reaction, and the emission of light:

$$\text{(a)} \quad \overset{H_2}{R-C-O-OH} + DH_2 \rightarrow \overset{H_2}{R-C-O-} + DH- + H_2O$$

(37C.6) $\quad$ (b) $\quad \overset{H_2}{R-C-O-} + DH- \rightarrow DH_2^* + \overset{H}{RC=O}$

$\qquad\qquad$ (c) $\quad DH_2^* \rightarrow DH_2 + h\nu$

$\overset{H_2}{R-C-O-}$ and DH— are free radicals, and their reaction, (b), should lib-erate enough energy to produce an electronically excited dye molecule, DH_2^*. It will be noted that reading reactions (c), (b), and (a) backwards, one gets the over-all reaction:

$$\text{(37C.7)} \qquad \overset{H_2}{RC=O} + H_2O \xrightarrow[+h\nu]{+DH_2} \overset{H_2}{R-CO-OH}$$

i. e., a dye-sensitized photochemical peroxide formation. This illustrates the inverse relation between photosensitization and chemiluminescence.

The chemiluminescence of photosynthesizing cells was discovered by Strehler and Arnold (1951), using sensitive methods of light detection. It can be observed in higher plants as well as in green and red algae. In its low yield, it resembles the weak luminescences which Audubert and co-workers have found to accompany many common chemical reactions. An important difference is that the emission occurs in the visible, not in the ultraviolet as in Audubert's experiments. Its spectrum could be deter-mined only rather crudely, but appeared to be identical with that of chloro-phyll fluorescence. The emission could be followed for several minutes after the cessation of illumination; about 0.1 sec. after the exciting light had been turned off, the intensity of the afterglow was about 0.1% of the intensity fluorescence has had during the illumination (in which less than saturating light had been used). The intensity of emission decays in the dark, following an approximately bimolecular law at $6.5°$ C. and a lower order law at higher temperatures.

That the emission is due to chemiluminescence (and is not a fluorescence or phosphorescence of long duration) is indicated by the many relations between the rate of photosynthesis and the intensity of the emission. Both show saturation in the same region of light intensities; both have a temperature maximum at about 35° C.; inhibitors of photosynthesis, including azide, cyanide, hydroxylamine, dinitrophenol and ultraviolet light, stop both photosynthesis and the "afterglow."

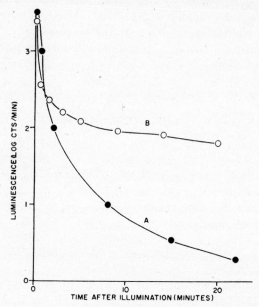

Fig. 37C.23A. Decay of "photosynthetic luminescence" at 25° C. (after Strehler 1951).   Curve A: Spinach, mustard leaf, *Chlorella*, spinach chloroplasts, washed mustard chloroplasts.   Curve B: Unwashed mustard chloroplasts.

The action spectrum of excitation of the afterglow appears to be the same as that of photosynthesis, in both green and red algae; in the latter case, this includes the region of predominant phycoerythrin absorption.

Five percent carbon dioxide reduces the emission by about 30%, compared to that in pure nitrogen.

All these observations are consistent with the assumption that the emission observed by Strehler and Arnold is a chemiluminescence associated with an energy-releasing back reaction between photochemical products, which becomes more probable when carbon dioxide is absent and photosynthesis cannot take its course.

Strehler (1951) made a similar study with a preparation of spinach chloroplasts, in which a comparison of the kinetics of chemiluminescence and of photochemical reaction could be carried out more easily than in whole cells (*e. g.*, by using ferricyanide as Hill oxidant and a potentiometric method for reduction measurement). Similar curves were found for the response of the two rates to changes in light intensity. The luminescence reached a maximum at 35° C., in common with photosynthesis and Hill reaction. The luminescence had two pH optima—at *p*H 5.2 and 8.8, with a minimum at *p*H 6.7, which is not in agreement with Hill reaction data (chapter 35, section B5).

The luminescence of spinach chloroplast preparations decayed in the same way (fig. 37C.23A) as that of the luminescence of *Chlorella* and of leaves of spinach and mustard (half-time of decay, about 3 min.). Mustard chloroplasts, washed only once, showed a different behavior, with a long luminescence "tail." Luminescence of the chloroplasts (similarly to their Hill reaction) showed no induction period, while one was present in *Chlorella* luminescence (as well as in photosynthesis). Carbon dioxide had no effect on the luminescence of chloroplasts (in contrast to that of *Chlorella*). Dinitrophenol, cyanide and azide inhibited the chemiluminescence of chloroplast material much less than that of *Chlorella;* the same was true of the relative effect of the last two (but not of the first one) of these inhibitors on the Hill reaction and on photosynthesis. Hydroxylamine inhibited the chemiluminescence of chloroplasts much stronger than that of *Chlorella*.

Arnold and Davidson (1954) improved the measurements so as to obtain a reliable spectral distribution curve of the luminescence. It proved identical with that of chlorophyll fluorescence *in vivo*. They estimated that each *Chlorella* cell emits, per second, about 33 quanta of delayed luminescence (at the beginning of the decay curve, at 25° C.).

6. Light Absorption by Pigments *in vivo*
(Addendum to Chapter 22)

(*a*) *Absorption Spectra of Leaves and Algae*

The previously unpublished investigation by Loomis and co-workers (1941), from which figures 1, 14, 30, 31, and 33 in chapter 22 had been taken, has since appeared (Moss and Loomis 1952). The paper contains some additional information. Fig. 37C.24 shows reflection and absorption spectra of leaves of four species. *Ficus* leaves—thick and dark green—absorb the most and reflect the least; cabbage leaves, with a highly reflecting surface layer, show the opposite behavior. A similar difference often exists between the upper and the lower surface of the same leaf; the lower, tomentuous surface reflects 2–3 times more light than the upper surface, and correspondingly less of the light falling onto it is absorbed.

The absorption peaks of the species studied were located at 680 mμ, with indication of bands at 640 and 600 mμ, and a minimum at 550 mμ (*cf.* table 22.III on p. 699). The average absorption was 92% at 400–500 mμ, 71% at 500–600 mμ, and 84% at 600–700 mμ; over-all average for

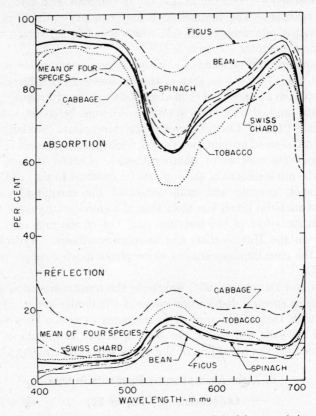

Fig. 37C.24. Absorption and reflection curves of singlel eaves of six species, together with smoothed average curves for bean, spinach, Swiss chard, and tobacco (after Moss and Loomis 1952). Average reflection of green light (550 mμ), 17%; average absorption, 62%.

the region 400–700 mμ was 82% absorption, 10% reflection and 8% transmission.

Boiled leaves showed a general slight reduction in absorption and reflection, and a slight shift of band peak toward shorter waves, *cf.* p. 698. (In some species, the changes were more drastic, indicating chemical decomposition of the pigment.) Dipping in *ether* caused in spinach leaves a much stronger decrease in absorption, particularly in the green, and a wider shift of the absorption peak, than did boiling (fig. 37C.25). In Swiss chard and tobacco leaves, on the other hand, dipping in ether caused an *increase* in absorption, particularly in the green; this increase was larger than the simultaneous decrease in reflection (fig. 37C.26). Spectra of *chloroplast preparations* showed the transition from the spectra of leaves to those of pigment extracts (fig. 37C.27).

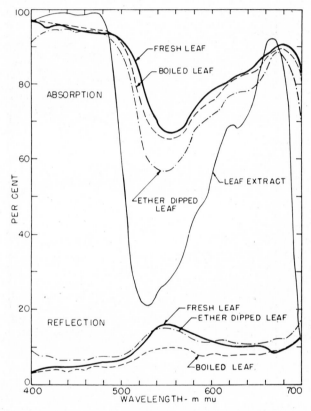

Fig. 37C.25. Absorption and reflection curves of fresh, boiled, and ether-dipped leaves of spinach (after Moss and Loomis 1952).

Strain (1950) discussed the participation, in the light absorption by photosynthesizing cells and tissues, of noncolored components with a weak general absorption, particularly at the shorter waves (*cf.* p. 684). He referred to this absorption as "cellular opacity" and suggested that it may account for some of the features of the action spectra of photosynthesis (described in chapter 30), such as the low yield in the far red and in the blue-violet region of the carotenoid absorption. (A weak absorption by other cell constituents should affect the action spectra most strongly in the regions where absorption by photochemically active pigments is relatively small.)

Krasnovsky and Brin (1948) gave the data listed in table 37C.IIIA (section 5) on the effect of boiling and freezing on the absorption spectrum

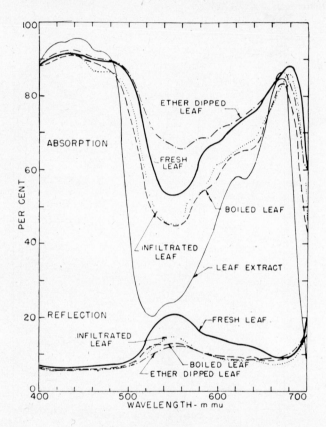

Fig. 37C.26. Absorption and reflection curves of fresh, boiled, water-infiltrated and ether-dipped leaves of tobacco (after Moss and Loomis 1952).

of leaves. Boiling shifts the red band to its position in solutions while freezing in liquid air leaves it unchanged.

Barer (1953) minimized scattering, in measuring the absorption spectra of cells, by suspending them in a protein solution with an index of refraction adjusted, by means of a phase contrast microscope, to match that of the cell material (Barer, Ross and Tkaczyk 1953). Fig. 37C.28 illustrates the success obtained with a suspension of purple bacteria; the residual scattering was somewhat stronger with chloroplast-containing algal cells.

Despite this improvement, the transmission curves, log (T_0/T), obtained by Barer (1955) with the green alga, *Chlorella variegata* and *Scenedesmus obliquus*, were similar to those given by earlier observers, except that transmission was almost constant, or even slowly declining (instead

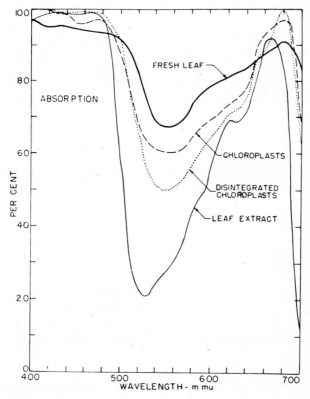

Fig. 37C.27. Absorption curves of equivalent quantities of pigments from spinach leaves, in four states.   Red band is at 680 mμ on all curves except that for methanol extract (Moss and Loomis 1952).

of steadily increasing, as in fig. 22.22) between 560 and 620 mμ.   In fact, the ratios of the optical densities in the *green trough* and the *red peak* were even higher than in previous experiments: 0.50 for *Scenedesmus*, 0.47 for *Closterium*, and 0.59 for (green) *Chlorella*, as compared to 0.28 and 0.33 given for *Chlorella* in table 22.VII.   The ratios of the optical densities in the *violet* and the *red* peak, were 1.36 for *Scenedesmus*, 1.59 for *Closterium*, and 1.36 for (green) *Chlorella*, in good agreement with the earlier data in table 22.VII.

The relative transmission in the *far red* also was, in Barer's curves, lower than in earlier measurements—*e. g.*, in (green) *Chlorella* the ratio of optical densities at 720 and 675 mμ was about 0.4, as compared with about 0.2 in fig. 22.22. This difference, too, is opposite in sense to what one would expect from an effective elimination of scattering! The problem of the true absorption curve of algal cells thus seems to need further attention.

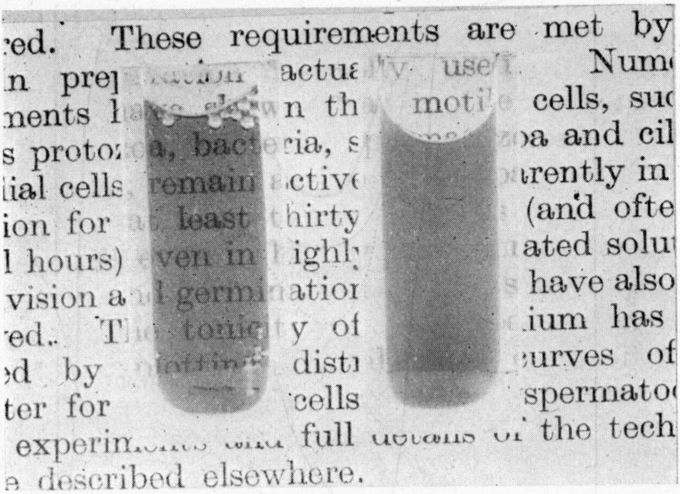

Fig. 37C.28. Removal of scattering in a bacterial suspension by the use of suspension medium with properly adjusted refractive index (Barer 1955).

One particular point, which needs clarification, is to what extent scattering can explain the high apparent absorption by cells in the green and in the far red. We will see below (section 6A) that, according to Duysens (1954), ordinary Rayleigh scattering can account for both the shallowness of the "green trough" and the existence of a "red tail" in the transmission curve; but that the observations of Latimer (1954) indicate the occurrence of a strong selective scattering on the long-wave side of the main absorption bands, which is bound to contribute to the diminution of transmission, particularly in the far red.

Sharp selective scattering bands are associated not only with the main absorption bands of chlorophyll, but also with those of the carotenoids, although the latter are merely ripples in the absorption curve of live *Chlorella* cells.

On p. 709, we noted that the dips in the green and in the red were as shallow in Noddack's "pure absorption" curve as in Emerson's "absorption + scattering" curve of *Chlorella*. In Noddack's measurements, however, scattering was not *eliminated* (as it was supposed to be in Barer's experiments), but merely *excluded from measurement;* therefore, the possibility of the scattering increasing significantly the true absorption in the minima (by the so-called "detour factor," *cf.* chapter 22) could not be ruled out.

Barer noted that the position of the main red peak varied, in different green algal suspension, between 675 and 680 mμ, and that of the main violet peak, between 435 and 440 mμ.

New absorption bands were found by Barer, in *Chlorella*, at 385 and 340 mμ, probably corresponding to the solution bands of chlorophyll *a* at 380 and 330 mμ, respectively (*cf.* fig. 21.3). In *Closterium*, an absorption band was noted at 620 mμ, of which only a slight indication can be found in the *Chlorella* spectrum; it was suggested that it is the equivalent of the 612.5 mμ band of chlorophyll *a* in solution (fig. 21.1). *Closterium* spectrum showed no evidence of the 645 mμ band, which would indicate the presence of chlorophyll *b*.

The absorption peaks of green algae at 480 and 490 mμ, presumably due to carotenoids, were noted by Barer to become progressively more pronounced in the transition from yellow, through yellow-green, to green *Chlorella* strains, indicating a parallel increase in the contents of chlorophyll and the carotenoids (unless the 480–490 mμ band is attributed—at least in part—to chlorophyll *b*!).

(b) Two Forms of Chlorophyll in vivo?

Krasnovsky and Brin (1948) suggested that chlorophyll is present in leaves in two different forms. The less abundant form, with a band at 665–670 mμ, they supposed to be "nonaggregated," but bound to a lipide, or lipoprotein. It was also supposed to be fluorescent and photochemically active. The main amount of chlorophyll, responsible for the band at 677–678 mμ, was supposed to be in an "aggregated" (colloidal), nonfluorescent and photochemically inactive form—a kind of "chlorophyll reserve." This hypothesis is very similar to that propounded earlier by Seybold and Egle (*cf.* p. 818). The argument used on pp. 746 and 819 against the latter's assumption that two different forms of chlorophyll account for the main absorption band and the fluorescence band *in vivo*—the approximately equal shifts of both bands from their positions in solution—was considered by Krasnovsky and Brin to be unconvincing because, in their opinion, self-absorption of fluorescence could have caused an apparent shift of the fluorescence band toward the longer waves. (The fluorescence band, corresponding to the absorption band at 665–670 mμ of the "nonaggregated" photoactive chlorophyll, could be located under the absorption peak of the "aggregated" form at 677–678 mμ, and distorted by absorption so as to show an apparent peak at 680 mμ. French's fig. 37C.45 shows this type of shift.)

No convincing spectroscopic evidence of a doublet structure of the red absorption band in mature plants has been published. Duysens (unpublished) has suggested, however, that the greater *width* of the absorption band of chlorophyll *in vivo* (compared to that of the same pigment *in vitro*), may be interpreted as due to the superposition of two bands, with peaks close enough to merge into a single band. The situation in green plants would then be similar to that in purple bacteria, where two (or three) infrared bands, present *in vivo*, are replaced by a single band after the destruction of the pigment complex. An alternative explanation of the broadening could be based, however, on enhanced coupling of electronic excitation with vibrations in the pigment-lipoid-protein complex (*cf.* the explanation of the greater width of the bands in chlorophyll crystals in section 3 above).

To sum up, from the point of view of absorption and fluorescence spectra, the hypotheses of Seybold and Egle, and of Krasnovsky and Brin, must be considered as unproved, even if not impossible.

The second postulate of Krasnovsky and Brin—that the bulk of chlorophyll is photochemically inactive—is quite implausible. The high quantum yield of photosynthesis seems incompatible with the assumption that the bulk of chlorophyll in the cell is photochemically inactive. The fluorescence experiments of Duysens, and of French and Young (chap. 24, sec. 7; this chapter, sec. 7), and action spectra of photosynthesis of green, brown and red algae, give convincing evidence that light quanta absorbed by all forms of chlorophyll are transferred, with high efficiency, to chlorophyll *a*, and utilized there for photosynthesis. Krasnovsky's "chlorophyll reserve," with an absorption band overlapping the fluorescence band of "active" chlorophyll would be a "sink" into which all excitation energy would disappear without the possibility of it ever being used for photosynthesis (assuming this "reserve" itself is photochemically inert, as suggested by Krasnovsky).

In a more recent publication, Krasnovsky, Kosobutskaya and Voynovskaya (1953) suggested that the "inactive, polymerized" Chl 678 contributes to photosynthesis by resonance energy transfer to the "active, monomeric" Chl 670. However, energy transfer in this direction should be negligible compared to that in the opposite direction, from Chl 670 to Chl 678, because of the relative position of the absorption and fluorescence bands of the two forms. We will see in section (c) below that Krasnovsky's analogous explanation of the several absorption peaks of bacteriochlorophyll *in vivo* runs into even greater difficulties.

The assumption of photochemical activity of "chlorophyll 670" and photochemical inertness of "chlorophyll 678" was based on the observation of Krasnovsky and Kosobutskaya (described in part B of this chapter, section 1) that, when plastid fragments from etiolated leaves, or these leaves themselves, are exposed to light, the protochlorophyll band (at 635 mμ) is first replaced by a band at 670 mμ, and only upon longer exposure of the leaves is shifted to 678 mμ; simultaneously with the latter transformation, the sensitivity of chlorophyll for photoxidation declines. These changes may well be associated with the formation of grana or lamellae, which can be considered as a special type of chlorophyll aggregation, or of chlorophyll attachment to proteins; and in any case, increased resistance to photoxidation does not necessarily mean general loss of photochemical activity, as postulated by Krasnovsky and co-workers.

We see in Krasnovsky's experiments no reason to abandon the—admittedly speculative—picture, developed in section A of this chapter, according to which chlorophyll is present, in green cells, in monolayers interlarded between proteidic and lipoidic layers. We consider it most likely that all of it contributes uniformly to fluorescence, and to photosynthesis as well.

Krasnovsky's observations on the shift of the absorption peak in the process of chlorophyll formation can perhaps be explained as indicating the transformation of "unorganized" chlorophyll-protein complexes into "organized" structures (such as cohesive monomolecular layers), the additional band displacement being due to pigment-pigment interaction, as discussed above in section 3. The spectroscopic difference between the "active" protochlorophyll of etiolated leaves (subject to photochemical conversion to chlorophyll and having a peak at 635 mμ, cf. Krasnovsky, Kosobutskaya and Voynovskaya 1953), and "inactive" protochlorophyll in pumpkin and squash seeds (with a peak at 645–650 mμ) can perhaps be explained in a similar way.

The situation may be different in those red and blue algae in which a large part of chlorophyll appears inactive, and only the part intimately associated with the phycobilins contributes to photosynthesis and fluorescence (cf. chapter 30, section 6 and chapter 32, section 6). It would be interesting to obtain evidence of a difference between the absorption spectra of these two fractions.

(c) *Absorption Spectra of Purple and Green Bacteria*

As mentioned in section (a) above, Barer (1953) suspended cells in protein solutions to minimize scattering. The results were particularly satisfactory with bacteria (cf. fig. 37C.28). Barer's absorption curves of the purple bacteria *Rhodopseudomonas spheroides*, *Rhodospirillum* (*rubrum*, *palustris*, and *capsulatus*), reproduced in fig. 37C.29, show (compared to figures 21.30A, 21.30B, 22.26, 22.27 and 22.36) not only a considerable extension of the spectral range, but also the elimination of much of the scattering (indicated by the higher ratios of the optical densities in the absorption peaks and the troughs between them).

Except for increased sharpness, the infrared absorption bands of the purple bacteria, measured by Barer, are similar to those observed earlier by the Dutch investigators; they, too, show two or three peaks of varying relative intensity. Barer suggested that the 585–590 mµ absorption band (cf. figs. 22.27 and 37C.29) is correlated with the band in bacterio-chlorophyll solutions located, depending on the solvent, between 575 and 610 mµ (cf. section 2(b) of this chapter). On p. 704, it was suggested that

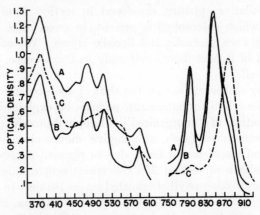

Fig. 37C.29. Absorption spectra of *Rhodopseudo-monas spheroides* (A) in the absence of iron, (B) in the presence of iron. Absorption spectrum of *Rhodospirillum rubrum* (C) (Barer 1955).

this solution band has no counterpart *in vivo;* Barer's interpretation implies that such a counterpart does exist, but that, in contrast to the two other main bands, it is not significantly shifted towards the longer waves. For comparison, the main near-ultraviolet band of bacteriochlorophyll is visible, on Barer's absorption curves of purple bacteria, at 375 mµ, indicating a shift by 1500 cm.$^{-1}$ from its position in ethereal solution (at 356 mµ, cf. section 2(b) above); while the long-wave band is shifted by 500–2000 cm.$^{-1}$ (assuming that all three peaks, at about 800, 850 and 890 mµ, correspond to the one solution band at 770 mµ).

Similarly to French's two differently colored varieties of *Streptococcus varians*, mentioned on p. 707, Barer obtained, from the same inoculum, two strains of *Rhodopseudomonas spheroides*, with the spectra shown in fig. 37C.30. The red variety is characterized by peaks at 550 (weak), 512, 477, and 450 mµ; the green one, by peaks at 490, 460, 425 and 405 mµ. Duysens (1952) found a difference between the absorption

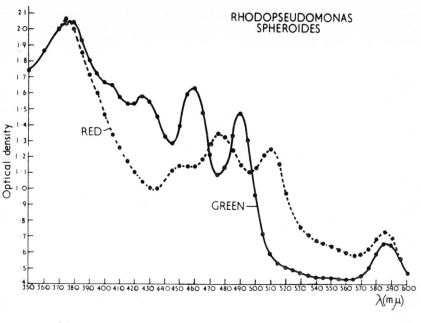

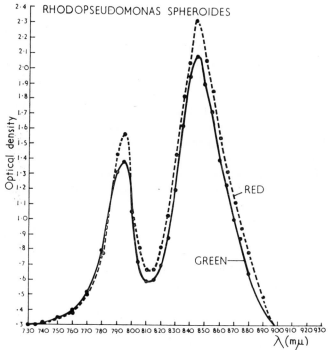

Fig. 37C.30. Absorption spectra of a red and a green strain of *Rhodopseudomonas*
(Barer 1955).

spectra of "young" and "old" cultures of *Rhodospirillum rubrum*, the former ones containing more rhodopin, the latter ones more spirilloxanthin (which is probably identical with rhodoviolascin, *cf.* this chapter 37B, section 2(*d*) and is characterized by a band at 550 mμ). Whether all these differences are based on analogous changes in the assortment of the carotenoids remains to be seen.

Krasnovsky, Voynovskaya and Kosobutskaya (1952) suggested a new interpretation also of the three infrared absorption bands of bacteriochlorophyll *in vivo*. As mentioned above, they attributed them to three different *states of aggregation* of bacteriochlorophyll (rather than to three different protein complexes, as suggested by Wassink and Katz, and Duysens); they pointed out that at least two, and perhaps all three, of these peaks can be observed also in colloids or solid films of chromatographed pigment containing no proteins or other foreign molecules (*cf.* section 3 above).

This is not an implausible alternative to Wassink's interpretation, since, apart from spectroscopic data, no other evidence for the existence of three different bacteriochlorophyll-protein complexes in bacteria is presently available. More difficult to reconcile with experimental data is, however, the additional hypothesis of Krasnovsky that the "aggregated" forms of bacteriochlorophyll, with absorption bands at 800, 850 and 890 mμ, which account for the bulk of the pigment *in vivo*, are "storage forms," nonfluorescent and inactive, while the monomeric form, with a (hypothetical) absorption peak at 780–790 mμ, is the only "active" one.

Krasnovsky, Kosobutskaya and Voynovskaya (1953) noted a preferential bleaching and extraction of "Bchl 890" (compared to "Bchl 850" and "Bchl 800"), and suggested that "Bchl 890" is the one of the three "polymeric" forms most easily decomposed into the "monomeric" form. However, they acknowledged that no absorption band of the "monomer" could be observed in the expected location (780–790 mμ). To these difficulties of Krasnovsky's hypothesis, one can add the physical impossibility of energy migration from the Bchl forms 890, 850 or 800, to the hypothetical, active "Bchl 780"; and the experimental proof by Duysens of energy migration in the opposite direction—towards Bchl 890. The fluorescence of the latter indicates that it serves as the final energy acceptor, and probably also as the actual photocatalyst in bacterial photosynthesis. We conclude that Krasnovsky's hypothesis is even less plausible in the case of purple bacteria than we found it to be in that of green plants.

Krasnovsky and co-workers made some observations on the effect of external factors on the three absorption peaks of colloidal dispersions of bacteriochlorophyll-bearing material from purple bacteria, which originally had the three bands (800, 850, 890 mμ) characteristic of live *Athiorho-daceae.*

Warming to 50–80° C. shifted the main absorption to 800 mμ; further heating to 100° C. brought it to 770 mμ (in analogy to the shift of the chlorophyll band in boiled leaves).

Wetting with methanol, acetone, pyridine or dioxane causes a gradual transformation of the spectrum into the single-peak spectrum of bacteriochlorophyll in solution, pyridine being the fastest acting agent.

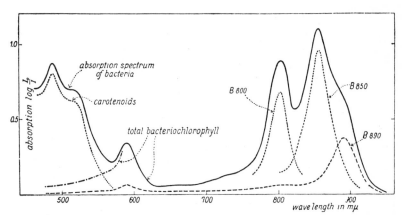

Fig. 37C.31. Absorption spectrum of *Chromatium* (after Duysens 1952). Absorption at 950–570 mμ is due to bacteriochlorophyll, that at 430–570 mμ mainly to carotenoids. The first region is analyzed into three bands, attributed to the three molecular species, "B 890," "B 850" and "B 800." Outside the infrared peak, the spectra of these species are similar, with a maximum at 590 mμ.

Action of acids weakens the 800 and 890 mμ bands, and enhances that at 850 mμ, indicating conversion to bacteriopheophytin, whose "aggregated form" has a band at 850 mμ. No band shift occurs when acid-treated bacteria are heated—in accordance with the behavior of bacteriopheophytin in solid films (*cf.* section 3 above).

Duysens (1952) gave fig. 37C.31 for the absorption spectrum of *Chromatium* and the contribution to it of the several carotenoids and the three bacteriochlorophyll-protein complexes, postulated by Wassink (p. 703). The latter have band peaks at 800, 850 and 890 mμ, respectively. Only the "890 mμ type" (with absorption peak at 873 mμ) is present in *Rhodospirillum rubrum.*

Upon heating autolysates from *Chromatium,* the absorption band at 890 mμ disappears; the other two infrared peaks are shifted slightly toward shorter waves and enhanced in intensity, thus compensating for the loss of absorption at the longer waves (fig. 37C.32). This change is plausibly explained by assuming that the "B 890" complex is converted, by heating, into the "B 850" and the "B 800" complexes.

In *Rhodospirillum*, heating causes the 873 mμ band to drop considerably in intensity, and a new band to arise at 780 mμ (fig. 37.33). Duysens suggested that this new band may indicate the formation of colloidal bacteriochlorophyll.

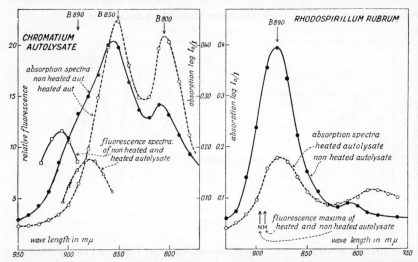

Fig. 37C.32. Absorption and fluorescence spectra of autolysates of *Chromatium* (after Duysens 1952). Constant concentration. The long-wave shoulder disappears in heated autolysate, while the absorption at 850 mμ, and particularly at 800 mμ, is enhanced. Fluorescence peak of non-heated autolysate indicates fluorescence of B 890, that of heated autolysate, fluorescence of B 850. As long as B 890 is present, B 850 transfers excitation energy to it and does not itself fluoresce.

Fig. 37C.33. Absorption spectra of autolysate of *Rhodospirillum rubrum* (after Duysens 1952). After heating, the main absorption maximum of the autolysate decreases and new absorption arises at about 780 mμ, indicating that bacteriochlorophyll had passed into a new state. (Location of the band and absence of fluorescence suggest colloidal state.)

The 590 mμ peak has a height proportional to the total amount of bacteriochlorophyll, as if all three complexes contributed equally to it—a striking fact, because one would expect complexing to influence also the higher excited electronic levels of the molecule, and not only the lowest one.

Fig. 37C.31 illustrates the predominant role of carotenoids in the absorption spectrum of *Chromatium* between 400 and 550 mμ.

Larsen (1954) gave an absorption curve of a suspension of the green sulfur bacteria, of which only the long-wave part had been described previously by Katz and Wassink (*cf.* p. 704). He found, in *Chlorobium thiosulfatophilum*, two main absorption peaks at 747 and 457 mμ; an ultraviolet band at 338 mμ, and shoulders, indicating hidden bands, at 423, 515 and 810 mμ (where Katz and Wassink observed a second strong infrared band). One enrichment culture showed a band peak at 732 mμ, instead of 747 mμ.

Barer (1955) also measured the absorption spectrum of *Chlorobium*. As shown by fig. 37C.34, he, too, found the two main bands at 745 and 455 mμ, respectively. No band at 810 mμ was visible.

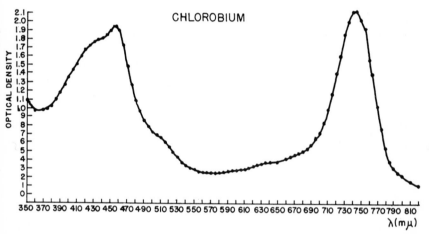

Fig. 37C.34. Absorption spectrum of green bacteria (after Barer 1955).

The blue-violet (Soret) band of green bacteria is, in both position and shape, very similar to that of chlorophyll *a* in green cells; but the position of the red band is quite different. Perhaps this indicates that chlorophyll *a* is present in these bacteria in a special form (Wassink, 1954, pointed out that 745 mμ is the approximate location of the absorption band of chlorophyll *a* in crystals!); more likely, however, "bacterioviridin" is a compound different from chlorophyll *a* (although belonging to the same type, as suggested by Fischer and Stern, *cf.* p. 445), and that its absorption band undergoes—in common with that of bacteriochlorophyll—a much wider red shift in the transition from solution to the living cell than does the absorption band of chlorophyll *in vivo*.

Experiments give even less support for the identification of bacterioviridin with bacteriochlorophyll, suggested by Seybold and Hirsch (1954) on the basis of absorption curves showing both a 750 mμ and an 850 mμ peak in green bacteria. One can only surmise that the cultures used by these investigators, had been contaminated with purple bacteria. Similarly, Seybold and Hirsch's finding of an absorption band at

750 mμ, in a culture of "Purpurspirillen" (and of a band at 660–670 mμ in extracts from this culture) points, according to Barer, to a contamination of purple bacteria cultures with green bacteria.

(d) Phycobilin Spectra in vivo.

New absorption curves of blue-green and red algae, with the allotment of absorption at selected wave lengths to the several pigments, were given by Duysens (1952); they will be reproduced in section 7 together with the action spectra of fluorescence (figs. 37C.51 and 53).

(e) Changes in Absorption Spectrum during Photosynthesis

An old problem is whether chlorophyll (or other cell constituents) undergo a chemical change during photosynthesis that could be detected

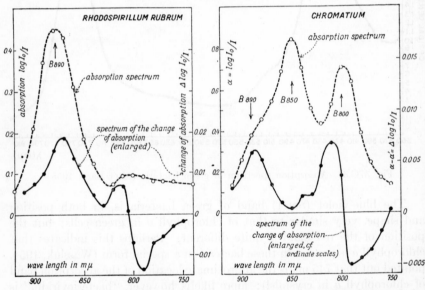

Fig. 37C.35. Absorption spectrum, and spectrum of the reversible change of absorption by irradiation of *Rhodospirillum rubrum*, in tap water (left); and of colloidal extract from *Chromatium* (right) (after Duysens 1952). The ordinates of solid curves are on a scale ten times (left) or fifty times (right) smaller than those of the dashed curves. Decrease in absorption is plotted upwards, increase downwards. The main absorption maximum of B 890 is indicated by arrow.

spectroscopically. Of the two previously known phenomena belonging to this field, one—the slow change in transmission of light by photosynthesizing leaves (p. 680)—has been attributed partly to chloroplast realignment, and partly to scattering by newly formed starch grains. The other—variation in intensity of chlorophyll fluorescence associated with variations in the rate of photosynthesis (*cf.* chapter 24, section 4, and chapter 33, part B)—has been explained by changes in the composition of compounds associated with chlorophyll in the "pigment complex" (oxidation, reduction, formation and deposition of "narcotics").

Bell (1952) found the transmission of leaves to *increase* rapidly, by 3–5% (in the region 350–670 mμ) upon exposure to strong light [intensity up to 185 kerg/(cm.^{2} sec.)], in the absence of carbon dioxide; the transmission *decreased* again (by about 0.6%) when carbon dioxide was admitted. The increase in transparency was ascribed by Bell to reversible chlorophyll

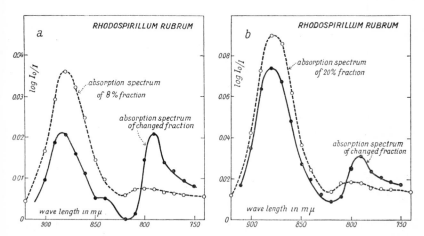

Fig. 37C.36. Absorption spectra of bacteriochlorophyll *in vivo* during illumination, calculated from fig. 37C.35 by assuming that 8% (left) or 20% (right) of bacteriochlorophyll (B 890) is transformed by irradiation (after Duysens 1952).

bleaching through transfer into a long-lived (> 0.02 sec.) excited state; he suggested that the back reaction is *accelerated* when the stored energy can be utilized for photosynthesis (*i. e.*, when carbon dioxide is present).

No evidence of a change in spectroscopic composition (of the transmitted or fluorescent light) has been sought in all these studies. Duysens (1952) found, however, that the absorption spectrum of bacteriochlorophyll changes when the bacteria are photochemically active. By a compensation method, permitting measurement of very small, sudden changes in transmission, Duysens found that illumination of a suspension of purple bacteria by a 500 w. lamp, [about 30 kerg/(cm.^{2} sec.)], causes an immediate change in the absorption spectrum, which is rapidly reversed in the dark. Figure 37C.35 (left and right) illustrates these changes for a *Rhodospirillum* suspension and in *Chromatium* extract. In *Rhodospirillum* (which contains "B 890" only) illumination causes a decrease in absorption above 805 mμ, and an increase below 805 mμ. In the first region, the changes are strongest at 872 and 812 mμ, in the second one, at 790 mμ. A similar picture was obtained with the colloidal extract from *Chromatium* (which has three absorption peaks). The maximum changes in fig. 37C.35 are of the order of 3 to 5%.

These effects were strongest in the absence of hydrogen donors, *i. e.*, when photosynthesis was prevented; as suggested by Bell (*cf.* above), spectral changes may be more pronounced under these conditions, because

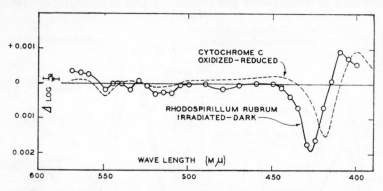

Fig. 37C.37. Changes in absorption spectrum in the green-blue-violet region in illuminated bacteria (after Duysens 1954[1]).

the usual path by which the photochemically changed pigment returns into its normal state, is closed.

It will be noted that the first maximum of the bleaching effect coincides with the absorption peak of "B 890." If the whole change is attributed to conversion of "B 890" into a different pigment, *at least* 8% of "B 890" must be changed. (Fig. 37C.36a and b show the spectrum of the changed pigment, calculated with two arbitrarily chosen percentage changes— 8 and 20%; one sees that, if one would assume < 8% conversion, the calculated absorption coefficient at 820 mμ would become negative.) Probably, much more than 8% of "B 890" is changed, in light, into a pigment (or pigment complex) with a spectrum only slightly different from that of "B 890" itself (as assumed in fig. 37C.24b).

Later, Duysens (1952, 1954[1]) noted that important reversible changes occur, in irradiated purple bacteria, also in the region 400–570 mμ. These are represented in fig. 37C.37, for *Rhodospirillum rubrum* suspended in peptone solution (or in 0.03 *M* sodium acetate + phosphate buffer, *p*H 6.8), under anaerobic conditions and in relatively low light. The change is complete within a time of the order of one second.

In stronger light, another spectral change becomes superimposed on the one represented in fig. 37C.37, probably correlated with the changes in the infrared represented in fig. 37C.35. While the latter reveals transformations in the pigment complex, the difference spectrum in fig. 37C.37 clearly indicates—as shown by the dashed line—the oxidation of a cytochrome-type pigment. A cytochrome similar to cytochrome *c* had been extracted from *Rhodospirillum rubrum* by Vernon (1953) and Elsden, Kamen and Vernon (1953).

Duysens (1954[2]) made similar studies with *Chlorella*. No significant effect could be noted in the long-wave region of chlorophyll absorption; characteristic changes were observed, however, in the violet, blue, and green

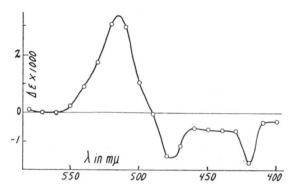

Fig. 37C.38. Changes in absorption spectrum in illuminated *Chlorella* (after Duysens 1954[2]).

(*cf.* fig. 37C.38); the peak at 420 mμ was tentatively attributed to the oxidation, in light, of cytochrome *f*—a compound found in chloroplast material by Hill and co-workers (*cf.* chapter 35, section B4(*f*)). The two other peaks—a "negative" one at 475 mμ and a "positive" one at 515 mμ—could not be associated with any known pigment. These two peaks were found also in an illuminated leaf, an algal thallus, and a grass blade. (No measurements were made on these objects at 420 mμ.)

The temptation is great to associate the 515 mμ band with bands in similar positions, which appear in reversibly reduced and reversibly oxidized chlorophyll *in vitro*, as well as in chlorophyll transferred, by intense illumination, into the metastable triplet state. We commented elsewhere in this chapter on the spectroscopic similarity of these products, and quoted Weller's suggestion that this similarity indicates that all of them are radicals (or biradicals) with interrupted all-round conjugation in the porphin system. There is, however, one difficulty in the way of attributing the 515 mμ band in illuminated *Chlorella* cells to chlorophyll-derived radicals:

The apparent absence of an equivalent loss of absorption in the main chlorophyll bands (*cf.*, however, page 1989).

Witt (1954) applied to photosynthesizing leaves and algae a flash illumination technique, similar to that used by Livingston and Ryan (cf. chapter 35, part A) on chlorophyll solutions. The apparatus he used permitted measurement of absorption changes of $<1\%$, produced by flash illumination. Witt found a new absorption band which arose, in light, at 515 mμ; it disappeared, in the dark, within about 10^{-2} sec. The absorption at 475 mμ was reversibly weakened during the flash; but no mention was made

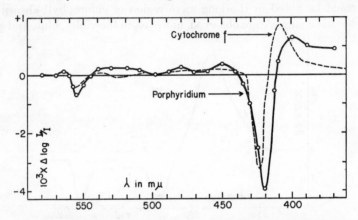

Fig. 37C.39. Changes in absorption spectrum of illuminated *Porphyridium* compared to the difference between the spectra of oxidized and reduced cytochrome f (after Duysens 1954[3]).

of a similar change at 670–680 mμ, so that an uncertainty remains as to whether the above-quoted objection against attributing the 515 mμ band to a chlorophyll-derived radical remains valid in the case of Witt's experiments. Witt himself suggested such an attribution, and identified the decay period of the 515 mμ band with the "Emerson-Arnold period" in photosynthesis. However, it was pointed out in the discussion of that period in chapters 32 and 34, that the catalytic agent requiring 10^{-2} sec. for recovery must be present in a much smaller concentration than chlorophyll to account for the observed saturation yield in flashing light and saturation rate in steady light.

Witt found a light saturation of the photochemical processes generating the 515 mμ band at flash intensities of the same order of magnitude as those known to cause flash saturation of photosynthesis.

We return now to those absorption changes which, Duysens suggested, were due to reversible photoxidation in the cytochrome system.

Lundegårdh (1954) observed such changes by a flow method, in which a pre-illuminated *Chlorella* suspension was conducted through the cuvette of a spectrophotometer. Only the narrow range 540–570 mμ was examined—a range in which the absorption spectrum of *Chlorella*, pretreated with ascorbic acid, shows the α-bands of the reduced cytochromes *b*, *c*, and *f*. (The amounts of *c* and *f* are similar, the concentration of *c* being much higher in *Chlorella* than in the leaves of the higher plants.) Upon illumination, the 556 mμ band of reduced cytochrome *f* is found to be weakened, indicating oxidation, while those of the cytochrome *b* and *c* are unchanged; that of *b* may be even slightly enhanced. Duysens

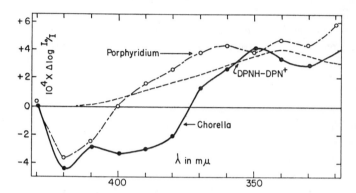

Fig. 37C.40. Changes in the ultraviolet absorption spectrum of illuminated *Chlorella* and *Porphyridium* (after Duysens 1954[4]).

fig. 37C.38 did not show any effects above 550 mμ, but his subsequent experiments (1954[3]) revealed a small dip at 555 mμ, in agreement with Lundegårdh's findings.

Duysens (1954[3]) applied his stationary crossed-beam method also to a suspension of the red algae *Porphyridium cruentum*. The difference spectrum is shown in fig. 37C.39. Bands at 420 and 555 mμ, characteristic of the oxidation of cytochrome *f* (or of another very similar pigment) appear more clearly on this picture, because the relatively stronger spectral effects, exhibited by *Chlorella* between these two bands are absent in the red alga.

Duysens (1954[3]) also noted a reversible increase, during the illumination of both *Chlorella* and *Porphyridium*, of the absorption in the near ultraviolet, with the indication of a peak at about 350 mμ (fig. 37C.40). This effect was tentatively interpreted as evidence of the reduction in light of a pyridine nucleotide; if this interpretation is correct, about one molecule of pyridine nucleotide must be reduced, in the photostationary state, for about 100 chlorophyll molecules present in the cell.

After addition to a *chloroplast suspension*, of 10^{-4} m./l. DPN, a reduction of 0.05% of the added nucleotide could be observed in the photostationary state. This very small shift in the oxidation-reduction equilibrium, whose discovery was made possible by the extreme sensitivity of the compensation apparatus, explains why no reduction of DPN could be observed directly in Hill reaction experiments (chapter 35, section B4(*f*)), and why DPNH$_2$-mediated reductions of organic substrates could be obtained, by means of illuminated chloroplasts, only with very low yields: the rate of the back reaction (reoxidation of DPNH$_2$) is so high as to make a significant accumulation of reduced DPN in the stationary state of the illuminated system impossible.

As to the significance of the observations of Duysens, and of Lundegårdh, concerning photostationary oxidation of cytochrome-like compounds in illuminated photosynthesizing cells, they can be interpreted either as evidence of direct participation of these compounds in the photochemical hydrogen transfer from water to carbon dioxide (or, rather, to an organic compound into which CO$_2$ had been incorporated, such as PGA), or as evidence of their participation in oxidative processes (back reactions), coupled with the reduction process. The first hypothesis (Hill, Lundegårdh) suggests photochemical transfer of electrons *from* reduced cytochrome to the organic acceptor (perhaps via DPN or TPN). The transfer of hydrogen (or electrons) from H$_2$O to the oxidized cytochrome would then require another photochemical reaction. To account for the observed shift, the relative probability of the two photochemical reactions would have to be such as to establish a photostationary state with most of the cytochrome in the oxidized state. The quantum requirement of the hydrogen transfer reaction as a whole would be (at least) 8, since two quanta will be needed to transfer each of the four required H atoms (or electrons), first from water to the cytochrome, and then from the cytochrome to the final acceptor.

The other hypothesis (preferred by Duysens) is that the photochemical hydrogen transfer from H$_2$O to TPN (or to another compound of a similar reduction potential), occurs directly, *i. e.*, by a single quantum, but that one part of the reduced photoproduct reacts back with the oxidized photoproduct, with a cytochrome as final or intermediate H acceptor, and the reoxidation energy may become available to assist in a further reduction step (as first suggested in the "energy dismutation" hypothesis in Vol. 1, chapters 7, p. 164 and 9, p. 233). If the reoxidation energy is stored as phosphate bond energy, the ATP produced in this way may, for example, enable reduced pyridine nucleotide to reduce PGA to a triose (as repeatedly suggested before, *e. g.*, in Chapter 36, p. 1717).

(f) *Calculation of True Absorption Spectra from Transmission and Fluorescence Spectra of Suspensions*

Duysens (1952) suggested two methods to determine the true absorption of light in small colored particles, such as *Chlorella* cells. The first method (Duysens and Huiskamp, 1953) is based on comparison of the intensities of fluorescence emitted "forward" and "backward" (in relation to the incident beam). If the particles are idealized as tiny plane-parallel vessels (thickness d) filled with pigment solution and illuminated normally to their "front wall," the intensity of fluorescence of wave length λ_f excited by monochromatic light of wave length λ_i, emitted through the "front wall" into a solid angle σ, is:

$$(37C.8) \qquad F''_{\lambda_f} = \frac{\sigma}{4\pi} \int_0^d I_0 e^{-\alpha_{\lambda_i} x} f(\lambda_f, \lambda_i) e^{-\alpha_{\lambda_f} x} \, dx$$

while that of the fluorescence escaping through the "rear wall" of the particle (into an equal solid angle) is:

$$(37C.9) \qquad F'_{\lambda_f} = \frac{\sigma}{4\pi} \int_0^d I_0 e^{-\alpha_{\lambda_i} x} f(\lambda_f, \lambda_i) e^{-\alpha_{\lambda_f}(d-x)} \, dx$$

where $f(\lambda_f \lambda_i)$ is the yield of fluorescence of wave length λ_f, excited by λ_i, while α_{λ_f} and α_{λ_i} are the (natural) absorption coefficients for these two wave lengths of the pigment solution inside the particle.

According to equations (37C.8) and (37C.9), the ratio of the "forward" and the "backward" fluorescence emissions is a function of the products $\alpha_{\lambda_f} d$ and $\alpha_{\lambda_i} d$. If a second relationship between these two products is known, α_{λ_i} and α_{λ_f} can be calculated from relative measurements of fluorescence intensity in the two directions. In applying this method to a suspension of *Chlorella* cells, Duysens and Huiskamp (1953) used the relationship:

$$(37C.9A) \qquad (1 - \exp(-\alpha_{\lambda_i} d))/(1 - \exp(-\alpha_{\lambda_f} d)) \doteq D_{p,\lambda_i}/D_{p,\lambda_f}$$

in which D_{p,λ_i} and D_{p,λ_f} are the optical densities of the cell suspension at the two wave lengths. (This relationship follows from equation 37C.16, derived below.) The wave length of the incident light (λ_i) was 420 mμ, that of the measured fluorescence (λ_f), 680 mμ.

The suspension was diluted so strongly that the transmission of the vessel was $> 80\%$. Since the transmission of each single cell is about 40%, practical absence of mutual shading of the cells was assured. (This is a necessary condition for the application of the above equations, derived for individual particles, to the fluorescence emission of the suspension as a whole.) The calculation was further improved by assuming spherical rather than plane-parallel particles. An absorption of 64% was calculated in this way for a single *Chlorella* cell, at 680 mμ.

The second method of calculation, also devised by Duysens and Huiskamp (1953), is based on the apparent depression of absorption coefficients by accumulation of colored molecules in small particles (as compared to the absorption caused by the same number of molecules in true molecular solution; *cf.* chapter 22, p. 714). The following derivation was made for the idealized case of cubic particles with one edge parallel to the incident beam. For a given wavelength, the optical density of a single particle (subscript p) is:

$$(37C.10) \qquad d_p = \ln(1/T)_p = \ln(I/I_0)_p = \alpha c_p d$$

where α is the molar absorption coefficient of the pigment, c_p its molar concentration (within the particles), and d the edge of the (cubic) particle.

If the area density of the particles in suspension is N (per cm.^{2}), dispersing the pigment uniformly would produce a solution (subscript S) with a molar area concentration $c_p N d^3$ (per cm.^{2}) and an optical density:

$$(37C.11) \qquad D_S = \ln(I_0/I)_S = \alpha c_p N d^3$$

Assuming the molecular absorption coefficient to be the same in (37C.10) and (37C.11), we have:

$$(37C.12) \qquad D_S = \ln(1/T)_p N d^2$$

Since d^2 is the cross section of a single particle, the average number p of particles the light beam crossing the suspension traverses is $N d^2$, and we can therefore write, instead of (37C.12):

$$(37C.13) \qquad D_S = p \ln(1/T)_p$$

When the molecules are bunched together in particles, the average optical density of the suspension can be calculated by using Poisson's formula for the probability of a beam encountering a certain number of particles, k, on 1 cm. of its path through the suspension. This probability is:

$$(37C.14) \qquad P_k = e^{-p} p^k / k!$$

where p is, as above, the *average* number of particles encountered. The beam that traverses k particles is weakened by the factor T_p^k; the average transmission of the suspension is therefore obtained by summation of:

$$P_k T_p^k = T_p^k e^{-p} p^k / k!$$

over all values of k from 0 to ∞. This gives:

$$(37C.15) \qquad \overline{T} = e^{-p(1-T_p)}$$

or an average optical density of suspension (subscript P):

$$(37C.16) \qquad D_P = p(1 - T_p)$$

as compared with the optical density (37C.13) of the same pigment in molecular dispersion. The optical density is thus reduced, in consequence of particle formation, in the ratio:

(37C.17)
$$\frac{D_P}{D_S} = \frac{1 - T_p}{\ln (1/T)_p}$$

which is dependent only on T_p, the transmission of a single particle, and not dependent on the concentration of particles. According to this reasoning, the "flattening" effect of particle formation on the absorption band should be independent of concentration. In other words, the "sieve effect" persists as "bunching effect" even when the concentration of particles is so high that no beam can traverse the cell without passing through several particles (*cf.* below).

Relationship (37C.17) can be derived even more simply by applying Beer's law first to the pigment "solution" in the particle, and then to the "solution" of particles (considered as giant molecules). If the absorption coefficient of a single molecule (its "cross section for photon capture," to use the language of corpuscular physics) is σ, and the number of molecules per unit area of the particle is n, we have, for the transmission of a single particle:

(37C.18)
$$T_p = (I/I_0)_p = e^{-n\sigma}$$

and for the absorption:

(37C.19)
$$A_p = 1 - T_p = 1 - e^{-n\sigma} = \Sigma$$

where Σ can be considered as the photon capture cross section of the particle as a whole. Applying Beer's law a second time, to a suspension containing N particles per unit area, we obtain:

(37C.20)
$$(I/I_0)_P = e^{-N\Sigma} = e^{-N(1-e^{-n\sigma})} = e^{-N(1-T_p)}$$

(37C.21)
$$D_P = \ln (I/I_0)_P = N(1 - T_p)$$

If the same total number of molecules, nN, is distributed at random over the same area, Beer's law gives:

(37C.22)
$$D_S = \ln (I_0/I)_S = nN\sigma = N \ln (1/T)_p$$

Thus, we again obtain relation (37C.17) between D_P and D_S.

The validity of these derivations is limited to a range of particle concentrations in which the total volume occupied by the particles is small compared to the volume of the suspension. (In the limit when particles are densely packed, the difference between the suspension and a solution containing the same total number of molecules obviously must disappear.)

Practically, suspensions used for absorption measurements fulfill this condition. Therefore our statements (Part 1, Vol. II, pp. 714, 716) that the effect of "bunching" must disappear when each beam traversing the suspension encounters several particles, and therefore must be insignificant in the usual suspensions of algae, were incorrect; the effect remains significant even in "dense" *Chlorella* suspensions (containing perhaps 10^7 cells, with a total volume of the order of 10^{-4} cc., in each cubic centimeter of the liquid). Only when the volume of cells reaches the same order of magnitude as the total volume of the suspension, does relation 37C.17 cease to be valid. These considerations should be taken into account in attempts to analyze transmission curves of cell systems in terms of the absorption curves of the several pigments as observed in extracts. In addition to band *shift*, one must consider band *flattening* by the sieve and bunching effects, before concluding that intrinsic changes in the absorption band shape have occurred. It will be noted that, for a particle transmission of 0.5, the ratio:

$$(1 - T_p)/ \ln (1/T)_p$$

is 0.5/0.7, or 70%; for a transmission of 0.1, it is 0.9/2.3, or close to 40%. This shows how strong the flattening effect is if single particles have a high optical density.

Applying the band flattening theory to *Chlorella* absorption at 680 mμ, Duysens found $1 - T_p = 0.63$, in agreement with the figure (64%) derived above from the asymmetry of fluorescence.

6A. Scattering by Pigment Bodies *in vivo*

All the above considerations did not take into account scattering, which can complicate the interpretation of absorption measurements on suspensions. Observations of Jacobs *et al.* on suspensions of chlorophyllide microcrystals (section 3) showed that, in addition to the "Rayleigh scattering," decreasing steadily from the shorter to the longer waves, one may have to consider *selective* scattering, with a peak on the long-wave side of the absorption band, dropping rapidly on the short-wave side and declining much more slowly on the long-wave side. The puzzle of the increased "absorption" of live cells and crude aqueous cell dispersions in the far red, noted on p. 715, may have its answer in such selective scattering.

In the absence of direct evidence it could be argued that, *in vivo*, pigments will not produce selective scattering, even if they are arranged in complete monolayers, because scattering requires an extension of the regular arrangement in all three dimensions. Duysens (1954) suggested, in fact, that a correction for Rayleigh scattering is adequate in this case, to take care of excessive apparent absorption in the far red as well as in the green.

However, preliminary experiments by Latimer (1954) have revealed a very pronounced selective scattering of light by *Chlorella* suspensions.

Sharp scattering peaks were found to correspond not only to the main chlorophyll bands, but also to the carotenoid bands, almost hidden in the absorption spectrum. Selective scattering was noted also in colloidal chlorophyll suspensions, indicating that it does not require a regular pigment lattice, but merely a sufficiently close packing of pigment molecules.

The occurrence of sharp selective scattering bands poses additional problems for the application of scattering correction to absorption measurements *in vivo*. On the other hand, it opens a new approach to the elucidation of the physical state of the pigments in the living cell; for example, the sharpness of the carotenoid bands in scattered light can be taken as an indication of a particularly close (or particularly regular) arrangement of their molecules (as compared to those of the other pigments).

Using an integrating sphere assures one against including scattering in absorption; but it does not prevent absorption from being itself affected by scattering, through increased pathway of the light in the absorbing medium ("detour factor").

7. Fluorescence of Pigments *in vivo*
(Addendum to Chapter 24)

(a) *Absolute Yield*

Duysens (1952, page 84 and page 88) made criticisms of the estimates of the *yield* of chlorophyll and bacteriochlorophyll fluorescence *in vivo*, which led Wassink *et al.* to figures of the order of 0.15%, for both *Chlorella* and *Chromatium*, while yields of $\backsim$1.5% were estimated for *Chroococcus* by Arnold and Oppenheimer (*cf.* chapter 24, section 2, and chapter 32, section 6). Duysens suggested that neglected geometrical-optical factors have reduced the observed yield in green algae and bacteria by a factor of perhaps 2.7, and that re-absorption of fluorescence accounted for a loss of another 50%; so that the true quantum yield of fluorescence in these cells may be of the order of 1% rather that 0.1%. Obviously, this criticism calls for careful experimental re-examination. Preliminary measurements by Latimer (unpublished) seem to support it (*cf.* page 1992).

Duysens further suggested that, conceivably, the "intrinsic" fluorescence capacity of chlorophyll (or bacteriochlorophyll) in the natural state is another order of magnitude higher (*i. e.* of the order of 10%, as *in vitro*), and that the reduction of the actual fluorescence to about 1% may be due to a 90% effective resonance energy migration to "reduction centers," where this energy is used for a photochemical transformation (*cf.* above section 3). Duysens estimated that this is possible if about 200 energy transfers are needed to reach a "center."

We can obtain a similar, but somewhat larger estimate, by the crude method used in section 3 for crystals. With a natural life time of 1.2×10^{-8} sec. (section 1), and a fluorescence yield of 1%, the time available for energy migration is 1.2×10^{-10} sec. Since the shape of the band indicates the maintenance of the coupling of electronic excitation with molecular vibrations having periods of the order of 10^{-13} sec., the possible number n of transfers during the actual life time is $n < 1.2 \times 10^{-10}/10^{-13} = 1200$. It is interesting to note that conditions for energy migration are more favorable *in vivo* than in crystal layers *in vitro*, the unfavorable effect of lesser density being more than offset by the favorable effect of a less efficient quenching through energy conversion into lattice vibrations.

(b) Sensitized Fluorescence in vivo

We now turn to *sensitized* fluorescence *in vivo*, and the evidence of energy transfer, derived from it.

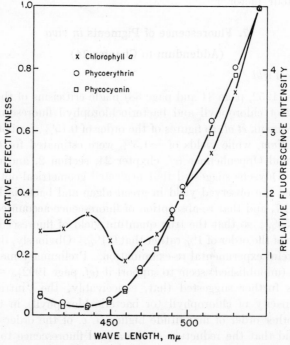

Fig. 37C.41. Relative intensity of fluorescence of three pigments in *Porphyridium cruentum*. Monochromatic excitation (after French and Young 1952).

In chapter 24 we gave a brief summary of the important work of Duysens, and of French and Koski, on the fluorescence of red algae. The two investigations have since been described in detail. In amplification of fig. 24.4* (p. 811), French and Young (1952) supplied figures 37C.41 to 37C.43. The first one shows the *intensities* of the fluorescences of chlorophyll *a* and of the two phycobilins, excited in *Porphyridium* by monochromatic light of constant quantum flux, as function of wave length.

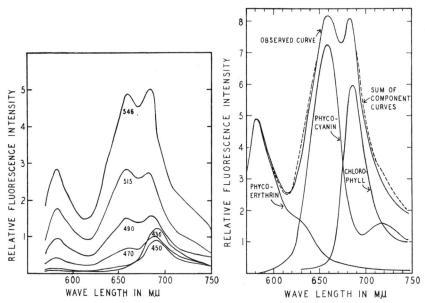

Fig. 37C.42. Fluorescence spectra of *Porphyridium* excited with monochromatic light of different wave lengths (marked on the curves) (after French and Young 1952).

Fig. 37C.43. Analysis of fluorescence of *Porphyridium* excited by λ 530 mμ (after French and Young 1952).

(The curves are arbitrarily adjusted to coincide at 546 mμ.) One notes the almost exclusive excitation of chlorophyll fluorescence by wave lengths below 450 mμ (*i. e.*, in a region of predominant chlorophyll absorption), and simultaneous excitation of all three pigments, with almost constant relative intensity, by wave lengths in the region of predominant phycobilin absorption, above 480 mμ. Fig. 37C.42 shows the *spectra* of fluorescence excited by six different wave lengths. Again, one notices that phycobilin fluorescence is not excited by violet light, which is absorbed mainly by chlorophyll, but that fluorescence excited by blue and green light, absorbed mainly by the phycobilins, contains bands of all three pigments. Fig. 37C.43 represents an analysis of the fluorescence spectrum excited, in

* This figure is by French and Koski; the attribution to Duysens was misplaced and belongs to fig. 24.5.

Porphyridium, by λ 530 mμ (fig. 37C.41 had been constructed from a large number of curves of this type). To permit the analysis, the fluorescence spectra of chlorophyll and of the phycobilins *in vivo* had to be constructed. This was done by shifting and broadening the fluorescence bands of chlorophyll *a* and phycoerythrin *in vitro* so as to fit the fluorescence spectrum

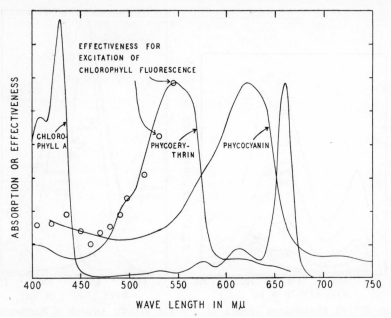

Fig. 37C.44. Action spectrum of excitation of chlorophyll fluorescence in *Porphyridium* (circles), compared to the absorption spectra of the three pigments (after French and Young 1952).

in vivo in regions where the latter can be attributed to one of these two pigments only; the fluorescence spectrum of phycocyanin was then calculated by subtraction.

Points in fig. 37C.44 trace the action spectrum of the excitation of cell fluorescence. Comparison with the absorption spectra indicates that, in the region of 450 to 550 mμ, the main absorber is phycoerythrin; the fluorescence of phycocyanin and chlorophyll (which, according to fig. 37C.41, are co-excited throughout this region, in a constant relation to that of phycoerythrin) must arise by excitation energy transfer from phycoerythrin.

One important observation of French and Young was that changes in fluorescence intensity during the induction period of photosynthesis (*cf.* section 4 in chapter 24, and chapter 33), are confined, in red algae, to chlorophyll fluorescence, and do not appear in the fluorescence of the phycobilins. In agreement with the observations Franck and Shiau made on green algae, induction effects were much stronger in "old" than in "young" cultures of red algae.

The effect of light intensity on fluorescence yield (*cf.* chapter 28, part B) also are restricted to chlorophyll. As mentioned briefly on p. 1051, the yield of fluorescence of phycobilins in *Porphyridium* is independent of light

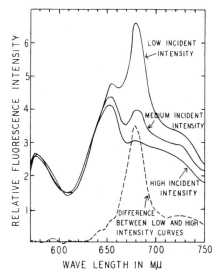

Fig. 37C.45. Effect of light intensity on fluorescence spectrum of *Porphyridium* (after French and Young 1952).

intensity, while that of chlorophyll (measured in the steady state, six minutes after beginning of illumination) is lower in stronger light. This leads to changes in the shape of the fluorescence spectrum with the intensity of illuminating light, illustrated by figure 37C.45.

All these observations agree with the hypothesis that chlorophyll is the only pigment directly related to the photochemical processes in photosynthesis.

Duysens' (1952) experiments dealt with the purple bacteria as well as with algae (*cf.* pp. 810 and 812, respectively). Figs. 37C.46 and 47 show the absorption and fluorescence spectra of the purple bacteria *Rhodospirillum rubrum* and *Chromatium*, respectively. The first species seems to contain only a single bacteriochlorophyll complex (it has a single infrared absorption band); the second, three such complexes (three infrared absorption bands).   Despite the difference in absorption spectrum, both species have the same fluorescence spectrum, making it likely that, in *Chromatium* as well as in *Rhodospirillum*, fluorescence is emitted by one pigment complex only.   The main fluorescence peak of *Chromatium* is located at 914 mμ, *i. e.*, 11 mμ on the long-wave side of that of *Rhodospirillum*, in agreement with the relative positions of the absorption bands (at 873 mμ in *Rhodospirillum* and 890 mμ in *Chromatium;* the latter band is only indicated by a hump on the absorption curve).   The fluorescent bacteriochlorophyll complexes thus must be somewhat different in the two species.

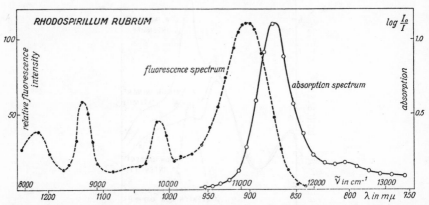

Fig. 37C.46. Absorption and fluorescence spectra of *Rhodospirillum rubrum* (after Duysens 1952).   The two spectra are approximately mirror-symmetrical.   This suggests that the absorption and fluorescence are due to the same molecule (B 890).

Upon heating to 100° C., autolysates of *Chromatium* and *Rhodospirillum* undergo changes in fluorescence shown in figs. 37C.32 and 33 together with the simultaneous absorption changes.   In *Chromatium*, the "B 890" complex disappears and the "B 850" complex becomes fluorescent— probably because the excitation energy of the latter is not lost any more by transfer to the former.   In *Rhodospirillum*, both the fluorescence band and the absorption band are shifted only very slightly by heating, but lose much of their intensity.   In this case, the destruction of the fluorescent "B 890" (more exactly "B 873") complex seems to be only partial, and the product (perhaps, colloidal bacteriochlorophyll, with an absorption band at 780 mμ) is nonfluorescent.

The intensity of infrared fluorescence of *Chromatium*, although it is due to "B 890" only, is nevertheless proportional to total absorption by all three forms of bacteriochlorophyll.   For example, the ratio of the fluorescence yields by illumination at 590 mμ and at 800 mμ is the same in *Chromatium* and *Rhodospirillum*, although in the first species most of the absorption at 800 mμ is due to "B 800." This indicates a better than 80% (perhaps, 100%) efficient transfer of excitation energy from "B 800" to "B 890." Fig. 37C.48 shows the action spectra of fluorescence and phototaxis of *Chromatium* (the latter is assumed by Duysens to represent also the action spectrum of photosynthesis, *cf.* p. 1188), in the region of predominant carotenoid absorption. Carotenoids clearly contribute their excitation energy

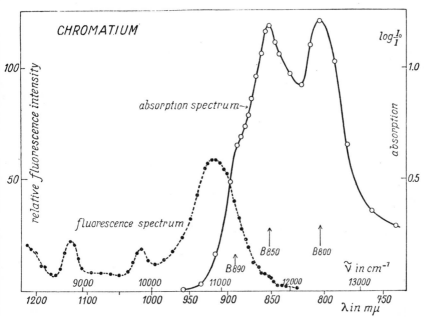

Fig. 37C.47. Infrared absorption and fluorescence spectra of *Chromatium* (after Duysens 1952). Except for a slight shift, the fluorescence spectrum is identical with that of *Rhodospirillum,* indicating that only B 890 fluoresces.

to both fluorescence and phototaxis, but with only about 35–40% efficiency (compared to that of bacteriochlorophyll in the 590 mμ band).

A marked difference between the shape of the absorption spectrum and that of the phototaxis action spectrum was noted by Duysens (in agreement with Manten, *cf.* p. 1188) in *Rhodospirillum* (*molischianum,* or *rubrum*), particularly in older (4–6 days old) cultures. As mentioned on p. 1188, Manten attributed this difference to the inactivity of spirilloxanthin. No such difference could be noted by Duysens between the action spectrum of fluorescence and the absorption spectrum; an efficiency of the order of 40% was indicated for sensitized fluorescence of "B 890" in spirilloxanthin bands as well as in the bands of other carotenoids (rhodopin). Duysens suggested that two different carotenoid-bacteriochlorophyll complexes are present in these bacteria, one of which is ineffective in phototaxis (and photosynthesis), despite a 40% efficient transfer of energy from the carotenoid in this complex to bacteriochlorophyll, and the capacity of the latter for fluorescence!

Duysens found that spirilloxanthin only appeared in old cultures grown in peptone.

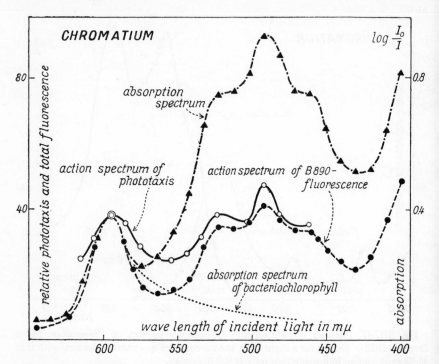

Fig. 37C.48. Absorption and action spectra of *Chromatium* (strain D) (after Duysens 1952). Absorption peak at 590 mμ is due to bacteriochlorophyll, absorption between 450 and 550 mμ, mainly to carotenoids. Curves were drawn to coincide at 590 mμ. Light absorbed by carotenoids is equally efficient in exciting phototaxis as well as the fluorescence of bacteriochlorophyll, and about 35–40% as efficient as light absorbed by bacteriochlorophyll.

The situation is further complicated by a report by Clayton (1951) that, in a different strain of *Rhodospirillum rubrum*, spirilloxanthin is active in stimulating phototaxis. (Duysens pointed out that Clayton's experiments were made in 10 or 100 times weaker light than those of Manten.)

With *Chlorella*, Duysens found the shape of the fluorescence spectrum to be practically the same whether excited by λ 480 mμ or 420 mμ, although in the first case, a substantial proportion of the absorbed quanta is taken up by chlorophyll b (Fig. 37C.49). The single fluorescence peak is located at 683 mμ; this indicates that chlorophyll a is the fluorescent pigment and suggests that practically all quanta absorbed by the b component are transferred to a before dissipation or re-emission. (This result is in disagreement with the earlier—and probably less reliable—observations listed in tables 24.I and 24.II, in which chlorophyll b fluorescence band was noted at 655–657 mμ, in *Ulva* and *Elodea*.)

Fig. 37C.50 shows the action spectrum of fluorescence of chlorophyll a in *Chlorella* (to minimize re-absorption, only fluorescent light above 720 mμ

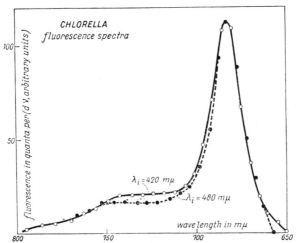

Fig. 37C.49. Fluorescence spectrum of *Chlorella* excited at λ 420 and 480 mμ (the latter appreciably absorbed by chlorophyll b) (after Duysens 1952). The fluorescence peaks are at 683 mμ, slightly beyond the main absorption peak of *Chlorella* at 680 mμ. No fluorescence peak is noticeable slightly beyond the absorption peak of chlorophyll b at 650 mμ. (Corrected for re-absorption of fluorescence in the cells.)

was measured; it belongs to the second fluorescence band and is not significantly re-absorbed). The yield is the same at 650 mμ (where 42% of total absorption is due to chlorophyll b) and in the region of exclusive chlorophyll a absorption (670 mμ). Whether the drop at $\lambda < 650$ mμ is real, or is caused by geometrical-optical conditions, is uncertain; the sharp drop at $\lambda > 680$ mμ undoubtedly *is* real (*cf.* table 37C.5). The yield was measured also at 480 mμ; analysis of these results indicated an about 40–50% effectiveness of energy transfer from carotenoids to chlorophyll a (*cf.* chapter 24, p. 813, and chapter 35, section 2).

Duysens also confirmed the observations of Dutton, Manning and Duggar (p. 814) of the carotenoid-sensitized chlorophyll fluorescence in brown algae. The fluorescence spectrum was the same whether excited at

500 mμ (predominantly absorbed by carotenoids) or 620 mμ (absorbed only by chlorophyll); the peak of the fluorescence band was at 682 mμ (or 683 mμ in *Chlorella*).   The fluorescence yield at 500 mμ was 70% of that at 680 mμ.   The same ratio was found in the action spectrum of photosynthesis in the same algae (*Nitzschia* DH$_2$).

Fig. 37C.51 shows the absorption spectrum of the blue-green algae *Oscillatoria* together with the action spectra of its photosynthesis (lower curve) (measured polarimetrically by Duysens and Goedheer 1952) and

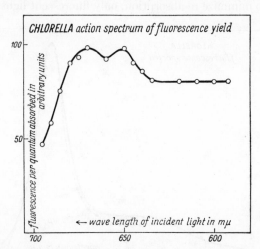

Fig. 37C.50. Fluorescence of an opaque layer of *Chlorella* cells (after Duysens 1952).   Quantum yield of chlorophyll *a* fluorescence same with excitation at 670 mμ (absorbed mainly by chlorophyll *a*) and at 650 mμ (much of it absorbed by chlorophyll *b*).

fluorescence (circles).   The two action spectra coincide, and both show that the effectiveness of phycocyanin absorption is higher (in a ratio of 10:4) than that of chlorophyll absorption—in confirmation of Haxo and Blinks' findings on the action spectrum of photosynthesis in red and blue algae (chapter 30).   The efficiency of absorption by carotenoids is low ($\sim$ 15% of that of phycocyanin), in agreement with Emerson and Lewis's estimates (20%) for *Chroococcus* (Emerson and Lewis found, however, no photosynthetically inefficient chlorophyll absorption; *cf.* chapter 30).

Fig. 37C.52 shows the fluorescence spectra of *Oscillatoria* excited by λ 420 and 578 mμ, respectively.   The contributions of chlorophyll and phycocyanin were calculated by shifting the fluorescence bands of the extracts so that the peaks coincided with those of the living cells (684 mμ for phycocyanin and 740 mμ for chlorophyll).   A striking discrepancy between the calculated sum of the fluorescences of the two pigments and the actual fluorescence of the cells appears above 700 mμ, indicating the presence of a third, strongly fluorescent, pigment, not noticeable in absorption (perhaps, chlorophyll *d*, *cf.* chapter 30, section 6 and 32, section 6).

The results obtained by Duysens with the red algae, *Porphyra lacineata* and *Porphyridium cruentum*, were mentioned briefly in Vol. II, Part 1 (pp. 807, 812). Fig. 37C.53 shows the absorption spectrum of *Porphyridium*, the action spectrum of its photosynthesis (after Duysens and Goedheer, 1952), and points on the action spectrum curve of chlorophyll *a*

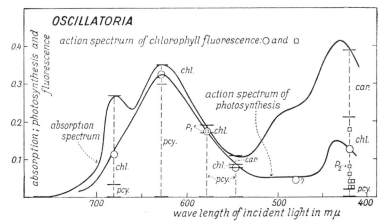

Fig. 37C.51. Absorption and action spectra of *Oscillatoria* (after Duysens 1952). At 680, 630, 578, 546 and 420 mμ, the contributions of chlorophyll *a* (chl.), phycocyanin (pcy.), and carotenoids (car.) to total absorption (upper curve) are indicated. Lower curve: action spectrum of photosynthesis; points (O) indicate action spectrum of chlorophyll fluorescence in an algal layer with negligible absorption. Points at λ 578 and 420 mμ, designated $\square$, were determined in a different way, and with various cultures. (At 578 mμ both points were made to coincide with the action spectrum of photosynthesis.)

fluorescence (calculated by analysis of total fluorescence spectrum, which contains contributions of chlorophyll, phycoerythrin and phycocyanin). The distribution of absorption between the pigments, as shown on vertical scales at several wave lengths, was obtained by shifting the peaks of extracted pigments to their positions *in vivo*, and flattening the absorption bands (using factors derived from the postulated inhomogeneity of pigment distribution, as suggested in section 4).

The curves show that photosynthesis is proportional to chlorophyll *a* fluorescence, indicating that fluorescent chlorophyll *a* is the immediate sensitizer, but that fluorescence of chlorophyll *a* is excited more effectively (in fact, about 2.5 times more effectively), by light absorbed by the phycobilins than by light absorbed by chlorophyll *a* itself! (Note, for example, the low fluorescence yield at 430 mμ as compared to that at 550 mμ.) The strength of sensitized fluorescence indicates effective resonance transfer of excitation energy from the phycobilins to chlorophyll *a;* the transfer efficiency is about the same for phycocyanin (630 mμ) and phycoerythrin (560 mμ).

A similarly constructed action spectrum for the excitation of phycocyanin fluorescence (based on combined data of French and Young, and

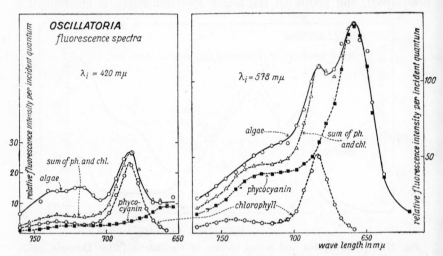

Fig. 37C.52. Fluorescence spectra of *Oscillatoria* excited by equal quantum fluxes at 420 and 578 mμ, in a layer with negligible absorption (after Duysens 1952); ordinates in (quanta)/(quantum × cm.² × sec.), multiplied by an arbitrary factor. Spectra analyzed in terms of fluorescence spectra of chlorophyll and phycocyanin. The difference found at 730 mμ (for λ_{exc} = 420 mμ) between the sum of the two fluorescence spectra and the fluorescence spectrum of the algae indicates the presence of an unidentified fluorescent pigment. Excitation by 570 mμ, absorbed mainly by phycocyanin, produces stronger chlorophyll fluorescence than excitation by 420 mμ, strongly absorbed by chlorophyll.

Duysens) shows the yield of fluorescence of phycocyanin to be proportional to the total absorption by the two phycobilins; this indicates effective energy transfer also from phycoerythrin to phycocyanin. No transfer appears to occur from chlorophyll (in the blue-violet band) to either of the two phycobilins.

An explanation of the paradoxical behavior of chlorophyll *a* fluorescence was mentioned in chapter 24, and also discussed in chapter 32. It postulated two types of pigment complexes, one "active," containing phycobilin together with (fluorescent) chlorophyll *a* (about 40% of total), and the other "inactive," containing the greater part (about 60%) of chlorophyll *a*, and an unknown, fluorescent pigment (chlorophyll *d?*). The fluorescence peak at 725 mμ, ascribed to the contaminating pigment (chlorophyll *d?*), is prominent in the fluorescence spectrum of *Porphyra* (fig. 24.5); its presence is less certain in *Porphyridium*.

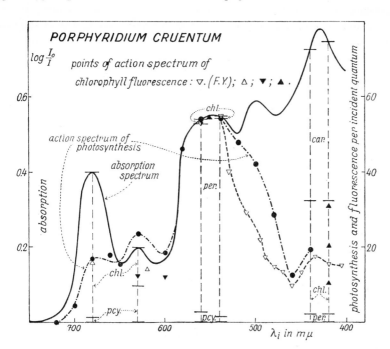

Fig. 37C.53. Absorption and action spectra of photosynthesis and chlorophyll fluorescence in red algae (after Duysens 1952). Contributions of the several pigments to total absorption are shown by line segments (chl. = chlorophyll, pcy. = phycocyanin, per. = phycoerythrin, car. = carotenoids). Action spectrum of chlorophyll fluorescence based on analysis of the fluorescence spectrum. Points marked ▽, after French and Young; points marked △, ▼, ▲, measurements with different cultures; the three points marked ▲ at 420 mμ, also obtained with different cultures. Photosynthesis roughly proportional to chlorophyll fluorescence. Comparison of action spectrum of fluorescence with absorption spectrum, at λ 680, 630 and 560 mμ, shows that light absorbed by phycobilins strongly excites chlorophyll fluorescence.

(c) Re-absorption of Fluorescence

In discussing their measurements, French and Young noted the effects of re-absorption of fluorescent light in the cells (concerning the same effect in solutions, see p. 746). This effect is most pronounced in the case of chlorophyll, where the fluorescence band overlaps strongly the absorption band; in dense green tissues, the first fluorescence peak can be shifted, by re-absorption, far toward the longer waves, and become subordinated to the second peak (fig. 37C.54). The fluorescence band of phycocyanin *in vivo* is distorted in the opposite sense by preferential re-absorption of its long-wave part by chlorophyll.

The extent of distortion of the fluorescence spectrum caused by self-absorption depends, for a given specimen, on the wave length of the exciting light. It is smaller in the case of excitation by red or blue light, which are absorbed in a thin layer in cells, and greater in that of excitation by

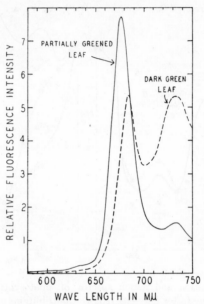

Fig. 37C.54. Fluorescence spectra of faintly green and dark green leaves showing the effect of self-absorption (after French and Young 1952).

green light, which penetrates deeper into the tissue (or cell suspension), thus causing the fluorescence to retrace a longer average path before emerging into pigment-free medium (French 1954).

Virgin (1954) showed that the fluorescence spectrum of leaves can be changed by infiltrating them with water. The elimination of air-filled spaces causes a reduction in scattering and re-absorption, with consequent enhancement of the main fluorescence band at 685 mμ relative to the first vibrational band at 735 mμ. The spectrum thus becomes similar to that of an optically thin chlorophyll solution or chloroplast suspension. A similar difference was found between the fluorescence spectra of (non-infiltrated) leaves immediately after a period of darkness and in the steady state after the induction period is over—as if the scattering, caused by air-filled spaces, increased considerably during the induction period and decreased again in darkness. In water-infiltrated leaves, or algal thalli containing no air spaces, the "initial" and the "steady state" fluorescence spectra show no significant differences.

(d) *Fluorescence of Protochlorophyll in vivo*

French (1954) gave spectral curves for the fluorescence of protochlorophyll in acetone solution (*cf.* section 4(*g*) above), in "chloroplastic material" from etiolated leaves of barley, in inner coats of squash seeds, and in the etiolated leaves after brief exposure to light. The unexpectedly complex shapes of the curves could be interpreted in terms of two phenomena: self-absorption of fluorescence, and the existence of two forms (or states) of protochlorophyll—one characterized by a fluorescence peak at 635 mμ and one having a peak slightly beyond 650 mμ. Self-absorption can explain why, in the fluorescence spectra of tissues rich in protochlorophyll (such as seed coats), both the 635 and 650 mμ bands, while present, are subordinated to a band at 705 mμ, which French interpreted as the sum of the first vibrational fluorescence bands of both "Pchl 635" and "Pchl 650."

The existence of two forms of protochlorophyll was first suggested, on the basis of absorption spectra, by Krasnovsky and co-workers (*cf.* section 1(*c*) above). The locations of their long-wave absorption bands were given as 635 and 645 mμ, respectively. According to Krasnovsky's hypothesis, "Pchl 635" is the fluorescent and photochemically active form, while "Pchl 645" (or 650) is a non-fluorescent and inactive polymerized form. However, the peak of the action spectrum of chlorophyll synthesis in etiolated seedlings has been found at 650 and not at 635 mμ (p. 1764); and according to French, both "Pchl 635" and "Pchl 650" are fluorescent. In this case, as in those of chlorophyll and bacteriochlorophyll, Krasnovsky's attribution of photochemical activity to the form with the higher excitation level seems to be in error. The photochemically active form again appears to be the one with the lower frequency absorption band—perhaps merely because the electronic excitation energy is apt to be transferred to this form by resonance before the photochemical change has had time to occur.

The finding of two photochlorophyll modifications has solved a difficulty mentioned once before—the apparent violation of Stokes' rule by this pigment whose fluorescence band *in vivo* was first reported at 635 mμ, while its absorption band was assumed to be, on the basis of action spectrum studies, at 650 mμ.

According to French (1954), Smith has observed that "Pchl 645" is converted into "Pchl 635" when freshly ground, etiolated barley leaves are heated, or allowed to stand in glycerol suspension.

(e) *Fluorescence of Chlorophyll c in Diatoms*

French (1954) could find no chlorophyll *b* fluorescence bands in living green plants, nor any chlorophyll *c* fluorescence bands in diatoms. The latter band should lie at 640 mμ; instead, the only additional fluorescence band observed in diatoms was located at 705 mμ. It may represent the first vibrational fluorescence band of chlorophyll *c*, in which case the main band must be presumed to be lost by effective re-absorption in chlorophyll *a*.

(f) *Changes of Fluorescence Intensity Related to Photosynthesis*

The kinetic relationships between the chlorophyll fluorescence *in vivo* and photosynthesis, described in chapter 24 (section 4), chapter 27 (part B) and 28 (part B) have again been reviewed by Wassink (1951). He argued that the hypothesis of Franck, which ascribes the most important changes in fluorescence intensity of living cells to metabolic formation and removal (by oxidation or displacement) of a "narcotic" from the surface of chlorophyll, is not basically different from the picture evolved by the Dutch group (in which the intensity of fluorescence is determined by the interaction of excited chlorophyll with an energy-accepting chemical system)—*if* one equates "narcotic cover" with "absence of energy-acceptor." However, this conciliation of the two views is purely formal and neglects basic physical differences. Franck's self-consistent, and physically plausible theory was again summarized in a paper (1951) which contained also an interpretation, in the terms of this theory, of Wassink and Kersten's observations on diatoms (*cf.* p. 1050, and figs. 28.28, 28.39 and 28.44). In these cells—in contrast to green algae and purple bacteria—the yield of fluorescence decreases—instead of increasing—when photosynthesis becomes light-saturated; Franck saw in this relation evidence that in diatoms substances engaged in primary photochemical reactions are better "fluorescence protectors" than narcotics, a conclusion supported by the observation (not mentioned on p. 1063) that ethyl urethane depresses the fluorescence of diatoms, while it increases that of other cells (*cf.* figs. 28.49 and 28.50).

Bibliography to Chapter 37C

Spectroscopy and Fluorescence

1929   Perrin, F., *Ann. physique*, **12**, 169, 261.
1940   Fischer, H., and Stern, A., "Chemie des Pyrrols," (Vol. II.2, *Pyrrol farbstoffe*), Akad. Verlagsges., Leipzig.
1944   Polgár, A., van Niel, C. B., and Zechmeister, L., *Arch. Biochem.*, **5**, 243.
1945   Lewis, G. N., and Kasha, M., *J. Am. Chem. Soc.*, **67**, 994.

1948 Krasnovsky, A. A., and Brin, G. P., *Compt. rend. (Doklady) acad. sci. USSR*, **63**, 163.

Karrer, P., and Jucker, E., *Carotinoide*. Birkhäuser, Basel.

1949 Simpson, W. T., *J. Chem. Phys.*, **17**, 1218.

Livingston, R., Watson, W., and McArdle, J., *J. Am. Chem. Soc.*, **71**, 1542.

Kuhn, H., *J. Chem. Phys.*, **17**, 1198.

Krasnovsky, A. A., and Vojnovskaya, K. K., *Compt. rend. (Doklady) acad. sci. USSR*, **66**, 663.

Lemberg, R., and Legge, J. W., *Hematin Compounds and Bile Pigments*. Interscience, N. Y.

1950 Evstigneev, V. B., Gavrilova, V. A., and Krasnovsky, A. A., *Compt. rend. (Doklady) acad. sci. USSR*, **74**, 315.

Platt, J. R., *J. Chem. Phys.*, **18**, 1168.

Strain, H. H., *Science*, **112**, 161.

Longuet-Higgins, M. C., Rector, C. W., and Platt, J. R., *J. Chem. Phys.*, **18**, 1174.

Watson, W. F., and Livingston, R., *J. Chem. Phys.*, **18**, 802.

Platt, J. R., *J. Chem. Phys.*, **19**, 101.

1951 Clayton, R., *Thesis*, California Inst. Technology, Pasadena.

Krasnovsky, A. A., and Voynovskaya, K. K., *Compt. rend. (Doklady) acad. sci. USSR*, **81**, 879.

Krasnovsky, A. A., and Kosobutskaja, L. M., *ibid.*, **82**, 761.

Linschitz, H., et al., Report NYO-654, AEC Contract A (30-1) 820 (Dec. 15, 1951).

Heller, W., and Marcus, A., *Phys. Rev.*, **84**, 809.

Strehler, B. L., and Arnold, W., *J. Gen. Physiol.*, **34**, 809.

Freed, S., and Sancier, K. M., *Science*, **114**, 275.

Franck, J., "A Critical Survey of the Physical Background of Photosynthesis," in *Ann. Rev. Plant Physiol.*, **2**, 53–86.

Strehler, B. L., *Arch. Biochem. and Biophys.*, **34**, 239.

Wassink, E. C., *Advances in Enzymology*, **11**, 91–199.

1952 Bell, L., *Compt. rend. (Doklady) Acad. Sci. USSR*, **83**, 477.

Duysens, L. N. M., "Transfer of Excitation Energy in Photosynthesis," *Thesis*, Univ. of Utrecht.

Duysens, L. N. M., and Goedheer, J. C., unpublished.

Foster, L. S., and Livingston, R., *J. Chem. Phys.*, **20**, 1315.

Freed, S., and Sancier, K. M., *Science*, **116**, 175.

French, S. C., and Young, V. K., "Pigment Spectra," manuscript prepared for Duggar, *Biological Effects of Radiation*, 2d ed., Vol. II, McGraw-Hill, N. Y.

Jacobs, E. E., "Condensed States of Chlorophyll and Related Pigments," *Thesis*, Univ. of Illinois.

Jacobs, E. E., and Holt, A. S., *J. Chem. Phys.*, **20**, 1326.

Krasnovsky, A. A., and Brin, G. P., *Compt. rend. (Doklady) acad. sci. USSR*, **89**, 527.

Krasnovsky, A. A., and Kosobutskaya, L. M., *ibid.*, **85**, 177.

Krasnovsky, A. A., Voynovskaya, K. K., and Kosobutskaya, L. N., *ibid.*, **85**, 389.

Kromhout, R. A., "Changes in the Absorption Bands of Ethyl Chlorophyllide during Crystallization," *Thesis,* Univ. of Illinois.

Linschitz, H., *et al.*, Ind. Res. Found. Syracuse Univ., N. Y., Report to Research Corp., New York (May 1, 1952).

Linschitz, H., *et al.*, Report NYO-656, AEC Contract A (30–1), 820 (Nov. 1, 1952).

Livingston, R., Thompson, L., and Ramarao, M. V., *J. Am. Chem. Soc.*, **74**, 1073.

Livingston, R., and Weil, S., *Nature*, **170**, 750.

Moss, R. A., and Loomis, W. E., *Plant Physiol.*, **27**, 370.

Nakajima, T., and Kon, H., *J. Chem. Phys.*, **20**, 750.

Neuberger, A., and Scott, J. J., *Proc. Roy. Soc. London*, **A213**, 307.

Rabinowitch, E., Jacobs, E. E., Holt, A. S., and Kromhout, R. A., *Z. Physik*, **133**, 261.

Scott, J. J., personal communication.

Strain, H. H., *Science*, **116**, 174.

Stupp, R., and Kuhn, H., *Helv. Chim. Acta*, **35**, 2469.

Watson, W. E., *Trans. Faraday Soc.*, **48**, 526.

Weigl, J. W., *J. Am. Chem. Soc.*, **75**, 999.

Weigl, J. W., and Livingston, R., *ibid.*, **74**, 3452.

1953   Barer, R., *J. Physiol.*, **119**, 52P.

Barer, R., Ross, K. F. A., and Tkaczyk, S., *Nature*, **171**, 720.

Duysens, L. N. M., and Huiskamp, J., (unpublished).

Elsden, S. K., Kamen, M. D., and Vernon, L. P., *J. Am. Chem. Soc.*, **75**, 6347.

Evstigneev, V. B., and Gavrilova, V. A., *Compt. rend. (Doklady) akad. sci. USSR*, **91**, 899.

Freed, S., and Sancier, K. M., *Science*, **117**, 655.

Holt, A. S., and Jacobs, E. E., (unpublished).

Jacobs, E. E., Vatter, A. E., and Holt, A. S., *J. Chem. Phys.*, **21**, 2246.

Koch, W., *Arch. Mikrobiol.*, **18**, 133.

Krasnovsky, A. A., and Kosobutskaya, L. M., *Compt. rend. (Doklady) acad. sci. USSR*, **91**, 343.

Krasnovsky, A. A., Kosobutskaya, L. M., and Voynovskaya, K. K., *ibid.*, **92**, 1201.

Larsen, H., *Kgl. Norsk, Videnskabsk. Selskabs Skrifter*, 1953, No. 1.

Livingston, R., Pariser, R., Thompson, L., and Weller, A., *J. Am. Chem. Soc.*, **75**, 3025.

Vernon, L. B., *Arch. Biochem. and Biophys.*, **43**, 422.

Weigl, J. W., *J. Am. Chem. Soc.*, **75**, 999.

Weigl, J. W., and Livingston, R., *J. Am. Chem. Soc.*, **75**, 2173.

1954   Arnold, W., and Davidson, J. B., *J. Gen. Physiol.*, **37**, 677.
Bannister, T. T., *Arch. Biochem. and Biophys.*, **49**, 222.
Barer, R., and Butt, V. S., (unpublished).
Blinks, L. R., *Symp. Gen. Microbiol.*, **4**, 224.
Duysens, L. N. M., *Nature*, **173**, 692.
Duysens, L. N. M., *Science*, **120**, 353.
Duysens, L. N. M., *ibid.*, **121**, 210.
Duysens, L. N. M., (unpublished).
Freed, S., and Sancier, K. M., *J. Am. Chem. Soc.*, **76**, 198.
French, C. S., "Fluorescence Spectrophotometry of Photosynthetic Pigments" (in manuscript).
Haxo, F. M., O'hEocha, C., and Strout, P. M., *Rapp. Comm. VIII Intern. Congr. Botany*, Paris, Section 17, p. 35.
Holt, A. S. (unpublished).
Holt, A. S., and Jacobs, E. E., *Am. J. Botany*, **41**, 710.
Holt, A. S., and Jacobs, E. E., *ibid.*, **41**, 718.
Holt, A. S., and Jacobs, E. E., (unpublished).
Jacobs, E. E., and Coleman, J., (unpublished).
Jacobs, E. E., and Holt, A. S., *J. Chem. Phys.*, **22**, 142.
Jacobs, E. E., Holt, A. S., Kromhout, R., Rabinowitch, E., and Vatter, A. E. (unpublished).
Jacobs, E. E., Holt, A. S., and Rabinowitch, E., *J. Chem. Phys.* **22**, 142.
Jacobs, E. E., Vatter, A. E., and Holt, A. S., *Arch. Biochem. and Biophys.*, **53**, 228.
Latimer, P. (unpublished).
Lundegårdh, H., *Physiol. Plantarum*, **7**, 375.
Seybold, A., and Hirsch, G., *Naturwiss.*, **41**, 258.
Virgin, H. I., *Physiol. Plantarum*, **7**, 560.
Wassink, E. C., *Proc. 8th Intern. Congr. Botany*, Paris, July 1954.
1955   Barer, R., *Science*, **121**, 709.
Witt, H. T., *Naturwiss.*, **42**, 72.

D. KINETICS OF PHOTOSYNTHESIS*
(ADDENDA TO CHAPTERS 1, 3, 12, 13, 27 AND 29)

1. The Carbon Dioxide Factor (Addendum to Chapter 27)

The most extensive kinetic work on photosynthesis, published since the appearance of Vol. II, Part 1, dealt directly or indirectly with the role of carbon dioxide in the photosynthetic process. The main new observations of importance in this field have been made with two entirely different objectives in mind.

The first objective was to clarify the role bicarbonate ions play in supporting photosynthesis (*cf.* chapter 27, section A.1). Steemann-Nielsen, Österlind, and Whittingham have contributed to this problem. Their experiments are described under (a) below.

The second objective was to maximize the quantum yield of photosynthesis. In continuing the work described in chapter 29, Warburg, Burk and co-workers reported that high partial pressures of carbon dioxide (as well as light of alternating intensity) are important for this purpose. This finding caused Whittingham, Emerson, Gaffron and Rosenberg, to re-investigate the influence of carbon dioxide concentration on the rate of photosynthesis in *Chlorella*. Emerson found no effect in weak, steady light, Whittingham none in either weak or strong light, Gaffron and Rosenberg considerable effect in strong light only. Their experiments are summarized under (d); a description of the quantum yield investigations of Warburg (and others) will be found in section 4 of this chapter.

(a) Utilization of Bicarbonate

In chapter 27 (p. 891) we treated the "carbon dioxide curves" of photosynthesis as functions of the concentration, $[CO_2]$, of *free* carbon dioxide, but mentioned that more recent investigations have re-opened the question—previously considered closed—of a possible direct participation of bicarbonate ions in photosynthesis. (By this, we mean participation in the flow of the reduction substrate into the cell and—perhaps—also separate entrance of bicarbonate ions into the first chemical reactions of photosynthesis, as contrasted to mere replacement of used-up carbon dioxide in the medium.) This subject has been further studied since, and additional evidence for the active role of bicarbonate has been supplied, particularly by Österlind, and Steemann-Nielsen.

* Bibliography, page 1975.

Österlind's first five papers (1947, 1948, 1949, 1950[1,2]) had been summarized in Part 1 of Vol. II (pp. 890–891). A difference was reported there between the two species, *Scenedesmus quadricauda* and *Chlorella pyrenoidosa*, in respect to the influence of bicarbonate ions on the rate of *growth*. The two species were found to contain different amounts of carbonic anhydrase (*cf.* chapter 14, p. 380 and chapter 37A, p. 1744, but the difference was not great enough to account for the wide discrepancy in the apparent capacity for bicarbonate utilization. Variations in membrane permeability to bicarbonate were suggested as the most likely explanation.

In the next paper, Österlind (1951[1]) measured manometrically the rate of *photosynthesis* (in light of about 6 klux) of the same two species. Ten-day old *Scenedesmus* cultures, and all the *Chlorella* cultures studied, showed no evidence of bicarbonate utilization, but five-day old cultures of *Scenedesmus* proved able to photosynthesize at maximum rate in 1×10^{-5} M NaHCO$_3$ (pH 8.1)—a solution that contains only insignificant amounts (0.02×10^{-5} mole/l.) of free carbon dioxide. At pH 4.0–4.6, the same cells produced oxygen at a rate proportional to the concentration of free carbon dioxide between $[CO_2] = 0.9 \times 10^{-5}$ and $[CO_2] = 9 \times 10^{-5}$ mole/l.; in this case, $[HCO_3^-]$ was much too low ($\leq 0.2 \times 10^{-5}$ mole/l.) to provide a contribution. From these two experiments, Österlind concluded that "young" cells of *Scenedesmus quadricauda* assimilate HCO$_3^-$ ions more effectively than CO$_2$ molecules (in agreement with the conclusions he had derived earlier from growth experiments).

Later, Österlind (1951[2]) suggested that the capacity of *Scenedesmus quadricauda* to use bicarbonate ions depends on an enzyme that requires "photactivation." At pH 5 ("CO$_2$ assimilation") oxygen liberation began at full rate immediately upon illumination; while at pH ≤ 7.3 ("HCO$_3^-$ assimilation"), the steady rate was reached only after an induction period of about one half hour. Österlind discussed two alternative mechanisms: either HCO$_3^-$ ions undergo "activation" *before* they can enter the cell, or their activation occurs *inside* the cell. In the latter case, activation may mean simply dehydration and the enzyme requiring activation may be none other than carbonic anhydrase.

Subsequently, Österlind (1952[1]) studied the inhibition of photosynthesis of *Scenedesmus quadricauda* by cyanide, at different pH values, in the hope of obtaining a clue to the alternative: utilization of bicarbonate as such, or its conversion to carbon dioxide inside the cell; but the results proved compatible with both interpretations (*cf.* section 2(*a*) below).

Österlind's suggestion—that the prolonged induction period he observed in CO$_2$-poor bicarbonate solutions (with algae that had been grown in ample [CO$_2$]) is caused by slow photactivation of an enzyme needed for bicarbonate utilization—was opposed by Briggs and Whittingham (1952) (*cf.* Vol. II, Part 1, p. 908). They suggested instead that cells grown in high [CO$_2$], and therefore full of metabolites, when exposed to strong light in CO$_2$-deficient medium, tend to form—as suggested in the induction theory of Gaffron and Franck—chlorophyll-enveloping "narcotics" (perhaps plant acids). This explanation was supported by the observation (cf. p. 909) that, in Chlorella, inhibition persisted even after cells had been transferred into a medium abundant in carbon dioxide. Österlind (1952[2]) could not confirm the last finding, and suggested that the induction effects observed by Whittingham in Chlorella must have been different from those in Scenedesmus quadricauda.

Whittingham (cf. Emerson and Whittingham 1953) measured the rate of photosynthesis of Chlorella pyrenoidosa at constant $[CO_2]$ (= 7×10^{-5} mole/l.) as function of $[HCO_3^-]$, in white light of varying intensity. Table 37D.I shows the results.

TABLE 37D.I

RATE OF PHOTOSYNTHESIS OF Chlorella AT DIFFERENT HCO_3^- CONCENTRATIONS [CO_2] = 7×10^{-5} MOLE PER LITER (AFTER WHITTINGHAM[a])

(Volumes O_2 per hour per volume of cells)

[HCO_3^-], mole/l.	White light					Red light	
	100	Relative intensity, I 44	14	7	3	Rate	Quantum requirement
0.26	22.4	17.0	8.2	4.6	1.5	1.39	10.7
0.085	26.4	21.3	8.8	5.3	1.3	1.32	11.5
0.037	19.3	14.4	7.5	3.5	1.3	1.45	9.9

[a] Cf. Emerson and Whittingham (1953).

Expressed in fraction of the yield in saturating white light ($I = 100$), the rates at all other white light intensities (3 to 44) are, according to Whittingham, independent of $[HCO_3^-]$, and of the correlated changes in pH, within the limits of experimental error. The rates in the (relatively weak) red light, from which the quantum yields shown in the last column were calculated, are definitely independent of $[HCO_3^-]$.

Since, in this study, the concentration of free carbon dioxide was in itself saturating (or almost saturating), it is not astonishing that addition of bicarbonate did not significantly improve the yield, particularly in weak light, where the absolute rate is low. We recall that Österlind found no evidence of bicarbonate contribution to photosynthesis in Chlorella pyrenoidosa even at much lower CO_2 concentrations.

In a not easily explainable contradiction to the findings of Whittingham and Österlind are the data of Gaffron (1953) and Rosenberg (1954), obtained (by electrochemical pH determination) with both Chlorella pyrenoidosa and Scenedesmus obliquus. As described in more detail in section (b), they found, in contrast to other observers, a decline in the yield of photosynthesis of these algae with decreasing concentration of free carbon dioxide, beginning as early as at 2% (7×10^{-5} mole/l.) CO_2 in saturating light, and somewhat later in weaker light. When the rate was thus "[CO_2] limited," bicarbonate was found able to serve as substitute for the deficient carbon dioxide. According to Gaffron, this cannot be attributed to removal of diffusion limitation in an insufficiently stirred vessel, because of the shape of CO_2 curves obtained at different light intensities (*cf.* under (*b*) below). Fig. 37D.1 represents a "CO_2 curve" obtained in dilute bicarbonate solution,

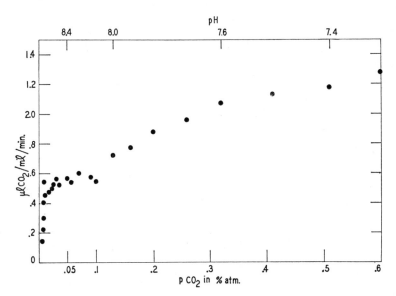

Fig. 37D.1. Carbon dioxide curve of *Chlorella* (determined with *p*H meter) in 2×10^{-3} *M* bicarbonate, in near-saturating green light (after Gaffron and Rosenberg 1953). CO_2 saturation at 1.2%. Sharp initial rise of the curve indicates contribution of bicarbonate. Suspension density, 0.9 volume percent.

which shows at $[CO_2] \simeq 0$ a "residual" rate attributable to bicarbonate. This residual rate increases with increasing bicarbonate concentration, until, in 0.01 or 0.1 *M* bicarbonate (*i. e.*, in the usual carbonate buffers), the "CO_2 curve" becomes practically flat down to $[CO_2]$ values as low as 0.1% (3×10^{-5} mole/l.), or less, as found by Emerson and other earlier observers. (However, this observation does not explain the finding by Emerson and Green, and by Whittingham, of CO_2 curves that remained flat down to very low $[CO_2]$ values also in acid media, containing no bicarbonate.) The contribution of bicarbonate to the yield was found by Gaffron to depend on the previous history of the cells. An extreme case is illustrated in fig. 37D.2. It shows that cells incubated in 50% CO_2, and then brought into an atmosphere of $0–5\%$ CO_2, at first show no capacity to utilize bicarbonate (downward run, triangles); a sojourn in the CO_2-deficient bicarbonate solution causes, however, a rapid adaptation to bicarbonate, illustrated by the dots obtained in a subsequent "upward run." It thus appears that *Chlorella* and *Scenedesmus* exposed to high CO_2 concentrations lose the capacity to take up bicarbonate, but regain it when placed in a medium deficient in free carbon dioxide.

It will be noted that the saturation rate in fig. 37D.2 is not affected by the "hysteresis loop," in contrast to Warburg's suggestions (*cf.* section 4(*a*)).

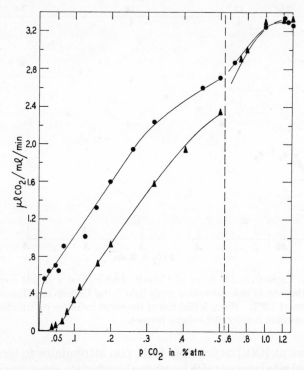

Fig. 37D.2. Adaptation to bicarbonate (after Gaffron and Rosenberg 1953). *Scenedesmus* in $2 \times 10^{-3} M$ bicarbonate. After incubation in 50% CO_2, cells were transferred into 4% CO_2 and illuminated until all CO_2 was consumed (lower curve). After 1 hour, 4% CO_2 was added and cells illuminated until all CO_2 was again used up (upper curve).

Steemann-Nielsen (1947) described in more detail the results of experiments on penetration of bicarbonate into the leaves of aquatic plants, summarized in an earlier note (1946). The question asked on p. 888 in connection with that note—whether the transportation of bicarbonate ions across the leaf, first noted by Arens, can be quantitatively significant for photosynthesis—had already been answered in the 1947 paper (see also

Steemann-Nielsen 1952): new measurements of the bicarbonate transport through leaves of *Potomageton lucens* showed the rate of this transportation to be high enough to play an important role in photosynthesis.

In contrast to Arens, Steemann-Nielsen observed that bicarbonate was taken up through the upper as well as through the lower leaf surface; the liberation of CO_3^{--} ions (or OH^- ions), on the other hand, occurred only on the upper surface. For example, after 180 min. illumination (24 klux) of a leaf placed between a $2.7 \times 10^{-3} N$ HCO_3^- solution (below) and distilled water (above), the upper solution was 25×10^{-5} N in OH^-, $37 \times 10^{-5} N$ in CO_3^{--} and $10 \times 10^{-5} N$ in HCO_3^- (pH 10.6, as against pH 7.9 before illumination). If the solutions in the two compartments were exchanged, no alkali was released into the lower compartment.

In the experiment with distilled water in the upper compartment, the amount of carbon transferred across the leaf was of the same order of magnitude as that used in photosynthesis. The results could be quantitatively accounted for by assuming that bicarbonate entered the leaf from below and suffered the following fate: about 15% diffused without change into the upper compartment; about 50% was dismuted ($2HCO_3^-$ $\rightarrow CO_3^{--} + CO_2 + H_2O$) and about 35% was split ($HCO_3^- \rightarrow CO_2 + OH^-$). The carbon dioxide produced in the leaf by these two processes was used for photosynthesis, while the OH^- and CO_3^{--} ions diffused out into the solution above. The result was the same, whether the light fell on the upper or on the lower surface of the leaf. No such directed transfer of ions could be observed with fronds of *Ulva lactuca*.

Steemann-Nielsen's experiments on *Potomageton* showed, in contrast to those of Arens, no significant difference between potassium bicarbonate and calcium bicarbonate in the ratio of CO_3^{--} and OH^- ions liberated on the upper side of the leaf.

From these experiments, Steemann-Nielsen (1951, 1952) concluded that the entrance of bicarbonate ions into *Potomageton* cells occurs by "passive" diffusion, at a rate proportional to the concentration gradient, while the excretion of OH^- ions is a directed "active" diffusion, the rate of which is independent of the concentration gradients.

The experiments of Österlind, Gaffron and Steemann-Nielsen provide strong evidence for the penetration of bicarbonate ions into the cells of certain species (or strains) of higher aquatic plants and algae. Other plants—not only terrestrial, but also aquatic—seem to be impermeable to bicarbonate. In the case of higher aquatics, the capacity to take in bicarbonate seems to be, to a certain extent, a matter of adaptation to the natural habitat—some of those living in alkaline waters, poor in free carbon dioxide, have acquired it, while those living in neutral or acid waters have not. However, not all aquatic plants appear capable of such adaptation; Steemann-Nielsen found *Fontinalis* picked in alkaline lakes (pH up to 8.2) to be as indifferent to bicarbonate as were plants of the same species collected in acid waters (pH down to 5.5), or as plants of *Fontinalis dalecarlica*, a species that grows only at pH 4.2–6.6. Gaffron's experiments seem to indicate that adaptation to bicarbonate can be very rapid in unicellular algae. In every case, adaptation is probably due to a change in the permeability of the cell membrane, rather than to an alteration in the chemical mechanism of carboxylation in photosynthesis. Changes in the amount of active carbonic anhydrase also may be involved. It can further be asked whether the bicarbonate ions that had penetrated into the cell (or had been produced in the cell sap by the hydration of CO_2 molecules) can participate in photosynthesis through a reaction independent of (and, perhaps, competitive with) the reaction by which carbon dioxide molecules enter it, e. g.:

$$(37D.1) \qquad\qquad CO_2 + A = ACO_2 \qquad \text{and}$$

$$(37D.2) \qquad\qquad HCO_3{}^- + A = ACO_2 + OH^-$$

The alternative is for the intercellular bicarbonate to participate in photosynthesis only by supporting the carbon dioxide level in the cell sap. The bicarbonate ions entering the cell would then be added to the internal bicarbonate reserve (cf. chapter 8, section B.2), and contribute to photosynthesis only via the relatively sluggish dehydration reaction, which, in strong light, may fail to keep pace with photosynthesis. (The efficiency of this "internal CO_2 buffering" must depend on the content of the sap in carbonic anhydrase; cf. Vol. I, p. 380. We mentioned above Österlind's suggestion that carbonic anhydrase in plants undergoes "activation" in light.)

(b) Carbon Dioxide Curves

The demonstration of the participation of $HCO_3{}^-$ ions in carbon transfer into photosynthesizing cells of some species (or strains) of aquatic plants brings a new element of uncertainty into plotting and interpretation of "carbon dioxide curves" of photosynthesis, $P = f[CO_2]$ (cf. table 27.I and figs. 27.2A to 27.4). In sections 5 and 9g of chapter 27, it was pointed out that the shape of many of the CO_2 curves found in the literature must have been determined by the supply of carbon dioxide to the cells (through diffusion and convection), so that the intrinsic relationship between the rate of photosynthesis and the carbon dioxide concentration in situ (i. e., at the chloroplast surface) has been more or less completely masked. It was suggested that even in experiments in which carbonate buffering, intense stirring, and use of small plant objects (unicellular algae) have assured the absence of a CO_2 concentration gradient outside the cells, it was still uncertain whether the observed residual dependence of P on $[CO_2]$ could not have been caused by slow diffusion of carbon dioxide through the cell wall, and from this wall to the chloroplast. Consequently, even calculations based on the shape of carbon dioxide curves obtained under ideal external supply condition can give only an upper limit for the dissociation constant of the hypothetical carbon dioxide-acceptor compound in photosynthesis (cf. p. 934).

The possible participation of HCO_3^- ions in the flow of carbon into the cell further complicates the situation, particularly since the relative role of CO_2 molecules and HCO_3^- ions appears to depend on the species and the strain used, and may be subject to change by individual adaptation. From this point of view, the only strictly comparable carbon dioxide curves are those obtained in gaseous carbon dioxide atmosphere, or in acid CO_2 solutions, such as the curves reproduced in figures 27.2B and 27.3. In plotting the results obtained in bicarbonate solutions, or carbonate-bicarbonate buffers, one faces the uncertainty whether one should use as abscissa $[CO_2]$, or $[HCO_3^-]$ or, more generally, $[CO_2] + x[HCO_3^-]$, with the coefficient x differing from species to species, strain to strain, and perhaps even changing, in a given specimen, from one measurement to another (cf. fig. 37D.2).

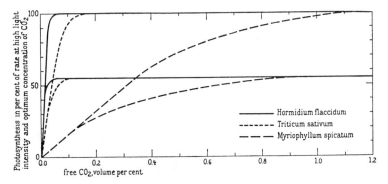

Fig. 37D.3. Three types of carbon dioxide curves, $P = f[CO_2]$ (at two light intensities) (Steemann-Nielsen 1952).

On p. 888 it was suggested that, when HCO_3^- ions contribute to the carbonic acid flow into the cell, they may traverse the cell membrane as neutral salt molecules, such as $KHCO_3$ and dissociate again in the cell sap. This remains a possible but unproved speculation.

Steemann-Nielsen (1952) suggested that the plants in which carbon dioxide has only a short liquid diffusion path (of the order of 1 μ) to reach the chloroplasts—such as the higher terrestrial plants and terrestrial algae (e. g., *Hormidium*), have no great difficulty in securing adequate supply of carbon dioxide, even when its concentration in the medium is low (free air, $[CO_2] = 0.03\%$, or 1×10^{-5} M). Their carbon dioxide saturation is reached at concentrations such as $[CO_2] = 7 \times 10^{-5}$ mole/l. (*Triticum*, fig. 27.3), or lower—e. g., 2×10^{-5} mole/l. in *Hormidium* (fig. 27.2B). Such plants do not need—and did not develop—a mechanism permitting bicarbonate to serve as vehicle for carrying carbon dioxide into the cell. The anatomy of some aquatic plants, on the other hand, is such that carbon dioxide has to diffuse through a liquid layer up to 40 μ thick to penetrate from the surface of the plant to some of the chloroplasts. Such plants would starve if they had to rely entirely on the supply of CO_2 molecules by diffusion from a medium containing only about 1×10^{-5} mole/l. CO_2. In fact, Steemann-Nielsen found the photosynthesis of *Myriophyllum spicatum* and *Fontinalis antipyretica* to reach saturation, in acid solution (containing free CO_2 only), only when $[CO_2]$ exceeded 50×10^{-5} mole/l. (The removal of thick terminal buds reduced, in the case of *Fontinalis*, the concentration needed for saturation, to $[CO_2] = 20 \times 10^{-5}$ mole/l.) In such plants, the rate of photosynthesis at $[CO_2] = 1 \times 10^{-5}$ mole/l. (water equilibrated with free air) would be insignificant, unless the medium contained also bicarbonate, and the cell walls were permeable to it. As an illustration of these relationships, fig. 37D.3 compares once again the carbon dioxide curves ($P = f[CO_2]$) in a medium containing CO_2 molecules only, of a terrestrial plant (*Triticum*), a terrestrial alga (*Hormidium*), and an aquatic plant (*Myriophyllum*).

Steemann-Nielsen pointed out that, even in the case of *Myriophyllum* (not to speak of *Hormidium*), the pairs of curves in fig. 37D.3 which correspond to different light intensities start with the same slope ("Blackman type," *cf.* fig. 26.2). He suggested that carbon dioxide curves of the "Bose type" (fig. 26.3)—such as had been found by Harder for *Fontinalis* (fig. 27.2A)—are always caused by insufficient rate of supply. (He could obtain such curves also with *Myriophyllum*, by using stagnant water.) According to chapter 27 (section A7b), diffusion resistance cannot produce curves of the "Bose type"; Steemann-Nielsen suggested, however, that such curves could be explained by *convection*, if it is assumed that the rate of the latter increases with the intensity of illumination; this would raise the "roof" imposed on the carbon dioxide curves of photosynthesis by CO_2 supply limitation (*cf.* fig. 26.6).

It was shown in chapter 27, that CO_2 curves of the "Bose type" must result also when the factor determining the shape of the curves is the carboxylation equilibrium, $A + CO_2 \rightleftharpoons ACO_2$. We expect this relationship to become revealed when all CO_2 concentration gradients are practically eliminated, and all "supply roofs" thus lifted. It is unlikely that these conditions could have been realized in Harder's measurements; his CO_2 curves rise much too slowly for such an interpretation.

Steemann-Nielsen (1952) criticized also the carbon dioxide curves Smith had given for *Cabomba caroliniana* (fig. 27.4), because of the use of "unphysiological," pure potassium carbonate buffers, and the curves Emerson and Green gave for *Chlorella pyrenoidosa* (fig. 27.2C) because their method (p. 897) did not take into account the possible contribution to photosynthesis, in a closed volume of gas, of intercellular carbonate reserves (which Steemann-Nielsen believes all cells must contain, *cf.* p. 196).

The observations on the shape of the carbon dioxide curves of *Chlorella* remain contradictory. In table 27.1, two measurements were listed, one by Warburg, showing half-saturation at 0.4×10^{-5} mole/l. and a slow approach to complete saturation somewhere above 7×10^{-5} mole/l. CO_2; and one by Emerson and Green, showing half-saturation at 0.35×10^{-5} mole/l. and sharp saturation at 0.7×10^{-5} mole/l. CO_2. Österlind (1950) published curves for the rate of *growth* of *Chlorella pyrenoidosa* as a function of $[CO_2]$, which showed half-saturation first at 2.5×10^{-5} mole/l. and full saturation at 10×10^{-5} mole/l. (free carbon dioxide, at pH 8).

Whittingham (1952) made a new determination of the carbon dioxide curve of *Chlorella pyrenoidosa*, in acid phosphate buffer (pH 4.6), using saturating light. The method was similar to that of Emerson and Green (*i. e.* the rate was measured as function of declining CO_2 content in a closed system), but the gas was circulated, and $[CO_2]$ was determined with a recording infrared spectrometer. Eight points were measured between 1.0 and 0.04×10^{-5} mole/l. CO_2 (table 37D.II), indicating half-saturation as early as at 0.1×10^{-5} mole/l. and full saturation near 1×10^{-5} mole/l. Whittingham's earlier measurements (1949) had indicated that, in carbonate buffer, the photosynthesis of *Chlorella pyrenoidosa* cultures acclimated to a medium of low CO_2 content may be half-saturated at even lower CO_2 concentrations—as low as 0.05×10^{-5} mole/l!

TABLE 37D.II

$P = f[CO_2]$ OF *Chlorella* IN THE STEADY STATE IN ACID BUFFER IN SATURATING LIGHT
(AFTER WHITTINGHAM 1952)

$[CO_2]$, %	0.030	0.011	0.0089	0.0070	0.0052	0.0033	0.0017	0.0013
" m./l. $\times 10^5$	1.0	0.37	0.30	0.23	0.17	0.11	0.057	0.043
P	18.0	16.8	16.3	14.6	12.5	11.5	8.5	6.8

Warburg and co-workers (1951) found a strong influence of free carbon dioxide concentration on the maximum quantum yield, $\gamma_{max.}$, of photosynthesis in *Chlorella pyrenoidosa*, as determined by the method of intermittent illumination. The experimental points fell on the same $\gamma_{max.} = f[CO_2]$ curve, whether determined in acid phosphate or in alkaline carbonate medium (*cf.* fig. 37D.27). We will discuss these results in section 4 of this chapter; what concerns us here is that Warburg's conclusions have caused Emerson to re-investigate the $[CO_2]$ dependence of photosynthesis in *Chlorella* in weak, steady light. Table 37D.III shows the results, in acid and alkaline media. No effect of $[CO_2]$ (or of pH) on the quantum requirement could be noted, between 0.2% (7×10^{-5} mole/l.) and 5% (16×10^{-5} mole/l.) free CO_2, corresponding to pH values from 9.0 to 4.8. This region has been generally known to be one of CO_2 saturation in *strong light,* and it was *a priori* unlikely that more carbon dioxide could be needed to reach CO_2 saturation in weak light, where the demand is smaller; but Warburg's observations in intermittent light made it advisable to look for a possible, even if unexpected, specific $[CO_2]$ dependence of photosynthesis in weak light.   The absolute values of the quantum requirements in table 37D.III (and 37D.I) will be discussed in Section 4.

TABLE 37D.III

QUANTUM REQUIREMENT OF *Chlorella* IN RELATION TO CO_2 CONCENTRATION
(AFTER EMERSON[a])

Illumination	$M/10$ buffer (85 p. bicarb., 15 p. carb.[b]), 0.2% CO_2 (6.2 × 10^{-5} M), pH 9.0	$M/5$ buffer (95 p. bicarb., 5 p. carb.[c]), 2% CO_2 (62 × 10^{-5} M), pH 8.5	Acid culture medium, 5% CO_2 (155 × 10^{-5} M), pH 4.8
Cd 643.8 mμ, 0.20 μeinstein per min.	9.0	9.2	8.8
Cd 643.8 mμ + Hg 579 mμ, 0.29 μeinstein per min.	9.5	9.6	8.9

[a] *Cf.* Emerson and Whittingham (1953).
[b] Warburg's buffer No. 9.
[c] Warburg's "new buffer," *cf.* section 4 below.

In subsequent papers, Warburg and co-workers (1953, 1954) mentioned that other *Chlorella* cultures did not show the same dependence of the yield on $[CO_2]$ as the culture described in the 1951 paper.

Steemann-Nielsen (1952), discounting the measurements of Emerson and Green, suggested that the *Chlorella* strain used by Whittingham (1949) might have been permeable to bicarbonate, or sensitive to changes in pH (which, in carbonate buffers, accompany changes in $[CO_2]$), rather than to charges in CO_2 concentration. He considered Österlind's growth measurements, showing CO_2 saturation at 10 × 10^{-5} mole/l. CO_2, as the only reliable determination of the CO_2 curve of *Chlorella pyrenoidosa*.   However, subsequent measurements of Whittingham (1952) have revealed no bicarbonate utilization by his strain of *Chlorella pyrenoidosa* (at least not at $[CO_2]$ = 7 × 10^{-5} mole/l.). Österlind's observations of a strong effect of pH on the growth of this species also have not been confirmed by measurements of photosynthesis (*e. g.*, those of Emerson and Green, *cf.* p. 340), except at pH > 9.   Furthermore, in Whittingham's measurements, a detrimental effect of high pH should have accelerated—and not delayed—the decline of the rate with increasing pH (since, in carbonate buffers, $[CO_2]$ is lower the higher pH). The suggestions of Steemann-Nielsen are therefore insufficient to explain the discrepancy.

Gaffron and Rosenberg (*cf.* Rosenberg 1954) also studied the dependence of photosynthesis in *Chlorella* on carbon dioxide concentration, at various light intensities, using a glass electrode.   They employed either a sealed reaction vessel, in which dilute bicarbonate solution was equilibrated with CO_2 gas of different pressure, or an open system, in which a gas stream, containing 0.25–1.25% CO_2, passed first through the reaction vessel (containing alkaline or acid suspension medium) and then through an electrode vessel filled with dilute bicarbonate solution; pH changes were recorded in this vessel, and CO_2 changes in the gas calculated from them. In experiments of both types, CO_2 saturation was found to require much higher CO_2 concentrations than anticipated from earlier data.

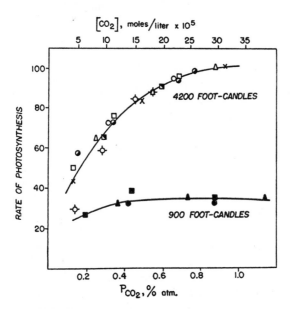

Fig. 37D.4. Carbon dioxide curves of *Scenedesmus* in 2.5×10^{-2} M KH_2PO_4 at two light intensities (after Rosenberg 1954). 28° C. Suspension density 1 volume percent. The curves are of "Bose-type" (fig. 26.3) rather than of "Blackman type" (fig. 26.2), as they should be if diffusion were the cause of $[CO_2]$-dependence (p. 923).

Fig. 37D.4 shows typical CO_2 curves obtained by Rosenberg (in bicarbonate-free medium). The relation of the curves obtained at two different light intensities argues against the attribution of the slow increase to diffusion limitations such as may occur in a vessel stirred only by the gas stream. (According to Chapter 27, diffusion limitation must produce curve families of the "Blackman type," rather than such of "Bose type," apparent in fig. 37D.4; compare above the remarks of Steemann-Nielsen on the measurements of Harder.) Very similar $[CO_2]$-curves were obtained also in 2×10^{-3} M $NaHCO_3$; at the higher bicarbonate concentrations saturation was reached earlier.

In Gaffron and Rosenberg's experiments, the saturation rate, once reached, was the same in "CO_2-adapted" and "bicarbonate-adapted" algae (*cf.* fig. 37D.2); this result does not support the suggestion of Warburg (section 4) that, whenever no dependence of the rate on CO_2 is found in the concentration region where the $\gamma = f\,[CO_2]$ curve in fig. 37D.27 rises steeply, this indicates that the cells are of poor photosynthetic efficiency. In Gaffron's experiments, all cells appeared equally efficient when provided with sufficient carbon dioxide, but CO_2-adapted cells lost this efficiency when CO_2 declined below a few per cent, while bicarbonate-adapted cells retained a high efficiency down to considerably lower CO_2 concentrations (provided sufficient bicarbonate was available as replacement).

Steemann-Nielsen (1953[1,2]) measured the rate of oxygen liberation by *Chlorella* as function of carbon dioxide concentration, using Winkler's method of oxygen determination, at different light intensities (up to 9 klux). At 21° C., at 7 klux, the $P = f[CO_2]$ curve was horizontal between 0.05 and 1% CO_2, and declined above 1% (CO_2-poisoning, *cf.* chapter 13, part B); the rate showed a decline also between 0.05 and 0.025%. At 0.6 klux, on the other hand, the rate of O_2 liberation rose between 0.05 and 3% CO_2, particularly clearly above 0.5%, in apparent support of the above-mentioned paradox: "the lower the illumination, the greater the CO_2-requirement!" However, Steemann-Nielsen refused to believe that this rise can represent a true dependence of P on $[CO_2]$ at low I, and suggested that it results from a blocking effect of concentrated carbon dioxide on respiration. True, no such effect could be detected when respiration was measured *in the dark;* but Steemann-Nielsen suggested that it may occur *in light.* (One could imagine, for example, that high CO_2 concentration favors photochemical "anti-respiration," *i. e.*, the detouring of respiration intermediates into the photoreductive cycle, as suggested by Franck and others in the interpretation of some of Warburg's data; but Steemann-Nielsen thought rather of the inactivation of a respiratory enzyme, in analogy to the ideas of Calvin and his co-workers, mentioned in chapter 36.) Steemann-Nielsen pointed out, in this connection, that Kok's and van der Veen's observations (reported on p. 1114; *cf.* also Kok 1951) of a doubling of the slope of $P = f(I)$-curves near the compensation point (interpreted by them as evidence of the existence of a photochemical "anti-respiration") had shown a clear-cut effect only in 5% CO_2, and that only much weaker, uncertain effects were noted in 0.2% CO_2 (a relation not noted by Kok).

Steeman-Nielsen used these findings to re-interpret Warburg's findings of a low quantum requirement at high CO_2-concentrations as a consequence of a photochemical inhibition of respiration, which requires only little light energy.

(c) Carbon Dioxide Compensation Point

In chapter 27 (section A) it was noted that "the carbon dioxide compensation point has not been studied in the same systematic way as the light compensation point." Since then, several papers have appeared dealing with this subject. Gabrielsen (1948) and Gabrielsen and Schou (1949) found the compensation point of excised leaves at 0.009% CO_2, in artificial light of 10 klux as well as in full sunlight. (The latter was a confirmation of an early observation of Garreau, 1849, 1851, not noted in Chapter 27.) Gabrielsen, as well as Audus (1947), believed to have observed a [CO_2] "threshold" of photosynthesis (at 0.0009%, or 0.006%

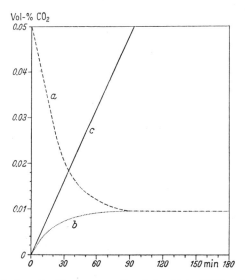

Fig. 37D.5. Carbon dioxide compensation (after Egle 1951). *Fegatella conica*, natural growth, 8 × 10 cm., with partially overlapping thalli: (a) 13 klux, 20° C., initial [CO_2] = 0.05%; (b) same, initially no CO_2; (c) same as (b), but in darkness.

CO_2, respectively), below which the net gas exchange was the same in light and in the dark (as if the photosynthetic mechanism were "shut off"). Similar conclusions by Chesnokov and Bazyrina were reported in chapter 21 (p. 907); we noted there their contradiction with the most reliably determined [CO_2] curves. The renewal of the "threshold" concept by Audus, and Gabrielsen, brought a rejoinder by Egle (1951). He gave figs. 37D.5 and 37D.6 for the gas exchange of *Fegatella conica* (observed with a heat conduction CO_2 meter, *cf.* chapter 25, p. 853), in a closed circulation system. The first figure shows the carbon dioxide concentration in the gas space to approach 0.009% after about 1.5 hours of exposure to light (13 klux), independently of whether the initial pressure was higher or lower. The deviation of curve b from the straight line c (which represents CO_2 liberation in darkness) proves that photosynthesis begins partially to compensate respiration long before the alleged "threshold" of 0.009% CO_2 is reached.   Fig. 37D.6 shows clearly the dependence of the CO_2 compensation point on light intensity (not found by Audus).   The compensation point moves from about 0.004% at 13 klux, to 0.016% at 2.1 klux, and > 0.04% at 1 klux.   Thus, compensation results from a dynamic equilibrium between a dark process of constant velocity, and a photochemical process that increases in rate (within certain limits) with increasing light intensity and carbon dioxide concentration, and *not* from "switching photosynthesis on and off."

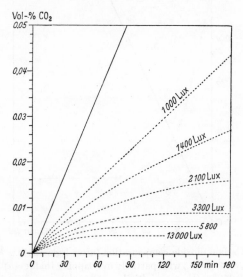

Fig. 37D.6. Carbon dioxide compensation as function of light intensity for same plant as in fig. 37D.5 (after Egle 1951).   Solid curve at left is respiration in dark.

Egle used stomata-free plants.   In leaves, which were used by Garreau, Audus, and Gabrielsen and Schou, stomatal movements, induced by low CO_2 concentration, complicate the results.   However, the observations of Heath and co-workers indicate that these movements should make the slowing-down of photosynthesis at low CO_2 concentrations more gradual rather than more sudden.   Heath (1948) and Heath and Milthorpe (1950) reported that stomatal openings grow wider as the CO_2 concentration declines from 0.03 to 0.01%; the response ceases below 0.009%.   Heath also found (1949, 1950, 1951) that a concentration of about 0.01% is established in air pumped through illuminated leaves (25 klux), at pumping speeds between 0.4 and 2.5 l./hr. (per 9 cm.[2]), whether the entering air carried 0.03% CO_2 or 0.14–0.18% CO_2.   It can thus be concluded that compensation occurs when the CO_2 concentration *in the substomatal spaces* is down to about 0.01%, and that the stomata respond to changes in the CO_2 pressure in these spaces, rather than in the outside air.   We expect that systematic study will prove this value to be dependent on light intensity—despite the remark by Heath (1951) that similar limiting pressures had been found at 25 klux (Heath), 11 klux (Gabrielsen), and 2.8–9.3 klux (Heath and Milthorpe).

A related question is that of the possibility of stopping photosynthesis altogether by rapid removal of respiratory carbon dioxide. This problem is of importance for the interpretation of the quantum yield measurements, since a positive answer (cf. chapter 29, p. 901) would mean that respiration intermediates are not drawn into photosynthesis, as substitute oxidants, if carbon dioxide (or the CO_2 acceptor complex) is available. The relevant experiments are therefore discussed in section 4 below.

(d) Carbon Dioxide Supply through Roots

Reference to this phenomenon was made in Vol. II Part 1 (p. 910). It was since studied quantitatively by Kursanov, Kuzin and Mamul (1951) and Kursanov, Krjukova and Vartapetjan (1952). *Phaseolus* plants, with roots immersed in C(14)-tagged carbonate solution or placed in a gas chamber containing CO_2, were found to take up C* and convey it up the stalk into the leaves. With roots immersed in water, the rate of C* supply through the roots was several times higher than that of the transpirational flow of water; in contrast to the latter, it occurred only in light. If the (green) stalk was illuminated, most of the C* was intercepted and assimilated there, before reaching the leaves. The absolute rate of CO_2 uptake through the root, observed in 9–15 day old plants, from an atmosphere containing 0.8–1% C*O_2 (a concentration common in podzol soils), corresponded to 3–5 mg. CO_2 per 100 cm.² leaf surface—about one fourth of the quantity these leaves can utilize if supplied with carbon dioxide from the air.

These measurements indicate the possibility of a substantial contribution of root-absorbed carbon dioxide (or bicarbonate?) to the photosynthesis of leaves, and especially of green stalks. This may be the explanation of the occurrence of chlorophyll in stalks, whose shape is unsuitable for the uptake of carbon dioxide from the air.

Kursanov (1954) summarized the studies of his group on the C*O_2 uptake by roots and its transportation and utilization in the plant. Chromatographic analysis indicated the conversion of the CO_2, absorbed into roots, to oxalacetic acid, by combination with pyruvic acid, and reduction of the latter to malic acid, which appeared as the first stable tagged compound; later, C(14), taken in through the roots, could be found also in citric and ketoglutaric acid. In the absence of enough light, a part of these acids, conveyed to the leaves, was decarboxylated there, liberating tagged carbon dioxide into the atmosphere.

(e) Isotopic Discrimination

The observations concerning the discrimination, in photosynthesis, between the carbon isotopes 12, 13 and 14 will be described in section 3 of this chapter (cf. p. 1927).

2. Other Chemical and Physical Factors
(Addendum to Chapters 1, 3, 12 and 13)

(a) *Catalyst Poisons*

Cyanide. The inhibition of photosynthesis by cyanide was discussed in chapter 12 (section A1). It has again been studied by Tamiya and Huzisige, Gaffron, Fager and Rosenberg, Calvin *et. al.*, Österlind, Whittingham, and by Brilliant and Krupnikova.

Tamiya and Huzisige (1949) investigated the cyanide inhibition in connection with a study of the inhibition of photosynthesis by excess oxygen (*cf.* section (*b*) below); they found that the effect of oxygen is weaker in the presence of cyanide (and vice versa). They suggested that cyanide does not affect the first carboxylation step (which they believed to be competitively inhibited by oxygen), but slows down a subsequent transformation (reduction?) of the carboxylation product. In support of this hypothesis, they referred to the observation of Ruben and co-workers (p. 203) that the cyanide inhibition of the dark carbon dioxide uptake requires as much as 10^{-2} mole/l. HCN; we will see, however, that a higher sensitivity was found by more recent observers. Furthermore, Tamiya and Huzisige believed that the inhibition of photosynthesis by cyanide does not depend on $[CO_2]$, and saw in this another indication that the carboxylation proper is *not* the cyanide-sensitive step. However, studies to be described below proved that cyanide inhibition *is* stronger the lower the CO_2 concentration.

Gaffron, Fager and Rosenberg (1951) measured the cyanide inhibition of the fixation of C^*O_2 by plants in the dark. They found, in $2 \times 10^{-3} M$ KCN, an inhibition of 86% if KCN was added in light, one minute before the darkening and admission of C^*O_2; an inhibition of 97% if KCN was added in light 2 minutes before the darkening and admission of C^*O_2; and an inhibition of 79% if HCN was added simultaneously with C^*O_2 in the dark. The uptake of C^* in the water-soluble fraction was particularly strongly affected by cyanide.

According to Calvin *et al.* (1951), cyanide ($3 \times 10^{-4} M$), added to a lively photosynthesizing *Scenedesmus* suspension two minutes before the introduction of $C(14)O_2$ (an addition that inhibits photosynthesis as a whole by 95%), reduces the $C(14)$-fixation in phosphorylated sugars much more strongly than its fixation in PGA, malic acid, and alanine—as if the most strongly cyanide-sensitive step in photosynthesis were *not* the primary carboxylation, but a subsequent reaction leading to sugar synthesis.

Whittingham (1952) measured the cyanide inhibition of photosynthesis in *Chlorella pyrenoidosa* at different concentrations of free carbon dioxide; the results are summarized in table 37D.IV. The pairs of values listed under $[CO_2] = 7.87 \times 10^{-5}$ mole/l. and $[CO_2] = 0.98 \times 10^{-5}$ mole/l.

correspond to different pH values; their identity confirms that only the concentration of free HCN molecules is significant for inhibition (as was suggested on p. 301).

TABLE 37D.IV

INHIBITION OF PHOTOSYNTHESIS OF *Chlorella pyrenoidosa*, IN SATURATING LIGHT, BY 3.8 $\times$ 10^{-5} MOLE PER LITER HCN (ONLY UNDISSOCIATED MOLECULES ARE COUNTED!), AT DIFFERENT [CO_2] (AFTER WHITTINGHAM 1952)

[CO_2], m./l. $\times$ 10^{-5}....	179		7.87		0.98		0.09
pH..................	4.6	9.4	8.3	10.08		8.3	10.6
% inhibition..........	7.2	49.0	48.0	54.4		53.7	82.5

Table 37D.IV shows the inhibition to increase with decreasing carbon dioxide concentration.

In varying the concentration of HCN, Whittingham obtained the results shown in table 37D.V.

TABLE 37D.V

EFFECT OF [HCN] ON RATE OF PHOTOSYNTHESIS OF *Chlorella* IN SATURATING LIGHT AND SATURATING [CO_2] (7.87 $\times$ 10^{-5} MOLE PER LITER) (AFTER WHITTINGHAM 1952)

[HCN],m./l..	0	1.9 $\times$ 10^{-2}	2.7 $\times$ 10^{-2}	4.4 $\times$ 10^{-2}
R...........	1.5; 1.4	1.5; 1.2	1.0	0.6
P (net)......	21.7; 20.6	−0.19; 0.0	−0.51	−0.52

Half-inhibition was reached, in Whittingham's experiments, at about 3 $\times$ 10^{-5} mole/l. HCN (in satisfactory agreement with the data in table 12. V).

Hill and Whittingham (1953)—similarly to Tamija, and to Calvin—suggested that cyanide inhibits, in photosynthesis, not the carboxylation reaction itself, but a reaction coupled with it, which, they suggested may be an oxidation. According to some recent evidence, (*cf.* chapter 36, section 00), the most likely mechanism of carbon dioxide uptake in photosynthesis is a reaction with pentose diphosphate, leading to two molecules of phosphoglyceric acid. Although the net reaction involves, in this case, no oxidation or reduction, it seems to require the presence of pyridine nucleotides (and thus probably involves a reversible oxidation-reduction).

Österlind (1952) made similar experiments with *Scenedesmus quadricauda*. The relative inhibition, (presumably in saturating light) was measured as a function of [KCN] at different pH and [CO_2] values (and correspondingly varying [CO_2]/[HCO_3^-] ratios). Fig. 37D.7 shows the effect between pH 6.0([CO_2] = 5.6 $\times$ 10^{-4} mole/l.) and pH 9.9 ([CO_2] =

1.5 × 10⁻⁷ mole/l.).   If, at the alkaline pH value, the concentration of HCN (rather than that of total cyanide) is used as abscissa, the curves indicate a consistent increase in inhibition with decreasing concentration of free CO_2 molecules (in agreement with Whittingham's findings)—apparently, irrespective of the amount of simultaneously present HCO_3^- ions.

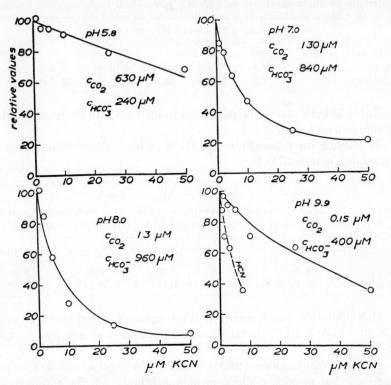

Fig. 37D.7. Inhibition of photosynthesis of *Scenedesmus quadricauda* by cyanide at various pH values and various KCN concentrations (Österlind 1952).   The broken curve refers to the concentration of undissociated HCN.

Österlind therefore classified the inhibition as "competitive." (This does not necessarily mean that HCN and CO_2 compete for the same enzyme; a similar kinetic relation can conceivably result also from mechanisms in which CO_2 shortage and HCN poisoning affect two *different* reaction "bottlenecks.")

As mentioned in section 1(a), Österlind hoped that experiments with cyanide could help to decide whether at high pH values, when most of the carbon entering the cells of *Scenedesmus quadricauda* is in the form of bicarbonate ions, these ions are used for photosynthesis as such, or first converted to carbon dioxide.   One possibility of interpreting fig. 37D.7 is to postulate that the reaction proceeds entirely through CO_2 molecules; however, a possible alternative is to assume that $HCO_3{}^-$ ions also enter photosynthesis, but their participation is inhibited by cyanide in a "noncompetitive" way (*i. e.*, in the same proportion at all [$HCO_3{}^-$] concentration).

Gaffron (1953) also found that the effect of cyanide on the photosynthesis of *Chlorella* is dependent on CO_2 concentration. The curves in fig. 37D.8 show that adding cyanide has the same influence as removing a certain fraction of carbon dioxide.

Brilliant and Krupnikova (1952) confirmed, on several species of algae and higher aquatic plants, an observation which Emerson and Arnold first made on *Chlorella*—that the effect of cyanide on the rate of photosynthesis in flashing light declines as the intervals between the flashes are prolonged. (These experiments have been described in chapter 34, section B3.) With some algae, addition of cyanide was observed to cause not only complete inhibition of respiration, but also oxygen liberation in the dark subsequent to a period of intense illumination—an observation which, if confirmed, may be significant for the identification of the cyanide "block" in photosynthesis.

Whittingham's observations (table 37D.IV) added another instance of cyanide affecting photosynthesis below the compensation point—as previously found by van der Paauw with *Hormidium*, but not by Warburg with *Chlorella* or by van der Paauw with *Stichococcus*.* According to Franck, the extent to which respiration intermediates can be utilized by the photosynthetic apparatus, depends on growth conditions and pretreatment of the cells. This offers a possible explanation of why different species (or even different cultures of *Chlorella*) have shown such a different response to cyanide below the compensation point: cells capable of using respiration

---

* It was suggested on p. 309 that the cells which show no cyanide-resistant residual photosynthesis are the ones in which respiration is as sensitive (or more sensitive) to cyanide than photosynthesis. Van der Paauw (personal communication) pointed out that one cannot quote, in this context, his data on *Hormidium* together with Gaffron's observations on *Scenedesmus*, since only one among his many experiments with *Hormidium* had shown an inhibition of respiration equal to that of photosynthesis; in all others, respiration was much less affected.

Concerning the stimulation of photosynthesis of *Stichococcus* in weak light by cyanide, whose reality was questioned on p. 309, van der Paauw himself had said that it "could not have been real." Since the enhanced rate of photosynthesis was calculated by using as correction the—strongly cyanide-stimulated—rate of respiration, he suggested that respiratory stimulation may disappear in light. One could hypothesize that in the presence of cyanide, respiration intermediates become more easily available for re-absorption into the cycle of photosynthesis (as assumed in Franck's interpretation of Burk and Warburg's experiments, *cf.* section 4 below), and that in this way respiration can be compensated with a quantum requirement much lower than that of true photosynthesis.

intermediates as substrates of photochemical "antirespiration" are not prevented by cyanide from doing so, since cyanide affects primarily one of the reactions through which carbon dioxide enters the photosynthetic cycle. (This is indicated by the several observations quoted on pp. 307–308, and by the indifference to cyanide of the Hill reaction.)

Whether the cyanide-sensitive reaction is the primary carboxylation itself, as suggested in chapter 12, or a follow-up reaction of the ACO_2 complex (as suggested by Tamiya and others) is as yet uncertain. (The

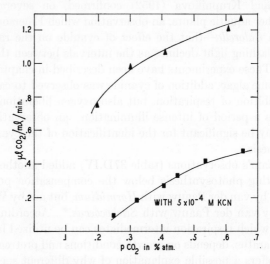

Fig. 37D.8. Carbon dioxide curves of *Scenedesmus* in the absence and presence of cyanide, in 2×10^{-3} M bicarbonate (determined with pH meter) (after Gaffron 1953, Rosenberg 1954). Suspension density, 0.5 volume percent. (Not corrected for changes in buffer caused by KCN.) Curves indicate that the $[CO_2]$-dependence is not a diffusion effect.

lack of sensitivity to cyanide of known carboxylases—except the "hydrogen lyase," which combines carbon dioxide and molecular hydrogen to formic acid—is an argument against the first hypothesis.)

Fluoride. Simonis (1949) investigated the effect of sodium fluoride on photosynthesis. (This agent is of interest because it inhibits transphosphorylation reactions.)

Previously, French (1946) had mentioned that the Hill reaction is sensitive to fluoride; but Warburg (1947) found no effect of fluoride on Hill reaction with quinone as oxidant. Simonis spread excised leaflets of *Mnium undulatum* on a metal net, covered them with fluoride solution and illuminated with white light (1.3, or 13 klux). Photosynthesis was determined manometrically. At 13 klux, one hour incubation (at 17° C.)

in 5×10^{-2} M NaF lead to marked inhibition; a similar treatment with 6.7×10^{-2} M NaF produced a 75% inhibition, while with 10×10^{-2} M NaF photosynthesis was replaced by photoxidation. Potassium fluoride had the same effect as sodium fluoride. The effect was stronger at the lower pH values—probably because of easier penetration through the cell membrane of neutral hydrogen fluoride molecules. The fluoride effect was considerably weaker (but still noticeable) at 1.3 klux. Respiration was not affected at all by fluoride in the concentrations used.

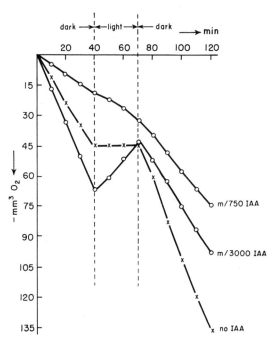

Fig. 37D.8A. Inhibition of photosynthesis and respiration in *Chlorella* by iodoacetic acid (IAA) (after Holzer 1954). 25° C., 18 mg. algae (dry weight) in vessel. Citrate buffer pH 5.4; 1% CO_2 in gas phase (Pardee buffer in side tube).

Simonis compared the effect of fluoride with the known inhibitions of photosynthesis by iodoacetate and azide (*cf.* p. 318, and below) which, too, are known to inhibit the formation of high energy phosphate esters. However, he recognized that the experiments do not prove that the observed (slow and only partially reversible) effect is due to direct inhibition of a photosynthetic enzyme.

The inhibition of respiration and photosynthesis of *Chlorella* by fluoride was investigated by Holzer (1954). The effect on both processes was about equally strong (the rate was reduced to one half by about 3×10^{-2} m./l. NaF); no evidence was found of the accumulation of oxidizable intermediates in light (as in fig. 37D.8B).

Hydroxylamine. Gaffron, Fager and Rosenberg (1951) reported that adding $6 \times 10^{-4}\ M$ hydroxylamine to photosynthesizing *Scenedesmus* two minutes before darkening and C(14)-tagging, inhibits the post-illumination

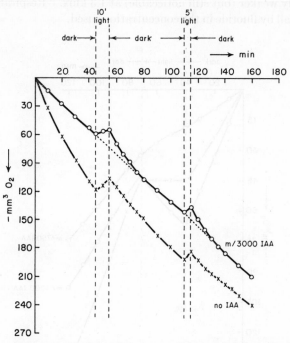

Fig. 37D.8B. Enhanced O_2 consumption following inhibition of photosynthesis in *Chlorella* by iodoacetic acid (IAA) (after Holzer 1954). 30° C., other conditions as in fig. 37D.8A.

C^*-fixation by about 40%; while $3 \times 10^{-3}\ M$ NH_2OH, added together with the tracer in the dark, have no effect. This is in agreement with the assumption that NH_2OH (in contrast to HCN), does not act on the primary carboxylation reaction, but affects the accumulation of the carbon dioxide-acceptor in light.

Calvin *et al.* (1951) found that given during active photosynthesis, $5 \times 10^{-3}\ M$ NH_2OH—which inhibits the rate of photosynthesis by 75%—affects more strongly the C^*-fixation in sugar phosphates (after one minute exposure to C^*O_2 in light) less strongly that in PGA, and least of all, that in malic acid. The fixation in glutamic, succinic, fumaric and citric acid is enhanced (not only relatively, but even absolutely) by hydroxylamine poisoning, suggesting, according to Calvin *et al.*, a reversal, by this poison, of the photochemical inhibition of respiration (*cf.* section 3 below).

Iodoacetate and Iodoacetamide. Earlier experiments by Kohn, showing especially high sensitivity of photosynthesis to these two compounds, were

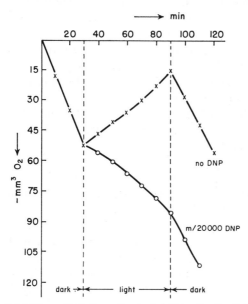

Fig. 37D.8C. Inhibition of photosynthesis in *Chlorella* by 2,4-dinitrophenol (after Holzer 1954). Conditions as in fig. 37D.8A, 20 mg. algae (dry weight).

described on pp. 318–319. In chapter 36 (page 1686), reference was also made to the observations (by Stepka and Calvin) of the effect of iodoacetamide on C(14)-fixation in light. These experiments, together with the observations (of Arnon, and of Holzer) of the effect of the same poison on the respiration of algae, were discussed in chapter 36 in relation to a plausible mechanism of photosynthesis, according to which the formation of PGA is followed by its reduction to triose, under the combined influence of photochemically reduced TPN (or DPN), and of ATP, produced from ADP and inorganic phosphate with the help of chemical energy derived from partial reoxidation of the reduced pyridine nucleotides. This reaction is catalyzed by triose dehydrogenase, specifically inhibited by the iodoacetyl radical.

Fraser (1954) found, as expected, that quinone reduction by *Chlorella* is much less sensitive to iodoacetate than photosynthesis.

Holzer (1954) described new experiments on the inhibition of photosynthesis and respiration of *Chlorella* by iodoacetate (fig. 37C.8A). He summarized them as showing an "approximately equal" inhibition of both processes; but the reproduced inhibition curves indicate (in agreement with Kohn's earlier data) a considerably stronger effect of iodoacetate on photosynthesis than on respiration. Interesting is the strong transient enhancement of oxygen consumption after a period of illumination in the presence of iodoacetate, illustrated by fig. 37D.8B; it seems to indicate rapid re-oxidation of intermediate products of photosynthesis (such as PGA), accumulated in light in front of the iodoacetate block. (However, no accumulation of tagged PGA was found by Calvin *et al.* when *iodoacetamide* was used as inhibitor of C(14)-fixation.)

A difference in the effects of iodoacetic acid and of its amide was noted already by Kohn, and attributed to differences in membrane permeability (*cf.* p. 319). Holzer (1954) reported that the amide (8×10^{-4} m./l.) inhibits photosynthesis of *Chlorella* at pH 9 almost completely, while leaving respiration almost unaffected.

2,4-Dinitrophenol. This inhibitor is known to uncouple the autoxidation of pyridine nucleotides, through the cytochrome system, from the production of high energy phosphates (ATP). Its effect on photosynthesis was mentioned on p. 319. Holzer made more systematic experiments on the inhibition of photosynthesis by dinitrophenol, first (1951) with relatively high DNP-concentrations in alkaline solution, and then (1954) with much lower concentrations in acid solution (acid reaction increases the concentration of the cell-penetrating, undissociated species of DNP). Fig. 37D.8C shows that photosynthesis is almost completely inhibited by 5×10^{-5} M DNP—an amount which affects respiration only very slightly. The observed effect is compatible with the hypothesis (Ruben, van der Veen) that photosynthesis utilizes energy produced by re-oxidation of a part of its intermediates—perhaps $TPNH_2$—by oxygen, or by oxidized intermediates such as a ferricytochrome; and that this energy is made available in the form of high energy phosphates, whose formation is coupled with this partial re-oxidation. Since the rate of re-oxidation must be, in strong light, considerably in excess of normal respiration, it is not inplausible that DNP inhibition markedly affects photosynthesis at lower concentrations than are needed to affect respiration.

"Vitamin K Antagonists." Wessels (1954) noted that the photoreduction of 2,6-dichlorophenol indophenol by chloroplasts is 50% inhibited by 5×10^{-4} M 2,4-dinitrophenol (*cf.* above), 10^{-4} M 2-Me-1,4-naphthaquinone, 6×10^{-5} M phthiocol, and 10^{-5} M dicoumarol-soluble substances related to, and known to act as antagonists of, the (water-insoluble) vitamin K. (This relation was first pointed out by Gaffron, in the study of the effects of these substances on photosynthesis and photoreduction in algae, *cf.* p. 314.)

Since vitamin K is known to occur in green plant cells, and to have a re-dox potential (about 0.025 volt) suitable for a Hill oxidant, Wessels suggested that this vitamin is the intermediate (often designated in this monograph as X), to which hydrogen is primarily transferred from chlorophyll by light (in photosynthesis as well as in Hill reaction). Wessels further suggested that vitamin K (which, like chlorophyll, contains a phytyl side chain) may be associated with chlorophyll in monolayers on protein-lipide interfaces (*cf.* chapter 37A) in the proportion—made plausible by

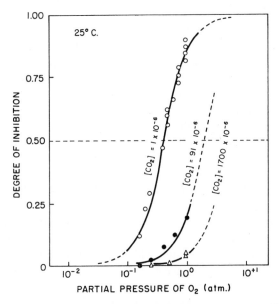

Fig. 37D.9. Inhibition of photosynthesis by excess oxygen at different carbon dioxide concentrations (after Tamiya and Huzisige 1949).

vitamin K assays (4×10^{-5} g. per g. dry matter in spinach, as compared to about 10^{-2} g. chlorophyll)—of one molecule vitamin K per several hundred molecules of chlorophyll (making it eligible to serve as Franck's limiting "catalyst B"). Partial reoxidation of photochemically reduced vitamin K by cytochrome (*c* or *f*) could produce high energy phosphates needed as "boosters" to permit the reduction of pyridine nucleotide by other molecules of reduced vitamin K.

The stabilizing influence of Cl^- and Br^- ions on chloroplasts exposed to light (mentioned in chapter 35, section B3(*c*)) can be related, in this picture, to a similar effect observed in photochemical destruction of vitamin K.

This hypothesis is mentioned here because Wessel's paper was not available in time for inclusion in the pertinent discussions in chapters 32 and 35.

(b) Oxygen

Inhibition by Excess Oxygen. Tamiya and Huzisige (1949) again studied the inhibiting effect of high oxygen tension on photosynthesis (*cf.* chapter 13, section A). Using *Chlorella ellipsoidea* in white light of 25 klux, at 25° C., they found fig. 37D.9 for the rate as function of $[O_2]$, with $[CO_2]$ as parameter. The curves could be represented by the quadratic equation:

$$(37D.3) \qquad \frac{P \text{ (inhibited)}}{P_0} = \frac{[O_2]^2}{K + [O_2]^2}$$

The constant K increased with $[CO_2]$, but appeared to be independent of temperature (4–25° C.). The oxygen inhibition was reversible. As mentioned on p. 316, carbon monoxide has no effect on photosynthesis; Tamiya and Huzisige therefore believed that the oxygen effect cannot be attributed to reversible binding of oxygen by a carrier of the type of hemoglobin. Oxygen—in contrast to cyanide—had no effect on the catalase activity of *Chlorella.*

Using the method by which Matsuyama and Hirano (1944) had determined the reduction state of ascorbic acid in *Chlorella*, Tamiya and Huzisige found that this state is not affected by changes in oxygen tension.

Tamiya and Huzisige interpreted the oxygen effect by assuming a reversible association of oxygen with the "Ruben factor" (as they called the carboxylation substrate, through which carbon dioxide enters the photosynthetic mechanism). To account for the quadratic form of equation (37D.3), the equilibrium was assumed to be:

$$(37D.4) \qquad 2O_2 + A \rightleftharpoons A(O_2)_2$$

Tamiya and Huzisige found the oxygen inhibition to be "competitive" with cyanide inhibition (*cf.* section (a) above). They assumed that cyanide does not affect the primary carboxylation step, but inhibits a follow-up reaction, by which the primary carboxylated product (designated by us as $RCOOH$, or ACO_2) is transformed into the substrate of photoreduction (perhaps phosphoglyceric acid). They argued that the "competitive" behavior of the two inhibitors (KCN and O_2) does not require that they act on the same reaction, but can be understood also if they affect two different links in a catenary reaction series. They derived equations for the separate and combined action of the two inhibitors, which could reproduce satisfactorily the experimental results. (That the problem of the primary cyanide-sensitive factor in photosynthesis is still open was stated above under (a).)

From the point of view of Tamiya and Huzisige's hypothesis, excess oxygen should not inhibit the Hill reaction in *Chlorella* cells. This conclusion should be checked.

Effects of Oxygen Deficiency. In chapter 13 (p. 326), a brief reference was made to Franck and Pringsheim's phosphoroscopic measurements of photosynthesis under anaerobic conditions. This study has since been published (Franck, Pringsheim and Lad 1945). The method used in it (quenching of trypoflavin phosphorescence by oxygen evolved by illuminated cells into a stream of pure nitrogen) is so sensitive that it permits detection of oxygen liberation by a single light flash. Many of the experiments described in this paper had been summarized in chapter 33 ("Induction Phenomena") and 34 ("Photosynthesis in Intermittent Light").

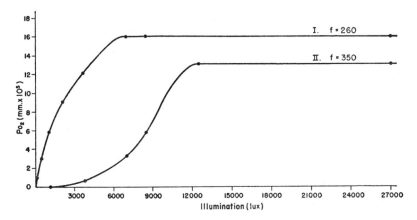

Fig. 37D.10. Anaerobic light curves of photosynthesis (Franck, Pringsheim and Lad 1945). The ratio of normal to anaerobic saturation level is designated *f*.

Working in a flow of gas permits measuring the weak residual photosynthesis going on under steady anaerobic conditions; Franck, Pringsheim and Lad have determined light curves of this residual photosynthesis in *Chlorella* and *Scenedesmus*, after varying periods of anaerobic incubation. These curves (fig. 37D.10) appeared similar to the light curves of severely poisoned cells, with saturation levels depressed by a factor of up to 10,000, compared to aerobic conditions. Saturation was reached at considerably lower intensity than ordinarily (*e. g.*, at 7 klux instead of 17 klux). As seen in fig. 37D.10, the shape of the saturation curves sometimes was changed from the usual hyperbolic type to a sigmoid one (commonly found in purple bacteria). When this change occurred—usually after an especially extended anaerobic incubation—the saturating intensity again became higher (occasionally, as high as under aerobic conditions).

Light curves of this general type were obtained with anaerobically pretreated cells of both *Chlorella* and *Scenedesmus*, in hydrogen as well as in nitrogen—despite the capacity of the second species for "hydrogen adaptation." The weak, but steady, residual photosynthesis was superimposed, in *Scenedesmus*, on photoreduction (the latter being protected from "reversion," which it usually suffers in strong light, by the continuous removal of oxygen by the stream of nitrogen). The temperature coefficient of the saturation rate, as well as the sensitivity to cyanide, were sharply reduced in the anaerobic state; the effect of lowering the carbon dioxide concentration also was much weaker than usual.

Contrary to the observations of Noack and co-workers (*cf.* chapter 33), anaerobically incubated *Scenedesmus* exhibited the same inhibition whether incubated at pH 6 or at pH 9.

One factor determining the effect of anaerobic incubation proved to be the density of the cell suspension. With only 1×10^5 wet algae per milliliter, three hours of dark anaerobiosis reduced the rate only by a factor of 10 at 20° C., and a factor of 2 at 0° C.—many times less than was observed with denser suspensions.

It can be concluded from these experiments that anaerobic incubation poisons a photosynthetic enzyme, and that the poison, produced by anaerobic metabolism, diffuses out of the cells into the medium. (It may be identical with Pratt's "chlorellin," *cf.* p. 880.) The occurrence of sigmoid-shaped curves can be taken as indication that two different poisons are involved, the second one affecting particularly strongly photosynthesis in low light.

Of the three enzymes (E_A, E_B, E_C) which Franck recognized as contributing to photosynthesis, the "carboxylase," E_A, does not seem to be influenced by anaerobiosis. (The temperature coefficient of E_A, is, according to Franck—*cf.* chapter 31, sect. 6—higher than that of the usually rate-limiting enzyme, E_B; poisoning of E_A should therefore impose a *higher* Q_{10} on photosynthesis as a whole. Furthermore, since E_A is the main cyanide-sensitive component, its poisoning should increase the sensitivity of photosynthesis to cyanide. The observed behavior contradicts both conclusions.) Inhibition of E_B seems to be excluded by the observations, (p. 1462) that the maximum yield per flash is relatively little affected by anaerobiosis (*cf.* chapter 32, section 4 for interpretation of this quantity as a titer of E_B). This leaves the "de-oxygenase," E_C, as the most likely object of anaerobic inactivation; the theory of the anaerobic inhibition thus becomes analogous to the Franck-Gaffron theory of the ordinary induction period (*cf.* chapter 33, section C4).

As to the additional, selective anaerobic inhibition of oxygen liberation at low light intensities, responsible for the sigmoid-shaped light curves, its cause was seen by Franck, Pringsheim and Lad in the formation of another "narcotic" poison, covering chlorophyll as well as the catalyst E_B; this poison is burned up by the "photoperoxides" formed in light, and this causes the yield to rise faster than linearly with increasing light intensity (*cf.* chapter 33, p. 1421, for discussion of this concept).

Experiments of this type support the conclusion—already enounced in chapter 13—that the inhibition of photosynthesis by anaerobic treatment is the consequence of slow metabolic formation of a poison (or poisons), and *not* of the necessity of oxygen for the functioning of the photosynthetic apparatus.   The latter view was, nevertheless, revived in the "new theory" of photosynthesis of Warburg and Burk (to be described in section 4 of this chapter).   According to the latter, the photosynthetic cycle includes a special kind of autoxidation, with a rate ten or more times that of normal respiration.   If this is the case, photosynthesis could not get under way in complete absence of oxygen.

Warburg and Burk's revival of the adage "no photosynthesis without oxygen," has caused Allen (1954; *cf.* Frank 1953) to repeat earlier experiments in Franck's and Gaffron's laboratory, in which algae showed continued photosynthesis under extreme anaerobic conditions (*cf.* chapter 33, section A6).   He found that the rate of photosynthesis of *Scenedesmus* in a nitrogen atmosphere containing $< 1 \times 10^{-9}$ part of oxygen can be as high as in air, after two or three hours of anaerobic incubation.   Even in the much more sensitive *Chlorella*, the rate remains unaffected by the absence of oxygen for 10–15 minutes, but inhibition sets in gradually afterwards.

The same study contains also extensive measurements of the oxygen produced under anaerobic conditions, by single, differently spaced light flashes, by photosynthesis and by quinone reduction.   These results were not published in time for detailed discussion in chapter 34, where they belong.

Brilliant (1940) observed that the rate of photosynthesis of *Elodea* increased with oxygen concentration up to 0.2%, and remained constant between 0.2 and 0.6%.

Isotopic Discrimination.   The relation between photosynthesis and isotopic composition of oxygen in the air, water, and carbon dioxide was mentioned in two places in Volume I.   In chapter 1, the question was raised whether the isotopic composition of atmospheric oxygen can be understood in terms of its probable photosynthetic origin; a hypothesis was suggested there according to which the relative prevalence of the heavier isotope O(18), in the air (compared to its content in oceanic water) is characteristic of a photostationary state, resulting from indiscriminate photochemical liberation of O(16) and O(18), and preferential fixation of O(16) in chemical oxidation (*e. g.*, by respiration).

This hypothesis presumed that *all* oxygen produced by photosynthesis originated in water—an assumption which is in agreement with the interpretation of photosynthesis as an oxidation-reduction reaction. Experimental tests of this assumption, reported in chapter 3, were of two kinds: Measurements in which O(18)-enriched water (or carbon dioxide) were used as substrates of photosynthesis (Ruben, Randall, Kamen and Hyde, 1941, cf. table 3.VI); and measurements with normal, isotopically equilibrated H_2O and CO_2, depending on the small difference in O(18)-content of these two compounds in isotopic equilibrium (Vinogradov and Teiss, 1941, 1947). Both types of measurements lead to the conclusion that the isotopic composition of the oxygen evolved in photosynthesis corresponds to that of water taking part in the reaction and is independent of that of carbon dioxide.

Kamen and Barker (1945, cf. also Kamen 1946) pointed out that measurements of the first type—with O(18) enriched water—are not entirely reliable. The rate of isotopic equilibration between water and carbon dioxide, which occurs via reversible hydration, e. g.:

(37.4A) $\quad CO_2{}^{(18)} + H_2O^{(16)} \rightleftharpoons H_2CO_3{}^{(16,18)} \rightleftharpoons CO_2{}^{(16,18)} + H_2O^{(16,18)}$

depends on acidity (cf. chapter 8, p. 176). In the interpretation of table 3.VI, the rate of equilibration was assumed to be that prevailing in the alkaline buffer medium, neglecting the possibility of a much faster equilibration inside the cells, where the reaction may be neutral or even slightly acid. The more convincing evidence of the origin of photosynthetic oxygen is therefore that provided by experiments with isotopically equilibrated reactants.

Two additional investigations of the latter type have been made since the appearance of Vol. I; and their results were contradictory. Yosida, Morita, Tamiya, Nakayama and Huzisige (1942) found that water prepared from photosynthetic oxygen (produced by *Elodea densa*) was 3.3 γ/ml. lighter than water prepared from atmospheric oxygen; from the known isotopic composition of atmospheric oxygen, and of oxygen present in natural water, it follows that photosynthetic water was about 3.5 γ/ml. heavier than natural (fresh) water. The Japanese authors interpreted this result as indicating that about one-third of the photosynthetically produced oxygen must have originated in carbon dioxide, and *not* in water— a result which they interpreted by the following equations ($\dot{O}$ is used to designate oxygen originally present in carbon dioxide):

(37D.4B) $\quad C\dot{O}_2 + 2\,H_2O \longrightarrow [H_2C\,(^2/_3\,\dot{O} + {}^1/_3\,O)] + ({}^1/_3\,\dot{O} + {}^2/_3\,O)_2 +$

$$H_2({}^2/_3\,\dot{O} + {}^1/_3\,O)$$

(37D.4B) $\quad H_2C\,({}^2/_3\,\dot{O} + {}^1/_3\,O) + {}^1/_6\,H_2O \longrightarrow H_2C\,({}^1/_2\,\dot{O} + {}^1/_2\,O\,) + {}^1/_6\,H_2\dot{O}$

Equation (37D.4B) describes photosynthesis from one molecule CO_2 and two molecules H_2O, leading to oxygen gas with $^1/_3$ of its oxygen atoms originating in CO_2, and a carbohydrate with $^2/_3$ of its oxygen atoms coming from the same source; (37D.4C) suggests that a secondary process dilutes $\dot{O}$, the "carbon dioxide oxygen," accumulated in the carbohydrate, by an exchange reaction with water, reducing the $3:1$ ratio resulting from reaction (37D.4B), to the experimentally found ratio of $1:1$.

It must be noted that the O-contribution to photosynthetic oxygen, claimed by the Japanese authors, is sufficient to account for only one-half of the "excess" $O(18)$ in the atmosphere (compared to water), and thus does *not* obviate the necessity of a special hypothesis to explain this excess.

The results of Yosida *et al.* were not confirmed by the measurements of Dole and Jenks (1944). In agreement with Vinogradov and Teis, they found that oxygen produced by various plants (aquatic higher plants, *Chlorella*, sunflower, *Coleus*) gave water which was similar to, or—more exactly—only $0.6-1.8\gamma/l$. heavier than the water from which it was liberated by the plants. The excess density corresponds to that predicted for the isotopic equilibrium (at $25°$ C.) between liquid water and oxygen gas. It could be therefore suggested that "photosynthetic" oxygen, produced indiscriminately from $H_2O(16)$ and $H_2O(18)$, is, after its liberation, equilibrated isotopically with water. However, this equilibration is known to be a very slow process *in vitro:* if it were catalytically accelerated in living plant cells the same final isotopic composition could result also from primary oxygen liberation from carbon dioxide, thus invalidating the whole method.

A satisfactory explanation of the isotopic difference between the oxygen in H_2O and in photosynthetically liberated O_2 remains to be given; but as to the amount of this difference, the smaller figure of Dole, Vinogradov, Kamen and their co-workers seem, by their approximate agreement, to carry more weight than the much larger figures of Yosida *et al.*

The discrepancy between the composition of the photosynthetic oxygen and of oxygen in the atmosphere, in any case, remains to be interpreted. The hypothesis of the photostationary state, referred to above, was tested by experiments of Dole, Hawkings and Barker (1947), who measured the isotopic composition of oxygen taken up from the air by soil bacteria. These organisms—which account for a large proportion of the total conversion of oxygen to water on the face of the earth—were found to discriminate in favor of $O(16)$, but only to an extent far too small to account for the excess $O(18)$ found in the air. Dole *et al.* therefore considered the earliest hypothesis, proposed by Dole in 1936, as the most satisfactory one. (This hypothesis suggested that an isotopic equilibrium between oxygen gas and carbon dioxide is established in the stratosphere, under the influence of ultraviolet radiation, at $-55°$ C., and is "frozen" when the gases descend into the lower atmosphere, where they are protected from ultraviolet light; the thermodynamic isotopic equilibrium at $-55°$ C., corresponds to an enrichment of $O(18)$ in O_2, which is somewhat short, but not too much short, of that actually found in atmospheric oxygen.

Dole (1952) found that the percentage of $O(18)$ in the photosynthetically produced oxygen in the sea is 0.2005%. On the other hand, measurement of the isotopic composition of dissolved oxygen in different depths in the sea (Rakestraw, Rudd and Dole 1951), were interpreted by Dole, Lane, Rudd and Zaukelies (1954) as indicating a fractionation factor of 1.009 in favor of $O(16)$ in the reverse process of oxygen consumption in the ocean (presumably by plankton respiration). This could account for a photostationary $O(18)$, concentration of $0.2005 \times 1.009 = 0.2023\%$ which is substantially less than the actual concentration of $O(18)$ in the atmosphere (which is 0.2039%). It thus again appeared that the "photostationary state" concept was insufficient to account for the $O(18)$-accumulation in the atmosphere; at the same time, however, no positive support for the "stratosphere equilibration" hypothesis could be derived from measurements of the $O(18)$-content in air at high altitudes.

More recent analyses of the isotope discrimination in respiration, by an improved technique (Dole 1954) gave, for certain objects (such as a species of fungus), discrimination factors as high as 1.02. This could account for a photostationary $O(18)$ concentration of $0.2005 \times 1.02 = 0.2045$—more than enough to explain the isotopic composition of atmospheric oxygen. However, it remains to be seen whether these new figures will prove applicable to respiration in general, including that of bacteria.

(c) Water Factor

Dehydration. Brilliant and co-workers have continued the study of relation between water content and photosynthesis (*cf.* p. 333), investigating in more detail the influence of the rate of dehydration (1943[1]), its duration (1943[2]) and its repetition (1943[3]). A summary of these studies, and of numerous other—to a large proportion, Russian—investigations concerning the influence of water content and osmotic state on the yield of photosynthesis, in land plants and aquatics, can be found in the monograph *Photosynthesis as Life Process of the Plant* by Brilliant (1949). Particular attention is devoted there to the occurrence, under certain conditions, of a yield maximum at a certain subnormal water content (*cf.* p. 333), to the dependence of the dehydration effect on the method of dehydration (*cf.* p. 335) and to "adaptation" of plants by repeated dehydration (Brilliant 1943[3]). Phenomena of this type are considered as evidence that water affects photosynthesis not as a reactant, in accordance with the law of mass action, but indirectly, by influencing the over-all state of the living protoplasm. This is undoubtedly correct (*cf.* p. 333) and is reflected in our treatment of hydration under the heading of "Inhibitions and Stimulations," rather than "Concentration of the Reactants." The implication that these effects illustrate the general fallacy of approaching photosynthesis from the point of view of physical chemistry rather than that of physiology, is an example of ideological "self-inhibition" which has weakened Russian research in photosynthesis ever since Kostychev had enunciated his "physiological concept" of photosynthesis in 1931 (cf. p. 872).

Effect of D_2O. In chapter 11 (section 5) the influence of heavy water on the rate of photosynthesis was described as similar to that of a catalytic poison (decrease in steady rate in saturating light, no effect in limiting light; decrease in yield per flash with brief dark intervals, disappearing as the intervals are prolonged, cf. figs. 25 and 26). These conclusions were confirmed by Horvitz (1954) who found, however, that with quinone as hydrogen acceptor (instead of carbon dioxide) the rate of oxygen production by *Chlorella* cells was affected by the substitution of D_2O for H_2O, at all light intensities—i. e., in this case heavy water acted like a "narcotic" rather than like a "catalytic" poison. To find out whether the effect of D_2O has anything to do with changes in the ionization of weak acids, the effect of pH changes on the rate of the quinone reaction in Chlorella also was compared in H_2O and D_2O. In this case the effect of heavy water was restricted to high light intensity. Consequently, the D_2O effect on the Hill reaction in weak light cannot be attributed to changes in ionization; its origin—and the reason why it does not occur in photosynthesis—remain to be explained.

(d) Inorganic Ions

pH Effect. The effect of $[H^+]$-ion concentration on the rate of photosynthesis (cf. chapter 13, section 2(a)) was again studied by Steemann-Nielsen (1952) on higher aquatic plants and by Thomas (1950) on purple bacteria. Steemann-Nielsen found that certain higher aquatic plants, such as *Fontinalis dalecarlica*, can survive, and photosynthesize at the normal rate, for several hours, at pH values between 3.0 and 10.5. Thomas, on the other hand, found a sharp maximum of bacterial photosynthesis (in saturating light) at pH 7.3 (in *Rhodospirillum rubrum*, in 0.015 M sodium butyrate). The effect of pH on the rate of the Hill reaction was described in chapter 35 (cf. p. 1600).

Ionic Inhibition Effects. Frenkel (1947) noted that endogenous respiration of *Chlorella* was only slightly affected by *uranyl* chloride, while respiration of added glucose was 80% inhibited by 10^{-3} mole/l. of this salt. No inhibition of photosynthesis could be noted up to 10^{-2} mole/l. UO_2Cl_2—a result that can be considered remarkable in view of the generally high sensitivity of photosynthesis to heavy metal ions.

Ionic Deficiency Effects.   The inhibition of photosynthesis by the deficiency of various *mineral salts* was described in chapter 13 (p. 336). It was pointed out there that, in certain cases, photosynthesis picks up very fast after the deficiency had been removed, while in others (particularly those of ions whose absence affects the formation of chlorophyll) the recovery is much slower.   One micronutrient of the first type—manganese—has been studied by several investigators.   Gerretsen (1949) found that manganese deficiency causes a reduction in the rate of photosynthesis in oats (*cf.* the observations of Emerson and Lewis, p. 338). He surmised that manganese is specifically involved in the oxygen-liberating stage of photosynthesis, and went on to study the effect on manganese salts on the oxidation-reduction potential of chloroplast suspension (*cf.* chapter 35, p. 1569).

Pirson and Wilhelmi (1950) found that manganese-deficient *Ankistrodesmus falcatus*, whose photosynthesis in saturating light had been reduced to one-third the normal value, recovered its full efficiency two hours after the addition of manganese salt.   This recovery was much more striking than that observed after the relief of potassium or nitrogen deficiency.   The photosynthetic ratio, Q_P, was the same in normal and in Mn-deficient cells.   The chlorophyll content (per g. dry matter) was, in Mn-deficient cells, only slightly lower than in normal ones.

Skvorzov (1952) found that addition of 3 mg. Mn salt to one liter tap water increased the rate of photosynthesis of *Chladophora, Elodea* and *Spirogyra*, in strong light, to 132–143% of controls; no significant effect could be noted in weak light or in darkness.   Higher amounts (up to 45 mg. Mn per liter) had no toxic effect (*cf.* fig. 34C, p. 341).

Stegman (1940) noted that *zinc* deficiency has a strong chlorotic effect on *Chlorella;* addition of zinc leads to rapid formation of chlorophyll.

Potassium (cf. p. 336).   Pirson and Wilhelmi (1950) gave new data illustrating the rapid and parallel recovery of oxygen liberation and carbon dioxide production in potassium-deficient *Ankistrodesmus* cells, upon provision of sufficient potassium, and prior to any marked increase in chlorophyll content.   Baslavskaya and Zhuravleva (1948) also found a strong effect of the removal of potassium deficiency on photosynthesis in *Elodea.*

Nitrate (cf. p. 339).   Pirson and Wilhelmi (1950) noted that the (previously described) rapid increase, upon addition of nitrate, of the rate of gas exchange in *moderately* nitrogen-deficient cultures, affects $\Delta O_2/\Delta t$ more strongly than $\Delta CO_2/\Delta t$, so that the ratio Q_P increases, 1.5 hours after the addition, to values such as 1.41, and only slowly returns to normal.   This indicates strong initial reduction of nitrate (as substitute oxidant either in photosynthesis, *cf.* p. 540, or in respiration, *cf.* p. 539).   With a culture whose chlorophyll content had been reduced 20% below normal by a more stringent nitrogen deficiency, addition of nitrate caused only a ve increase in $\Delta O_2/\Delta t$, and a considerable *decline* in $-\Delta CO_2/\Delta t$, so photosynthetic ratio rose as high as 1.8. The earlier assertion (p. that inhibition of photosynthesis by nitrogen deficiency is immediately relieved by nitrate supply, thus needs qualification: in case of *extreme* deficiency, "nitrate respiration" (eq. 19.1) may be the main or only effect, at least for several hours. No "nitrate photosynthesis" (eq. 19.2)—which would cause an increase in $\Delta O_2/\Delta t$—becomes apparent in this period.

It is mentioned in Pirson and Wilhelmi's paper that, according to an earlier study by Pirson (1938), the effect of nitrogen deficiency on photosynthesis cannot be rapidly relieved by a supply of ammonium salt.

(e) Various Organic Compounds

Dam (1944) found *vitamin K* in *Chlorella*, after having previously noted its presence in chlorophyll-bearing tissues, and relative rarity in nonchlorophyllous tissues of the higher plants. This caused him to speculate on the possible relation of this compound to photosynthesis. Of two synthetic vitamin K substitutes, menadione inhibited photosynthesis within 24 hrs., while dicumarol had no effect.

Freeland (1949) sprayed bean plants with indoleacetic acid, and other synthetic *auxins*. All—except β-naphthoxyacetic acid—diminished the (net) photosynthesis; all but indoleacetic acid temporarily stimulated respiration. The effect on net photosynthesis was in part—but not entirely—attributable to the increase in respiration.

Skvorzov (1950) reported that photosynthesis is stimulated by naphthylacetic acid in weak as well as in strong light.

Brebion (1948) and Gavaudan and Brebion (1951) compared the effects of *benzene, chloroform,* different *alcohols, colchicine,* etc., on photosynthesis, chlorophyll synthesis and certain physiological processes in animal tissues.

(f) Ultraviolet Light

The effect of ultraviolet light on photosynthesis was discussed in chapter 13 (p. 344). It was tentatively suggested there that 253.7 mμ photons attack an enzymatic compound—perhaps the CO_2 acceptor—rather than chlorophyll (since the latter appears intact). However, since the relative inhibition was found to be the same in steady and in flashing light (*cf.* chapter 34, p. 1465), and could not be offset, in flashing light, by longer dark periods, it appears that ultraviolet light must affect also (or exclusively) the enzyme (E_B) that we have assumed to limit the rate in saturating continuous light, as well as in saturating light flashes. (An alternative is to assume that each molecule E_B can operate only in conjunction with a

certain localized group of "reduction centers"—such as ACO_2 complexes—
so that "knocking out" a center leaves the attached E_B molecule "un-
employable"; cf. Rabinowitch 1951.)

Holt, Brooks and Arnold (1951) found that in *Scenedesmus* D_1, a given
dose of 235.7 mμ reduces, in the same proportion, the rates of photosynthesis, photoreduction (with H_2 as reductant) and Hill reaction (with quinone as oxidant). The dark oxyhydrogen reaction (p. 138) is much less
sensitive. Measurements with different cell densities (6.5 to 65 mm.[3]
Scenedesmus cells in the vessel) showed no difference in the extent of inactivation; since the rate of absorption (of visible light) increased with increasing density, it was concluded that ultraviolet light affects photosynthesis equally at all light intensities (*cf.* below for direct confirmation of
this conclusion in the case of chloroplasts). When photosynthesis was
reduced to one third of its full rate by cyanide, or to one-half of its full
rate by hydroxylamine, the effect of ultraviolet irradiation was proportionally the same as in normal cells.

Chlorella pyrenoidosa was found to be much more sensitive to 253.7 mμ
photons than *Scenedesmus* D_1. At a certain intensity of irradiation, the
rate of photosynthesis in *Chlorella* was reduced to 54% after 50 sec., 5%
after 150 sec., and to zero after 240 sec. of exposure, while in *Scenedesmus*,
the rate was 82% of the initial one after 150 sec., and 40% after 240 sec. of
the same irradiation.

Glucose respiration also was much less affected by ultraviolet irradiation
in *Scenedesmus* than in *Chlorella pyrenoidosa*. The exogenous respiration
of the latter was even more sensitive to ultraviolet than its photosynthesis.
(The *endogenous* respiration is relatively insensitive to λ 253.7 mμ in *Chlorella* as well as in *Scenedesmus*, cf. fig. 37D.11.) The curve of log R as
function of time consisted, in the case of exogenous respiration of *Chlorella*,
of two straight sectors, as if two different first-order inactivation processes
were involved. The capacity of *Scenedesmus* D_1 for colony formation was
also reduced by exposure to 253.7 mμ much more strongly than its photosynthesis.

One peculiar effect, noted in these experiments, was the enhanced
influence of continuous (as compared to interrupted) ultraviolet irradiation
on the rate of photosynthesis of *Chlorella* in carbonate buffer No. 9. (For
example, two 90 sec. irradiation periods, interrupted by a 20 min. photosynthesis period, resulted in an inactivation by 46%, while a solid 3 min.
exposure resulted in 78% deactivation.) No such difference was noted in
acid phosphate medium or with *Scenedesmus*, in either acid or alkaline medium. In the latter species, the inactivation was the same at low and at
high pH values, with interrupted as well as with continuous irradiation.

The log $(P/P_0) = f(t)$ curves showed a definite deviation from straight line, indicating a superposition, upon the main first-order inactivation process, of higher order effects, particularly noticeable at low exposures. Fig. 37D.11 (to be compared with fig. 36 on p. 345) shows this deviation, and incidentally illustrates once again the steadiness of endogenous respiration. With *Chlorella*, the solid exposure curves deviate from linearity much stronger than those obtained by interrupted exposure.

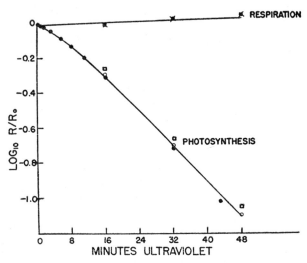

Fig. 37D.11. Inhibition of photosynthesis by ultraviolet light (253.7 mμ) (after Holt, Brooks and Arnold 1951). 20 mm.[3] cells of *Scenedesmus* D_1, 20% C. R = rate. ($\square$), Cells from fresh culture, in buffer No. 9. (O), same culture stored at 4° C. for 6 days and resuspended in 0.05 M KH$_2$PO$_4$ under 5% CO$_2$ in air. ($\bullet$), same culture stored at 4° C. for 7 days; resuspended in buffer No. 9. Interrupted exposures.

In isolated chloroplast fragments (from *Phytolacca americana*), the capacity for the Hill reaction (measured by the initial rates of oxygen liberation from ferricyanide solution, and by decoloration of phenolindophenol solution) also was strongly affected by irradiation with 253.7 mμ. It disappeared after 25 min. of irradiation. The catalase and the polyphenol oxidase activity of the same preparation was, on the contrary, unchanged even after 60 min. of irradiation; the cytochrome oxidase activity was down by only 12% after 25 min., and by 55% after 60 min. None of these three enzymes is thus responsible for the ultraviolet injury to the chloroplasts, nor is chlorophyll, since it showed no spectroscopic change after irradiation.

The inactivation of the chloroplast fragments was found to affect in the same proportion the rates of the Hill reaction in light of all intensities, posing the same problem as the above-mentioned equality of inactivation of photosynthesis in continuous and intermittent light.

Holt, Brooks and Arnold discussed whether fractional inactivation by ultraviolet irradiation means equal partial inactivation of all cells, or complete inactivation of a fraction of cells. *A priori*, it seems unlikely that a single hit can destroy the photosynthetic apparatus in the whole cell. The observation that, in *Scenedesmus* suspensions partially inhibited by 253.7 mμ and then adapted to hydrogen, reversion to normal photosynthesis in strong light required a longer time than in nonirradiated cells, supported the concept that *all* cells had been partially incapacitated (rather than that certain cells had been knocked out altogether).

In addition to *immediate* effects of irradiation, further damage to the photosynthetic apparatus results from slow processes, initiated by irradiation but not becoming manifest for several hours. These affect endogenous respiration as well as photosynthesis.

Redford and Myers (1951) also made a study of the effect of 253.7 mμ irradiation on growth, respiration and photosynthesis of *Chlorella pyrenoidosa*. They, too, found endogenous respiration to be insensitive (except for slight transitory stimulation) and exogenous respiration (supported by acetate or glucose), highly sensitive to ultraviolet irradiation (table 37D.VI). The inactivation of exogenous respiration was an exponential function of total dosage, intensity $\times$ time, and independent of the specific values of the two factors.

Photosynthesis after irradiation was found to remain constant for 30–50 min. and then to fall off (delayed effect). The rate in the initial, steady-rate period after irradiation was an exponential function of irradiation time, up to a certain limit, but showed strong deviations at higher dosages. As shown in fig. 37D.12, a certain dosage had a stronger effect if given within a shorter time (*i. e.*, at higher intensity).

TABLE 37D.VI

COMPARATIVE SENSITIVITY TO 253.7 mμ OF DIFFERENT FUNCTIONS OF *Chlorella pyrenoidosa* (AFTER REDFORD AND MYERS 1951)

Function	Relative sensitivity calculated from	
	Slope of survival curve	Time needed for half-inactivation
Glucose respiration............	1	1
Growth.....................	0.27	0.30
Initial photosynthesis.........	0.04	0.045

Frenkel (1949) compared the effect of ultraviolet irradiation on photosynthesis with its effect on catalase activity of *Chlorella pyrenoidosa* in bicarbonate solution. While 6 min. exposure to a certain flux reduced the rate of photosynthesis of a cell suspension to 50% of the original value, and an exposure of 11 min. brought it down to practically zero, catalase activity was about doubled after 6 min. irradiation, and increased eightfold after 11 min. It was noted that, after exposure to ultraviolet, the (not obviously altered) chlorophyll became subject to relatively rapid bleaching in visible light.

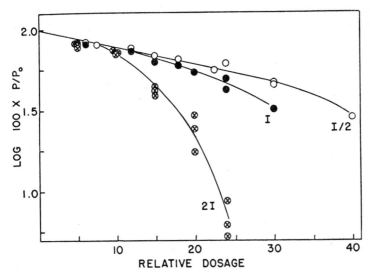

Fig. 37D.12. Effect of ultraviolet pre-irradiation on the initial rate of photosynthesis in 10 klux (Redford and Myers 1951). Dosage in minutes × relative intensity. 9 ml. of Knop's solution, containing 1.75 to 1.90 mm.³ cells/ml., plus 4 ml. fresh Knop's solutions, 5% CO_2 in air. I is the intensity of irradiation.

3. Photosynthesis and Respiration (Addendum to Chapter 20)

In chapter 20, the relation between photosynthesis and respiration was described as obscure and the data on this subject as contradictory. Since then, the relation has become even less clear and the data even more controversial. The experimental conclusions and theoretical interpretations now range from a substantial *reduction* of respiration in light (Calvin, Weigl), through *no general effect* of photosynthesis on respiration at all (Brown) to an *enhancement* of respiration by a factor of 10 or more (Warburg, Burk).

Warburg and co-workers made two studies pertaining to the relation of respiration and photosynthesis. The first one—by Warburg, Burk, Shocken, Korzenovsky and Hendricks (1949)—was summarized in Part 1 of Vol. II (p. 901). The finding was that, with a dense, strongly shaken *Chlorella* suspension, exposed to a narrow beam of light, respiratory carbon dioxide can be removed into the gas so effectively that switching the light on or off has no noticeable effect on the rate of CO_2 uptake by alkali in a side arm.   This was taken as proof that, with photosynthesis inhibited by lack of carbon dioxide, respiration continues at the same rate in light as in darkness; and that, consequently, it cannot be postulated—as Franck did—that respiration intermediates are drawn into the reaction cycle of photosynthesis when the carbon dioxide supply fails (for Franck's answer to this argument, see section 4(d) below).

Kok (1951) was unable to reproduce the experiment of Warburg et al.   In a mano-metric vessel with a center-well containing KOH-soaked filter paper, and a very thin layer of algal suspension in the main compartment, the rate of oxygen consumption was found by him to decrease even upon very weak illumination, indicating a beginning com-pensation of respiration (presumably by photochemical "antirespiration").

While these experiments indicated that, in the absence of photosyn-thesis, respiration was unaffected by light, subsequent experiments by Burk, Warburg, Geleick and Briese (cf. sect. 4(a) below) lead them to the conclu-sion that, when carbon dioxide is supplied, and photosynthesis thus allowed to proceed, an "extra respiration" occurs in light, involving the consump-tion of at least 2.8 volumes of oxygen (and the liberation of an equal volume of carbon dioxide) for each volume of these gases liberated and consumed, respectively, in "net" photosynthesis (meaning by this now the rate of gas exchange in light, corrected for *steady* respiration, as observed in an ex-tended dark period).

Because of the significance of these observations for Burk and War-burg's work on the quantum yield, they will be described in more detail in section 4.

(a) C(14) Studies

Weigl and Calvin (1949) and Weigl, Warrington and Calvin (1951) first used the isotopic tracer technique to find out whether the rate of respi-ration underwent a change in light.   For this purpose, plants (barley seed-lings) were exposed to a circulating gas mixture, ($N_2 + CO_2$), containing tracer carbon, $C^*(14)$.   The total carbon dioxide content was monitored by an infrared photometer (p. 852), the oxygen content by a Pauling mag-netic oxygen meter, and the content of C^*O_2 by an ionization chamber. The curves showing the change in specific activity, $[C^*O_2]/[CO_2]$ of the circulating gas as function of time, obtained in this way, appeared com-plex (fig. 37D.13).   If the nonphotochemical uptake of C^*O_2 by isotopic *exchange* (cf. chapter 36, section A1, 2) was neglected (compared to the up-take by *reduction* in light), these curves could be explained by taking into ac-count, in addition to the known rates of net carbon dioxide evolution in dark and consumption in light, two more factors: rate of respiration in light, and the discrimination between $C(12)$ and $C^*(14)$ in photosynthesis.   Additional complications arise, however, from the possibility of incomplete mixing of the products of photosynthesis and respiration with the pools of respiratory substrates in the plant and of photosynthetic substrates in the gas.

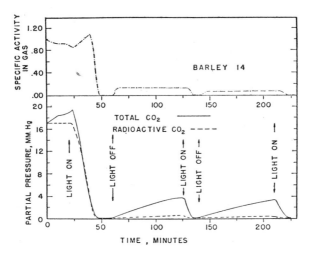

Fig. 37D.13. Time curves of CO_2 exchange, showing C(12)–C(14) discrimination in the photosynthesis of barley (Warrington and Calvin 1951).

From an approximate mathematical analysis of the specific activity *vs.* time curve during one dark-light-dark cycle, in which complications seemed to be least disturbing, Weigl and Calvin concluded that C*(14) was taken up in light at a rate 17% slower than C(12)—a remarkably strong isotopic discrimination—and that the rate of respiration in light was only one half of that in light. Weigl, Warrington and Calvin also inferred that the products of photosynthesis were not drawn into respiration as long as the illumination was on, but began to be autoxidized immediately after the cessation of illumination, in agreement with the conclusion drawn by Calvin *et al.* from C(14) distribution in the products of photosynthesis, *cf.* chapter 36, pages 1645 and 1666. As mentioned on page 1666, Steward and Thompson (1950) proposed another explanation of the C(14) findings. They suggested that, in light, the Krebs cycle is maintained (in green cells) at the cost of glutamic acid formed from proteins, rather than of pyruvic acid formed from sugars. The C(14) fixed by photosynthesis must then pass through the cellular pool of amino acids before it can be drawn into respiration.

A similar study was made by Van Norman and Brown (1952), using the mass-spectroscopic method of continuous gas analysis described by Brown, Nier and Van Norman (1952). *Chlorella* suspensions and barley leaf tissues were investigated.   The $C(12)O_2 \rightleftharpoons C(13)O_2$ exchange was found to be too large to be neglected.   In contrast to Weigl *et al.*, Van Norman and Brown found the assumption that light does *not* interfere with respiration to be compatible with observations.   Assuming such constant respiration,

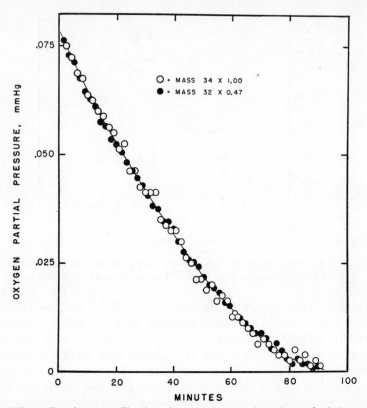

Fig. 37D.14. Respiratory utilization of oxygen isotopes by tobacco leaf tissue.   The tissue was permitted to consume oxygen until too little remained for accurate measurement (Brown 1953).   The two isotopes were used up in proportion to their partial pressures.   This result could not have been obtained if gaseous oxygen participated in isotope exchange with water or if respiration discriminated between the isotopes.

the isotopic discrimination factors for $C(13)O_2$ and $C(14)O_2$ (relative to $C(12)O_2$ as unity) were calculated to be 0.96 and 0.85, respectively.   The second figure agrees with Weigl's result (0.83).   It was unexpected to find the rate constant for $C(13)O_2$, not half-way between those for $C(14)O_2$, and $C(12)O_2$, but close to that of $C(12)O_2$.   Similar results have been reported for other chemical reactions, but the reason is as yet unexplained.

According to Buchanan, Nakao and Edwards (1953) the $C(13)$–$C(12)$

discrimination factor is in approximate agreement with theoretical expectation, but the high value for the C(14)–C(12) discrimination—first obtained by Weigl *et al.* and confirmed by Brown—is about twice that expected theoretically even for a totally irreversible (not to speak of a reversible) reaction; growth experiments of the same authors with *Scenedesmus obliquus* gave results in agreement with theoretical expectation for a partially reversible CO_2 uptake.

(b) O(18) Studies

The assumption that respiration is essentially unchanged in light was confirmed by measurements with isotopic oxygen tracer, O(18)O(16).

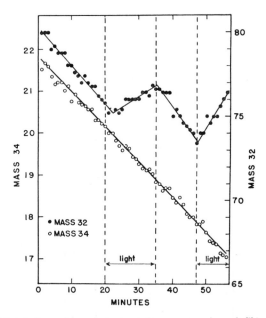

Fig. 37D.15. Metabolism of oxygen isotopes by a suspension of *Chlorella pyrenoidosa* in phosphate buffer in dark and in light (Brown 1953). Mass 32 (ordinary oxygen) decreased in the dark due to respiration and increased in light due to respiration and photosynthesis. Mass 34 (tracer oxygen) decreased in the dark and in light, due to respiration. The illumination intensities for the two light periods were different.

Plants containing only ordinary oxygen, O(16), exposed to air enriched in O(18)O(16) were found by Van Norman and Brown (1952) to consume O(18)O(16) uniformly through the dark and the light periods, while O(16)O(16) was consumed by respiration in the dark, and evolved by photosynthesis in light. These experiments give clearer results than those with

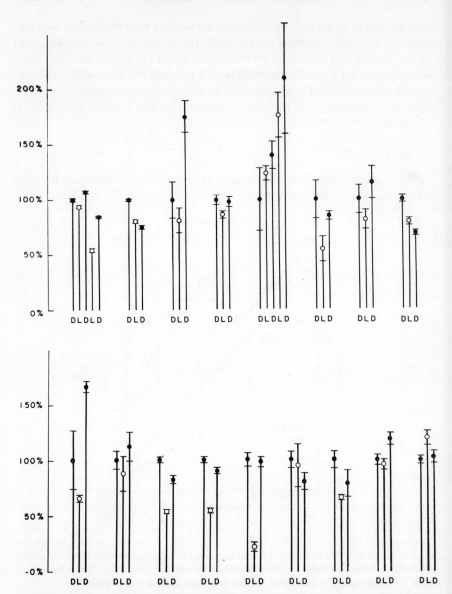

Fig. 37D.16. Seventeen consecutive experiments in the effect of light on respiration of one strain of *Chlorella pyrenoidosa* (Brown 1953).   Dark and light indicated by D and L.   Rates of mass 34 (tracer oxygen) consumption are plotted as closed circles (rate in dark) and open circles (rate in light), with horizontal lines indicating standard error. The initial dark rate is plotted as 100%.

C(14)O₂, because no isotopic discrimination is observed, and no isotopic
exchange (*e. g.*, of oxygen in O_2 for that in H_2O) seems to occur (fig. 37D.14).
In continuation of Van Norman and Brown's preliminary studies, more
detailed measurements of respiration in light were carried out by Brown
(1953). A representative experiment, in which respiration (consumption of

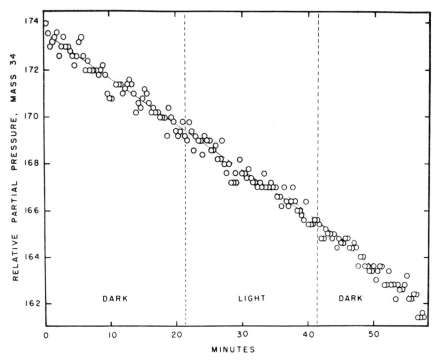

Fig. 37D.17. Tracer oxygen consumption by a *Chlorella* suspension (Brown 1953).
Cells harvested after 4 days growth. 160 μl. cells suspended in 4 ml. Burk and War-
burg's medium at 22.9° C. Red light; intensity near compensation. Oxygen, 8.4%.
Carbon dioxide, 0.8%. Background gas, helium. Data recorded at 20 sec. intervals.

O(18)O(16)) continues unchanged through two dark and two light periods,
is shown in fig. 37D.15. The results were not always so clearcut. Fig.
37D.16 summarizes seventeen dark-light-dark cycles (all on *Chlorella
pyrenoidosa*). It shows variations in behavior ranging from practically no
change (last experiment in the second row) to a 70% drop of respiration in
light (middle of last row); occasionally, a steady respiration increase, continuing through both light and dark periods (typified by the fifth cycle),
was observed. This trend could be, however, prevented by avoiding prolonged periods of anaerobiosis in the preparation of the suspensions. If, in

addition to this precaution, the cells were conditioned to the intensity of light to be used in the measuring period, practical constancy of O(18)O(16) consumption in light and in the dark became the general rule—provided the partial pressure of oxygen was high enough (and light intensity low enough)

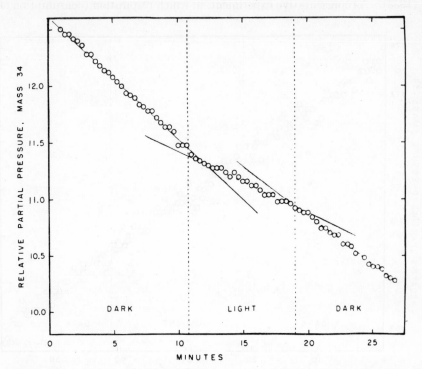

Fig. 37D.18. Tracer oxygen consumption by a *Chlorella* suspension (after Brown 1953). Cells harvested after 7 days growth.   300 μl. cells suspended in 5 ml. at 23.5° C. Burk and Warburg's medium. Red light; intensity about 3 times that giving compensation. Oxygen, 0.7% in helium. Data at 20 sec. intervals.

to avoid marked *dilution,* during the light periods, of tracer oxygen in the gas by the photosynthetically evolved O(16)O(16). Figs. 37D.17 and 18 illustrate the latter point, by comparing a curve obtained in 8.4% O_2, close to compensation, with a curve measured at 0.7% O_2, at three times the compensating light intensity. (Correcting for isotope dilution would restore the linearity in the second case.) Low oxygen tension, and high light intensity also increase the danger of incomplete *mixing* of photosynthetic oxygen with the oxygen pool in the gas. Re-utilization of photosynthetic oxygen probably has been responsible for the apparent inhibition of respiration by light in some of the experiments in fig. 37D.16.

Experiments such as those in fig. 37D.19 showed that, in the case of cells whose respiration is found increased after a period of illumination (a behavior typical of dark-incubated cells which have received a considerable dose of light), this increase takes place, not gradually over the whole illumination period, but suddenly, when the light is turned off. This confirms the conclusion of Weigl and Calvin that products of photosynthesis do not become available for respiration immediately after their formation. However, it seems implausible that this "protection" could remain in force

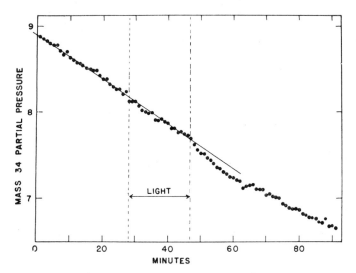

Fig. 37D.19. Time course of tracer oxygen uptake by a *Chlorella* suspension after Brown 1953). Knop's solution used for culture and experiment. Gas phase: *ca.* 2% $O_2(34)$-enriched oxygen in nitrogen. Data for $O_2(34)$ only.

indefinitely if illumination should continue.   Rather, one must assume that, after sufficiently long illumination, the photosynthesized materials will begin drifting into the respiratory metabolism.   It is, however, significant, that switching off the light accelerates this transfer.   Conceivably some enzyme (or enzymes), involved in it, are kept in an inactive (perhaps, reduced) state in the illuminated chloroplast.   (For a specific suggestion along these lines, made by Calvin *et al.*, see chapter 36, p. 1698.)

These experiments gave no support to Warburg and Burk's concept of strongly *enhanced* respiration in light.   Since it was conceivable that enhancement could only be observed in intermittent light, as used by Warburg, Burk *et al.*, Brown made mass-spectroscopic runs also with this type of illumination.   Fig. 37D.20 shows a typical result: enhancement is absent in intermittent as well as in continuous light.

Brown and Webster (1953) made a similar study of the blue-green alga *Anabaena*, in which respiration during 10–20 min. periods of illumination proved to be subject to much stronger changes in response to light than

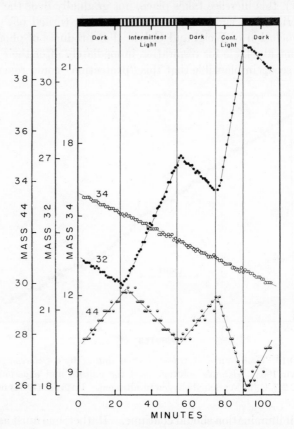

Fig. 37D.20. Oxygen and carbon dioxide metabolism of *Chlorella* in light and in darkness (Brown 1953). Cells cultured in Knop's solution. 110 μl. cells in 5 ml. *M*/15 potassium phosphate, *p*H 6.7, 20.9°C. White fluorescent light. Shaking, 195 oscillations per minute at 19 mm. excursion. Gas phase: helium, oxygen (isotope-enriched), carbon dioxide. Ordinates are partial pressures in arbitrary units. Total volume, 28.8 ml. To obtain volume (N.T.P.) of gas in milliliters, multiply by 13.4 for masses 32 or 34; by 18.5 for mass 44. Mass 44 (CO_2) value corrected for buffer retention.

was found before with *Chlorella*. These changes ranged from complete suspension of respiration in light to an enhancement by up to a factor of 2.5. The sign and extent of the effect seemed to be related to two factors: light intensity and oxygen tension (fig. 37D.21). Inhibition occurred in weak and moderate light intensity (expressed through the ratio P/R, to bring into a single picture data obtained with suspensions of widely differing density). At higher light intensities—the greater [O₂], the earlier —inhibition was replaced by stimulation.

The extreme inhibition observed at low [O₂] may be at least partially apparent rather than real, because of the possibility (mentioned earlier in this section) of preferential re-utilization of photosynthetically produced oxygen for respiration. No similar explanation is, however, possible for

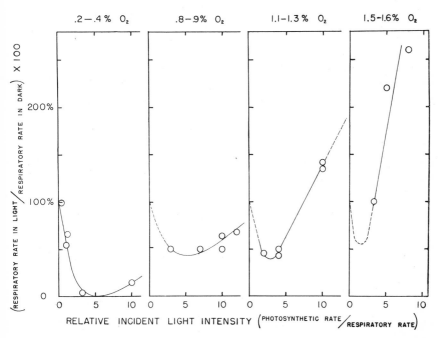

Fig. 37D.21. Uptake of isotopic oxygen, O(16)O(18), by blue-green alga *Anabaena* in light, in relation to light intensity and oxygen concentration (after Brown and Webster 1953). Illumination periods 10–20 min.

the stimulation of respiration at the higher [O₂] values. The latter may, however, be associated with photoxidation (which is more strongly [O₂] dependent than respiration, *cf.* figs. 58 and 59 in vol. I). However, photoxidation has been observed before only under the conditions of inhibited photosynthesis (*e. g.*, in absence of carbon dioxide). Another mechanism of O(16)O(18) uptake in light, in which Brown and Webster saw a not unlikely explanation of the apparently enhanced "respiration" of *Anabaena* in light, is the utilization of molecular oxygen as "Hill oxidant"—a reaction which results in no net chemical change, $(H_2O + \frac{1}{2}O_2 \rightarrow \frac{1}{2}O_2 + H_2O)$, but must lead to accelerated isotopic exchange between O_2 and H_2O, and will thus be registered as "oxygen uptake" in Brown's apparatus. We recall that the capacity of oxygen to serve as Hill oxidant (first suggested on p. 543 in vol. I) was made plausible experimentally by Mehler's experiments with chloroplasts (chapter 35, section B4(c)). The mechanism, suggested by Mehler on the basis of indirect chemical evidence, was confirmed by a mass-spectroscopic study of Mehler and Brown (p. 1565). Brown and Webster quoted an (as yet unpublished) investigation of Good, which showed this kind of "closed-cycle Hill reaction" to occur also in whole cells. There, is, however, no explanation as to why this process should occur in *Anabaena* more easily than in *Chlorella*, and why it should occur at all in carbonate buffers, *i. e.*, with an abundant supply of carbon dioxide.

Johnson and Brown (1954) used the O(18) method to confirm directly van Niel's surmise (*cf.* page 110) that light *inhibits* (rather than compensates) the oxygen consumption by (aerobic) *Athiorhodaceae*.

(c) Polarography

Polarographic respiration (oxygen consumption) measurements at 10 sec. intervals—*i. e.*, with a much better time resolution than is possible in manometry—have been carried out by Brackett, Olsen and Crickard (1953). Characteristic changes are illustrated by figs. 37D.31 and 37D.32.

Brackett concluded from these measurements that changes in the rate of oxygen uptake result from the superposition of several phenomena. If intermittent illumination is preceded by a sufficiently long period of dark (aerobic) incubation, respiration starts at a very low rate and increases logarithmically through the whole period of intermittent illumination. (This concept led to the interpolation of respiration during the light periods, shown by dashed line in fig. 37D.32.) During each dark interval, this main trend of increasing respiration is superimposed by a—also logarithmic—decline, which begins, however, not immediately, but only 2–3 minutes after the cessation of illumination. In consequence of this delay, the average respiration during the dark periods of intermittent illumination (with dark and light intervals not longer than 2–3 minutes) may be *higher*—instead of lower—than that during the light periods.

In addition to these two, relatively slow respiration trends, a sharp "gulp" of oxygen occurs in the first 0.5–1 minute of darkness.

The two main trends become clear only when the initial dark period had been long enough, and the "light dose" sufficiently large, as in fig. 37D.32. Without previous dark adaptation, and with smaller light doses (shorter periods, or lower light intensity) the fluctuations of oxygen uptake during the dark intervals, and its change after a light period, begin to appear irregular (although the O_2 "gulp" in the first 0.5–1 minute of darkness, and the maximum of respiration about 2 minutes later, remain recognizable in most, if

not all, of the plots). All "wiggles" (except the initial oxygen "gulp")
are smoothed if the cells are suspended in 1% glucose solution (+0.1 M
KCl) instead of in pure KCl.

Brackett *et al.* concluded that the uncertainty caused by the fluctuations
of respiration, may account for the "Kok effect" (*cf.* Vol. II, Part 1, p.
1113). If the respiration correction on every point is interpolated as described on p. 1960, this effect disappears (*cf.* figs. 37D.33 and 34) and the
calculated rate of photosynthesis (uppermost line in fig. 37D.32), becomes
proportional to light intensity and constant through the light period
(except for an "induction period" of 1–2 minutes).

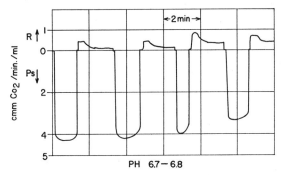

PH   6.7 – 6.8

Fig. 37D.22. CO_2 exchange by *Scenedesmus* in dark and in light, followed with a
pH meter, in saturating light (after Gaffron 1953).   Decreasing depth of the troughs
shows the decline in yield with decreasing CO_2 concentration (increasing pH).   Note
immediate return to the state of compensation after the switching-on and the switching-
off of the light, followed, in dark, by an outburst of respiration.

These observations of Brackett *et al.* show qualitative similarity to the
results of Warburg *et al.* in that they, too, indicate an enhancing effect of
photosynthesis on respiration, delayed by 1–2 minutes, and therefore "out
of phase" with photosynthesis in alternating light.   However, quantitatively the results are quite different, as a comparison of figs. 37D.30 and
33.6A will show (both of which refer to a 3 minute light–3 minute dark
cycle).   There is nothing in Brackett's broken lines resembling the bends
of Warburg's curves, on which the concept of "one quantum process" is
based.   Rather, Brackett's results confirm the conclusions of Emerson
and co-workers about the great variability of respiration.

Whittingham (1954) was unable to find, by spectrophotometry of the
hemoglobin-oxyhemoglobin transformation, any extra O_2 exchange by
Chlorella in light-dark cycles of 1–3 minutes.

While Brackett *et al.* registered rapidly the changes in oxygen uptake
immediately following a period of illumination, Gaffron (1953) did the same

with changes in carbon dioxide liberation.   Fig. 37D.22 shows a typical recording.   Its most striking feature is the practically instantaneous return of cells into the state of compensation after switching the light on; after this, photosynthesis sets in suddenly with almost the maximum rate. When the light is switched off, the cells again instantaneously return—for up to twenty seconds—into the compensation state.   This is followed by an outburst of respiration, during which the CO_2 production rate may be several times higher than the steady rate the respiration approaches later.   This "CO_2-burst" coincides with, but seems to be considerably more extensive than, the "O_2 gulp" observed by Brackett *et al.* (*cf.* figs. 37D.31 and 32).

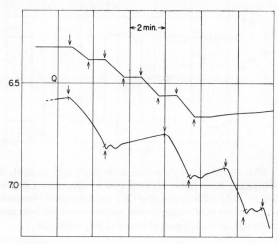

Fig. 37D.23. Carbon dioxide exchange (measured by pH change) of hydrogen-incubated *Scenedesmus,* exposed to alternating light and dark periods (after Gaffron 1953).   Photosynthesis begins at once at full rate.   Respiration gets under way after the fourth cycle, and characteristic induction effects in light and darkness follow its appearance.   The lower curve is the continuation of the upper one.   Ordinate is pH.

Fig. 37D.23 represents the sequence of events following the incubation of a *Scenedesmus* culture in hydrogen.   Upon switching on the (very strong and thus immediately de-adapting) light, carbon dioxide uptake starts at full rate without any induction loss, showing that the presence of oxygen is not needed at all to initiate photosynthesis (*cf.* section 2(*b*) above).   After four one-minute light periods, separated by dark periods during which no CO_2 exchange occurs at all, respiration gradually gets under way (at the cost of oxygen accumulated in the four light minutes).   As soon as respiration has developed, characteristic "wiggles" begin to appear after each illumination interval.   These include, in addition to momentary cessation of CO_2

exchange, followed by an outburst, also a secondary "wave"—first a CO_2 gulp, then a "burst." A short "compensation period" now appears also at the beginning of each light interval.

These experiments clearly show the complex course of the carbon dioxide exchange—and indicate that it is due to the influence of light on the respiration mechanism, rather than to the complexity of photosynthesis itself.

While the exact mechanism of mutual interaction of respiration and photosynthesis remains to be elucidated, experiments with tracer carbon, described in chapter 36, indicate that certain compounds, known to occur as intermediates in respiration (such as phosphoglyceric acid, and malic acid) also appear as intermediates (or, in the case of malic acid, as rapidly formed side-products) in photosynthesis.

Unless spatial segregation intervenes, these compounds should provide a cross-link between catabolic and anabolic processes— reservoirs fed both by photosynthetic CO_2 fixation, and by the Krebs cycle in respiration, and into which both the reductive processes of photosynthesis and the oxidative processes of respiration could dip. Depending on the relative rates of the two processes, this cross linkage may lead either to the reoxidation of intermediate products of photosynthesis, or to the utilization of respiration for reduction in light.

Imagine that a reservoir, situated midway on a gravity waterway (respiration), is also used as midway reservoir of an uphill pumping system (photosynthesis). When the latter pumps much faster than the stream runs down (*i. e.*, when illumination is strong), the water level in the common reservoir will be determined practically completely by the *uphill* movement of water; the situation will be reversed when the gravity stream is fast compared to the pumping velocity (weak light). If the stationary level of water in the reservoir as determined by pumping alone is *lower* than it would be if it were determined by gravity stream alone, strong pumping will cause the level of water in the reservoir to drop, and the amount of water running down from the reservoir to decline (*i. e.*, strong light will inhibit respiration). If, to the contrary, strong pumping causes the halfway reservoir to be filled to a higher level than it would have assumed under the influence of the downward stream alone, then pumping will increase the downhill flow of water from the reservoir (*i. e.*, strong photosynthesis will accelerate respiration). Similarly, in weak light (near or below the compensation point) photosynthesis (defined as the effect of light on the uptake of CO_2 and liberation of O_2) could be either increased or decreased by respiration, depending on the sign of the difference between the steady levels of the common reservoir as determined by each process separately.

4. Maximum Quantum Yield (Addendum to Chapter 29)

The "quantum yield controversy" was followed in Vol. II, Part 1, (p. 1104), through 1950, when Warburg, Burk and co-workers (1949, 1950) reported minimum requirements of 2.5–5 quanta per molecule oxygen for the photosynthesis of *Chlorella* in phosphate buffers equilibrated with 5% carbon dioxide. In most of these experiments, the yield was determined from the increment of gas exchange, caused by the addition (for a period of 5–20 min.) of measured red light ("bright" period) to unmeasured white background illumination ("dim" period). The beam was narrow, the suspension very dense, and the shaking very rapid, so that each *Chlorella* cell went through rapid and wide fluctuations of light intensity during each bright period, in addition to the slower alterations caused by the changes from "dim" to "bright" and back.

The ratios $-1/Q_P$ ($= \Delta CO_2/\Delta O_2$), derived from two-vessel experiments, showed no deviations from -1 (in excess of $\pm 20\%$) which would indicate "one-sided" induction phenomena (CO_2 exchange without corresponding O_2 exchange, or vice versa).

A methodological criticism of these experiments by Nishimura, Whittingham and Emerson (1951) also was reported in Part 1 of Vol. II (p. 1109). They concluded that the observations of Warburg and Burk can be reproduced, but that the method is of low precision and subject to systematic error. The magnitude of the latter could not be estimated, but its direction was that of an increase in apparent efficiency.*

One of the points in this controversy was the occurrence and relative importance of the "carbon dioxide burst" which Emerson and co-workers (chapter 29, section 1, and chapter 33, section 3) made responsible for some of the high yields calculated by Warburg and co-workers. Emerson and co-workers suggested (p. 1111) that when Warburg and co-workers found manometric curves without any induction bends, this was due to accidental, approximate compensation of the physical lag of the manometer by the carbon dioxide burst. It was important in this connection to check the reality of the burst by an independent method—if possible, one permitting unambiguous identification of the gas responsible for the pressure changes. Brown and Whittingham (1954) were in fact able to observe the burst, by mass spectroscopy, and identify it as due to CO_2-molecules. It was noted in both *Chlorella* and *Scenedesmus;* in agreement with Emerson's findings, it increased strongly with the partial pressure of carbon dioxide, and with the length of the dark period preceding illumination.

With 5% CO_2, the effect of the burst could be noted even in repeated (1 minute dark, 1 minute light) cycles. When cells were exposed to C(13)-

*Pirson, Krollpfeiffer and Schaefer (1953) supplied a thorough discussion of the reliability of the two-vessel technique, with equal and unequal volumes of suspension.

labelled carbon dioxide in the dark, the "carbon dioxide reservoir" from which the burst originates, was found to be tagged within a couple of minutes—even more rapidly than this reservoir is refilled after it had been emptied in light (a "pick-up" which has a half-time of about 5 minutes). It is unexpected for an isotopic CO_2-*exchange*—presumably, $RC(12)OOH + C(13)O_2 \rightleftarrows RC(13)OOH + C(12)O_2$, where R is an organic radical—to be more rapid than the *carboxylation* $RH + CO_2 \rightarrow RCOOH$!

Cyanide was found to affect the burst more strongly than photosynthesis; the inverse relation prevailed with *o*-phenanthroline.

(a) Experiments by Warburg and Co-workers since 1950

The studies of Warburg, Burk and co-workers, carried out in Germany after 1950, were mentioned only in a footnote in chapter 29 (p. 1113), and require more detailed presentation here.

Approach to Perfect Energy Conversion Yield. Warburg, Burk and Schade (1951) described improvements in the previously employed technique. A divided beam was used to illuminate the two reaction vessels

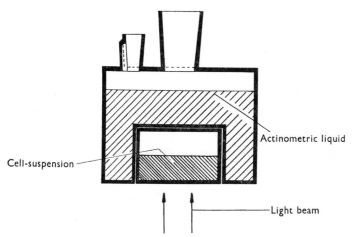

Fig. 37D.24. Actinometric vessel for measuring light transmission of cell suspensions (Warburg, Burk and Schade 1951).

equally and simultaneously, thus avoiding errors caused by differences in the time and order of treatments of the cells in the two vessels. Mixing was further accelerated (to 220 swings per minute); the vessel volume was increased (from 13 and 20 ml. to 20 and 30 ml., respectively) so that the smaller, as well as the larger, vessel provided adequate space for circulation of the liquid (7 ml.). Respiration was compensated by white light; it was believed that this reduces the uncertainty of the respiratory correction, because the respiratory state of cells maintained near compensation throughout the experiment should not be much affected by the relatively small increment in average illumination during the "bright" periods.

An interesting innovation (*cf.* fig. 37D.24) was the use of a reaction vessel (20 ml.) enclosed, from all sides but one, in a larger vessel (120 ml.) containing an actinometric solution (chlorophyllide, or pheophorbide, and

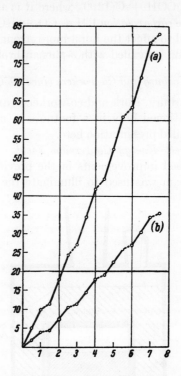

Fig. 37D.25. Pressure changes in two manometric vessels with *Chlorella* (after Warburg and Geleick 1951): (*a*) small vessel, (*b*) large vessel. Dotted lines, unmeasured background light, λ 436 mμ; solid lines, same plus intermittent green light, λ 546 mμ. 21% absorption, 0.9 μeinstein/min. Calculated quantum requirements for successive hour periods: $1/\gamma = 5.1; 5.2; 3.2; 3.3; 3.5$; photosynthetic quotient, $1/Q_P = 1.2, 1.10, 1.28, 1.01, 1.18$. Abscissa, hours. Ordinate, pressure change in millimeters.

thiourea in pyridine, *cf.* p. 839). This permits measurement of the light absorption in the reaction vessel, and thus determination of quantum yields of incompletely absorbing suspensions.

A new precaution was recommended in the preparation of cell suspensions—gentle centrifugation; it was suggested that too densely packed cells can be damaged mechanically during resuspension. It was reported that such damaged cells regain full efficiency after several hours of strong shaking (a treatment earlier described by Warburg as injurious!).

Quantum requirements of 3–5 quanta per molecule oxygen were found in these experiments with dense suspensions, low light intensities, and bright intervals of 5, 10 or 15 min. However, induction periods of considerable duration were observed, both in light and in dark, making calculations uncertain. With not totally absorbing suspensions, stronger light had to be used; the quantum requirement was somewhat higher, and showed a dependence on intensity and duration of illumination.

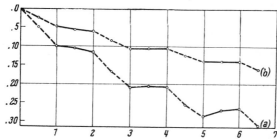

Fig. 37D.26. Same as in fig. 37D.25, but without background light (after Warburg and Geleick 1951). Quantum requirement in successive light period: 4.3, 4.3–5.2, 3.3–3.6; photosynthesis quotients $1/Q_P$ = 1.20, 1.20–1.10, 1.30–1.23.

In a companion paper, variations of the manometric method, employing one, two or three vessels, were described by Burk, Schade, Hunter and Warburg (1951). A new method was suggested for manometric determination of ΔCO_2 in which ΔO_2 was eliminated by an oxybiscobaltodihistidine buffer. The newly discovered "Pardee buffer" (diethanolamine), able to maintain a constant CO_2 pressure over nonalkaline solutions, also was used. None of these new buffers proved itself satisfactory enough to become a standard tool in the study of photosynthesis.

In experiments with all these devices, quantum requirement of about 4.0 (±0.5) were obtained, for "bright" periods of up to 30 min. and "dim" periods of up to 2 hours.

In some experiments, the respiratory quotient in "dim" light, $Q_R(= -\Delta CO_2/\Delta O_2)$ was as high as 1.26; yet, the extra gas exchange in light had a ratio close to 1.0, indicating, according to Burk et al., that the "light effect" consisted not in partial reversal of respiration (as suggested by Franck), but in the superposition, upon unchanged respiration, of a photochemical process with $Q_P = 1.0$. This was seen as further confirmation of the conclusion of Warburg et al. (chapter 29, p. 901 and this chapter, section 3) that respiration is not affected by light.

The quantum requirement rose to 5.5 when optically thin suspensions (20% absorption of incident light, measured in the vessel of fig. 37D.24), were exposed to five times the compensating light intensity.

Warburg and Geleick (1951) made experiments that lasted 7–9 hours, during which respiration was compensated by "background" light, and alternating, measured green light (alternation frequency, 1/min. or 2/min.)

was superimposed on it for periods of 30 or 60 min.   The suspensions were dilute, absorbing only 20% of the green beam.   An "over-all" requirement of 5 quanta per molecule of oxygen was observed at the beginning of the runs, declining to 4 or 3.5 in the subsequent hours (fig. 37D.25).

Similar results were obtained also without a respiration-compensating background light, but the rates were less steady (fig. 37D.26) and calculation had to be based on the comparison of light and dark periods immediately following each other.   Variations in the color of background light or of the measured beam had no effect.   The action spectrum appeared constant throughout the visible region—including 436 mμ, where carotenoids account for a considerable fraction of total absorption (in disagreement with Emerson's action spectrum of *Chlorella* in fig. 30.1).

These experiments were considered by Warburg as the first definite proof that the minimum over-all quantum requirement of photosynthesis is less than 4; 3.5 quanta was suggested as a possible true minimum.

The ratio $\Delta CO_2/\Delta O_2 = -1.2$, found in these experiments, was taken as indication that carbon dioxide was reduced only to the average level of glyceric acid ($L = 0.83$ according to eq. (5.13), p. 103, corresponding to $-1/Q_P = -1.2$).   Nevertheless, Warburg and Geleik used 112 kcal/mole as the energy stored per oxygen molecule evolved. This is permissible, because, as noted on p. 216, the heat of combustion of all saturated carbon-hydrogen-oxygen compounds is approximately the same *per oxygen atom* consumed (about 100 kcal/mole O_2).   The lower energy of combustion of an "under-reduced" compound (such as glyceric acid) is therefore compensated by the smaller amount of oxygen needed for its combustion.

The maximum energy conversion yield of 77%, reported in this paper, was raised to practically 100% in the next paper, by Warburg, Geleick and Briese (1951).   This boost resulted mainly from the unexpected finding that the minimum quantum requirement, as determined by the new procedure, was strongly dependent on *carbon dioxide concentration*.   A very high concentration (9–11% CO_2) was used before; it was now found that an optimum existed at 5% CO_2.   Another way to improve the yield was to substitute, during the measuring period (even if it lasted for several hours), distilled water for nutrient salt solution.   In water, the yield was high from the beginning, without the prolonged "induction period" seen in fig. 37D.25.

When these changes in procedure were combined with those described earlier—particularly, low cell density (incomplete absorption) and intermittent illumination—the calculated quantum requirement went down to about 2.8, corresponding to practically complete conversion of light into chemical energy (112 kcal:2.8 = 40 kcal; equal to the energy of 1 einstein of red quanta at 713 mμ, or to 95% of the energy of one einstein of quanta at 680 mμ).

The dependence of quantum yield on [CO_2] was found not only in acid phosphate media, but also in alkaline carbonate buffers. In fig. 37D.27 the crosses correspond to two-vessel measurements in acid media of varying carbon dioxide content, while circles are quantum yields derived from one-vessel measurements in carbonate buffer, with [CO_2] varied by changing the total concentration and the bicarbonate-carbonate ratio. The highest

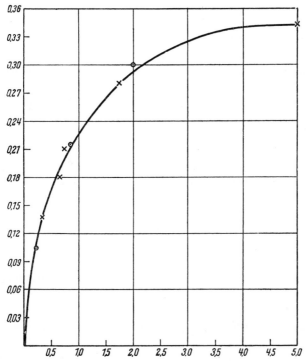

Fig. 37D.27. Quantum yield $1/\gamma = \Delta O_2/h\nu$, as function of carbon dioxide concentration (in vol. %) at 20° C. (after Warburg, Geleick and Briese 1951). Crosses, two-vessel measurements in acid medium; circles, one-vessel measurements in carbonate-bicarbonate buffers. Abscissa, % CO_2. Ordinate, γ.

conveniently accessible [CO_2] value in carbonates corresponds to 2% CO_2 in the atmosphere, and is reached in 0.2 M mixture of 95 parts bicarbonate and 5 parts carbonate. (The buffering capacity of this mixture is rather limited but sufficient for an experiment of several hours duration.) In this buffer, a quantum requirement of about 3.3 was observed, as compared to 9–10 in buffer No. 9 (0.1 M, 85 parts bicarbonate + 15 parts carbonate buffer, 0.2% CO_2). Warburg suggested that this explains why Emerson (and others) have never found minimum quantum requirements lower than about 10. However, this explanation does not apply to the results described in sections 1 and 2, in which Emerson and Whittingham found no dependence of the yield of photosynthesis in *Chlorella* on CO_2 concentration in the range 0.2 to 5% CO_2, in weak as well as in strong light, and obtained minimum quantum requirements between 8.8 and 8.9 (in 5% CO_2) and 9.0 and 9.5 (in 0.2% CO_2), according to Emerson (table 37D.3); and between 9.9 in 0.037 M HCO_3^-, and 10.7 in 0.26 M HCO_3^-, according to Whittingham (table 37D.1). True, Gaffron (*cf.* sections 1 and 2) found an increase in photosynthesis in acid-grown algae with increasing $[CO_2]$, up to and above 2%; but this effect was noted in saturating light; and the ultimate level of saturation was not higher for the algae showing it than for the algae grown in bicarbonate and showing no $[CO_2]$ dependence down to 0.2%.

The quantum yields obtained by Emerson, Rieke, and others, in earlier experiments in phosphate buffers equilibrated with 5% CO_2, also did not differ from those they observed in buffer No. 9, by more than 10–15% (p. 1095). Therefore, the reason for the contradictory findings of Warburg and co-workers, could not lie simply in different carbon dioxide concentration. Rather, it must be sought in the totality of the conditions used, including, in addition to high CO_2 concentration, also intermittency of illumination, and certain procedures in the culturing of the algae.

Warburg called these results "the end of a long road . . . which could be foreseen for several years, but was hard to reach." In Warburg and Burk's earlier paper (1950) the statement had been made that "in a perfect world, photosynthesis is perfect, too"; Warburg now repeated this assertion, implying that the anticipated perfection has now been experimentally reached.

Warburg, Geleick and Briese (1952) described additional experiments on the yield in carbonate buffers. Using a thin suspension, and compensating respiration with white light, they found, in buffer No. 9, a quantum requirement of 9 to 10 for added green light, in agreement with Emerson and others. In the "new buffer" (95 parts 0.2 M HCO_3^- + 5 parts 0.2 M CO_3^{--}; K^+, Na^+ or $K^+ + Na^+$ could be used as cations; Li^+ or Cs^+ proved unsuitable) the yields were much better. However, if cells were washed twice with this buffer before resuspending them for the measurement (as has been customary in working with buffer No. 9), the quantum requirement was found to be high, and rising with time—*e. g.*, 6.75 in the first hour and 11.6 in the third hour; in the fourth hour, photosynthesis was replaced by photoxidation. If washing was omitted, a quantum requirement of 3.95 was found in the first hour, and 4.25 in the fourth hour. The damaging effect of washing was attributed by Warburg *et al.* to bicarbonate penetration into the cells (*cf.* section 1 above).

Adding nutrient salts ($MgSO_4$, $Ca(NO_3)_2$) to the carbonate medium was found to improve the yield.

The decline of the yield with time, observed in bicarbonate-washed cells, was taken as evidence that factors other than the momentary CO_2 concentration can affect the rate in alkaline media. Therefore, the yields observed in a carbonate buffer with a certain [CO_2] value sometimes may not fall on the curve of fig. 37D.27; in particular, one might conceivably find the same (low) yield at *all* CO_2 concentrations. (This remark by Warburg *et al.* forestalls criticism which could be based on Emerson's and Whittingham's findings of the independence of quantum yield from carbon dioxide concentration.) Warburg *et al.* suggested that, whenever the yield in carbonate buffer is below the values predicted by fig. 37D.27, this is "a sure sign of progressive changes in the cells, probably, a diffusion of bicarbonate into them." Gaffron's experiments (*cf.* section 1) agree with these conclusions in that they, too, indicate that *Chlorella* cells may or may not respond to changes in [CO_2] between 0.2 and 5%, depending on the conditions of their culturing. However, Gaffron's measurements indicated (for strong light) an *early decline* of the rate with decreasing [CO_2] in cells conditioned to high CO_2 concentrations, rather than—as suggested by Warburg's observations—a *continued increase* of the rate, in these algae, with increasing [CO_2], beyond the saturation rate of the "bicarbonate algae."

The above-described results of Warburg and co-workers contradicted not only the quantum yield measurements of other observers (despite the assertion, made in 1950, that the quantum yield measurements have become so simple as to be suitable for student's experiments!), but much of the general experience in the field of photosynthesis—such as observations on the dependence of the yield on [CO_2] (chapter 27, and this chapter, sections 1 and 2) and wave length (chapter 30); the radiocarbon data (chapter 36); and the induction and intermittency studies (chapters 33, 34). Furthermore, the successive results, presented by Warburg and co-workers in the 1924, 1948, 1950 and 1951 papers, contradicted each other in many respects (*e. g.*, in the pretreatment recommended to obtain cells of highest efficiency, and the best conditions—light intensity, pH, intermittency, etc.—needed to demonstrate this efficiency).

If one nevertheless accepts all the reported observations as experimentally correct, one is led to the conclusion that, for each pretreatment, different conditions and a special schedule of measurements must be worked out to calculate the highest yields. These facts made Franck suggest in 1953 that Warburg, Burk *et al.* were measuring, in 1950–52, not normal, steady photosynthesis, but certain transient phenomena, which can be strongly enhanced by various treatments—including starvation, prolonged shaking, high carbon dioxide concentration, etc. These transient phenomena affect the calculated quantum yields most strongly if the cells are kept in an unsteady state throughout the measurement by exposing them to intermittent illumination. Manometric measurements of Emerson and co-workers, to be described in section (b), and polarimetric studies by Brackett et al., summarized in section (c) below, gave evidence of the actual occurrence, variety and long duration of such transients.

The above summary of Warburg's 1950–52 papers, as well as the review of the related findings of other investigators in parts (b), (c) and (d) of this section, have been written down in 1953. Since then, Warburg's long "road to perfection" proved to lead beyond the "end" he assumed to have reached in 1951. Two new unexpected vistas opened in 1952 and 1954, respectively. First, Warburg, Krippahl, Schröder and Buchholz (1952), and Warburg, Krippahl, Buchholz and Schröder (1953), described cultures of *Chlorella pyrenoidosa*, capable of many hours of sustained photosynthesis with a quantum requirement of 3–4, in steady light of an intensity sufficient to compensate respiration 30 or 40 times over, i. e., under conditions where the respiration correction (and the possible contribution of transients) are practically insignificant! Then, Warburg, Krippahl, Schröder, Buchholz and Theel (1954) found that a very small "photocatalytic" amount of blue-green light enhances strongly the efficiency of photosynthesis in light of other colors, fully replacing in this respect the (relatively strong) white "background illumination" previously used by Warburg et al.

Unfortunately, Warburg's description of the way in which the new, exceptionally efficient *Chlorella* cultures have been grown does not indicate anything markedly different from the ways such cultures have been generally grown in the past (unless growing at a window with northern exposure, and supplementing natural light with light from a xenon arc, has a special effect on photochemical efficiency). One procedure used in the new experiments, which may be important (although it, too, has not remained untested by other observers in the past, and was said by Warburg in 1951 to lead to poorer yields), was to measure the quantum yield directly in the culture solution (rather than in a buffer, or in distilled water—we recall that the latter was recommended by Warburg in 1951). Warburg et al. (1954) used either the same medium in which the cells had been grown, or a fresh medium, to resuspend the cells after centrifugation. The growth medium was distilled water with a complete assortment of nutrient elements, including vanadium (as recommended by Arnon).

Dilute suspensions were used in these studies, and the whole vessel was illuminated uniformly by means of a mirror shaken together with the vessel; the two procedures combined to give as uniform an illumination of all cells as possible, and thus to create the most favorable conditions for extensive linearity of the light curve. Nevertheless, it seems remarkable that this linearity was found to continue up to 30 or even 40 times the compensation rate (in other words, up to $(R + P)/R = 30$ or 40). Since the rate of respiration of the cells, used in this work, was given as about one volume oxygen per volume of cells per hour, their saturation rate of oxygen production by photosynthesis must have been (at 20° C.) in excess of 40 times their own volume per hour. (The more commonly reported values for oxygen production by *Chlorella* cultures are 25–30 times the cell volume per hour, cf., e. g., table 28.V, or Tamija and Huzisige, 1949.)

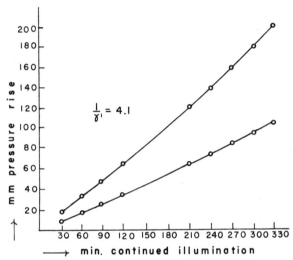

Fig. 37D.27A. Oxygen liberation by a dilute *Chlorella* suspension (initial absorption, 6.2%) (after Warburg *et al.* 1953). Upper curve: smaller vessel; lower curve: larger vessel. λ546 mμ, incident flux, 4.1 μeinstein/min. Quantum requirement ($1/\gamma' = 4.1$) calculated without respiration correction, at 18× compensation ($P + R = 18R$).

The (relative) absorption (10–25% of incident monochromatic light at 546, 578 or 644 mμ) was measured in an integrating sphere, while the (absolute) quantum flux was determined by the pheophorbide-thiourea actinometer.

The actinometer had a volume of 184 cm.³, containing 120 ml. liquid. A quantum yield of 1.0 was assumed to prevail in the actinometric reaction up to a light flux of about 1 μeinstein per minute. We will see below that a quantum yield of 0.7 had been given by Burk and Warburg in 1951 for an apparently similar 120 ml. actinometer, also with pheophorbide as sensitizer, between 1 and 5 μeinstein per minute; the reasons why the quantum yield was raised to 1.0 in the new experiments, were not explained.

As illustrated by fig. 37D.27A, oxygen liberation remained nearly constant for 4½ hours. During this time, absorption changed somewhat because of continuous chlorophyll synthesis; therefore, only the gas exchange in the first hour was used to calculate the quantum requirement. A value of 4.3 was obtained in this way for $1/\gamma'$, where γ' is the "net" quantum yield, uncorrected for respiration. In shorter experiments, with light intensity varied so as to overcompensate respiration by a factor between 5 and 40, $1/\gamma'$-values between 4.2 to 5.2 have been found, corresponding to (respiration-corrected) $1/\gamma$-values between 3.4 and 4.9.

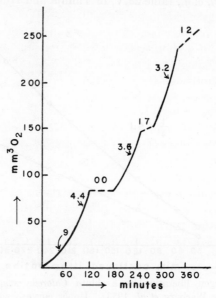

Fig. 37D.28. Effect of weak blue-green light (0.013 μeinstein/min.) on oxygen liberation by *Chlorella* in red light (0.73 μeinstein/min.) (after Warburg 1954). Solid line: red + blue-green; broken line: red only. Figures indicate net quantum requirements $(1/\gamma')$ per molecule oxygen at times indicated by arrows.

The photosynthetic ratio, $Q(-\Delta O_2/\Delta CO_2)$, was about 0.9 in all experiments, except a single one in which this ratio became infinitely large ($\Delta CO_2 = 0$) after the first $1\frac{1}{2}$ hours; this was explained by assuming deterioration of the cells in one of the two vessels, making the use of two-vessel equations in the calculation of $1/\gamma$ inappropriate.

The effect of weak blue-green light, illustrated by fig. 37D.28, was discovered by Warburg *et al.* as the result of inquiry into the differences in the efficiency of *Chlorella* cultures grown in daylight (supplemented by incandescent light) in summer and in winter; and into the—previously described—capacity of white background light to assure constant high efficiency of added red light (*cf.* above p. 1941). Warburg had suggested earlier that the beneficient influence of background light is due to compensation of respiration in the "dim" periods; now, however, it was found that much weaker background illumination than needed for compensation can suffice if it contains blue-green light. With the help of very weak blue-green additional light, hour-long periods of uninterrupted photosynthesis with a "net" quantum requirement of $1/\gamma' = 3.2$ could be obtained (fig. 37D.28), corresponding to a "true" quantum requirement of $1/\gamma = 2.85$; it was suggested that "from now on, it will be very difficult to obtain bad energy yields in photosynthesis."

As explanation of the effect of blue-green light, Warburg suggested reversible activation of a photosynthetic enzyme containing a carotenoid as active group (in analogy to the known reversible photochemical stereoisomerization of carotenoids in the visual cycle).

These new observations of Warburg and co-workers shifted the maximum quantum yield problem to an entirely new ground. Of their results obtained in 1950–52, the $[CO_2]$-dependence of the quantum yield could not be confirmed by other observers, and Warburg himself did not find it with some of his cultures; while all data obtained with light of intermittent intensity (with or without a constant background) appeared uncertain after Emerson's demonstration of the variability and long duration of transients. The results with the new *Chlorella* cultures are not similarly open to reinterpretation; if they prove experimentally reproducible, the controversy will have to be considered as settled in favor of the plant's capacity to convert absorbed light energy quantitatively, without any losses, into chemical energy, as suggested by Warburg. Even the most convincing physical objections against the possibility of such a friction-free mechanism will have to be withdrawn in the face of experimental evidence—if it was to be confirmed.

The "One Quantum Process." A second independent discovery was reported by Burk and Warburg (1950). As mentioned in section 3, an extraordinary strong interaction of photosynthesis with respiration was found in these experiments. Specifically, in the first minute after return into darkness (or dim light), of cells exposed for a minute to strong illumination, the rate of oxygen consumption was observed to be up to twelve times the steady rate of respiration; as a corollary, a quantum yield approaching unity was observed for the additional oxygen exchange during the (also one-minute long) "bright" periods.

This previously unsuspected interaction of respiration and photosynthesis could be discovered in these experiments, according to Burk and Warburg, because of the use of much higher light intensity (2 μeinsteins per minute in a narrow light pencil), and of shorter intervals of measurement. High intensity naturally enhances the light effect, and minute-to-minute measurements reveal transient changes that had remained concealed in the earlier studies (where 5 minute light-5 minute dark was the shortest cycle used). Some doubts can be entertained concerning the reliability of minute-to-minute measurements because of the physical lag in the response of the manometer, and of its insufficient precision. (Simple, not differential, manometers were used, so that the pressure changes, which were of the order of 1 mm. per minute, could be read only to ± 0.5 mm.) Burk and Warburg believed (*cf.* p. 1104) that strong shaking eliminated all instrumental lag; and that repetition of measurements assured sufficient reliability of the average.

These experiments were described in more detail in a second paper (Burk and Warburg 1951). The light beam from a high-pressure mercury or cadmium lamp, made monochromatic by filters, was divided into two beams by four totally reflecting prisms. Each beam had an intensity of 2–3 μeinsteins per minute. They were tested for equality by the Warburg-Schocken actinometer, and for equal absorption in the two vessels, by comparing the yields of photosynthesis produced in both of them when they were filled with carbonate buffer. Absolute intensity was checked by a bolometer.

The quantum yield of the actinometer was now found to be significantly smaller than 1 (0.69–0.86), even at low light intensities (*cf.* p. 839 for the different earlier findings of Warburg and Schocken). Addition of piperidine (6 mg. in 7 ml.), increased this yield to 0.82–1.03 (for beam intensities from 0.05 to 1 μeinstein per minute). With ethyl pheophorbide as sensitizer, and a larger actinometer vessel (120 ml.), the quantum yield was remarkably constant—about 0.70—between 1 and 5 μeinstein per minute; this system was recommended for future use (*cf.*, however, p. 1949!).

The quantum requirement of photosynthesis in alternating light (1 minute dark-1 minute light) was found to be as high as 7 in carbonate buffer No. 9 (*p*H 9.4); but in phosphate buffer (*p*H 4.5, 10% CO_2, *cf.* below), it went down to close to unity.

In a typical experiment in phosphate buffer, the pressure in the large vessel changed by 0 to 0.5 mm. in 1.5 min. light periods (green light, λ 546 mμ), and by -0.5 mm. during 1.5 min. dark periods; in the smaller vessel, the changes were by $+1.5$ to -2.0 mm. in the light periods, and -2.0 mm. in the dark periods. Adding together the effects of six light periods, and of six dark periods, and subtracting the second sum from the first, a quantum requirement of 1.27, and a $-1/Q_P$ value of 1.15 were calculated.

With slower alternations, the quantum requirement increased from 1.27 (1.5 min. periods) to 1.4 (2.5 min. periods), 4.1 (5 min. periods) and 5.3 (7.5 min. periods); the ratio $(-1/Q_P)$ declined, in the same series, from 1.15 to 0.97. The gas exchange in the dark declined with decreasing frequency of alternations, in the same proportion as that in light. With the shortest periods used, the oxygen consumption in the dark periods was about 12 times the steady respiration rate.

In experiments in which unmeasured, white background light compensated respiration, and a measured green beam (546 mμ) was added for one minute at one minute intervals, the differences between the total gas exchanges in the two vessels in 20 dark periods and 20 light periods, corresponded to a requirement of 1.29 quanta per molecule oxygen, and to a ratio $-\Delta CO_2/\Delta O_2 = 1.29$. In a similar experiment with a measured blue beam (436 mμ), the requirement was 1.15 quanta per oxygen molecule, and 1.0 quanta per CO_2 molecule. A similar result was obtained with red cadmium light, λ 644 mμ, superimposed on compensating white illumination.

When the gas exchange in continuous white light (steady respiration + steady photosynthesis) was subtracted from the net gas exchange in an equal period of alternating light, an over-all quantum requirement of 3–5 quanta per oxygen molecule was calculated for the additional light, in agreement with the earlier results of Warburg and Burk. (The rate of gas exchange in the background light was found in these experiments to be the same before and after a period of additional alternating illumination, thus making the calculation unambiguous.)

The conclusion Warburg and co-workers drew from these observations was that the light process in photosynthesis can be separated from the dark process by minute-to-minute alternations of light intensity. At the beginning of the light periods, oxygen is liberated and carbon dioxide is absorbed (in equal amounts), with a quantum requirement of only one quantum per molecule ("one-quantum process of photosynthesis"). Since the energy of 1 red quantum (40–45 kcal) is insufficient to bring about the elementary process of photosynthesis (which requires 112 kcal), Warburg suggested that the extra "respiration" which develops after a minute or two of exposure to light and is carried over into the first minute or two of darkness, re-oxidizes two thirds of the carbohydrates (or other photosynthetic products) synthesized in light, and that the energy of this autoxidation is stored in an unknown chemical compound. The latter thus becomes able to reduce one molecule of carbon dioxide to carbohydrate, and to oxidize one molecule of water to oxygen, with the help of a single additional light quantum. This concept Warburg, Burk et al. called the "new theory of photosynthesis."

It is misleading to refer to the suggested mechanism as "one-quantum mechanism of photosynthesis." The minimum quantum requirement, according to Warburg, Burk et al. is 2.8, not 1. That the energy of one quantum is used in a way different from that in which the energy of the other 1.8 quanta is used, does not change the fact that the combined action of 2.8 quanta is needed to achieve complete photosynthesis. It has been suggested by many before Warburg that, in photosynthesis, the energy of several quanta is brought to bear on a single molecule of carbon dioxide (or water) by reversing one part of the primary photochemical processes and utilizing the liberated chemical energy to "promote" the reducing (or oxidizing) power of the remaining primary photochemical products. This was called "energy dismutation" in chapters 7 and 9. (Ruben, and van der Veen, *cf.* p. 1116, suggested more specifically that the chemical energy, obtained by reversal of the primary photochemical processes, is stored for subsequent use in phosphate bonds.)

New in Warburg and Burk's theory was *first*, the concept that the energy-storing back reaction is so slow that it can be substantially separated from the photochemical forward reactions by light intermittency with a frequency as low as 1 min.$^{-1}$; and, *second*, that the back reaction involves molecular oxygen, in other words, that it is a form of complete respiration, and not the reversal of one or several intermediate oxidation-reduction steps in photosynthesis (which would not be detectable by manometry).

Warburg *et al.* supported their hypothesis by reference to the inhibition of photosynthesis by absence of oxygen; however, we have seen (*cf.* section 2(*b*) above) that anaerobic conditions prevent photosynthesis only if, during the dark period, fermentation has taken place, and poisonous products have accumulated.

Warburg, Geleick and Briese (1951) listed the following conditions as important for the successful separation of the photochemical and the dark reaction: (*1*) precompensation of respiration by background light, "making certain that any decrease of pressure in the dim period must be due to back reactions of photosynthesis," (*2*) low density of the cell suspension, and (*3*) intermittency of illumination. Warburg *et al.* noted that the type of intermittency at which photosynthesis appeared most clearly separable into its component reactions was the one known to be least favorable for the *growth* of algae—1 minute light-1 minute dark (*cf.* fig. 34.2) but suggested no explanation of this peculiar relation. The situation appears even stranger if one recalls that this type of intermittency has been found (*cf.* fig. 34.4) to give also the lowest over-all yield of *photosynthesis* (in moderately strong light).

The "photosynthetic back reaction" decays in the dark, according to Warburg *et al.*, in about three minutes; a 3 minute "bright" + 3 minute "dim" cycle was therefore chosen to study this process in more detail. Fig. 33.6A represents such a cycle (with points obtained by averaging corresponding on-the-minute readings from ten cycles). In this particular case, with $[CO_2] = 11\%$, and 100 mm.^{3} of cells in the vessel, the over-all quantum requirement for the whole cycle was 5.1. Warburg *et al.* converted this figure into a "minimum requirement" (to be expected at 5% CO_2), by means of the previously determined curve $\gamma = f[CO_2]$ (of which the beginning is shown in fig. 37D.27), and obtained in this way a value of 3.8; with 22 mm.^{3} cells in the same vessels, the similarly calculated minimum over-all requirement was 2.7 to 2.8—the smallest thermochemically possible value. After a "bright" period of 30 min., the change in the rate of oxygen consumption in the first 3 min. of "dimness" was the same as that observed in the first 3 min. of "dark" after 3 min. of "light."

The minimum quantum requirement for oxygen liberation *at the beginning of a light period*—calculated from the initial slope of the curve in fig. 33.6A—was the same (about 1.0) for carbon dioxide concentrations between 5 and 50%; however, the oxygen loss in the back-reaction became "larger than needed" above 5% CO_2, thus causing a decline in the over-all quantum yield. The oxygen gulp after an illumination period took the same *time* (3 min.) at the higher CO_2 pressures as at 5% CO_2, but the *amount* of oxygen consumed in this gulp was larger. At 50% CO_2, the net gain in the cycle was down to zero.

The back-reaction appeared to be much faster in alkaline media; at least, no oxygen gulp could be observed in carbonate buffers, even those that gave an over-all quantum requirement of about 3.0 (0.1 N bicarbonate saturated with 10% CO_2, pH 7.7; or 0.2 N bicarbonate saturated with 2% CO_2, pH 8.9). However, Burk (1952) reported that, using *Chlamidomonas*, he was able to observe the separation of the two reaction stages also in alkaline buffers.

Assuming a first order back-reaction, Warburg and co-workers derived the equation:

(37D.5) $$\Delta O_2/\Delta t = A(1 - \epsilon)t + \epsilon A(1 - \epsilon^{-kt})/k$$

for the rate of net oxygen liberation, with A designating the number of absorbed einsteins of light, ϵ the oxygen fraction that reacts back, and k the rate constant of the back-reaction. When $\epsilon = 1$ (as in 50% CO_2), no net oxygen production occurs.

The experiments of other observers on the relation of photosynthesis and respiration, summarized in section 3 of this chapter—in particular, the unambiguous mass-spectroscopic data—taken in conjunction with the observations of transients by Emerson *et al.* (described in chapter 33, section 2 and in section (*b*) below) and by Brackett *et al.* (*cf.* section 3 above, and section 4(*c*) below), and with the newly confirmed capacity of algae to photosynthesize under completely anaerobic conditions (referred to in section 2(*b*) above), leave little doubt that Warburg and Burk's "one quantum process" is an unwarranted generalization of arbitrarily selected data. It needs hardly to be repeated that this criticism does not apply to the concepts of a single primary photochemical process, and of energy-supplying dark back reactions in photosynthesis as such (both concepts antedate the investigations of Warburg and Burk, and have been made increasingly plausible by recent biochemical studies), but only to the specific form these concepts were given by Warburg and Burk (including the slowness of the energy-supplying back reaction, permitting its separation from the light reaction by one minute light-one minute dark cycles, and the participation of molecular oxygen in this reaction).

(b) Other New Manometric Measurements

In tables 37D.I and 37D.III were listed the quantum requirements found by Whittingham, and Emerson, respectively, with *Chlorella pyrenoidosa*, while looking into the possible effect of bicarbonate concentration (table 37D.I) and carbon dioxide concentration (table 37D.II) on the yield. Whittingham found $1/\gamma = 9.9 - 11.5$, at $[CO_2] = 7 \times 10^{-5}$ mole/l. and $[HCO_3^-] = 0.037 - 0.26$ mole/l.; Emerson's values were between 8.8 and 9.5, for $[CO_2]$ between 155×10^{-5} mole/l. and 6.2×10^{-5} mole/l. (pH 4.8 to 9.0), with $[HCO_3^-]$ present in large excess in the alkaline buffers.

Emerson and Chalmers (1955) have used an improved manometric technique (two differential manometers, read simultaneously by means of four cathetometers; split beam illumination of the two vessels) to better resolve the transients in the pressure changes upon switching the illumination on or off. The results were described in chapter 33 (section A.3). They proved, *first*, the occurrence of a physical lag in the manometric response, under conditions similar to those under which Warburg and Burk assumed the absence of such a lag, and the importance of the relative shapes of the two manometric vessels for the equilization on these lags (*cf.* fig. 33.6C); and *second*, the variety and long duration of transients following each change in illumination (*cf.* fig. 33.6D). These transients can include one (or several) bursts (or gulps) of CO_2, or O_2, or both gases, and permit calculation of almost any desired quantum yield by appropriate selection of measuring periods. If only the rates measured after the transients were over were taken into consideration, no quantum requirements <7 could be derived from the data of Emerson and Chalmers.

(c) New Nonmanometric Measurements of Quantum Yield*

New measurements have been made by Brackett, Olsen and Crickard (1953[1,2]) with a variation of the polarographic method (*cf.* p. 850), described by Olsen, Brackett and Crickard (1949), employing a fixed platinum electrode (25 μ in diameter) and a square wave potential (10 sec. cycle). The current, proportional to the momentary concentration of dissolved oxygen, was recorded every 10 sec. at the end of the negative half-cycle. The estimated time resolution was 1-2 sec.—a much faster recording than has yet been possible with a manometer. A dilute cell suspension (absorption 20-30% at λ 578 mμ) was contained in a flat, round cuvette. It was illuminated simultaneously from the two sides with filtered light from a mercury lamp, thus assuring approximately uniform exposure of all cells.

* See also page 1989.

Absorption was determined by moving a photocell around the cuvette and comparing the integral of the light transmitted and scattered in all directions, when the cuvette was filled with pure potassium chloride solution and when it contained cells suspended in the same medium. (Within 1%, the same absorptions were found when the suspension was transferred into an integrating sphere.) Fig. 37D.29 illustrates the relation between the

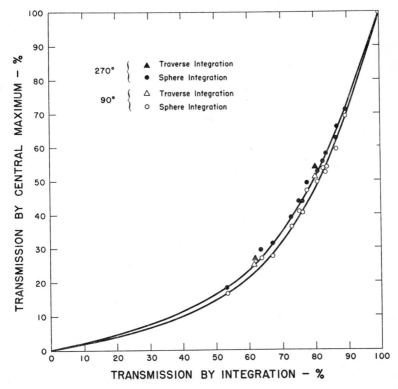

Fig. 37D.29. Straight-line transmission of *Chlorella* suspensions as function of integrated transmission (straight line-transmission + scattering) (after Brackett *et al.* 1953).

straight-line transmission, T, and the sum of transmission and scattering, $T + S$, for suspensions of different density. It shows that, when T is 30%, $T + S$ is 70%, so that the true absorption is only 40%. This example shows how erroneous absorption measurements can be on cell suspensions in which scattering is neglected. However, the true optical density (as determined by integration) was found to be proportional to the apparent optical density (as determined from straight-line transmission), at least up to a certain cell density. The cumbersome integration procedure could therefore be replaced, in most experiments, by multiplication with a constant proportionality factor, care being taken to assure unchanged alignment of the beam (to which the proportionality factor is sensitive).

About 0.66 μl. of cells was used, suspended in about 0.4 ml. of potassium chloride solution, equilibrated with 5% CO_2; the (incident) intensity was from 0.25 to 0.015 μeinstein/(cm.^{2} $\times$ min.). (The compensation point

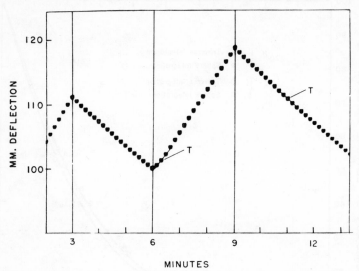

Fig. 37D.30. Polarographic record of oxygen exchange in 3 min. light–3 min. dark cycle (after Brackett *et al.* 1953). *I* (incident) = 8.35 $\times$ 10^{-4} watt/cm.^{2}, λ 578 mμ; dilute suspension of *Chlorella pyrenoidosa* (about 1.5 μl. cells/ml.), T: tangent to curve laid through three adjacent points.

was at about 0.07 μeinstein.) Fig. 37D.30 shows a typical reading for a 3 minute dark-3 minute light cycle. The rates were determined either by the "best straight line" approximation of a whole light or dark period, or by fitting tangents to curves laid through three adjacent points; a typical result of the second procedure (for a six minute cycle) is shown in fig. 37D.31. This figure also illustrates the reproducibility which was regularly obtained with several samples of the same culture.

Respiration in fig. 37D.31 shows typical changes with time. When the illumination starts after an extended period of darkness, the respiration is low. It increases after each light period and declines again in each dark period. The decline is sharp in the first half-minute of darkness; the oxygen uptake then increases again slightly, exhibiting a flat maximum 1 or 2 minutes after darkening. It then declines slowly and approximately logarithmically, with a decay constant of about 20 min. $^{-1}$, so that a steady rate of respiration, characteristic of dark-adapted aerobic suspensions, is reached only after several hours. In alternating light, this course is repeated again and again, starting each time at a higher initial rate, until the steady respiration rate of light-adapted suspension is reached. Brackett *et al.* suggested that the respiration increase in light also follows a logarith-

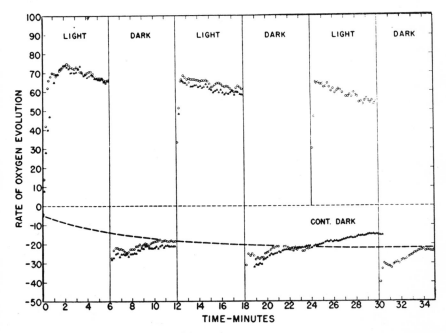

Fig. 37D.31. Plot of slopes derived from experimental data, of the type shown in preceding figures, by constructing the tangent T in every point (after Brackett *et al.* 1953[2]). Six minute cycles. Two runs with the same suspension show the same time course, including minor details. (In one run, the second dark period is extended to >12 min.) Dashed line represents interpolated main trend of respiration (for a 6 min. cycle of the intensity used).

mic course, and interpolated the respiration curves over the light periods as indicated by dashed lines in fig. 37D.32 (the "burst" of oxygen consumption, observed in the first 1–2 minutes of the dark periods, is disregarded in this interpolation!). Using the so interpolated respiration values, the rate of photosynthesis was computed point-by-point; the result is shown by the uppermost curve in the figure.

Calculated in this way, photosynthesis appeared constant except for an induction period, declining in duration with the repetition of the cycle.

(For more detailed discussion of the induction results, see chapter 33, section A2.)

Experiments of this type were made with varying intensities of illumination. If an average respiration correction was applied to the rates obtained at different light intensities (or a single "best fitting straight line" was used for the whole dark or light period), the light curves, $P = f(I)$, calculated in this way, showed a "Kok effect"—i. e., their slope changed

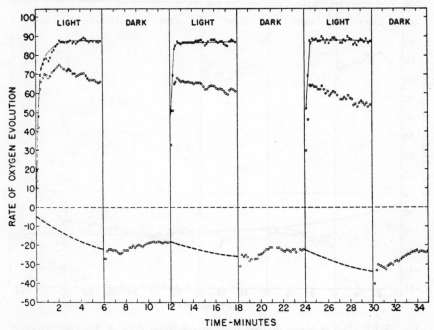

Fig. 37D.32. Rate of photosynthesis calculated from the same data as in fig. 37D.31, by interpolating respiration during the light periods as shown by dashed lines (i. e., by connecting by logarithmic curves the respiration level at the end of one dark period with that at the beginning of the next dark period, but disregarding the "oxygen gulp" in the first 1–2 minutes of darkness) (after Brackett et al. 1953[1]). The so calculated rate of photosynthesis is constant except for an induction period of about 2 min. in the first light period, dropping to < 1 min. in the two following light periods.

abruptly, by about a factor of two, near the compensation point (cf. p. 1113). If, however, the respiration course during the light period was evaluated point-by-point as described above, attributing all variations in the net gas exchange (outside the "induction periods") to changes in respiration, the "Kok effect" disappeared, and the light curves became straight lines. (This procedure amounts to calculating the rate of photosynthesis by adding to the rate of oxygen liberation at the end of a light period, the rate of oxygen consumption at the beginning of the subsequent dark period, but omitting the oxygen "gulp" in the first 1–2 minutes of darkness.)

Figs. 37D.33 and 34, represent the $P = (I)$ curves calculated in these two ways. The first one shows the Kok effect, while the second one is a straight line through the origin of the coordinates. The "Kok bend" appears, according to Brackett *et al.*, on curves constructed as in fig. 37D.33, because the increase of respiration, caused by

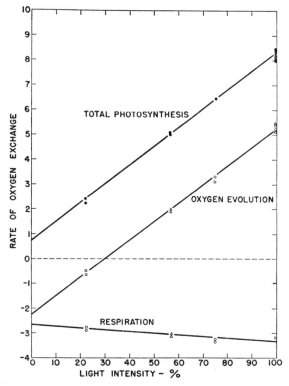

Fig. 37D.33. Light curves of respiration and photosynthesis calculated from "best straight lines" drawn through all experimental points during 3 min. dark and 3 min. light periods (after Brackett *et al.* 1953[1]). The light curve of photosynthesis does not extrapolate to zero ("Kok effect").

exposure to light, rises rapidly with light intensity, but becomes "saturated" even before compensation had been reached. Consequently, the error made by neglecting the change of respiration in light affects most strongly the quantum yields calculated from experiments in low light, particularly below compensation.

Not only the time course of the gas exchange, but also the absolute quantum requirements, found by Brackett, Olsen and Crickard (1953[2]), differed strongly from those of Warburg, Burk *et al.* A given culture showed the same requirement in repeated experiments, but the requirements of different cultures varied from 6.1 to 13.5 (quanta per oxygen molecule). Of the various factors studied, concentration of chlorophyll (produced by accidental fluctuations, not by systematic changes in the conditions of culturing), was found to be the most relevant one. Fig. 37D.35 shows the decline in quantum requirement with increasing [Chl] value. The median value of all the measurements in this chart is $1/\gamma = 8.5$; but since the variations appear systematic, and exceed the limits of experimental error, the lowest value found, 6.1, was considered significant.

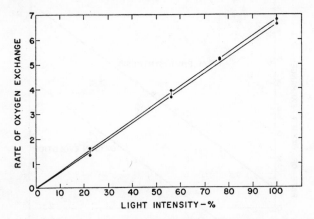

Fig. 37D.34. Light curves of photosynthesis derived from the same experiments as in fig. 37D.33, but using slopes determined separately for each point, as in fig. 37D.32 (after Brackett *et al.* 1953[1]). The curves extrapolate linearly to zero (no Kok effect).

Some errors to be watched for in this type of experiments, lie in the relation between straight-light transmission and absorption. Increasing the total pigment content of the vessel by *increasing the number of cells* in the suspension, can have a different effect on scattering than *increasing the amount of chlorophyll in each cell;* the calibration curve (fig. 37D.29) should therefore be determined separately for each suspension used.

(d) Franck's Interpretation of Warburg's 1950–1952 Experiments

Franck (1953) tried to provide a consistent interpretation of all quantum yield requirements, including the 1950–1952 results of Warburg and coworkers. His basic postulate remained the same as in an earlier paper (*cf.* p. 1117)—namely, that quantum requirements of 4 or less are indicative of the substitution of intermediate products of respiration for carbon dioxide as substrate of photochemical reduction. This substitution causes no change in the ratio $\Delta CO_2/\Delta O_2$ of the net gas exchange, since the "light action" amounts simply to a partial or complete photochemical *inhibition or respiration* (we could call this effect "photochemical antirespiration").

Three of Warburg's experiments challenged this interpretation. (*1*) The experiment in which the rate of oxygen consumption by respiration was found to be the same in light and in the dark, if carbon dioxide was

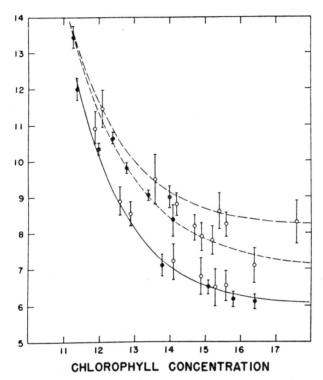

CHLOROPHYLL CONCENTRATION

Fig. 37D.35. Quantum requirement of photosynthesis of *Chlorella pyrenoidosa* in relation to variations in chlorophyll concentration in units, c, related to true concentration of chlorophylls inside the cells, $[Chl]_i$, by the relation $[CHl]_i = c/8.5$ (after Brackett *et al.* 1953[2]). The curves are logarithmic curves with limits 6, 7 and 8, respectively.

effectively removed by alkali (p. 901); this could be taken as proof that respiration intermediates cannot replace deficient carbon dioxide as substrate of photochemical reduction. (*2*) The experiments in which the quantum requirement of photosynthesis was found to be 4 or less, *far above the compensation point*, over periods of the order of 30 min. or 1 hr. (fig. 37D.25); this could be taken as proof that the high quantum yield belongs to true photosynthesis and not to mere photochemical "anti-respiration." (*3*) The separation of the "light process" from the "dark back-reaction" in minute light-minute dark (or minute bright-minute dim) experiments; these seem to indicate that respiration, far from being inhibited, proceeds, during intense photosynthesis, at up to 12 times its steady rate in the dark.

Franck has endeavored to show that these experiments, too, can be plausibly explained by assuming that respiration intermediates can serve as alternative substrates of photochemical reduction.

(1) The experiment on respiration in CO_2-free medium (p. 901) was made with a dense suspension, and a narrow pencil of light. Therefore, at any given moment, only about 5% of algae received light. The experiment thus merely proved that irradiation of 5% of algae in a suspension cannot affect significantly the total respiration of all of them. (The method is not sensitive enough to disclose a 5% decline in respiration!) Furthermore, Franck had deduced from other observations (cf. below) that a high concentration of carbon dioxide favors the entry of respiration intermediates into the photochemical process, while effective removal of CO_2 (as achieved in Warburg's experiment) makes this substitution improbable.

In contrast to Warburg, others who have attempted to study respiration in light by making the medium free of carbon dioxide, have not succeeded in preventing partial compensation of respiration in light. Franck attributed this to a more diffuse illumination.

Whenever light is found to have an effect on gas exchange in a CO_2-free medium, one is uncertain whether the compensation of respiration occurs by re-utilization of respiratory CO_2 before it has had time to escape from the cell, or by chemical reversal of an intermediate step in respiration, such as the oxidation of triose to glycerate (in other words, by the utilization of glycerate as a substitute reduction substrate in the CO_2-denuded photosynthetic mechanism). Franck considered the second mechanism as indicated in the experiments of Kok (1951), in which a very thin (1 mm. thick) layer of a cell suspension was used, permitting very efficient carbon dioxide removal. Despite this efficiency, Kok found that the yield of photosynthesis (according to Franck, one should say "anti-respiration") was quite as high as when carbon dioxide was present, even close to compensation.

(2) The experiments illustrated by fig. 37D.25 seem to be quite convincing, since, in them, considerable net amounts of oxygen were produced, over periods of time of the order of an hour, with an average quantum requirement of 3 (or less). However, it must be kept in mind that the quantum yield was calculated in these experiments by assuming that the "background" process (which is a combination of dark respiration with approximately compensating photosynthesis caused by the steady background light), is not affected by the superimposed alternating illumina-

tion. Warburg, Burk *et al.* thought that when respiration is about compensated by steady, diffuse illumination, the suspension remains for hours in a state of "physiological equilibrium." They found this surmise confirmed by the steadiness of the pressure during long "dim" periods (fig. 37D.25), as contrasted with changes in the rate of respiration in protracted dark periods (fig. 37D.26). When cells in this state of physiological equilibrium are exposed to additional, rather intense, even if locally restricted, alternating illumination, it is not immediately obvious that their physiological background will be undisturbed; but Warburg *et al.* decided that this is the case because they found such suspensions to return immediately to the original steady compensation state after 30 or 60 min. of alternating illumination. Also, they noted that the net gas exchange was the same in two successive alternating illumination periods of 30 min. each (fig. 37D.25).

Franck suggested that this apparent steadiness is deceptive and that the physiological state reached during the "dim" period, is significantly altered by superimposed alternating illumination. According to Franck, this superposition causes the photosynthetic apparatus to become deficient in the carbon dioxide acceptor, A. Consequently, true compensation of respiration, which, during the "dim" period, is achieved by normal photosynthesis with a quantum requirement of (presumably) 8 quanta per molecule of oxygen, is replaced, during the "bright" period, by "antirespiration" (photochemical reduction of half-oxidized respiration products), with the same net result, but with a quantum requirement which—Franck assumed—can be as low as 3, if the respiration intermediate involved is PGA (phosphoglyceric acid) or even 2 (if it is PGAP, *i. e.*, diphosphoglyceric acid containing one "high energy" phosphate bond).

The difference between the rates of gas exchange in the dim and the bright period is in this picture due to a combination of additional photosynthesis with the replacement of the part of photosynthesis that compensated respiration in dim light, by "anti-respiration." If the quantum yield of the additional photosynthesis is calculated on the assumption of unchanged background reaction, an excessively high value is obtained.

To determine whether this qualitative interpretation is quantitatively sufficient to explain results such as those shown in fig. 37D.25, the rate of steady respiration and the intensity of background illumination must be known; these data were not given in the paper by Warburg *et al.;* Franck assumed that the volume of respiration was 1.5 times the volume of cells per hour (a value given in another of Warburg's papers for a similar culture) and that the intensity of background light was such as to compensate this respiration with a quantum yield of $1/8$. Applying these two postulates to the extreme example of high quantum yield above the compensation point, given in Warburg's paper ($1/\gamma = 2.91$, at $P = 2R$), Franck calculated that, if 85% of the respiration intermediates, of the type of PGAP, formed in the period of alternating illumination, could be utilized for "anti-respiration," this would be enough to account for the calculated quantum requirement.

The calculation can be made as follows: If the steady respiration is R (moles O_2 per unit time), we assume that its compensation requires $8R$ einstein in the dim period, but could be achieved by $2R$ einstein in the bright period, if "anti-respiration" were 100% effective in the second case. More generally, $[8(1 - x) + 2x] \times R = 8R - 6Rx$ quanta will be needed, where x is the fraction of total respiration reversed in light. This switch frees $6Rx$ einsteins for photosynthesis. If the observed increment of photosynthesis in unit time during the "bright" period is ΔP, and the number of additional photons absorbed from alternating light, I_A, Warburg calculates the quantum requirement from the simple equation $1/\gamma = n = I_A/\Delta P$ ($= 2.9$). Franck's equation for the calculation of the "true" yield, n_0, is, on the other hand, $1/\gamma_0 = n_0 = (I_A + 2 \times 6Rx)/\Delta P$.

The factor 2 in parentheses reflects the fact that the $6Rx$ einsteins are available during *both* phases of alternating light—the 1 minute periods when the monochromatic beam is "on," as well as the 1 minute period when this beam is "off."

With $\Delta P = 2R$, this equation gives $n_0 = 2.9 + 6x$; for n_0 to be equal to 8.0, x must be 0.85, *i. e.*, 85% of total respiration must be compensated by "antirespiration" during alternating illumination.

Franck's interpretation is thus quantitatively possible, even in a case in which the average net photosynthesis in the one hour "bright" period is twice the steady respiration in the "dim" period. However, one needs in this case the somewhat extreme assumption that respiration in the whole cell (not only in the chloroplast) is, on the average, 85% inhibited (or, more exactly, reversed) in alternating light.

(3) The observations illustrated by fig. 33.6A are interpreted by Franck as demonstrations of a new kind of induction phenomena, rather than as revelation of the two-stage mechanism of photosynthesis. The pecularity of these induction effects is that they cause (apparent) *gains* rather than the—more familiar—*losses* in the photosynthetic yield in the first minute or two of illumination.

This interpretation has caused us to deal with the minute light-minute dark experiments in chapters 33 ("Induction Phenomena") and 34 ("Photosynthesis in Flashing Light"). The essential point in their interpretation by Franck is the attribution of the exceptionally high quantum yield in the first minute of illumination to temporary shortage of the carbon dioxide acceptor (called A or RH in chap. 27, specified as ribulose diphosphate in chapter 36). This shortage, caused by metabolic destruction of the acceptor during the dark period, invites respiration intermediates (PGA, or PGAP) to enter the photosynthetic cycle; as long as they are being utilized, the quantum requirement of the photochemical process can be as low as 2. If alternation is not between light and dark, but between "bright" and "dim," the level of [A], established in dim light, will be too low to support the higher rate of photosynthesis during the bright half-cycles, and this, too, may cause respiration intermediates to rush into the emptied photosynthetic mechanism. In both cases—that of transition from dark to light, and that of transition from dim to bright—a "priming" of the CO_2 cycle is necessary, and, while this "autophotocatalytic" adjustment is effected, respiration intermediates are reduced with a relatively low quantum requirement. This picture does not immediately explain why respiration appears enormously increased in the first minute after the return into dark (or dim) conditions; nor why a value approaching 1 is obtained for the quantum requirement if the gas exchange at the beginning of the first minute of "dim light" is subtracted from that at the beginning of the first minute of "bright light" (cf. fig. 33.6A). Details of Franck's interpretation of these transient phenomena have been given in chapter 33 (part C). In essence, Franck assumes that the induction caused by shortage of A does not affect ΔO_2 in the same way as ΔCO_2. In other words, the ratio $\Delta O_2 / \Delta CO_2$ is variable during the minute light-minute dark cycle (while Warburg and Burk's calculations are based on the assumption of a constant $Q_P \simeq 1$). Franck thinks that the on-the-minute manometric readings lacked the precision needed to assert the constancy of Q_P, and that the curves of Burk, Warburg et al.—from which the "one quantum process" was derived —are, for this reason, not reliable enough to calculate quantum yields for fractions of a minute, even by averaging five or ten measurements. Doubts on this account were expressed also by Brown (1953).

A similar suggestion was made by Schenk (1952), but rejected by Warburg (1952) with reference to the constant value of $Q_P \cong 1$ obtained by averaging the results of the two-vessel experiments.

Franck's interpretations do not cover the subsequently published papers of Warburg et al. (1953, 1954). As stated before, these extremely interesting papers bring the maximum yield controversy onto a new plane. In the light of the past history, they require, first of all, independent experimental confirmation—in respect to both the $1/\gamma$ and the Q_P values; this will be awaited with the greatest interest.

(e) Quantum Yield of Hill Reaction

The quantum requirement of the Hill reaction (cf. chapter 29, section 4) was again measured by Wayrynen (1952) and by Warburg (1952). Wayrynen used sugar beet chloroplasts with ferricyanide as oxidant and measured the rates potentiometrically. A quantum requirement of 8.3 was calculated by extrapolation to zero light intensity (the light curves of Hill reaction bend early, cf. chapter 35, page 1620). This value, which is in satisfactory agreement with the data of Ehrmantraut and Rabinowitch (p. 1130) was obtained at pH 3 and 675 mμ; the yield was lower at other pH values and declined at the shorter wave lengths, until a minimum was reached at 575 mμ; it was higher again at 475 mμ.

Warburg (1952), using spinach chloroplasts and quinone as oxidant, found quantum requirement as high as 70 at 400 mμ, and 100 at 644 mμ. He considered this extremely low efficiency, as well as its dependence on wave length, as striking demonstrations that the Hill reaction has nothing in common with photosynthesis (the latter having, according to Warburg, a quantum requirement of less than 3, independent of wave length). Comparison with the results of Ehrmantraut and Rabinowitch (p. 1130) and of Wayrynen shows that Warburg must have used a very poor, almost inactive preparation—perhaps because the quinone concentration (0.05 M) was far above the optimum (about 0.005 M, according to fig. 35.25).   Warburg also reported that his chloroplast preparation gave no reaction at all with ferrocyanide.

(f) Quantum Requirement of Bacteria

Larsen, Yocum and van Niel (1952, cf. also Larsen 1953) measured the quantum requirement of a species of green sulfur bacteria, *Chlorobium thiosulphatophilum*, with thiosulfate, tetrathionate or molecular hydrogen as reductant.   With dense bacterial suspensions, the light curves of CO_2-consumption were distinctly sigmoid; the same was true, albeit to a distinctly lesser degree, for light curves of the hydrogen consumption (compare figs. 28.8 and 28.11; concerning the interpretation of sigmoid light curves, see pp. 948 and 1126).   Because of the inflection at the beginning of the light curve, maximum quantum yield measurements on bacteria were best carried out in dilute suspensions, and as high up the linear part of the light curve as possible.

Measurements were made in monochromatic light (interference filter, $\lambda_{max.} = 732$ mμ), with absolute intensity measured by thermopile, and absorption by means of an integrating sphere.   Yields were measured manometrically, in 30–40 minute runs, eliminating from calculation the first 10 minutes of illumination, in oxygen-free nitrogen atmosphere containing 2–5% CO_2.   In ten experiments with H_2 as reductant, quantum requirements of 7.8–11.8 were measured (average, 9.1); in eight experiments with $Na_2S_2O_3$, such of 8.9–11.4 (average, 9.3); and in five experiments with $Na_2S_4O_6$, such of 8.9–9.7 (average, 9.3).

In this case, again, a quantum yield measurement on a new type of organism, having a different kind of photochemical metabolism, gave practically the same results as so many previous measurements on green plants, chloroplasts and bacteria had given—between 8 and 10 quanta per four hydrogen atoms (or four electrons) moved. The standard free energy change is, in the reduction of carbon dioxide by H_2, only about 2 kcal/mole CO_2; in the reduction by $H_2S_2O_3$, about 29 kcal/mole, and in that by H_2-S_4O_6, about 30 kcal/mole—as contrasted to about 120 kcal/mole in ordinary photosynthesis. The identical results obtained with the three reductants clearly show that the maximum quantum requirements are determined by the (probably identical) *mechanism*, and not by the (vastly different) *energy requirement* of the photochemical process. No utilization of the abundant excess quantum energy, enabling the over-all process to proceed at the cost of a smaller number of quanta, is attempted by nature in these cells. (Such a utilization has been suggested for higher plants in various "energy dismutation" hypotheses of photosynthesis.)

The results of Larsen *et al.* are in reasonable agreement with the earlier data for purple bacteria and hydrogen-adapted green algae (chapter 29, section 3).

5. Thermochemical Considerations

Franck (1953) reviewed once again the question of the probable *practical* energy requirement of photosynthesis—*i. e.*, energy requirement that includes the inevitable (or highly probable) losses in the presently recognizable individual steps of the process. This analysis is similar to the earlier one, reported on p. 1089, but makes use of new and more specific ideas concerning the photochemical and enzymatic stages of photosynthesis.

When Warburg and Negelein's finding of a quantum requirement of 4 stood unchallenged, Franck had tried to devise a mechanism of photosynthesis incorporating this feature, but noted that this offered great thermochemical di culties (noted also by Wohl). The experimental criticism of Warburg and Negelein's conclusions by Daniels *et al.* (p. 1121) and Emerson and Lewis (p. 1091) provided a welcome way out of these difficulties and the search for the mechanism of photosynthesis was switched to models involving more than four elementary photochemical steps—with eight a favorite number, both for experimental reasons, and because of its easy interpretation in terms of a two-stage transfer of four hydrogen atoms (*cf.* chapter 7, "Eight Quanta Mechanisms"). Alternative hypotheses, envisaging $4 + x$ photochemical reactions, storing the energy of x quanta in high energy phosphate esters, also have been discussed (*cf.* for example, the hypotheses of Ruben, and of van der Veen, p. 1116).

This sequence of events, already told in chapter 29, is recalled here because of Warburg's repeated assertions that Franck had concluded on theoretical grounds that the quantum requirement of photosynthesis must be 11 (or, in another of Warburg's papers, 13) *before* Daniels and Emerson (and others) began finding quantum requirements supporting his theory. The origin of the quantum yield controversy lies in different experimental findings and not, as Warburg asserts, in a conflict between theoretical dogmatism and "unbiased" experimental approach.

The basis of Franck's thermochemical considerations is the belief—which most physical chemists will support, but some biologists may refuse to countenance—that the elementary steps in a photochemical and enzymatic process *in vivo* must obey the rules known to apply to similar processes *in vitro*. Not only the law of conservation of energy must be preserved by the over-all reaction—as everybody concedes—but the individual reaction steps must be kinetically plausible. If this postulate is accepted, the conclusion follows that many steps involved in photosynthesis cannot occur without some energy dissipation into heat. These losses must be added to the net energy requirement of the over-all process of photosynthesis (as illustrated in fig. 29.2).

Losses must first occur immediately following light absorption, in the conversion of the excitation energy of chlorophyll—or another pigment—into chemical energy (potential energy of re-arranged atoms, either in chlorophyll itself or in a sensitization substrate).

Fluorescence experiments indicate that all energy absorbed in excess of that of the transition from the (nonvibrating), lowest excited electronic state to the (nonvibrating) ground state is lost practically instantaneously. (The fact that the quantum requirement of photosynthesis remains constant through a large part of the visible spectrum, is in agreement with this conclusion.) All electronic energy in excess of that of the lowest "red" excited state is thus dissipated prior to fluorescent re-emission or photochemical utilization. The energy of the $0 \rightarrow 0$ transition is slightly less than the quantum corresponding to the peak of the red absorption band (located, *in vivo*, at 675–680 mμ); the corresponding energy is 42 kcal/einstein.

The next question is: Is the excitation energy of 41 kcal, which we know to be available for fluorescence, also available for photochemical utilization, or are all chlorophyll molecules that escape fluorescence (the yield of the latter *in vivo* is $< 1\%$) transferred into the metastable (triplet) state, presumed to exist below the fluorescent (singlet) state (*cf.* p. 790), before they take part in photosynthesis? The evidence for the existence of this state in chlorophyll is indirect (kinetics of chlorophyll-sensitized autoxidations *in vitro*); but the general theory of the molecular states of conjugated double bond molecules predicts that a metastable triplet state should exist below the lowest singlet state; this conclusion has been verified on many dyestuff molecules.

In the absence of spectroscopic evidence we do not know how deep under the 41 kcal level the metastable state lies. Franck considers 5 kcal/mole a conservative estimate. Therefore, if the chlorophyll molecule is transferred into the metastable state before participating in photosynthesis, it has only 37 kcal/mole (or less) to contribute. However, it is not certain that sensitization occurs only after the chlorophyll molecule has been transferred into the metastable state; in a condensed system, sensitization may successfully *compete* with this transfer. If it does, all 42 kcal are available for photosynthesis.

Livingston and Ryan (*cf.* chapter 35, page 1498) found that chlorophyll solutions illuminated with a strong flash of light, acquire a transient absorption band at 515 mμ, which could be attributed to a metastable chlorophyll molecule. Witt (1955) noted the same band in plants exposed to a sudden, intense flash (in the same way as chlorophyll solutions in Ryan's experiments). These observations add circumstantial evidence for the existence of the (theoretically anticipated) metastable chlorophyll molecule, and its formation in light, both *in vitro* and *in vivo*, but give no clue to what the energy of this state is.

We do not know by what specific mechanism the electronic excitation energy of chlorophyll—be it 37 or 42 kcal—is first converted into potential energy of atoms, by displacing their nuclei. What we know, however, is that such transformation never occurs without some energy being converted into kinetic energy of the nuclei and ultimately lost as heat. (To prevent this loss, the whole process would have to be conducted "adiabatically," *i. e.*, infinitely slowly—while electronic excitation or deactivation by absorption or emission of a photon is practically instantaneous, and electronic energy transfers between two molecules occur very quickly compared to the speed with which nuclei can re-arrange themselves into a new stable pattern.) Consequently, in accordance with the so-called "Franck-Condon principle," we can expect the sensitizer (chlorophyll molecule), after its electronic energy has been transferred to the sensitization substrate (*e. g.*, an appropriately bound HOH or ROH molecule), to be left behind in a configuration that was stable while the electronic system was in the excited state, but appears distorted after the electronic system has reverted into the ground state. The nuclei will therefore begin to vibrate, like a released spring. This means that a part of the excitation energy of chlorophyll will be "left behind," after sensitization, as vibrational energy of the chlorophyll molecule. By the same token, the products of the sensitized reaction (*e. g.*, the radicals H and OH, or R and OH attached to appropriate "acceptors," such as X and Z in chapter 7) will be created not in the state of rest, but endowed with more or less violent motion, and some energy will be dissipated in the medium in stopping them. Incidentally, since a single quantum is likely to move only one electron, these primary photo-chemical products in all probability will be radicals (the product of attach-ment of free radicals to valence-saturated "carriers" also are free radicals). Unless these radicals are given sufficient energy in the act of their formation, to break out of the "cage" (in the terminology of Franck and Rabinowitch), before they are stopped, they will be in danger of "primary recombination."

The amount of energy lost in the conversion of electronic to chemical energy will depend on whether the sensitized reaction is brought about by the unstable singlet, or the metastable triplet state. In the first case, the residual vibrational energy must be equivalent to roughly the distance between the peaks of the absorption and the fluorescence bands (in the case of chlorophyll *in vivo*, about 1 kcal/mole). If the triplet state participates in sensitization, the vibrational energy residue will be larger (because the change in stable nuclear configuration must be greater for the triplet-singlet than for the singlet-singlet transition).

Franck's tentative estimate of total energy losses in the photochemical steps is 7 kcal per quantum, leaving 35 kcal if the singlet state is involved, and ≤ 30 kcal if the triplet state is responsible for sensitization.

After the two free radicals, formed in the primarily photochemical step, have separated (the sensitizer itself may be one of them) the chemical stage of photosynthesis begins. We do not know its details, except for the conclusion, derived from radiocarbon studies, that phosphoglyceric acid (PGA) is the first identifiable organic product. It is presumed to be formed by carboxylation of a C_2 phosphate (or of a C_5 diphosphate, the product splitting into two PGA molecules). Probably, this carboxylation is followed by the reduction of PGA to a triose, as first step in a cycle in which one part of the reduction products is stabilized as hexose sugars, and another is converted back into the CO_2–acceptor, to take up more carbon dioxide.

Whether in this or in another specific way, the chemical stage of photo-synthesis undoubtedly consists of a complex series of reactions, mostly or entirely enzymatic. It probably includes, in addition to oxidation-reduc-tions, also phosphorylations, condensations and carboxylations. Consider-ing the low concentration of the intermediates (particularly radicals) which can be present in the steady state, each step can proceed rapidly and com-pletely in the desired direction only if it is at least slightly exothermal; and this means that a certain amount of energy must be converted into heat in each step. The more steps are involved in a suggested mechanism, the larger are the expected energy losses. (Warburg and Burk's "new scheme" of photosynthesis, in which at least three times more oxygen molecules are produced as intermediates than are left in the net result, would, for this reason, entail considerably greater losses than the earlier, simpler schemes.)

Franck counted "on the reduction side" of photosynthesis a minimum loss of about 6 kcal in the enzymatic dismutation of four photochemically formed radicals (XH in chapter 7) into two molecules of a saturated reductant, and one of 13 kcal in the formation of PGA by reduction, phosphorylation and carboxylation of the C_2 "acceptor." To this, one would have to add the losses in the second stage of the reduction process—probably the conversion of PGA into a triose phosphate (followed by polymerization of the latter to hexose phosphate, and dephosphorylation). Even without these additional items, we have by now accumulated losses of at least 7 kcal per quantum in the primary photochemical process, and at least 19 kcal per carbon dioxide molecule in the carboxylation and reduction reactions. For a four quanta mechanism, this amounts to a total loss of $7 \times 4 + 19 = 47$ kcal per reduced CO_2 molecule; for a three quanta process, the minimum loss would be $7 \times 3 + 19 = 40$ kcal. These amounts must be added to the free energy of formation of a mole of CH_2O groups.

As Franck pointed out, *free* energy rather than total energy of photosynthesis must be used in such calculations. This amounts to 120 kcal/mole in the free atmosphere, and to 116–117 kcal/mole in CO_2-enriched media (*cf.* chapter 1). The total free energy requirement, established so far, is therefore 163–167 kcal/mole for a four quanta process, and 156–160 kcal/mole for a three quanta mechanism. Four quanta of red light (168 kcal/einstein) are barely enough to cover these requirements; four metastable quanta (148 kcal/einstein) are too little; three quanta are insufficient in both cases.

The calculation so far has neglected all losses on the "oxidation side" of photosynthesis, *i. e.*, in the conversion of the primary photochemical oxidation product into molecular oxygen. This conversion probably involves at least two steps (*cf.* chapter 11). The first one transforms the primarily produced free radicals (called Z, or {OH}, in chapter 7) into peroxides ("photoperoxides"), while the second one dismutes the peroxide into oxygen and an oxide. The latter process is known to be very wasteful of energy. Whether the peroxide is hydrogen peroxide (which is unlikely), or an organic peroxide, its dismutation into oxygen and an oxide liberates, according to the general experience in peroxide chemistry, an energy amount of the order of 45 kcal (per mole of liberated oxygen). Adding this huge loss to the previously estimated losses would make photosynthesis unachievable even by 5 quanta of red light (requirement: $7 \times 5 + 19 + 45 + 116$ or $120 = 215$ or 219 kcal/mole), and make six quanta the smallest plausible number. (If the reaction occurs *via* the metastable state, even six quanta would be hardly enough: available energy $\leq 6 \times 37 = 222$ kcal; required energy, $7 \times 6 + 19 + 45 + 116$ or $120 = 222$ or 226 kcal/mole.)

Two criticisms of the assumption of a 45 kcal loss in the "photoperoxide" mechanism of oxygen liberation can be made. One is that mechanisms of oxygen production are conceivable which would not involve a peroxide at all, or involve a peroxide of lower energy, capable of dismutation with a relatively small loss of energy (or a peroxide with such high energy that it is capable of straight decomposition, $R_1OOR_2 \rightarrow R_1R_2 + O_2$). In other words, one is not under obligation to postulate an energy-wasting "catalatic" mechanism of oxygen liberation. The second objection is that the energy of decomposition of the peroxide could be somehow fed back into the reaction cycle (*e. g.*, by coupling the peroxide composition with the formation of high energy phosphate esters, and utilizing the latter in reactions such as the reduction of PGA to glyceraldehyde).

To the first suggestion—which was discussed in some detail in chapter 11—one can say that no mechanism of oxygen evolution not involving peroxide as intermediate has yet come to light, and that it is unlikely that the $O{=}O$ double bond can be formed in one act without preliminary formation of an $O{-}O$ single bond. However, the possibility of a peroxide thermochemically radically different from H_2O_2 (or from typical organic peroxides) cannot be denied *a priori* (*cf.* chapter 11, p. 293); the 45 kcal item in the energy balance may therefore be too large.

As to the possibility of feeding the peroxide dismutation energy back into the reaction cycle, two arguments against this hypothesis come to mind. No such coupling has yet been demonstrated in respiratory processes; and the yield determinations on purple bacteria and adapted algae (where no oxygen is evolved, and correspondingly more energy is available for "ploughing back" into photosynthesis), indicate no energy saving compared to true photosynthesis. Admittedly, both arguments are suggestive rather than conclusive.

To sum up, the conclusions that can be derived from these estimates (differing in some numerical detail from those of Franck, but in general agreement with the latter) are as follows:

(*1*) If 3 quanta (or less) would be proved to suffice for steady photosynthesis, this would mean that plants have found a way to get around all general rules of reaction kinetics and photochemistry, except the law of conservation of energy.

(*2*) A quantum requirement of 4 is thermochemically only possible— and then unlikely—if plants have found a way to liberate oxygen without a peroxide as an intermediate, or to re-utilize the peroxide decomposition energy.

(*3*) If a peroxide with even one half of the dismutation energy of H_2O_2 is involved in photosynthesis, and its dismutation energy is dissipated, the minimum plausible quantum requirement is 6, with 7 or 8 the more likely alternatives.

Bibliography to Chapter 37D

Kinetics of Photosynthesis

1849 Garreau, *Ann. sci. natur. (Botan.)*, **13**, 321.

1851 Garreau, *ibid.*, **15**, 5; **16**, 271.

1936 Dole, M., *J. Chem. Phys.*, **4**, 268.

Greene, C. H., and Voskuyl, R. J., *J. Am. Chem. Soc.*, **58**, 693.

1938 Pirson, A., *Forschungsdienst*, **I**, 92.

1940 Stegmann, G., *Zeitschrift Botanik*, **35**, 385; *cf.* also Noack, K., Pirson, A., and Stegmann, G., *Naturwiss.*, **28**, 172.

Brilliant, V. A., *Eksperim. Botanika*, **4**, 53.

1941 Vinogradov, A. P. and Teis, R. V., *Compt. rend. (Doklady) Acad. Sci. USSR*, **33**, 490.

Ruben, S., Randall, M., Kamen, M. D., and Hyde, J. L., *J. Am. Chem. Soc.*, **63**, 877.

1942 Yosida, T., Morita, N., Tamiya, H., Nakayama, H. and Huzisige, H., *Acta Phytochimica (Jap.)*, **13**, 11.

1943 Brilliant, V. A., *Compt. rend. (Doklady) Acad. Sci. USSR*, **41**, 82, 134, 231.

1944 Steemann-Nielsen, E., *Dansk. Botan. Arkiv.*, **11**, No. 8.

Matsuyama, H., and Hirana, J., *Acta Phytochimica (Jap.)*, **14**, 131.

Dam, H., *Am. J. Botany*, **31**, 492.

Dole, M., and Jenks, G., *Science*, **100**, 409.

1945 Kamen, M. D., and Barker, H. A., *Proc. Nat. Acad. Sci. U. S.*, **31**, 8.

Franck, J., Pringsheim, P., and Lad, D. T., *Arch. Biochem.*, **7**, 103.

1946 Steemann-Nielsen, E., *Nature*, **158**, 594.

French, C. S., *Annual Review Biochemistry*, **15**, 397.

Kamen, M. D., *Am. Museum Nat. Hist. Bull.*, **87**, 101.

1947 Dole, M., Hawkings, R. C., and Barker, H. A., *J. Am. Chem. Soc.*, **69**, 226.

Vinogradov, A. P., and Teis, R. V., *Compt. rend. (Doklady) Acad. Sci. USSR*, **56**, 57.

Steemann-Nielsen, E., *Dansk. Botan. Arkiv.*, **12**, No. 8.

Frenkel, A. W., Report AEC D-2143 (Nov. 13, 1947).

Warburg, O., *Naturforschung und Medizin in Deutschland* **1939–46**, **39**, p. 211.

Österlind, S., *Nature*, **159**, 199.

Audus, L. J., *Ann. Botany*, **11**, 165.

1948 Österlind, S., *Nature*, **161**, 319.

Baslavskaja, S. S., and Zhuravleva, *Botan. Zhurn. USSR*, **34**, 420.

Heath, O. V. S., and Williams, W. T., *Nature*, **161**, 178.

Winokur, M., *Am. J. Botany*, **35**, 207.

Brebion, G., *Gallica Biol. Acta*, **1**, 24.

1949 Gabrielsen, E. K., *Nature*, **163**, 359.

Gerretsen, F. C., *Plant and Soil*, **1**, 346.

Heath, O. V. S., *Nature*, **164**, 822.

Weigl, J. W., and Calvin, M., *J. Chem. Phys.*, **17**, 210.

Österlind, S., *Symp. botan. upsal.*, **10**, No. 3.

Gabrielsen, E. K., and Schou, L., *Experientia*, **5**, 116.

Simonis, W., *Z. Naturforsch.*, **4b**, 109.

Frenkel, A., *Biol. Bull.*, **97**, 222.

Brilliant, V. A., "Photosynthesis as Life Process of the Plant" (Russian), pp. 48–80, Acad. Sci. USSR, 1949.

Burk, D., Hendricks, S., Korzenovsky, M., Schocken, V., and Warburg, O., *Science*, **110**, 225.

Tamiya, H., and Huzisige, H., *Acta Phytochimica (Jap.)*, **15**, 83.

Warburg, O., Burk, D., Schocken, V., Korzenovsky, M., and Hendricks, S., *Arch. Biochem. Biophys.*, **23**, 330.

Freeland, R. O., *Plant Physiol.*, **24**, 621.

1950   Österlind, S., *Physiol. plantarum*, **3**, 353.

Österlind, S., *ibid.*, **3**, 430.

Skvorzov, S. S., *Compt. rend. (Doklady) Acad. Sci. USSR*, **67**, 1155.

Warburg, O., Burk, D., Schocken, V., and Hendricks, S., *Biochem. Biophys. Acta*, **4**, 335.

Burk, D., and Warburg, O., *Naturwiss.*, **37**, 560.

Warburg, O., and Burk, D., *Arch. Biochem. Biophys.*, **25**, 410.

Heath, O. V. S., *J. Exptl. Botany*, **1**, 29.

Heath, O. V. S., and Milthorpe, F. L., *ibid.*, **1**, 227.

Pirson, A., and Wilhelmi, G., *Z. Naturforsch.*, **5b**, 211.

Thomas, J. B., *Biochim. et Biophys. Acta*, **5**, 186.

Steward, F. C., and Thompson, J. F., *Nature*, **166**, 993.

1951   Rabinowitch, E., *Ann. Rev. Phys. Chem.*, **2**, 361.

Holzer, H., *Z. Naturforsch.*, **6b**, 424.

Stepka, W., "The Path of Carbon in Photosynthesis; the Influence of Enzyme Poisons," *Thesis*, Univ. Calif., Berkeley.

Rakestraw, N. M., Rudd, D. P., and Dole, M., *J. Am. Chem. Soc.*, **73**, 2976.

Kok, B., *Symposia Soc. Exptl. Biol.*, **5**, 211.

Österlind, S., *Physiol. plantarum*, **4**, 242.

Österlind, S., *ibid.*, **4**, 514.

Österlind, S., *ibid.*, **4**, 528.

Steemann-Nielsen, E., *ibid.*, **4**, 189.

Redford, E. L., and Myers, J., *J. Cell. Comp. Physiol.*, **38**, 217.

Gaffron, H., Fager, E. W. and Rosenberg, J. L., *Symp. Soc. Exptl. Biol.*, **5**, 262.

Burk, D., and Warburg, O., *Z. Naturforsch.*, **6b**, 12.

Holt, A. S., Brooks, I. A., and Arnold, W. A., *J. Gen. Physiol.*, **34**, 627.

Egle, K., *Naturwiss.*, **38**, 350.

Kursanov, A. L., Kuzin, A., and Mamul, J., *Compt. rend. (Doklady) Acad. Sci. USSR*, **79**, 685.

Nishimura, M. S., Whittingham, C. P., and Emerson, R., *Symp. Soc. Exptl. Biol.*, **5**, 176.

Warburg, O., Burk, D., and Schade, A. L., *ibid.*, **5**, 306.

Burk, D., Schade, A. R., Hunter, J., and Warburg, O., *ibid.*, **5**, 312.

Weigl, J. W., Warrington, P. M., and Calvin, M., *J. Am. Chem. Soc.*, **73**, 5058.

Gavaudan, P., and Brebion, G., *Exptl. Cell. Res.*, **2**, 158.

Warburg, O., and Geleick, H., *Z. Naturforsch.*, **6b**, 134.

Warburg, O., Geleick, H., and Briese, K., *ibid.*, **6b**, 285.

Warburg, O., Geleick, H., and Briese, K., *ibid.*, **6b**, 417.

Heath, O. V. S., *Symp. Soc. Exptl. Biol.*, **5**, 94.

1952 Österlind, S., *Physiol. plantarum*, **5**, 372.

Österlind, S., *ibid.*, **5**, 403.

Egle, K., and Schenk, R., *Beitr. Biol. d. Pflanzen*, **29**, 75.

Briggs, G. E., and Whittingham, C. P., *New Phytologist*, **51**, 236.

Steemann-Nielsen, E., *Physiol. plantarum*, **5**, 145.

Warburg, O., Geleick, H., and Briese, K., *Z. Naturforsch.*, **7b**, 141.

Whittingham, C. P., *Nature*, **169**, 838.

Brilliant, V. A., and Krupnikova, T. A., *Compt. rend. (Doklady), Acad. Sci. USSR*, **85**, 1383.

Skvorzov, S. S., *ibid.*, **85**, 1391.

Brown, A. H., Nier, A. O. C., and Van Norman, R. W., *Plant Physiol.*, **27**, 320.

Van Norman, R. W., and Brown, A. H., *ibid.*, **27**, 691.

Schenck, R., *Naturwiss.*, **39**, 89.

Whittingham, C. P., *Nature*, **170**, 1017.

Kursanov, A. C., Kryukova, N. N., and Vartapetjan, B. B., *Compt. rend. (Doklady) Acad. Sci. USSR*, **85**, 913.

Warburg, O., *Naturwiss.*, **39**, 185.

Warburg, O., *Z. Naturforsch.*, **7b**, 443.

Larsen, H., Yocum, E. C., and van Niel, C. B., *J. Gen. Physiol.*, **36**, 161.

Wayrynen, R. E., "Quantum Yield of Photoreduction Reaction in Photosynthesis," *Thesis*, Univ. Utah.

Dole, M., *Chem. Rev.*, **51**, 263.

Steemann-Nielsen, E., *Physiol. plantarum*, **5**, 211.

1953 Allen, F. L., "Observations on Photosynthesis and Related Reactions under Anaerobic Conditions," *Thesis*, Univ. Chicago.

Brackett, F. S., Olson, R. A., and Crickard, R. G., *J. Gen. Physiol.*, **36**, 529, 563.

Brown, A. H., *Am. J. Botany*, **40**, 719.

Brown, A. H., and Webster, G. C., *ibid.*, **40**, 753.

Buchanan, D. L., Nakao, A., and Edwards, G., *Science*, **117**, 541.

Burk, D., *Federation Proc.*, **12**, 611.

Damaschke, K., *Biochim. et Biophys. Acta*, **12**, 347.

Emerson, R., and Whittingham, C. P., (private communication).

Franck, J., *Arch. Biochem. and Biophys.*, **45**, 190.

Gaffron, H., (private communication).

Larsen, H., *Norsk Videnskabs. Selskab. Skrift.*, **1953**, No. 1.

Pirson, A., Krollpfeiffer, I., and Schaefer, G., *Marburg. Sitzungsber.*, **76**, No. 2.

Steemann-Nielsen, E., *Nature*, **171**, 1106.

Steemann-Nielsen, E., *Physiol. plantarum*, **6**, 316.

Warburg, O. (with G. Krippahl, W. Schröder, and W. Buchholz), *Biochim. et Biophys. Acta*, **12**, 356.

Warburg, O., Krippahl, G., Buchholz, W., and Schröder, W., *Z. Naturforsch.*, **8b**, 675.

1954 Brown, A. H., and Whittingham, C. P., *Plant Physiol.* (in press).

Dole, M., (personal communication).

Dole, M., Lane, G. A., Budd, D. P., and Zaukelies, D. A., *Geochim. et. Cosmochim. Acta*, **6**, 65.

Frazer, I. M., *Australian J. Exptl. Biol. Med. Sci.*, **32**, 49.

Holzer, H., *Angew. Chemie.*, **66**, 65.

Horwitz, L., *Plant Physiol.*, **29**, 215.

Johnson, J. A., and Brown, A. H., *ibid.*, **29**, 177.

Kursanov, A. L., *Proc., 8th Intern. Congr. Botany, Paris* July 1954 (in press); reprinted in *Voprosy Botaniky*, **1954**, No. 1, Acad. Sci. USSR, Moscow-Leningrad, pp. 131–156.

Rosenberg, J. L., *J. Gen. Physiol.*, **37**, 753.

Warburg, O., and Krippahl, G., *Angew. Chem.*, **66**, 493.

Warburg, O., Krippahl, G., Schröder, W., Buchholz, W., and Theel, E., *Z. Naturforsch.*, **9B**, 164.

Wessels, J. S. C., *Rec. trav. chim. Phys-Bas*, **73**, 529.

Whittingham, C. P., *Plant Physiol.*, **29**, 473.

1955 Witt, H. T., *Naturwiss.*, **42**, 72.

Emerson, R., and Chalmers, R., *Plant Physiol.* (in press).

CHAPTER 38

EPILOGUE

When this monograph was begun in 1938, students could still read, in most textbooks of plant physiology, that von Baeyer's formaldehyde theory of 1870—either in its original form, or as elaborated by Willstätter and Stoll in 1918 (*cf.* p. 287)—provided the most plausible picture of the chemical mechanism of carbon dioxide reduction in photosynthesis. The—still older—plant acid theory of Liebig (*cf.* p. 51), which we now recognize as being much closer to truth, has been completely displaced by von Baeyer's theory, even though no convincing support of the latter, through identification of its suggested intermediates, could be obtained during the many years of its sway.

The formaldehyde theory made photosynthesis appear as something quite different from, and unconnected to, all the other biochemical activities of the organism. Because of the failure of the attempts to separate photosynthesis from the living cell, or to divide it into individual steps which could be reproduced in cell-free preparations, it seemed that there must exist one central "secret of photosynthesis," a simple photochemical transformation, whose elucidation will suddenly make us "understand" photosynthesis, and, very likely, will permit us to repeat it outside the living cell.

Looking back on the change which has come upon the field in the last ten or fifteen years, it seems that it consists, above all, in the abandonment of the idea of a single and simple "solution" of the photosynthesis problem. We have come to realize that photosynthesis is a complex sequence of photochemical and enzymatic reactions. If, for the sake of convenience, we still speak occasionally of the "Blackman reaction" as the non-photochemical component of this sequence, it is generally understood that this term covers a number of consecutive and parallel, forward, backward and side reactions, set into motion, accelerated, or retarded, by the action of light.

As a survival from the period when photosynthesis appeared a mysterious, but perhaps uniquely simple reaction, one or the other discovery is still being occasionally hailed as the "final solution" of the problem of photosynthesis. However, the complete mechanism of photosynthesis cannot be revealed by a single new finding—however significant—any more than a complicated jigsaw puzzle can be solved by the fitting of a single bit, however large, into its proper position.

Since photosynthesis is the source of all our food and fuel, the progress in its elucidation is followed with great interest by the public, which, in our time, has become aware of the limitations the supply of these commodities imposes on the material progress of the rapidly expanding human race. Every time a "solution" of photosynthesis is announced, the press indulges in the description of the great relief this discovery is likely to bring to the food and fuel hunger of the world. The hope that research on photosynthesis will provide a spectacular solution of one of the gravest—if not the gravest—difficulty that confronts mankind, is one of the reasons why this research has found public encouragement to the extent usually reserved only for problems of great practical significance.

It is only to be hoped that the public opinion will not be too disappointed by the probable failure of photosynthetic research to lead, in any foreseeable future, to a marked alleviation of the world's food and fuel shortages. The understanding is as yet sadly deficient in the public opinion—as well as in national leadership of most countries—of the way science progresses, and of its relation to technology. The progress of science occurs by probing in various directions, in which many scientists from different countries, take part, motivated by an urge to understand nature; and only to a much lesser extent by competitive efforts, spurred by a desire to obtain immediate solutions of practical difficulties. The prevailing public attitude that science is to be judged by its practical dividends, exposes research workers in fields such as photosynthesis to the temptation at least to abet—if not to encourage—excessive hopes and claims put out on their behalf by the press; and not all scientists successfully resist this temptation.

The study of photosynthesis is certain to lead to important insights into the fundamental processes of life; and out of these insights, there are certain to arise many at present unpredictable consequences for better agricultural or industrial processes, including perhaps ways for substantially enhancing the efficiency of solar energy conversion by plants. In this sense, the public interest in the study of photosynthesis is not misplaced, and the funds invested in it will not be wasted. But if mankind is ever to become independent from plants in the utilization of solar energy for making food or fuel, this emancipation is not likely to come directly from the elucidation of the complex mechanism of photosynthesis, or its successful reproduction outside the living cell. The utilization of solar energy for *heat* and *power* is much more likely to come from new processes as different from natural photosynthesis as industrial combustion of fuel is different from cellular respiration; and as to the *food* the most reasonable hopes in this area lie, for the time being, not in "artificial photosynthesis,"

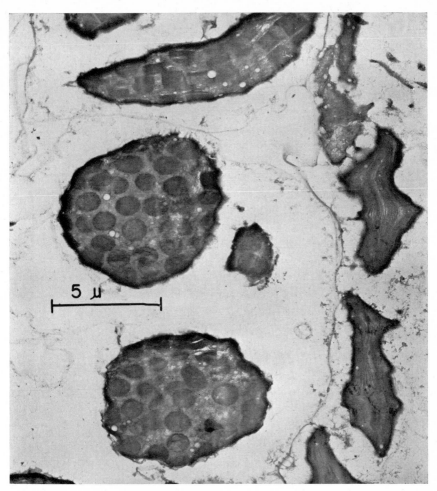

Fig. 38.1. Granular and laminar chloroplasts in *Zea mais*, sectioned after fixation by OsO₄. The granular chloroplasts on the left (two are sectioned parallel, one normal to the main plane) belong to the parenchyma, laminar chloroplasts on the right to a vascular bundle (after Vatter, unpublished; see p. 1991).

but in the development of new strains of more productive plants and of new methods of their cultivation (of which the now extensively studied large-scale growth of microscopic algae is a first example).

This does not mean that the achievement of photosynthesis outside the living cell would not be an important milestone in man's mastery of natural processes; but the importance of this achievement will not lie in immediate practical applications.

With the increasing understanding of the different aspects of the photosynthetic process in nature, the very definition of what is to be considered as "imitation of photosynthesis outside the living cell" becomes difficult. Which of the many facets of natural photosynthesis have to be faithfully reproduced for the experiment to be called "repetition of photosynthesis *in vitro*"? Certainly not every reduction of carbon dioxide to carbohydrate level by the action of light, can be called so (as has often been done *in* the past). At the very least, simultaneous evolution of an equivalent amount of oxygen is to be required. Beyond this, a certain similarity of the energy conversion yields is essential, as well as a capacity for continuing the process steadily for a reasonable length of time. No experiment performed as of January 1, 1955 can claim to have satisfied all these requirements; we can thus say that, at the termination of this monograph, photosynthesis outside the living cell still remains unachieved. This is true not only of artificially compounded chemical systems, but even of preparations derived from cells and containing various intact cell structures and cell ingredients.

*   *   *

Considerable progress has been achieved, since the writing of this monograph began, in the separation of some of the most important partial reactions in photosynthesis from their former bondage to the intact cell structure. In Chapter 4, the discovery of the "Hill reaction" in chloroplast preparations could just be announced; while in Chapter 35, a long series of studies could be described, revealing the analogy and the differences between this reaction and the true photosynthesis. These studies climaxed in the coupling of the Hill reaction with the reduction of certain carbonyl and—with the help of high-energy phosphate—also of some carboxyl compounds: the nearest approach to date to true photosynthesis in cell-free preparations. After Chapter 35 was completed, the photochemical incorporation of tagged carbon dioxide into organic compounds in light could be demonstrated by Tolbert on squeezed-out cell contents, and by Arnon on whole chloroplasts (*cf.* p. 1535). It now seems more likely than ever that the complete enzymatic system of photosynthesis is contained in chloroplasts. (Certain early experiments with the isotope

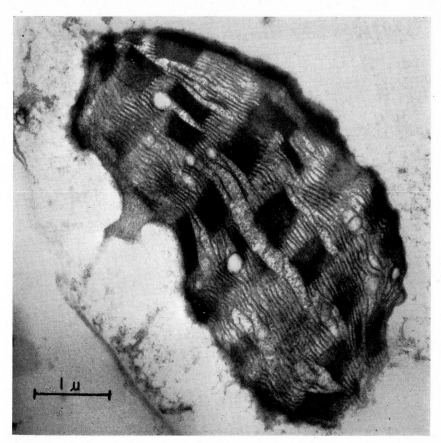

Fig. 38.2.   Fixed and sectioned mature chloroplast of *Zea mais*, lamellar connections between the grana (Vatter 1955, unpublished; see p. 1991).

C(11), and the lack of ability of chloroplast fragments to use carbon dioxide as hydrogen acceptor in the Hill reaction, had made it appear likely, for a while, that the cytoplasm has an essential function in the carbon dioxide reduction.) However, this conclusion needs confirmation, since complete separation of chloroplasts from residues of cytoplasm, which may include mitochondria or similar enzyme carriers, is not easy. Furthermore, it is not yet excluded that separated chloroplasts may be able to continue the photochemical reduction of carbon dioxide only for a very short time, before some chemical agents, normally supplied by the cytoplasm, become exhausted.

*   *   *

With the help of the long-lived radioactive carbon, C(14), several important landmarks could be identified in the field of photosynthetic intermediates, which at the time this book was begun still was the *terra incognita* (and has now become merely the "dark continent") on the biochemical maps. Certain paths have been identified connecting these landmarks, and we can hopefully look forward to a gradual mapping-out of the whole area—even if this is likely to take as much time and effort as did the unraveling of another tangled skein of enzymatic reactions—the respiratory degradation of carbohydrates in the cell. Although the mechanism of the latter seemed to have been essentially clarified by the establishment of the tricarboxylic acid cycle by Krebs, new intermediates and new alternative paths are being added almost every year.

The two main landmarks which the application of tracer technique has established, as of 1955, in the domain of CO_2-reduction intermediates in photosynthesis are *phosphoglyceric acid* (PGA) and *ribulose diphosphate* (RDP). The role of the first one as the immediate product of CO_2-fixation and substrate of photochemical reduction seems to be established beyond all reasonable doubt; while the function of the second as the carbon dioxide acceptor, whose carboxylation leads to PGA, seems eminently plausible, and is supported by enzymatic experiments *in vitro*.

Calvin and co-workers have outlined a complete mechanism of sucrose synthesis incorporating, in addition to PGA and RDP, other intermediates (on the reduction level of carbohydrates). Most of these—dihydroxyacetone phosphate, sedoheptulose mono- and diphosphates, glucose and fructose monophosphates, and uridine diphosphoglucose (but not erythrose phosphate!)—have been identified among the early C(14)-tagged products of photosynthesis.* This reaction sequence requires, in addition to the

---

* See scheme on p. 1697. A more detailed presentation was given by Calvin and Bassham in a paper at the Geneva Conference on Peaceful Uses of Atomic Energy, August 1955 (*cf.* in particular figs. 5 and 14 of that paper).

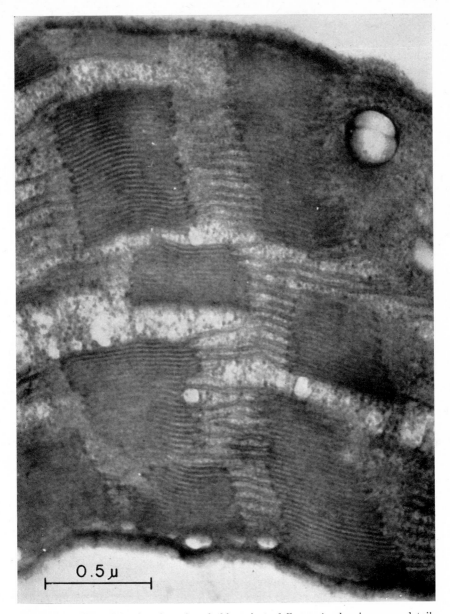

Fig. 38.3.   Part of fixed and sectioned chloroplast of *Zea mais*, showing more details of the grana and intergranular lamellae.   Darker layers must be richer in lipoids, which take up more OsO_4 than proteins.   Note double sheets in grana, with space between them closed up on both ends by lipoids (Vatter 1955, unpublished; see p. 1991).

recently discovered RDP-carboxylating and dismuting enzyme ("ribulose carboxydismutase"), only enzymes (PGA hydrogenase, phosphotriose, isomerase, aldolase, transketolase, phosphopentokinase, phosphatase, phosphopentoisomerase) which are known to exist. According to this scheme, the reduction of a molecular of carbon dioxide to sucrose could proceed without the help of light, if two molecules of $TPNH_2$ and three molecules of ATP could be made available in appropriate concentrations, and in proper location within the cell: a conclusion which challenges experimental confirmation.

The hypothesis that the photochemical reduction of PGA leads to phosphoglyceraldehyde seems almost unavoidable; the suggestion that this is the *only* photochemically induced reduction step in photosynthesis has all the temptation of plausible simplicity. That this reduction occurs by combined action of a reduced pyridine nucleotide and a high-energy phosphate, in exact reversal of the corresponding step in respiration, is undoubtedly suggestive, but remains to be proved. The demonstration that high-energy phosphate (ATP) actually is synthesized in light by whole cells as well as by chloroplasts (*cf.* p. 1702–1709), lends support to this hypothesis. However, the possibility that PGA is reduced in photosynthesis, either directly by excited chloroplasts or by an intermediate other than TPN (and not requiring the assistance of high-energy phosphate), is not yet excluded.

Despite the demonstration that phosphoglyceric acid alone is tagged in the first second or two of exposure, the large variety of acids, phosphate esters, and aminoacids, which tagging experiments of slightly longer duration characterize as early products of photosynthesis, remains bewildering. The elucidation of their genesis (and fate) remains a large task for the future. Most puzzling is the role of *malic acid*, which appears in large quantities immediately upon the beginning of tagging in light. So does alanine, and, to a lesser extent, certain other aminoacids. Whether the appearance of the latter is indicative of an early branching-off of protein synthesis from sugar synthesis, remains to be established.

*   *   *

Not only does the reduction of carbon dioxide in photosynthesis, as we see it now, involve a complex interplay of enzymatic transformations, similar in many respects to those that occur in respiration, but running generally in the opposite direction, but it also shows evidence of being connected to respiration, and probably to other metabolic processes as well, by multiple crosslinks, on different levels of reduction and carbon chain synthesis, with common pools of intermediates, to which several reactions can contribute, or into which several of them can dip.

Fig. 38.4. Lamellated chloroplast from a light green part of the inner leaf of a young shoot of *Aspidistra elatior* (after Leyon, *Exptl. Cell Research*, **7**, 265 (1954)). See page 1732.

The nature of these links between photosynthesis and respiration still is only dimly perceived. A blocking of the citric acid cycle in light is postulated by Calvin *et al.* on the basis of tagging observations, but is not confirmed by Brown's mass-spectroscopic studies, which reveal a more or less steady continuation of respiration in light. If it is true—as it now seems likely—that the reaction sequence converting CO_2 to $\{CH_2O\}$, begins and ends within the chloroplasts, *cytoplasmic* respiration could have a less close relation to photosynthesis than chloroplastic respiration; and the results of Calvin's experiments may perhaps indicate, not that the citric acid cycle in the whole cell is stopped by light, but that the tagged products of photosynthesis are prevented from leaving the chloroplasts, and joining the reservoir from which the respiration in the cytoplasm is sustained. Another facet of this interpretation is the conclusion that in cells showing in Brown's experiments, a practically unchanged respiration in light, by far the most important part of respiration occurs outside the chloroplasts.

A very important conclusion, derived from tagging experiments, is that in synthesis, as in the breaking down of carbohydrates, a cyclic mechanism operates, with the carbon dioxide acceptor (such as ribulose diphosphate) being "thrown into the pot" at the beginning of the reaction cycle, and regenerated at its end (together with the hexose which leaves the cycle as its final product). There is something striking—and perhaps significant—in this "reproductive cycle" of a relatively simple molecule.

* * *

It was repeatedly emphasized in this monograph that the biochemical mechanism of the transformation of CO_2 to $\{CH_2O\}$ is only one of the three main components of photosynthesis—the other two being the enzymatic mechanism of oxidation of water to oxygen and the third—and photochemically perhaps the most interesting one—the mechanism of photochemical hydrogen transfer from the system H_2O/O_2 to the system $\{CH_2O\}/CO_2$. Of these three parts of photosynthesis, the first one is much better understood now than the second and the third.

The enzymatic mechanism of oxygen liberation, for example, remains entirely unknown; nothing can be added, after fifteen years, to the vague general speculations indulged in in Chapter 11. (A similar darkness spreads, incidentally, also over the mechanism of the reverse process—the "mobilization of oxygen" in respiration.) Is water oxidized, in photosynthesis, as in certain inorganic systems, *directly*, i.e., by removal of an electron from an OH^--ion and transformations of the so obtained OH-radical into O_2 (either involving, or not involving, the biradical, H_2O_2, as intermediate)? Or is the H_2O molecule incorporated in an organic molecule, as CO_2

is incorporated in PGA (*e.g.*, $R_1 = R_2 + H_2O \rightarrow R_1H.R_2OH$), and the organic hydroxyl group then oxided photochemically, with or without the intermediate formation of an organic peroxide? Are compounds of the cytochrome type involved in this part of the reaction sequence? Or carotenoids, with their known capacity to form peroxides?

Little progress has occurred, since 1940, also in the understanding of the chemical nature of the photochemical process proper. Is chlorophyll a chemical participant in it? It is most likely that this process is a light-induced oxidation-reduction against the gradient of chemical potential with chlorophyll as a possible intermediate acceptor of hydrogen atoms or electrons. The alternative suggestion that this process involves, not an (intra- or intermolecular) H-transfer, but the dissociation of an S—S bond, leading to the formation of a biradical, made by Calvin and co-workers (p. 1698) does not seem convincing. Is there something to the suggestion, made recently by Wessels, that vitamin K is the oxidant in this reaction? May lipoic acid serve in this capacity? Or cytochromes—*c*, or *f*—(as suggested by Hill)—or are the last two taking part only in the back reaction between the primary oxidation and reduction products, leading to the production of high-energy phosphates (*cf.* below)?

Whether chlorophyll *a* (or bacteriochlorophyll "890") plays the role of the H-donor in the primary photochemical process (or that of the H-acceptor in this process, or of both), remains a matter of speculation (encouraged by observations of reversible photochemical oxidation, and reversible photochemical reduction of chlorophyll *in vitro*, described in Chapters 18 and 35).

The reversible changes of the absorption spectrum of photosynthesizing cells have at first indicated only transformations of components other than chlorophyll (*cf.* Chapter 37C, section 7e). Since then, however, Coleman and Holt* have observed a reversible bleaching of chlorophyll *in vivo* at 680 mμ together with the appearance of a band at 515 mμ (observed already by Duysens). This finding seems to indicate a reversible photoreduction of chlorophyll *in vivo* analogous to that studied by Krasnovsky *et al.* *in vitro*.

The study of chlorophyll reactions and the investigation of the spectroscopic properties of this compound, suggest that the cyclopentanone ring, with its keto-enol isomerism, may be the part of the chlorophyll molecule most directly involved in the photocatalytic action; the presence of the magnesium atom in the center of the molecule appears to influence the properties of this group in a significant way.

Since four H-atom transfers are needed to reduce one molecule of carbon dioxide to the carbohydrate level (or to liberate one molecule of oxygen

* Coleman, J. W., Holt, A. S., and Rabinowitch, E., *Science* (in press).

from two molecules of water), the hypothesis of H-transfer as primary photochemical process naturally suggests that the quantum requirement of photosynthesis (in higher plants as well as in bacteria) should be at least 4. We say "at least," because one quantum is likely to give the H-atom an insufficient reductive potential to enable it to reduce carbon dioxide to the carbohydrate level (e.g., the hydrogen in reduced pyridine nucleotide cannot be transferred to a carboxyl group without an additional supply of energy). A "booster" effect could be derived from the reversal of a part of the primary photochemical processes, and storage of the chemical energy liberated in the back reactions ("energy dismutation" hypothesis, cf. p. 164). For example, back reaction could be made to create high-energy phosphate esters (ATP), which, we know, can assist reduced pyridine nucleotides in reducing phosphoglycerate to phosphoglyceraldehyde. "Energy dismutation," if it does occur, should increase the minimum quantum requirement above 4—how far above, depends on the effectiveness with which the energy of the back reactions is utilized for the forward reaction. Calvin suggested recently that the additional quantum requirement is close to 3, leading to a total quantum yield of about 1/7.

The hypothesis, according to which the primary chemical process of photosynthesis is the transfer, by one quantum, of one hydrogen atom (directly or indirectly) from water to pyridine nucleotide; and that re-oxidation of a fraction of the reduced pyridine nucleotide molecules produces high-energy phosphates, permitting other molecules of the reduced pyridine nucleotide to reduce phosphoglyceric acid to triose phosphate, seems, at this writing, the most popular (but by no means finally established) mechanism of the primary photochemical process in photosynthesis. It is supported—as mentioned above—by the observations of the accumulation of adenosine triphosphate in illuminated cells (cf. p. 1702). The "quantum yield controversy" (cf. Chapters 29 and 37D), remains unsettled, but it seems that its most likely final outcome will be the experimental establishment of a minimum quantum requirement of between 6 and 8 quanta per oxygen molecule*—a value compatible with the above described theoretical picture. On the other hand, it is not yet impossible that the actual minimum quantum requirement will turn out to be 8, thus supporting the "eight quantum hypothesis" (cf. Chapter 8), which suggests that two quanta are used for the transfer of each hydrogen atom from water to its ultimate desitination.

Continued assertions that the minimum quantum requirement is *less* than 4 are, on the other hand, highly implausible; this applies in particular to the suggestion that the true minimum requirement is as low as 2.83,

---

* New results, falling into this range, were published by Yuan, Evans and Daniels (*Biochim. et Biophys. Acta*, **17**, 185, 1955) and Bassham, Shibata and Calvin (*ibid.*, **17**, 332, 1955).

corresponding to a 100% conversion of light energy into chemical energy, and thus implying a complete absence of "friction losses" in the whole reaction sequence of photosynthesis. There is, however, considerable evidence that at low light intensities (or in short illumination periods) intermediates of respiration can be used as substrates of photosynthesis, with an apparent decrease in quantum requirement.

*   *   *

One area in which great progress has been achieved since this monograph was begun, is the *morphology* of the photosynthetic organs. We now know, from electron-microscopic evidence, that a general feature of these organs are lamellae, 70–200 A thick, either running through the whole chloroplast, or forming cylindrical stacks ("grana") perhaps 2 μ thick, suspended in the "stroma." It seems likely that these lamellae are formed by single or double protein layers, coated with monomolecular layers of chlorophyll; but the precise arrangement of chlorophyll molecules remains to be established, and practically nothing is known as yet about that of the "accessory" pigments, the carotenoids, and the phycobilins.

Since Chapter 37A was completed, the technique of sectioning, permitting the preservation of much of the original structure of the chloroplasts, has been further improved, and the relation between laminar and granular chloroplasts has emerged with new clarity. As dimly perceived before, the whole chloroplast has a laminar structure, with lamina converging and merging at the two poles (*cf*. fig. 38.4). In a certain stage of the development of most (but not all) chloroplasts of the higher plants, the lamina become thicker and denser in certain regions, until, in many cells, these denser regions acquire the sharp outlines of "grana." The latter remain, however, connected by thinner lamina. The lamina probably contain more lipoids than the interlaminar material (since they are preferentially fixed by OsO_4). This structure was demonstrated by Steinmann and Sjöstrand* in *Aspidistra elatior;* even more revealing in their clarity were the electron micrographs obtained by Vatter† with maize (*cf*. figs. 38.1–38.3).

The two-dimensional, lamellar structure may serve the purpose of easy access to, and removal away from, the light-activated pigment molecules, of chemical agents ("co-enzymes") or of reaction intermediates, including organic acids or aldehydes (intermediates in the reduction of carbon dioxide), and peroxides (intermediates in the oxidation of water). In addition, however, this structure may also permit the migration of excitation energy toward the reaction substrates or enzymes. The actual occurrence and extent of such energy migration between the chlorophyll molecules

* Steinmann, E., and Sjöstrand, F. S., *Experimental Cell Research*, **8**, 15 (1955).
† Vatter, A., Thesis, University of Illinois, 1955. See figures 38.1, 2, and 3.

remains to be established; but an energy exchange of this type is definitely known to occur between the accessory pigments, absorbing light of higher frequency (the carotenoids, the phycobilins, and chlorophyll b) on the one hand, and chlorophyll a (bacteriochlorophyll "890" in purple bacteria) on the other hand. The latter two pigments seem to be the only ones directly participating in the primary photochemical process (in higher plants and bacteria, respectively). The spatial arrangement of the pigment molecules, which makes this energy exchange possible (and in some cases, highly efficient), remains to be elucidated; a great puzzle in this field is presented by the low effectiveness of quanta absorbed directly by chlorophyll a in some red and blue-green algae (as compared to the quanta first absorbed by the phycobilins and then transferred to chlorophyll a).

The low yield of fluorescence of chlorophyll *in vivo* (which, however, may be of the order of 1%, rather than 0.1% as formerly assumed, *cf.* p. 1867)*, puts a rather low upper limit on the life time of excitation, and thus also on the extent of excitation energy migration in living cells. It is nevertheless possible—although by no means certain—that this migration is important in the transition from the photochemical process proper (in which a 10^{-2} molar "photoenzyme," chlorophyll, is involved), to reactions mediated by the much less abundant (perhaps, 10^{-5} or 10^{-6} molar), non-photochemical biocatalysts.

The high yield of resonance transfer from accessory pigments to chlorophyll poses a challenge to submicroscopic morphology—to elucidate the relative position of the molecules of the various pigments in the living state. Are the chromoproteids (phycobilins), for example, located inside the protein discs, on which chlorophyll (according to the above-mentioned hypothesis) forms a monomolecular adsorpticn layer?

$$* \quad * \quad *$$

Among the problems of reaction kinetics of photosynthesis, that of the "limiting" reaction (or reactions), determining the maximum rate in constant light and the maximum yield per flash in flashing light, stands at present in the center of interest. A ratio of $2500:n$ between the concentrations of chlorophyll and of a "limiting" enzyme (with $n = 1$, or 4, or 8) accounted satisfactorily for the essential features of the instantaneous flash light experiments (such as those of Emerson and Arnold), the maximum yield of such a flash being about one molecule oxygen per 2500 molecules of chlorophyll. The time constant of 2×10^{-2} sec., derived from the dependence of the "instantaneous" flash yield on the length of the dark period between flashes, explained well, in conjunction with the

---

* New integrating sphere measurements by Latimer (unpublished) gave, for various algae, fluorescence quantum yields extrapolating to 2% for light intensity zero, and increasing to and above 3% in stronger light.

above concentration value, the maximum rate of photosynthesis in constant light, which is equivalent (at room temperature) to about 0.025 molecules oxygen per chlorophyll molecule per second $(1/(2500 \times 2 \times 10^{-2}) = 0.02)$. However, this satisfactory agreement was spoiled by the more recent observations (by Tamiya *et al.*, and by Kok) of a higher flash yield, obtainable by flashes which, though not "instantaneous," still are much shorter than the "Emerson-Arnold period" of 2×10^{-2} sec. The yield of these "extended" flashes continues to increase with the length of the dark interval, in the region (up to 1 sec. or beyond) in which that of "instantaneous" flashes become constant; furthermore, it depends on temperature, while the yield of the "instantaneous" flashes is independent of the latter. The explanation of these complications must be sought in the interaction of two "limiting" reactions. Franck's suggestion that one of them (the "Emerson-Arnold reaction") consists in the transformation of the primary photochemical products, which "stabilizes them against back reactions, while the second one is concerned with the primary carbon dioxide fixation, may be correct for some of the results, but does not account for similar observations made by Gilmour *et al.* on the Hill reaction, in which no carboxylation is involved. It seems that more than one "limiting" reaction is involved in the oxygen-liberating photochemical process itself. A closer quantitative analysis of flash light results promises important revelations concerning these reactions. The important point to be kept in mind in this analysis is that the maximum yield of a reaction involving a "catenary series" of enzymatic (or other) steps of limited capacity, is not always equal to the maximum rate of the "slowest" of these reactions, but may be dependent on several of them (if their maximum rates are not too different), as demonstrated in Chapter 27 (section A7).

The existence of a second "limiting" reaction, which can utilize effectively dark periods of the order of 0.1–1 sec., is indicated, in addition to flashing light experiments, also by observations in alternating light with equal light and dark periods.

This brief passing in review of some of the problems of photosynthesis in which the most progress has been achieved in the last ten years, or in which unexplained experimental results have posed a clear challenge to further experimentation and theoretical interpretation, shows that at the time this monograph is completed, the field is in great flux. The author hopes that the method he has adopted to describe critically all the experiments, and discuss all the theories suggested to explain them, without committing himself too strongly to any one of them (and committing himself against them only when they infringe on general principles of physical chemistry, which —the author believes—cannot be violated by organisms any more than by non-organic chemical systems), will prevent this monograph from becoming *obsolete* as rapidly as it will inevitably become *incomplete*.

AUTHOR INDEX OF THE MAIN INVESTIGATIONS DESCRIBED IN VOLUME II, PART 2

A

Åberg, B.: Ascorbic acid content of leaves, 1750.

Albers, V. M. *See* Knorr, H. V.

Albertson, P. A., and Leyon, H.: Electron microscopy of *Chlorella*, 1726–1727.

Algera, L., Beijer, J. J., Iterson, W. van, and Thung, T. H.: Electron microscopy of chloroplasts, 1721–1722.

Allard, H. A. *See* Garner, W. W.

Allen, F. L.: Photosynthesis in the absence of oxygen, 1915.

Allen, M. B. *See* Arnon, D. I.

——, Gest, H., and Kamen, M.: Distinguishing C^*O_2 uptake by photosynthesis and respiration, 1635–1636.

Altman, K. I. *See* Salomon, K.

Andreeva, T. F. *See* Zubkovich, L. E.

Anson, M. L. *See* French, C. S.

Arnold, W.: Effect of ultraviolet light on flash yield, 1465; flashing light effect with purple bacteria, 1481–1482. *See also* Emerson, R.; Holt, A. S.; Strehler, B. L.

——and Davidson, J. B.: Chemiluminescence in *Chlorella*, 1841.

——and Kohn, H.: Maximum flash yield and Chl, 1273–1274; photosynthetic unit, 1281; photosynthesis yield in flashing light as function of dark intervals, 1454.

——and Oppenheimer, J. R.: Energy transfer from phycocyanin to chlorophyll in blue-green algae, 1300; disintegration of blue-green algae by squeezing, 1543.

Arnon, D. I.: Coupling of Hill's reaction in chloroplasts to malic enzyme system from the same plant, 1583–1584; polyphenol oxidase in leaves, 1607; inhibition of plant respiration by iodoacetamide, 1687; malic enzyme in leaves, 1745; polyphenol oxidase in plants, 1747. *See also* Whatley, F. R.

——, Allen, M. B., and Whatley, F. R.: C^*O_2 fixation and ATP* formation in light by whole chloroplasts, vii, 1537, 1982; differential inhibition of Hill's reaction, C^* and P^* uptake by whole chloroplasts in light, 1615.

——, Bell, M. A., and Whatley, F. R.: C^*O_2 fixation in whole chloroplasts, 1701.

——and Whatley, F. R.: Deterioration of chloroplasts by heat, 1544; by shaking, 1544; with time, 1546; influence of buffer, 1546; of chloride, 1550; of anions, 1551; maximum rate of Hill's reaction, 1595; maximum utilization of different oxidants, 1598; pH effect on Hill's reaction, 1601; temperature effect on Hill's reaction, 1602–1603; inhibition of Hill's reaction by azide, 1610.

Aronoff, S.: Deterioration of chloroplast preparations, 1546; fractionation of chloroplast material and activity of supernatant, 1556–1557; various quinones as Hill oxidants, 1572; aldehydes as Hill oxidants, 1589; light curves of Hill's reaction with different quinones, 1595–1596; Hill's reaction inhibition by KCN, 1609; by azide and NH_2OH, 1610; by o-phenanthroline and urethane, 1611.

——, Barker, H. A., and Calvin, M.: C(14) distribution in glucose molecule after 1 hour photosynthesis in barley, 1631.

D

Hunter, J. *See* Burk, D.
Hutner, S. M. *See* Provasoli, L.
Huzisige, H. *See* Tamiya, H.; Yosida, T
Hyde, J. L. *See* Ruben, S.

I

Iggena, M. L.: Growth in alternating light, 1438–1439.
Inman, O.: Chlorophyll in thermophiles, 1228; photosynthesis begins with first traces of chlorophyll, 1267.
Irvin, A. A.: Chlorophyll formation and beginning of photosynthesis, 1267.
Ivanov, L. A., and Orlova, I. M.: Lower temperature limit of photosynthesis in conifers, 1219.

J

Jacobs, E. E.: Life-time of lowest excited state of chlorophyll, 1798; absorption of chlorophyll monolayers, 1818. *See also* Holt, A. S.; Rabinowitch, E.
——, Holt, A. S., Kromhout, R., and Rabinowitch, E.: Calculation of excitation states in chlorophyll crystals and monolayers, 1295–1297.
——, Holt, A. S., and Rabinowitch, E.: Absorption spectra of chlorophyll monolayers, 1297, 1818.
——, Vatter, A. E., and Holt, A. S.: Crystalline chlorophyll, 1782; absorption spectra of crystalline chlorophyll, 1815.
Jacquot, R. *See* Wurmser, R.
Jelley, E. E.: Energy migration in dye polymers, 1292.
Jenks, G. *See* Dole, M.
Jucker, E. *See* Karrer, P.
Jumelle, H.: Photosynthesis at $-30°C$?, 1218.
Jungers, V., and Doutreligne, Soeur, J.: Color of grana, 1717–1718.

K

Kachan, A. A., and Dain, B. J.: Reversible bleaching of chlorophyll in rigid solvent by ultraviolet light, 1499.
Kalishevich, S. V. *See* Godnev, T. N.
Kamen, M. D. *See* Allen, M. B.; Gest, H.; Ruben, S.
—— and Barker, H. A.: Interpretation of isotopic oxygen experiments, 1916.
—— and Spiegelmann, S.: Products of P(32) fixation in plants, 1704.
Kandler, O.: Phosphate fixation in *Chlorella* in light and dark, 1705; nitrate metabolism and photosynthesis, 1705.
Karmanov, V. G.: Temperature of leaves in incandescent light, 1217.
Karrer, P., and Tucker, E.: Absorption of violaxanthin, 1810.
Kasha, M. *See* Lewis, G. N.
——, and Becker, R. S.: Phosphorescence and metastable state of chlorophyll, ix.
Kaspers, J. *See* Bucher, Th.
Katheder, F. *See* Scheibe, G.
Katz, E.: Photoelectric model of photosynthetic unit, 1299. *See also* Wassink, E. C.
——, Wassink, E. C., and Dorrestein, R.: Temperature effect on fluorescence in bacteria, 1245.
Kautsky, H.: Temperature effect on fluorescence, 1245; fluorescence-time curves during photosynthesis induction, 1376–1405; induction theory, 1428.
Kawaguchi, S. *See* Benson, A. A.

L

N

Nagai, S.: Silver precipitates in chloroplasts, 1736–1737.

Nakajima, T., and Kon, H.: Theory of chlorophyll spectrum, 1793.

Nakao, A. *See* Buchanan, D. L.

Nakayama, H. *See* Yosida, T.

Neuberger, A., and Scott, J. J.: pH variation and porphyrin spectrum, 1799.

Nezgovorov, L.: Amylase in chloroplasts, 1749.

Nezgovorova, L. A.: C(14) uptake and distribution after long photosynthesis and in darkness, 1632.

Niel, C. B. van. *See* Larsen, H.; Polgar, A.

Nier, A. O. C. *See* Brown, A. H.

Niggli, F. *See* Baur, E.

Nishimura, M. S. *See* Whittingham, C. P.

Noack, K.: Chlorophyll decomposition, 1768.

——, Pirson, A., and Michels, H.: Anaerobic inhibition of photosynthesis caused by an acid fermentation product, 1366.

Noddack, W., and Kopp, C.: Time effect in photosynthesis at high temperature, 1221–1222; no temperature effects on quantum yield, 1234; temperature coefficient of photosynthesis, 1235, 1237, 1240; assimilation numbers of *Chlorella*, 1262.

Northcote, D. H. *See* Hill, R.

O

Ochoa, S. *See* Vishniac, W.

O'hEocha, C. *See* Haxo, F.

Olson, R. A. *See* Brackett, F. S.

—— and Brackett, F. S.: Anaerobic inhibition of *Chlorella*, 1371.

——, Brackett, F. S., and Crickard, R. G.: Polarographic method for measuring quantum yield, 1956.

Oppenheimer, J. R. *See* Arnold, W.

Ordin, L. *See* Whatley, F. R.

Orlova, I. M. *See* Ivanov, L. A.

Osipova, O. P., and Timofeeva, I. V.: Nitrogen deficiency effect on chloroplasts, 1743.

Osterhout, W. J. V., and Haas, A. R. C.: Temperature coefficient of photosynthesis, 1236; first induction measurements, 1317; long induction period, 1361; two possible mechanisms of induction, 1408.

Österlind, S.: Induction in algae after increase in pH, 1363–1364; role of bicarbonate ions in photosynthesis, 1887; effect of cyanide on photosynthesis, 1903.

Ouellet, C. *See* Calvin, M.

Owens, O. H. *See* Goodwin, R. H.

P

Paauw, F. van der: Temperature coefficient of photosynthesis, 1235, 1237, 1238.

Palade, G. E. *See* Wolken, J. J.

Pardee, A. B., Schachman, H. K., and Stanier, R. Y.: Ultracentrifuge studies of chloroplast material, 1740–1741.

Paris, C. H. *See* Thomas, J. B.

Pariser, R.: Chlorophyll sensitized oxidation of ascorbic acid by butter yellow, 1525. *See also* Livingston, R.

Pearse, H. L. *See* Gregory, F. G.

V

Van Amstel, J. E.: Thermal injury in *Elodea*, 1223.

Van der Paauw, F. *See* Paauw, F. van der.

Van der Veen, R. *See* Veen, R. van der.

Van Niel, C. B. *See* Niel, van, C. B.

Van Norman, R. W. *See* Brown, A. H.

—— and Brown, A. H.: Mass spectroscopic method for studying relation of respiration to photosynthesis, 1927; consumption of O(18) and O(16) by plants, 1929.

——, Franch, C. S., and Macdowall, F. D. H.: Phycocyanin-sensitized chlorophyll fluorescence in red algae, 1301; no Hill reaction with chloroplasts from red algae, 1561.

Van Pee, M. *See* Dunicz, B.

Varner, J. E., and Burrell, R. C.: C*O$_2$ fixation in deacidification of succulents, 1702.

Vartapetjan, B. B. *See* Kursanov, A. L.

Vatter, A.: Electron microscopy of grana, 1719–1722, 1726, 1741, 1986; no chloroplast membrane, 1722; grana discs, 1723, 1981, 1983, 1985, 1991. *See also* Jacobs, E. E.

Vavilov, S. I.: Fluorescence quenching and depolarization by resonance, 1284, 1286; experiments on energy transfer in solution, 1308.

——, Galanin, M. D., and Pekerman, F. M.: Experiments on energy transfer in solutions, 1308–1309.

Vecher, A. S.: Chloroplast ash, 1749.

Veen, R. van der: Diaferometric measurement of induction, 1330–1331; CO$_2$ induction studied with diaferometer, 1342, 1348–1355, 1370.

Vennesland, B.: Carboxylases and malic enzyme in chloroplasts, 1745.

Vereshchinsky, I. V.: Snap freezing of chloroplasts in liquid air, 1546.

Vermeulen, D. *See* Wassink, E. C.

Vernon, L. *See* Aronoff, S.

Vertregt, N. *See* Thomas, J. B.

Vinogradov, A. P., Boichenko, E. A., and Baranov, V. I.: C(14) studies with chloroplast preparations, 1533.

Virgin, H. I.: Effect of imbibition on fluorescence spectrum of leaves, 1880.

Vishniac, W.: Restoration of photochemical activity of extracted chloroplasts by addition of chlorophyll, viii.

—— and Ochoa, S.: Pyridine-nucleotide specific enzymatic reductions tied to Hill's reaction, 1577–1579.

Vogler, K. G., and Umbreit, W. W.: Phosphate energy storage in chemosynthetic bacteria, 1703.

Vojnovskaja, K. K. *See* Krasnovsky, A. A.

Voynovskaya, K. K. *See* Krasnovsky, A. A.

W

Warburg, O.: *Chlorella* photosynthesis survives immersion in liquid air?, 1219; no temperature effect on photosynthesis in weak light, 1233; temperature coefficient of photosynthesis, 1236, 1239, 1241; discovery of short induction, 1317; photosynthesis in alternating light, 1437; quantum yield of Hill's reaction, 1593, 1967. *See also* Burk, D.; Damaschke, K.

——, Burk, D., and Schade, A. C.: Quantum yield measurements, 1941–1956.

——, Burk, D., Schocken, V., Korzenovsky, M., and Hendricks, S.: Relation of photosynthesis to respiration, 1925; quantum yield of photosynthesis, 1940.

—— and Geleick, H.: Quantum yield measurements, 1942–1944.

Wolken, J. J.: Space relationship in laminar chloroplasts, 1735–1736.

—— and Palade, G. E.: Laminated chloroplasts in flagellates, 1728–1730.

Wood, J. G.: High photosynthesis optimum of desert plants, 1228.

Wood, R. W. *See* Franck, J.

Working, E. B. *See* MacDougal, D. T.

Wurmser, R., and Jacquot, R.: Upper temperature limit of photosynthesis, 1221; thermal injury, 1223.

Y

Yabusoe, M.: Temperature coefficient of photosynthesis, 1236, 1239, 1241.

Yocum, C. S.: CO and HCN inhibition of chlorophyll formation, 1768. *See also* Larsen, H.

Yosida, T., Morita, N., Tamiya, H., Nakayama, H., and Huzisige, H.: Preparation of water from photosynthetic oxygen, 1916.

Yoshii, Y.: Temperature coefficient of photosynthesis, 1235; several temperature optima?, 1244.

Young, V. K. *See* French, C. S.

Yuan, E. L., Evans, R. W., and Daniels, F.: Quantum requirement of photosynthesis, viii.

Z

Zaukelies, D. A. *See* Dole, M.

Zechmeister, L. *See* Polgar, A.

Zhuravleva, M. *See* Baslavskaya, S. S.

Zill, I. P. *See* Tolbert, N. E.

Zubkovich, L. E., and Andreeva, T. F.: Loss of efficiency and change in other properties of chloroplasts in storage, 1547–1548.

SUBJECT INDEX

Volumes I, II.1, and II.2

The following abbreviations are used: ATP, *adenosine triphosphate;* BChl, *bacterio-chlorophyll;* Chl, *chlorophyll;* CS, *chemosynthesis;* DPN, *diphosphopyridine nucleotide;* HR, *Hill's reaction;* PGA, *phosphoglyceric acid;* Pheo, *pheophytin;* PO, *photoxidation;* PR, *photoreduction;* PS, *photosynthesis;* R, *respiration;* and TPN, *triphosphopyridine nucleotide*

Volume I, pp. 1–599; Volume II.1, pp. 601–1208; Volume II.2, pp. 1209–2088

A

Absorption

Absorption acts, frequency, 838, 1411

Absorption bands. See *Absorption spectra*

Absorption of light, by algae, in different depths, 735

by pigments *in vitro,* 603–71, 1793–1827

by plants, 672–730, 735, 1841–66

changes during PS, 1406, 1856–62, 1985

induction, 1406

chloroplast motion effects, 679–81

non-uniformity in depth, 865, 1007–12

by single cells, calculated from transmission and fluorescence, 1863–66

Absorption spectra, 603–71, 686–717, 1793–1827, 1841–66. See also under specific pigments

deformations caused by pigment segregation, 672–76, 698, 700, 709–17, 1865–66

"bunching" effect, 1865–66

scattering effect, 682–83, 698–700, 709–16, 1880–81, 1844, 1846, 1849

selective scattering effect, 1846, 1866

"sieve effect," 672, 697, 709–17, 1865–66

Absorption spectrum, of bacteria (purple and green), 693–94, 702–05, 707, 729, 1844–46, 1849–56, 1871–74

changes during induction, 1856–62

of bacteriochlorin, 620

of bacteriochlorophyll and bacterio-chlorophyllide, 616–18, 637–49, 1806–08

in colloids, 1826–27

in crystals, 1817, 1820

infrared, 1811

in monolayers, 1818, 1820

in vivo, 702–05, 1849–56

of bacteriopheophytin, 1807

of bacterioviridin, 618–19, 1807–08

in vivo, 704, 1854–56

of blue-green algae, 699, 708–30, 1876–77

of brown algae and diatoms, 690, 699, 706–08, 723–27, 1173

of carotenes, 658, 660

of carotenoids, 656–64, 1810

in vivo, 705–07, 1849–53, 1876–79

theory, 662–63

of chlorin, 620

of chlorin-e4, 621

of chlorophylls and chlorophyllides (a, b, and isomers), 603–614, 615, 629, 644–45, 652, 1173, 1495, 1799–1806

allomerized, 613–14, 1804–05, 1812, 1815

in colloids and adsorbates, 649–56, 1815, 1825–27

in crystals and monolayers, 1295, 1815–27

infrared, 610–12, 1811–15

in vivo, 697–702, 705, 1766, 1841–49

organic, conversion to carbohydrates by succulents, 265, 1702

as intermediates in PS and R, 35, 51, 246–48, 267–73, 1630–1702

occurrence and role in plants, 34, 262–69

production by succulents, 264–267

as reductants for Chl *in vitro?*, 1054

as substrates of bacterial PR, 102, 106–11

production and consumption ("gushes" and "gulps"), during induction in PS, 1334-55

production by HR, 1539–40, 1590, 1607–08

as stimulants of PS?, 343

Aconitic acid, as intermediate in R, 1690

Acrylates, polymerization, as test for free radicals, 1499, 1576

Actinometer, (Warburg-Schocken) with chlorophyllide, protoporphyrin, or pheophorbide as sensitizer, 839, 841, 1526–28, 1949, 1952

Action spectra. See also under *Blue-green algae, Brown algae,* etc.

Action spectra, of AgNO₃ reduction by chloroplasts (Molisch reaction), 1739–40

of BChl fluorescence *in vivo,* 813–14, 1302, 1873–74

of Chl *a* fluorescence *in vivo,* in blue-green algae, 813–14, 1303–04, 1876–78

in brown algae, 814–15, 1303, 1875–76

in green algae, 812–13, 1302–03, 1874–76

in red algae, 815–16, 1870, 1877–79

of Chl formation *in vivo,* 430–31, 1763–64

decline at long-wave end, in PS, 1154–55, 1180–83

in fluorescence, 752–53, 1828–29, 1875–76, 1877, 1879

definition, 1142–47

of phototaxis, in bacteria, 1188, 1302, 1873–74

in chloroplasts, 557, 681

of phycocyanin fluorescence, *in vivo,* 1878

of PO, *in vivo,* 531

of PR, in purple bacteria, 1187–89, 1302

of protochlorophyll-Chl transformation, 1763–64

of PS, 1142–87, 1303–04, 1876–79

in blue-green algae, 1178–80, 1183, 1184, 1303–04, 1876–77

in brown algae and diatoms, 1168–78, 1181, 1182, 1303

in green plants, 1142–1168, 1181–82, 1185–86

in red algae, 1178–87, 1877, 1879

Activated states, long-lived (metastable), 1023, 1290–91

of Chl *in vitro,* 748, 790–95, 1492–98

role in PS, 1970–71

Activation energy

Activation energy, of chloroplast deterioration, 1544

of heat injury, 1224

of HR, 1603

of PS, 1235–42, 1247–54, 1969–74

Adaptation

Adaptation, of algae, chromatic, 421–27, 532, 1357–58

to H₂, 128–36

poisoning, 310, 313

to light intensity and color, 421–27, 532, 1357–58

of plants, to light periodicity, 874

thermal, 1225–31

"Adapted algae," 120, 128–48, 168–70, 239, 1374–75, 1701

C(14) fixation in light, 1701

induction effects, 1374–75

metabolism, 120, 128–48, 168–70, 239

Adenine phosphate, C(14) tagging in PS, 1686

Adenosine phosphates

Adenosine diphosphate (ADP), P(32) tagged, in PS, steady state concentration in dark and light, 1708

Adenosine monophosphate (AMP), C(14) tagged in PS, 1686

Adenosine triphosphate (ATP), formed in light, by chloroplasts, 1537, 1614, 1709

by green cells, 227–28, 1406, 1702–09
by purple bacteria, 1709
inhibits CO_2 uptake by chloroplasts in light, 1536
P(32) tagged, steady state concentration in dark and light, 1708
role, in PS and CS, 115, 150, 201–02, 226–29, 1115–17, 1674, 1700, 1702–09, 1952, 1990
in R, 224–26, 1687
Adsorption, competitive, of PR substrate and narcotic, on Chl, 1422–23
fractional, of chloroplast material, 1556
Afterglow. See *Phosphorescence*
Aged cell cultures, decline of PS, in flashing light, 1273–74
in steady light, 285, 332, 339, 1270–71
"*Aggregation*" of Chl and BChl *in vitro* and *in vivo*, 1753–54, 1826, 1847, 1852
Aging effect, on Chl-content, 1264, 1271–72
on chloroplast structure, 1730–31
on PS, 285, 332, 339, 873, 879, 880–83, 1003, 1271–74, 1454
Alanine
Alanine, C(14) tagged, in light and after, 1681
photostationary concentration, 1679
preferential in carboxyl, 1663
time course of tagging, 1668
Alcohols, CO_2 uptake by, 179–80, 186
as H donors in bacterial PR, 107
in plants, 253–56
Aldehydes, in plants, 253
Aldolase, in chloroplasts, 1749
Algae. See also *Blue-green, Brown, Green, Red, algae; Chlorella*, and *Scenedesmus*
Algae, feeding with low molecular weight compounds, 257–62
forming Chl in dark, 430
as material for PS study, 833–36
pigments, 405–07, 408–11, 415–16, 472, 1786, 1809–10
unicellular, chloroplast preparation from, 1541
Alkali
Alkali, effect, on anaerobic PS induction, 1366, 1367
on Chl fluorescence induction, 1405

on reversible reduction of Chl and Pheo, 1506
production, by chloroplast preparations, 1540
Alkali ions, in chloroplasts and cytoplasm, 376–77
effect on PS, 321
Alkaloids, effect on PS, 321
"*Allomerization*" *of Chl.* See *Chlorophyll reactions, allomerization*
"*Allomerized*" *Chl*, fluorescence, 748, 754 786
spectrum, 613–14, 1804–05, 1812–15
Allyl thiourea, Chl-sensitized autoxidation, 510, 513, 839, 1525–26
effect on Chl bleaching and fluorescence, 487–88, 516, 783, 788–89, 1488, 1835. See also *Thiourea*
Alpine plants, leaf temperature, 1216
PS yield, 997, 1001
temperature curves of PS, 1226
Alternating light (= intermittent light with $t_l = t_d$), effect, on growth, 1437–38
on PS, 1435–47
on R, 1933–34
Amines
Amines, association with Chl, 1507, 1834
Chl-sensitized autoxidation, 509–13, 1525–28
CO_2 uptake, 181–83
effect, on Chl absorption spectrum, 638, 642, 646–48, 1780–82, 1801, 1803
on Chl-fluorescence, 766–72, 777, 783, 788–89, 1834
on reversible reduction of Chl and Pheo, 1504, 1506–07
reaction with Chl. See *Aminolysis*, and *Chlorophyll reactions*
Amino acids
Amino acids, in chloroplasts, 1743
CO_2 uptake, 182
C(14) tagging, in darkness and light, 1637–41, 1644, 1657, 1666, 1668, 1669, 1677, 1681, 1682, 1709
in leaves, 373–374
source of oxalic and malic acids in succulents, 264
Aminolysis, of Chl, 1780–82

Ammonia, effect on reversible reduction of Chl and Pheo, 1506

Ammonium ions, effect on PS, 340

Amylase, in chloroplasts, 1749

Anabolic cycle, in PS, 1664–65, 1692, 1695–98

Anaerobiosis

Anaerobiosis, effect, on absorption spectrum of Chl, 648

　on "adapted" algae, 128–36

　on ATP synthesis, 1706, 1709

　on Chl bleaching, 486, 490, 498, 501–02, 1493

　on Chl fluorescence, in chloroplasts, 1404

　　in solution, 492, 547

　　in vivo, 1393, 1399–1404, 1405

　on C*O$_2$ fixation in dark, 1648

　on PS induction, 1316–17, 1321, 1364–71

　on steady PS, 326–28, 976, 1364–65, 1913–15

Aniline, effect on reversible reduction of Chl, 1504

Anions

Anions, effect, on coagulation of chloroplast material, 1552–53

　on HR activity of chloroplasts, 1549–54

　on PS, 341–42

Anthocyanins, 401, 479–80, 541, 684–85, 717

"Antiphotosynthesis," 1326, 1898, 1906

"Antirespiration," 1117, 1898, 1905, 1963

Arginine, effect on reversible bleaching of Chl and Pheo, 1506

Arrhenius function, 1235, 1238, 1240, 1247–54

Arsenate, effect on C*O$_2$ fixation by chloroplasts, 1537

Ascorbic acid

Ascorbic acid, BChl-sensitized autoxidation, 511

　Chl-sensitized oxidation, by azo dyes, 1525

　　by riboflavin or safranin T, 1514–22

　deuterated, isotopic exchange with Chl in light, 1525

effect on Chl fluorescence, 1500

occurrence and function in green cells, 93, 259, 269–73, 1749–50

as reductant, for AgNO$_3$ in chloroplasts, 1737, 1740

as stimulant, of HR with O$_2$ as oxidant, 1568

　of C*O$_2$ fixation and ATP formation in chloroplasts, 1537

　of PS, 343

as "substitute reductant" in PS, 1588–89

Assimilation numbers

Assimilation numbers, 834–35

　of algae, 1262

　of *Chlorella* cells, cultivated in different lights, 1271

　　strongly illuminated, 1266

　　thermophilic, 1272

　of chlorotic plants, 1263

　of etiolated plants, 1267

　of leaves, aurea, 993, 1263–64

　　autumn, 1264

　　Chl-deficient, 1266

　　"normal," 1262

Assimilation time, definition, 1263. See *Assimilation numbers*

Athiorhodaceae (= purple non-sulfur bacteria). See *Bacteria, photosynthetic*

ATP. See *Adenosine triphosphate*

Aurea leaves

Aurea leaves, 401, 403, 408–09, 684–85, 1136–37

　assimilation numbers, 993, 1263–64

　flashing light yield, 1277

　light curves, 1261–66

　quantum yield of PS, 1137

　PS at extreme Chl deficiency, 1266

　temperature effect on PS, 1241

Autocatalysis, of PS activation after induction, 1388, 1393

　of Chl synthesis in leaves, 430, 1763, 1764

Autotrophic bacteria, 99–111

　role in nature, 123–24

Autoxidation. See also *Photoxidation.*

Autoxidation, 70

　of BChl, 495, 1501, 1786–87

　of carotenoids, 474

of Chl, 293, 459–63, 499–501, 1501, 1773, 1776–77

Chl sensitized, 508–11, 513, 528, 786, 788–90, 1508, 1525–28, 1949, 1952

Autumnal leaves, absorption spectra, 401, 705

PS, 1264–65, 1269

reflection spectra, 697

transformation of pigments, 412, 415

Auxin, effect of PS, 1921

Azide

Azide, effect, on CS, 113

  on HR, 1610, 1612

  on PR in bacteria, 957–59

  on PS, 318

  on sensitized cytochrome reduction, 1586

Azo dyes, Chl-sensitized reduction, 513, 1507–13, 1525

reaction with Chl, 503–05, 511

B

Back reactions, in HR, 1574, 1597–1600

in PS, first and second order, 1470–75

  with O_2 or its precursors?, 1708

  primary, 1020–33

  rate constant, 1326

  as source of phosphate energy, 1707–08, 1985

Bacteria

Bacteria, chemosynthetic (= chemautotrophic), 111–125

photosynthetic (= photoautotrophic), 99–112

  absorption spectrum, 170, 654–55, 692–94, 702–05, 707, 729–30, 1302, 1849–56

  changes in light, 1406, 1856–59

  action spectrum, of fluorescence, 1871–74

  of phototaxis, 1302, 1873–74

  of PR, 1187–88

  C(14) fixation in light, 1701

  energy transfer, 1301–02, 1871–74

  fluorescence, 809–11, 954, 1871–74

  kinetics, 1052–55, 1057, 1059, 1061–66, 1070, 1077

  sensitized, 813–14, 1301–02, 1871–74

grana, 1725, 1740–41

green, 101, 402, 445, 704

  absorption spectrum, 618, 694

hydrogenase content, 131

kinetics of PR, 836, 893, 943–49, 952–60, 969, 972, 977–78, 980, 1009–11, 1014, 1274, 1481–82, 1919, 1968–69

  flash yield, 1274, 1481–82

  *p*H effect, 1919

  sigmoid light curves, 948, 974, 977, 979, 1009–11, 1126

phosphatase, heat-resistant, 1686

phototaxis, 1302

pigments, 99, 101, 170, 384–89, 402, 407, 416–17, 444–45, 447, 473, 495, 616–18, 620, 622, 641–42, 748, 947, 1501, 1505, 1519–20, 1753, 1782, 1784, 1785, 1786–87, 1794–97, 1806–08, 1809–10, 1811, 1817–20, 1823, 1826, 1837–38, 1871–74

  state *in vivo*, 1753, 1849–56

primary photoprocess, 168–70

products of PR, C(14) tagged, 1671, 1701

quantum requirement of PR, 1125–28, 1968–69

respiration, 100, 110, 564

Bacteriochlorin, absorption spectrum, 620

Bacteriochlorophyll

Bacteriochlorophyll, 99, 101, 170, 388–89, 402, 407, 447, 495, 616–18, 631–33, 641–42, 651, 654–55, 702–05, 748, 749, 751, 810, 813, 817, 825, 947, 1301–02, 1307, 1482, 1501, 1505, 1519, 1782, 1784, 1786, 1787, 1806–07, 1811, 1817, 1818, 1820, 1823, 1826–27, 1837–38, 1849–54, 1874–75

absorption spectrum, 101, 170, 389, 616–18, 631–33, 651, 653–55, 702–05, 810, 1806–07, 1811, 1820–26, 1849–54

  in colloids, 651, 653–55, 1826

  in crystals and monolayers, 1817–23

  infrared, 1811

  in vivo, 170, 389, 655, 702–05, 810, 1849–54

  changes during PR, 1856–58

C₆ chain, formation by head-on condensation of two trioses, 1671

C(11) tracing, of C exchange in Chl, 557
of CO₂ fixation in PS, 37, 202–05, 241–44, 1634
of CO₂ role in metabolism of methane bacteria, 122
of reversibility of decarboxylation, 185–86, 201

C(13) mass spectrography, of CO₂-induction burst, 1940–41
of isotopic discrimination in PS, 1928–29
of R during PS, 1927–28

C(14) mass spectrography, of isotopic discrimination in PS, 1926–28

C(14) tracer studies

C(14) tracer studies, 244, 939, 1533, 1535–37, 1548, 1577–85, 1614, 1630–98, 1671, 1701–02, 1927–29
of CO₂ fixation, by reversal of decarboxylations in R, 1630, 1632–34, 1635–37, 1642, 1647–48, 1660, 1691
of CO₂ fixation and reduction, by HR, in chloroplastic preparations, 1533, 1535–37, 1548, 1577–85, 1614, 1635, 1701
by PR, in bacteria and H₂-adapted algae, 1671, 1701
by PS, 244, 939, 1630–98
anaerobic, 1648–49
in dark after pre-illumination?, 1632, 1634–44, 1646–55
early intermediates other than PGA, 1646–66
effect of inhibitors, 1686–88
intramolecular distribution of label, 1631–32, 1663–64, 1665–66, 1671–72
kinetics, 1676–84
occurrence in cytoplasm?, 1635
paper chromatography of products, 1655–66
PGA as first tagged product, 1644–46, 1651–55
post-photosynthetic tagging of tricarboxylic acids, 1645–46, 1660, 1666, 1680–82, 1698–99
proof of a cycle, 1664–66

role of a C₂ body as CO₃ acceptor?, 1675–76
role of C₅ and C₇ sugars, 1670–86
role of malic acid, 1666–76
sequence of intermediates, 1688–98
sequence of sugars, 1684–86
in squeezed-out cell material, 1537, 1701
stationary concentration of tagged intermediates, 1679
tagging after 1 hour of PS, 1631–32
tagging of uridine, adenine, and adenosine sugar phosphates, 1686
time course of tagging, 1668–70, 1676–86
two different CO₂ acceptors?, 1666–70, 1688–98
of CO₂ uptake in the deacidification of succulents, 1702

Calcium carbonate, in aquatics, 197
in leaves, 194, 377

Carbamates, formation from amines and CO₂, 181–83

Carbamination, 123, 182, 188, 191, 194, 289
of Chl, 454

Carbohydrates

Carbohydrates, 38–43
effect, on greening, 429
on PS, 331–33
on R, 333
energy, 49
as "internal factor" in PS, 875
occurrence in leaves, 44–45
as products of CS and PS, 33, 36–38, 118, 140, 241–42, 853, 1684–86
role in succulents, 265

Carbon, cycle on earth, 19
as reductant in CS, 112, 118
sublimation energy, 213

Carbon dioxide

Carbon dioxide, "free" and "bound," 189–90

Carbon dioxide absorption, by alcohols, 179–80
by alkaline earth carbonates, 179
by amines, 181–83
by bacteria, 110, 114, 209
by blood, 182

by Chl, 455–56
by *Escherichia coli*, 209
irreversible and reversible, 192–93
by leaves, dry, 191–95
living, 188–209
by phosphate buffers, 190–95
by plants, in dark, 190–95, 200–08
in PR, by organic H donors in bacteria, 106–111
in PS. See *Carbon dioxide acceptor in vitro*, 173–188
by water, 180, 181, 209
Carbon dioxide acceptor in PS (ACO₂, {CO₂}, or RCOOH), 173, 188, 198, 200–08, 346, 871, 898, 917, 1413–19, 1635, 1642, 1644–45, 1654–55, 1665, 1688–98
"blockade" by reduction intermediates, 933, 934, 936
cyclic regeneration, 1664–65, 1695–98
formation in light, survival in dark?, 1642, 1653–55
located in cytoplasm?, 66, 204, 1635
a "loose" and a "stable" form of CO₂ complex?, 1654–55
PGA as carboxylation product, 1644–55
a PS product (ribulose diphosphate), 1418–19, 1644–45
role in induction, 1413–19
as the ultraviolet-sensitive factor?, 346
Carbon dioxide addition, to C—H bonds, 183
to C—metal bonds, 186
to C—OH bonds, 180
to H—OH bonds, 176
to N—Mg bonds, 454
Carbon dioxide concentration, effect, on CO₂ burst, 1346
on dark C*O₂ fixation, 1643–44
on deacidification of succulents, 265
on fluorescence induction, 1381, 1391–95
on HCN poisoning, 303, 320
on induction, 1317, 1318, 1406
on rate of tagging of PS intermediates, 1684
on urethan poisoning, 322
as factor in PS, 851–53, 870–72, 879, 886–943

in nature, 174, 902, 904–05
Carbon dioxide curves, of dark C*O₂ fixation in pre-illuminated cells, 1644
of PS, $P = f[CO_2]$, 870, 871, 886–98, 916–39, 1892–98
carboxylation constant calculation, 934–37
compensation point, 898–901, 1243, 1898–1901
effect of narcotics and poisons, 954–960
in flashing light, 1461
half-saturation, 891–98, 916–36, 1018, 1038
are they hyperbolae?, 937–39
interpretation, 916–43
role of stomatal resistance, 914
saturation, 867, 892–98, 903–10, 916–34
time effect, 908
Carbon dioxide deficiency, stimulates PO in plants, 526–31
Carbon dioxide determination, 851–53
Carbon dioxide diffusion, to PS sites, 903–10
kinetic theory, 921–24
Carbon dioxide effect, on Chl and BChl fluorescence *in vivo*, 167, 939–43, 949–51, 1051–52, 1381, 1391–95
on Chl bleaching, 488
on H₂ uptake by algae, 142
on maximum quantum yield of PS, 1944–47
on stomata, 331, 1900–01
Carbon dioxide fertilization, 901–03
Carbon dioxide hydration, *in vitro*, 74, 173–79, 186–87
in vivo, 182, 198–99, 1744–46, 1891–92
Carbon dioxide induction phenomena in PS, 167, 1086–87, 1334–55, 1363–64, 1367, 1376–77, 1407–08, 1413–19, 1887–91
"CO₂ bursts," 1086–87, 1343–48, 1350–51, 1353–55, 1416–19, 1940
"CO₂ gulps," 1338–42, 1345, 1339–43, 1349–53
Carbon dioxide inhibition, of PS, 330–31, 903, 1898
Carbon dioxide liberation, in deacidification of succulents, 265–66

Carbowaxes, effect on phycobilin retention in chloroplasts, 1754–55

Carboxylases, in plants, 1673, 1745–46. See also *"Catalyst E_A"*

Carboxylation

Carboxylation, chemosynthetic, 114, 138–42

of Chl, 454

coupled with phosphorylation, 201

effect of cyanide on rate, 1455–1460

energy, 217, 935

equilibrium and kinetics in PS, 200–08, 917–21, 924–30, 934–37, 938, 941–43

in vitro, 183–87

in vivo, 183–86, 200–08

first step in PS, 80

of H_2, 208

in heterotrophants, 128, 208–09

one or two in PS?, 1666–70, 1694–95

in plants, 188, 200–08

rate derived from "pick-up," 1444

reductive, 939, 1633

relation to true reduction of CO_2, 123, 187–88

respiratory, 1633

reversible, 1632–33

of ribulose diphosphate to 2PGA, 1418, 1672–74

role in intermittency effects, 1443–45

Carboxyl group, energy, 215–18, 221, 1578, 1674. See also *Oxidation-reduction potentials*

first C(14) tagged group in light, 1632–35, 1638, 1663–64

high energy phosphate ester, 224–25

as intermediates of R and substrates of PS, 563

as reduction substrate in PS, 80

Carotenes and carotenoids

Carotenes, α and β, absorption spectra, 660

β, no reversible photoreduction by ascorbic acid, 1506

Chl-sensitized oxidation, 510

conversion to "xanthophyll," 554

photochemical reaction with Chl *in vitro*, 1528

in plants, 401, 412–16

in seeds, 430–31

Carotenoids, 413–16, 470–76, 521–22, 656–64, 705–09, 798–99, 1147–48, 1151–52, 1169–78, 1180, 1187–89, 1302–03, 1307, 1809, 1867, 1873–78, 1877, 1879

absorption spectra, *in vitro*, 656–64, 1809–11

effect of solvents, 656–62, 721–23

in vivo, 706–09, 723, 1874

theoretical considerations, 662–64

algal, 401, 415–16, 472, 657–61

bacterial, 99, 101, 416, 473, 659, 662, 1809, 1873

chemical structure and properties, 292–93, 470–76

as Chl protectors, 501

in colloidal cell extracts, 388, 475–76

effect on protochlorophyll — Chl transformation, 1764

fluorescence, 402, 798

formation, in dark-grown seedlings, 1765

in vivo, 423, 427–31

inheritance, 431

of leaves, 401, 412–16, 656–61

autumnal transformations, 415

life-time of excitation, 798

peroxide formation, 292–93, 474

photochemistry, 521–22

role, in energy transfer, 813–15, 1302–04, 1307, 1873–76

in light absorption, by bacteria, 729–30

by blue-green algae, 728–30, 1877

by brown algae, 723–27, 1169–74

by green algae, 720–23, 1147–52

by red algae, 1879

in PS and PR, 473–75, 522, 527, 557–58, 561, 569, 813–15, 1147–52, 1168–78, 1180, 1182, 1302–04, 1307, 1873–76

as sensitizers, of phototaxis of bacteria, 557, 1188, 1302, 1806, 1873–74

of phototaxis of chloroplasts, 681–82

of PO?, 557, 568, 1166, 1302, 1948, 1951

of R?, 1302

by oxygen excess, 328–30, 976, 1911–13

"self-inhibition" by high cell density, 880–82

by ultraviolet light, 344–46, 1921–25

by vitamin K "antagonists," 1921

interaction with R, 901, 1324–34, 1338, 1339. 1342, 1343, 1345–48, 1353–55, 1366–70, 1371, 1372–73, 1925–35, 1951–56, 1959–61

mass-spectroscopic study, 1927–35

kinetics, CO_2 curves, 893, 896, 906, 908

light curves, 969, 973, 974, 975, 976, 978, 980–81, 1009, 1015, 1159–66. See also under *Flashing light, Inhibition, Temperature effect, and Quantum yield*

maximum rate, 991, 993

quantum yield, 1085–95, 1097–1118, 1120–25, 1132–36, 1234, 1947–69

effect of blue-green light?, 1950–51

effect of [Chl]?, 1962–63

effect of [CO_2]?, 1945–56

photoxidation in, 530, 531–36

R, 901, 1922–24

effect of ultraviolet light, 1922–24

suspensions, culturing and characteristics, 833–36, 880–82

light absorption in relation to density, 1009–10

rate of CO_2 consumption, 904

scattering of light, 676

selective scattering, 1847, 1866–67

thermophilic strain, 1228–29

"*Chlorellin*," 882, 883

Chloride

Chloride ions, activating effect on chloroplasts, 1549–54, 1601, 1911–12

no effect on methemoglobin reduction in HR, 1588

effect on PS, 341–42

effect on vitamin K, 1911–12

in leaves, 376–77

Chlorin-e₄ dimethyl ester, 622

absorption spectrum, 621, 627

Chlorin-e₄ trimethyl ester, absorption spectrum, 627

Chlorins, 447, 457, 467

absorption spectrum, 620–21

excited states, 752

term system, 631

fluorescence, 749

Chloroform, effect, on infrared Chl spectrum, 1813–15

effect, on PS, 320–21

on C^*O_2 and P^* fixation by chloroplasts, 1615

on HR, 1613, 1615

Chlorofucin. See *Chlorophyll c*

"*Chloroglobin*," 389

p-Chloromercuribenzoate, effect on CO_2 fixation by chloroplasts, 1614

Chlorophenol indophenol. See *Quinonoid dyes*

Chlorophyll

Chlorophyll (a or b), 382–94, 402–12, 438–70, 483–521, 526–57, 603–56, 697–702, 705, 719–21, 740–55, 763–95, 805–26, 1258–99, 1375–1407, 1452–55, 1487–1501, 1501–28, 1736–40, 1750–54, 1755–86, 1793–1806, 1815–37, 1838, 1860, 1866–67, 1867–81, 1989

"allomerized," 293, 400, 459–62, 492–93, 613–14, 748, 754, 786, 787–88, 1773, 1804–05, 1812–15

absorption spectrum, 613, 1804–05

infrared, 1812–15

fluorescence, 748, 754, 786

location, in chloroplasts, 361–62, 1717–18, 1736–40

metastable. See *Chlorophyll molecule, metastable state*

as "photocatalyst," 56, 69, 384

preparations, stability, 604, 1782, 1785

Chlorophyll absorption spectrum

Chlorophyll absorption spectrum, 362, 383, 403, 427, 443–44, 603–35, 637–49, 645–56, 697–702, 705, 1772, 1773, 1775, 1778–79, 1793–1806, 1811–15, 1815–27, 1841–49

analysis, 630–35, 749–51, 1793–99, 1811–15, 1822–25

blue-violet band, 1797

in crystals and monolayers, 1822–25

oscillator strength and life-time of

excitation, *in vitro*, 633–35, 751–55, 790–95, 817, 1798–99
in vivo, 817, 1867–68, 1987
long-lived states, 753–54, 790–95. See also *Metastable state.*
in colloids and adsorbates, 649–56, 1815, 1819–21, 1822, 1825–27
infrared, 610–12
in crystals and monolayers, 1295–97, 1815–27
infrared, 1811–14
in vivo, 686–717
blue-violet band, 699, 701, 705
peak ratios, 708
red band, 695–702, 721
two forms?, 1752–54, 1847
in solution, 603–14, 615, 629, 635–49, 1799–1806, 1811–15
blue-violet band, variations, 607, 642, 646–48
effect of allomerization, 613, 1774–75, 1804–05, 1812, 1814
in infrared, 1812–14
effect of amines, 642, 1780–81, 1801–04
effect of dissolved gases, 648
effect of isomerization, 403, 1771–73
effect of low temperature, 1772–73, 1801–04
effect of pH, 1799
effect of reduction, 1805
effect of salt, 644
effect of solvents, 635–49, 1780–81, 1801–04
relation to dipole moment and polarizability, 641–42
ultraviolet, 610
in vacuum (extrapolated), 642
Chlorophyllase, 380–81, 447, 467
Chlorophyll association
Chlorophyll association, with bases, 1506–07
with CO, 648
in vivo, with oxidants and reductants in PS, 544–47
with proteins and lipides, 68, 382–89, 391–94, 502–03, 537, 776–77, 1753–54
with CO₂, 287, 451–56, 545

with fluorescence quenchers, 649, 786, 788, 1834
with gases, "zeolithic," 455
with O₂, 460–62, 492, 520–21. See also *Chlorophyll peroxide*
with oleate in coacervates, 776
with phenyl hydrazine, 1513, 1834
with polar molecules (fluorescence activators), 647–48, 766–71, 777, 1835
with proteins (artificial), 388, 502–03, 777, 1753–54
with sensitization substrates, 520–21
with solvents, 1771–73, 1801–04
protein:Chl ratio, 387, 389–91
two associated forms?, 166–67, 556
with water, 450–51, 648, 766–772
Chlorophyll biodecomposition, 1768
Chlorophyll biogenesis, 1768
Chlorophyll biosynthesis, from protochlorophyll, 1759–68
Chlorophyll as catalyst, in dark, 466, 504
Chlorophyll chemiluminescence, in vitro, 751, 794, 1838–39
in vivo, 1473, 1839–41
Chlorophyll colloids and adsorbates, 68, 394, 449, 452–53, 502–03, 644–56, 1815, 1819–21, 1820, 1822, 1825–27
absorption spectrum, 649–56, 1815, 1819–21, 1822, 1825–27
effect of detergents, 1826
films, 68, 394, 449
fluorescence, 385–88, 392, 394, 775–77, 1825–26, 1837
infrared spectra, 610–12
photochemical properties, 1507
Chlorophyll concentration, effect on Chl-sensitized reactions, 509, 512, 519
on reversible bleaching, 1491–92
Chlorophyll content, of algae, 389, 408–11
unicellular, 204, 410–11, 833–34
chlorophyll:carotenoid ratio, 413–14
effect of culturing methods, 410, 834
of cells, chloroplasts and grana, 204, 391, 411–12, 834, 1733–36
of leaves, 407–09. See also under *Chlorophyll a, b*, etc.
chlorophyll:carotenoid ratio, 413–14, 422–23
chlorophyll:protein ratio, 387, 389–91

diurnal variations?, 419, 420

in lipoid fraction, 375

unchanged by PS, 549–50

of plants, as adaptation phenomenon, 419–27

as kinetic factor in PS. *See Chlorophyll factor*

ontogenetic and phylogenetic adaptation, 424–27

Chlorophyll crystals, 448–49, 1751–52, 1782–86, 1815–27

absorption spectra, 1815–27

of Chl-protein complexes?, 1751–52

fluorescence, 1824

stability, 1785

"*Chlorophyll curves*," of PS, 1259, 1260

Chlorophyll-deficient cells, respiration, 983

See *Aurea leaves* and *Chlorosis*

Chlorophyll-deficient leaves. See *Aurea* and *Chlorotic leaves*

Chlorophyll extracts, aqueous from plants, 382–87, 394. See also *Chlorophyll colloids, Chloroplast suspensions*, and *Chloroplastin*

Chlorophyll Factor in Photosynthesis

Chlorophyll factor, in PS, 285, 304, 834–35, 1016, 1258–99, 1359–61, 1963

effect, on maximum flash yield, 1272–80

on maximum quantum yield, 1963

relation to catalase activity, 285

role in HCN poisoning, 304

role in induction phenomena, 1359–61

role in light saturation?, 1016

Chlorophyll Fluorescence *in vitro*

Chlorophyll (a and b) fluorescence, 546–48, 740–98, 806–26, 939–43, 1047–67, 1299–1310, 1375–1406, 1827–38, 1867–82

in "chloroplastin," 776

in chloroplast suspensions, 1382, 1404, 1415

in Chl-protein complexes, 1754

in colloids and adsorbates, 385–88, 392, 393, 394, 775–77, 1825–26, 1837

in crystals, 1824–25

in solutions, 546–47, 740–98, 1827–38

activation, by phenylhydrazine, relation to quenching, 1834

by polar molecules, 646–48, 763–72, 788, 1835

concentration quenching. See *Self-quenching*

fading, 492, 495, 497, 501

long-lived infrared, 749, 794, 795, 1291, 1835

polarization, 1830–31

"protection" by lipides and lipophilic solvents, 775–77

quantum yield, 751–54, 1828–30

quenching, 167, 483, 490, 518, 777–90, 1831–35. See also *Self-quenching*

by allyl thiourea 780

by o-aminophenol, 782

by benzidine, 780

by chloranil, 782, 784

by 2,6-diaminopyridine, 782

by dimethylaniline, 782

by m-dinitrobenzene, 782–84

by duroquinone, 782, 784

by hydroquinone, 783

by methyl red, 782, 784

by nitric oxide, 782, 784

by nitrobenzene, 782

by β-nitro-β,γ-hexene, 782

by β-nitro-β-methylstyrene, 782

by β nitroso-α-naphthol, 782, 784

by β-nitrostyrene, 782, 784

by O_2, 546–48, 778–80, 782, 784

by oxidants, 783–84

by oxidation substrates, 518, 780

by phenylhydrazine, 782, 786, 1513, 1834. See also under *Activation*

by 2-phenyl-3-nitrobicyclo-[1,2,2]-heptene-5, 782

by quinone, 782, 784

by reductants, 783–84

by trinitrotoluene, 782, 784

self-quenching, 755, 759–61, 772–77, 789, 1831, 1832

effect of temperature, 774, 1833

protection by lipides, etc., 775–77

sensitization, 1835–36

solvent effect on yield. See *Activation* and *Quenching*

spectrum, 740–47, 749–51, 1827–28

effect of re-absorption, 745–46
effect of solvent, 743–45, 747, 765
effect of wave length of exciting
light, 748–49
an infrared band?, 749, 794, 795,
1291, 1835
.erm system, 750–51
yield, 485, 751–90
yield-limiting mechanisms (quenching, self-quenching, sensitization), 483–84, 545–47, 755–64,
769–75, 777–79, 781–82, 784–87,
795–98, 1284–86, 1303–04
See also under *Fluorescence*

Chlorophyll Fluorescence *in vivo*
Chlorophyll fluorescence in vivo, 321–23,
328, 383, 392–94, 547–48, 558, 806–
26, 939–43, 1046–67, 1299–1310,
1375–1406, 1867–82
action spectrum, 558, 811–16, 1301–07,
1868–71, 1874–79
in blue-green algae, 1303–04, 1306,
1876–77
in brown algae, 558, 814–15, 1303,
1307, 1875–76, 1877–79
in green algae, 813–14, 1302–03,
1307, 1874–75
in red algae, 815–16, 1301, 1304–05,
1306, 1307, 1868
theoretical considerations, 1301–07
induction curves, 1377–78, 1380
first and second "wave," 1378–80,
1394–95, 1398, 1404
in grana and stroma, 361–62, 1718
parallel and antiparallel with PS induction curves, 1378
temperature effect, 1384–85
induction phenomena, 1301, 1375–
1406, 1482, 1870–71
after decrease or increase in I, 1388–89
effect, of age, 1381
of anaerobiosis, 1379, 1391, 1396,
1399–1404
of cell density, 1380
of CO_2 supply, 1379, 1381, 1391–95
of dark period, 1382–86
of inhibitors, 1395–98, 1405, 1482
of light intensity, 1384–85, 1386–90,
1394, 1397, 1398, 1404

theory, 1419–25, 1428
relation to PS, 819–26, 940–43, 949–51,
958, 1047, 1050, 1067–78, 1882
sensitized, 812–17, 1868–79
spectrum, 392–93, 805–12, 1869, 1871,
1875, 1878–79, 1879–81
effect of re-absorption, 1879
yield (steady), 321–23, 328, 383, 392–93,
546–47, 805, 812–19, 819–26, 939–
43, 1047–78, 1871, 1872. See also
under *Induction phenomena*
effect, of anaerobiosis, 328, 1063,
1066–67
of boiling, 393
of CO_2 concentration, 939–43, 951,
1048, 1051–52
of cyanide, 310–11, 1057, 1060–
62
of heat and desiccation, 817–19,
1872
of light and intensity, 1047–78,
1871, 1992
of temperature, 1055–59
of urethan, 322–23, 1063, 1065
kinetic analysis, 1069–78

Chlorophyll Formation
Chlorophyll formation in cells, 427–31,
1267, 1759–68
action spectrum, 1763–64
autophotocatalysis?, 430, 1763, 1764
and beginning of PS, 1267, 1767
in dark, 404, 430, 431, 1765, 1766
effect, of heavy metals, 429
of light, 429–30, 1759–68
of magnesium deficiency, 428–29
of mutations, 431, 1616, 1766
of nitrogen deficiency, 428
of pine seedlings extract, 1765
of potassium deficiency, 1428, 1920
of streptomycin, 1766–67
of sugars, 429
of temperature, 430–31, 1760–61,
1765
of zinc deficiency, 1920
inhibition by CO and HCN, 1768
an oxidation?, 404, 429, 431
a reduction?, 431, 1764–65
slow but permanent in virescent corn,
1764

reduction, 505–07, 1501–07, 1513–25
potentiometric study ("photogalvanic effect"), 1520–22
reversible (by ascorbic acid, riboflavin, phenylhydrazine, etc.), 1501–07, 1513–25, 1805
ermal, 450–67, 483–506, 507–21, 1487–1528, 1771–86
alcoholysis, 381, 459
allomerization, 293, 400, 459–62, 492–93, 613–14, 754, 787–88, 1773, 1804–05, 1812–15
aminolysis, 646–49, 1780–82, 1801
with ascorbic acid, 273
autoxidation. See Reaction with O_2
carbamination, 183, 454
with CO, 316
with CO_2, 451–56
dismutation?, 460, 489, 519
enolization, 444, 459, 493, 771, 1779, 1812–14
with Fe^{3+}, 295, 464–66, 1499–1501, 1776
with H_2O, 450–51, 454–55
isomerization, 403, 444, 770–71, 1771–73, 1801–02. See also Enolization
isotopic exchange with Mg*, 467
with O_2, 293, 463, 499
CuAc-catalyzed, 463
oxidation, 459–66, 1773, 1776–77
by Fe^{3+}, quinone, iodine, etc., 295, 464–66, 1499–1501, 1776–78
to protochlorophyll?, by AgO or molybdicyanide, 463
"phase test," 457, 459, 465–66, 1778–79
pheophytinization, 467
reduction, 90, 456–66, 491, 765, 1779–80
spectroscopic evidence of irreversibility, 457
Chlorophyll (a and b) reactions in vivo, photochemical, 529, 537–38, 550, 1359–61, 1753, 1859–60, 1989
"deactivation" (in strong light), 1359–61

oxidation by nitrous gases and SO_2, 538
oxidation by O_2, 529, 537–38, 1753
reversible, 1359–61, 1859–60, 1989
reversible bleaching, 1989
Chlorophyll-Sensitized Reactions
Chlorophyll-sensitized reactions, in chloroplast preparations, 61–67, 1528–1616. See also Hill's reaction
in vitro, 484, 489, 504, 507–21, 545–47, 1507–25, 1525–28
autoxidation, of benzidine, 510
of thiourea, 509, 510, 513, 1525–28
of thiourea, effect of Chl concentration, 509, 513, 519
competition with fluorescence and internal conversion, 484, 489, 519, 545–47
CO_2-reduction?, 67–69, 89, 90–94
H_2O_2 formation?, 78
oxido-reductions, 504, 509, 512, 513–14, 1507–25
of butter yellow with ascorbic and deuteroascorbic acid, 1525
of DPN with ascorbic acid, 1515–17
effect of Chl concentration, 509, 513
of methyl red with phenylhydrazine, 512, 513–14, 1507–14
no isotopic exchange with deuterated reductant, 1525
potentiometric study, 1522–23
of riboflavin or safranin T with ascorbic acid, 1514–22
of thionine, quinone, methylene blue, etc., with ascorbic acid, 1518–19
in vivo (other than PS), 526–48, 1616–26. See also Hill's reaction, in whole cells
autoxidations, 526–38
of Chl itself, 538
in excess light, 532–38
in excess oxygen, 531–32
in narcotized, poisoned or starved plants, 528–31
oxido-reductions, 538–43, 1616–26
with $AgNO_3$ as oxidant (Molisch

reaction), 271, 360, 1737–39
  with nitrate as oxidant, 538–41
  with organic oxidants, 541–43
  with quinone as oxidant, 1616–26
  with various inorganic oxidants,
    541
Chlorophyll state in vivo, 367, 382–94, 650,
  1736–40, 1750–51
  photoactive and photoinactive forms?,
    818–19, 1267, 1752–54, 1767
Chlorophyll tagging with C(14), after 20
  min. PS, 1651
Chlorophyll term system, 630–33, 749–51,
  1793–99
Chlorophyll *a*
Chlorophyll a, absorption spectrum, *in
    vitro*, 605–07, 610, 613, 629, 630,
    638–40, 643–44, 646, 652, 1778,
    1780, 1802–03, 1804, 1805–06,
    1811–13
  infrared, 1811–13
  in monolayers, 1819–20
  in vivo, 697–701, 705
  association, with "activators," 768–770
  content in plants, 402–04, 405–06, 407–11
    ratio to that of Chl *b*, 402–04, 408–11,
      419, 422–24, 559
  crystalline, 1782–84
    x-ray diffraction pattern, 1784
  discovery, 402
  fluorescence in solution, activation, 766–
    72
    life-time of excited state, 754, 1798
    polarization, 1830–31
    quenching, 782–86, 1833–35
    self-quenching 775, 1831–33
    sensitized by Chl *b*, 1303, 1835–36
    spectrum, 741–45, 750
    spectrum, effect of self-absorption,
      746
    yield and action spectrum, 754,
      787, 1828–30
  in vivo, induction phenomena, 1301,
    1375–1406, 1482
    kinetics, 139–43, 1047–67
    self-absorption, 1880
    sensitized by other pigments, 811–
      16, 1301–07, 1868–71, 1874–79
    spectrum, 806–09, 1869

  yield and action spectrum, 812–17,
    1868, 1870, 1871, 1875
  formation in plants, precedes that
    Chl *b*, 1759, 1762
  "inactive" form, in blue-green and
    algae, 1304, 1305
  isomers and tautomers, 403, 607
    617, 1771–73, 1779, 1801–02
  molecular structure, 439–44, 608
  purification, 604–05
  role in PS, 1142–87, 1301, 1302–08
  See also *Chlorophyll*
Chlorophyll a′, 403, 608–09, 1772
Chlorophyll *b*
Chlorophyll b, absorption spectrum, *in
    vitro*, 605–07, 610, 626, 629, 638–
    39, 643, 645, 647, 652, 1802–03,
    1805–06, 1811–13
  effect of C=O group, 626
  infrared, 1811–13
  in vivo, 701–02, 721
  bleaching, reversible, in flash light,
    1488, 1496–97
  changes after photoreduction and re-
    oxidation, 1504
  content in plants, 402–04, 405–06, 407–11
    absence in red algae, 616
    deficiency and formation in barley
      mutants, 1766
    ratio to Chl *a*, 402–04, 408–10, 419,
      422–24, 554
  conversion to *a*?, 466, 534
  crystalline, 1782–84
    x-ray diffraction patterns, 1784
  discovery, 402
  fluorescence, *in vivo*, 702, 1882
    in solution, life-time of excited state,
      1708
    quenching by Chl *a*, 790
    quenching by iodine, etc., 787
    long-lived, 749, 795
    spectrum, 742–45, 750
    yield and action spectrum, 752,
      1828–30
  formation follows that of Chl *a*, 1759,
    1762
  function, in PS, 150, 403, 406, 422
    contribution to light absorption, 403,
      719–21

energy transfer to Chl *a*, 1302–03, 1305

isomers and tautomers, 403, 607–08, 1771–73, 1801–02

molecular structure, 439–44, 608

phosphorescence, 749, 795

purification, 604–605

See also *Chlorophyll*

Chlorophyll b', 403, 609, 1803

Chlorophyll b'', 1772

Chlorophyll *c*

Chlorophyll c (*chlorofucin*), 402, 406–07, 439, 614–19, 623, 1786

absorption spectrum, *in vitro*, 614–15, 720

in vivo, 720–21, 727, 1173

chemical structure, 1786

fluorescence, in diatoms, 1882

in vitro, 747

occurrence in nature, 402, 406–07, 616

role in PS, 1173–75, 1769–70

Chlorophyll *d*

Chlorophyll d, absorption spectrum, *in vitro*, 615

in vivo, 720–21

chemical properties, 616

as "energy sink" *in vivo*, 1289–90, 1304, 1879

fluorescence, *in vivo*, 811–12, 816, 1304

in solution, 748

isomers, 616

occurrence, 407, 616

Chlorophyll d', *iso-d, iso-d'*, 407, 615–16

Chloroplastic Matter

Chloroplastic matter, 269, 368–81, 411–12, 1528–1616, 1721, 1723–24, 1725, 1728, 1732–36, 1991

absorption spectrum in suspensions, 649–50, 652–53, 688–89, 1843, 1845

activation, by anions, 1549–1554

by cations, 1553

by chelating agents, 1553

by coagulation, 1556

by lipoid solvents, 1559

composition, 269, 369–81, 1721, 1723–24, 1725, 1728, 1732–36, 1991

amino acids, 373–74

ascorbic acid, 269–71

ash, 376–79

carbonic anhydrase, 380

catalase, 379–80

chlorophyllase, 380–81

chlorophyll:protein ratio, 389–91

enzymes, 379–81

heavy metals (Cu, Fe), 376–79

lipoproteins, 1734

peroxidase, 380

phospholipides, 374–75

phosphorus content, 376

pigments, 382–91, 411–12, 1733–34

proteins and lipoids, 371–76, 1723–24, 1725, 1728, 1732–36, 1991

fractionation, 1554–61

loss of activity, 1543–49

photochemical activity, 61–67, 1528–1616. See also *Hill's reaction*

loss and re-activation, 1543–62

relation to particle size, 1552, 1553, 1559–61

preparation, 61–62, 368–69, 1541, 1542–43

from greening etiolated plants, 1542

from plants of different species, 1537–42

from unicellular algae, 1541–42

preservation, 1545–49

by anaerobiosis, 1546

by buffers, 1546–47

by chemical preservatives (glycol, etc.), 1548–49

by cooling and lyophilization, 1544–46

by methanol, 1548–49

by polymers, 1549

by preillumination of leaves, 1547, 1549

by sucrose, 1548

quantity in cells, 370–71

"*Chloroplastin*," 385–86, 389, 537, 817, 1750–51

fluorescence, 776

"*Chloroplastonem*," 1717

Chloroplasts

Chloroplasts, 63–67, 354–97, 1542–61, 1714–55, 1991

absorption of light, by single chloroplasts, 683, 864, 1021, 1863–67

absorption spectrum, 654–55, 688–89, 692, 699, 1843, 1845

alignment in light, 549, 551, 679–81

birefringence, 364–67, 718, 1741–42

composition. See *Chloroplastic matter*

dichroism, 366–67, 718

membrane, 357, 1722–23, 1733

morphogenesis, 359, 1717, 1731–32, 1991

number in cells, 357–58

pH in, 451

pigments, location and state, 382–94, 1736–40

shape, 356–57, 1733–36

structure, 354–67, 1714–42, 1983, 1985, 1987, 1991. See also *Chloroplast membrane, Grana, Lamina,* and *Stroma*

 electron microscopy, 363–64, 1718–40, 1983, 1985, 1987, 1991

 in *Chlorella*, 1726–27

 in flagellates, 1728–29

 microscopy, 358–65, 1714–18

 optical study, 364–67, 1741–42

 ultracentrifuge study, 1740–41

volume, 357, 371, 1733–36

water content, 382

whole, composition, 369–70, 377, 390–91

 photochemical activity (C* and P* fixation and ATP formation), 1537, 1543, 1701

See also *Chloroplastic matter*

Chloroporphyrin-e₄ dimethyl ester, 622

absorption spectrum, 621

Chlorotic plants

Chlorotic plants, 337–39, 373, 414, 428, 429

carotenoid content, 414

kinetics of PS, 1268–70, 1273

produced by ionic deficiency, 337–39, 428

Chromate, as oxidant in HR, 1563–64

pH effect, 1602

Chromatic adaptation, 421–27, 730–36, 995

"*Chromatophores,*" precipitation by ultra-centrifuge, 1740

"*Chromatoplasm,*" 355

Chromidia, 1732

Chromophyllin, 1751

Chromoplasts, 354–67

Chromoproteids, 382, 417–19, 1561

Citric acid

Citric acid, C(14) tagged, after illumination, 1680–82

 C(14) tagging, in dark, 1660

in light, enhanced by NH₂OH, 1908–09

none in light, 1666, 1681

occurrence, in nonsucculent plants, 250, 267–69

 in succulents, 264, 1702

 as plant food, 261, 262, 266

 as R intermediate, 268–69, 1690

Cleavage test, 460

Coacervates, of Chl, 392

Coenzyme A, 1690, 1699

Coenzymes I and II. See *Pyridine nucleotides*

Colchicine, effect in Chl synthesis *in vivo,* 1766

Combustion energy, of C—H—O compounds, 214–16

Compensation point

Compensation point, on CO₂ curves, 898–901, 1898–1901

 on light curves, 981–85, 1234

  quantum yield below and above it, 1113–16, 1132, 1898

  temperature dependence, 1234

Complementary chromatic adaptation, 421–27

Complexon. See *Ethylenediaminetetracetic acid*

"*Conditioning*" *light,* effect on induction, 1322

Conifers, Chl formation in dark, 430

low temperature PS, 1218–19

Conjugation, influence on bond energy, 183–84, 214, 218–19

Copper, in chloroplasts, 379

role in PS, PO, and R, 320, 538

Copper acetate, as catalyst for Chl autoxidation, 463

Copper pheophorbide, non-fluorescence, 749, 752

Coproporphyrin III, role in chlorophyll biosynthesis, 1770

Coupled reactions, in CS, 141, 142, 235

in PS, 234

Crotonic acid, preparation from purple bacteria, 110

Cryophilic plants, 1218

PS, 1218–20, 1225–27

R, 1230

Crystals, shift of absorption bands, 1815–25

of Mg porphyrin, Zn chlorin, and Zn porphyrin, 1835

on photolysis of CO_2, 82

on PS, 333–35, 1918

Dehydrogenases, in plant material, 1748–49

Dehydrogenation, of Chl, by AgO or molybdicyanide, 463

Denaturation of proteins, as cause of thermal injury, 1225

Deoxidases, NH_2OH and H_2S sensitivity, 286, 312, 316

role in PS, 134–36, 173, 281, 282, 291, 293–95, 312, 379, 867

Desert plants, PS at high temperature, 1228

PS rate under natural conditions, 997, 1000

Detergents, effect, on colloidal leaf dispersions, 387, 652–53

on fluorescence of artificial Chl-protein complexes, 1825

on proteins from chloroplasts, 1559

use in fractionation of chloroplast proteins, 1556, 1559

"*Detour factor,*" 672. See also *Scattering*

Deuterium oxide. See *Heavy water*

Deuteroascorbic acid. See *Ascorbic acid*

Diadinoxanthol, absorption spectrum, 659, 661

Diaferometry (measurement of heat conductance), 853, 1330–31, 1339–43, 1348–55

2,6-Diaminopyridine, as fluorescence quencher, 782

Diatoms

Diatoms, absorption spectrum, *in vivo*, 699, 706–08, 710, 725–27, 1173–75

of pigments, 657–62, 692, 699, 1169

action spectrum, of fluorescence, 814–15, 1303

of PS, 1169–76

adaptation to H_2S, 128

energy transfer to Chl *a*, 814–15, 1303

fluorescence, 814–15, 940–41, 959, 1050–51, 1056–57, 1059, 1062, 1169–76

effect, of $[CO_2]$, 940–41, 1051

of HCN, 1062

of temperature, 1056–57

of urethane, 959

of wavelength, 814–15

oil storage, 34

pigments, 401–02, 405, 416, 425, 1169

PS, 836, 954–55, 959, 969, 972, 976, 1097, 1169–76

effect, of HCN, 954–55

of light intensity, 969, 972, 976

of urethan, 959

of wavelength, 1169–76

quantum yield, 1096–97, 1173–75

Diatoxanthol, absorption spectrum, 661

Dichroism, of chloroplasts, 366–67, 718

Differential manometer, 850

Diffusion

Diffusion, as limiting factor in HR, 1596

as source of induction, 1407–08

as source of $[CO_2]$ dependence of PS, 903–16, 921–24

Dihydroacetone phosphate, C(14) tagging in PS, 1683

Dihydropheophorbide, absorption spectrum, 629

Dihydroporphins, 445, 633, 1794

Dihydroxyacetone (= *triose*) *phosphate*, C(14) labelling in PS, 1656, 1670, 1679, 1683, 1685

Dimethylanaline, as fluorescence quencher, 782

Dinitrobenzene, Chl-sensitized reduction by phenylhydrazine, 1524–25

as fluorescence quencher, 782, 784

as Hill oxidant, 1589

as inhibitor, of C* and P* fixation in chloroplasts, 1614–15

of HR, 1612, 1613, 1615

of PS, 113, 143, 319, 1910–12

Diphosphopyridine nucleotide (DPN). See *Pyridine nucleotides*

Dipole moment, of Chl, 444

of electronic transitions. See *Oscillator strength*

Discrimination, isotopic. See *Isotopic discrimination*

Discs, in grana, 1723–28, 1735

Dismutation

Dismutation, chemical, 48, 80, 121, 130, 217, 230, 282, 287, 460, 485, 519, 542–43, 1708

of Chl?, 460, 489–90, 519

in blue-green algae, 801, 817, 1300–01, 1876–77

to Chl d?, 1289–90, 1878–79

in diatoms, 522, 558, 814–15, 1303, 1875–76

between different molecules (transfer), 812–17, 1299–1310, 1868–79

as explanation of PS unit, 1281, 1288–89

in green algae, 813–15, 1302–03, 1874–75

between identical molecules (migration), 1280–99

in red algae, 815–16, 1868–71, 1877–79

revealed by sensitized fluorescence, 812–17, 1868–79

to O_2?, 514–15, 779

theory, 1282–99

See also *Photosynthetic unit*

Enolization of chlorophyll. See under *Chlorophyll reactions*

Enol-pyruvic acid, 1667, 1692

Enzymes

Enzymes, in chloroplasts, 379–81, 1744–49

concentration, as limiting factor in PS, 172–73, 921–30, 1016, 1017–43, 1452–55, 1456–60, 1467–78

in leaves, 41–42

Erythrobilin. See *Phycoerythrobilin*

Ethanol

Ethanol, in bacterial metabolism, 121

effect, on Chl in leaves, 383

on PS, 321

on reversible reduction of Chl, 1504

occurrence in plants, 249, 251, 254

reaction with CO_2, 180

Ether, effect on PS, 320–21, 342

Ethyl chlorophyllide. See *Chlorophyllide*

Ethylenediaminetetracetic acid (= complexon), as stimulant of HR, 1611

Ethylene glycol, as inhibitor of C^*O_2 and P^* fixation in chloroplasts, 1548

as stabilizer of photochemical activity of chloroplasts, 1548

Ethyl urethan. See *Urethan*

Etiolated plants

Etiolated plants, 404, 429–31, 1267, 1759–68

assimilation numbers, 1267

chlorophyll formation, 429–31, 1759–60

protochlorophyll content, 404, 1759

PS, 1267

Etioporphyrin, absorption spectrum, 620

Excitation energy migration. See *Energy migration*

Exciton, 1283

F

Fats, formation in algae, 1744

occurrence in chloroplasts, 375

Fatty acids, C^* tagged, in brief PS, 1651

in dark, 1638

as H donors in PR of bacteria, 102, 106, 108, 110–11

as oxidants for reduced Chl *in vitro*, 1519

Feedback mechanism, for self-regulation of PS?, 1075

Feeding, of albino plants with organic compounds, 47

of algae and flagellates with low molecular compounds, 260–62

of algae with formaldehyde, 257–60

Fermentation

Fermentation, 110, 121–22, 129, 130, 136–38, 217, 265, 327, 563

in algae under anaerobic conditions, 327, 563, 1366

energy, 217

in H_2-adapted algae, 129–30, 136–38

in methane bacteria, 121–22

in succulents, 265

in sulfur bacteria, 110

Ferri and ferro compounds

Ferric oxalate, as photoxidant for H_2O_2 in ultraviolet light, 64

Ferric salts, effect on fluorescence-time curve of chloroplasts, 1405

as Hill oxidants, 64–66, 1562–63, 1596–98, 1601

in *Chlorella*?, 541, 1616–17

reaction with Chl in solution, 295, 464–66, 490–91, 504, 512, 1494, 1499–1500

Ferricyanide, as Hill oxidant, 1562–63, 1590, 1593, 1596–97, 1598, 1601, 1603

Ferri-ferro systems, potential, 222

possible role in O_2 liberation, 294

Ferrous ions, occurrence in chloroplastic matter, 378

reaction with oxidized Chl, 488, 490

as reductants in CS, 116

Field plants, efficiency of energy conversion, 1005–07

"Finishing catalysts," 1276–77

"Finishing" dark reactions, kinetic role in PS, 1033–41

Firefly extracts, use in ATP determination, 1705

Flagellates, chloroplast structure and Chl content, 1728–31, 1735–36

organic nutrition, 261–62

pigments, 405–07

Flashes, grouped, 1458–60, 1482–83

single, yield of PS, 1448, 1462

Flashing light. See also *Alternating light* and *Intermittent light*

Flashing light experiments, on HR, 1478–81

on PR, 1481–83

on PS, 133, 169, 296–97, 307–08, 310, 311 ,313, 338, 346, 1272–80, 1433–83

Flash yield, of HR, 1475, 1478–81

of PR, 1481–83

of PS, 1272–80, 1452–78

depends only on integrated flash energy?, 1435, 1448, 1473–74, 1476

effect, of age of cell cultures, 1273

of anaerobiosis, 1371, 1462–64

of [Chl], 1272–80, 1454, 1464

of CO_2 concentration, 1461–62, 1464, 1465

of cyanide, 1455–60

of dark interval, 1452–53, 1456–61, 1463, 1466, 1467–72, 1478, 1482, 1993

of dehydration, 1465

of H_2O, 1465–66

of flash duration, 1463–64, 1467–72, 1473–74

of flash energy (integrated light intensity), 1449–52, 1453, 1467–72, 1479

of grouping of flashes, 1458–60, 1482–83

of narcotics, 1464–65

of temperature, 1241–42, 1454, 1460–61, 1464, 1467–72, 1953

of ultraviolet irradiation, 1465

maximum, as function of Chl content, 1272–80, 1454, 1464

interpretation, 1274, 1454, 1475–76

reciprocity law valid?, 1435, 1448, 1473–74, 1476

Flattening, of absorption spectra. See *Absorption spectra, deformation*

Flavones, 401, 402, 479–80, 541, 684, 717

light absorption, 684

reduction in light, 547

Fluctuations, of PS rate under natural conditions, 876–77

Fluorescence

Fluorescence, of allomerized chlorophyll, 748

of bacteriochlorophyll, *in vitro* and *in vivo,* 571, 748, 809, 812–13, 823–24, 941–43, 949–51, 952–54, 958, 959–60, 1049–50, 1052–55, 1057, 1059, 1062–63, 1064–66, 1301–02, 1307, 1837–38, 1854, 1871–75. See also under *Bacteriochlorophyll*

of bacterioviridin, *in vivo,* 811

of carotenoids, 798

of chlorins, 749

of Chl *a* and *b, in vitro* and *in vivo,* 385–88, 392–94, 546–48, 740–98, 775–77, 806–26, 939–43, 1047–67, 1299–1310, 1375–1406, 1415, 1824–38, 1867–82, 1992. See under *Chlorophyll, fluorescence*

of Chl *b,* delayed infrared (phosphorescence), 749, 757, 793–95

of Chl *c, in vitro,* 747

of Chl *d, in vitro* and *in vivo,* 748, 812, 1304–05

concentration depolarization, 1284–85

concentration quenching. See *Self-quenching*

of dye solutions, 1307–09

of dye vapors, 1309–10

of etioporphyrin, 742

general theory, 755–64, 773, 779, 781, 795–98, 1284–86

induction, in chloroplasts, 1404–05

in vivo, 1375–1406

kinetic schemes and equations, 769–70, 772–75, 784–89, 795–98

of mesoporphyrin, 1829, 1833

of pheophorbides, 742, 749

of pheophytin, 1829

of phycobilins, *in vitro* and *in vivo*, 402, 417, 799–801, 811–12, 813, 815–17, 1303–04, 1306, 1309, 1868–71, 1876–79

of phylloerythrin, 742

of porphin, 750

of porphyrins, 749

of protochlorophyll, *in vitro* and *in vivo*, 748, 811, 1838, 1881

of protoporphyrin, 1833

"pseudo-quenching," 787

quenching, chemical, 756–57, 761, 764, 777, 781, 782

by complex formation, 757, 777–78, 782

in linear polymers, 1298

by monomolecular reactions, 756, 757, 764, 773

physical, 757–59, 764, 779, 781

by transfer of energy, 757–59, 778, 797, 1303–05

relation to primary photoprocess, 483–84

self-quenching, by bimolecular reactions, 761–63, 773

by dimer formation, 759–62, 765, 771, 772

by energy transfer, 759–61, 1284–86

by internal conversion, 755–56, 764, 773, 797

sensitized, in gases, 758

in vivo, 812–17, 1868–79

in solution, 1835–36

Fluorescence spectra. See under individual pigments, also *Blue-green algae, Brown algae, Green algae, Leaves,* and *Red algae*

Fluorescence yield. See *Chlorophyll, fluorescence; Phycobilins, fluorescence,* and *Quantum yield of fluorescence*

Fluoride, effect, on C^*O_2 uptake by chloroplasts, 1536

on HR, 1613, 1621

on PS, 1906

Formaldehyde

Formaldehyde C(14) tagged in PS, 1693

Chl-sensitized formation *in vitro?*, 89, 90–94

decomposition by plants, 257, 260

does not stimulate HR, 1614

energy content, 48–49, 218

feeding to plants, 257–60

formation, from Chl, 91

from CO_2 *in vitro*, 79, 82, 83

by electric discharges, 83

from percarbonate, 289

from phosgene and bicarbonate by H_2O_2, 79

hydrate, 53

an intermediate in PS?, 48, 51, 247–48

occurrence in plants, 249, 253, 255–57

as plant poison, 257–59

polymerization, 247, 259, 273

as product of PO, 68, 267, 495–96

in rain water, 82

reaction with nitrate and nitrite in light, 87

as stimulant, 343

Formic acid

Formic acid, biosynthesis, 218

C(14) tagging in PS, 1693

effect on reversible Chl bleaching, 488, 1488

energy, content, 216

of decarboxylation, 184

of hydrogenation, 218

feeding to plants, 261

an intermediate in PS?, 51

occurrence in plants, 249–51, 253

photochemical production in chloroplasts?, 1530, 1533

production by bacteria, 110

reversible decarboxylation, 185

Four quanta theories, of PS, 154, 288

Franck-Condon principle, 746–47, 1283, 1586, 1971

Free energy. See *Energy*

Free radicals

Free radicals, in Chl reactions, *in vitro*, 494–501, 1503, 1521, 1805–06

in Chl-sensitized reactions *in vitro*, 515

in CO_2 reduction, 80

energy, 81, 217, 229–34
in HR, 1576
in PS, 233–39, 287, 293, 1971–72
Freezing, effect, on chloroplast activity, 1544
  on PS. See under *Photosynthesis* and *Inhibition of Photosynthesis (by frost)*

Fructose
Fructose, 40, 43, 44, 46, 49
  C(14) tagging in PS, 1685, 1686
  follows that of fructose phosphate, 1685
  precedes that of glucose, 1686
  diphosphate, P(32) tagging in light, 1661
  phosphates, C(14) tagging in PS, 1661, 1671, 1677, 1678, 1685–86
  initial rate, 1683
  photostationary state, 1679

Fucoxanthol
Fucoxanthol, 401, 413, 415–16, 423, 472, 612–13
  absorption bands *in vivo*, 657, 706–07, 723–27
  absorption spectrum *in vitro*, 659, 661
  energy transfer to Chl *in vivo*, 1303
  light absorption *in vivo* and role in PS, 1168–78

Fumaric acid
Fumaric acid, biosynthesis, 209
  C(14) tagging, in dark, 1640, 1660
  in light, 1659–60
  enhanced by NH₂OH, 1908–09
  chloroplast-sensitized photoreduction to succinic acid, 1578
  energy content, 184, 218
  as H acceptor in bacteria, 131
  as intermediate, in PS, 1689, 1691
  in R, 224, 1689–90
  occurrence in plants, 250–51

G

Galactose, 39, 49
Glucose
Glucose, 39–42, 46
  C(11) tagging in PS, 1631–32
  C(14) tagging in PS, 1656, 1662, 1678, 1685
  follows that of fructose, 1686

follows that of glucose phosphate, 1685
  effect, on metabolism of H₂-adapted algae, 133, 137, 140, 141, 143, 147
  on PS, 331–33, 562
  energy content, 49
  as product of PS, 44–46
  as substrate, of PO, 528, 529, 535
  of R, 308
Glucose monophosphate, C(14) tagging in PS, 1662, 1664, 1671, 1676–79, 1683, 1685
  first tagged product to disappear, 1678
  follows fructose phosphate, 1685
  photostationary concentration, 1679
  time course, 1676–77, 1683
Glucose uridine diphosphate, C(14) tagging in PS, 1656, 1676, 1686
Glucuronic acid, in plants, 250, 252
  as intermediate in respiration, 269
Glutamic acid, C(14) tagging, during and after PS, 1666, 1669, 1681, 1682
  in light, enhanced by NH₂OH, 1908–09
Glutathione, as stimulant of HR with O₂, 1568
Glyceraldehyde. See also *Phosphoglyceraldehyde*
  energy, 49
  occurrence in PS, 46
  role in R, 223
Glyceric acid, C(14) tagging in light, 1662.
  after pre-illumination, 1639
    See also *Phosphoglyceric acid*
Glycerol, in bacterial metabolism, 209
  conversion to sugar by plants, 260, 261
  effect on PS and PO, 528
Glycine, C(14) tagging in PS, 1656, 1659, 1675
  role in porphyrine synthesis, 1769
Glycogen, in algae, 43
Glycol, conversion to starch by plant, 261
Glycolaldehyde, occurrence in plants, 249, 251, 254
Glycolic acid. See also *Phosphoglycolic acid*.
  C(14) tagged in PS, 1656, 1659, 1675, 1693

feeding to algae, 1675–76

intermediate in PS?, 1694

occurrence in plants, 249, 251

Glycolytic enzymes, in chloroplasts, 1748–49

Glyoxal, enhancing effect on C^*O_2 fixation in chloroplasts, 1536

Glyoxylic acid, occurrence in plants, 249, 251

intermediate in PS?, 1694

Grana

Grana, in bacteria?, 1740–41

in chloroplasts, 44, 254, 357–61, 362, 1714, 1715–28, 1730, 1740–44, 1991–92

arrangement, 1715–18

Chl:protein ratio, 390–91

fluorescence, 361, 1382, 1718

number, size, and volume, 390–91, 1733–34

PR of silver nitrate, 1737–39

structure, 1723–28

ultracentrifugation, 1740

"*Grana sediments*," O_2 uptake?, 503

Granular vs. laminar chloroplasts, 1730, 1991–92

Green algae

Green algae, absorption and scattering of light, 676, 683, 689, 691, 698–700, 706, 708, 714, 715, 720, 721–23, 725, 735, 842–43, 1845–47, 1866

absorption changes during PS, 1859–61

action spectrum, of fluorescence, 813, 1874–76

of PS, 1147–60

chemiluminescence, 1839–41

Chl content and PS, 1267–72

fluorescence, 807, 809, 812–15, 1867–68, 1992

HR, in chloroplasts and whole cells, 1541–43, 1616–26

pigments, 405–07, 408–16, 423

formation, 428–430

PO, 531–36

PR of nitrate and organic oxidants, 538–41

R and PS, 562–63, 568–70

See also *Chlorella, Scenedesmus, Inhibitors, Photosynthesis (Chemical mechanism, Kinetics, Quantum yield, etc.)*

Green bacteria

Green bacteria, 99, 101, 102, 103, 402, 704, 1787–88, 1849–51

absorption spectrum, 704, 1849–51

fluorescence, 811

pigments, 402, 1787–88, 1807–08

Greening, 427, 429, 1267, 1542, 1767. See also *Protochlorophyll, conversion to chlorophyll*

Growing algae, in intermittent light, 1446, 1476–78

Growing plants, in intermittent light, 1437–39

Guard cells, 334, 910–12

"*Gulps*" and "*gushes*," of CO_2 and O_2. See *Induction phenomena*

H

Half-saturating CO_2 concentration, in PR, 893

in PS, 892–93, 920, 922, 923, 924, 926, 927, 928, 930, 931, 932, 934

Half-saturating light intensity, in fluorescence transition *in vivo*, 1072–74

in PR, 969

in PS, 966–69, 1018, 1019, 1028, 1038–39, 1043–44

Heat

Heat of activation, of PS, 1231–54

of thermal injury, 1224–25

Heat inhibition and injury, 993, 1223–25

Heat transfer, effect on leaf temperature, 1212–13

Heat pretreatment, effect on CO_2-induction phenomena, 1331, 1350, 1371

Heavy metals, in chloroplasts, 376–77, 1749

effect, on Chl formation, 2128–29

on HR, 1612–13

on PS, 340–42

Heavy oxygen $O(18)$. See $O(18)$ *tracer*

Hg^{++}, 336, 341
Na$^+$ and NH$_4^+$, 340, 834–35
Ni^{++}, 340–41
UO$_2$$^{++}$, 1919
Zn^{++}, 341
by dehydration, 333–35, 341, 944, 1918–19
by excess carbohydrates, 331–33
by excess carbon dioxide, 330–31
by excess light, 531–36, 909, 1355–61, 1372–74
by excess oxygen, 328–30, 531–36, 960, 1912–13
by frost and heat, 1218–25
by injury, 343–44
by ionic deficiencies, 336–39, 1920–21
  K$^+$, 336–37
  Mg^{++}, 337–38, 1920
  Mn^{++}, 338–39
  nitrate, 339
by narcotics, 300, 320–24, 959–60, 975–76, 979, 1344, 1463–65
  chloroform, 320–21
  ethanol and ether, 320–21
  excess CO$_2$, 330–31
  thymol, 320–21
  urethans, 284, 300, 321–24, 959–60, 1463–65
by photoxidation, 526, 532
by physical agents, 344–47, 1465, 1921–25
  ultraviolet light, 344–46, 1921–25
by poisons, 286, 300–20, 340–41, 974–76, 1455–60, 1686–88, 1887, 1902–12
  alkaloids, 321
  azide, 318, 1907
  carbon monoxide, 316–17
  cyanide, 301–11, 955, 1887, 1902–06
  dicumarol, 1910
  dinitrophenol, 319, 1910
  fluoride, 1906–08
  heavy metals, 336, 340–42, 1919
  hydrogen peroxide, 286, 318
  hydrogen sulfide, 315–16
  hydroxylamine, 311–15, 1908–09
  iodoacetyl compounds, 318–19, 1907–10
  1,4-naphthaquinone, 1910

nitrous oxides and sulfur dioxide, 317–18
  phthiocol, 314, 319, 1910
  thiocyanide, 318
  thiourea, 320
  vitamin K "antagonists," 1910, 1921
by products of PS, 880–81
thermal, 1220–25
See also under *Hill's Reaction, Photoreduction, Photosynthesis, Photoxidation, Respiration,* and under individual inhibitors
Inositols, 39–40, 46, 244
Intensity adaptation, of algae, 421–22, 425
of leaves, 423–27, 986–89
Intermediates
Intermediates, of CO$_2$ reduction, 35, 51, 239–80, 1630–98
  stationary concentration, 1679
  of O$_2$ liberation, 133–36, 173, 281–99, 312, 379, 1698–1701
  role in PS induction, 1408–13
Intermittency factors, 1433–41, 1446, 1447–52
  for equal intensity and time (of constant and intermittent illumination); intensity and energy; and energy and time, 1434–35, 1445–52
  as function of frequency of alternating light, 1435–41
  See also *Alternating light and Flashing light*
Intermittent illumination, resulting from stirring, 1106, 1433, 1476–78
Intermittent light, 1272–80, 1433–83. See also *Alternating light* and *Flashing light*
"Internal conversion," 749, 1300
"Internal factors" in PS, 872–73
Inulin, 43, 49
Invertase, in chloroplasts, 1749
Iodide ions, effect on PS, 341
  sensitized PO, 511
Iodine, effect, on Chl bleaching in methanol, 1489, 1490–91
  on Chl reaction with Fe^{3+}, 1494
Iodoacetate
Iodoacetate and iodoacetamide, effect, on catalase, 284–85

on C(14) uptake in PS, 1686–87
on C(14) and P(32) uptake by chloro-
    plasts in light, 1614–15
on CS in sulfur bacteria, 113–14
on HR, 1612, 1613, 1615
    in *Chlorella*, 1621
on PS, 318–19, 342, 1686–87, 1907–10
on R, 1687
Ions, effect, on chloroplast preparations,
    1549–54
    on HR, 1612–13
    on PS, 335–42, 951–54, 1919–21
    See also *pH*

Iron
Iron, in chloroplasts, 376–79, 429
    role in PS inhibition by SO_2, etc., 317–18
Iron bacteria, 112, 116
Iron complexes, redox potentials, 222, 1746
    role in PS?, 239–40, 293–95, 1586–87,
    1858–61
Iron deficiency, effect, on Chl formation,
    338, 428–29, 1268–70
    on PS, 338, 1268–70
Isoamylamine, Chl-sensitized oxidation,
    511
    no effect, on Chl bleaching, 487–88
    on Chl fluorescence, 788–89
    stimulation of Chl "phosphorescence,"
    793–94
Isochlorophyll (d,d'). See *Chlorophyll d*,
    isomers
Isocitric acid, C(14) tagging, in light, in
    succulents, 1702
    post-photosynthetic, 1666
    intermediate in R, 1690
Isoelectric point, of chloroplast prepara-
    tions, 386
    of phycobilins, 478
Isomerization, of Chl. See *Chlorophyll iso-
    mers*, and *Chlorophyll reactions*
    energy, 217
Isotopic discrimination, in PS, 854, 1915–
    18, 1926–28
    in R, 10, 1918
Isotopic distribution, of O(18) and O(16),
    between atmosphere and oceans, 10,
    1916–18
Isotopic exchange, of C, between Chl and
    CO_2, 557

between CO_2 and RCOOH, 185–86,
    202–03, 1632, 1634
of H, between Chl and H_2O, 557
of Mg, between Chl and Mg^{++}, 555

J

Janus green, photochemical reaction with
    Chl, 504

K

α-Ketoglutaric acid, reductive carboxyla-
    tion, sensitized by chloroplasts, 1578
Kinetic curves, types, 858–64, 868–72
    first (Blackman), 859–60, 868–72, 894,
    1014
    second (Bose), 861–62, 868–72, 894,
    1014
    third, 862, 866, 894, 959, 1014
Kinetics, of C(14) incorporation, in PS
    intermediates, 1676–84
    of HR, in *Chlorella*, 1616–26
    in chloroplast preparations, 1589–1616
    in flashing light, 1478–80
    of PS, 831–1486, 1886–1978
    in flashing light, 1272–80, 1433–86
Knallgas bacteria. See *Hydrogen bacteria*
"*Kok effect*," 981, 1113–18, 1132, 1898,
    1960–62, 1964
"*Krasnovsky reaction*," 1501–07, 1514–22,
    1805–06
    in vivo?, 1589
Krebs cycle, 1689–90
    intermediates, no C(14) tagged during
    PS, 1645–46, 1666, 1680–82
    tagging in dark after PS, 1645–46,
    1666, 1680–82
    tagging in light in presence of hy-
    droxylamine, 1908–09
Kundt's rule, 641–42

L

Lactaldehyde, occurrence in plants, 249,
    250, 251, 254
    as plant food, 261
Lactic acid, formation from pyruvate, by
    HR, 1578
    occurrence in plants, 249, 250, 251, 254

effect of chlorophyll content, 1260, 1265, 1269

in flashing light, 1449–51, 1468, 1471–72, 1479

general shape, 987–89, 994, 1008–09, 1012–17, 1043–47

half-saturation, 1018, 1019, 1028, 1038, 1039, 1043, 1044

initial slope, 979, 1016, 1017, 1019, 1029, 1037, 1042

interpretation, 1007–47

   effect of back reactions in the photosensitive complex, 1020–33

   effect of cell density in suspension, 1007–10

   effect of "finishing" dark reactions, 1033–41

   effect of inhomogeneity of light absorption, 1007–12

   effect of "narcotization," 1041–43

   effect of preparatory dark reactions, 1017–20

   linear range, 979–81

   in monochromatic light, 1158–68

   saturation, 985–96, 1018, 1019, 1027, 1028, 1029, 1035, 1038, 1042, 1043–45, 1047

of umbrophilic plants, 995, 1262

Light effect, on R, 527, 563–69, 1108–09, 1325–26, 1333–34, 1347, 1427, 1666, 1926, 1930, 1934–36, 1951–52

"*Light fields*," natural, 730–36

effect on pigment formation, 403, 423

Light inhibition and injury, 529, 532–36, 858–59, 992, 995, 1355–61

Light intensity

Light intensity, effect, on $AgNO_3$ photoreduction by chloroplasts, 1738

on anaerobic induction, 1371

on ATP content of *Chlorella*, 1705–06

on Chl bleaching, 487, 489, 1494

on Chl-sensitized reactions, 519

on fluorescence yield *in vivo*, 1047–78, 1386–90, 1398, 1871, 1992

on H_2 metabolism of algae, 142–43, 147

on HR, 65, 1479, 1593–94, 1619

on induction, in Chl fluorescence *in vivo*, 1386–90, 1398

in PR, 146, 1374

in PS, 1317, 1318, 1335–36, 1342, 1346, 1351–54, 1356–59, 1410

on inhibition of PS, 302, 303, 306, 309, 312, 319, 333. 337–39, 341 1907, 1913

on PO, 531, 532

on PS, 296–98, 526, 531–37, 964–1141, 1372–74

on relative PGA and malic acid C(14) tagging, 1667–68

See also *Light curves*

Light intermittency effects, 1272–80, 1433–83, 1993. See under *Alternating light*, *Flashing light*, and *Intermittent light*

Light measurement, methods, 837–44

   Warburg-Schocken actinometer, 839, 1526–28, 1952

   units, 837, 838, 839, 965

Light saturation

Light saturation, of HR, 65, 1593–95

of PO, 535

of PR, 145

of PS, 532, 866, 964–79, 985–96, 1012–17, 1018, 1019, 1028, 1030, 1035, 1038, 1042, 1043–47

Light scattering. See *Scattering*

"*Limiting factors*," 858–64, 868–72, 923–24, 964–65

Lipmann reaction, 1691

Lipochromes, 382

Lipoic acid (= thioctic acid), an intermediate catalyst in PS?, 1698–1701

occurrence in plants, 1699

Lipoids

Lipoids, assay in leaves, 375

association with carotenoids, 475–76

C(14) tagging after 1 min. PS, 1651

in chloroplasts, grana and stroma, 361, 365–68, 371–76, 382–84, 391–94, 537, 1722, 1724, 1734–35, 1742, 1991. See also *Myelin*

effect, on Chl fluorescence, 392

   on photoxidation of Chl in solution, 503

Lipoprotein-chlorophyll, crystallized?, 1751–52

Lipoproteins, in chloroplasts, 1725, 1732, 1734. See also *Chloroplastin*

Long-lived active products, formed by Chl *in vitro,* 483–86, 514, 749, 753–54, 790–95, 1291, 1495–99, 1835

formed by Chl *in vivo,* 544–47, 1970–71

Luminescence. See *Chemiluminescence, Fluorescence,* and *Phosphorescence*

Luminous bacteria, as reagents for O_2, 62, 100, 327, 845

Luteol, 415, 416, 470–72, 474

absorption spectrum, 660–61

in vivo, 700

Lycopene, absorption spectrum, 660

Lyophilizing, effect on chloroplast activity, 1544–45

M

Macromolecules, in chloroplast stroma, 1721–22

in grana, 1728

Magnesium

Magnesium, deficiency effect, on Chl formation, 428

on PS, 337–38

effect on absorption spectrum of chlorins, 628, 629, 630

influence of Chl and BChl properties, 383, 450–53, 454, 461–62, 467, 493–94, 498, 1501, 1504, 1505, 1506, 1507, 1519, 1528, 1780, 1800, 1807, 1809, 1823–24, 1826, 1829, 1835

isotopic exchange with chlorophyll, 555

loss by pheophytinization, 456, 467, 493–94, 498, 1777, 1779–90

organic binding, in Chl synthesis, 1759–60

position, in Chl molecule, 440, 442, 443, 448

as reductant, for CO_2, 79

Magnesium porphyrin, fluorescence in non-polar solvents, 1835

Magnesium vinyl pheoporphyrin a_5, in *Chlorella* mutants, 1768

phytyl ester, role in Chl biosynthesis, 1770

Malic acid

Malic acid, biosynthesis, 209

C(14) tagging, 1638–41, 1645, 1656, 1658–60, 1662–63, 1666–70, 1677–78, 1681, 1683, 1686, 1691, 1693–96, 1698

after brief illumination, 1658–60, 1662, 1666–70, 1677–78, 1683

after darkening, 1681

inhibition by malonate, 1667, 1686, 1693

preferential in carboxyl, 1663

after pre-illumination, 1638–41

time course, 1668, 1669, 1677–78, 1683

conversion to citric acid, in leaves, 269

as intermediate, in PS, 51, 224, 1638–41, 1645, 1656, 1658–60, 1662–63, 1666–70, 1677–78, 1681, 1683, 1686, 1691, 1693–96, 1698

a link to R?, 1694–98

a primary carboxylation product?, 1666–70, 1691, 1694–95, 1697, 1698

in R, 51, 224, 1640, 1660, 1690, 1695

C(14) tagging in dark, 1640, 1660

in succulents, 264–67, 1702

C(14) tagging, 1702

occurrence, in plants, 247, 250, 251, 262–69

as plant food, 261

as reductant, for bacteria, 108

Malic enzyme, in chloroplasts, 1745

Malic enzyme system, coupling, to HR *via* TPN, 1577–78, 1582–84

Malonate, as inhibitor, of C(14) fixation in malate in light, 1667, 1686, 1693

of HR in *Chlorella,* 1621

Maltose, 41

Manganese, content in leaves, 195

effect, on HR, 1568–69

on PS and Chl, 338–39, 429, 1920

Mannose, 39, 46

Mannose phosphate, C(14) tagging in PS, 1677, 1679

Manometry, 845–50, 1085

Mass spectroscopy

Mass spectroscopy, application, to HR, 1530, 1565, 1567, 1592, 1624–25

to PS, 54–55, 1333–34, 1930, 1927–36, 1940

induction study, 1333–34, 1940
simultaneous measurement of PS
and R, 1333–34, 1927–36
Maximum rate and yield. See *Photosyn-
thesis, Photoreduction, Hill's Reaction,*
etc.
Mechanical injury, effect on PS, 343–44
Mehler reaction, (HR with O_2 as oxi-
dant), 1565–67, 1625–26
Membrane, chloroplastic, 358, 1722–23
Mercuric ions, effect on HR, 1612
inhibitors of PS, 336
Mesobilirhodin, 1788
Mesobiliviolin, 1788
Mesomerism, of Chl, 442–43
Mesoporphyrin, fluorescence quenching of,
1833
Metastable state, of Chl. See *Chlorophyll
molecule, long-lived state*
Methane bacteria, 118–19, 120–22
Methanol
Methanol, Chl-catalyzed oxidation, by
Fe^{3+}, 466, 504, 512
conversion to starch, by algae, 261
occurrence, in plants, 249, 251
stabilizing effect, on chloroplast suspensions, 1547–49
Methemoglobin, as oxidant in HR, 1587–88
as oxygen indicator in HR, 64–65
Methyl bacteriochlorophyllide, absorption
spectrum, in solution, crystals, and
monolayers, 1817–18, 1820
Methyl chlorophyllide, absorption spectrum, 628
Methylene blue, as oxidant, in HR, 1573, 1575
dimerization and fluorescence, 762
Methyl pheophorbide a, absorption spectrum, 627, 628
Methyl red, Chl-sensitized reduction, by
phenylhydrazine, 512–14, 1507–13
effect, on Chl bleaching, 1489
on Chl fluorescence, 782, 784
Mg (27), 555
Micronutrients, effect, on CO_2 burst in PS
induction, 1347
on PS, 338–39, 1920
"Midday depression," of PS, 331, 334, 824,
873–76, 997
Molisch reaction (AgNO_3 reduction by

chloroplasts in light), 254, 270–71
360, 541, 1736–40
Molisch test. See *Chlorophyll reactions in
solution, thermal, phase test*
Moloxides, as intermediates in PS and PO,
156, 292, 499, 508, 511
Monocotyledons, absence of starch, 47
pigments, 424
"Mono-dehydrochlorophyll," 1503
Monolayers, of Chl, BChl and derivatives,
on water, 394, 449, 1295–96, 1818–24
of Chl, *in vivo?*, 368, 391–94, 1733–36
*Monomolecular and bimolecular limiting
reactions,* in PS, 1023–28, 1031, 1452–
54, 1456, 1470–75, 1480–81, 1839
Morphine, effect on PS, 321
Motile bacteria, 100
Multilayers, of Chl, 394, 449, 1821
Mutants, of *Chlorella,* variations in pigments, PS and HR activity, 1266–67,
1616, 1766, 1768
Myelin, in chloroplasts, 375–76, 1722,
1724, 1725, 1732

N

Naphthaquinone, as oxidant in HR, 1571,
1572
Narcotics
Narcotics, effect, on Chl and BChl
fluorescence during induction,
1396–97
in vivo, 322, 819, 959–60, 1063,
1070–71, 1396–97
on Chl fluorescence in the steady-
state *in vivo,* 821, 824–25, 942–43,
1387
on Chl synthesis, 1766
of excess CO_2, 903
on formic acid synthesis by *E, coli.*
208
on HR, 1611–13
on PR in bacteria, 958–59, 977, 979,
1015
on PS, 300, 320–24, 959, 976, 979
in flashing light, 1463–65
during induction, 1344–45
on R, 322
internal, as kinetic factor in PS, 820,
824–26, 875, 929, 942–43, 950,

effect, on reversible Chl-bleaching, 1488, 1491

energy, content, 216

of formation from H_2 and CO_2, 184

as intermediate, in PS, 51

in R, 269

occurrence in plants, 249, 262–63

as plant food, 201

PO, in ultraviolet light, 267

Oxalosuccinic acid, intermediate, in R, 1690

Oxidants, effect on fluorescence induction, 1404–05

for HR. See *Hill's reaction, oxidants*

Oxidases, activation in algae, 135, 286

in chloroplasts, 1746–48

Oxidation

Oxidation, of carotenoids, 473–75

of Chl, 293, 295, 456–66, 491–93, 499, 503–05, 1499–1501, 1773–79. See also *Chlorophyll reactions, oxidation*

as primary process in PS, 551–57

Oxidation-reduction

Oxidation-reduction, of Chl, internal, 450–59

Oxidation-reduction potential(s), 53, 217–22

of ascorbic acid/dehydroascorbic acid system, 272, 1514, 1518

of carbon dioxide, 218

of carbonyl/carboxyl and alcohol/carbonyl systems, 218, 1674

of C—C/C═C systems, *e.g.* succinate-fumarate system, 225

of Ce^{3+}/Ce^{4+} system, 74

of CH—CH/C—C and CH_2—CH_2/-CH═CH systems, 218

of Chl, 295, 556–57

in chloroplast suspensions, in darkness and light, 1537

in *Chlorella* suspensions, 1653

in *Chromatium* suspensions, 1653

of dehydrogenases, 226

of dyes (leucodye/dye systems), 76, 222. 1573, 1575, 1599–1600, 1604

cresyl blue, 1575

indigo derivatives, 1573, 1575

indophenol derivatives, 1573, 1575, 1599, 1600, 1604

methylene blue, 1573, 1575

safranin T, 1514, 1575

thionine, 152, 1573, 1575

toluylene blue, 1575, 1600

viologen, 233

of excited molecules, 152

of Fe^{2+}/Fe^{3+} systems, 222, 240, 1585, 1586

cytochromes, 222, 226, 1585, 1586

hemoglobin, 222

of formaldehyde/formic acid system, 79, 218

of free radicals 230–33

of H_2O_2/H_2O system, 79, 283

of HR oxidants, 1572, 1573, 1575–76, 1585, 1586, 1591, 1599, 1600

of hydrogenase, 222

of hydroquinone/quinone systems, 221–22, 1572

in illuminated systems (photogalvanic effect), 1522–24, 1599–1600, 1604–06

of "Krasnovsky reactants," 1514, 1518, 1520–21

in leaves, 431

of oxygen (H_2/O_2 system), 79, 226, 283, 1585

of phosphate esters, 225

of pyridine nucleotides, 222, 1518, 1585

of quinones, 222, 1572, 1575, 1911

anthraquinones, 1572

benzoquinones, 222, 1572

chloranilic acid, 1572

naphthaquinones, 1572

phthiocol, 1572, 1575

rosindone sulfonate, 222

vitamin K, 1911

of riboflavin, 222, 1514

of sulfhydryl compounds (2SH/S—S systems), 222, 1700, 1701

cystin/cysteine system, 222, 1701

thioctic acid, 1700

of water, H_2O/O_2 and H_2O/H_2O_2 systems, 79, 283, 1518, 1585

of xanthin, 1518

Oxidation-reduction reactions as cause of reversible bleaching of Chl, 489–93

with dyes, 503–05

with oxidants or reductants, as mechanism of sensitization, 515–18 with solvents, 485–86, 500–01

Chl-sensitized *in vitro*, 509, 512–14, 1507–25

"Oxidizing power," of photostationary systems, 1523

Oxidoreductions. See *Oxidation-reductions*

"Oxychlorophyll," 295, 464–67, 556

"Oxygenases." See *Catalyst E_C* and *Catalyst E_O*

Oxygen

Oxygen, in complex binding, need for PS?, 325, 1400

  cycle on earth, 10

  deficiency effect, on Chl fluorescence *in vivo*, 1063, 1067, 1399–1404

    on PS, 326–28, 1364–71, 1913–15

    during induction, 1316–17, 1321, 1364–71. See also *Anaerobiosis*

  determination, methods, 844–51

  effect, on ATP synthesis by cells, 1706

    on Chl fluorescence *in vitro*, 492, 547, 778–79, 782, 784, 786, 788

    in vivo, 1063, 1067, 1393, 1399–1404

    on CS, 139

    on greening, 429

    on nitrate reduction by *Chlorella*, 539

    on PS, 326–30, 1364–71, 1912–15

    on conversion of PS to PO, 531–32

  metastable, 150, 514–515, 779

  origin, in HR, 64, 1529–30

    in PS, 54–56, 1915–17

    in sulfate produced by CS of bacteria, 113

  as oxidant in HR, in chloroplasts, 1565–69

    in *Chlorella*, 1625–26

Oxygen excess, effect, on PS, 328–30, 530–32, 1912

Oxygen isotopes, distribution in nature and PS, 10, 54–56, 1915–18

  utilization in study of PS and HR. See *O(18)*.

Oxygen-liberating enzymes, in PS. See under *Deoxidases, Catalyst E_C,* and *Catalyst E_O*.

Oxygen liberation, absence in bacterial PS, 100

  absence in conversion of protochloro-

phyll to Chl, 1764

in "artificial PS," 92, 93

in deacidification of succulents, 265

in HR, in chloroplast preparations, demonstration, 62–67, 1528–30, 1580–83

  with O_2 as oxidant, 1565–69

  in *Chlorella*, 541–43, 1616–25

  with O_2 as oxidant, 1624–25

by nitrate-reducing plants, 539

by PS, chemical mechanism, 281–99, 1698–1701

  continued in distilled water, 200

  by first light flash, 133, 327

  induction phenomena, 1317–34, 1355–60, 1362–63, 1364–67, 1369, 1371–74

  role of carotenoids?, 474–75

Oxygen pressure, effect on Chl fluorescence, *in vitro*, 778–79, 782, 784, 786, 788

  in vivo, 1063, 1067, 1399–1404

  on Chl-sensitized autoxidations, 513

  on PO, *in vitro*, 502–03, 523, 526–27

  in vivo, 530–36

  on phosphorescence of adsorbed dyes, 778, 851

  on PS, 326–30, 530–31, 1364–71, 1912–15

  in induction, 1364–71

  on R, 527, 530–31

Oxygen uptake, in actinometer (Warburg-Schocken), 1526–27, 1949, 1952

  by "adapted" algae, 139

  by Chl *in vitro*, 293, 455, 460–61, 492, 498–99, 520

  role in Chl bleaching in killed plants, 538

  by chloroplast preparations, in light, 1569

  by Chl-sensitized autoxidations *in vitro*, 508–11, 1525–28

  by CS of bacteria, 110, 114

  by grana, 503

  by HR ("Mehler reaction"), 1565–67

  stimulation, by ascorbic acid, 1568

    by quinone reduction, 1567–68

  by PO *in vivo*, 528–36, 538

  by soil bacteria, 1917

  See also *Photoxidation, Respiration*

Oxyhydrogen reaction, in "adapted" algae, 129, 132, 134, 138–42, 286, 310, 1701
    C(14) fixation, 1701
    effect of cyanide, 310
    H_2O_2 as intermediate, 286
  in bacteria, 116, 118
  in vitro, Chl sensitized, 512

P

P(32), as tracer, in chloroplast reactions, 1537, 1614
    in plant metabolism, 1660–61, 1679, 1682–83, 1702–05, 1708–09
  use in determination of phosphorus content in chloroplasts, 1743
Paper chromatography, of C(14) and P(32) tagged compounds, 1640–41, 1655–61
Palisade tissue, 357
Parabenzoylamine, effect on Chl absorption spectrum, 1801
Paramagnetism, of phosphorescent state, 792–93
  use for O_2 determination, 850
Pentoses (and pentose phosphates), 38, 43, 49
    C(14) tagging in PS, 1670–75
    function in PS, 1696–98, 1984
    no C(14) tagging in squeezed-out cells, 1537
  See also *Ribulose diphosphate*
Peracids, energy, 291
Percarbonic acid, 79, 288–89
Performaldehyde and performic acid, role in PS?, 287–88
Permeability, of cell membranes, role in induction, 1424
  role in CO_2 diffusion, 916
Peroxidase, 281, 380, 431
Peroxides
Peroxides, of Chl, 293, 461
  decomposition, as nonphotochemical reaction in PS, 172
  formation, in Chl bleaching, 495
  in dead tissues?, 63
  as intermediates, in HR with O_2 as oxidant, 1565–67
  in oxyhydrogen reaction, 140

  in PO, 293, 499, 508, 511
  in PS, 48, 156, 281–86
  monomolecular and bimolecular decomposition, 80, 291
  reversible, 291–93
  See also *Amine peroxides, Catalyst peroxides, Chlorophyll peroxide, Hydrogen peroxide, Organic peroxides, Percarbonic acid*, and *Performaldehyde*
PGA. See *Phosphoglyceric acid*
pH effects
pH effect, on anaerobic induction, of Chl fluorescence *in vivo*, 1405
  of PS, 327, 1366–67
  on BChl fluorescence *in vivo*, 953–54
  on Chl monolayers, 449–50
  on CO_2 solubility, 173–79
  on fermentation, 137
  on HCN solutions, 301
  on HR, 1600–02
  on PS, 198, 339–40, 952–54, 1919
  on redox potentials, 220
Phase test, 457, 459–60, 462–63, 465, 492–93, 1778–79
  intermediates "frozen" at low temperature, 1778–79
o-Phenanthroline, effect, on "adaptation" and PR in algae, 135, 314, 319–20
  resistant half of PR, 314
  on Chl fluorescence induction curves, 1405
  on HR, 1612, 1614
  on PS, 319–20
Phenol, as Chl "protector," 501
  conversion to starch by algae, 261
  energy of carboxylation, 185
Phenol indophenol. See *Quinonoid dyes* and *Hill's reaction*
Phenylhydrazine, activation of Chl fluorescence, 768, 1834
  Chl-sensitized PO, by methyl red, 512–14, 1507–13
  by *o*-dinitrobenzene, 1524
  by O_2, 1508
  complexing with Chl, 649, 768, 1509, 1513, 1834
  effect, on absorption spectrum of Chl, 649, 786, 1834

on reversible reduction of Chl and Pheo, 1506, 1805

photochemical shift of equilibrium with methylene blue, 509

quenching of Chl fluorescence, 782, 786, 1513, 1834

as reductant, for Chl, 1502, 1805

for oxidized Chl, 504–05

2-Phenyl-3-nitrobicyclo-[1,2,2]heptane-5, as quencher of Chl fluorescence, 782

Phenylurethan, effect, on CO_2 burst, 1346–47

on fluorescence induction, 1396, 1398

on HR, 1611–13

on PR in bacteria, 959

on PS, 321–23, 959

in flashing light, 1463–64

See also *Urethans*

Pheophorbides (a, b), 447, 458, 462

absorption spectra, 629, 1799, 1800, 1801

in crystals, 1820, 1823

fluorescence spectra 742, 749

as sensitizer in thiourea actinometer, 1528

Pheophyceae. See *Brown algae*

"*Pheophytin*," of protochlorophyll. See *Protopheophytin*

Pheophytinization, of Chl, 456, 467, 493–94, 498

prevention during extraction, 1774

in reversible reduction or oxidation of Chl, 1504, 1777

Pheophytins

Pheophytins (a, b), 447, 452–54, 456, 467, 493–94, 498, 604, 616–17, 626–27

absorption spectra, 627, 1804

no effect of polar molecules, 648, 772, 788

CO_2 absorption, 452–54

d, d', iso-d, and *iso-d'*, 616–17

fluorescence spectra, 748

no effect of polar groups, 648, 772, 788

formation from Chl. See *Pheophytinization*

photogalvanic and photovoltaic (Bec-

querel) effect, 1520–22

as sensitizers of oxido-reductions, 1519–20

Pheoporphyrin a_5, absorption spectrum, 629

Phorbins, 447

Phosphatase, in cytoplasmic fraction of leaves, 1748

in higher plants and bacteria, heat-resistant, 1686

Phosphate bond energy. See *High energy phosphates*

Phosphate buffers, and CO_2 uptake by leaves, 190–95

Phosphate esters, C(14) tagging in PS, 1639–41, 1656–60, 1670–74, 1676–86

precedes that of free sugars, 1685

P(32) tagged in PS, 1660–61, 1702–03, 1708–09

See also *Phosphoglyceric acid, Phosphopyruvic acid, Uridine Phosphate*, etc.

Phosphates, high energy. See *Adenosine triphosphate (ATP)*, and *High energy phosphates*

role in plant metabolism. See *Phosphorus metabolism*

Phosphatidic acid, in leaves, 374–75

Phosphoacetaldehyde, possible role in PS, 1692

2-Phosphoenolpyruvic acid, possible role in PS, 1692

Phosphoglucomutase and phosphofructokinase, in chloroplasts, 1749

Phosphoglyceraldehyde, C(14) tagged in PS, 1645

Phosphoglyceric acid (PGA)

Phosphoglyceric acid, C(14) tagging, in chloroplasts, 1535

in dark after preillumination, 1639–40, 1642, 1653–55

distribution of label, between α, β, and γ-carbon, 1653, 1663–64, 1665–66, 1671–72

between α and β-phosphates, 1661–62

effect of darkening, 1680

effect of drop in [CO_2], 1684

first product labelled, 1644–46, 1650–53, 1658–59, 1682, 1683

inhibition by poisons, 1687–88

last product unlabelled, 1677–78

photostationary concentration, 1679, 1683–84

in PS, 1639, 1641, 1644–46, 1650–53, 1656, 1658–59, 1661–62, 1665–66, 1668, 1677–78, 1679–80, 1682–84, 1687–88

time course of tagging, 1668, 1677, 1680, 1682, 1683, 1684

isomers (α and β), order of tagging, 1661–62

isotopic equilibration with free acid, 1662

P(32) tagged, 1661

photostationary concentration, 1708–09

role in PS, 1535, 1664–65, 1672–74, 1675–76, 1685, 1687, 1691–98, 1984, 1986

formed by carboxylation, of a C_2 compound?, 1675–76, 1691–96

of ribulose diphosphate, 1535, 1672–74, 1680, 1697–98

reduced by light to phosphoglyceraldehyde?, 1578, 1687, 1703, 1986

regenerated in a cycle, 1664–65, 1685, 1691–98

Phospholipides, in leaves, 374–76, 393

role in chloroplast structure, 368, 393

Phosphopyridine nucleotides (DPN, TPN). See *Pyridine nucleotides*

Phosphopyruvic acid, C(14) tagging, in dark after pre-illumination, 1639–41

in light, 1656, 1658, 1662, 1677, 1683

equilibration with phosphate-free acid, 1662

Phosphorescence, 757, 790–95

of Chl, 749, 790–95, 1291

effect of O_2, 793–94

Phosphorescence quenching, as method of O_2 determination, 327, 1534–35, 1580

Phosphorus, content in chloroplast ash, 376–77

in chloroplasts, determined with P(32), 1743

Phosphorus compounds, soluble in ether, appearance in greening seedlings, 1761

soluble in trichloracetic acid, formation by *Chlorella* in light, 1704–05

Phosphorus deficiency, effect on PS, 339

Phosphorus metabolism, of chloroplasts, 1537, 1614

of plants, 228, 1679, 1682–83, 1702–09

induction phenomena, 1704, 1706–07

P(32) studies, 1660–61, 1679, 1682–83, 1702–05, 1708–09

See also *Adenine phosphate, Adenosine diphosphate, Adenosine monophosphate, Adenosine triphosphate, High energy phosphates*, etc.

Phosphorylation, coupled with carboxylation, 115, 201

with CS, 114, 229

with PS, 150, 226–29, 1537, 1614, 1702–09

with R, 222–26

"photosynthetic," 1537, 1614, 1702–09

of ribulose phosphate, requires high energy phosphate, 1674

Photoactivation, of enzyme permitting to use bicarbonate for PS, 1887

Photoautotrophic bacteria, 99, 101

Photoautoxidation. See *Photoxidation*

Photocatalysis, 56, 161–62, 507

"*Photochemical antirespiration*," 1963

Photochemical intermediates, role in induction, 1409–12

Photochemical reactions, of "adapted" algae, 142–48

of carotenoids and phycobilins, 521–22, 1487

of Chl, *in vitro*, 483–507, 1487–1507

sensitized by Chl, in chloroplast preparations, 61–69, 1528–1616

in vitro, 507–21, 1507–28

in vivo (other than PS and PR), 526–60, 1616–26

Photochemiluminescence, of Chl, *in vitro*, 794, 1838–39

in vivo, 1839–41

"*Photodismutation*," 485

Photodynamic reactions, 56, 76, 317, 507–10, 520

Photoelectric conductivity, of Chl in PS units?, 1299

Photogalvanic effect, in Chl–ascorbic acid system, 1520–22

in Chl, Pheo, or phthalocyanine-coated electrodes, 1521–22

in chloroplast-dye systems, 1575

in chloroplast-quinone systems, 1572, 1598–1600

Photogalvanic and photovoltaic (Becquerel) effects, 76, 1521–24

Photoheterotrophic bacteria, 101, 106–11

Photo-oxidation. See *Photoxidation*

"Photoperoxides," 825, 948, 950, 1014

role in induction, 1369, 1421, 1422

Photoreduction

Photoreduction, of acids in succulents, 34, 264–67, 1702

of BChl and bacteriopheophytin, reversible, 1505

of Chl, as primary process in PS, 551, 553–57

in vitro, activation by bases, 1500–07

not quite reversible, 1502, 1504

reversible, 505–06, 1500–07

in vivo, revealed by absorption changes?, 1989

of CO_2, by "adapted" algae, 111, 128–36, 146–48, 169–70, 310–11, 314, 316–17, 319–20, 956, 1374–75, 1701

adaptation and de-adaptation, 128–36, 310–11, 314, 316–17, 319–20, 956, 1701

C(14) study, 1701

induction, 1374–75

inhibition, 310–11, 314, 316–17, 319–20, 956

by bacteria = bacterial PS. See also *Bacteria, photosynthetic,* and *Bacteriochlorophyll*

action spectrum, 1187–89, 1301–02, 1871–74

C(14) study, 1701

chemistry and energetics, 99–111

effect of [CO_2], 893, 941, 972

effect of inhibitors, 950–60, 977, 1061–64

effect of light intensity, 948, 969,

972, 974, 977–79, 1009–11, 1049, 1052–55, 1059, 1061–63

effect of mixed reductants, 947

effect of pH, 978–79, 1064, 1919

effect of reductant concentration, 941–43, 943–49, 972

effect of temperature, 974, 1057, 1059

flash yield, 1274, 1481–82

induction phenomena, 1406

quantum yield, 1125–29, 1968–69

sigmoid light curves, 974, 977, 979, 1009–11, 1126

of neutral red and phenol indophenol, reversible, 1506

of phthalocyanine and its Mg complex, reversible, 1504–05, 1506

as primary process in PS, 154, 157–59, 161, 551, 553–57

of protochlorophyll, 1505

of riboflavin and safranin T, reversible, 1506

"Photorespiration," 527, 567, 569–70, 1325–26, 1347, 1926, 1951–56

"Photosensitive complex," effect of secondary reactions in it on kinetics of PS and fluorescence, 930–34, 936, 941, 942, 947, 950, 959, 960, 1020–33, 1073–76

Photostationary concentration, of PS intermediates, 1679, 1708–09

Photosynthesis

Photosynthesis, action spectrum, 1142–87, 1303–04, 1876–79

anaerobic, 1364–71, 1915

artificial, 84, 86–87, 93, 1982

bacterial. See *Photoreduction of CO_2 by bacteria*

in cell-free chloroplast preparations?, 1537, 1701

chemical mechanism, of CO_2 fixation and reduction, general chemical and energetic considerations, 38–51, 172–246

pre-tracer search for intermediates, 246–81

tracer studies, 241–44, 1630–1714

early theories, by v. Baeyer, 48, 51

by Baur, 248

by Chl or chlorophyllide, of benzidine, 510, 528

by Chl or chlorophyllide, of carotene and xanthophyll, 510, 1528

by Chl or chlorophyllide, of ergosterol, 511

by Chl or chlorophyllide, of horse serum, 510

by Chl or chlorophyllide, of iodide, 511

by Chl or chlorophyllide, of isoamylamine, 511, 788–89

by Chl or chlorophyllide, of oleate and pyruvate, 511

by Chl or chlorophyllide, of phenylhydrazine, 1508

by Chl or chlorophyllide, of rubrene, 511

by Chl or chlorophyllide, of thiourea, 1526–28, 1949, 1952

by pheophorbide or protoporphyrin, 1526, 1528, 1952

in vivo, 526–38

in absence of CO_2, 527–31, 900, 909

of benzidine, 528

as cause of enhanced fluorescence in starved cells, 942

as cause of induction effects, 1420–25

of Chl, irreversible, 537–38

reversible, as primary process in PS, 551–53, 554–57

effect on PS, 328, 526, 531–32, 1359–61, 1371–74

induction after it, 1371–74

inhibition, 526, 532

in excess light, 526, 532–36, 965, 1359, 1360–61

in excess oxygen, 526, 531–32

of metabolites, leading to "internal narcotization," 825, 942, 1420–25, 1425–28

under narcotization, 526, 528, 909

of plant acids in succulents, 34, 265–66

in poisoned plants, 317

as primary photoprocess in PS, 161, 527–28, 543–44

relation to R, 527, 530–31, 563–66, 900, 1425–28

Phthalocyanine (and its Mg complex), activation of fluorescence by polar molecules, 772, 1835

influence of polar molecules on absorption spectrum, 648

photogalvanic and photovoltaic effects, 1521–22

reversible photoreduction by ascorbic acid, 1504–05, 1506

as sensitizer of oxidoreduction, 1514–15

Phthiocol

Phthiocol, inhibiting effect, on "adaptation" and PR in algae, 314, 319–20

"resistant half" of PR, 314

on HR, 1613

on PS, 314, 319, 1910

as oxidant, in HR, 1572, 1575

Phycobilins

Phycobilins (phycocyanin and phycoerythrin), 417–19, 420–21, 424–27, 476–79, 664–68, 707–09, 1306

absorption spectra, in solution, 664–68, 728, 800, 1789–90, 1809–10

in vivo, 707–09, 728–30, 1856, 1876–77, 1879

association with a part of Chl *in vivo?*, 816

chemistry, 476–79, 1788–90

energy transfer, to Chl *in vivo*, 815–16, 1300–01, 1303–05, 1306

from Chl to them, 816

from phycoerythrin to phycocyanin, 1306, 1878

from protein to chromophore, 1790, 1838

fluorescence, *in vitro*, 799–801, 1838

action spectrum, 1838

sensitized by protein, 1838

in vivo, 811–12, 813, 815–16, 1868–69, 1876, 1878

yield independent of light intensity, 1051, 1871

isoelectric point, 478

location in chromoplasts, 1304, 1306, 1754–55

molar extinction coefficient of the chromophore, 666–67, 1789

molecular weight of proteins, 478–79, 1790

occurrence, 417–19, 420–21, 424–27, 1789–90

varieties, 417, 1789–90, 1809–10

participation in light absorption by red and blue-green algae, 728–30

photochemical reactions, 521–22, 1487, 1790

proteins, composition, 1789

separation from chromophore, 477–78, 665, 1790

retention in cells by high-polymer solutes, 1306, 1549, 1561, 1754–55

separation from Chl-bearing grana by ultracentrifuging, 1741

Phycobilin-sensitized Chl fluorescence, 801, 811–13, 815–16, 1301, 1303–05, 1868–71, 1876–79

Phycobilin-sensitized PS, 426, 479, 522, 558, 801, 1178–87, 1303–05, 1771, 1876–79

Phycochromoproteins, chromatographic separation, 1789

Phycocyanins (C, P and R), 1789. See also *Phycobilins*

Phycocyanobilin, 477, 1788–89

Phycoerythrins (C, P, and R), 1789–90. See also *Phycobilins*

Phycoerythrobilin, 477, 1788–89

Phyllins, 447

Phylloerythrin, fluorescence spectrum, 742

Phylloporphin, absorption spectrum, 620

Phylogenetic adaptation of pigment system, to light color and intensity, 419–24, 532, 987, 995

to light exposure, 987, 995–96

to temperature, 1218

"Physiological concept" of PS (Kostychev), 872–73, 875

Phytins, 40, 447

Phytofluene, 798

Phytol

Phytol, 439–40

CO_2 uptake, 180

effect on crystallizability of Chl, 448, 1782

infrared spectrum, 610–12, 1811

ingredient for artificial PS?, 93, 1524

relation to carotene, 471–72

Pigments

Pigments concentration, in cells, effect on light absorption, 672, 686, 697, 709–17, 1007–12, 1258–61, 1863–66

as kinetic factor in PS, 1258–1312

Pigment content, in algae, 409–11, 834

in chloroplasts and grana, 389–91, 411–12, 1735–36

in leaves, 407–09

Pigment system, adaptation phenomena, 419–27

ontogenetics, 424–27

phylogenetics, 420–24

composition, in algae, 401, 405–07, 408–11, 413–16, 417–18, 419, 420–22, 472–73, 476–79, 616, 658–59, 665–66, 834, 1786, 1788–90, 1809–10

in bacteria, 99, 101, 402, 407, 416, 444–45, 473, 659, 1286–88, 1806–08, 1809, 1849–56

in higher plants, 402–05, 407–09, 412–15, 439, 445, 470–72, 479–80, 658–59, 1766, 1808, 1847–49, 1881

Piperidine, effect, on absorption spectrum of Chl, 638, 642, 1780

on reversible reduction of Chl and Pheo, 1506

Plankton, contribution to PS on earth, 6

Plasmolysis, effect on PS, 334–35

Plastides. See *Chloroplasts*

"Plastidogen," 1717

Poisoning. See *Inhibition*

Polar molecules, effect, on Chl bleaching, 1495, 1501, 1504

on Chl fluorescence, 764–72

Polarography, for O_2 determination, 850, 1120–23, 1319–22, 1326–27, 1936, 1956

Polymerization

Polymerization, of carbohydrates, energy, 217

sensitized by Chl *b*?, 150

of formaldehyde, catalyzed by ascorbic acid, 273

as test for free radicals, in Chl reaction with ascorbate, 1499

in HR, 1576

Polyphenol oxidase, in chloroplasts and cytoplasm, 1606–08, 1747–48

role in PS, 1653, 1667
role in R, 223, 224, 1633, 1689–91
sensitized PO, 508–11
See also *Enol-pyruvic acid* and *Phospho-pyruvic acid*

Q

Quantum efficiency, quantum requirement, definition, 1085. See *Quantum yield*

Quantum yield. See also *Action spectra*

Quantum yield, of bleaching, of Chl and chlorophyllide, irreversible, 488, 496–98, 1489, 1494
reversible, 486–88, 1489, 1494–95
of Chl-sensitized reactions, 546–47
autoxidations, 509, 513, 841, 1526, 1528, 1949, 1952. See also *Warburg-Schoken actinometer*
oxidation-reductions, 513, 1508, 1511–13, 1525
of "CO$_2$-burst," 1103
of fluorescence (φ), of Chl, Pheo, and mesoporphyrin, in solution, 546–47, 1828–30, 1992
of Chl and BChl *in vivo*, 812–13, 1867, 1992
as function of light intensity, 1049, 1183, 1992
as function of wavelength. See under *Action spectra*
of HR, in *Chlorella*, 1130–31, 1619–20
in chloroplast preparations, 1129–31, 1593, 1967–68
as function of wavelength. See under *Action spectra*
of photochemical reactions, empirical equations, 509, 1511–12
Stern-Volmer equation, 1023
of PR, in "adapted" algae, 169, 1128–29
in bacteria, 1125–28, 1968–69
as function of wavelength. See under *Action spectra*
of PS, (γ), 1083–1142, 1940–67
in *aurea* leaves, 1137
in blue-green algae, 1095, 1096, 1179
in brown algae (diatoms), 1096–97, 1170
effect, of age, 1097, 1113, 1138, 1947

of "background light," 1107, 1942–44, 1950–51, 1956
of bicarbonate, 1956
of blue light?, 1948, 1950–51
of carbonate buffers, 1095, 1102–08, 1945–47, 1952
of Chl concentration?, 1962–63
of CO$_2$ concentration?, 1896, 1945–46, 1951
of induction phenomena, 1086, 1092–94, 1100, 1101–02, 1329, 1940–41, 1948–49, 1956, 1966–67
of light intensity, 1113–17, 1132–37. See also *Kok effect* and *Light curves of PS*
of light intensity, in strong light, 1136–37, 1948–50
of light intermittency?, 1106, 1942–44, 1951
of pH, 835–36, 1095, 1097, 1107–08, 1113–14, 1947
of temperature?, 1138, 1232–35
of wavelength. See *Photosynthesis action spectrum*
in leaves and thalli, 1095, 1119, 1136–37, 1162
measured, by calorimetry, 1123–25
by gas analysis, 1119–20
by manometry, 1085–1118, 1941–56
by manometry, physical lag, 1101, 1111, 1940
by manometry, three-vessel method, 1943
by manometry, two-vessel method, 1093, 1100, 1103–04, 1109–13, 1941–56
by polarimetry, 1120–23, 1956–62
theoretical limitations, 1022–24
theory, 155–56, 1089–92, 1117–18, 1137–39, 1278–79, 1951–56, 1962–74
four quanta and eight quanta theories, 155–66, 1089–90, 1969–74
"one quantum process," 1951–56
quanta collection problem, 1278–79
theoretical *vs.* actually observable yield, 1137–39

thermochemical considerations, 1089–90, 1969–74

utilization of respiration intermediates ("antirespiration"), 1091–92, 1107, 1117–18, 1962–69

of Warburg-Schocken actinometer, 513, 841, 1526–28, 1949, 1952

of water oxidation by ceric ions, 74

Quenching, of fluorescence, of Chl and chlorophyllide in solution, 167, 483, 490, 518, 777–90, 1831–35. See also *Chlorophyll fluorescence, in solution (quenching and self-quenching)*

of phosphorescence, of adsorbed dyes, 793–94, 851

Quercetin, 185, 480

Quinine, effect on PS, 321

as sensitizer, 78

Quinoline, effect on reversible bleaching of Chl and Pheo, 1506

Quinones

Quinones, decomposition in light, 1622–23

as oxidants, for BChl, in light and dark, 1501

for Chl, in dark, 461

in light, 1500–01

after PR, 1518–19

for HR in *Chlorella*, 1617–26

in flashing light, 1620–21

inhibition, 1621

kinetics, 1618–21

maximum utilization, 1618

pre-illumination effect, 1621–23

quantum yield, 1130–31, 1619–20

self-inhibition, 1618–19

for HR in chloroplast preparations, 954, 1131, 1175, 1530, 1546, 1566–68, 1569–72, 1575, 1591, 1593, 1596, 1598, 1601–02, 1609–12, 1967–68

competition with O_2, 1566–68

inhibition, 1609–12

kinetics, 1591, 1593, 1596

maximum utilization, 1598

pH effect, 1601–02

quantum yield, 1130–31, 1593, 1967–68

self-inhibition, 1596

peroxides, 292–293

as quenchers, of Chl fluorescence, 782, 784, 1500

redox potentials, 221–22, 1575

as removers of anaerobic inhibition of PS, 1366–67

fluorescence changes, 1405

reversible reduction, 221–22

Quinonoid dyes

Quinonoid dyes, as oxidants in HR, 1530, 1572–76, 1594, 1595, 1598, 1600, 1609–14, 1615–16

inhibition, 1609–14

kinetics, 1594, 1595, 1598

maximum utilization, 1598–1600

role of redox potentials, 76, 1573, 1575

redox potentials, 76, 222, 1573, 1575

See also *Methylene blue, Thionine*, etc.

Quotient, photosynthetic (Q_p). See *Photosynthetic quotient*

respiratory (Q_r). See *Respiratory quotient*

R

Radicals. See *Free radicals*

Radioactive rays, effect on PS, 337, 346–47

Radioautography, 1657

Radiocarbon. See $C(11)$ and $C(14)$

Radiohydrogen. See *Tritium*

Radiomagnesium. See $Mg(27)$

Radiophosphorus. See $P(32)$

Reciprocity law, photochemical, for PS in flashing light, 1435, 1448, 1473–74, 1476

Recovery of PS, after freezing, 1218, 1219–20

after heating, 1218, 1223, 1225

after strong illumination, 1321–24

Red algae

Red algae, absorption of light, 689–90, 707–09, 1870, 1879

changes during PS, 1860–62

in different depths, 735

action spectrum of PS, 1178, 1180–83, 1305–06, 1879

energy transfer, 815–16, 1183, 1289, 1301, 1304–07

to a "minor pigment" (Chl d?), 1183, 1289, 1305, 1878–79

fluorescence, of Chl a, 811–12, 813, 815–16, 1051, 1868–71, 1877–79
    sensitized by carotenoids and phycobilins, 815–16, 1877–79
  of phycobilins, 1868–70, 1878–79
  of "unknown pigment" (Chl $d?$). 812, 1289, 1305, 1878–79
habitat, 418, 420–22, 424–25
pigments, 402, 405, 407, 410, 413, 417–19, 420–22, 425–26, 476–79, 615–16, 811–12, 816, 1304, 1788–90, 1809–10
  absence of Chl b, 405
  Chl d, d', etc., 407, 615–16, 811–12, 816, 1304
  chromatic adaptation, 418, 421, 424–25
  preservation by high molecular weight solutes, 1306, 1549, 1561–1759
  variety of phycobilins, 417, 478, 1788–90, 1809
Redox potentials. See *Oxidation-reduction potentials.*

Red shift
Red shift of spectral bands, of bacterioviridin *in vivo*, 704, 1807–08, 1855
  of BChl, in adsorbates, 1826
    in colloids, 651–56, 1826–27
    in crystals, 1817, 1820, 1822–24
    in monolayers, 1818, 1820, 1822–24
    in solutions, 641–42, 1806–07
    orange band, 1806–07
    in vivo, 651, 653, 702–04, 1850, 1852
  of carotenoids, in colloids, 706
    in solutions, 656–59
    in vivo, 706–07, 725–26, 727, 728, 1171, 1174–75
  of Chl and chlorophyllides, in adsorbates, 651–52, 1825
    in colloidal solutions and extracts, 649–55, 776, 1825
    in crystals, 1815–18, 1820, 1822–24
    effect of size, 1815–16, 1822–24
    in monolayers, 1818–19, 1820, 1822–24
    in solutions, 637–43, 649, 786, 810
    upon cooling, 1802–03
    in fluorescence, 745, 747, 810. 1746–47
    in vivo, 697–02, 722–23, 725–27, 728, 808–10, 1171–74, 1175, 1825,

1847–49
  of Chl b, 701–02, 705, 721
  of Chl c, 727
  in fluorescence, 808–10
  in condensed systems (general), 635–37, 1822–24
  of fucoxanthol, 657, 706–07, 727, 1171, 1175
  of Pheo, in crystals, 1820, 1823
  of phycobilins, in fluorescence, 799
    in protein complexes, 665
    in vivo, 707–09, 728
  of protochlorophyll, *in vivo*, 1764, 1808

Reducing power
Reducing power, 1691
  of photostationary systems, 1519, 1523–24
  of pre-illuminated chloroplast suspensions?, 1615–16
  of pre-illuminated plants, 1636, 1642, 1643, 1644, 1653–54

Reductants
Reductants, for CS in bacteria, 113, 115, 116, 117, 118
  for the photochemical apparatus of plants, 543
  for PR in bacteria, 102, 106–08
  for reversible PR of Chl, 1504

Reduction
Reduction, of BChl and BPheo, chemical, 1505
  photochemical, 1519–20
  of Chl, *in vitro*, chemical, 457–58, 1779–80
    photochemical, 505–06, 1501–07, 1513–23, 1805–06
    in vivo, photochemical, as primary process in PS, 551, 553–57, 1517, 1989
  of Mg-phthalocyanine, photochemical, 1521
  of Pheo, photochemical, 1519–21
  of protochlorophyll, chemical, 1780
  photochemical, 1516

Reduction level
Reduction level of C—H—O compounds, 105–10, 216, 247–48
  of acids acceptable as food for algae, 261–62, 266

of low molecular weight leaf components, 249–50, 254

of pentoses, 1673

Reflectance, of leaves, 676–77, 696

Reflection spectra, of algae, 689–90

of leaves, 685–87, 694–97, 1841–44

Reservoirs

Reservoirs, of CO_2 in plants, 188–95

emptied in CO_2 burst, 1346

of photochemical products, revealed by flash kinetics, 1481

of PS intermediates, revealed by C(14) and P(32) studies, 1667, 1679–80, 1683–86, 1708

of R and PS intermediates, communicating, 1316, 1426, 1939

Resorcinol, effect on HR, 1612

Respiration

Respiration, 876, 882, 983, 989

change in light, in *Anabaena,* 1333–1334

of chloroplast preparations, 1569, 1606–08

compensation, as function of $[CO_2]$, 899

as function of light intensity, 1108, 1109

constancy in light, in *Chlorella,* 1333–34

correction in PS, 32, 561, 1085–86, 1099, 1107, 1113, 1926–39, 1956–62

in cryophilic plants, 1230

cycles, 222–24, 268, 1689–91

effect, of light, 527, 566–70, 1108–09, 1926–39, 1956–62

O(18) studies, 1929–36

of O_2 pressure, 530

of temperature, 899

as hydrogen transfer, 52

induction phenomena, after PO, 565–66

after PS, 563–66, 1085, 1092–93, 1316, 1325–33, 1344–47, 1354–57, 1933, 1938–39, 1951–55, 1958–60

inhibition, 301–06, 308, 311, 315, 316, 318–19, 320–24, 569–70, 1687, 1907, 1909

by light?, 900, 1645–46, 1666, 1681–82, 1698, 1926–27

in blue-green algae, 1334, 1934–36

by ultraviolet light, 345, 1922–23

interaction, with PO, 565–66

with PS. See *Photosynthesis, interaction with R*

intermediates, as Hill oxidants, 1576–89

in purple bacteria, 100, 110–11

role, in fluorescence induction, 1386

of phosphorylations, 222–26

in PS induction, 1421, 1425–28

stimulation, by blue light, 557, 567–69

See also *Respiration, induction after PS and PO*

by light, 1334, 1934–36

by poisons, 301, 304, 316

of umbrophilic plants, 988–89, 1230

Respiratory CO_2 fixation, 1630–36

Respiratory decarboxylations, 1633, 1643, 1691

Respiratory quotient $(Q_R = -\Delta CO_2/\Delta O_2)$, 32, 34, 109, 266, 1325–26, 1943

Reversible bleaching, of Chl. See *Chlorophyll reactions*

Reversible oxidation, of Chl. See *Chlorophyll reactions*

Reversible oxidation-reduction systems, 221, 231–32

Reversible peroxide formation. See *Peroxides, reversible*

Reversible reduction, of Chl. See *Chlorophyll reactions*

Rhodamine B, as sensitizer, 78, 92

as stain for chloroplasts, 361, 367

Rhodins, 447

absorption spectrum, 620

Rhodochlorin dimethyl ester, absorption spectrum, 626

Rhodophyceae. See *Red algae*

Rhodopin (rhodopol), 416, 473, 659, 1873–74

Rhodoporphyrin, absorption spectrum, 620

Rhodopurpurin, 416, 473

Rhodovibrin, 416, 473

Rhodoviolascin (= spirilloxanthol?), 416, 473

absorption spectrum, 659, 1809

inactivity as sensitizer in bacteria?, 1302, 1873–75

Riboflavin, Chl-sensitized reduction by ascorbic acid, 1514–22

Ribulose

Ribulose, C(14) tagged in PS, 1671

intramolecular distribution of label, 1671

Ribulose diphosphate, as CO_2 acceptor, 1672–1673

C(14) tagging in PS, 1669, 1670–74

distribution of label, 1672

photostationary concentration, 1679

time course, 1669, 1676–79, 1686

carboxylase, in spinach and *Chlorella,* 1746

carboxylation to 2 PGA, 1672–74, 1984, 1986

role in PS, 1674, 1696–98, 1984, 1986

Rubene. See *Rubrene*

Rubidium, as K substitute, 337, 428

Rubrene, peroxide, 292

PO, 511

S

Safranin T, Chl-sensitized reduction by ascorbic acid, 1514–22

Salt effects, on Chl reaction with Fe^{3+}, 465

on chloroplast activity, 1549–54

on CO_2 solubility, 179

on PR of dyes, 506

on PS, 336–42, 835

Salting-out, of chloroplastic matter, 369–71, 1555–56

of Chl "coacervates," 392

of CO_2 from solution, 179

Salt-water algae, dependency of PS on salinity, 336

Saturation

Saturation, of absorption band shift, with crystal size, 1816, 1822–24

of C(14) uptake in various PS intermediates, with time, 1668–69, 1676–81

of carbon-tracer uptake by algae, in dark, with time, 202–03, 1637, 1647

of Chl with CO_2, 452

of Chl-chemiluminescence following PS, with light, 1840–41

of flash yield, of HR in *Chlorella,* with dark time, 1478

with flash energy, 1479

of PR in bacteria, with dark time, 1482

of PS, with [CO_2], 1461, 1463

with dark time, 1452, 1457, 1460, 1461, 1467, 1469, 1471, 1472, 1478

with flash energy, 1468

of HR, in *Chlorella,* with light, 1619, 1594–95

in chloroplast preparations, effect of inhibitors, 1612–13

with light, 65, 1540–42, 1594–96

of leaves, with CO_2, 191, 195

of PO, with light, 532, 535–36

of PR in bacteria, with light, 969, 972, 973, 976–78

with reductants, 944–46

of PS, with CO_2, 196, 892–97, 916–43, 1889–90, 1892–95

effect of bicarbonate, 886–89, 1889–90, 1892–95, 1897

effect of inhibitors, 1906

effect of light intensity, 895–97, 1897

theory: acceptor blockade, 934

theory: accumulation of photo-products, 932

theory: back reactions, 931

theory: carboxylation equilibrium, 920

theory: slow carboxylation, 924, 926, 927, 928, 930

general discussion of kinetics, 859–64, 866–72

with light, 965–69, 1048–49

effect of age, 879

effect of anaerobiosis, 1364–65, 1913

effect of cell extract, 88

effect of Chl content, 1260, 1265, 1269–70

effect of [CO_2], 970–72

effect of D_2O, 296

effect of inhibitors, 302, 312, 323, 342, 974–76, 978, 985–89.

effect of light color, 1059–61

effect of O_2, 976

effect of temperature, 973, 1619

effect of thermophily and cryophily, 1226–27, 1229

effect of umbrophily and heliophily, 986–89, 995

in flashing light, 1449–51

Stokes' rule, 751

Stomata

Stomata, as cause of dehydration effect, on
PS, 334, 944

    of inhibition by excess CO_2, 331

  by excess light, 532

  of midday depression?, 875–86

  diffusion resistance, 912–14

  opening in intermittent light, 1438

  role, as limiting factors in PS, 914–16

    in PS induction, 1407

  structure and function, 357, 910–12

Streptomycin, effect on chlorophyll formation, 1766

Stroma, of chloroplasts, 358, 361, 362,
369–370, 1720, 1725, 1732–33

Strychnine, effect on HR, 1612, 1613

"Substitute" reductants and oxidants, in PS,
67, 124, 514–43. See also *Hill's
reaction* and *Photoreduction*

Succinic acid

Succinic acid, biosynthesis, 209

  C(14) tagging, in dark, 1636, 1638, 1640

    enhanced by NH_2OH, 1908–09

    in light, 1640

  content in plants, 250, 251, 263

  energy, content, 216

    of dehydrogenation, 218

  as food for algae, 261–62

  an intermediate, in PS, 1691, 1693

    in R, 224, 268, 1690

  not photoreduced by Chl, 1505

  oxidation coupled with phosphorylation,
226

  PO in ultraviolet light, 267

Succulents

Succulents, acid metabolism, 264–67

  $C(14)O_2$ fixation, 1702

  energy balance and leaf temperature,
1216

  occurrence of sedoheptulose, 1621

  PS quotient, 34

Sucrose

Sucrose, 41–42

  C(14) tagging in PS, 1631, 1640–42,
1656, 1659, 1663, 1676–77, 1680,
1685

    in dark after illumination, 1640, 1642

    label distribution, 1631, 1663

    in light, 1641, 1659

    precedence over free hexoses, 1685

    time course, 1676, 1677, 1680

  energy content, 49

  first sugar formed in PS, 37, 44–46, 1685

  influence on PS, 334–35, 341

  uptake of CO_2, 180

Sucrose monophosphate, C(14) tagged, in
PS, 1686

Sugar diphosphates, P(32) labelling in
photostationary state, 1708–09

Sugar phosphates, C(14) tagging, in dark
after pre-illumination, 1639–42,
1653

  in light, 1639–42, 1658–59, 1671

  photostationary concentration, 1679

  precedence over free sugars, 1685

  time course, 1669, 1670–72, 1676–78,
1680, 1682–86

  P(32) tagging in light, 1660–61, 1708

Sugars

Sugars, C(14) tagging, in dark after preillumination, 1639

  label distribution, intramolecular,
1631, 1663

    between sugars, 1671

  in light, 1631, 1639, 1645

  order of labelling, 1684–86

  time course, 1669, 1676–78

Sulfanilamide, effect on HR, 1613

Sulfate, in chloroplast ash, 377

  formation, by CS in bacteria, 115–16,
119

    by PR in bacteria, 102, 103

  as reductant for CS in bacteria, 113

Sulfhydryl inhibitors, effect on HR, $C*O_2$,
and $P*$ fixation in chloroplasts, 1612,
1614. See also under *Inhibition, by
dinitrophenol and iodoacetyl (of HR,
PS, and $C*$ fixation)*

Sulfide, as photoreductant, for bacteriochlorophyll in solution, 1519, 1520

  in blue-green algae, 148

  for Chl, 1504–05, 1506, 1519, 1520

  for Pheo and BPheo, 1520

  for PR in bacteria, 99, 101, 102, 103

Sulfite, effect on PS, 317

Sulfur, in chloroplastic ash, 377

  in chloroplastic proteins, 374